45.3

GU00836546

10 650 5532

THE DUTCH SCHOOL

NATIONAL GALLERY
CATALOGUES

THE DUTCH
SCHOOL

1600–1900

by Neil MacLaren
Revised and expanded by
Christopher Brown

VOLUME 1
TEXT AND COMPARATIVE
PLATES

National Gallery Publications Limited
The National Gallery
London

National Gallery Publications
Published by order of the Trustees

© The National Gallery 1991

All rights reserved. No part of this publication
may be transmitted in any form or by any means,
electronic or mechanical, including photocopy,
recording, or any information storage and
retrieval system, without the prior permission in
writing from the publisher.

**British Library Cataloguing in Publication
Data**
National Gallery
    The Dutch School, 1600–1900 – (National
    Gallery catalogues).
    1. Paintings, history
    I. Title II. MacLaren, Neil III. Brown,
    Christopher 1948–
    759.9492034421
    ISBN 0-947645-20-9 Vol. 1
    ISBN 0-947645-80-2 Vol. 2
    Boxed set: ISBN 0-947645-99-3

Designed by James Shurmer

Printed and bound in Great Britain by
Grosvenor Press (Portsmouth) Limited

FRONT COVER
Hendrick ter Brugghen: *The Concert* (detail)

BACK COVER
Johannes Vermeer: *A Young Woman standing at a
Virginal*

Pictures painted before 1600 in the Northern
Netherlands are discussed in the catalogue of
the Early Netherlandish School.

WEST SUSSEX LIBRARIES

Copy No. 6505532	Class No. 759.949		
Supplier MACAULAY	Date Invoiced 15 NOV 1991		
Loc. WS	Initials eh	2nd Loc.	Initials
Loc.	Initials	4th Loc.	Initials

IN MEMORY OF NEIL MACLAREN
(1909–1988)

Curator of Dutch Paintings at the
National Gallery from 1935 until 1961 and author of
the first edition of this catalogue.

The publication of this catalogue
has been supported by a generous donation from
Unilever

National Gallery Catalogues

The first series of major catalogues of the Schools of Painting in the National Gallery was launched in 1945. The series is now being extensively revised.

Revised edition

THE EARLY ITALIAN SCHOOLS BEFORE 1400 by Martin Davies revised by Dillian Gordon

Reprints

Each of the following volumes has been reissued without alteration to the text, but a list of paintings in the relevant school acquired since the publication of the last edition is added as an appendix.

THE SIXTEENTH-CENTURY ITALIAN SCHOOLS by Cecil Gould

THE SEVENTEENTH AND EIGHTEENTH CENTURY ITALIAN SCHOOLS by Michael Levy

THE FLEMISH SCHOOL 1600–1900 by Gregory Martin

THE EARLY NETHERLANDISH SCHOOL by Martin Davies

THE SPANISH SCHOOL by Neil MacLaren, revised by Allan Braham

Contents

Foreword to the Second Edition

When it was published thirty years ago, the first edition of this catalogue immediately established itself as an outstanding catalogue of Dutch seventeenth-century paintings and a model for catalogues of public collections of Dutch pictures. It was therefore with very considerable temerity that I undertook the preparation of a second edition. In the event, because of my increasing administrative duties at the National Gallery, it has taken far longer than I anticipated. I have attempted to bring up to date the entries on all the paintings included in MacLaren's catalogue and have added entries for all the paintings acquired since then. Three paintings, Jan van Os's *Fruit and Flowers in a Terracotta Vase*, Aelbert Cuyp's *River Landscape with Horseman and Peasants* and Jan van der Heyden's *View of the Westerkerk, Amsterdam*, arrived too late to be incorporated in the main body of the text and short entries are included in a supplement. I had the benefit of draft entries by my predecessor as Curator of Dutch and Flemish paintings, Gregory Martin, for the paintings acquired during the period 1958 to 1970.

In the course of the many years during which I have been at work on this catalogue I have had assistance from numerous colleagues and friends, among them Ronni Baer, Hans-Ulrich Beck, Ingvar Bergström, Albert Blankert, Josua Bruyn, Cees de Bruyn Kops, Alice Davies, Jan van Gelder, Egbert Haverkamp-Begemann, Frima Fox Hofrichter, J. R. Judson, Jan Kelch, George Keyes, Frederik van Kretschmar, Walter Liedtke, Anneliese Mayer-Meintschel, Fred Meijer, Ulrike Middendorf, Sir Oliver Millar, Kristi Nelson, William Robinson, Margarita Russell, Willem Russell, Birgit Schumacher, Sam Segal, John Sillevis, Seymour Slive, Joaneath Spicer, Wolfgang Stechow, Werner Sumowski, Peter Sutton, Pieter van Thiel, Irena Warsink, Willem van de Watering, Ernst van de Wetering, and Majorie Wieseman. It is a particular pleasure to be able to thank two friends who were also thanked by MacLaren in his preface to the first edition, Christopher White and Michael Robinson. The entries for the paintings by Willem van de Velde the Younger depend very heavily on the extensive notes supplied to me by Michael Robinson. Two long-suffering friends, Ivan Gaskell and Otto Naumann, were kind enough to read through the entire typescript. They suggested a number of important changes and improvements which have been acted upon. I am most grateful to them.

Many of my former and present colleagues at the National Gallery assisted with this volume. David Bomford looked at every painting with me in order to help me prepare the notes on condition and I have discussed many particular problems with Martin Wyld, Tony Reeve, Kenneth Malcolm and Jill Dunkerton. Joyce Plesters and Ashok Roy have undertaken scientific investigations of a large number of paintings and I have gratefully incorporated their findings. Sir Michael Levey, Director of the National Gallery from 1973 to 1986, and his successor, Neil MacGregor, have been helpful and patient during the extended genesis of this volume.

No catalogue of this type can be written without the constant use of research facilities. The National Gallery Library, so ably run by Elspeth Hector, has been my first resource. I have had several extended stays in The Hague, the first in 1975, using the remarkable holdings of the Rijksbureau voor Kunsthistorische Documentatie. There I have been treated with kindness and constant helpfulness by Dr J. Nieuwstraten and his staff, in particular Gerbrandt Kotting. In London I was given much valuable help by Rupert Hodge at the Witt Library. More recently, Burton Frederickson and his team at the Getty Provenance Index have sent me a steady stream of corrections and additions to the provenances of National Gallery paintings.

Sara Hattrick and her colleagues in the Photographic Department have tirelessly provided numerous technical and detail photographs. Sue Curnow of National Gallery Publications Ltd and the designer James Shurmer have fashioned a huge amount of unwieldy material into an attractive and accessible format. Charlotte Roberts and Lucy Trench edited the manuscript in the early stages, and Diana Davies guided it with conscientious care through to publication. Among the many others who have generously assisted with the preparation of the manuscript, I would especially like to thank Amanda Bennett, Joanna Kent and Louise Woodroff.

DR CHRISTOPHER BROWN
London, July 1990

Explanatory Notes on the Catalogue

SEQUENCE The paintings are arranged alphabetically according to the name of the artist or school.

ATTRIBUTION A picture catalogued under the name of the artist is considered to be by him. 'Attributed to' qualifies the attribution. 'Ascribed to' indicates a greater degree of doubt. 'Workshop of' or 'Follower of' are self-explanatory. 'Style of' indicates that the painting is an imitation or copy painted after the artist's lifetime. A list of attributions which have been changed from the first edition of this catalogue (published in 1960) is given on pages 510–13.

INVENTORY NUMBER The National Gallery inventory number is to be found to the left of the picture title.

MEASUREMENTS These are given in centimetres, followed by inches in brackets. Height precedes width.

RIGHT AND LEFT These indicate the viewer's right and left, unless the context clearly implies the contrary.

BIOGRAPHIES MacLaren's biographical notes on painters have been expanded and brought up to date when there is no accessible and reliable modern literature. Where such literature exists, these notes have been kept to a minimum.

REFERENCES The bibliographical references, though selective, include publications which appeared before mid-1989. References to books and articles which appeared subsequently and which the author considered to be of importance are referred to within square brackets but could not be taken into account in the catalogue entries themselves.

LISTS AND INDEXES At the back of this volume are lists of paintings acquired since the last edition of this catalogue and changed attributions. There are also indexes to religious subjects, profane subjects, topography, previous owners, years of acquisition and inventory number.

ILLUSTRATIONS The plates of the paintings included in the catalogue are in the second volume, together with all the signatures which could be reproduced. The comparative plates are included in Volume 1.

VAN 'van' has been used in lower case throughout in accordance with *The Oxford Dictionary for Writers and Editors*. The 'van' has been omitted for certain artists as is customary, e.g. 'Jacob van Ruisdael', but 'Ruisdael'.

BIBLIOGRAPHICAL REFERENCES 'op. cit.' may refer back to books and articles referred to under the artist's biography (rather than in the particular catalogue entry).

CHRISTIE'S AND SOTHEBY'S Unless another location is mentioned, the sales referred to took place in London.

CLEANING The cleaning of paintings which took place before 1945 is not referred to, unless the circumstances were exceptional.

CONDITION All the paintings have been examined during the preparation of this catalogue. In many cases the condition is described, sometimes in considerable detail. If the condition is not described, the painting can be presumed to be in good condition.

PROVENANCE AND EXHIBITIONS There are separate headings for provenance and exhibitions in individual catalogue entries. In certain cases, when nineteenth-century paintings were included in dealers' exhibitions for example, these two sections have been conflated,

VAN GOGH The National Gallery's four paintings by Van Gogh (Inv. nos. 3861, 3862, 3863 and 4169) are not catalogued in this volume but in *The French School* by Cecil Gould.

CORNELIUS JOHNSON The one painting (Inv. no. 6280) in the National Gallery by Johnson, who was born in London of Dutch parents but moved to the Netherlands after the outbreak of the Civil War, is not included in this catalogue but in *The British School* by Martin Davies.

Abbreviations used in the Catalogue

1 BIBLIOGRAPHICAL ABBREVIATIONS

Van der Aa
A. J. van der Aa, *Aardrijkskundig Woordenboek der Nederlanden*, 3 vols, 1848

Bartsch
[J. A. B. von Bartsch, *Le peintre graveur*, 21 vols, Vienna, 1803–21] *The Illustrated Bartsch*, ed. W. L. Strauss, New York, 1978–

Bartsch, *Rembrandt*
A. Bartsch, *Catalogue Raisonné de toutes les estampes qui forment l'oeuvre de Rembrandt . . .*, second edition, Vienna, 1797

Bauch
K. Bauch, *Rembrandt Gemälde*, Berlin, 1966

Benesch
O. Benesch, *The Drawings of Rembrandt*, 6 vols, second edition, London, 1973

Bergström
I. Bergström, *Dutch Still-Life Painting in the Seventeenth Century*, London, 1956

De Bie
Cornelis de Bie, *Het Gulden Cabinet, vande edele vry schilder-const . . .*, Antwerp, 1662

Van Bleyswijck
Dirck van Bleyswijck, *Beschryvinge der Stadt Delft*, Delft, 1667

BM
The Burlington Magazine, London, 1903–

Bode and HdG
W. Bode and C. Hofstede de Groot, *The Complete Work of Rembrandt*, 8 vols, Paris, 1897–1906

Bredius, *Künstler-Inventare*
A. Bredius, *Künstler-Inventare: Urkunden zur Geschichte der holländischen kunst des XVIten, XVIIten und XVIIIten Jahrhunderts*, 8 vols, The Hague, 1915–22

Bredius, *Rembrandt*
A. Bredius, *Rembrandt*, third edition (revised by H. Gerson), London, 1969

Buchanan
W. Buchanan, *Memoirs of Painting*, 2 vols, London 1824

Charrington/Alexander
Compiled by John Charrington and revised by David Alexander, *A Cata-*

logue of Mezzotints after, or said to be after, Rembrandt. In C. White, D. Alexander and E. D'Oench, *Rembrandt in Eighteenth-Century England*, New Haven, 1983, Appendix C, pp. 119–49

Descamps
 J. B. Descamps, *La vie des peintres flamands, allemands et hollandois*, 4 vols, Paris, 1754–63

DNB
 Dictionary of National Biography, Oxford, 1917–

Dublin, *Dutch Paintings*
 H. Potterton, *Dutch seventeenth and eighteenth century paintings in the National Gallery of Ireland: a complete catalogue*, Dublin, 1986

Van Eijnden and van der Willigen
 R. van Eijnden and A. van der Willigen, *Geschiedenis der Vaderlandsche Schilderkunst sedert de helft der XVIII eeuw*, 3 vols, Haarlem, 1842

Farington
 Ed. K. Garlick et al., *The Diary of Joseph Farington*, 16 vols (vols 1–6 edited by K. Garlick and A. Macintyre; vols 7 onwards edited by K. Cave), New Haven/London, 1978–84

GB–A
 Gazette des Beaux-Arts, Paris, 1859–

Geisberg
 M. Geisberg, *Die Stadt Münster (Bau- und Kunstdenkmaler von Westfalen)*, 2 vols, Münster, 1933

Grimm
 C. Grimm, *Frans Hals : Das Gesamtwerk*, Stuttgart/Zürich, 1989

Van Gool
 J. van Gool, *De Nieuwe Schouburg der Nederlantsche Kunstschilders en schilderessen . . .*, 2 vols, The Hague, 1750–1

Van Hall
 H. van Hall, *Portretten van Nederlandse beeldende kunstenaars*, Amsterdam, 1963

Havard
 H. Havard, *L'art et les artistes hollandais*, 4 vols, Paris, 1879–81

HdG
 C. Hofstede de Groot, *Catalogue raisonné of the Works of the most eminent Dutch Painters of the Seventeenth Century*, 10 vols (vols 9 and 10 are in German), London/Stuttgart/Paris, 1907–28

HdG, *Urkunden*
 C. Hofstede de Groot, *Die Urkunden über Rembrandt (1575–1721)*, The Hague, 1906

Hind
 A. M. Hind, *Catalogue of Drawings by Dutch and Flemish Artists . . . in the British Museum*, 5 vols, London, 1915–32

Hoet
G. Hoet, *Catalogus of Naamlyst van Schilderyen met derzelver pryzen . . .*, 3 vols, The Hague, 1752 and 1770

Hollstein
F. W. H. Hollstein, *Dutch and Flemish Etchings, Engravings and Woodcuts, 1450–1700*, 19 vols (unfinished series), Amsterdam, 1949–

Hoogstraten
Samuel van Hoogstraten, *Inleyding tot de Hooge Schoole der Schilderkonst : anders de zichtbaere werelt . . .*, Rotterdam, 1678

Houbraken
Arnold Houbraken, *De Groote Schouburgh der Nederlantsche Konstschilders en Schilderessen*, 3 vols, Amsterdam, 1718–21

Jantzen
H. Jantzen, *Das Niederländische Architekturbild*, Leipzig, 1910

JKPK
Jahrbuch der Königlich Preussischen Kunstsammlungen, Berlin, 1880–1943

Kramm
C. Kramm, *De levens en werken der hollandsche en vlaamsche kunstschilders . . .*, 7 vols, Amsterdam, 1857–64

Lebrun
J. B. P. Lebrun, *Galerie des peintres Flamands, Hollandais et Allemands*, 3 vols, Paris; vols 1 and 2, 1792; vol. 3, 1796

Lugt
F. Lugt, *Repertoire des catalogues de ventes, 1600–1900*, 3 vols, The Hague, 1938–64

van Mander
Carel van Mander, *Het Schilder-Boeck*, Haarlem, 1604

Moes
E. W. Moes, *Iconographia Batava . . .*, 2 vols, Amsterdam, 1897–1905

Muller
S. Muller, *Schilders-vereenigingen te Utrecht*, Utrecht, 1880

Nieuwenhuys
C. J. Nieuwenhuys, *A Review of the Lives and Works of some of the most eminent painters*, London, 1834

NKJ
Nederlands Kunsthistorisch Jaarboek, The Hague, 1947–9, 1955–

NNBW
Nieuw Nederlandsch Biografisch Woordenboek, 10 vols, Leiden, 1911–37

Northbrook catalogue
W. H. J. Weale and J. P. Richter, *Descriptive Catalogue of the Collection of Pictures belonging to the Earl of Northbrook*, London, 1889

Obreen
F. D. O. Obreen, *Archief voor Nederlandsche Kunstgeschiedenis*, 7 vols, Rotterdam, 1877–1890

OH
Oud Holland, Amsterdam, 1883–1972, The Hague, 1973–

Van Puyvelde
L. van Puyvelde, *The Dutch Drawings in the Collection of His Majesty the King at Windsor Castle*, London, 1944.

Rademaker
A. Rademaker, *Kabinet van Nederlandsche Outheden en Gezichten*, 3 vols (Amsterdam), 1725

Rembrandt Corpus
J. Bruyn, B. Haak, S. H. Levie et al., *A Corpus of Rembrandt paintings*, The Hague/London, 1982–

Sandrart, *Teutsche Academie*
Joachim van Sandrart, *Academie der Bau-, Bild- und Mahlerey-Kunste von 1675*, ed. A. R. Peltzer, Munich, 1925

Schatborn 1985
P. Schatborn, *Catalogus van de Nederlandse Tekeningen in het Rijksprenten-kabinet, Rijksmuseum, Amsterdam: Tekeningen van Rembrandt en zijn onbekende leelingen en navolgers*, The Hague, 1985

Scheen
P. A. Scheen, *Lexicon Nederlands Beeldende Kunstenaars 1750–1830*, The Hague, 1981

Smith
John Smith, *A Catalogue Raisonné of the works of the Most Eminent Dutch, Flemish and French Painters . . .* (with Supplement), 9 vols, London, 1829–42.

Stechow
W. Stechow, *Dutch Landscape Painting of the Seventeenth Century*, London, 1966

Strauss *Doc.*
W. L. Strauss and M. van der Meulen, *The Rembrandt Documents*, New York, 1979

Sumowski, *Drawings*
W. Sumowski, *Drawings of the Rembrandt School*, 9 vols, New York, 1981–5

Sumowski, *Gemälde*
W. Sumowski, *Gemälde der Rembrandt Schüler*, 5– vols, Landau/Pfalz, 1983–

Terwesten
P. Terwesten, *Catalogus of Naamlyst von Schilderyen*, The Hague, 1770

Thieme/Becker
U. Thieme and F. Becker, *Allgemeines Lexikon der bildenden Kunstler*, 37 vols, Leipzig, 1907–50

De Vries, Bredius, Muller
    A. D. de Vries, A. Bredius and S. Muller, *Catalogus der Schilderijen in het Museum Kunstliefde te Utrecht*, Utrecht, 1885

Vroom
    N. R. A. Vroom, *De Schilders van het Monochrome Banketje*, 1945 (second edition, in English, *A Modest Message as intimated by the Painters of the 'Monochrome Banketje'*, 2 vols, Schiedam, 1980)

Waagen, 1854
    G. F. Waagen, *Treasures of Art in Great Britain*, 3 vols, London, 1854

Waagen, 1857
    G. F. Waagen, *Galleries and Cabinets of Art in Great Britain*, London, 1857 (Supplement to Waagen 1854)

Weyerman
    J. C. Weyerman, *De Levens-Beschryvingen der Nederlandsche Konst-Schilders . . .*, 4 vols, The Hague, 1729–69

White
    C. White, *The Dutch Pictures in the Collection of Her Majesty the Queen*, Cambridge, 1982

White and Boon
    C. White and K. Boon, *Hollstein's Dutch and Flemish Etchings, Engravings and Woodcuts*, vols 18 and 19, *Rembrandt van Rijn*, Amsterdam, 1969

Van der Willigen
    A. van der Willigen, *Les artistes de Harlem*, Haarlem, 1870

Wurzbach
    A. von Wurzbach, *Niederländisches Künstler-Lexikon*, 3 vols, Vienna/Leipzig, 1906–11

2 EXHIBITION CATALOGUES

Amsterdam 1976
    Tot Lering en Vermaak: Betekenissen van Hollandse genrevoorstellingen uit de zeventiende eeuw, Rijksmuseum, Amsterdam, 1976

Amsterdam 1989/90
    De Hollandse Fijnschilders van Gerard Dou tot Adriaen van der Werff, Rijksmuseum, Amsterdam, 1989–90

Arts Council 1958
    Dutch Genre Paintings, Arts Council of Great Britain (Aberystwyth, National Library of Wales; Cardiff, National Museum of Wales; Swansea, Glyn Vivian Art Gallery), 1958

Bath 1953
    Coronation Exhibition of Flower Paintings, 1652–1952, Victoria Art Gallery, Bath, 1953

Birmingham 1934
    Commemorative Exhibition of the Art Treasures of the Midlands, City of Birmingham Museum and Art Gallery, 1934

Birmingham 1950
Some Dutch Cabinet Pictures of the 17th Century, City of Birmingham Museum and Art Gallery, 1950

Birmingham 1953
Works of Art from Midland Houses, City of Birmingham Museum and Art Gallery, 1953

Brighton 1979
Painters of the Sea, Art Gallery and Museum, Brighton, 1979

Glasgow 1888
Glasgow International Exhibition, Glasgow, 1888

The Hague 1979
Zo wijd der wereld strekt, Koninklijk Kabinet van Schilderijen Mauritshuis, The Hague, 1979

The Hague/Cambridge, Mass. 1981–2
Jacob van Ruisdael, Koninklijk Kabinet van Schilderijen Mauritshuis, The Hague, 1981–2; The Fogg Art Museum, Cambridge, Mass., 1982

Hull 1961
Dutch Painting of the Seventeenth Century, Ferens Art Gallery, Kingston-upon-Hull, 1961

Leiden 1988
Leidse Fijnschilders van Gerrit Dou tot Frans van Mieris de Jonge, 1630–1760, Stedelijk Museum de Lakenhal, Leiden, 1988

London 1947–8
An Exhibition of Cleaned Pictures (1936–1947), The National Gallery, London, 1947–8

London 1972
The Alexander Gift, The National Gallery, London, 1972

London 1974a
Dutch Townscape Painting, The National Gallery, London, 1974

London 1974b
The Working of the National Gallery, The National Gallery, London, 1974

London 1976
Art in Seventeenth-Century Holland, The National Gallery, London, 1976

London 1978–9
The National Gallery lends Dutch Genre Paintings: Newcastle, Hatton Art Gallery; Bolton, Museum and Art Gallery; Lincoln, Usher Art Gallery; Southampton, Art Gallery; London, The National Gallery, 1978–9

London 1982
The National Gallery lends Paintings of the Warm South; Coventry, Herbert Art Gallery; Derby, Museum and Art Gallery; Doncaster, Museum and Art Gallery; Bath, Victoria Art Gallery; London, The National Gallery 1982

London 1983
The Neglected National Gallery, The National Gallery, London, 1983

London 1986
Dutch Landscape: The Early Years: Haarlem and Amsterdam 1590–1650, The National Gallery, London, 1986

London 1988
The Harold Samuel Collection. 17th Century Dutch Painting. Barbican Art Gallery, London, 1988

London, 1988/9
Art in the Making: Rembrandt, The National Gallery, London, 1988–9

London, NACF, 1945–6
Exhibition in honour of Sir Robert Witt of the principal acquisitions made for the National Gallery through the National Art-Collections Fund, The National Gallery, London, 1945

Manchester 1857
The Art Treasures of the United Kingdom, Manchester, 1857

Manchester 1929
Dutch Old Masters, City of Manchester Art Gallery, 1929

Manchester 1957
Art Treasures Centenary: European Old Masters, City of Manchester Art Gallery, 1957

Paris/London/The Hague/1983
The Hague School: Dutch Masters of the Nineteenth Century, Paris, Grand Palais; London, Royal Academy of Arts; The Hague, Gemeentemuseum, 1983

Philadelphia/Berlin/London 1984
Masters of Seventeenth-Century Dutch Genre Painting, Philadelphia, Museum of Art; Berlin-Dahlem, Gemäldegalerie, Staatliche Museen Preussicher Kulturbesitz; London, Royal Academy of Arts, 1984

RA 1928
Seventeenth Century Art, Royal Academy of Arts, London, 1928

RA 1929
Exhibition of Dutch Art 1450–1900, Royal Academy of Arts, London, 1929

RA 1938–9
Seventeenth Century Art in Europe, Royal Academy of Arts, London, 1938–9

RA 1952–3
Dutch Pictures 1450–1700, Royal Academy of Arts, London, 1952–3

RA 1954–5
European Masters of the Eighteenth Century, Royal Academy of Arts, London, 1954–5

San Francisco/Toledo/Boston, 1966–7
The Age of Rembrandt, California Palace of the Legion of Honor, San Francisco; The Toledo Museum of Art; Museum of Fine Arts, Boston

Sheffield, 1956
Dutch Masterpieces, Graves Art Gallery, Sheffield, 1956

Utrecht 1965
> *Nederlandse 17e Eeuwse Italianiserende Landschapschilders*, Centraal Museum, Utrecht, 1965 (second edition, revised and enlarged, Soest, 1978)

Washington/Detroit/Amsterdam 1980–1
> *Gods, Saints and Heroes: Dutch Painting in the Age of Rembrandt*, National Gallery of Art, Washington; Institute of Arts, Detroit; Rijksmuseum, Amsterdam, 1980

Washington/London/Haarlem 1989–90
> *Frans Hals*, National Gallery of Art, Washington; Royal Academy of Arts, London; Frans Halsmuseum, Haarlem, 1989–90

3 OTHER ABBREVIATIONS

BI
> *British Institution*

NACF
> *National Art Collections Fund*

NMM
> *National Maritime Museum*

RA
> *The Royal Academy of Arts, London*

RBK
> *Rijksdienst Beeldende Kunst, The Hague*

RKD
> *Rijksbureau voor Kunsthistorische Documentatie, The Hague.*

List of Paintings

		VOL. 1 page	VOL. 2 plate

CATALOGUE

JOHANNES VAN DER AACK, 1635/6 – after 1680

Johannes Claesz. van der Aack or *Aeck* was the son of a Leiden wine-merchant.[1] The date of his birth is not known but he was said to be fourteen when he was admitted to Leiden University in May 1650.[2] In April 1658 he entered the guild in Leiden[3] and bought a house there in the same year.[4] He appears in the Leiden guild records from 1658 to 1680;[5] in 1673–4 he was a *hoofdman* and dean and in 1676 a *hoofdman* again.[6] He is presumably the 'Johannes van der Aack' who is described in 1676 as a wine-merchant in Leiden.[7] According to Moes he is mentioned in the Leiden guild until 1700[8] but 1680 is the latest date concerning him in the guild records published by Bredius[9] or in the latter's unpublished extracts from the Leiden archives.[10]

REFERENCES:

1. According to a document of 1659 in the Leiden archives (unpublished extracts made by A. Bredius from this and other documents relating to van der Aack are in the RKD).
2. Entry in the MS 'Volumen inscriptionum . . . studiosorum Academiae Leijdensis' in Leiden University Library (vol. 4, 1645–62, p. 242).
3. Obreen, vol. 5, p. 216.

4. See note 1.
5. Obreen, vol. 5, pp. 216–17, 223 and 250–51.
6. Obreen, vol. 5, pp. 216–17.
7. See note 1.
8. E.W. Moes in Thieme/Becker, vol. 1, p. 94.
9. See note 5.
10. See note 1.

1397 *An Old Woman seated sewing* — Plate 1

On the wall, at the right, hangs an engraved portrait of Christian, Duke of Brunswick; the oval border of the portrait is inscribed, starting at the top to the right: VIN [CERE] AU[T] MORI.[1]

Signed in the lower margin of the engraving, between the lines of simulated inscription: Joannes-Ab Aack fecit/16 55.[2]

Oil on canvas, 108.8 × 82 ($42\frac{7}{8}$ × $32\frac{1}{8}$).

Christian, Duke of Brunswick (1599–1626), was a Protestant general in the early part of the Thirty Years' War and fought for a time in the service of the United Provinces. He was noted as a violent partisan of the Protestant cause and described himself as 'friend of God and enemy of the priests'. The print on the wall is Willem Jacobsz. Delff's engraving of 1623 after a portrait of Christian by Michiel van Miereveld.[3] The same print hangs on the wall in J. D. de Heem's *Interior with a Young Man seated at a Table* (Oxford, Ashmolean Museum, Ward Bequest).

PROVENANCE: Presented by Henry J. Pfungst in 1894.

REFERENCES:

1. The inscription on the oval border of the engraved portrait, which was noted in this form by MacLaren and which is based on that around the engraving, is very hard to read even with the assistance of infra-red photography and may be partially simulated.
2. Although the signature and date are darker than the simulated inscription surrounding them, they are neither later additions nor retouched.
3. Hollstein, vol. 5, no. 14. The impression seen in the present painting is the first state, i.e. without the moustache and chin-tuft added in the second. Van der Aack has added flesh tints to the face of Christian of Brunswick in the painting.

ARENT ARENTSZ., 1585/6–1631

He was the son of a sailmaker, Arent Jansz., who lived on the Zeedijk in Amsterdam in a house called *de Cabel*. On 19 May 1619 he married in Sloten near Amsterdam. On 4 May 1622 he is mentioned as the owner of a plot of land on the Prinsengracht facing the Noordermarkt on which he built a house which he named *de Cabel* after his family house. He was himself known by the name *Cabel*. He was buried in the Old Church in Amsterdam on 18 August 1631.[1]

These are the few known facts of Arentsz.'s life. Nothing is known of his artistic training. He painted landscapes, often in an oblong format, with prominent figures of peasants, fishermen and hunters in the foreground. His work is dependent on that of Hendrick Avercamp; that it was Avercamp rather than Arentsz. who was the innovator of this kind of landscape can reasonably be assumed from the fact that Arentsz.'s earliest extant dated painting is from 1629, later than the earliest related works by Avercamp.

REFERENCE:
1. I.H. van Eeghen, 'Meerhuizen of de Pauwentuin en Arent Arentsz. genaamd Cabel', *Maandblad Amstelodamum*, 54, 1967, pp. 219–21.

3533 *Fishermen near Muiden Castle*   Plate 2

The castle is in the left background.

Signed at the left end of the bridge: AA (in monogram).

Oil on oak, 23.3 × 38.8 ($9\frac{3}{16}$ × $15\frac{1}{4}$).

The Castle of Muiden, here seen from the west, is $7\frac{1}{2}$ miles east of Amsterdam (cf. Beerstraaten No. 1311). The church in the right background bears a slight resemblance to that in Muiderberg,[1] which lies, however, to the east of the castle.

The figure of the fisherman on the left occurs, in reverse, almost exactly in a painting which in 1963 was in the collection of Dr H. Wetzlar in Amsterdam.[2]

The picture was apparently at one time ascribed to Esaias van de Velde.[3]

VERSIONS: A signed version, with variations, was in the possession of W. Paech, Amsterdam, before 1940. A painting showing the left-hand side of the composition, signed in monogram on the box carried by the fisherman, was in a sale at Christie's, 31 March 1989 (lot 157).[4]

PROVENANCE: Possibly identical with a painting of very similar description, attributed to Hendrick Avercamp, in the Simon Fokke sale, Amsterdam, 6 sqq. December 1784 (lot 19),[5] bought by Belie (2 guilders 15 stuivers). In the [Mrs M.S. Cole] sale, Christie's, 2 June 1919 (lot 81), bought by Dr J. Seymour Maynard, by whom presented (through the NACF) in 1920.

EXHIBITION: London 1978–9, No. 1.

REFERENCES:
1. Cf. the engravings of Muiderberg church in 1640 and 1660 in Rademaker, vol. 2, nos. 248 and 249.
2. Panel, 43 × 59 cm. It was in the exhibition, 'Nederlandse Landschappen uit de 17e eeuw', Dordrechts Museum, 1963, cat. no. 1.
3. On the back is a label, inscribed: 14. Izias vandavil/shipping [sic].
4. Panel, 18.1 × 15.6 cm.
5. 'Dit verbeeld een Gezigt van het Slot van Muiden, op de voorgrond staat een Man met zyn

Hengeltuig op zyn schouder, ziende naar twee Viss-chers, die eenige Visch uit een Korf in eene Tobbe storten; verder ziet man eenige zoo vaartende als dryvende Vaartuigen.' The size is not given in the sale catalogue. C.J. Welcker, *Hendrick Avercamp en* *Barent Avercamp*, 2nd ed., Doornspijk, 1979, p. 287, No. T. 292, includes it in her list of lost draw-ings, but although the Fokke sale was mostly of drawings, the first fifty lots were paintings.

HENDRICK AVERCAMP, 1585–1634

Hendrick Barentsz. Avercamp, also known as 'de stom (stomme) van Campen', since he was dumb. He was baptised in the Old Church in Amsterdam on 27 January 1585. In the following year his parents moved to Kampen, where his father was town apothec-ary (he died in 1602). Avercamp spent his early years in Kampen but he may be 'de Stom' living in the house of the painter Pieter Isaacsz. in Amsterdam in March 1607 who bought some drawings at a sale of the latter's possessions. Avercamp is recorded in Kampen in January 1613, and also in 1622 when the town paid 12 guilders to 'Hendrick Avercamp d'Stomme van twee peerden te schilden op de stadsstal'. He was buried in the Sint Nicolaaskerk in Kampen on 15 May 1634.[1]

Pieter Isaacsz. (c. 1560–1625), who may have been Avercamp's teacher, is known as a history painter, portraitist and draughtsman, in an elegant, late Mannerist style, quite unlike that of Avercamp, whose manner was based in the first place on that of the Flemish followers of Pieter Bruegel the Elder. It is possible that he came into contact with one of Bruegel's followers who settled in Amsterdam, such as David Vinckboons (1576–c.1632). Avercamp principally painted winter scenes and also made many col-oured drawings of winter scenes, fishermen and peasants. (There is a particularly important group of these drawings in the Royal Collection.) There are dated paintings of the years 1608,[2] 1609, 1620, 1626 and 1632.

His nephew, Barent Petersz. Avercamp, who also lived and worked for much of his life in Kampen, was a close follower, as was Arent Arentsz.

REFERENCES:
General: C.J. Welcker, *Hendrick Avercamp en Barent Avercamp*, 2nd ed., Doornspijk, 1979. Ex. cat. (by A. Blankert, G. Keyes, D. B. Hensbroek-van der Poel and others), *Hendrick Avercamp, Barent Aver-camp: Frozen Silence*, K. and V. Waterman, Amster-dam, 1982.
In text:
1. The documents concerning Avercamp's life etc., are to be found in Welcker, op. cit. (especially pp. 56–71).

2. In H. Vey and A. Kesting, *Katalog der Niederlän-dischen Gemälde . . . im Wallraf-Richartz-Museum*, Cologne, 1969, p. 14, it is noted that a version of a monogrammed painting in that collection (No. 1319) is dated 1605. The version was lot 43 in a sale in Copenhagen (Rasmussen) on 12 March 1966 (illustrated in the catalogue). There is also a photo-graph in the RKD. It is therefore possible that the Cologne painting, which is more 'Flemish' in style than the one of 1608 in Bergen, dates from 1605.

1346 *A Winter Scene with Skaters near a Castle* — *Plate 3*

On the back of the carved and gilt sledge on the right is a lion rampant, which is also on the side. The barrel in the middle distance, centre, is marked with a crescent and star.

3

Signed at the bottom, left of centre: HA (in monogram).

Oil on oak, circular; diameter 40.7 (16). (Let into a later square surround, also of oak. Cleaning in 1983 revealed that the painting has been extended onto this surround by a later hand and subsequently these additions have been painted out.)

Some damage around the outer edge of the original circular panel.

The castle is an invention of the artist. A very similar composition – with a central castle, prominent tree on the left and groups of farm buildings to left and right – treated in a closely related manner and with the skaters in comparable costumes can be seen in a winter landscape of 1608 in the Billedgalleri, Bergen.[1]

This is also an early work, and should be dated to c.1608/9.[2]

PROVENANCE: In the collection of Edward Habich, Cassel, and exhibited with others from that collection in the Gemäldegalerie, Cassel, from 1881–91.[3] Purchased with Nos. 1336–45, 1347 and 1348 from Edward Habich in 1891.

EXHIBITION: Cassel, Gemäldegalerie, 1881–91.[4]

REFERENCES:
General: Welcker, op. cit., No. S54.
In text:
1. Welcker, op. cit., No. S3; see also W. Stechow, 'Significant dates on some 17th-century Dutch land-scape paintings', OH, 75, 1960, pp. 80–83.
2. Blankert, in the 1982 Amsterdam exhibition cata-logue, op. cit., p. 27, argues that No. 1346 predates the Bergen painting. He places it in a detailed sequence between the Cologne painting which may date from 1605 (see note 2 of the biographical notice above) and a painting in the Rijksmuseum (1976 cat., A1718). In the same ex. cat. G. Keyes relates No. 1346 to an anonymous etching after David Vinckboons' *Winter*, which is strikingly similar in composition. It is illustrated as fig. 13.
3. JKPK, 1881, *Amtliche Berichte*, col. 91, no. 13, and O. Eisenmann, *Führer durch die Kgl. Gemälde-galerie zu Cassel*, 5th ed., [1883], p. 44.
4. See note 3.

1479 *A Scene on the Ice near a Town*   Plate 4

The sleigh at the left edge has a painted panel with two figures on the side and one with a horseman on the back. Several groups of men in the distance are playing *kolf*.

Signed on the wooden boarding in the centre foreground: HA (in monogram; worn).

Oil on oak 58 × 89.8 ($22\frac{13}{16}$ × $35\frac{3}{8}$).

Cleaned in 1969. There is an area of damage at the left edge in the sky.

It has been supposed[1] that the building on the right is the Half Moon brewery in Kampen, but there are only the half-a-dozen barrels outside to suggest it is a brewery and the rather vaguely indicated town in the distance does not seem at all like Kampen;[2] the tower bears a vague resemblance to that of the St Cunerakerk in Rhenen (Province of Utrecht).

In this painting Avercamp has moved away from the markedly 'Flemish' style of No. 1346. It should be dated later than that painting, probably c.1615.[3]

DRAWING: A coloured drawing of the man seated in the right background is at Windsor.[4]

COPY: A copy (with variations in the figure groups and an extended area of sky) was in the Plumier collection, Brussels, in 1970 (photograph in RKD: support not specified and dimensions not given).

PROVENANCE: Purchased from J. St Hensé of Bradford (out of the Lewis Fund) in 1896.

EXHIBITIONS: Arts Council 1945, No. 1; London 1976, No. 4.

REFERENCES:
General: Welcker, op. cit., No. S55.
In text:
1. Welcker, loc. cit., who claims that barrels marked with a half moon often occur in Avercamp's works.
2. Cf. Wenzel Hollar's etched view of c.1644, the drawing of c.1633 in the Geschiedkundig Over-ijsselsch Museum, Zwolle, reproduced in Welcker, op. cit., pl. 47, and Barent Avercamp's painting of

1663 in the Raadhuis, Kampen (reproduced in Welcker, op. cit., pl. 41).
3. Blankert, in the 1982 Amsterdam ex. cat. (op. cit.), p. 27, also dated No. 1479 to c.1615. He relates it to a painting in Schwerin (Panel, 67.5×117 cm. Not signed. Inv. no. 2678; Welcker, op. cit., No. S73; exhibited in Amsterdam 1982 as cat. no. 8).
4. Welcker, op. cit., No. T158.

LUDOLF BAKHUIZEN, 1630/1–1708

He signed his name also *Ludolph Bakhuisen*, *Backhuysen* and *Backhuyzen*. He was born in or near Emden, East Friesland, in 1630 or 1631.[1] He came to Amsterdam in about 1650 as a merchant's clerk[2] and was also a calligrapher,[3] but soon turned to making pen drawings of shipping.[4] He later learned painting from Allart van Everdingen and also from Hendrick Dubbels,[5] whose influence is clear in his early works. His more mature style shows that he studied the work of the younger van de Velde, especially the storm scenes. There are dated paintings from 1658 onwards. In 1665 he was commissioned by the burgomasters of Amsterdam to paint a view of the town for presentation to one of Louis XIV's ministers.[6] After the two van de Veldes went to England in 1672 he was the leading marine painter in Holland and became one of the most successful artists of his time, being patronised by Peter the Great and various German princes.[7] He lived all his life in Amsterdam and died there on 7 November 1708.[8]

Nearly all his paintings are seascapes, often with rough water; he also painted a number of portraits and a few religious and genre scenes, landscapes and town views.[9] In addition he made a number of etchings.

Among his pupils were Jan Claesz. Rietschoof (1652–1719), Pieter Coopse (active 1657/8) and Michiel Maddersteeg (c.1659–1709).

REFERENCES:
General: HdG, vol. 7; Exhibition catalogue, *Ludolf Bakhuizen*, Nederlands Scheepvaart Museum, Amsterdam, 1985 (for his biography, see W.L. van de Watering, 'Ludolf Bakhuizen, zijn leven en werk', pp. 3–10 of that catalogue). H. Nannen, *Ludolf Backhuysen (Emden 1630–Amsterdam 1708)*, Emden, 1985.
In text:
1. Houbraken (vol. 2, p. 236) writes that he was born on 18 December (old style = 28 December new style) 1631 in Emden but van de Watering (in ex. cat. *Bakhuizen*, 1985, op. cit., pp.3–4) has pointed

out that his baptism is not recorded in the Emden *doopboek*. See also E. Starcke, 'Ist Emden der Geburtsort des Malers Ludolf Backhuysen?', *Jahrbuch der Gesellschaft für bildende Kunst und vaterländische Altertümer zu Emden*, 7, 1887, pp. 67–72 and discussion in Nannen, op. cit., pp. 15–17.
2. Houbraken, loc. cit.
3. As late as 15 November 1656 he was described as 'schrijver en factor'.
4. In 1657 and 1660 he is called a draughtsman ('*teyckenaer*'); he is described as a painter in 1664.

5

5. Houbraken, vol. 2, p. 237.

6. OH, 1893, pp. 30–3; Ex. cat. *Bakhuizen*, 1985, op. cit., p. 8 and cat. no. 58.

7. Houbraken, vol. 2, p. 240.

8. Houbraken, vol. 2, p. 242, and OH, 1916, pp. 242–43.

9. Ex. cat. *Bakhuizen*, 1985, op. cit., pp. 9ff.

204 *Dutch Men-of-War and Small Vessels in a Fresh Breeze off Enkhuizen*   *Plate 5*

In the foreground towards the left is a *kaag* with a blue and red vane. In the right middle distance are two men-of-war with Dutch ensigns before the wind; the nearer, which lacks her main topmast, has the arms of Amsterdam on her stern and is firing a salute. Farther to the right is a yacht. A third man-of-war, with a Dutch flag at the main, is in the left middle distance. The town of Enkhuizen is visible in the centre distance.

Signed twice, once on the wale of the small vessel in the left foreground: 1683 L Bakhuizen; and a second time in a cartouche on the stern of the yacht on the right: L B.

Oil on canvas, 100.5 × 136.5 ($39\frac{5}{8}$ × $53\frac{3}{4}$).

Cleaned in 1960.

Enkhuizen is here seen from the south-east, surrounded by its sea wall. The tall tower in the centre is that of the Zuiderkerk and the pointed roof immediately to the left of it is the Zuiderpoort; the long low building on the extreme right of the town is possibly the East India Company's house. Enkhuizen appears in several paintings by Bakhuizen; the same view of it, but seen from a less distant viewpoint, is in a painting in the Royal Collection.[1]

PROVENANCE: In the possession of John Smith, who sold it in 1822;[2] in the collection of Richard Simmons by 1835.[3] Richard Simmons Bequest, 1846.

REFERENCES:
General: Smith No. 123; HdG No. 197.
In text:
1. HdG No. 116; White No. 13.

2. Smith, loc. cit., as 'View on the Texel'.
3. Smith, loc. cit.

223 *The Eendracht and a Fleet of Dutch Men-of-War before the Wind*   *Plate 6*

In the centre is the *Eendracht*, on her stern the lion of the United Provinces and below the stern gallery a *cartellino* with the inscription: EEND[R]ACHT; she wears a Dutch ensign and, at the main, the flag and pennant of the commander-in-chief. In the right middle distance is a flute (*fluitschip*) with Dutch colours; on her stern is carved a female figure. Numerous other men-of-war are in the centre and right distance, some with plain red ensigns. In the left middle distance a yacht with a Dutch vane is firing a salute. The row-barge in the right foreground pulling towards the *Eendracht* has a white ensign with an orange escutcheon.

Oil on canvas, 75.5 × 105.5 (29½ × 41½).

Cleaned in 1973. Some damage along the right edge.

The man-of-war in the centre is apparently the *Eendracht* (Union) of 76 guns which was built in 1653. She was the flagship of Lieutenant-Admiral Jacob van Wassenaer van Obdam during the Dutch expedition against the Swedes in 1658–9, and at the battle of Lowestoft on 3 June 1665 when she blew up with the loss of almost all her crew including the Admiral. The battle ended with an English victory.[1] A larger *Eendracht* was built to replace her in 1666.[2] Judging from the drawing of the first *Eendracht* off Kronborg Castle in 1658 or 1659 by Heerman Witmont (*c.*1605–83) and that of her in action at the battle of the Sound, October 1658, by Willem van de Velde the Elder (both in the National Maritime Museum[3]), the present representation is not entirely accurate; the lion of the United Provinces should be rampant and enclosed within a fence, and there are minor variations in the structure of her stern. Despite these differences, it is probable that the ship in the present picture is intended to represent the *Eendracht* of 1653; M. S. Robinson points out that she flies the flag of command and pennant of a full admiral and that, while this was the case with the 1653 *Eendracht* (see above), the later *Eendracht* was apparently never the flagship of a full admiral.[4] The present picture has been described as *Admiral de Ruyter and his Officers embarking*[5] but de Ruyter's flag was never carried by either *Eendracht*.

Although the picture almost certainly shows a ship that was destroyed in 1665, the style suggests it was painted later, probably in the early 1670s. The inaccuracies in the detailed representation of the ship may therefore be due to Bakhuizen having painted it from memory, some years after its destruction.

VERSIONS OR COPIES: A repetition or copy was in the Chaix d'Est-Ange collection, Paris, by 1907;[6] another was in the possession of Arthur Tooth and Son, London, in 1928.[7] (A repetition or copy which was on the London market in 1946 is perhaps to be identified with one or other of these.)

PROVENANCE: In the collection of Lady Holland, Cranbury, near Winchester; Lady Holland sale, London, 22 April 1826 (lot 85), bought by Woodin (167 gns). In the collection of Charles A. Bredel by 1828 when lent to the BI. Bredel Bequest, 1851.

EXHIBITIONS: BI 1828, No. 126; BI 1835, No. 170; BI 1851, No. 57.

REFERENCES:
General: Smith No. 76; HdG No. 229.
In text:
1. See the NMM catalogue, 1937, pp. 39–40 and 42.
2. NMM catalogue, p. 97, No. 24.
3. NMM catalogue, p. 94, No. 8 and p. 93, No. 4
4. Oral communication, 1954.
5. In the catalogue of the BI exhibition, 1851, No. 57.

6. Canvas, 75 × 104 cm.; signed: L.B. Reproduced in *Les Arts*, July 1907, p. 14. Chaix d'Est-Ange sale, Paris, 11 December 1934 (lot 8), as acquired from Mons. Crosnier.
7. Reproduced in an advertisement in BM, vol. 53, No. 307, October 1928.

818 *A Beach Scene with Fishermen*   *Plate 7*

On the right is a fishing pink.

Signed, bottom left: L.B.

Oil on oak, 34.2 × 48.5 (13½ × 19⅛).

A fairly early work still showing the influence of Dubbels, and probably of the mid-1660s.

ENGRAVING: Engraved (in reverse) by Robert Daudet, 1785.[1]

PROVENANCE: Identified by Smith[2] with a *Sea Beach with Figures and Ships* of the same size by Bakhuizen in the Willem Lormier sale, The Hague, 4 sqq. July 1763 (lot 51),[3] bought by Balden or J. Phalte[4] (200 guilders), but according to the sales catalogue this was on canvas. It was in the possession of J.-B.-P. Le Brun, Paris, by 1785;[5] in the collection of Robert de Saint-Victor, Rouen; R. de Saint-Victor sale, Paris, 7 sqq. January 1823 (lot 152), bought by Pérignon (3,850 francs). Possibly in the Ralph Bernal sale, London, 8 May 1824 (lot 32,[6] apparently bought in for 145 gns). By 1835 it was in the collection of Sir Robert Peel, Bart.[7] Purchased with the Peel collection, 1871.

REFERENCES:
General: Smith Nos. 65 and (?)93; HdG Nos. 230 and (?)325.
In text:
1. In Le Brun, vol. 2, opposite p. 62.
2. Smith No. 65.
3. (L. Bakhuizen) 'Un rivage de Mer, avec figures and Vaisseaux'; canvas, 1 *pied* 1 *pouce* × 1 *pied* 6¾ *pouces*. The Dutch edition of the catalogue gives the same description and size. (HdG No. 230 erroneously as lot 49.)
4. Some marked copies of the sale catalogue give Balden as the purchaser, others have J. Phalte.

5. When engraved by R. Daudet (cf. note 1).
6. 'Bakhuysen Sea view. Vessels with a Sea Beach and Figures, &c . . . the surge rolling in upon the shore'; further described by Smith (No. 93) as 'A View from the Beach, looking out seaward, with several vessels at sea, and figures on the shore. The rolling of the waves over the sands is remarkably true to nature.'
7. Smith No. 65.

819 *An English Vessel and a Man-of-War in a Rough Sea off*   *Plate 8*
a Coast with Tall Cliffs

The two-masted vessel running before the wind in the centre foreground has the English ensign and a vane with St George's cross; she has no fore topmast. In the left middle distance is a man-of-war shortening sail; she has the Union flag at the main and at the fore a vane with St George's cross. On the right, in the middle distance, is a snow (*snaauwschip*) and beyond her, two ships with sails furled.

Oil on canvas, 98.5 × 132 (38¾ × 52).

The old identifications of this as a view off Deal[1] and the mouth of the Thames[2] are incorrect; the coast differs from that in the preparatory drawing in the Royal Collection (Fig. 1) and is almost certainly imaginary.

    Probably a work of the 1680s or a little later.

DRAWING: A preparatory study, with variations, is in the Royal Collection at Windsor Castle.[3]

PROVENANCE: In the Lafontaine sale, London, 7 May 1824 (lot 74),[4] bought in (1,450 gns) and sold later.[5] It was in the collection of Sir Robert Peel, Bart., by 1835.[6] Purchased with the Peel collection, 1871.

REFERENCES:

General: Smith No. 88; HdG No. 231 (with the description of a different picture).
In text:
1. In the Lafontaine 1824 sales catalogue (see note 4).
2. Smith, loc. cit.

3. Van Puyvelde No. 64.
4. As 'View off Deal, with Vessels in a stiff breeze'.
5. According to Smith, loc. cit.
6. Smith, loc. cit.

1000 *A View across the River near Dordrecht(?)*   *Plate 9*

On the right is a snow (*snaauwschip*) flying a blue ensign with a coat-of-arms in gold which is only faintly visible; beyond her, broadside on, is a man-of-war under Dutch colours with sails furled. The small gaff-rigged vessel on the left behind the jetty has a Dutch vane.

Oil on oak, 34.1 × 47.8 ($13\frac{7}{16}$ × $18\frac{13}{16}$).

The town on the horizon seems to be Dordrecht, with the Grote Kerk on the left and, towards the right, the Groothoofdspoort. The small vessel in the left foreground has a white vane with red borders: these are the colours of both Dordrecht and Hoorn but in each case the bands of red and white should properly be of equal width.

    If the building towards the right of the town is the Groothoofdspoort in Dordrecht, as seems almost certainly to be the case, the picture was presumably painted before *c.*1692–4 when the spire was replaced by a dome (cf. Calraet No. 3024 and Attributed to Willem van Drielenburgh No. 960). The style is of the mid-1660s.

PROVENANCE: (Previously identified erroneously with a picture in a [Lafontaine] sale, London, 8 May 1813, lot 71.[1]) No. 1000 was in the collection of William Wells, Redleaf, by 1832, when it was exhibited at the BI; William Wells sale, London, 12–13 May 1848 (lot 84), bought by Fuller[2] (156 gns). In the collection of Wynn Ellis by 1850 or 1851.[3] Wynn Ellis Bequest, 1876.

EXHIBITION: BI 1832, No. 168.

REFERENCES:

General: Smith No. 120; HdG No. 232.
In text:
1. The description in the sale catalogue shows that this was a different composition.
2. The 1929 National Gallery catalogue states that it was bought by Brown for Holford, but the auctioneer's copy of the sale catalogue gives Fuller as the purchaser.
3. Waagen, 1854, vol. 2, p. 297.

1050 *Dutch Men-of-War entering a Mediterranean Port*   *Plate 10*

On the left is a man-of-war with Dutch colours and the arms of Amsterdam on her stern. Another man-of-war, in the right middle distance, has a red and blue jack, the flag of the States-General at the main and a plain red ensign; a boat is being rowed towards her. The small vessel in the left foreground has a Dutch vane. Between the warehouse and the tower on the far side of the port a galley is anchored, and the masts of others are visible beyond a headland. In the centre distance are other men-of-war with Dutch colours.

Signed on the ensign of the man-of-war on the left: L Back[huizen] ft[1] and dated on a floating spar, bottom right: 1681.

Oil on canvas, 118.5 × 163 ($46\frac{5}{8}$ × $64\frac{1}{8}$).

The view is imaginary; the galleys show that it is meant to be a Mediterranean scene.

PROVENANCE: Edward Solly sale, London, 31 May 1837 (lot 85), bought by Anthony (135 gns). Later in the collection of Solly's daughters, the Misses Lavinia and Sarah Solly.[2] Miss Sarah Solly Bequest, 1879.

REFERENCES:
General: HdG No. 282.
In text:
1. The signature is worn and only the first four letters of Backhuizen can be made out.

2. Miss Sarah Solly's will, which mentions that the picture had belonged to her father, is dated January 1873.

BARTHOLOMEUS VAN BASSEN, active 1613; died 1652

The place and date of his birth are not known; his close stylistic connection with the Antwerp School (see below) suggests that he may have been Flemish. He is first mentioned in October 1613, when he was inscribed in the Delft guild (as coming from outside Delft).[1] The earliest known dated picture is apparently of 1614 (Lord Clinton sale, London, 19 July 1950, lot 6). He had settled in The Hague by 1622, in which year he became a member of the guild there.[2] In Berlin there is a church interior dated 1624 and signed by him and Frans Francken II of Antwerp (who painted the figures); there is no indication that he went to Antwerp and the picture may have been sent there for the figures to be added. There is no firm evidence that he went to Italy or England, as has been suggested, though he painted several Italian church interiors, in particular that of St Peter's in Rome.[3] Van Bassen was also an architect and as such was in the service of The Hague burgomasters from 1639 onwards;[4] the Nieuwe Kerk, built 1649–56, is in part from his designs. He was buried in The Hague on 28 November 1652.[5]

He painted imaginary church interiors and imaginary views of palaces. His earlier style is closely related to that of the Antwerp architectural painters, for example the Steenwycks and Pieter Neeffs. In some of his pictures the figures are by other painters, such as Frans Francken II (see above) and Esaias van de Velde.

REFERENCES:
1. Obreen, vol. 1, p. 12.
2. Obreen, vol. 3, p. 258. Van Bassen was a *hoofdman* of the guild in 1627, 1636 and 1640–41 (Obreen, vol. 3, p. 276, and vol. 5, pp. 73–74).
3. *Interior of St Peter's*, panel, 51 × 72 cm, signed and dated 1650: dealer J. O. Leegenhoek, Paris, 1968; exhibited Dorotheum, Vienna, 18 March 1969, no. 7, illustrated; another *Interior of St Peter's*, panel, 35.2 × 50.1 cm. Signed. Národní Galerie, Prague (Inv. no. 0127; 1912 cat., no. 19).
4. and **5.** A. J. Servaas van Rooyen, *Catalogus . . . van het Gemeente-Museum van 's-Gravenhage*, 1890, p. 4.

3164 *Interior of the St Cunerakerk, Rhenen* Plate 11

The tablet on the column behind the two men in the left foreground is inscribed DOM, followed by simulated lettering.

Signed, bottom left: B:.van · Bassen ·. 1638.

A large monogram ⅋ is incised on the back of the panel.

Oil on oak, 61.1 × 80.5 ($24\frac{1}{16}$ × $31\frac{11}{16}$).

A retouched split runs the entire width of the panel about 7 cm. from the top.

This is a view of the west end of the St Cunerakerk in Rhenen. It is taken from a point close to the north-east crossing pier, beneath the north side of the rood loft at the entrance to the choir. The identification has been made on the basis of comparison with drawings made by Pieter Saenredam in 1644.[1] The brick walls, vaults and piers are represented here as if constructed in stone.[2] The arches of the vaults have been given rounder profiles,[3] the small impost capitals are eliminated,[4] the pilaster bases above the pier bases are van Bassen's invention, and the irregular stone floor of the church is here replaced by more orderly stones in a tile-like pattern. In the left background is a stairway to an outbuilding which no longer exists;[5] van Bassen modifies the staircase and adds an ornate banister (as well as the carved moulding on the wall above). The doorway in the last bay on the right should be a wall with a window and no engaged piers. The church furniture would largely seem to be van Bassen's invention.[6]

The fifteenth-century church in Rhenen which contains the relics of St Cunera was the court chapel of Frederick V of Palatinate and Elizabeth Stuart, the King and Queen of Bohemia, who were in exile in The Hague.[7] Van Bassen was the architect of the Koningshuis or 'Palace of the Winter King' which was built in 1630–1 on the site of the St Agnieten nunnery immediately adjoining the St Cunerakerk.[8] Although van Bassen painted a few other pictures which show life at the Rhenen court,[9] this is one of the very few paintings by him which represent an actual building more or less accurately.[10]

PROVENANCE: J. D. Ichenhauser sale, London, 3 December 1910 (lot 32), bought by Gooden and Fox (35 gns). Presented by F. A. White (through the NACF), 1917.

REFERENCES:
1. This identification is due to Walter Liedtke, *Architectural Painting in Delft*, Doornspijk, 1982, p. 28. For the Saenredam drawings, see Utrecht, Centraal Museum, *Saenredam*, 1961, Nos. 104–10, esp. No. 109 (pen and wash, 40.8 × 44.6 cm., signed and dated 5 and 6 July 1644: Institut Néerlandais, Paris).
2. See *Kunstreisboek voor Nederland*, 1969, p. 297. The present white plaster surface of the vaults dates from after the fire of 1897; at the same time the original plastering of the walls was abandoned in favour of bare brick.
3. Compare *Saenredam*, op. cit., No. 109.
4. Three and four on each of the simpler piers (compare *Saenredam*, op. cit., Nos. 108–10). The present

pier capitals are additions of *c.*1900.
5. See *Saenredam*, op. cit., No. 109 for this outbuilding, and figs. 110–11 for the actual form of the staircase.
6. No seats, pulpits or pulpit enclosures are found in the bare interior sketched by Saenredam six years later. The memorial tablets are not depicted by Saenredam who does, however, show two chandeliers in the nave and an organ very similar to that in No. 3164.
7. See No. 6362 in this catalogue; and Heidelberg, Schloss, *England und Kurpfalz*, exhibition cat., 1963; and London, National Portrait Gallery, *The Winter Queen*, 1963. Frederick V died in 1632 but, according to his daughter Sophie, 'La Reine (Elizabeth) se

11

retiroit ordinairement tous les estées dans une maison de chasse, nommé Rhenen' (writing in 1680, Sophie was referring to events of *c*.1640; see A. Köcher, *Memoiren der Herzogin Sophie* . . . [Publication aus den K. Preussischen Staatsarchiven, IV], Leipzig, 1879, p. 37).

8. See S. Muller, 'Het Koningshuis te Rhenen', *Bulletin van den Nederlandschen Oudheidkundigen Bond*, vol. 4, 1911, pp. 66–73; and H. E. van Gelder, 'Iets over Barthold van Bassen, ook als bouwmeester van het Koninghuis te Rhenen', ibid., pp. 234–40.

9. See, for example, van Bassen's *The King and Queen of Bohemia dining in Public* in the Royal Collection (White No. 14).

10. His earliest known painting (of 1614: ex-Clinton collection, see above) shows Antwerp Cathedral, but this could have been derived from an earlier Flemish representation. In 1650 he painted the exterior of the New Church in The Hague (Gemeentemuseum, The Hague; 1955 cat. No. 36); as at Rhenen, van Bassen was involved there as an architect.

Attributed to BARTHOLOMEUS VAN BASSEN

924 *Interior of a Church*   *Plate 12*

Falsely signed at the bottom of a wall tablet above a tomb on the right: P. NEEFS. f. 1644. The 'signature' is of a slightly different colour from the date, which is in the same paint as the simulated lettering of the inscription above it, and is a little more coarsely painted than either of the latter. The date is centred on the imitation inscription; the 'signature' being squeezed in on the left of the date. It may also be observed that Neeffs almost invariably spelled his name with two fs, usually in capitals with the fs alone in cursive.

Oil on oak, 68.5 × 98.5 (27 × 38¾).

There is retouching along an original join about 18 cm, from the top.

Previously attributed to Pieter Neeffs the Elder,[1] but the 'signature' is false and the style not that of Neeffs. The picture is close to van Bassen's work but is somewhat coarser than No. 3164 above. The date may be original but could equally well have been added at the same time as the false signature.

PROVENANCE: Presented by (Sir) Henry H. Howorth, 1875.

REFERENCE: **1.** Jantzen, p. 45, considers it one of Pieter Neeffs the Elder's best works.

GERARD VAN BATTEM,
See JACOB VAN RUISDAEL No. 1390

JAN BEERSTRAATEN, 1622–1666

Jan Abrahamsz. Beerstraaten; he also signed his Christian name *Johannes, Johannis* and *Joannes*, and his surname *Beerstraten* (the latter sometimes in two parts – cf. No. 1311 below). He was born in Amsterdam;[1] there are two candidates – Jan, the son of Abraham Jansz., baptised in Amsterdam on 31 May 1622[2] and Johannes, son of Abraham Danielsz., baptised in Amsterdam on 1 March 1622.[3] The painter was said to be twenty in August 1642[4] and about twenty-eight in November 1649,[5] which puts his birth in 1621 or 1622. He married in Amsterdam in 1642[6] and appears to have lived there until his death;[7] his topographical paintings, often very accurate, prove that he visited other parts of Holland. He was buried in Amsterdam on 1 July 1666.[8]

He painted topographical views of Dutch towns and castles (often as winter scenes), imaginary seaports and a few sea-battles; there are dated pictures of 1653–66.[9]

It has been suggested[10] that the pictures signed 'J. Beerstra(a)ten' in capitals are by Jan Abrahamsz. Beerstraaten and those signed in cursive characters, sometimes with the Christian name 'Johannes' or 'Joannes' in full, are by a different painter, 'Johannes Beerstraaten'; it is claimed that the dates of some of the 'Johannes Beerstraaten' pictures are later than Jan Abrahamsz.'s death and therefore confirm this hypothesis. There does not, however, seem to be any appreciable difference of style between the two groups and no J. or Johannes Beerstraaten picture dated or datable after Jan Abrahamsz.'s death has been traced.[11]

The situation is further complicated by the existence of a group of pictures of the same subjects and in the same style signed 'A. Beerstra(a)ten' (occasionally 'A. Beerstraeten' and 'A. Beerestraaten'); these are perhaps the work of 'Abraham Beerstraaten' (possibly Jan Beerstraaten's son of that name who was twenty-one in 1665[12]) or 'Anthonie Beerestraeten' (a picture with this signature is said to exist, dated 1664; he is otherwise unrecorded[13]).

REFERENCES:

General: Havard, vol. 3, pp. 1–60; Bredius, *Künstler-Inventare*, vol. 3, 1917, pp. 814–20; W. F. H. Oldewelt in *Jaarboek van het Genootschap Amstelodamum*, vol. 35, 1938, pp. 81–87; C. N. Fehrmann, 'Vier 17de eeuwse Kamper stads gezichten', *De Kamper Almanak*, 1957/8, pp. 9–17; Stechow, p. 204, note 61; P.J.J. van Thiel, 'De kerk te Sloten door Jan Abrahamsz. Beerstraaten', *Bulletin van het Rijksmuseum*, vol. 16, no. 2, June 1968, pp. 51–6 (with extensive bibliography on the 'Beerstraaten problem', p. 56, note 7).
In text:
1. According to entries in the Amsterdam marriage register, 1642 (Havard, vol. 3, p. 10) and the Weeskamer records, 1666 (Oldewelt, op. cit., p. 84).
2. Havard, vol. 3, pp. 9–14.
3. Oldewelt incorrectly stated (pp. 85–6) that he was baptised in Amsterdam on 27 February 1627; he was followed by MacLaren. The correct date is given by van Thiel, op. cit., p. 56, note 7.

4. Havard, vol. 3, p. 10.
5. Bredius, *Künstler-Inventare*, p. 817.
6. Havard, vol. 3, p. 10, and Oldewelt, op. cit., p. 84.
7. He is recorded there in 1649, 1651 (when he bought a house) and 1659 (Bredius, *Künstler-Inventare*, p. 817); children of his were baptised in Amsterdam in 1652, 1658, 1660 and 1661 and he remarried there in 1665 (Oldewelt, op. cit., p. 84).
8. Oldewelt, op. cit., p. 82.
9. The view of the Hoofdtoren, Hoorn, in the Kunsthalle Hamburg shows a tablet dated 1651 on the tower; this is not the date of the picture and the dated tablet is still on the tower.
10. C.G. 't Hooft in Thieme/Becker, vol. 3, p. 171.
11. The only one specified in Thieme/Becker (see note 10) is a winter scene in Amsterdam [actually a view of the Paalhuis], then in Amsterdam Town Hall, said to be signed 'Joannes Beerstraten 1668'. This picture, now in the Rijksmuseum (1976 cata-

logue, A20), is in fact signed 'I. Beerestraten'. It is not dated. A sea-fight, also in the Rijksmuseum, formerly thought to represent a battle between Dutch and English ships which took place on 12 June 1666 (catalogue, A22), has since been identified as the Battle of Terheide on 10 August 1653. A painting of the Dutch attack on Sheerness fort in June 1667 (Culp sale, Amsterdam, 3–10 July 1951, lot 541), said to be signed by J. Beerstraaten, is not connected in style with any known J. or A. Beerstraaten picture. Van Thiel (op. cit.) claimed that *The Church at Sloten* (Canvas, 90 × 128 cm., Rijksmuseum A4134) signed 'J. Beerstra. . . .', is far superior in quality to the painting of the same subject signed 'J: Beerstraaten' in the Metropolitan Museum of Art, New York (Canvas, 92 × 131 cm.; inv. no. 11.92). He suggested that the latter was the work of 'Johannes Beerstraten'. The existence of this unrecorded member of the Beerstraaten family would explain, in his view, the reference noted by Oldewelt (op. cit., p. 82) in the inventory of 1664 to a winter scene by the 'Young Beerstraten'. However, in the view of the present writer, the discrepancies between the two paintings are not great enough to justify their attribution to two different hands. The most likely explanation is that Jan Beerstraaten simply changed the form of his signature at one period of his career. This was not an unusual practice in seventeenth-century Holland (W. Stechow, 'Uber das Verhältnis zwischen signatur und Chronologie bei einigen holländischen Künstlern des 17. Jahrhunderts' in *Festschrift Dr E. Trautscholdt*, Hamburg, 1965, pp. 111ff).

12. Havard, pp. 9 and 149–50. For Abraham Beerstraaten see Bredius in OH, 1900, p. 183, and *Künstler-Inventare*, vol. 3, pp. 819–20, and HdG in OH, 1904, p. 114. The attribution of some of the 'A. Beerstraaten' pictures to an Abraham Beerstraaten is based solely on a painting in the Lansdowne collection at Bowood which is supposedly signed in full by him. This signature, however, appears to be damaged and repainted, and is not altogether trustworthy. The date 1645 which appears twice on the view of St Olof's chapel, Amsterdam, by A. (Abraham?) Beerstraaten in the Six collection is not that of the picture but was carved on the building and can still be seen on it (cf. *Zeven eeuwen Amsterdam*, vol. I, 1942, p. 228).

13. See Bredius in OH, 1900, p. 183, and *Künstler-Inventare*, vol. 3, p. 820, and Wurzbach, vol. I, p. 71. For a possible *third* A. Beerstraaten see Stechow, p. 204, note 61.

1311 *The Castle of Muiden in Winter* *Plate 13*

The castle is seen from the north-east. Over the entrance in the eastern side, which is approached by a wooden drawbridge, is a coat-of-arms with a bend sinister[1] in stonework within a Gothic arch. Beyond the dyke on the left is a river, at the mouth of which, on the left bank, is a beacon; in the distance is the sea. In the right background are houses and a church. Some of the skaters on the frozen moat of the castle have *kolf* clubs.

Signed, below, towards the right: I. BEER-STRAATEN./1658 (the N is reversed).

Oil on canvas, 96.5 × 129.5 (38 × 51).

The painting was cleaned in 1973: there is considerable damage in the sky.

The castle of Muiden is 7½ miles east of Amsterdam, at the entry of the Vecht River into the Zuider Zee. It was commenced in about 1285 by Court Floris V of Holland. It is best known as the residence of the Dutch poet and historian, Pieter Cornelisz. Hooft, who was governor of the castle from 1609 until his death in 1647. During his governorship a circle of poets and scholars, the so-called *Muiderkring* which included the most eminent Dutch poets of the day, often met there, and the castle is frequently mentioned in Dutch poetry of the time.[2] At the time this picture was painted, the governor of the castle was Gerard Bicker.[3]

Most of the existing castle, which remains very much as it appears in Beerstraaten's painting,[4] is probably of the fourteenth century.[5] The wooden bridge shown in the picture (later replaced by one of stone) is perhaps that which Hooft, writing in 1630, declared to be so dangerous in a high wind that several people had been blown off it into the moat.[6] The partly visible building on the left may be the *Torentje*, a summer-house formerly in approximately this position, which Hooft often used as his work-room; it was presumably demolished when the existing fortifications were laid out from 1672 onwards.[7]

It seems that Beerstraaten has arbitrarily rearranged the view. In the left background are what appear to be the mouth of the Vecht River and beyond it, the Zuider Zee; a map of 1623[8] does, in fact, show a beacon at the mouth of the Vecht on the left (i.e. western) bank of the river as in the present picture. The viewpoint of Beerstraaten's painting, however, is north-east of the castle,[9] and from this point the view would not be towards the sea but southwards up the Vecht. Furthermore, it seems likely that the buildings in the right background are intended for part of the town of Muiden; these would not have been visible to a spectator looking towards the mouth of the Vecht, although they could have been seen from a viewpoint north-east of the castle.

Views of the castle were painted and engraved by a number of artists: there is an etching of 1617 by C. J. Visscher and a view of the castle from the west appears in the background of Arent Arentsz. No. 3533 of this catalogue.

No. 1311 is one of the pictures ascribed by C. G. 't Hooft[10] to the hypothetical 'Johannes Beerstraten' (see the biographical notice above) despite the fact that it is signed in capitals whereas 't Hooft maintains that the signatures of 'Johannes' are always in script. In any case it is difficult to believe the present picture is not by the same hand as, for example, the *Ruins of the Old Amsterdam Town Hall* in the Rijksmuseum which 't Hooft accepts as the work of Jan Abrahamsz. Beerstraaten and which bears a signature of exactly the same form as that on No. 1311.[11]

A winter view of Poelgeest Castle (near Leiden) similar in size to No. 1311 and with the same signature was sold at Christie's in 1974.[12]

VERSION (?) AND COPY: A picture of Muiden Castle in winter, of the same size as No. 1311 but said to be signed by A. Beerstraaten, was in the Jan Gildemeester Jansz. sale, Amsterdam, 11 sqq. June 1800 (lot 18), bought by Labouchère, and later apparently in the collection of Christiaan Kramm.[13] An early copy, reduced in size (c.21 × 28 in.) was in the possession of Mr I. Weiss, Colchester, Essex, in 1973.

PROVENANCE: A painting of Muiden Castle in winter, with skaters, by Beerstraaten (without initials) was in an anonymous sale, Amsterdam, 16 September 1739 (lot 114);[14] another (or the same?) was in the Coenraad van Heemskerck sale, The Hague, 7 October 1765 (lot 7),[15] bought by Le Heule (44 guilders). A *Muiden Castle, Winter Scene*, by Beerstraaten (without initials) was in the Bryan sale, London, 7 sqq. May 1804 (2nd day, lot 55), 50 gns. No. 1311 was bought from Messrs P. & D. Colnaghi, London, in 1890.

REFERENCES:

1. There is apparently no other charge on the escutcheon which is small and carelessly painted. The brushstrokes on the tablet beneath the coat-of-arms (which are well preserved) do not seem ever to have been intended as legible characters. See also note 4.

2. See R. van Luttervelt, *P. C. Hooft, Drossaert van Goeylant en Castelein op thuys te Muyen*, 1947, passim.

3. Gerard Bicker was governor 1649–66.

4. In the part visible in the painting the principal differences are that the round tower on the left, the gate tower and the walls between the towers are now castellated; some windows have been condemned and others opened. The escutcheon and arch above the entrance in the painting no longer exist. The wooden bridge has been replaced by one of stone. A drawing by A. Rademaker (1675–1735), perhaps after a painting, shows the castle from the

same viewpoint but with a different background, and with some variations in architectural details (reproduced in Luttervelt, op. cit., opp. p.3).

5. See Luttervelt, op. cit., p. 4.

6. See the letter quoted by Luttervelt, op. cit., pp. 6–7.

7. See Luttervelt, op. cit., p. 20.

8. In M. Boxhorn's *Tooneel der Steden van Holland*, 1623; the relevant part of the map is reproduced in Luttervelt, op. cit., opp. p. 21.

9. This is quite certain, since the entrance to the castle (still in existence) is in the east side.

10. Thieme/Becker, vol. 3, p. 171.

11. 1976 cat., A21. Both signatures are in backhand capitals, and both have the final N reversed.

12. Christie's, 29 March 1974, lot 79. Canvas, 91 × 127 cm. Signed: I. BEER-STRATEN.

13. See Kramm, vol. 1, p. 67.

14. Hoet, vol. 1, p. 605.

15. 'Beerstraten. Le Chateau à Muyden, représentant un Hiver, rempli de Patineurs & autres Figures.' Canvas, 3 *pieds* 1 *pouce* × 4 *pieds* 1½ *pouces*.

ABRAHAM BEGA *See* BEGEIJN

CORNELIS BEGA, 1631/2–1664

Cornelis Pietersz. Bega, son of a gold- and silversmith, Pieter Jansz. Begijn or Bega, and of Maria Cornelisdr., a daughter of Cornelis van Haarlem.[1] He was born in Haarlem; in a document of April 1650 he is said to be eighteen, i.e. born in 1631 or 1632.[2] In 1634 the Bega family is recorded as living on the Koningstraat in a house owned by Cornelis van Haarlem. Soon after they moved to a house in the Lange Begijnestraat owned (until 1652) by Pieter Begeijn. According to Houbraken,[3] Bega was the 'first and best pupil' of Adriaen van Ostade.[4] A drawing inscribed 'Bega Romae' has been adduced as evidence of a visit to Italy: in fact it is by Abraham Begeijn (Bega of Leiden) who was in Italy *c.* 1660.[5] In 1653 he travelled in Germany and Switzerland with the painter Vincent Laurensz. van der Vinne (who kept a journal of his travels) and the Haarlem shoemaker, Joost Boelen.[6] He entered the guild in Haarlem in September 1654.[7] He was a friend of Leendert van der Cooghen, a Haarlem artist who had studied with Jacob Jordaens in Antwerp.[8] He died in Haarlem on 27 August 1664.[9]

The greater part of his pictures are peasant scenes in a style derived from Adriaen van Ostade; there are extant dated works from 1652 onwards. He also made etchings of similar subjects.[10]

REFERENCES:

General: P.J. Begheyn, 'Biografische gegevens betreffende de Haarlemse schilder Cornelis Bega (ca. 1632–1664) en zijn verwanten', OH, vol. 93, 1979, pp. 270–8. M.A. Scott, 'Cornelis Bega (1631/32–1664) as Painter and Draughtsman' (University of Maryland PhD thesis, 1984), Ann Arbor, 1987.

In text:

1. Houbraken, vol. 1, p. 349. An inventory of 1639 records that Cornelis van Haarlem left part of his estate including all his drawings in red chalk to his daughter Maria.

2. C. A. van Hees, 'Nadere gegevens omtrent de Haarlemse vrienden Leendert van der Cooghen en Cornelis Bega', OH, vol. 71, 1956, p. 244. The Haarlem Doepboek records the baptism on 22 January 1632 of 'Cornelis. V[ader] Pieter Jansen van Haerlem M[oeder] Barbara Cornelis'. The mother's name could be a mistake for Maria. See Scott, op. cit., pp. 7–8.

3. Loc. cit.

4. An early signed painting on copper (33 × 40 cm.) which is wholly in the style of

Adriaen van Ostade was at Sotheby, New York, 12 January 1979 (lot 152).

5. *The Dentist*, Schlossmuseum, Weimar, inv. no. 4763. The drawing is discussed and correctly attributed by Begheyn, op. cit., p. 274.

6. Houbraken, vol. 2, p. 211; van der Willigen, p. 76; and Ed. B. Sliggers jr., *Dagelijckse aentekeninge*

van Vincent Laurensz. van der Vinne, Bussum, 1979.

7. Van der Willigen, p. 76.

8. Van Hees, op. cit., pp. 243–4.

9. Houbraken, vol. 1, p. 349, and van der Willigen, p. 76.

10. See Hollstein, vol. 1, pp. 203–32.

1481 *An Astrologer* *Plate 14*

On the table behind the astrologer is a celestial globe; on the right-hand page of the book before him is an illustration of a hand. On the wall, left, is a drawing of a skeleton.

Signed, bottom left: CP bega/ A° 1663 (CP in monogram).

Oil on oak, 36.9 × 29.6 ($14\frac{9}{16}$ × $11\frac{5}{8}$).

The man has traditionally been identified as an astrologer because of the presence of a globe on the table behind him. The illustration of a hand suggests that he is also interested in palmistry. There was a widespread belief in the seventeenth century that it was possible to discover a person's fate by the study of lines and mounds on their hands. Much of the contemporary literature concerned with palmistry is of a popular kind – almanacs and crudely printed broadsheets – but there were also more scholarly publications. One of these, replete with references to Aristotle and Galen, is Meyens' *Chiromantia Medica* (The Hague, 1665).

The presence of the globe and the book on palmistry imply that this man, dressed in the traditional scholar's cap and black cloak, is attempting to foretell the future using astrology and palmistry. His posture, slumped in his chair, lost in thought, his eyes averted from his books, suggests melancholy. If this is the case, the painting would take its place in a visual tradition of *Melancholia*, the scholar's malady, of which the best-known example is Dürer's famous print, *Melencolia I*. In this tradition melancholy was thought to be the inevitable outcome of the scholar's investigations, which serve only to bear in upon him the futility of his efforts and the certainty of his own mortality.

DRAWING: There is a related drawing (Fig. 2) in the Musée des Beaux-Arts, Besançon (Inv. no. 120; black chalk and brown ink, 269 × 188 mm.), attributed to Thomas Wijck.

PROVENANCE: Perhaps 'Un Philosophe' in the Baronne Douaieriere de Boonem sale, Brussels, 15 July 1776 ('H. 1p. 3p., 1.11 pouces': HdG fiche in RKD); bought from P.J. Thijs by Gerrit van der Pot, Rotterdam, in July 1799;[1] Gerrit van der Pot sale, Rotterdam, 6 sqq. June 1808 (lot 8), bought by M. van Noort (605 florins). Charles Scarisbrick sale, London, 11 sqq. May 1861 (lot 742), bought by Lawrence (£14); Edwin H. Lawrence sale, London, 6 May 1892 (lot 362), bought by Martin H. Colnaghi (250 gns) by whom presented in 1896.

EXHIBITIONS: RA 1893, No. 61; London, Guildhall, 1894, No. 71; London 1978–9, No. 14.

REFERENCES: General: Scott, op. cit., cat. no. 145.

In text: **1.** It appears in G. van der Pot's MS list of his pictures in the Gemeente Archief in Rotterdam (Bibliotheek van Handschriften, No. 353): '1799 Julij Een Alchimist, zittende te peinzen in zijn Laboratorium op Paneel hoog. – breed – dm. van P. I. Thijs gekogt voor f.200.'

ABRAHAM BEGEIJN (or BEGA), active from 1655; died 1697

Abraham Cornelisz.(?) Begeijn (the patronymic Jansz. sometimes assigned to him is apparently erroneous); he also signed himself, less frequently, *Begein, Begeyn, Begheyn* and *Bega*.

Born in Leiden.[1] The date of his birth is not known; E.W. Moes gives it as 1637 or 1638[2] but does not state on what evidence. He was in Italy *c.* 1660;[3] he had entered the Leiden guild in 1655 and remained a member of it until 1667 or 1668.[4] He was living in Amsterdam in 1672 and in December of that year he was given a letter of recommendation from the Reformed Church there to the Dutch community in London.[5] He presumably came to London shortly afterwards and at this time painted the pictures at Ham House (W. van de Velde the Younger and Dirck van Bergen were also working at Ham in the early 1670s).[6] It is not known how long he remained in England; in 1681 he was living in The Hague.[7] He became a member of The Hague painters' confraternity, *Pictura*, in 1683 and is documented there until 1685.[8] In 1688 he was appointed court painter to the Elector of Brandenburg in Berlin, and died there on 11 June 1697.[9]

Begeijn painted Italian landscapes in the manner of both Jan Asselijn and Nicolaes Berchem and port scenes in the style of Jan Baptist Weenix, also plants with reptiles and insects in imitation of Otto Marseus van Schrieck. In addition he made a few etchings and, in Berlin, cartoons for tapestry.

REFERENCES:
1. Weyerman, vol. 4, 1769, p. 58.
2. Thieme/Becker, vol. 3.
3. See the biography of Cornelis Bega above (p. 16 and footnote 5).
4. Obreen, vol. 5, p. 216.
5. J.H. Hessles, *Register of the Attestations . . . Preserved in the Dutch Reformed Church . . . London*, 1892, p. 93; see also OH, vol. 4, 1886, p. 42.

6. For Ham see P.K. Thornton and M.F. Tomlin, *The Furnishing and Decoration of Ham House*, London, 1980.
7. Obreen, vol. 4, p. 116.
8. Obreen, vol. 5, pp. 136 and 152.
9. P. Seidel in JKPK, vol. 11, 1890, p. 134.

78 Peasants with Cattle by a Ruin   *Plate 15*

Falsely signed, bottom right, on the end of a stone block: NB (in monogram).[1]

Oil on canvas, 54.3 × 66 ($21\frac{3}{8}$ × 26).

Prominent craquelure throughout.

Included by Hofstede de Groot[2] in his catalogue of Berchem's works. The signature is certainly false and the picture is clearly not by Berchem. Comparison with signed works by Begeijn[3] makes it plain that he was the author.[4]

PROVENANCE: Bequeathed by Richard Frankum,[5] 1861.

REFERENCES:
1. Under magnification the monogram can be seen to be painted on top of slight damage in the original paint of the stone.
2. HdG, Berchem, No. 607.

3. In particular the following: *Cattle fording a Stream by a Ruin* in an anonymous sale, London, 10 February 1936 (lot 144), signed and dated 1664; *Mountainous Landscape with Peasants and Cattle* in the

possession of Douwes, Amsterdam, 1928, signed and dated 1665; and, especially, *Landscape with Peasants and Cattle* in an anonymous sale, London, 2 March 1951 (lot 145), signed and dated 1690.

4. The picture was independently attributed to Begeijn by E. Schaar (in OH, vol. 69, 1954, pp. 241–42 and p. 245, note 3). Schaar reads the 'signature' as

AB; it is, however, certainly NB and in any case it is a false addition (cf. note 1 above).

5. In some editions of the National Gallery catalogue, 1892–1901, this picture appears with the same National Gallery number as Reynolds's *Holy Family*; the number of the latter was changed after 1906 to 78A.

Nicolaes BERCHEM, 1620–1683

Nicolaes (or *Claes*) *Pietersz.*, son of the still-life painter, Pieter Claesz.;[1] he adopted the surname *Berchem*. In his earlier years he also signed *Berghem* and, occasionally, *Berighem* and *Berrighem* – cf. No. 1005 below – sometimes preceded by C or, rarely, C P; after about 1660 the initial is almost invariably N.[2] He was baptised in Haarlem, 1 October 1620.[3] He was a pupil of his father who in 1634 is mentioned in the records of the Haarlem Guild of St Luke as 'teaching drawing to his son'. Houbraken[4] says he studied subsequently with Jan van Goyen, Nicolaes Moeyaert, Pieter de Grebber, Johannes Wils (later his father-in-law) and, lastly, his cousin, Jan Baptist Weenix; the last-named is unlikely since he was not even Berchem's age. Berchem entered the Haarlem guild in June 1642[5] and already in August of that year is recorded as having three pupils.[6]

Although there is no firm evidence that Berchem travelled to Italy, his familiarity with southern landscape makes such a trip (or trips) likely. It has been suggested that Berchem accompanied Jan Baptist Weenix to Italy,[7] where Weenix is recorded in Rome from the winter of 1642/3 to 1645.[8] Berchem married in Haarlem in 1646[9] and in 1649 he and his wife, Catrijne Claesdr. de Groot, made a will. A visit to Italy in the years between 1650 and 1654 (when he was probably back in Haarlem) seems likely. Recently a painting of 1651 in a strongly Italianate manner has been discovered in Milan.[10] The artist is not definitely mentioned in the Netherlands until 1656, when he was in Haarlem, where he is also documented the following year;[11] in November 1660 he was in Amsterdam (where he was a witness at the betrothal of Johannes Wils);[12] he was living in Haarlem in 1670.[13] By 1677 he had settled in Amsterdam,[14] where he died in 1683.[15] He was buried in the Westerkerk.

Berchem was a highly productive artist (there are more than 800 items in Hofstede de Groot's *Catalogue Raisonné*) and one of the comparatively few well-paid Dutch painters of his day. The Italianate landscape scenes of his early years reflect his study of the work of Pieter van Laer and Jan Both. He also painted imaginary Mediterranean harbour scenes, water and dune landscapes, allegories, religious and mythological subjects, and genre scenes. He also often painted the figures in the landscapes of others, among them Willem Schellinks, Jacob van Ruisdael, Johannes Hackaert (see No. 829 of this catalogue) and Meindert Hobbema. He collaborated with J. B. Weenix.[16] He etched more than fifty plates, the majority of them depicting animal subjects. His work was frequently engraved in the seventeenth and eighteenth centuries.

He had many pupils and followers; of the former, Houbraken[17] names Pieter de Hooch, Jacob Ochtervelt, Karel Dujardin, Jan Glauber, Jacob van Hughtenburgh, Dirk Maas and Justus van Huijsum; others are mentioned in contemporary documents and include Willem Romeyn and Simon du Bois.[18] Among his closest imitators are Romeyn, Abraham Begeijn, Dirk van Bergen and Johannes van der Bent.

REFERENCES:

General: HdG, vol. 9, 1926; Ilse von Sick, *Nicolaes Berchem*, Berlin, 1930; Hollstein, vol. 1, pp. 249–80; Eckhard Schaar, 'Studien zu Nicolaes Berchem', Dissertation, University of Cologne, 1958; Utrecht 1965, cat., pp. 147–49, 261.

In text:

1. Houbraken, vol. 2, 1719, p. 110.
2. For a discussion of Berchem's signatures, see W. Stechow, 'Uber das Verhältnis zwischen Signatur und Chronologie bei einigen holländischen Künstlern des 17. Jahrhunderts', *Festschrift Dr E. Trautscholdt*, Hamburg, 1965, pp. 111–17.
3. Van der Willigen, p. 76.
4. Houbraken, vol. 2, p. 111.
5. Van der Willigen, p. 77.
6. Van der Willigen, p. 252.
7. G.J. Hoogewerff in OH, 1931, p. 84.

8. I. von Sick, op. cit., p. 7, and Hoogewerff, loc. cit.
9. Thieme/Becker, vol. 3, p. 371.
10. G. Jansen, 'Berchem in Italy: notes on an unpublished painting', *Mercury*, 2, 1985, pp. 13–17.
11. Van der Willigen, p. 77.
12. Bredius, vol. 7, p. 292.
13. Van der Willigen, p. 77.
14. Thieme/Becker, loc. cit.
15. Houbraken, vol. 2, p. 114, and Kramm, vol. 1, p. 76.
16. F. J. Duparc Jr., 'Een teruggevonden schilderij van N. Berchem en J. B. Weenix', OH, vol. 94, 1980, pp. 37–43.
17. Houbraken, vol. 2, p. 35, and vol. 3, pp. 56, 217, 362 and 387.
18. Van der Willigen, p. 252, and OH, 1899, p. 177.

240 *Peasants with Cattle fording a Stream*   Plate 16

Signed, lower left: Berchem.

Oil on oak, 29.5 × 45.3 ($11\frac{5}{8}$ × $17\frac{7}{8}$).[1]

Cleaned in 1981. At the time of cleaning a false strip 2.6 cm. deep at the top of the panel was removed. A narrower false strip along the bottom (measuring 0.8 cm.) was retained and is concealed by the frame.

MacLaren described the painting as 'ascribed to Berchem' and wrote that 'the handling is in the style of Berchem's later work, but the picture is rather feeble and may well be by an imitator, possibly Johannes van der Bent'. Schaar[2] had accepted the painting as the work of Berchem himself: he considered it to be one of a group of very late paintings (*c.*1672–9) and compared the loose handling with a picture of 1672 in the Wallace Collection, London,[3] and a second, of 1679, in Copenhagen.[4]

When the painting was cleaned the signature was found to be original. The present writer agrees with Schaar that the painting's handling is entirely consistent with Berchem's style in the 1670s.

PROVENANCE: In the Randon de Boisset sale, Paris, 27 February sqq. 1777 (lot 109), bought by Julliot for the Comte du Luc (2,000 francs); Comte du Luc sale, Paris, 22–23 December 1777 (lot 2),[5] bought by Le Brun (1,501 francs); [Tronchin] sale, Paris, 12 sqq. January 1780 (lot 45),[6] bought by Lenglier (2,400 francs). In the collection of N.W. Ridley Colborne (later Lord Colborne) by 1821 when it was exhibited at the BI. Lord Colborne Bequest, 1854.

REFERENCES:
General: Smith Nos. 59 and 335; HdG No. 376.
In text:
1. This is the true size of the panel without the false strip along the bottom edge.
2. Schaar, op. cit., pp. 106–7.
3. HdG No. 194; Inv. no. P183.
4. HdG No. 374; Royal Museum of Fine Arts, *Catalogue of Old Foreign Paintings*, 1951, no. 54.
5. As from the Randon de Boisset collection.
6. As from the Randon de Boisset collection.
7. See Smith No. 335 (who gives the date of the BI

exhibition wrongly as 1822). Two Berchems were lent to the 1821 exhibition by N.W. Ridley Colborne: No. 66 'Cattle and Figures passing a River', and No. 98 'Cattle and Figures passing a Brook'. One of these was the National Gallery picture, the other was Smith No. 334 (HdG No. 264), *Peasants with Cattle fording a Stream, with a Herdsman playing a Pipe*. Lord Colborne's seal is on the back of the panel (photograph in National Gallery archives).
8. 'Cattle and Figures passing a Brook', see note 7.
9. 'Figures and Cattle crossing a Brook', see note 7.

820 *Peasants with Four Oxen and a Goat at a Ford by a Ruined Aqueduct*

Plate 17

Signed, bottom left: Berchem.

Oil on oak, 47.1 × 38.7 (18½ × 15¼).

Cleaned in 1958.

MacLaren argued that the picture probably dated from the late 1650s on the basis of a comparison with a painting of 1658 in the Rijksmuseum.[1] Schaar[2] preferred a dating in the 1670s on an analogy with the figure group in a painting in the Royal Collection[3] and a second last recorded in the possession of A. Brod, London,[4] both of which he believed to be from that decade. The present writer prefers, however, MacLaren's dating, finding the comparison with the dated Rijksmuseum landscape especially telling.

ENGRAVING: Engraved in reverse by C.W. Weisbrod and F. Godefroy, 1781.[5]

PROVENANCE: HdG suggests this may be the 'Four cows in a landscape' of the same size by Berchem in the Samuel van Huls sale, The Hague, 3 sqq. September 1737 (lot 31),[6] 50 guilders. It was in an anonymous sale, Amsterdam, 18 March 1767 (lot 2), bought by van Diemen (525 guilders); Gerret Braamcamp sale, Amsterdam, 31 July sqq. 1771 (lot 20), bought by P. Fouquet (830 guilders); Poullain sale, Paris, 15 sqq. March 1780 (lot 65), bought by the Duc de Chabot (1,651 francs); Duc de Ch[abot] sale, Paris, 10 sqq. December 1787 (lot 32), bought by Le Rouge (4,801 francs); Claude Tolozan sale, Paris, 23 sqq. February 1801 (lot 8), 4,650 francs, bought (according to HdG) by P.J. Thijs for Crawford of Rotterdam; [Crawford of Rotterdam] sale, London, 26 April 1806 (lot 9), (bought in);[7] Anon. sale, Christie's, 20 February 1807 (lot 65) (bought in);[8] John Humble sale, London, 11 April 1812 (lot 61),[9] bought by Pinney (355 gns). It was in the collection of Sir Simon H. Clarke, Bart., by 1823, when it was exhibited at the BI; Sir S.H. Clarke sale, London, 8–9 May 1840 (lot 43), bought for Sir Robert Peel, Bart.,[10] by Seguier (385 gns). Purchased with the Peel collection in 1871.

EXHIBITIONS: BI 1823, No. 68; London 1982, cat. p. 24.

REFERENCES:
General: Smith No. 72 and Supplement No. 45; HdG No. 377.
In text:
1. HdG No. 359; Rijksmuseum, 1976, cat. A680.

2. Schaar, op. cit., pp. 97–98
3. HdG No. 493; White No. 19. White rejects Schaar's dating in favour of a date around 1660.
4. HdG No. 714.

5. In *Collection de cent-vingt estampes . . . d'après les Tableaux . . . du Cabinet de M. Poullain*, 1781, No. 11.
6. 'Vier Koetjes in een Landschap'; 1 *voet* 5 *duim* × 1 *v*. 2 *d.* (Hoet, vol. 1, p. 481).
7. Campbell is given as the purchaser in the auctioneer's copy of the sale catalogue, but in fact all the paintings bought by Campbell were bought in. No. 820 reappeared in the 20 February 1807 sale, when it

was bought in again, but not in the subsequent Crawford sale in July 1807.
8. According to Buchanan (vol. 2, p. 182) it was bought by Walsh Porter presumably between February and July 1807 (see above, note 7). It was not in the Walsh Porter sales in London, 30–31 January 1810, 14 April 1810 or 21 June 1811.
9. As from the Crawford of Rotterdam collection.
10. Smith Supplement No. 45.

1004 *Mountainous Landscape with Muleteers*

Plate 18

Signed at the bottom, towards the left, on some rocks: 1658 Berchem.

Oil on canvas, 109 × 126 ($42\frac{7}{8}$ × $49\frac{5}{8}$).

Cleaned in 1950.

The painting is very close in style to Italianate landscapes by Jan Both (for example, Nos. 71 and 1917). Schaar,[1] who was apparently unaware of the date on the painting, considered it to be from the early 1660s. There is no reason to doubt the authenticity of the date.

COPIES: A copy is in the Kiev Museum (information from J. Kuznetzov). A drawing of this design, inscribed J. Both, was in the Klinkosch sale, 1889; it agrees closely with the picture and is probably a copy after it.

PROVENANCE: In the collection of Loveden Pryse, Buscot Park; Loveden Pryse[2] sale, London, 12 March 1859 (lot 171), bought by Pearce (£735), probably for Wynn Ellis.[3] Perhaps the 'Landscape and Figures' by Berchem exhibited at the BI 1861, by Wynn Ellis; Wynn Ellis Bequest, 1876.

EXHIBITION: Perhaps exhibited at the BI 1861, No. 29.

REFERENCES:
General: HdG No. 173.
In text:
1. Schaar, op. cit., pp. 72–73.
2. Not *Povre*, as HdG states incorrectly.
3. Pearce apparently often bought for Wynn Ellis. Besides the present picture, he seems to have bought at least eleven others which were afterwards in the

Wynn Ellis collection (Berchem No. 1006; Both No. 958; Cappelle No. 964; Cappelle No. 965; Cuyp No. 961; Dujardin No. 985; Verbeecq No. 1009 – all in this catalogue; also Bouts No. 943; Claude No. 1018; Italian, sixteenth century No. 932 and Canaletto No. 938).

1005 *A Man and a Youth ploughing with Oxen*

Plate 19

Signed at the bottom, left of centre: cBerghem (cB in monogram).

Oil on canvas, 38.2 × 51.5 ($15\frac{1}{16}$ × $20\frac{1}{4}$).

Cleaned in 1970. There is some wearing in the sky.

MacLaren dated the picture to the early 1650s. Schaar, however, believed that it adopted a landscape format from Berchem's early period – as seen, for example, in a picture of 1653 in the Academy in Vienna[1] – and reworked it in the style of the late 1660s. The present writer cannot detect the discrepancy in style to which Schaar refers and considers that the painting should, as MacLaren believed, be dated at about the same time as the Vienna Academy picture. As MacLaren stated, this dating receives some support from the form of the signature.[2]

The painting was owned by François Boucher (see PROVENANCE).

VERSION: A probable version or copy on wood was in an anonymous sale, Amsterdam, 11 October 1810 (lot 9),[3] bought by Posthumus (35 guilders).

PROVENANCE: In the François Boucher sale, Paris, 18 sqq. February 1771 (lot 12), bought by Foliot (400 francs). Possibly among the pictures from the collections of Dr [Thomas] Newton (Bishop of Bristol), Richard Cumberland and others, exhibited for sale in London, 8 sqq. April 1788 (No. 190).[4] In the collection of Wynn Ellis, London; Wynn Ellis Bequest, 1876.

REFERENCES:

General: HdG No. 319.

In text:

1. HdG No. 217; Inv. no. 1365; R. Trnek, *Niederländer und Italien: Italianisante Landschafts- und Genremalerei von Niederländern des 17. Jahrhunderts*, Akademie, Vienna, 1982, pp. 73–75, esp. note 3.

2. Berchem not infrequently signed pictures Berrighem, Berighem or Berghem, usually preceded by a c (in monogram with B), until the mid-fifties but rather rarely later.

3. 'Een aangenaam Boomrijk Landschap, gestoffeerd met een Landman en een Jongen bij een Ploeg, met twee Ossen bespannen . . . door denzelven [N. Berchem]'; panel 15 × 20 *duim*.

4. 'Berchem The plough.' On canvas; the size, *including the frame*, 22 × 27 in.

1006 *A Peasant playing a Hurdy-Gurdy to a Woman and Child in a Woody Landscape, with Oxen, Sheep and Goats*

Plate 20

Signed in the bottom left corner: Berchem 1658.[1]

Oil on mahogany,[2] 34.5 × 38.3 ($13\frac{5}{8}$ × $15\frac{1}{8}$).

Cleaned in 1958.

PROVENANCE: Probably in the Marquis de Ménars (formerly Marquis de Marigny) sales, Paris, 18 March–6 April 1782 (lot 7),[3] bought by Rubis (525 francs). In an anonymous sale ('a foreign collection'), Amsterdam, 9 April 1783 (lot 2), bought by Valet (605 guilders); Stephanus Loquet et al. sale, The Hague, 8 September 1789 (lot 1), bought by Prins (920 guilders); Elisha Biscoe sale, Wheatley (near Oxford), 23–27 April 1833 (fifth day, lot 56), bought by Pennell (£106); perhaps in an anonymous sale, London, 26 May 1836 (lot 112), bought by Scott (142 gns). Sir Thomas Baring, Bart., sale, London, 2–3 June 1848 (lot 103),[4] bought by Evans (143 gns); Charles Scarisbrick sale, London, 11 sqq. May 1861 (lot 113), bought by Pearce (230 gns), probably for Wynn Ellis.[5] Perhaps lent by Wynn Ellis to the Leeds Exhibition, 1868, No. 692;[6] Wynn Ellis Bequest, 1876.

REFERENCES:

General: Smith No. 248; HdG Nos. 247, 266 and 769b.

In text:

1. There have been various readings of the last figure of the date; it is certainly 8.

2. Identified as mahogany (*Swietenis* species) by B.J. Rendle, Forest Products Research Laboratory (letter of 1953 in the National Gallery archives).

3. The description, size and support of the Ménars picture given in the sale catalogue agree with those of No. 1006 except that the former is said to have twelve figures and animals; in No. 1006 there are three figures (if the baby is included), three oxen, two sheep, two goats and a dog (i.e. eleven in all).

4. There is a contemporary note in the auctioneer's copy of the Scarisbrick sale catalogue identifying the picture with that formerly belonging to Sir T. Baring.

5. Pearce apparently often bought for Wynn Ellis (cf. Berchem No. 1004, note 3). HdG (No. 247) wrongly identifies the National Gallery picture with the 'Herdsman and woman with two cows and two goats' by Berchem seen in the Wynn Ellis collection by Waagen (1854, vol. 2, p. 296); the description in the catalogue of the Scarisbrick sale of 1861 agrees closely with the present picture.

6. 'Merry-making. Signed, and dated 1655.'

For BERCHEM *see also* JAN HACKAERT No. 829

GERRIT BERCKHEYDE, 1638–1698

Gerrit Adriaensz. Berckheyde (he also wrote his surname *Berkheyde, Berckheijde* etc., sometimes in two parts). He was baptised in Haarlem, 6 June 1638,[1] and was probably taught painting by his elder brother, Job Berckheyde (who was born in 1630).[2] Together they visited Germany, going to Cologne and thence to Heidelberg where they worked for a time at the court of the Elector Palatine.[3] They returned from Heidelberg to Haarlem, where they lived in the same house.[4] Gerrit entered the Haarlem guild in 1660.[5] He was buried in Haarlem on 14 June 1698.[6]

He painted a few landscapes and interiors of churches (cf. No. 1451 below) but the bulk of his work consists of views of towns, chiefly Haarlem, Amsterdam and The Hague, which he frequently repeated with little variation.

REFERENCES:

1. Van der Willigen, p. 79.
2. Van der Willigen, p. 78.
3. Houbraken, vol. 3, pp. 191–95.

4. Houbraken, vol. 3, p. 195.
5. Van der Willigen, p. 79.
6. Houbraken, vol. 3, p. 197.

1420 *The Market Place and the Grote Kerk at Haarlem*   *Plate 21*

The market place (Grote Markt) is seen from the north-west from a point beside the town hall, the Doric portico of which is visible on the right. On the opposite side of the square is the Grote Kerk (St Bavo), to the left of which is the fish market; beyond the latter, partly hidden by the north transept of St Bavo, is the bell tower. The last of the row of houses on the right, just in front of St Bavo, is the Vleeshal (meat market). Over the shop visible between the columns on the right is a painted sign of a woman in a shop, with simulated lettering above and, below, an inscription beginning with M (probably not intended to be legible).

Signed on the base of the third column from the right: Gerrit Berck Heyde/1674.

Oil on canvas, 51.8 × 67 (20⅜ × 26⅜).

Cleaned in 1973.

The Grote Kerk (St Bavo) was built between the end of the fourteenth and the end of the fifteenth centuries (cf. No. 1451 below), the spire being an addition of 1519–20; it remains in much the same state as in this painting. The Vleeshal (the former meat market) was constructed by Lieven de Key in 1602–3 and still stands; the houses beside it on the south side of the market place no longer exist, nor those opposite the north side of the church. The stalls on the north side of the Grote Kerk are those of the former fish market and have long since been removed. The bell tower of St Bavo (here seen beyond the fish market) was built in 1479; it was removed in the nineteenth century.

The portico on the right was added to the town hall in 1633 and destroyed c.1886.

Gerrit Berckheyde painted the Haarlem market place from the west side many times; the earliest known dated one is of 1665 (see below). The National Gallery version appears to be the only one in which the portico of the town hall is seen on the right of the picture.

VERSIONS: There are dated variants of this view, from a slightly different viewpoint and without the portico (and with different figures) in the collection of the Earl of Northbrook (dated 1665),[1] Basel Museum (dated 1678),[2] Leipzig Museum (dated 1683),[3] the Uffizi Gallery (dated 1693),[4] Haarlem Museum (dated 1696)[5] and in an anonymous Amsterdam sale, 15 November 1938, lot 8 (dated 1697).[6] There are also a number of undated versions.[7] There are, too, some views taken from farther to the right, in one of which the town hall portico is visible on the left (Lyons Museum, dated 1675),[8] one view of the market place seen from beneath the portico (Cambridge, Fitzwilliam Museum; dated 1674),[9] and some from the south-west corner of the market place (e.g. Brussels Museum,[10] Springfield Museum, Mass.,[11] Detroit Institute of Arts).[12]

PROVENANCE: Perhaps in the [Lespinasse de Langeac] sale, Paris, 16–18 January 1809 (lot 22),[13] 401 francs. Adrian Hope sale, London, 30 June 1894 (lot 16), bought for the National Gallery.

EXHIBITIONS: London 1974; Edinburgh, National Gallery of Scotland, 'Dutch Church Painters', 1984, No. 30.

REFERENCES:
1. Apparently in the part of the Baron Verstolk van Soelen collection bought by Chaplin in 1846 (cf. Northbrook catalogue, 1889, pp. 200–01); in the Col. A. Ridgway sale, 14–16 January 1886 (lot 166). Exhibited at Agnews, London, 1957, No. 4.
2. According to the Basel 1966 catalogue, p. 150 (inv. no. 1118) it is dated 1678 (or 1673); the date is, however, damaged and difficult to read.
3. Inv. no. 1555.
4. Uffizi Catalogo Generale, 1979, p. 199. From Poggio Imperiale, 1796.
5. Frans Halsmuseum 1969 catalogue, No. 464a (on loan from the RBK); from the Comte Greffülhe sale, London, 22 July 1937 (lot 55).
6. Reproduced in the sale catalogue. From the Hope heirlooms sale, London, 20 July 1917 (lot 28).
7. References to at least eight signed but undated versions occur in the National Gallery dossier.
8. Lyons Museum cat. 1960, No. 34.
9. Fitzwilliam Museum cat. 1960, No. 47.
10. Inv. no. 33.
11. James Philip Gray collection, 41.04. Museum catalogue 1979, No. 196.
12. Dated 1695. Museum catalogue 1930, No. 11.
13. As by Job and Gerrit Berckheyde: 'Une Vue de la grande Place de Harlem. Entr'autres bâtimens, l'on y voit une Eglise qui en occupe le milieu. Auprès sont différentes Maisons avec Boutiques, et sur le devant à gauche s'élève un Monument surmonté d'une balustrade qui . . . porte son ombre sur une grande partie du devant . . . un nombre infini de Figures . . . distribuées sur différens plans . . .'; on canvas, 18 × 26 pouces. It should be noted that in this description left means the picture's left, not the spectator's; this is proved by the description of, for example, lot 34 in the same catalogue, the Lady and Maidservant by Vermeer (now in the Frick Collection; HdG No. 33) where the seated woman is said to be on the left (she is actually on the spectator's right).

1451 *The Interior of the Grote Kerk at Haarlem* Plate 22

The church is seen from the west door, looking towards the choir. In the left foreground is an alms chest; the tablet on a post attached to it has a simulated inscription dated, below, 16(5?)1 with carved and painted figures of a girl and a boy from the orphanage on either side. The hatchment above it on a column (*de gueules, au lion d'or*) is inscribed below 16 · · (the last two figures are not intended to be legible). On the north side of the choir is an organ; on the inner side of its right door is painted the Resurrection.[1] The centre panel of the pulpit on the right is inscribed: Psalm 138 (less probably, 135); the inscription on the sounding-board is not intended to be legible.

Around the base of the gallery of the organ in the south aisle[2] is visible part of an inscription ZA ZYIN E [*sic*]; on the wall below the gallery hangs a painting of the exterior of the Grote Kerk (see below). The hand of the clock in the vaulting of the crossing stands between two and three.

Signed below, in the centre: Gerrit Berkheijde 1673.

Oil on oak, 60.8 × 84.9 ($23\frac{15}{16}$ × $33\frac{7}{16}$).

Cleaned in 1954.

This is an accurate view of the interior of the Grote Kerk (St Bavo) in Haarlem, the choir of which was built *c.*1400 and the nave after 1470; it remains much as it is in the present painting. The wooden vaulting of the nave and choir, erected in 1530–8, is still in existence, as also the choir-screen (of 1509–17). The canopy and sounding-board of the pulpit have survived; the pulpit and its stair were replaced in 1679. The organ in the choir has now gone,[3] so also has the smaller one in the south aisle.[4] The picture below the latter is of the exterior of the Grote Kerk seen from the north, and still hangs in the church; it appears in the same position in several of Saenredam's views of the interior (e.g. No. 2531 of this catalogue) and is attributed to Geertgen tot sint Jans in Carel van Mander's *Schilder-Boeck* of 1604.[5] The pews around the columns of the nave have been altered. As is the practice in the Dutch Reformed Church, the congregation is seated around and facing the pulpit (compare E. de Witte, No. 1053 of this catalogue).

Although most of their work consists of street views, both Job and Gerrit painted a few church interiors. As with his other pictures, Gerrit's interiors are close in style to Job's. This seems to be the only known dated interior by Gerrit; there are views of other parts of the same interior by Job dated 1665 (Dresden Gallery), 1666 (P. de Boer, 1951), 1668 (Haarlem Museum) and 1676 (Detroit Institute of Arts). H. Jantzen[6] has drawn attention to the similar view of the interior of St Bavo during a sermon in Samuel Ampzing's *Beschrijvinge ende Lof van de Stad Haerlem*, 1628, etched by Jan van de Velde after a drawing of 1627 by Pieter Saenredam.[7]

PROVENANCE: This is perhaps the interior of the Grote Kerk during a sermon, by Gerrit Berckheyde, of the same size, which was in the Seger Tierens sale, The Hague, 23 July 1743 (lot 204),[8] bought by Schouman (182 guilders), and the Hendrik van der Vugt sale, Amsterdam, 27 April 1745 (lot 116),[9] bought by Jacob Haegen (66 guilders); it may be the 'interior of the Groote Kerk with figures', by G. Berckheyde, in the David Jetswaart sale, Amsterdam, 22 sqq. April 1749 (lot 147),[10] bought by Wandelaar (40 guilders). It was in the collection of the Hon. G. Agar Ellis (created Baron Dover, 1831; died 1833) by 1828 when it was exhibited at the BI. It passed with the Dover collection to the 4th Viscount Clifden;[11] at his sale in London, 21 sqq. May 1895 (lot 790), it was purchased for the National Gallery.

EXHIBITIONS: BI 1828, No. 117; BI 1858, No. 126 (lent by Lady Dover).

REFERENCES:
1. For this organ, see M.A. Vente in the catalogue *Nederlandse Orgelpracht*, Haarlem, 1961, pp. 1ff. The wings were painted by Frederick Hoorn in 1464/6 (loc. cit., p. 20).
2. For the small organ in the south aisle, see *Nederlandse Orgelpracht*, op. cit., no. 21.
3. See note 1. The organ can be seen better in Pieter Saenredam's painting of 1636 (Amsterdam, Rijks-

museum, 1976, catalogue A359).
4. See note 2.
5. Van Mander, f. 206 recto. M.J. Friedländer, *Early Netherlandish Painting*, Leiden/Brussels, 1969, vol. 5, cat. no. 15 and p. 101, note 7: 'It is generally accepted now that the picture was painted by Pieter Gheryts of Haarlem in 1518.'
6. Jantzen, p. 88.

7. There is a painting of the same view by Saenredam, from *c*.1635, in the J.G. Johnson collection, Philadelphia Museum of Art (1972 catalogue, No. 599).

8. 'De Haarlemsche Kerk, waar in gepredikt werd, vol Toehoorders, door dito' [Gerrit Berckheyde]; 1 *voet* 11½ *duim* × 2 *v. 8 d.*

9. 'De Groote Kerk te Haarlem, waar in gepredikt werd voor veel Toehoorders, van denzelven' [G. Berckheyde]; 1 *voet* 11½ *duim* × 2 *v. 8 d.* In the copy

of the van der Vugt sale catalogue in the RKD in The Hague, this lot is marked in a contemporary hand: 'Thierens No. 204. 182$^{ff.}$' (Hoet, vol. 2, p. 165, gives the lot number wrongly as 115).

10. 'Een de Groote Kerk van Haarlem van binnen, met Beeldjes, van denzelven' [G. Berckheyde] (Hoet, vol. 2, p. 248, wrongly as lot 141).

11. See the title-page of the 1895 Clifden sale catalogue.

1863 *The Market Place and Town Hall, Haarlem*   *Plate 23*

The view is of the west side of the market place (Grote Markt). Facing the spectator is the town hall; on the gable of the projecting part of the building is a statue of Justice and, above it, the arms of Haarlem (indistinct). On the right, beside the town hall, is the beginning of Zijlstraat. The entrance to Grote Houtstraat is between the houses on the extreme left. The boxes on the roof of the town hall are nesting boxes for storks.

Signed at the bottom edge to the left: G Berck Heyde.

Oil on oak, 31.9 × 40.3 ($12\frac{9}{16}$ × $15\frac{7}{8}$).

Cleaned in 1974.

The town hall was built in the fourteenth century as a palace of the Counts of Holland. The entrance towards the left and the windows were remodelled in 1630; the projecting part with the balcony, on the right, was rebuilt externally in 1633.[1] The wing in the Zijlstraat was added in 1620–*c*.1630.

The town hall has survived but has undergone some further alterations: the principal changes since Berckheyde painted it are that the balcony supported by columns on the right has gone, as also the seven dormer windows in the roof and the turret on the left corner. The doorway beneath the staircase on the left and the central window opening on to the balcony have also been altered. The original tower was destroyed in 1772, the present one being a reconstruction of 1914.

The houses visible in Zijlstraat have been replaced by later buildings; of those visible on the south side of the square only the second and third after the Grote Houtstraat survive, much altered. The archway to the left of the town hall, the Pandpoort, still exists but the buildings above and to the left of it have been rebuilt. In an earlier version in the Northbrook collection (see VERSIONS) the arcade immediately to the right of the town hall staircase is filled in (but pierced by windows and doors); in the other versions mentioned below the architecture is the same as in the National Gallery picture.[2]

It is possible that in this composition Berckheyde had in mind the similar view of the Grote Markt etched by Jan van de Velde after Pieter Saenredam in Samuel Ampzing's *Beschrijvinge ende Lof van de Stad Haerlem*, 1628.[3]

The present picture is a late version of a composition repeated a number of times by Berckheyde (see below). It was probably painted at about the same time as the version dated 1691.

VERSIONS: Earlier versions, painted from the same viewpoint but with different figures, are in the collection of the Earl of Northbrook (said to be dated 1661)[4] and the Frans Halsmuseum, Haarlem (dated 1671).[5] A later version from a slightly remoter viewpoint, so that more of the Zijlstraat can be seen, was with Richard Green in 1974 (dated 1691);[6] another late version is in the Wadsworth Atheneum, Hartford, Mass.;[7] and another was with Duits, London, in 1967.[8]

COPY: There is a painted copy by Vincent van der Vinne the Younger, signed and dated 1729, in the Frans Halsmuseum, Haarlem (Inv. no. 297).

DRAWING: A chalk sketch by Berckheyde of the left half of this view (excluding the first house on the left and without figures) is in the Teylers Museum, Haarlem (Fig. 3).[9]

PROVENANCE: In the collection of George Mitchell, London; George Mitchell Bequest to the South Kensington (now Victoria and Albert) Museum, 1878.[10] Lent to the National Gallery from 1895 onwards.

EXHIBITION: London 1974a.

REFERENCES:
1. A view of the town hall before these alterations is in S. Ampzing, op. cit. (engraved after Pieter Saenredam; reproduced in P. T. A. Swillens, *P. J. Saenredam*, 1953, fig. 57).
2. In the Wadsworth Atheneum version alone the chimneys of the town hall wing in the Zijlstraat are all of equal height.
3. Reproduced in Swillens, loc. cit.
4. Reproduced in the Northbrook catalogue, 1889, No. 32. On panel, 59 × 81.5 cm. Bought in 1846 from the collection of Baron J. G. Verstolk van Soelen. According to the 1889 catalogue, the picture is signed and dated 1661, but the date is uncertain (cf. the catalogue of the Exhibition of Pictures from Hampshire Houses, Winchester/Southampton, 1955, No. 1).
5. Canvas, 33 × 42 cm. Bought in Paris, 1878. 1969 cat. no. 16.
6. Catalogue of the Summer Exhibition 1974 (34),

from the Lilienfeld collection: see G. Glück, *Niederländische Gemälde aus der Sammlung . . . Leon Lilienfeld in Wien*, 1917, opp. p. 40. On canvas, 53 × 63 cm.
7. Sumner Collection, 1947, no.363; Wadsworth Atheneum Paintings, catalogue 1: *The Netherlands and the German-speaking Countries, 15th–19th Centuries*, Hartford, 1978, p. 119. Signed: on panel, 32 × 40.5 cm. See also note 2.
8. Exhibited: 'La vie en Hollande au XVIIe siècle', Musée des Arts Décoratifs, Paris, 1967 (no. 26). Signed: on canvas, 52.7 × 62.6 cm.
9. Black chalk, 22.2 × 16.5 cm. (H. J. Scholten, *Catalogue raisonné des dessins des écoles française et hollandaise [du] Musée Teyler*, 1904, p. 243, Portefeuille R, No. 3.)
10. *Catalogue of the National Gallery of British Art at South Kensington*, 1893, part 1, p. 175, Nos. 344–78

DIRCK VAN DEN BERGEN, c.1640–1690

He also spelt his name *Dirck van (den) Berghen*. Little is known of his life. Houbraken[1] says that he was born in Haarlem. This was probably in about 1640. He also says that van Bergen was a pupil of Adriaen van de Velde in Amsterdam and van Bergen's work consists entirely of Italianate landscapes in a manner closely related to van de Velde. He travelled to England but there, Houbraken recounts, Fortune did not smile on him. Van Bergen was, however, one of the artists involved in the decoration of Ham House for the Duke and Duchess of Lauderdale in the 1670s. Subsequently he returned to Haarlem and died there. Van Gool[2] says that he was a close friend of the landscape painter Jan Vermeer of Haarlem.

REFERENCES:
1. Houbraken, vol. 3, pp. 91–92.
2. Van Gool, vol. 2, p. 461.

984 *Two Calves, a Sheep and a Dun Horse by a Ruin* *Plate 24*

Oil on oak, 23.8 × 30 (9⅜ × 11¹³⁄₁₆).

This picture is in the style of Adriaen van de Velde's later years and was included by
Hofstede de Groot in his catalogue of van de Velde's work. MacLaren, however,
catalogued the painting as 'Ascribed to Adriaen van de Velde', noting that much of it,
especially the landscape and the recumbent calf, seemed too weak for van de Velde and
raising the possibility that it was by Dirck van den Bergen. The present writer considers that it is close enough to signed paintings by van den Bergen to justify the attribution to him: for example, the *Landscape with Herdsmen and Cattle* in the Rijksmuseum.[1]
Van den Bergen's work is based on van de Velde's late style.

PROVENANCE: Wynn Ellis Bequest, 1876.

REFERENCES:
General: HdG No. 209 (Adriaen van de Velde).
In text:
1. 1976 cat., No. A37.

For JAN VAN BIJLERT *see* pages 68–69

FERDINAND BOL, 1616–1680

Ferdinand(us) Bol, son of Balthasar Bol, was baptised in Dordrecht, 24 June 1616. In
Dordrecht he may have been the pupil of Jacob Cuyp: he was still in the town in 1635
when he witnessed four documents with the signature *Ferdinandus bol, schilder*. Shortly
afterwards he went to Amsterdam, where he lived for the rest of his life, and was a
pupil of Rembrandt. A note by Rembrandt on the back of a drawing from the second
half of the 1630s (Benesch, No. 159) mentions copies by Bol which Rembrandt had
sold; in 1640 he witnessed a document for Rembrandt. He appears to have remained
with Rembrandt until *c.*1641 (the year of his father's death). His first dated paintings
are from 1642 and from then until 1669 there are dated works virtually every year.
In 1649 Bol received his first major commission, a group portrait of the Governors
of the Amsterdam Leper House. His reputation continued to grow and he was
acknowledged to be one of the city's leading painters – he played an important
part in the decoration of the town hall. His *Pyrrhus and Fabricius* there, for which
he was paid in 1656, was greatly admired by contemporaries. Bol had become a
citizen of Amsterdam in 1652 and married in the following year. In the 1660s Bol's
reputation stood at its highest point – he received numerous major municipal and
institutional commissions. Among his patrons were the Amsterdam Admiralty and
the Leiden town council.

Many of his earlier works, especially the portraits, display the powerful influence of Rembrandt. After 1650, however, he turned more and more towards the manner of Bartholomeus van der Helst in portraiture, although in his subject pieces he remained closer to Rembrandt. Bol's first wife died in 1660. His second marriage, in 1669, was to the widow of a rich merchant and he seems to have given up painting then; the last known dated picture is of 1669. He was buried in Amsterdam on 24 July 1680. Cornelis Bisschop and Gottfried Kneller were his pupils. He also etched in the style of Rembrandt (the earliest dated prints are of 1642).

REFERENCES:
A. Blankert, *Ferdinand Bol: Rembrandt's Pupil*, Doornspijk, 1982 (for his biography, see pp. 15–25 and 71–87 [documents transcribed]); Sumowski, *Gemälde*, vol. 1.

679 *An Astronomer* *Plate 25*

On the table, left, is a celestial globe and, behind it, a terrestrial one. In the centre of the man's belt is a medallion with the bust of a Roman emperor(?).

Signed on a paper below left: fBol feci(t)/1652 (fB in monogram); the signature and date are worn.

Oil on canvas, 127 × 135 (50 × 53¼).

Cross-sections reveal that the painting has a double ground – of red-brown ochre directly on the canvas, lead-white and charcoal black on top – of a type found in most of Rembrandt's paintings in the National Gallery (see the discussion of Rembrandt No. 4930 in this catalogue). The flesh shadows, hair and background are worn; the blacks are badly rubbed. A horizontal tear runs through his right hand and neck and two parallel vertical tears run from this one through his body to the bottom edge of the picture.

Cleaned in 1952–3.

On the celestial globe the figure to the left is clearly intended for the constellation Boötes (Bubuleus);[1] the dark shape on the right of it is therefore presumably the constellation Hercules.

The man's abstracted manner may be intended to suggest melancholy, a sense of the futility of his endeavours in face of the inevitability of death (see above, under Bega No. 1481).

Mellaart[2] thought the painting was 'possibly a self portrait' and van Hall[3] reproduced it as such. Blankert[4] considered that it 'closely resembled' the man in a double portrait in the Philips collection in Eindhoven.[5] There is no authenticated self portrait of Bol but if he is the man shown in a group of portraits of 1646/7,[6] as seems likely, No. 679 is not a self portrait. Nor is the similarity with the Philips collection portrait striking.

PROVENANCE: *An Astronomer* by Bol was exhibited for sale by private contract with other paintings belonging to J. Hickman in Edinburgh (lot 66) in or after 1802(?).[7] Presented by Miss E.A. Benett, 1862.

REFERENCES:
General: Blankert, op. cit., cat. no. 70. Sumowski, *Gemälde*, vol. 1, no. 127.
In text:
1. Cf. Olivier van Deuren No. 2589 of this catalogue.
2. J.H.J. Mellaart, 'Self-portraits by Bol', BM, vol. 43, 1923, p. 154.
3. Van Hall, No. 20.
4. Blankert, op. cit.

5. Blankert, op. cit., cat. no. 168.
6. Blankert, op. cit., cat. nos. 60–65.
7. *A catalogue of . . . original pictures, the property of Mr J. Hickman . . . exhibition and sale by private contract, in Adam's Square, Edinburgh . . . printed by Robert Allan, Caledonian Mercury Office*. This catalogue is undated; the National Gallery's copy has a watermark: W S1802.

5656 *Portrait of a Young Lady with a Fan* *Plate 26*

Oil on canvas, 83.5 × 69.5 (32$\frac{7}{8}$ × 27$\frac{3}{8}$).

There is some loss of paint in the area of the parapet at the bottom of the picture.

There are *pentimenti* in the fan.

MacLaren considered that both the style and costume (especially the collar) of this portrait suggested a date in the middle or late 1640s. Blankert[1] agreed with this dating.

It is not included in Sumowski's catalogue of Bol's works (op. cit.).

PROVENANCE: Possibly inherited from Robert Philips, The Park, Prestwick, by his son, Robert Needham Philips (died 1890), who certainly owned it.[2] Passed to the latter's daughter, Miss Anna Maria Philips, who lent it to the Dutch Exhibition, Manchester 1929. Miss A.M. Philips Bequest, 1946.

EXHIBITION: Manchester 1929, No. 26.

REFERENCES:
General: Blankert, op. cit., cat. no. 123.
In text:
1. Blankert, op. cit.

2. Information supplied by Miss A.M. Philips's nephew, W.R. Price (letter of 1949 in the National Gallery archives).

GERARD TER BORCH, 1617–1681

Gerard ter Borch[1] (he often signs *Geraert ter Borch*) was the son of Gerard ter Borch the Elder (1584–1662), an artist who had lived in Italy in his youth. He was born in Zwolle (Province of Overijssel) in the last days of 1617. His first master was doubtless his father, as Houbraken says.[2] In 1632 he was apparently in Amsterdam and in 1634 in Haarlem, where he was a pupil of Pieter de Molijn. He is said to have entered the Haarlem guild in 1635; in July of that year he was in England working with his uncle, the engraver Robert van Voerst, but may have been back in Zwolle by April 1636. Houbraken[3] says that after he had studied in Haarlem he travelled in Germany, Italy, England, France, Spain and the Netherlands; he may have been in Rome in the late 1630s.[4] Subsequently, he went to Münster and painted miniature portraits of some of the plenipotentiaries engaged in the peace negotiations of 1646–8 (see No. 896 below). Houbraken[5] relates that the Spanish envoy there, the Conde de Peñaranda, took ter Borch with him to Madrid, where ter Borch painted the king and members of the court, and that afterwards he worked in England and France before returning home. It is true that Peñaranda had an unnamed Dutch painter in his service in March 1648[6] but if this were ter Borch he cannot have accompanied his patron to Spain since the count, who left Münster for Brussels in June or July 1648, did not return to Madrid until September 1650[7] while ter Borch is recorded in Amsterdam in November 1648 and in December 1650 was apparently in Kampen[8] (near Zwolle). There is no trace of ter Borch in Spain; it is, however, conceivable that he visited it in his earlier days, c.1636–7. On 22 April 1653, ter Borch witnessed a document in Delft with the young Johannes Vermeer.[9] In February 1654 he married in Deventer (Overijssel) and in 1655 he acquired citizenship there; he seems to have lived there for the rest of his life. He became a common councillor (*gemeensman*) of Deventer and in 1667 painted a group portrait of its regents.[10] He died in Deventer on 8 December 1681.

His early genre scenes are connected in style with those of the Haarlem *corps de garde* painters and Pieter Codde and Willem Duyster of Amsterdam; in the 1640s he was painting miniature portraits. In the fifties he evolved an individual style in genre painting; he also introduced a new type of small full-length portrait. His most distinguished pupil was Caspar Netscher.

REFERENCES:

General: S.J. Gudlaugsson, *Gerard ter Borch*, 2 vols., The Hague, 1959.

In text:
1. For the details of ter Borch's biography, see Gudlaugsson, op. cit.
2. Houbraken, vol. 3, p. 34.
3. Loc. cit.
4. See Gudlaugsson, op. cit., vol. 1, pp. 35–8.
5. Op. cit., pp. 34–36.
6. In a letter written in Münster in March 1648, Peñaranda mentions 'un pintor que tengo, holandés'; see [F.J.] S[ánchez] C[antón] in *Archivo Español de Arte y Arqueología*, vol. 7, 1931, p. 174.
7. Sánchez Cantón, loc. cit.
8. In December 1650 the magistrate of Kampen presented him with 100 guilders in return for some prints.
9. J.M. Montias, 'New Documents on Vermeer and his Family', OH, vol. 91, 1977, pp. 280–1.
10. Gudlaugsson, cat. no. 205.

864 *A Young Woman playing a Theorbo to Two Men*   Plate 27

The card beneath the table is the ace of spades; on the table is a Turkey carpet. In the background is a bed.

Oil on canvas, 67.6 × 57.8 ($26\frac{5}{8}$ × $22\frac{3}{4}$).

Cleaned in 1971.

The same spaniel is seen in several other paintings by ter Borch (for example, No. 5847 below).

MacLaren suggested that the picture was painted in the late 1660s or, at the latest, in the earlier years of the following decade. Gudlaugsson dated it to c.1667/8. The lute-player appears alone in a painting in Cassel (Fig. 4) – also dated by Gudlaugsson to

$c.1667/8^1$ – and the man on the right who leans on the table holding a songbook appears with a different female figure in another painting in Cassel (Fig. 5).[2] (MacLaren believed that painting to be a pastiche but Gudlaugsson – correctly in the view of the present writer – accepted it as an authentic picture of $c.1670$.) The silver box and candlestick can also be found in other paintings by the artist. There is another version of this composition in the collection of Baroness Bentinck[3] in which the main differences are that the woman is leaning farther forward, the table-covering is plain grey with a gold fringe and the dog has been omitted; Gudlaugsson believed it to be a good workshop painting based on No. 864 and the single lute-player in Cassel.

In Dutch genre painting music-making is often suggestive of love. Here, as in many of his interior scenes from the 1650s and 1660s with two or three figures, ter Borch creates a deliberately ambiguous situation in which the spectator is teased by the relationships between the figures.

Several versions are known of a composition rather similar to that of No. 864 but, except for the background, in the opposite direction.[4] In these the same woman and the man on the right appear (in different poses) and the background is almost exactly repeated; the style and costume are of the same date as in the National Gallery, Bentinck and Cassel pictures.

ETCHING: Etched (in reverse) by B.A. Dunker, 1771.[5]

VERSIONS AND COPIES: A workshop version and several variants are discussed above. In addition, Gudlaugsson (cat. no. 220) lists two copies after No. 864, two paintings which seem to be compilations of elements of No. 864 and the Bentinck painting (see above), and a pastiche.

PROVENANCE: In the Chevalier de Julienne collection by 1754;[6] Julienne sale, Paris, 30 March sqq. 1767 (lot 141), bought by the Duc de Choiseul (2,800 francs); Duc de Choiseul sale, Paris, 6 sqq. April 1772 (lot 26), bought by Boileau (3,500 francs) for the Prince de Conti; Prince de Conti sale, Paris, 8 sqq. April 1777 (lot 295), bought by Langlier (4,800 francs); Marquis de Pange sale, Paris, 5 sqq. March 1781 (lot 23), bought by Langlier (5,855 francs). Perhaps in the collection of Comte de la Motte.[7] Incorrectly stated by Smith to have been in the Choiseul-Praslin sale, 1808, and the Séréville sale, 1812.[8] It was in the [Prince Galitzin][9] sale, Paris, 28 February sqq. 1825 (lot 38), bought by Delahante who sold it to Joseph Barchard;[10] [Barchard] sale, London, 6 May 1826 (lot 22), bought by (Sir) Robert Peel (Bart.) (920 gns). Purchased with the Peel collection, 1871.

REFERENCES:

General: Smith No. 7; HdG No. 132; Gudlaugsson, op. cit., cat. no. 220.
In text:
1. Panel, 51 × 37 cm. Gudlaugsson, op. cit., cat. no. 218; *Gerard Ter Borch*, catalogue of the exhibition held at the Mauritshuis, The Hague, and the Landesmuseum, Münster, 1974, No. 53.
2. Canvas, 58 × 46 cm. Cassel Gallery cat. 1929, no. 288; Gudlaugsson, op. cit., cat. no. 258.
3. Canvas, 61.5 × 47.5 cm.; signed with monogram. Gudlaugsson, op. cit., cat. no. 220d. To Gudlaugsson's provenance it can be added that the painting was in the John Smith sale, London, 2–3 May 1828 (lot 34). It was almost certainly not the painting mentioned by Waagen (vol. 2, 1854, p. 116) as being in the collection of Michael Peacock (that appears to be Gudlaugsson, op. cit., cat. no. 221 [II]).

The painting was No. 407 in the 1937 catalogue of the Schloss Rohoncz collection; it was passed to Baron Thyssen's daughter, Baroness Bentinck, and has recently been on loan at the Kunstmuseum, Düsseldorf (Inv. no. Dep 31/1970). HdG (No. 132, note) described it as a copy of the National Gallery picture but later apparently accepted it as the work of ter Borch.
4. All are listed by Gudlaugsson (op. cit.) under his cat. no. 221.
5. In *Recueil d'estampes . . . d'après les tableaux du Cabinet . . . Choiseul*, 1771, No. 12.
6. Descamps, vol. 2, p. 126.
7. On the back is an old inscribed label: 'No. 22/le Cte Delam( )'. A similar label with the name fully legible is on the back of Netscher's *Lady seated at a Spinning-Wheel* (No. 845 of this catalogue) which,

like the present picture, came from the Galitzin collection.
8. Smith No. 7. The only ter Borch in the Choiseul-
Praslin and Séréville sales was an entirely different
composition, *The Glass of Lemonade*, now in the
Hermitage, Leningrad (HdG No. 87; Gudlaugsson,
op. cit., cat. no. 192), which was lot 25 of the 1772
Choiseul sale.

9. Prince Galitzin was the vendor of at least some of
the pictures in this anonymous sale; a seal with the
Galitzin arms is on the back of the lining of
the present picture (see also Metsu No. 5225 and
Netscher No. 845).
10. Smith No. 7.

896 *The Swearing of the Oath of Ratification of the Treaty of Münster, 15 May 1648* Plate 28

The interior of the Ratskammer in the Rathaus in Münster, seen from the south side. In
it are seventy-seven persons; of some only the top of the head can be seen. Standing
round the table in the centre with their right hands raised are six of the Netherlands
delegates: (from left to right) Willem van Ripperda, Frans van Donia, Adrian Clant van
Stedum, Adriaen Pauw, Jan van Mathenesse and Barthold van Ghent, the last holding a
paper (with the words of the oath – see below); all are in black except for van Ripperda.
On their left are the two Spanish plenipotentiaries: the Conde de Peñaranda in dark
grey with silver embroidery, holding a copy of the oath, and on his left Anton Brun in
light grey. The count's chaplain, Don Miguel Lopez de Barnuevo, holding an open
Bible with a silver crucifix on it, stands before the two Spaniards, whose right hands
are laid on the Bible. Behind the chaplain, holding a document, is a man in a red cloak,
probably Anton Brun's secretary, Johannus Christopherus Belne. On the extreme
right is a Franciscan monk, probably the prior of the monastery in which Peñaranda
stayed during the negotiations. On the extreme left, behind a man with his hand on a
chair, is ter Borch. (For further identifications, see Plate 28a.)

On the table are, from left to right, a box covered in red and bound with gold braid
on which lies a document with seals; a round silver box and, behind it, a large seal; a
casket covered with red velvet and edged with silver braid, before which lies a document with a seal.

The walls of the Ratskammer are lined with carved wooden stalls; those at the back
have a painted wooden canopy. From the ceiling hangs a circular ironwork candelabrum around which are escutcheons with the arms of Münster and, in front, a gilded
statuette of the Virgin and Child in an aureole. The corners of the room are decorated
with foliage and on either side of an (invisible) tribunal at the back is a flag.

Signed on a tablet hanging on the left-hand wall: GTBorch. F. Monasterij. A. 1648
(GTB in monogram).

Oil on copper, 45.4 × 58.5 (17$\frac{7}{8}$ × 23).

Cleaned in 1982. Overpainting was removed in three principal areas: (1) The monk at
the right edge: his robe had been painted dark brown and the back of his head extended
to conceal the profile of the man behind.[1] (2) The man holding the feathered hat, his
hand on the chair, left side: his jerkin had been made longer. (3) The self portrait of the

artist, left edge: the face had been completely repainted, the complexion made redder, the moustache turned up and the hair darkened (Figs. 6 and 7).

The candelabrum was at first wider by more than 5 cm.[2] and another *pentimento* is in the legs of the man in the red cloak to the right.

Recent cleaning (see above) has revealed that the head of ter Borch had been over-painted, apparently to make him more clearly resemble the well-known *Self Portrait*[3] in the Mauritshuis of about twenty years later. The face, which after cleaning appears fairer, thinner and younger, is still recognisably ter Borch's.

The ratification of the Treaty of Münster was an event of exceptional historical significance for the Dutch. Since 1568 the United Provinces of the Netherlands had been at war almost continuously to free themselves from the dominion of Spain. Although the Spaniards had been forced to recognise their independence *de facto* in 1609 it was not until the conclusion of the Peace of Münster in 1648 that *de jure* recognition was accorded. This treaty brought to an end eighty years' struggle and was a complete triumph for the Dutch; Spain renounced for ever her claim to sovereignty, recognising the United Provinces as free and independent, and accepted their conquests including those in the Portuguese colonies.

The negotiations began in 1646 in Münster in Westphalia. The peace treaty was signed by the delegates in Münster on 30 January 1648 and was ratified by Philip IV of Spain on 1 March and by the Dutch on 18 April. The final act, the swearing of the oath of confirmation, took place in the town hall of Münster on 15 May 1648. Of the eight Dutch delegates only six were present. These were Barthold van Ghent, delegate of the Province of Gelderland and leader of the delegation; Jan van Mathenesse (Province of Holland and West Friesland); Adriaen Pauw (also for Holland and West Friesland); Frans van Donia (Friesland); Willem van Ripperda (Overijssel); Adrian Clant van Stedum (Groningen). Godard van Reede, the Utrecht delegate, was unable to attend because of illness, and Johan de Knuyt was absent since Zeeland, which he represented, refused until later to ratify the treaty.[4] The Spanish plenipotentiaries were Don Gaspar de Bracamonte y Guzman, Conde de Peñaranda, and Anton Brun, a member of the Supreme Council of Flanders.

A detailed account of the ceremony of ratification was published in the same month by Johan Cools, who witnessed it.[5] According to this, the room where the oath was sworn (the Ratskammer, see below) was decorated with foliage and flowers. The Conde de Peñaranda was dressed in grey with silver embroidery and the Dutch delegates were all in black. The delegates seated themselves at a round table (this and the seats had green coverings); first the count, next Anton Brun on his left, then Barthold van Ghent, followed by Jan van Mathenesse, Adriaen Pauw, Frans van Donia, Willem van Ripperda and Adrian Clant; they kept their hats on but the spectators all stood uncovered. On the table stood two caskets containing the treaty documents: the Spanish one covered in red with gold edges and silver fittings, that of the Dutch also red. After speeches by Anton Brun and Barthold van Ghent the treaty was read aloud in full, first in French by Anton Brun's secretary, Belne, and then in Dutch by the secretary to the Dutch delegation, Jacob van der Burgh. Afterwards, while the delegates stood around the table, came the swearing of the oath. The first to swear were the Spanish plenipotentiaries. As the count recited the oath in Spanish he and Brun raised their left hands and placed their right hands on the Gospels, which, with a silver crucifix, were held by the count's chaplain; they afterwards kissed the crucifix. Then, in the name of his colleagues, Barthold van Ghent read out the oath in French; at the words 'we swear' the Dutch delegates raised their right hands with fingers extended. With this the ceremony ended. Abraham de Wicquefort, writing in 1667–9, adds that the doors of the Ratskammer were left open and the ceremony took place publicly in the presence of some of the Münster magistrature and of many members of the suites of the plenipotentiaries then in the town.[6]

Ter Borch's painting agrees closely with Cools' account. For example, the removal of yellowed varnish during the recent restoration of the painting has revealed the colour of the table-covering and the seat of the only visible chair to be green, just as Cools describes them (viridis). He has, however, represented the two sides taking the oath simultaneously and it is also obvious that the placing of the figures in a half-circle facing the spectator is an arbitrary arrangement dictated by the pictorial requirements. The picture differs from Cools' report in only a few minor matters. The latter describes the six Dutch delegates as all dressed in black; ter Borch shows Willem van Ripperda in grey edged with silver braid.

The woodwork and some of the objects seen in the picture have survived and prove that ter Borch was at pains to achieve accuracy. The act of ratification took place in the Ratskammer of the Münster Rathaus; from the eighteenth century onwards it has been known as the 'Friedenssaal'.[7] It was destroyed in 1944 together with most of the Rathaus but the sixteenth-century woodwork had been removed previously and was installed in the reconstructed Ratskammer in 1948. The painted iron candelabrum is also preserved and hangs in the Ratskammer. It now has a polychrome Virgin and Child carved in wood (probably Flemish sixteenth century) in place of the statuette seen in the picture, which is presumably the Virgin and Child in glory made for the Ratskammer by Johann Gröninger and paid for in 1636.[8] The red and gold casket containing the United Provinces' copy of the treaty is preserved in the Algemeen Rijksarchief in The Hague.[9] Despite the small scale of the painting all these are reproduced in accurate detail.

The six Dutch delegates and the two plenipotentiaries have been identified by the engravings of them in Anselmus van Hulle's *Celeberrimi . . . Legati, Monasterium et Osnabrugas . . . missi*, of which there are various editions, 1648–1717; these prints are after portraits made by van Hulle at Münster, 1646(?)–8.[10] According to Arnold Houbraken the artist's self portrait here is a particularly good likeness.[11] The man in a red cloak behind the Spanish chaplain, with a paper in his hand, is presumably one of the two secretaries who read out the treaty before the oath-swearing (see above); if so he must be Johannes Christopherus Belne since the man in black on his right, seen in profile, can be identified as the other secretary, Jacob van der Burgh, whose features are known from Pieter Holsteyn's engraving after ter Borch's lost portrait of him.[12] Most of the other figures, at least in the principal group, also appear to be portraits.

Gudlaugsson[13] identified Joannes Cuyermans, Don Miguel Lopez de Barnuevo, Don Diego Bahac, Eleazer Lootius, Graf Kratz von Scharfenstein, Wolfgang Konrad von Thumbschirn, Caspar van Kinschot and Arnoldus Teckmanus. He also suggested the two further figures might be identified as Johann Vultejus and Henrich Herdingh.

Ter Borch painted portraits of a number of the people who had come to Münster for the peace negotiations but only a few are known to have survived, most of them being miniatures on copper or wood.[14] Examples are the bust portrait of the Conde de Peñaranda in Rotterdam[15] and that of Godard van Reede in the Rijksmuseum.[16]

It is not known whether ter Borch painted the present picture as a commission. It is worth noting that the Conde de Peñaranda had an unnamed Dutch painter in his service (see the biographical notice of ter Borch) and ter Borch certainly painted a miniature of Peñaranda. Houbraken[17] merely says that ter Borch asked six thousand guilders for No. 896 but as he was offered less he kept it, and it does in fact appear to have remained either in his possession or that of his family (see PROVENANCE).

COPIES: There are later copies in the Rijksmuseum, Amsterdam,[18] and the Rathaus in Münster;[19] these agree in detail with the original except that the self portrait of the artist has very long hair (or a wig) and a lace cravat, both of a type that can hardly be dated before 1670. A copy by Claude Jacquand (1804–78) is in Versailles.[20] In the Landesmuseum in Münster (Fig. 8) is a pastiche made up of most of the figures in the present composition grouped about a tomb with the recumbent figure of a man (who has been identified as Joseph de Bergaigne, Archbishop of Cambrai, and Hugo Grotius);[21] a copy of this pastiche was in an anonymous sale, London, 27 July 1956 (lot 152).[22] Three small panels with half-length copies of ten of the principal figures in No. 896 and five heads of background figures, arbitrarily regrouped, are apparently in the Gemäldegalerie in Berlin-Dahlem.[23] A drawing by Gesina ter Borch, Gerard's half-sister, after one of the figures in No. 896 is in a book of drawings by members of the ter Borch family in the Rijksmuseum.[24]

ENGRAVINGS: Engraved by Jonas Suijderhoef (the same size as the painting; Fig. 9)[25] and anonymously (with verses by J. de Dekker).[26] An engraving by Simon Fokke, 1754, is after Suijderhoef's print.[27]

PROVENANCE: In the collection of Hendrick ter Borch, burgomaster of Deventer and a distant cousin of the painter, in Deventer in 1672/4.[28] It passed to Hendrick's son, Bernard Heidentrijck ter Borch,[29] in whose collection it was seen by Houbraken.[30] It is not in the 1736 will of B.H. ter Borch[31] (who died in 1738) but apparently remained in the hands of his family since it was bought from one of his descendants by van Leyden of Amsterdam.[32] Van Leyden sale, Paris, 5 sqq. November 1804 (lot 91), bought by de La Roche (16,000 francs). It is said to have been in the collection of Chevalier de Lespinasse de Langeac (born c.1750, died 1842).[33] By June 1814 it belonged to the Prince de Talleyrand, Paris.[34] It is in the catalogue of the [Talleyrand] sale announced for 9 July 1817 (lot 38); the sale did not take place and almost the whole collection was bought in the same year by William Buchanan,[35] from whom it had passed by 1833 to the Duc de Berry;[36] it was among the Duc de Berry's pictures exhibited for private sale in London, April 1834 (No. 69). At the Duchesse de Berry's sale, Paris, 4–6 April 1837 (lot 1) it was bought by Octave Taunez (45,500 francs) for Prince Anatole Demidoff. In the Demidoff collection at San Donato, Florence; Prince Anatole Demidoff sale, Paris, 18 April 1868 (lot 18), bought by the 4th Marquess of Hertford (182,000 francs). Inherited with Lord Hertford's collection in 1870 by Sir Richard Wallace, who presented it in 1871.

EXHIBITIONS: The Hague, Mauritshuis, and Münster, Landesmuseum, 'Gerard ter Borch', 1974, No. 15; London 1976, No. 11.

REFERENCES:

General: Smith No. 1 and Supplement No. 2; HdG No. 6; Gudlaugsson, op. cit., cat. no. 57; Ex. cat., The Hague, Mauritshuis, and Münster, Land-esmuseum, *Gerard ter Borch*, 1974, No. 15.

In text:

1. The face is fully visible in the copies in Amsterdam and Münster and J. Suijderhoef's engraving (see COPIES, ENGRAVINGS).

2. This can be clearly seen in an infra-red photograph.

3. Gudlaugsson, op. cit., cat. no. 232. It is not clear when this change was made, though it is unlikely to have been before 1700. Gudlaugsson (op. cit., cat. no. 57, p. 83) had noted this discrepancy and suggested that ter Borch himself might have added his older self in this area.

4. Both added their signatures to the ratification a little later.

5. *Tractatvs Pacis Inter Catholicam svam Maiestatem, et Dominos Ordines Generales Prouinciarum Vnitarum Inferioris Germaniae. Signatus vtrinque 30. Ianuarij: Ratihabitus & Iuratus 15 Maij: Publicatus 16. eiusdem Mensis, Monasterij Westphalorum, Anno 1648. E Gallico & Belgico sermonibus, subrogatis subrogandis, alliisque nuspiam antehac editis, in Latinum, nunc primum, tenuissimo filo, optima fide, Magnatûm Legatorumque auctoritate & inuitatu, translatus à Iohanne Cools IC. Hornabatauo, negotiorum Pacis quadriennali, publicae Pacis amore, priuato suo Aere, inspectore. Accedvnt Acta Qvatridvi sive Solennitates Ratificationum, Ivramenti, Pvblicationis, Aliaque mox illas consecuta Solennia. Auctore praepropero, Plerorumque, si non omnium, oculo aut aure, Translatore, qui supra. Monasterij Westphaliae . . . M.DC.XLVIII. ipso Mense Maij.* The description of the ratification ceremony is on pages 46–50.

6. A. de Wicquefort, *L'histoire des Provinces-Unies des Pais-Bas*, vol. 1, 1719, book ii, p. 67 (1861–74 edition, vol. 1, p. 112): '. . . les cérémonies de l'échange [des ratifications] et du serment . . . se firent publiquement, les portes de la salle estant ouvertes, en la présence de quelques uns du Magistrat, & d'un grand nombre de domestiques de la pluspart des Ministres, qui se trouvoient dans la ville.' Book ii was written in 1667–69.

7. For a description and reproductions of the Ratskammer before its destruction, see Geisberg, vol. 2, pp. 348ff., and figs. 508 and 509.

8. See F. Koch, *Die Gröninger*, 1905, pp. 134ff., and Geisberg, vol. 2, pp. 364–66, and fig. 524. It was in the Peace of Münster exhibition, Delft, 1948 (No. 413).

9. Exhibited in Delft, 1948 (No. 436; reproduced in the catalogue opposite p. 34) and in the ter Borch exhibition, The Hague, Münster, 1974 (not in the catalogue).

10. *Celeberrimi ad pacificandum christiani nominis orbem Legati, Monasterium et Osnabrugas ex omni pene gentium nationumque genere missi: vivum Anselmi van Hulle penicillo expressi, eiusque cura et aere per insigniores huius aevi sculptores caelo repraesentati*, Antwerp, 1648 (for the various editions, 1648–1717, see A. Pieper in F. Philippi's *Der Westfälische Friede*, 1898, pp. 187–90). In the Ratskammer of the Münster Rathaus is a series of thirty-six portraits, thirty-two being of the plenipotentiaries. They are feeble con-

temporary copies or derivations, apparently by Jan Baptist Floris, from the engravings in *Celeberrimi . . . Legati* or, more probably, from van Hulle's studies for the engravings (cf. Geisberg, op. cit., p. 390).

11. Houbraken, vol. 3, p. 40.

12. Reproduced in Hollstein, vol. 9, p. 76 (HdG No. 216).

13. Gudlaugsson, op. cit., cat. no. 57.

14. e.g. Gudlaugsson, op. cit., cat. nos. 49, 51, 55 and 56.

15. Gudlaugsson, op. cit., cat. no. 56: Rotterdam, Museum Boymans-van Beuningen, inv. no. 2529, copper, 10.5 × 9 cm. (oval).

16. Gudlaugsson, op. cit., cat. no. 47; Amsterdam, Rijksmuseum, A 3842, copper, 14.5 × 11 cm. (oval).

17. Op. cit., p. 40.

18. Rijksmuseum, A405, copper, 46 × 60 cm.

19. Canvas, 59.5 × 45 cm. Peace of Münster exhibition, Delft, 1948 (No. 441).

20. E. Soulié, *Notice du Musée Impérial de Versailles*, vol. 2, 1860, p. 211, No. 2197. 44 × 57 cm.

21. Gudlaugsson, op. cit., cat. no. 57F, canvas, 51 × 44.5 cm.; falsely signed: G. Terburg F. Joseph de Bergaigne was one of the Spanish plenipotentiaries until his death in October 1647; he was buried in the Observantenkloster in Münster; his tomb was moved later to the 'Friedenssaal' and remained there until the middle of the nineteenth century. The Münster pastiche shows in the left background an altar with a painting of the Resurrection. HdG (note to No. 6) thought that this pastiche was probably by Gerrit Lundens but this is not convincing; if it shows de Bergaigne, it was presumably painted after his tomb was removed to the 'Friedenssaal'. For the identification of the recumbent figure as Hugo Grotius, see C. Gellinek, 'Hugo Grotius und Gerard ter Borch: Neues zum Kampf um den Westfälischen Frieden', *Simpliciana* (Schriften der Grimmelshausen Gesellschaft), 3, 1981, pp. 17–38. This rather fanciful identification was accepted by the author of the exhibition catalogue *Münster 800–1800: 1000 Jahre Geschichte der Stadt*, Stadtmuseum Münster, 1985, cat. no. 198.

22. Gudlaugsson, op. cit., cat. no. 57g, canvas, 48 × 39.5 cm.

23. Gudlaugsson, op. cit., cat. no. 57e, panel, centre portion 14 × 14 cm., side portions 14 × 9 cm., framed together. Not in the 1975 Berlin catalogue.

24. See A. Bredius in *Zeitschrift für bildende Kunst*, vol. 18, 1883, p. 407.

25. J. Wussin, *Jonas Suyderhoef; Verzeichniss seiner Kupferstiche*, 1861, No. 103. The subject (*not* plate) size is 43.5 × 57 cm. Inscribed in engraving with the subject: 'Geraert ter Burch pinxit. Jonas Suijderhoef sculpsit' and in the lower margin: 'ICON EXACTISSIMA, QUA AD VIVUM EXPRIMITUR SOLENNIS CONVĒTUS LEGATORUM PLENIPOTENTIARIORUM HIS-PANIARUM REGIS PHILIPPI IV. ET ORDINUM/GENER-ALIUM FAEDERATI BELGII, QUI PACEM PERPETUAM PAULLO ANTE SANCITAM, EXTRADITIS UTRINQUE IN-STRUMENTIS, IURAMENTO CONFIRMARUNT,/MONAS-TERII WESTPHALORŪ IN DOMO SENATORIA. ANNO CIƆ IƆ CXLVIII. IDIBUS MAII.' The only variation from the National Gallery painting is that the tablet on the wall has, instead of the signature, the inscription: 'PAX OPTIMA RERVM'. This print was apparently made before Dec. 1650 (see Gudlaugsson, op. cit., cat. no. 57, p. 81).

26. Engraved inscription (within the subject): 'Vraeght ghij Wat ghij hier siet? ick sal u't stuck Verklaren;/sta, leser, slechs Wat stil. Alhier Word door den Vrê/Een oorlogs Vier gestuijt Van Vier-mael twintig jaren,/En't Spaensch en Neêrlandsch stael Verzegelt in de Scheê.//En lust u van de plaets oock Wat bescheyds te Weten,/Alwaer soo nut een stuck Voltoijt is en Verrecht?/Te Münster Wierd God Mars geslagen aen te keten,/En 't monster Van den krijg in boeijen Vast gelegt. I. de Decker.' Plate size: 18.4 × 24.8 cm. This print follows the Nation-al Gallery picture rather carelessly. The tablet on the wall is inscribed: 'PAX OPTIMA RERVM' in place of the signature.

27. Inscribed in engraving: 'G. Terburg Pinx S. Fokke del et fec/1754'. Plate size: 18.7 × 25.4 cm. This engraving is a careless copy after Suijderhoef's

print. The tablet is inscribed: 'PAX OPTIMA RERVM'.

28. It is described in his collection by Mr Cost Jor-dens, 'Deventer door den Keurvorst van Keulen en den Bischop van Münster ingenomen en beset, 1672-74', *Overysselsche Almanak*, 1842, p. 20 (quoted by Gudlaugsson, op. cit., p. 83).

29. M.E. Houck, *Mededeelingen betreffende Gerhard ter Borch* etc., Zwolle, 1899, p. 405.

30. Houbraken (vol. 3, p. 40) says it then belonged to 'Heer Rentmeester Terburg' in Deventer. Ber-nard Heidentrijck ter Borch is described in a docu-ment of 1695 as 'rentm[eeste]r van 't convent van Diepenveen' (see Houck, op. cit., p. 43). The *Groote Schouburgh* was apparently written between about 1717 (or 1715?) and Houbraken's death in October 1719.

31. Houck, op. cit., p. 81.

32. According to the catalogue of the van Leyden sale, 1804.

33. According to *Le cabinet de l'amateur*, vol. 1, 1842, p. 377. It was not in the [Langeac?] sale, Paris, 8 sqq. March 1808, nor in the [Lespinasse de Langeac] sale, Paris, 14–15 December 1808, nor in the Lespinasse de Langeac sale, Paris, 16–18 January 1809.

34. It was then seen there by Sir David Wilkie (A. Cunningham, *The Life of Wilkie*, 1843, vol. 1, pp. 424–25). See also the catalogue of the Talleyrand sale announced for 9 July 1817, p. 1.

35. Buchanan, vol. 2, pp. 305ff. and 339–40.

36. Smith No. 1.

1399 *Portrait of a Young Man*

Plate 29

Oil on canvas, 67.3 × 54.3 (26$\frac{1}{2}$ × 21$\frac{3}{8}$).

The face and hair are somewhat worn and retouched, as are the legs of the chair and the shadows on the ground.

Cleaned in 1982. Damages at the edges caused by the canvas having at one time been mounted on a smaller stretcher.

There are *pentimenti* in the hat.

MacLaren dated the painting by the costume to the early 1660s. It was dated by Gudlaugsson[1] on grounds of style and costume to *c*.1663/4. He believed that it was probably a pair to the *Portrait of a Young Woman* in Cleveland.[2] The present writer would agree; the two portraits are of approximately the same date, have com-plementary backgrounds, furniture and overall tonality, and are very close in size.

PROVENANCE: In the collection of the Earl of Northwick, probably by 1846;[3] Earl of Northwick sale, Thirlestane House, Cheltenham, 26 July–24 August 1859 (lot 1114), bought by Sir Charles L. Eastlake (65 gns). Bought from the estate of his widow, Lady Eastlake, in 1894.

EXHIBITION: London 1983, No. 1.

REFERENCES:
General: HdG Nos. 307 and 345; Gudlaugsson, op. cit., cat. no. 193.
In text:
1. Gudlaugsson, op. cit.
2. Gudlaugsson, op. cit., cat. no. 194. Cleveland Museum of Art, canvas, 63.3 × 52.7 cm., inv. no. 44.93. 1982 Cleveland catalogue, p. 222. The provenance of neither the National Gallery nor the Cleveland painting is known before the nineteenth century by which time the portraits, if they were a pair, had been parted.

3. It is presumably the sole ter Borch mentioned in *Hours in Lord Northwick's Picture Galleries*, 1846, p. 14, No. 59. In 1850 or 1851, G.F. Waagen saw at Thirlestane House a 'male portrait; delicate but somewhat empty' by ter Borch (1854, vol. 3, p. 207.) but this might, conceivably, be the only other ter Borch in the Northwick collection, a supposed portrait of Dr Harvey that was apparently acquired after 1846 since it does not appear in the 1846 *Hours* etc. (see *Hours* etc., 1858, p. 10, No. 3; Northwick sale, 1859, lot 1053, bought by Grundy).

4596 *Portrait of Hermanna van der Cruis*

Plate 30

Oil on canvas, 71.9 × 57.7 ($28\frac{5}{16}$ × $22\frac{11}{16}$).

Hermanna van der Cruis, Cruijs or Cruysse was born in 1615 and died in 1705. She was the wife of Abraham van Suchtelen (1600–61), a burgomaster of Deventer.[1]

The identification of the sitter rests on a painted inscription on the back of a repetition formerly in the collection of Viscount D'Abernon:[2] 'Hermanna van der Cruis/ Weduwe van Abraham van/Suchtelen.' This inscription, which is on the lining canvas, is modern, but, judging by the style of writing, it has been copied from a seventeenth- or eighteenth-century one, and the picture comes from the collection of a collateral descendant of Hermanna van der Cruis.[3]

Both MacLaren and Gudlaugsson[4] dated the painting on the grounds of style and costume to the second half of the 1660s; this would agree with the apparent age of the presumed sitter, who would then have been in her fifties. Of the two repetitions mentioned below, that at Vienna (which has no variations from the National Gallery version other than the still life on the table) seems to be of about the same date (Fig. 10). In the D'Abernon version the collar, at first of the same depth as in the National Gallery portrait, was afterwards made narrower by the painter himself; the alteration, which corresponds to a change in fashion, makes it clear that the D'Abernon picture is a slightly later repetition.[5] Gudlaugsson[6] suggests *c.*1669/70.

VERSIONS: A slightly smaller version of identical design except for the addition of a salver, a wine-pot and a wineglass on the table, is in the Kunsthistorisches Museum, Vienna;[7] a repetition with slight variations, probably a little later (see above), was formerly in the collection of Viscount D'Abernon.[8]

PROVENANCE: In an anonymous[9] sale, London, 15 May 1858 (lot 39), bought by Peters (30 gns); [Peters] sale, London, 4 June 1859 (lot 189),[10] bought by Pearce (28 gns). In the collection of (Sir) Otto Beit (Bart.) by 1913;[11] Sir Otto Beit Bequest, 1931.

REFERENCES:
General: Gudlaugsson, op. cit., cat. no. 210(I).
In text:
1. See M. E. Houck, *Mededeelingen betreffende Gerhard ter Borch* etc., 1899, *passim*; and Gudlaugsson, op. cit.
2. HdG No. 221; Gudlaugsson, op. cit., cat. no. 210 (III). Canvas, 79.5 × 64 cm. Viscountess D'Aber-

non sale, London, 18 March 1955 (lot 51). Present whereabouts unknown.
3. The picture was inherited by the wife of A. J. Dijckmeester (see provenance given in Gudlaugsson, op. cit., cat. no. 210 (III)); she was the great-granddaughter of Wilhelm Umbgrove who was given a number of van Suchtelen family portraits by

his uncle, G. G. J. van Suchtelen, the great-grandson of Hermanna van der Cruis (see Houck, op. cit., pp. 136–38a). There are similar inscriptions with the sitters' names on other ter Borch portraits of members of the van Suchtelen family (see J. D. Breckenridge in *Art Quarterly*, vol. 17, 1954, pp. 345–49 and 351).
4. Gudlaugsson, op. cit.
5. There are also slight differences in the shape of the cap between the National Gallery and Vienna versions on the one hand, and the D'Abernon version on the other.
6. Gudlaugsson, op. cit.
7. Vienna 1938 catalogue, No. 1365A. Canvas, 62 × 50.5 cm. Gudlaugsson, op. cit., cat. no. 210 (III). To Gudlaugsson's provenance can be added

that the painting was bought by the museum from E. Wendlinger in 1918.
8. See note 2.
9. In the catalogue of the [Peters] sale, 4 June 1859, the picture is among several described as 'purchased at the Sale of Colonel H. Baillie's Pictures'; the auctioneer's copy of the sale catalogue shows that lot 39 of the 1858 sale did not belong to Col. Baillie, but was sold anonymously; the name of the vendor is not recorded.
10. The markings relating to this sale are on the back of the picture.
11. W. Bode, *Catalogue of the Collection of . . . Mr Otto Beit*, 1913, p. 10 and p. 84, no. 62.

5847 *An Officer dictating a Letter while a Trumpeter waits* Plate 31

The man on the left wears a cuirass and a helmet (morion). On the left end of the stretcher of the table are the worn remains of a signature: GTB (in monogram).

Oil on canvas, 74.5 × 51 (29⅜ × 20); the edges have been made up.

Cleaned in 1948. There is a pronounced craquelure.

PENTIMENTI: Infra-red photographs (Fig. 11) show that at first the table was narrower and not covered by a cloth, so that the legs of the man in the centre were visible beneath; the head of the writing man was bent over his letter, he did not wear a morion and had an aquiline nose. A playing-card, the ace of hearts, has been painted out near the dog's hind leg and the left sleeve of the man in the centre has also been altered.[1]

MacLaren considered that, judging by the style and costume, the picture could have been painted in the later 1650s or earlier sixties. Gudlaugsson[2] dated it *c.*1658/9; he pointed out that the model for the young man in the centre was Caspar Netscher (it is clear from a comparison with Wallerant Vaillant's mezzotint [Fig. 12] after a lost Netscher self portrait).[3] Netscher[4] was probably born in 1635 and was ter Borch's pupil in or about 1655; he left Holland in 1658 or 1659 and almost certainly did not return before 1661, perhaps not until 1662. If the young man in the present picture was painted from the model, it seems likely, on grounds of style and costume, to have been done shortly before his departure rather than after his return.

In Dresden[5] there is a variant of the present composition which is probably from ter Borch's workshop and may be by Caspar Netscher: the table is narrower than in No. 5847 and has no covering; the man on the left is bent over his letter and is bare-headed, and an ace of hearts lies by his right foot; the man in the centre, the bed and the dog do not appear at all; the trumpeter has a fur cap. In its first state (see PENTIMENTI above) the National Gallery picture agreed exactly with these variations as far as the letter-writer, the table and the playing-card are concerned. The central man, the bed and the dog may also have been added later by the artist; their *absence* from the earlier stage would not necessarily be revealed by infra-red photography or radiography. It could be a pastiche but more probably is either a copy of the National Gallery picture before ter Borch altered it or after a lost work by him very similar in design to the picture in its first stage. The second hypothesis is the more likely one since (1) it is a good deal smaller than the National Gallery canvas (which has not been enlarged); (2) it is improbable that the light-coloured fur cap worn by the trumpeter appeared in the earlier state of No. 5847 as it would almost certainly be visible in an infra-red photograph if it lay under the present reddish paint about the head.

The fireplace reappears in the *Woman sewing by a Cradle* (Aerdenhout, Nienhuys collection)[6] and the *Woman playing a Theorbo* (New York, Metropolitan Museum):[7] also, with variations, in the *Three Soldiers by a Fireplace* (Paris, Baroness E. de Rothschild collection)[8] and the *Soldier offering Money to a Woman* (Paris, Louvre).[9] The outer garment worn by the trumpeter also occurs in other pictures by ter Borch.[10] The man seated in the centre is repeated, with slightly different dress, in the *Woman playing a Theorbo* in the Dresden Gallery (Fig. 13),[11] which appears to be a pastiche compiled from various ter Borch originals.

ETCHING: Etched by F. Milius, 1881.[12]

VERSIONS AND COPIES: E.H. Pool et al. sale, London, 4 December 1869, no. 121 ('Interior with a gentleman seated with two attendants': no measurements given. Sold to Davis for £4.15s).[13] The variant in Dresden has been discussed above. Copies after it are listed by Gudlaugsson.[14]

PROVENANCE: The present picture was confused by HdG[15] with one in the collection of Comte de Bendern (formerly Baron de Forest), Biarritz, which is in fact a copy of the *Officer writing a Letter* in the Elkins collection, Philadelphia Museum;[16] the provenance he gives for the Bendern picture is that of the National Gallery painting, i.e. in the collection of Lothar Franz, Graf von Schönborn in Pommersfelden, near Bamberg by 1719;[17] Schönborn (Pommersfelden) sale, Paris, 17 sqq. May 1867 (lot 117), bought by Khalil Bey; Khalil Bey sale, Paris, 16–18 January 1868 (lot 103), 7,800 francs; Baron de Beurnonville sale, Paris, 9 sqq. May 1881 (lot 518), bought by Gautray (19,500 francs); Amédée G[autray] sale, Paris, 23 February 1883 (lot 57), 15,100 francs; E. Secrétan sale, Paris, 1 sqq. July 1889 (lot 172),[18] bought by Colnaghi, London (11,500 francs). It was in the collection of Arthur James, London, in 1890, when it was exhibited at the Royal Academy; among the pictures of the Arthur James collection bequeathed by his widow, Mrs Mary Venetia James, 1948.

EXHIBITIONS: RA 1890, No. 75; London 1976, No. 12.

REFERENCES:
General: HdG Nos. 29 and 30. Gudlaugsson, op. cit., cat. no. 141.
In text:
1. The earlier head of the letter-writer was clearly visible after the removal of the old retouchings in 1948, the original overpaint having worn thin; it was covered again when the picture was restored. The ace of hearts can be seen through the overpaint.
2. Gudlaugsson, op. cit.
3. J.E. Wessely, *Wallerant Vaillant: Verzeichniss seiner Kupferstiche* etc., 1881 ed., No. 51. Inscribed in state 2: 'CASPARVS NETSCHER Casp. Netscher pinxit W. Vaillant fecit'. This engraving was done in Netscher's lifetime (Vaillant was born in 1623 and died in 1677).
4. For biographical data concerning Netscher, see pp. 280–1.

5. Canvas, 51.5 ∧ 38.5 cm.; 1982 cat. no. 1829 [as ter Borch(?)]. HdG No. 26; Gudlaugsson, op. cit., cat. no. 141b ('perhaps Caspar Netscher'). The painting is mentioned in the Guarienti inventory of 1747–50 (no. 1535) as a copy but it may well be a studio work or a work by the young Netscher. Gudlaugsson, op. cit., notes that no. 69 in the 1694 inventory of Netscher's widow is 'een Officier, schrijvende een brieff om een trompetter af te vaerdigen'.
6. HdG No. 72; Gudlaugsson, op. cit., cat. no. 115.
7. HdG No. 135; Gudlaugsson, op. cit., cat. no. 140.
8. HdG No. 36; Gudlaugsson, op. cit., cat. no. 123.
9. HdG No. 161; Gudlaugsson, op. cit., cat. no. 189.
10. e.g. in *A Trumpeter delivering a Letter* (Munich; HdG No. 173; Gudlaugsson, op. cit., cat. no. 124).

A Soldier reading a Letter (Dresden; Gudlaugsson, op. cit., cat. no. 130) and *An Officer writing a Letter* (Warsaw; Gudlaugsson, op. cit., cat. no. 129).

11. HdG No. 131; Gudlaugsson, op. cit.. cat. no. 140b.

12. In the catalogue of the Beurnonville sale (see PROVENANCE).

13. HdG No. 195c; Gudlaugsson, op. cit., cat. no. 141a.

14. Gudlaugsson, op. cit., cat. nos. 141c-j. A further-er copy of the Dresden variant was lot 369, Sotheby's, 31 July 1968. Another copy (after either No. 5847 or the Dresden variant) is mentioned by HdG in a note to No.26; 41 × 30 cm., Brukenthal Museum, Sibiu, Rumania.

15. See HdG No. 29.

16. The Bendern painting – Gudlaugsson, op. cit., cat. no. 143a – is probably to be identified with the 'replica' of the Elkins composition mentioned by HdG (note to his No. 31) as formerly in the collection of Baron Königswarter, Vienna; it has the same variations as those noted by HdG in the Königswarter composition. Count de Bendern's picture came from the collection of Baron Hirsch de Gereuth.

17. According to the Pommersfelden sale catalogue of 1867, the picture is mentioned in the Schönborn catalogues of 1719 and 1746. [J.R. Byss, *Fürtrefflicher*

Gemählde- und Bilder-Schatz . . . des Churfürstl. Pommersfeldischen . . . Privat-Schloss, Bamberg, 1719, and *Beschreibung des fürtreffl. Gemahld- und Bilder-Schatzes, welcher in denem hochgräfl. Schlössern . . . deren Reichs-Grafen von Schönborn, Bucheim, Wolfsthal &c. Sowohl in . . . Oesterreich zu ersehen . . .*, Würz-burg, 1746.] The picture is also described in the *Verzeichniss der Schildereyen in der Gallerie des hochgräflichen Schönbornischen Schlosses zu Pommersfelden*, Ansbach, [1774], p. 5, No. 19; this is apparently a word for word reprint of Byss's catalogue (see J. Heller, *Die gräflich Schönborn'sche Gemälde-Sammlung zu Schloss Weissenstein zu Pommersfelden*, 1845, p. 11, note). The ter Borch is mentioned in Pommersfelden in J.G. Meusel's *Museum für Künstler und Kunstliefhaber*, vol. 2, 1788, p. 16, and Heller, op. cit., p. 29. The Pommersfelden collection was formed by Lothar Franz, Graf von Schönborn, apparently after 1710, when he inherited the estate of Pommersfelden (see Heller, op. cit., pp. 6–11).

18. The identity of the Schönborn/Secrétan ter Borch with the National Gallery picture is put beyond doubt by the photogravure in the *édition de luxe* of the Secrétan 1889 sale catalogue (vol. 2, opposite p. 66), in which it can even be seen that the craquelure is identical.

ANTHONIE VAN BORSSUM, 1630–1677

Anthonie van Borssum was baptised in Amsterdam on 2 January 1631. Sumowski[1] believes that he was probably a pupil of Rembrandt in about 1645–50. He is recorded in Amsterdam in 1671 and was buried there on 19 March 1677.

Van Borssum worked in various differing styles. Most of his paintings, which are rare, are landscapes with cattle in the manner of Paulus Potter and moonlight or winter scenes in the manner of Aert van der Neer. There are, however, also landscapes which show a knowledge of contemporary Haarlem works, notably those of Cornelis Vroom and Jacob van Ruisdael, and others which display his familiarity with the landscapes of Philips Koninck; a picture of plants and animals in the Rijksmuseum, Amsterdam, is in imitation of Otto Marseus van Schrieck;[2] and a church interior, dated 165( ), is very close to those of Hendrik van Vliet.[3] There are other dated paintings of 1655, 16(6)6 and 1671.[4] Many drawings by him have survived, chiefly landscape studies some of which contain topographically accurate elements.[5] He also made a few etchings of animals and birds.

REFERENCES:
General: Sumowski, *Gemälde*, I, pp. 426–56.
In text:
1. Sumowski, op. cit., p. 426.
2. 1976, cat. no. A1535.

3. RBK, inv. no. NK2467; Sumowski, op. cit., cat. no. 210.
4. Sumowski, op. cit., cat. nos. 187, 191, 190.
5. Sumowski, *Drawings*, vol. 3, pp. 617–779.

3314 *A Garden Scene with Waterfowl*   *Plate 32*

Signed, bottom right: A V Borsfom f (AVB in monogram).

Oil on canvas, 33.7 × 45.8 ($13\frac{5}{16}$ × $18\frac{1}{16}$).

Sumowski,[1] noting the relationship with paintings of fowl by Melchior d'Hondecoeter, dated the painting to the early 1660s.

PROVENANCE: In the collection of Sir Edmund Lechmere, Bart., Rhydd Court, Worcestershire;[2] Sir E. Lechmere sale, London, 27 March 1918 (lot 6), bought by Greenstreet (10 gns). Presented by John P. Heseltine, 1918.

REFERENCES:
General: Sumowski, op. cit., no. 196.
In text:
1. Sumowski, op. cit.
2. According to the 1918 Lechmere sale catalogue.

JOHANNES BOSBOOM, 1817–1891

Born in The Hague, 18 February 1817. In 1831 he became a pupil of Bartholomeus Johannes van Hove, painter of town views and theatrical decorator, assisting him with the painting of stage sets. Only two years later, in 1833, Bosboom exhibited two paintings at the *Tentoonstelling van Levende Meesters* in The Hague. In 1835 he travelled to the Rhineland with a fellow pupil, Sam Verveer. In the following year, Bosboom left van Hove's studio and set up as an independent painter: in the same year, 1836, he won the Gold Medal of Honour in a competition organised by the Felix Meritis Society. It was the first of many Dutch and foreign honours. In 1837 Bosboom visited Belgium and, two years later, Paris and Rouen. At this time he began to paint church interiors, which proved such a great success that he came to specialise in this genre. In 1851 he married Anna Louisa Geertruida Toussaint, a well-known historical novelist, and settled in The Hague. Subsequently he travelled extensively within the Netherlands and (in 1865) to Coblenz and Trier. He died in The Hague on 14 September 1891.

Bosboom painted town views, landscapes, beach and seascapes and scenes from country life, but he is best known for his interiors of churches, cloisters and synagogues, in which the figures often wear seventeenth-century costumes. He was also a distinguished watercolourist.

REFERENCE: Paris/London/The Hague, 1983, pp. 171–9 and 325 (Bibliography).

2712 *The Interior of the Bakenesserkerk at Haarlem*   *Plate 33*

The figures are in seventeenth-century costume.

Signed, bottom left: I Bosboom.

44

Oil on mahogany, 24.7 × 34.1 (9¾ × 13 7/16).

Most of the Bakenesserkerk was built in the fifteenth century. It is a two-aisled church; the north aisle was rebuilt in the seventeenth century. The present picture shows a view of the south aisle, looking towards the east end.

Bosboom made a number of paintings and drawings of the interior of this church. Versions of the present composition are listed below; the National Gallery picture is closest to the large one in the Fodor Museum, Amsterdam, which must have been painted in 1860 or very shortly before (Fig. 14).[1] The National Gallery version is broader in execution and is dated *c*.1870–5 by Marius and Martin.[2]

VERSIONS: A larger version with slight variations, of 1860 or earlier, is in the Fodor Museum, Amsterdam.[3] A watercolour version, probably of about the same date, with a flat door-case on the left instead of a projecting one, is in the Teylers Museum, Haarlem.[4] A little oil sketch in the J. van Stolk et al. sale of 1928[5] and a wash drawing in the Lenaertz Wagner sale, 1922,[6] are connected with the National Gallery and Fodor Museum compositions. A version in oils in the possession of P. A. Scheen in The Hague in 1950/1[7] and wash drawings in the D. van Houten collection in Dordrecht (Fig. 15)[8] and the Dentz van Schaick sale, 1934,[9] are related in design to the Teylers Museum watercolour. A painting in the James Staats Forbes sale in Munich, 1906,[10] appears to be a copy of the Fodor Museum picture. In these pictures and drawings the figures vary more or less but in all, as in the National Gallery composition, they are in seventeenth-century costume.

PROVENANCE: In the collection of John Forbes White, Dundee, by 1888 when it was lent to the International Exhibition in Glasgow, No. 825; exhibited at Dowdeswell Galleries, London, April–May 1889, No. 170.[11] Acquired from J. Forbes White by the Goupil Gallery, London,[12] and exhibited there in March 1899, No. 30; said to have been later in the collection of Alexander Young,[13] Blackheath; sold by A. Preyer of The Hague in February 1907 to J.C.J. Drucker, London,[14] by whom it was lent to the National Gallery in March 1907 and presented in June 1910. Transferred to the Tate Gallery *c*.1920;[15] transferred back to the National Gallery in 1956.

EXHIBITION: Glasgow, International Exhibition, 1888, No. 825.

REFERENCES:
1. See note 3.
2. G. Marius and W. Martin, *Johannes Bosboom*, The Hague, 1917, p. 145.
3. Canvas, 88 × 113 cm. Fodor Museum catalogue, 1863, No. 14; reproduced in Marius and Martin, op. cit., pl. 19. In his autobiography Bosboom speaks of it as a work of about 1862 (A. Glavimans' edition, 1946, p. 10) but it was certainly painted at least two years earlier since C. J. Fodor, to whom it belonged, died in December 1860. On the other hand, the style suggests it could not have been painted much before 1860. Marius and Martin (op. cit., p. 137) identify it with the 'Bakenesse-kerk te Utrecht' [sic] by Bosboom mentioned in *Kunst-kronijk*, 1860, p. 24, in a review of an exhibition at the Arti et Amicitiae Society, Amsterdam (*not* 1861 as Marius and Martin state; furthermore the review is dated April 1860). This exhibit, however, was a drawing; there were no oil paintings in the exhibition (see *Kunstkronijk*, 1860, p. 21). The Fodor paintings, among them the Bosboom, were exhibited at the Amsterdams Historisch Museum in 1975; see I. Hagenbeek-Fey, *Carel Joseph Fodor . . . en zijn schil-*

derijenverzameling, Amsterdams Historisch Museum, 1975, pp. 10–11.
4. 31 × 43.7 cm.; signed. H.J. Scholten, *Musée Teyler . . . Catalogue raisonné des dessins des écoles française et hollandaise*, 1904, p. 571, No. 77.
5. J. van Stolk et al. sale, Amsterdam, 20–22 June 1928 (lot 83); reproduced in the sale catalogue. Panel, 9 × 12 cm.; signed.
6. Len
eartz Wagner sale, Amsterdam, 19 December 1922 (lot 53); reproduced in the sale catalogue. 16 × 26 cm.; signed.
7. Panel, 16 × 19 cm.; signed. Reproduced in the catalogue of the Daniel Cottier sale, Paris, 27–28 May 1892 (lot 11).
8. 28 × 44 cm.
9. Dentz van Schaick sale, Amsterdam, 13 November 1934 (lot 22), 42 × 52 cm.; signed.
10. J. Staats Forbes sale, Munich, 21 March 1906 (lot 6); reproduced in the sale catalogue. Panel, 33 × 44 cm.; inscribed: 'J. Bosboom'.
11. The exhibition catalogue does not name the owner of each picture individually but J. Forbes White is listed among the lenders.

12. Note in a Goupil Gallery stockbook now at the Tate Gallery.
13. and 14. Letter of 15 September 1914 from J.C.J. Drucker (in the National Gallery archives): 'Matthew Maris "Montmartre" I bought from A. Preyer (The Hague) together with J. Bosboom's Church at Haarlem (from the Alexander Young Collection, previous[ly] at the 1899 Marchant – Goupil Gallery – Exh.ⁿ who got it from the Collection of Mr Forbes White at Dundee) . . . This was 13/2/1907.'
15. Tate Gallery Modern Foreign catalogue, 1926–34.

PIETER VAN DEN BOSCH, c.1613/15–after 1663

His place and date of birth are not known. In April 1649, van den Bosch was said to be about thirty-four and in October 1650, about thirty-seven.[1] (It has been suggested that he was the 'Pieter Jansen (Jansz.) van den Bos' living in Leiden 1631–5; this man, however, was said to be twenty-six in January 1631, i.e. born in 1604 or 1605.[2]) He is first mentioned in January 1645, in Amsterdam, when he contracted to paint for twelve months for the collector, Marten Kretzer, at 1,200 guilders a year, the subjects of the pictures to be specified by Kretzer.[3] He was living in Amsterdam in 1649 and 1650[4] and is mentioned as the owner of a house there in 1660.[5] In December 1663 a 'Pieter van den Bosch', a painter, was said to be living in London.[6] (A Pieter Jansz. van den Bosch was living in Franeker, East Friesland, in 1684 and a Pieter van den Bosch was buried in Amsterdam in 1686[7] but there is no reason to suppose either was the painter.)

The Pieter van den Bosch active in Amsterdam 1645–c.1660 has been generally accepted, though on very slight grounds, as the author of a very small group of genre interiors, of which two or three are signed 'P. v. Bos'.[8] Their author must have studied in Leiden since most of these paintings are in the manner of Dou's immediate following and one, in Leningrad, is close in style to Quiringh van Brekelenkam. A still life signed 'P.v.d.Bosch f 1655'[9] that seems to be by a Leiden-trained painter is not necessarily by the same hand as the interiors, yet in 1650 J. de Renialme of Amsterdam had still-life pictures by 'Pieter van den Bosch'.[10] A further complication is the existence of a painter, 'Paulus van den Bos', who was born in Amsterdam in 1614 or 1615, married there in 1649 and died there in 1664.[11]

REFERENCES:
General: W. Bode and A. Bredius in JKPK, 14, 1893, pp. 41–48.
In text:
1. A. Bredius in OH, 1934, p. 188.
2. Ibid.
3. Bredius, op. cit., p. 189.
4. See note 1.
5. Bredius, op. cit., p. 189.
6. Bredius, op. cit., p. 188.
7. Bredius, op. cit., p. 189.
8. The proposed identification is due to Bode and Bredius, loc. cit.
9. Reproduced in OH, 1934, p. 190.
10. JKPK, 1890, p. 123; see also Hoet, vol. 1, pp. 2 and 21.
11. Bredius, op. cit., p. 190.

Attributed to PIETER VAN DEN BOSCH

2551 *A Woman scouring a Pot*

Plate 34

Oil on oak, 19.4 × 25.8 (7⅝ × 10³⁄₁₆).

The picture[1] has been attributed to Pieter van Slingeland[2] (1640–91) and Quiringh van Brekelenkam.[3] The ascription to Pieter van den Bosch, due to W. Bode and A. Bredius,[4] is based principally on its resemblance to the signed picture of a similar subject in Berlin.[5] The artist of No. 2551 is to be found among the followers of Gerrit Dou and the painting would seem to be datable to the 1650s. It does have stylistic affinities with other paintings attributed to Slingeland and thought to be from his early period.[6] On the RKD mount there is a suggested attribution to Willem van Odekerken (active *c.*1631 in The Hague; 1643–77 in Delft) but comparison with the signed painting in the Rijksmuseum[7] makes this unlikely.

PROVENANCE: An old label on the back of the panel is inscribed: Dom.ᶜᵒ Pedrini/Ang.ˡᵒ Ferri/1(7?)95. No. 2551 was bought from Donaldson by 1883 by George Salting, London;[8] Salting Bequest, 1910.

REFERENCES:

1. MacLaren considered that there are possibly the illegible remains of a signature on the shaded side of the tub in the right foreground. In fact these are just brushstrokes indicating the structure of the tub and the shadow.
2. and 3. When in the Salting collection.
4. In JKPK, vol. 14, 1893, p. 44.
5. Berlin, 1931 catalogue, No. 1011. Signed: P.v B( ) and inscribed on the back in a seventeenth-century hand: Pieter van den Bosch. (See JKPK, p. 42, and the Berlin catalogue, 1911, vol. 2, p. 201, and 1912, p. 45. The 1931 catalogue, p. 55, mentions only the inscription on the back.)

6. It appears to be by the same hand as a painting from the collection of E.H.M. Luckock, London, sold at Sotheby's, 23 September 1949 (lot 96: bought Slatter), as Slingeland. It is also related to a picture in the Bacon collection at Raveningham Hall, Norfolk, which HdG attributed to Slingeland (HdG No. 46).
7. 1976, cat. no. A 1279.
8. Salting notebook in the National Gallery archives.

JAN BOTH, *c.*1615–1652

He was born in Utrecht,[1] the son of a glass-painter or engraver, Dirck Both, according to Sandrart and Houbraken.[2] The date of his birth is not known but it was probably *c.*1615.[3] Houbraken says that Jan trained with his father before entering the studio of Abraham Bloemaert. Sandrart[4] says Jan and his brother Andries were pupils of Abraham Bloemaert (in Utrecht) when he himself was studying with Honthorst, i.e. about 1625/7, but Andries was born about 1611/12[5] and is probably the unnamed son of 'Derrick Boot' who was a pupil of Abraham Bloemaert in 1624,[6] while Jan is probably the unnamed son of 'Dirck Bot, glass-engraver', who was a pupil of an unspecified master at some time in the years 1634–6.[7] According to Sandrart[8] the brothers went to France and then to Rome. Andries was living in Rome by 1635;[9] Jan is first recorded there in July 1638[10] and was living with his brother in the Strada Vittoria in the years

1639 and 1641.[11] Jan probably returned to Utrecht shortly after this: Houbraken says that Hendrick Verschuring, whose birth he places in 1627, was apprenticed to Jan in Utrecht in his 'thirteenth year',[12] i.e. in 1639 or 1640; he may have meant 'at the age of thirteen' since Both was still in Rome for at least part of 1641. It may have been in that year that Andries Both drowned in Venice and his brother's death could have prompted Jan's return.[13] Jan Both appears to have lived in Utrecht for the rest of his life;[14] he was an *overman* of the painters' college there in 1649[15] (at the same time as Cornelis van Poelenburgh, who painted the figures in No. 209 below, and Jan Baptist Weenix). He died (or was buried) there on 9 August 1652.[16]

Almost all Both's works are landscapes based on Italian scenery, occasionally with religious or mythological subjects in them; there are also views of Rome and Tivoli. In Rome he collaborated, probably in 1639/40, with Claude, Poussin, Dughet, Swanevelt and others, on a series of paintings for the Buen Retiro Palace in Madrid.[17] There are very few dated works; the earliest appears to be a drawing of 1643.[18] Sandrart[19] states that Andries painted figures and animals in Jan's pictures and indeed those in the Buen Retiro paintings do seem to be by Andries. After his brother's death, Jan painted figures in his paintings in a style very similar to that of Andries; in some of Jan's paintings they are the work of other painters (e.g. in No. 209 below). Verschuring and the little-known Barend Bispinck were pupils of Both. Close followers who may also have been pupils include Willem de Heusch and Jan Hackaert. His influence on the development of Dutch landscape painting was immense: Nicolaes Berchem, Frederick de Moucheron, Adam Pynacker, Herman Saftleven and, particularly importantly, Aelbert Cuyp were profoundly indebted to Both.[20]

He made a number of landscape etchings as well as some after figure subjects by Andries.

REFERENCES:
General: HdG vol. 9; J.D. Burke, *Jan Both: Paintings, Drawings and Prints*, New York/London, 1976.
In text:
1. Utrecht is first named as his birthplace in the title of Coenrad Waumans' engraved portrait of him published in 1649 in Antwerp (in Jan Meyssens' *Images de divers hommes d'esprit sublime*; this engraving was reprinted in de Bie, p. 157).
2. Sandrart, *Teutsche Academie*, vol. 2, p. 312; Houbraken, vol. 2, p. 114.
3. For recent extended discussions of Both's date of birth, see the Utrecht cat., 1965, pp. 113–14, note 2, and Burke, op. cit., pp. 37–8, notes 2 and 3.
4. Loc. cit.
5. He is recorded in Rome in 1636 as 'Andrea Botti, fiammengo pittore, di anni 24' (G.J. Hoogewerff, *Nederlandsche kunstenaars te Rome*, 1942, p. 280).
6. Muller, p. 118.
7. Muller, p. 122.
8. Loc. cit.
9. G.J. Hoogewerff, *De Bentvueghels*, 1952, pp. 88–89; see also note 5.
10. G.J. Hoogewerff, *Bescheiden in Italië* etc., vol. 3, 1913, p. 53.
11. G.J. Hoogewerff, *Nederlandsche kunstenaars te Rome*, 1942, pp. 108 and 110.
12. Houbraken (vol. 2, p. 193) says Verschuring stayed with his first master 'tot zyn dertiende Jaar, wanneer hy besteet wierd by den beruchten Jan Bot tot Uitrecht . . .'
13. Sandrart, *Teutsche Academie*, p. 185. According to Sandrart, Jan returned to Utrecht after Andries' death in Venice. Houbraken, however, says that Andries died in 1650.
14. He is recorded in Utrecht in 1644, 1648, 1649 and 1650. See Utrecht cat. 1965, p. 112 and notes 11–14.
15. Muller, p. 129.
16. Lia de Bruyn, in OH, 1952, pp. 111 and 112, note 12.
17. Burke, op. cit., pp. 81–101.
18. Burke, op. cit., 154–56.
19. Loc. cit.
20. Burke, op. cit., pp. 17ff.

71 A Rocky Landscape with Peasants and Pack Mules

Plate 35

Signed ten cm. from the bottom, below the man beating a mule: JBoth f. (JB in monogram).

Oil on canvas, 119.5 × 160 (47 × 63). Original edges on all sides, those at top and bottom irregular.

Cleaned in 1958. There is an area of damage in the lower left centre.

Dated by Burke to *c*.1645.[1]

ENGRAVING: Engraved by William Byrne and J. Schuman, 1790.

VARIANT/COPY: Burke[2] notes that a variant (in which the landscape is the same but the figures different), by the hand of a student, was with the Amsterdam dealer, F. Buffa en Zonen, in 1943. Judging by the photograph in the RKD, this painting may in fact be a free copy. An early nineteenth-century miniature copy (8 × 9½ in.), perhaps painted when the picture was in Beaumont's collection, was in the collection of R.F. Fairbairn in 1960.

PROVENANCE: The suggestion[3] that this may be a picture in the Lucas Merens (Burgomaster of Hoorn) sale, Amsterdam, 15 April 1778 (lot 19), bought by Fouquet (698 florins) is probably incorrect.[4] By 1790 in the collection of Sir George Beaumont, Bart.,[5] who presented it to the British Museum in 1823; it was transferred to the National Gallery in 1828.

REFERENCES:
General: Smith No. 69; HdG No. 192; Burke, op. cit., no. 48.
In text:
1. Burke, op. cit.
2. Burke, op. cit.
3. HdG, loc. cit.
4. The Merens picture is described in the sale catalogue as 'Een Bosch en Bergagtig Landschap, wordende door een sterk Zonlicht beschenen; het geen veelerlei dartele Lichtjes doet speelen door 't Geboomten, en door zyn breede schaduwe en hel- dere slagschaduwe, een groote party van Licht en Donker veroorzaakt, waar door dit Tafereel ten uiterste bevallig is; 't is daarenboven ryklyk gestoffeerd met Ryzende Lieden, Paarden en Muilezels . . . zynde een der beste Stukken van deeze groote Meester.' The description is very vague but in any case there are no horses in No. 71.
5. Byrne's picture is inscribed: 'MORNING./Engraved from the Original Picture in the Possession of Sir George Beaumont, Bar* . . . / . . . Published . . . 15 May 1790 . . .'

956 A Rocky Italian Landscape with Herdsmen and Muleteers

Plate 36

Signed on the rocks, half way up on the right edge: JB . . . (f?); JB in monogram.

Oil on canvas, 103 × 125 (40½ × 49¼).

Cleaned in 1967.

Dated by Burke[1] to the mid-1640s.

VERSIONS: A repetition, with different figures, was in the collection of the Hon. H.B. Robson, Pinewood Hill, Surrey, in 1942. There is a smaller variant, with some differences in the foliage and with only the two central figures, in the Maharaja Gaekwar of Baroda's collection, Baroda.[2]

PROVENANCE: In the Sir Gregory Page Turner, Bart., sale, London, 19–20 April 1815 (lot 206),[3] bought by Baring (490 gns); afterwards in the hands of several dealers,[4] including Delahante in 1822.[5] Héris of Brussels sale of pictures collected for Col. de Biré, Paris, 25–26 March 1841 (lot 4), bought by Mennechet and Leroy (14,800 francs); by 1842 in the possession of Brown,[6] by whom it was sold in 1845 to Wynn Ellis.[7] Possibly exhibited by Wynn Ellis at the BI, in 1856 and 1863. Wynn Ellis Bequest, 1876.

EXHIBITIONS: Possibly BI 1856, No. 70,[8] BI 1863, No. 33.[9]

REFERENCES:
General: Smith No. 46 and Supplement No. 3; HdG No. 156; Burke, op. cit., No. 50.
In text:
1. Burke, op. cit.
2. HdG No. 189; *Baroda State Museum and Picture Gallery: Catalogue of the Pictures*, 1935, No. 70. Canvas, 24 × 34½ in. Exhibited at the Royal Academy exhibition, 1912 (No. 58).
3. 'Both View in Italy, with Figures by his Brother.'

4. Smith, Supplement No. 3.
5. According to the Héris sale catalogue, 1841, the picture belonged to Delahante in 1822.
6. Smith, Supplement No. 3.
7. According to HdG No. 156. It was seen in the Wynn Ellis collection in 1850 or 1851 by Waagen (1854, vol. 2, p. 297, No. 1).
8. 'Landscape.'
9. 'Landscape and Waterfall with Figures.'

957 *Muleteers, and a Herdsman with an Ox and Goats by a Pool*

Plate 37

Signed at the bottom, towards the left: J Both (JB in monogram).

Oil on oak, 57.2 × 69.5 (22½ × 27⅜).

Burke[1] stated that the animals in the foreground were by Jan Baptist Weenix. There is no need to attribute them to another hand as they are perfectly consistent with animals by Both himself. He also stated that Pynacker's *White Cow* in Munich[2] was a 'free adaptation of this picture'. While Pynacker was undoubtedly influenced by Both's work, the resemblances in this particular case are not precise enough to consider Pynacker's landscape a variation on Both's.

PROVENANCE: Wynn Ellis Bequest,[3] 1876.

REFERENCES:
General: HdG No. 229; Burke, op. cit., No. 51.
In text:
1. Burke, op. cit.
2. Munich, Bayerische Staatsgemäldesammlungen, inv. no. 868.

3. HdG, loc. cit., suggests that No. 957 is the small picture seen in the Wynn Ellis collection in 1850 or 1851 by Waagen (1854, vol. 2, p. 297, No. 2) but this was more probably Both No. 959 below.

958 *A View on the Tiber, near the Ripa Grande, Rome(?)*

Plate 38

Signed on a rock, bottom left: JBoth fc (JB in monogram).

Oil on oak, 42.1 × 55 (16⁹⁄₁₆ × 21⅝).

Cleaned in 1951.

Since the third quarter of the last century, this picture has been described as a view on the Tiber.[1] The tower in the centre background does, in fact, resemble that of S. Maria della Torre, which was beside the Ripa Grande, the old port of Rome opposite the Aventine, and this may be intended for a view from the north of the buildings around the Ripa Grande. The fenestration of the tower here, however, is different, and the other buildings do not seem to be identifiable. There is a painting of the Ripa Grande from the south-west by Both (in the Städelsches Kunstinstitut, Frankfurt[2]) which, to judge by the drawings of Pieter Bruegel the Elder[3] and Claude,[4] is a more or less accurate view; the present picture is probably a slightly fanciful reminiscence of the same place seen from a different point. A similar view, with variations, of the same gate and wall was formerly in the collection of Lady Balogh, Oxford, attributed to Jan Asselijn but perhaps by Willem Schellincks,[5] and a drawing of a very similar view by Schellincks is in the British Museum;[6] in these the other buildings and the distance are different.

It appears to be a relatively early work. It is on an oak panel and is therefore unlikely to have been painted when Both was in Italy, but even so it must have been done shortly after his return to Holland.

COPIES: There is a drawn copy by Willem van Bemel (1630–1708) in the Kestner Museum, Hanover;[7] a copy on panel was in the M.K. Mainwaring sale, London, 5 April 1946 (lot 92);[8] an enlarged copy (eighteenth century?) on canvas, with slightly different figures and accessories, was in an anonymous sale, London, 18 June 1954 (lot 112).[9]

PROVENANCE: Said to have been purchased at a Brentano sale[10] but not in the Josephus Augustinus Brentano sale, Amsterdam, 13 sqq. May 1822,[11] nor in the sale of paintings 'including the Brentano Pictures from Amsterdam', London, 22–23 June 1832.[12] It was almost certainly in an anonymous sale, London, 30 May 1863 (lot 103), bought by Pearce[13] (101 gns), and was certainly in the Wynn Ellis collection, London, by 1864, when it was exhibited at the BI; Wynn Ellis Bequest, 1876.

EXHIBITIONS: BI 1864, No. 90;[14] London 1976, No. 15.

REFERENCES:
General: HdG No. 29; Burke, op. cit., No. 52.
In text:
1. BI 1864 exhibition catalogue, No. 90, as *View on the Tiber*; in the National Gallery catalogue from 1877 onwards the view is described as outside the walls of Rome, on the banks of the Tiber. It is probably the picture similarly described in a sale of 1863 (see PROVENANCE and note 11 below).
2. Städelsches Kunstinstitut 1924 catalogue, No. 42; HdG No. 100; Burke, op. cit., No. 35. It was identified as a view of the Ripa Grande by H. Gerson (in OH, vol. 66, 1951, pp. 65–66), together with another view from the same point ascribed by him to Reinier Nooms (on the Berlin market, 1936). In addition to those published by Gerson, there is a drawing of the same view by Thomas Wijck in the British Museum Printroom which agrees very closely with them (reproduced in Hind, vol. 4, p. 67, No. 6).
3. Collection of the Duke of Devonshire, Chatsworth. Inscribed: a rypa. Ex. cat. *Pieter Breugel d.A. als Zeichner*, Kupferstichkabinet, Berlin-Dahlem, 1975, No. 26.
4. British Museum. M. Röthlisberger, *Claude Lorrain: The Drawings*, 2 vols., Berkeley/Los Angeles, 1968, No. 280.
5. Panel, 47 × 58.5 cm. Sold, as Jan Asselijn, at Sotheby's, 27 March 1974 (lot 3).
6. Black chalk and grey wash, 23.4 × 37.2 cm. Inscribed: 'W Schellinx'. Acquired in 1958.

7. Inv. no. N189. C. von Heusinger, *Handzeichnungen der Niederländer des 16. bis 18. Jahrhunderts. Bildkatalog des Kestner Museums, Hannover*, vol. 3, Hanover, 1960, No. 36.
8. 46 × 54.5 cm. A photograph is in the National Gallery archives.
9. 82.5 × 125 cm. From the Hon. F. Bowes-Lyon sale, London, 25 June 1948 (lot 31). A photograph is in the National Gallery archives.
10. According to the National Gallery catalogues of 1877 onwards.
11. The only two Boths in this sale were: lot 39, attributed to Andries Both: 'In een aangenaam Italiaansch Landschap . . . de ruine van een oud gebouw, waarnevens, steil gebergte; ter zijde een bergachtig verschiet. Zonachtig . . .', panel, 3 *palmen 9 duimen* × 4 *p.* 9 *d.* (*c.*37 × *c.*46.5 cm.); lot 40, attributed to Jan and Andries Both: 'Bij een' aangenaamen avondstond . . . op een Plein, langs eene Hofstede, eenige Boeren zich met Kaatsen vermaken; op den voorgrond een' man, zittende op een' ezel, verder een' drijver met koeijen . . .', panel, 4 *palmen 4 duimen* × 5 *p.* 4 *d.* (*c.*42 × *c.*51.5 cm.). The first (Smith No. 53; HdG No. 116; Burke, op, cit., No. 84) was in the B. de Geus van den Heuvel sale, Sotheby Mak van Waay, Amsterdam, 26/27 April 1976 (lot 6), the second (Smith No. 54, HdG No. 108; Burke, op. cit., No. 44) is in the Marquess of Lansdowne's collection at Bowood (Lansdowne collection exhibition, Agnew's, London, 1954–5, No.

7) but *not* in *Catalogue of Paintings at Bowood House,* 1982. Burke, following HdG, has apparently confused this painting with one sold in Munich in 1902 and in the collection of D. Cevat in 1976.
12. There were no pictures attributed to Both in this sale.
13. 'Both A View on the Banks of the Tiber, at the entrance to Rome, with picturesque buildings and numerous peasants. A clear and sunny work . . .'
Pearce apparently purchased a number of paintings for Wynn Ellis (see Berchem, No. 1004 of this catalogue, note 3) and the National Gallery picture was certainly in the latter's collection in the following year, when it was exhibited at the BI (see note 1).
14. See note 1.

959 *Peasants with Mules and Oxen on a Track near a River* Plate 39

Signed on a stone at the left edge and towards the bottom: J Both (JB in monogram).

Oil on copper, 39.6 × 58.1 ($15\frac{5}{8}$ × $22\frac{7}{8}$).

Cleaned in 1974.

Dated by Burke[1] *c.*1640–3.

PROVENANCE: Imported into England by John Smith in 1826;[2] in the collection of Artis, London, by 1835,[3] and sold by him to Wynn Ellis in 1845.[4] Wynn Ellis Bequest, 1876.

EXHIBITIONS: London 1974b (in partially cleaned state); London 1976, No. 16.

REFERENCES:
General: Smith No. 107; HdG No. 226; Burke, op. cit., No. 53.
In text:
1. Burke, op. cit.
2. Smith, loc. cit.
3. Smith, loc. cit.
4. According to HdG, loc. cit. It may well be the small picture by Both seen in the Wynn Ellis collection by Waagen in 1850 or 1851 (cf. Both No. 957, note 3). According to the National Gallery catalogue, 1877–81, it was purchased at a Brentano sale, but it was not in the J. A. Brentano sale, Amsterdam, 13 sqq. May 1822 (see Both No. 958 above, note 11) and there were no paintings attributed to Both in the sale, 'including the Brentano Pictures from Amsterdam', London, 22–23 June 1832.

1917 *A Rocky Landscape with an Ox-Cart* Plate 40

Signed in the middle of the large rock on the right: J Both (JB in monogram).

Oil on canvas, 120.5 × 160.5 ($47\frac{1}{2}$ × $63\frac{1}{4}$).

Cleaned in 1956.

Burke[1] dates the painting *c.*1641–5 and notes its similarity in composition and treatment of the sunlight to a landscape by Both in the Mauritshuis.[2]

PROVENANCE: Earl of Shaftesbury sale, London, 15 May 1852 (lot 57), bought in (500 gns). Lent by Lord Shaftesbury to the BI in 1855. [Hon. J.S. Wortley][3] sale, London, 19 May 1860 (lot 197), bought by Owen (300 gns); anonymous [Fordham?][4] sale, London, 7 May 1864 (lot 99), bought by Graves (305 gns). In the collection of the 3rd Earl of Onslow (d. 1870) and in the Onslow executors' sale, London, 22 July 1893 (lot 30), bought by Lord Cheylesmore (830 gns). Lord Cheylesmore Bequest, 1902.

EXHIBITION: BI 1855, No. 16.

REFERENCES:
General: HdG Nos. 129 and 136 (HdG No. 136, also suggested that the present picture might possibly be the same as his No. 134 but this was of different composition and smaller; cf. Smith No. 2); Burke, op. cit., No. 55.

In text:
1. Burke, op. cit.
2. Canvas, 108.2 × 125.8 cm. Inv. no. 20. Mauritshuis cat., *Hollandse Schilderkunst: Landschappen 17de
Eeuw*, The Hague, 1980, pp. 15–16.
3. HdG (No. 136) gives the vendor as P. Ashburn-

ham; the correct name of the vendor of this lot is
given in the auctioneers' copy of the sale catalogue.
4. In Messrs Christie's copy of the sale catalogue,
lots 96–99 are bracketed and marked F; lot 95, which
is on the preceding page is marked as the property of
'Fordham'.

JAN BOTH and CORNELIS VAN POELENBURGH

209 *A Landscape with the Judgement of Paris*   Plate 41

Paris, behind whom a seated river god sits, is handing the apple of discord to Venus; on
either side of her, Minerva and Juno. Two water nymphs are on the river bank.

Signed on the rocks in the left foreground: J Both (JB in monogram).

Oil on canvas, 97 × 129 (38¼ × 50¾).

The figures are by Poelenburgh, the landscape and animals by Both. That Both and
Poelenburgh knew one another is well documented[1] and an example of their collaboration is recorded as early as 1679.[2] This particular collaboration appears to have been
recognised as early as 1752 (see PROVENANCE). There is a painting with figures by
Poelenburgh and landscape by Both, *Landscape with Nymphs*, monogrammed by
Poelenburgh, in the Busiri-Vici collection in Rome.[3] Its similar size and subject matter
caused Burke[4] to suggest that it could have been a pair to No. 209 but there is no real
evidence for this. He dated No. 209 to *c.*1645–50.[5]

PROVENANCE: Perhaps the Both landscape of the same size with figures by Poelenburgh in the Benjamin da
Costa collection in The Hague by 1752[6] and in the Benjamin da Costa sale, The Hague, 13 August 1764 (lot
2),[7] bought by Theodati (351 guilders). In the Randon de Boisset sale, Paris, 27 February sqq. 1777 (lot 99),
bought by the Prince de Rohan Chabot (5,601 francs); Duc de Ch[abot] sale, Paris, 10 sqq. December 1787
(lot 20), bought by Dulac (4,952 francs). In the collection of the 1st Baron Gwydyr, Grimsthorpe Castle, by
1812;[8] Lord Gwydyr sale, London, 8–9 May 1829 (second day, lot 83), bought by Alexander Baring (£483).
Sold by Smith to Richard Simmons by 1835.[9] Richard Simmons Bequest, 1847.

EXHIBITION: BI 1829, No. 6.

REFERENCES:
General: Smith No. 7; HdG No. 23. Burke, op. cit.,
No. 49.
In text:
1. Utrecht 1965 cat., p. 121, note 3.
2. Utrecht 1965 cat., p. 121, note 2.
3. Canvas, 100 × 120 cm., monogrammed near
left: CP. Utrecht 1965 cat., no. 50.
4. Burke, op. cit.
5. Burke, op. cit.
6. See Hoet, vol. 2, p. 469.

7. 'Jan Both. Een Landschap gestoffeert door Cornelis Poelenburgh.' Canvas, 3 *voet* 1½ *duimen* × 4
voet 2 *d*.
8. It appears in a MS list of pictures in Grimsthorpe
corrected up to 1 January 1812: 'Judgement of Paris
The figures by Poelenburg The landscape by
Both.' (A copy of the inventory is in the National
Gallery library.)
9. Smith, loc. cit.

JAN DE BRAIJ, *c.*1626/7(?)–1697

Jan Salomonsz. de Braij (less frequently, *de Bray*), son of the painter, architect and poet, Salomon de Bray (1597–1664), was born in Haarlem.[1] The date of his birth is not known; his father married in May 1625[2] and Jan was the eldest son.[3] The earliest known works – a portrait drawing of 1648 in the British Museum and a painted portrait of 1650 in Prague – suggest he was a pupil of his father. He was often an officer of the Haarlem guild in the years 1667–84[4] and he spent most of his life in Haarlem, but in January 1688 he declared that he had lived in Amsterdam for the last two years.[5] In June 1688 he was again living in Haarlem[6] and went bankrupt there in 1689.[7] He was buried in Haarlem, 4 December 1697.[8]

Most of his works are portraits; he painted some religious pictures and a few mythological and genre subjects. There are some twenty etchings by him. He was also active as an architect.

REFERENCES:
General: J.W. Moltke, 'Jan de Bray', *Marburger Jahrbuch für Kunstwissenschaft*, vols. 11/12, 1938–39 [1941], pp. 421–523.
In text:
1. Van der Willigen, p. 96.
2. Van der Willigen, p. 92.
3. Van der Willigen, p. 96.
4. Van der Willigen, pp. 23–24.
5. W.F.H. Oldewelt, *Amsterdamsche Archiefvondsten*, 1942, p. 170.
6. Oldewelt, loc. cit.
7. and **8.** Van der Willigen, p. 97.

1423 *Portrait of a Woman with a Black Cap* — Plate 42

Inscribed on the left, bottom centre: 1657/Ouwt 52 jaar. and signed below this: Braij (the initial letter is near the present edge of the panel and a preceding letter or letters may have been cut off).

Oil on oak, 66.4 × 50.5 (26$\frac{1}{8}$ × 19$\frac{7}{8}$); possibly cut down along the left edge (cf. the note on the signature above).

Cleaned in 1971.

PENTIMENTI: X-radiographs (Fig. 16) show that the head was at first much farther to the left (the sitter's right eye was outside the present contour of her right cheek) and the collar was much lower and farther to the left; there is also a *pentimento* in the peak of the cap.

PROVENANCE: In the Edward H. Pares collection, Hopwell Hall, Derby; E. H. Pares sale, London, 24 January 1891 (lot 16),[1] bought by Colnaghi (9$\frac{1}{2}$ gns). Presented by Alfred Fowell Buxton, 1894.

REFERENCES:
General: Moltke, op. cit., No. 143.
In text: **1.** As by Jan Anthonisz. van Ravesteyn (so also in the National Gallery catalogue, 1894–1911).

BARTHOLOMEUS BREENBERGH,[1] 1598–1657

In the earlier part of his life he usually spelt his name *Breenborch*; afterwards *Breenberch*, *Breenberg* or, most frequently, *Breenbergh*. He was born in Deventer in 1598, the son of a merchant, Jan Bre(d)enbergh, who had been appointed town apothecary in 1591. Soon after his father's death in 1607, the family left Deventer, perhaps for Hoorn. Nothing is known of Breenbergh's training: Poelenburgh and Poelenburgh's master Abraham Bloemaert (1564–1651) have both been suggested as Breenbergh's teacher but there is no evidence to support either proposal. In October 1619, Breenbergh is described as a painter living in Amsterdam. By the end of the same year he was in Rome, living in the same house as the Flemish painter Frans van de Kasteele and listed as a Catholic. In Rome he was in close contact with the Flemish landscape painter Paul Bril (who died in 1626), a number of whose paintings he copied. Breenbergh was one of the founders, in 1623, of the society of Netherlandish painters in Rome, the *Schilders-bent*. Among his Italian patrons was the Duke of Bracciano, whose country estate at Bomarzo he probably visited.

It is not known exactly when Breenbergh returned to Holland. It may have been in 1629. He is recorded in Amsterdam in 1633. In 1648 he is recorded as a tenant of the collector Joan Huydecoper on the Lauriersgracht; in 1652 he is mentioned as a merchant. In the following year he (and a son Pieter) witnessed a document for the engraver van der Laegh. In 1654 Breenbergh had moved to the Prinsengracht and in 1655 he is again recorded as a merchant. In 1657 he was living on the Herengracht; he was buried on 5 October 1657 in the Oude Kerk.

Breenbergh's earliest dated work, *The Finding of Moses* (Stockholm, Hallwyl Museum)[2] of 1622 reveals the influence of Jacob Pynas but subsequently he followed the powerful example of Cornelis van Poelenburgh. On his return to Holland he developed his own, independent Italianate style in which religious and mythological figures increasingly assume a greater importance.

Antique ruins – which are more and more removed from the Italian reality – play an important part in his compositions. His later history paintings reveal his study of the work of Pieter Lastman and Claes Moeyaert. He also made a number of etchings.

REFERENCES:
General: M. Roethlisberger, *Bartholomeus Breenbergh: The Paintings*, Berlin/New York, 1981.
In text:
1. Utrecht 1965 cat., pp. 75ff; Roethlisberger, op. cit., pp. 2–5.

2. Utrecht 1965, cat. no. 23. The attribution to Breenbergh was denied by J. Nieuwstraten, BM, vol. 107, 1965, p. 272, but accepted by Roethlisberger, op. cit., cat. no. 64.

208 *The Finding of the Infant Moses by Pharaoh's Daughter*   Plate 43

Signed on a stone, bottom right: BBreenberg.f./A° 1636 (BB in monogram).

Oil on oak, 41.5 × 56.7 ($16\frac{3}{8}$ × $22\frac{5}{16}$).

Cleaned in 1951.

The Finding of Moses (from Exodus 2: 1–6) is also the subject of Breenbergh's earliest dated picture, painted in 1622 under the strong influence of Jacob Pynas (see above). In No. 208, Breenbergh has opened up the composition, assuming a higher viewpoint over an extensive landscape, reduced the size and prominence of the figures and given greater emphasis to the Classical (and pseudo-Classical) monuments. According to Roethlisberger,[1] the stela is based on J. della Porta's Forum fountain.

VERSION: Another painting of this subject by Breenbergh, of different size, was in the Count de Fraula sale, Brussels, 21 sqq. July 1738 (lot 353).[2]

PROVENANCE: Président Le Rebourg sale, Paris (Remy), 27 April 1778.[3] Apparently lot 20 in the Vassal de Saint-Hubert sale, Paris (Remy), 24 April et seq., 1784 (as dated 1636).[4] Probably bought by the Vicomte de Morel Vindé (grandson of Paignon Dijonval);[5] No. 208 was in the Paignon Dijonval and Morel Vindé sale, Paris, 17–18 December 1821 (lot 10), bought by Paillet (299 francs), i.e. probably bought in.[6] Probably among those pictures from the collection bought by William Buchanan or Thomas Emmerson.[7] Richard Simmons Bequest, 1847.

EXHIBITION: London 1976, No. 18.

REFERENCES:
General: Roethlisberger, op. cit., cat. no. 182.
In text:
1. Roethlisberger, op. cit.
2. 'Een schoon Landschap, verbeeldende het uyt-visschen van Moyses, door Breenberg, h. 1 v[oet]. 6 d[uim]. br. 2 v. 10 en een half d.' (47 florins). See Hoet, vol. 1, p. 549.
3. 'Moyse sauvé des eaux et presenté à la fille de Pharaou. La composition est de 9 figures principales: on voit encore dans l'eloignement un pont et plusieurs figures dont un homme conduisant 2 elephants et un troupeau de moutons. Les fonds sont tres ornés de fabriques et de petits arbres. Ce tableau distingué est daté de 1636. Il est peint sur bois et portes 15 pouces de haut sur 20 pouces 9 lignes de large.' This lot differs from No. 208 in one small detail: there is only one elephant. (Thanks to Mme J. Nouhaut for bringing this entry to the attention of the present writer: correspondence of October 1972 in the National Gallery archives.)

4. Roethlisberger, op. cit.
5. The back of the panel of No. 208 is inscribed in ink in an old hand: 'from Dijon Valle(s?) collection Paris'.
6. There is a contemporary MS annotation in the British Museum copy of the sale catalogue: 'cette vente a été suspendue au milieu de la 2ᶜ vaccation [sic] à cause de la modicité des enchères, et les objets adjugés ont été presque tous retirés par Mʳˢ Paillet et Bénard' [i.e. the auctioneers]. This note is confirmed by comparison of the marked copy of the catalogue with the *feuille des vacations* of the sale.
7. Buchanan (vol. 2, p. 372) says that he bought the whole collection: Smith (Dou No. 99) says it was bought *en bloc* by Emmerson (cf. also Smith: W. van Mieris No. 26, and Wouwermans No. 298, etc.). This purchase presumably refers to those pictures withdrawn at the 1821 sale (cf. note 6).

QUIRINGH VAN BREKELENKAM, active 1648; died 1668

Quiringh Gerritsz. van Brekelenkam. The place and date of birth are not known. He may have been born, as his sister Aeltje (wife of the painter Johannes Oudenrogge) was, in Zwammerdam[1] (about twelve miles from Leiden); the date of birth usually given, *c*.1620, is a conjecture based on his being a founder member of the Leiden guild in March 1648,[2] which is the first documentary record of him. His earliest dated painting is of 1644.[3] He married in Leiden in the same year and is recorded there continuously until his death in 1668.[4]

His paintings show peasant and bourgeois interiors.

REFERENCES:

General: Havard, vol. 4, pp. 90–146.

In text:

1. Havard, vol. 4, pp. 103–4.
2. Obreen, vol. 5, p. 206.

3. Panel, 37.5 × 49 cm. RBK inv. no. NK2924.
4. Havard, vol. 4, pp. 104–6, and Obreen, vol. 5, p. 207.

1329 *An Interior, with a Man and a Woman seated by a Fire*   Plate 44

In the right background is a map of Holland, with the lion of Holland in the top right corner, and inscribed at the top: H(?)AR(E?) GE(R?)WANIC UM and, lower down: DE NO(O?)RT ZEE.

Signed on the lower edge of the cupboard in the right background: Q.VB.1653 (VB in monogram). The date is faint.

Oil on oak, 51.4 × 70.5 (20¼ × 27¾).

In the map, as is often the case in the seventeenth century, north is not at the top but on the right.[1] The first line of the inscription on it is a careless or ignorant transcription of MARE GERMANICUM.

PROVENANCE: In the [Lt.-Col. Worthington Wilmer] sale, London, 21 June 1890[2] (lot 85), bought by Horace Buttery (63 gns), from whom purchased (out of the Walker Fund) in 1891.

REFERENCES:
1. cf. P. de Hooch No. 834 of this catalogue.
2. The markings for this sale are on the back of the panel.

2549 *Interior of a Tailor's Shop*   Plate 45

In the background, on the left, hangs a still-life painting with a jug, a glass and a fish on a plate.[1]

Oil on oak, 42.7 × 50 (16¹³⁄₁₆ × 19¹¹⁄₁₆).

The still-life painting in the background is in the manner of Pieter Claesz.; Brekelenkam himself occasionally painted still life in this style and this may be after one of his own works.[2]

Brekelenkam painted the subject of *The Tailor's Shop* many times using the same basic composition in which he rearranged the figures and details of the interior. The earliest dated treatment of the subject is in the painting of 1653 in the Worcester Art Museum (Fig. 17); two other versions are dated 1661; and a fourth, 1664 (see VERSIONS). No. 2549 is difficult to date with any confidence. It may be later than the Worcester painting but is probably a little earlier than the Rijksmuseum picture of 1661.

VERSIONS: Four versions are dated: those in Worcester (1653);[3] the Rijksmuseum, Amsterdam (1661);[4] Goudstikker sale, 3 December 1940, lot 28 (1661);[5] F. Bennett collection, London, 1958 (1664).[6] Other versions are: Kleinberger sale, New York, 1918;[7] C. von Pannwitz collection;[8] Johnson collection, Philadelphia Museum of Art;[9] Bonn, Rheinisches Landesmuseum, 1927;[10] Komter sale, Amsterdam, 1926;[11] art

57

market, Berlin, *c*.1930;[12] L. Koetser Gallery, London, 1972;[13] Galeries Nackers sale, Brussels, 1964;[14] J.D. Waller collection, Heemstede;[15] Gunther Oberlaender sale, New York, 1939.[16] This list may contain some pastiches and copies. A copy of No. 2549 was sold at Christie's, 10 April 1970 (lot 27).[17]

PROVENANCE: The National Gallery picture may be identifiable with one or other of the following *Tailor's Shops* by Brekelenkam: Lord Rendlesham sale, London, 20 June 1806 (lot 9),[18] 45 gns; BI 1832 (No. 127),[19] lent by William Hastings; W. Hastings sale, London, 28 March 1840 (lot 54), bought by Woodin (37 gns); [W.C. Higgins] sale, London, 8 March 1875 (lot 126),[20] bought by Wigzell (£105). It was in the collection of George Salting, London, by 1902, when it was exhibited at the RA; Salting Bequest, 1910.

EXHIBITIONS: BI 1832, No. 127(?); RA 1902, No. 216; London 1978/9, No. 4.

REFERENCES:

1. MacLaren considered that there are perhaps the illegible traces of initials on the fire pot in the foot-warmer under the foot of the woman on the right. In fact these are just brushstrokes indicating the shape of the pot in the foot-warmer.

2. It is quite close, for example, to a still life (panel, 35 × 49 cm.) signed and dated 1660, which in 1959 was in the collection of D.G. Buxton, Norwich (formerly Brod Gallery, London; previously Goudstikker, Amsterdam. Included in the exhibition of *Het Stilleven*, Goudstikker, Amsterdam, 1933, no. 39).

3. Panel, 60 × 85 cm. Signed QVB 1653 (VB in monogram). Inv. no. 1910.7, Worcester Art Museum, 1974 catalogue, pp. 88–90. This painting was exhibited in Philadelphia/Berlin/London, 1984, No. 18, where it is discussed at length, with the variants, by O. Naumann.

4. Canvas, 66 × 53 cm. Signed QB 1661. Inv. no. C112. Rijksmuseum, 1976 catalogue, p. 149.

5. Panel, 59 × 82 cm. Signed and dated 1661. Exhibited Goudstikker, The Hague, 1916; subsequently at the Sackville Gallery, London (see advertisement in the BM, vol. 36, 1920, p. 39). This may be identical with the version in the Rheinisches Landesmuseum, Bonn (see below, note 10). This is suggested by Naumann in ex. cat. Philadelphia/Berlin/London, 1984, No. 18, note 1.

6. Panel, 49 × 38 cm. Signed and dated 1664. Sale Valentin-Roussel, Brussels, 14 June 1899; Brod Gallery, London, 1956. Exhibited Arts Council 1958, No. 528 (as from the collection of F. Bennett, London).

7. Panel, 60 × 82 cm. Kleinberger sale, American Art Association, 23 January 1918, lot 58 (variant of Worcester composition: without old woman).

8. Panel, 60 × 75 cm. Kellner sale, Berlin, 3 December 1929, lot 29. Art market, New York, 1988. Now in the collection of Michal Hornstein, Montreal.

9. Panel, 56.8 × 82 cm. 1972 catalogue, No. 534. Purchaser unknown but in Johnson's possession by 1908.

10. Wesendonck collection, Bonn (No. 112); Bonn, Provinzial Museum, 1927 catalogue, No. 30 (pl. 53). Not in the 1936 Wesendonck-Bissing sale.

11. Panel, 41 × 52 cm. Collection Jules Porgès, Paris; J. de la L. . . . sale, Brussels, 3 July 1919 (lot 60); D. Komter sale, Amsterdam, 9 January 1926 (lot 20).

12. Panel, 68 × 88 cm. (with woman on right combing out girl's hair).

13. Signed. Panel, 43 × 62.8 cm. L. Koetser Gallery, Autumn Exhibition, October–November 1972, cat. no. 4. Formerly Dr H. Schäffer, Berlin. (Same composition as recorded in note 11; perhaps same painting, though measurements differ.)

14. Panel, 83 × 59 cm. Nackers sale, Brussels, 15 January 1964, lot 133 (illustrated in catalogue). Possibly a copy of the left half of the painting described in note 12.

15. Panel, 48 × 64 cm. Reproduced in *Beeldende Kunst*, vol. 3, 1916, fig. 9, no. 71 (woman talking to the tailor and another woman sewing by the fire).

16. Gunther Oberlaender sale, New York, 25 May 1939, lot 227.

17. Panel, 41.9 × 62.2 cm. Illustrated in catalogue. From an American collection (seated woman on right combing child's hair).

18. Brekelenkam, 'The Taylor's Shop, an Interior . . .'; size is not given.

19. Brekelenkam, 'The Interior of a tailor's shop'; size not given in the exhibition catalogue nor in the Hastings sale catalogue.

20. 'Interior of a tailor's shop.' In the printed catalogue of the sale this picture is attributed to P. de Hooch, but in the auctioneer's copy this is crossed out and Brekelenkam's name substituted.

2550 *A Woman Asleep by a Fire, an Open Bible(?) in her Lap*   Plate 46

The stoneware jug on the table has, in relief, Adam and Eve before God the Father. (The jug is very similar to a *Siegburger Schnelle*, with a relief of the same subject, in the Rheinisches Landesmuseum, Bonn.)

Oil on oak, 43.7 × 32.8 ($17\frac{3}{16}$ × $12\frac{15}{16}$).

It apparently once bore a signature or inscription;[1] no trace of this is now visible.

The subject of an old woman seated in a chair, dozing, spinning, or gazing into a fire, is a favourite one of Brekelenkam and his Leiden contemporaries. There are paintings of 1658,[2] 1662[3] and 1663[4] comparable to No. 2550 but there is also a similar painting – the old woman is seated on the left, facing to the right – in the Louvre which has a false signature and date: N. Maes 1648.[5] It is possible that this date presumes an original inscription and that No. 2550 is also *c.* 1648. It is not very different in style from a painting of 1648 in Leiden.[6] Brekelenkam's style changed little in the 1650s and 1660s.

COPY: A copy on porcelain by Jean-Etienne Liotard, signed and dated 1760, is in the Kunsthistorisches Museum, Vienna (Fig. 18).[7]

PROVENANCE: In the Floris Drabbe sale, Leiden, 1 April 1743 (lot 39), 34 guilders;[8] by 1760 in the collection of Jean-Etienne Liotard at Geneva.[9] Perhaps sold by Liotard (who died in 1789) to François Tronchin of Geneva;[10] it was in Tronchin's sale, Paris, 23–24 March 1801 (lot 22),[11] bought by Constantin (102 francs). It is said to have been in a Countess of Holderness sale as by Frans van Mieris;[12] it was not in her only recorded sale, London, 6 March 1802,[13] but it was in an unidentified British sale, apparently before 1830, as by Frans van Mieris.[14] It was in the [Lady Stepney] sale, London, 1 May 1830 (lot 75),[15] apparently bought in (40 gns). In the collection of Jean-Gilles-Marie-Joseph Schamp d'Aveschoot (1765–1839), Ghent.[16] In the collection of H.F. Broadwood by 1892, when it was lent to the Royal Academy; H.F. Broadwood sale, London, 25 March 1899 (lot 27), bought by Agnew (370 gns). Collection of George Salting; Salting Bequest, 1910.

EXHIBITION: RA 1892, No. 90.

REFERENCES:
1. Catalogue of the Stepney sale, 1830 (see note 14).
2. *An Old Woman gazing into a Fire*. Panel, 44 × 36 cm. Sale in Paris (Galliera), 23 November 1972 (lot 27): previously J. Wilson sale, Paris, 14–16 March 1881 (lot 33); sale A. Schloss, Paris (Charpentier), 5 December 1951 (lot 4). Photo in RKD. The handling is cruder than No. 2550.
3. Panel, 16 × 13 in. Collection P. de Keyser, Rotterdam, 1940 (exh. Rotterdam, 23 December 1939–29 January 1940, cat. no. 5, illustration in catalogue). Formerly Lord Aldenham collection: Aldenham sale, London, 24 February 1937 (lot 99): ill. in catalogue). Very similar in composition to No. 2550: the old woman is seated at a slightly different angle.
4. *An Old Woman sleeping at her Spinning-wheel*. Panel, 14 × 9¾ in. Signed and dated 1663. With Nijstad, The Hague, 1953, and Brod, London, 1964.
5. Panel, 545 × 41 cm Inv. no. M.I. 939. Louvre cat., *Ecoles Flamande et Hollandaise*, 1979, p. 33.
6. Panel, 57 × 53.5 cm. Stedelijk Museum De Lakenhal cat. 1983, inv. no. 47.
7. Vienna 1938 catalogue, No. 590. 44 × 34 cm. It was in the Imperial collection in Vienna by 1783 (see C. von Mechel's *Verzeichnis der Gemälde der Kaiserlich Königlichen Bilder Galerie in Wien*, 1783, p. 145, No. 16).
8. Hoet, 1752, vol. 2, p. 78. The provenance from the Drabbe collection is mentioned in the Tronchin 1801 sale catalogue.
9. It appears in a list of paintings in Liotard's collection made by Johann Friedrich Reiffenstein for the Markgräfin Karoline Luise of Baden in 1761: 'Breckelenkamp Betende Alte nach Tisch eingeschlafen.' cf. Archives of the Grand Ducal House of Baden in Karlsruhe. Papers and manuscripts of Karoline Luise, supp. 2, vol. 17. This reference is published by M.N. Benisovich, 'Liotard et sa collection de tableaux', *Genava*, vol. 29, 1953, p. 152. Identity of Liotard's picture with No. 2550 is established by his copy in Vienna, which is dated 1760, by which time the original presumably belonged to him (according to Benisovich, op. cit., pp. 3 and 4, Liotard bought his collection of Dutch paintings in Holland in 1755–56, mostly from Gerard Hoet).
10. Cf. Benisovich, op. cit., p. 13, note 1; *De*

59

Genève à l'Ermitage: Les collections de François Tron-chin, Musée Rath, Geneva, June–September 1974, cat. no. 81. The author quotes from a manuscript of Tronchin, unfortunately undated, in which he described the paintings in the collection of Liotard: '. . . Une vieille femme vue de face, assisse, les pieds sur une chaufferette, ses souliers à terre à côté. Elle s'endort la Bible ouverte sur ses genoux et ses lunettes à la main qui pose sur la Bible. Elle est entre la cheminée et une table couverte d'une serviette sur laquelle sont un plat à bière de grès avec un couvercle d'étain, un couteau dont la manche est à moitié hors de la table; un demi pain de seigle, un poisson dans un plat, un demi fromage de cumin sur lequel est un plat de fayance. Une grande écuelle de bois dans lequel est un pain blanc entier. Une étoffe brune verdâtre est pôsée sur le coin de la table. Sur bois de Brekelcam [sic]. h. 16⁰. l. 12⁰. 3⁰⁰' (cf. Archives Tronchin 195/3. Bibliothèque publique et universitaire, Geneva). The painting was in Tronchin's second collection; 1780 catalogue, p. 16: 'Quirinus van Breekelenkamp Une vieille femme vue de face assisse, dormant la bible ouverte sur ses genoux; ses lunettes dans la main droite posée sur la bible; la gauche appuyée sur le bras de sa chaise. Elle a les pieds sur une chausserette, & ses souliers sont sur le plancher. Elle est entre la cheminée & une table couverte d'une nappe sur laquelle sont un plat de Schellevisch, la moitié d'un fromage; sur le fromage une assiette de fayance pleine de beurre; dans une écuelle de bois est un pain blanc. Un pot de grès dont le couvercle est d'étain, la moitié d'un pain de seigle, un couteau, un morceau d'étoffe brune couvrent le reste de la table, au pied de laquelle est une terrine avec une cuillère dedans. Au coin de la cheminée est un panier à tourbes; &, dans le fond, une armoire sur laquelle sont de vieux livres & de la vaisselle de fayance. Un chapeau de femme est pendu à côté

au-dessus d'un fauteuil couvert d'un oreiller. B. h. 16⁰. 2⁰⁰. l. 12⁰. 3⁰⁰. (40 × 29.5 cm.). Les tableaux de ce maitre sont recherchés: celui-ci, d'un dessin pur, d'une couleur très-vraie; riche d'accessoires, & fini comme un Gerard Dou, est vraiment précieux. Il vient du cabinet de Floris Drabbe, vendu à Leyden in 1743.'

11. The sale catalogue mentions the provenance from Floris Drabbe's collection and the copy by Liotard in the Imperial collection in Vienna.

12. In the catalogue of Lady Stepney's sale, 1830.

13. It is the only Countess of Holderness sale of paintings recorded in Lugt.

14. Stuck on the back of the panel is a cutting from an unidentified sale catalogue: 'F. MIERIS . . . 59 Interior of a Dutch Apartment, in which a table/is spread with refreshments: an old woman/with a bible on her lap, has fallen asleep, with/her spectacles in her hand. From the Holder-/nesse collection.' Since the attribution to F. van Mieris is mentioned and corrected in the catalogue of the Stepney sale of 1 May 1830 (see the following note), this cutting is presumably from the catalogue of an earlier sale; indeed, it seems probable that the reference to the appearance of the picture as a van Mieris in the Holderness sale, made in the Stepney sale catalogue, derives from this cutting.

15. As by Brekelenkam: 'An elderly Female in her Chair, asleep, after dinner, with a large Bible in her Lap . . . This Picture was sold in the Sale of the Countess of Holdernesse, as a work of Fr. Mieris – it is inscribed with the name of the Painter.' The cutting on the back of No. 2550 (see the preceding note) shows that this is the same picture.

16. A posthumous sale of the collection took place in Ghent in 1840. The Brekelenkam is No. 214 in the sale catalogue. According to the marked copy in the National Gallery library, it was sold for 1000 francs.

HENDRICK TER BRUGGHEN, 1588(?)–1629

Hendrick Jansz. ter Brugghen. The place and date of his birth are not securely documented. In 1707 his son Richard presented to the town of Deventer (Province of Overijssel) pictures of the four Evangelists by his father; in the minute of acceptance of 1707 in the Deventer records, Hendrick ter Brugghen is said to have been a native of the Province of Overijssel[1] and an inscription, probably made at the time of the gift, on the frame of the St Matthew states that he was born in 1588.[2] The same place and date are given in the title of a 'portrait' of ter Brugghen engraved by Pieter Bodart (after Gerard Hoet) probably early in the eighteenth century.[3] When ter Brugghen testified in April 1615 his age was given as 'about twenty-five'.[4] De Bie (1661)[5] says he died in 1629 (which is correct) at the age of forty-two.

Recently discovered documents[6] have identified the painter's father as Jan ter Brugge who may well have left Deventer in 1581. He is recorded in Utrecht in that year: he was appointed secretary to the Court of Utrecht on 20 June 1581. He had moved to The Hague by 1589 when he bought a house there. Hendrick was therefore born either in Utrecht or The Hague. (Hendrick's father is not recorded in The Hague after 1602; by 1613 he was back in Utrecht, although he later apparently moved to Amsterdam.) Sandrart says Hendrick was a pupil of Abraham Bloemaert in Utrecht and afterwards visited Italy.[7] According to Houbraken[8] and the title of the print mentioned above, ter Brugghen lived in Rome for ten years; if this is true, he must have gone there about 1604 since he was travelling home in mid-1614 and was again in Utrecht before April 1615. The source of the information about his stay in Italy was probably Richard ter Brugghen,[9] who was only about eleven when his father died;[10] it is perhaps a little unlikely that the painter went to Italy when only sixteen (or even younger if the document of 1615 is accurate) or that all trace of his activity in Italy could have disappeared had he worked there for a decade.[11] In any case he was in Milan on his way back to Holland in the summer of 1614 and probably arrived in Utrecht by the end of the year, certainly before April 1615.[12] He married in Utrecht in October 1616,[13] entered the guild there in 1616 or 1617 (probably the former)[14] and apparently lived there for the rest of his life.[15] A recently published manuscript annotation, however, appears to support earlier speculation based on ter Brugghen's apparent knowledge of Italian painting executed after 1615, that he made a second trip to Italy between 1619 and 1621.[16] He was buried in Utrecht, in the Buurkerk, on 7 November 1629.[17]

Ter Brugghen's style is in the main a very individual interpretation of the manner of Caravaggio and, perhaps even more, of Caravaggio's Roman followers (notably Bartolommeo Manfredi, Orazio Gentileschi and Carlo Saraceni), and he was the first of the northern *Caravaggisti* to return to Holland. No work of his Italian years is known. The first dated picture is of 1616;[18] the monumental *Adoration of the Magi* in the Rijksmuseum is dated 1619.[19] Ter Brugghen seems to have worked closely, perhaps even sharing a studio, with Dirck van Baburen from the time of that artist's return from Italy (probably in 1620, certainly by 1622) until his death in 1624.

His pictures are mainly of religious subjects and genre, the latter often musicians and drinkers; he also painted some mythological and literary subjects.

REFERENCES:
General: B. Nicolson, *Hendrick Terbrugghen*, 1958; B. Nicolson, 'Second Thoughts about Terbrugghen', BM, vol. 102, 1960, pp. 465–73; P. van Thiel, 'De aanbidding der Koningen en ander vroeg werk van Hendrick ter Brugghen', *Bulletin van het Rijksmuseum*, vol. 19, no. 3, 1971, pp. 91–116; B. Nicolson, 'Terbrugghen since 1960', *Album Amicorum J.G. van Gelder*, 1973, pp. 237–41; B. Nicolson, *The International Caravaggesque Movement*, Oxford, 1979, pp. 97–101. M.J. Bok and Y. Kobayashi, 'New data on Hendrick ter Brugghen', *Mercury*, 1, 1985, pp. 7–34 (with transcriptions of all documents relating to ter Brugghen and his family); C. Schuck-man, 'Did Hendrick ter Brugghen revisit Italy?', *Mercury*, 4, 1986, pp. 7–22; *Nieuw Licht op de Gouden Eeuw; Hendrick ter Brugghen en zijn tijdgenoten*, Centraal Museum, Utrecht, and Herzog-Anton Ulrich Museum, Braunschweig, 1986–7; *Hendrick ter Brugghen und die Nachfolger Caravaggios in Holland, Beiträge eines Symposions im Hersoz Anton Ulrich-museum, Braunschweig, 23/25 March 1987*, Braunschweig, 1988.
In text:
1. See HdG, *Arnold Houbraken und seine 'Groote Schoubrugh'*, 1893, p. 439.
2. The frames of the four pictures are inscribed as

follows: (*St Matthew*) A⁰ 1621 PINXIT HENRICVS TER-BRVGGHEN NATVS. 1588; (*St Mark*) DENATVS 1629. FILIVS RICHARDVS CVRIÆ TRAIE –; (*St Luke*) CTINÆ. ADVOCATVS · CIVITATI · DAVENTRIENSI; (*St John*) IN MEMORIAM DONAVIT ANNO 1707 · ÆTATIS SVÆ 89.

3. HdG, *Houbraken*, op. cit., pp. 437–38.

4. Document published by J.J. Dodt van Flensburg in *Berigten van het Historisch Genootschap te Utrecht*, vol. 1, 1846, pp. 133–35, and (in an improved transcription) by M.E. Houck, *Mededeelingen betreffende Gerhard ter Borch . . . en Henrick ter Brugghen*, 1899, pp. 355–57; Bok and Kobayashi, op. cit., Doc. no. 17.

5. De Bie, p. 132.

6. Bok and Kobayashi, op. cit., pp. 7–9. Publication of these documents substantially amends the account given of ter Brugghen's life in Nicolson, op. cit.

7. Sandrart, *Teutsche Academie*, vol. 2, p. 308.

8. Houbraken, vol. 1, p. 133.

9. HdG, *Houbraken*, op. cit., pp. 273–4 and 437–8.

10. He was eighty-nine in 1707 (see note 2).

11. Nothing is known of a large picture by him said by Houbraken (pp. 133–34) to be over the high altar of Naples Cathedral.

12. See note 4.

13. Bok and Kobayashi, op. cit., Doc. no. 20.

14. Bok and Kobayashi, Doc. no. 18.

15. Cf. Bok and Kobayashi, op. cit. Ter Brugghen lived on the Snippevlucht where his neighbours included Gerard van Honthorst and the fish painter Marcus Ormea.

16. Schuckman, op. cit.

17. Bok and Kobayashi, Doc. no. 36. The funeral was held on the 7th and registered on the 9th.

18. *St Peter Praying* (Utrecht, Centraal Museum; 1971 cat. no. 18) and a *Supper at Emmaus* (Toledo Museum of Art, Inv. no. 83.1, Utrecht/Braunschweig cat., op. cit., no. 1.).

19. 1976 cat. A4118. See van Thiel, op. cit.

4164 *Jacob reproaching Laban for giving him Leah in place of Rachel(?)* Plate 47

Laban is seated; Jacob stands before him. Leah(?) is beside Laban, and Rachel(?) in the left background.

Signed on the base of the table: HTBrúgghen · i627 (HTB in monogram).

Oil on canvas, 97.5 × 114.3 (38⅜ × 45).

There are *pentimenti* in Jacob's legs, in the outline of his face and hat, the outline of the drapery behind Laban and the profile of Leah(?). There was at first a deep dish on the ground in the bottom left corner.

Cleaned in 1979–80.

For the marriage of Jacob and the substitution of Leah see Genesis 29: 21–6. The subject, first identified as *Jacob and Laban* by Collins Baker and Schneider,[1] is generally thought to be the same as that in the painting of 1628(?) by ter Brugghen in the Wallraf-Richartz Museum in Cologne (Fig. 19).[2] This supposition is probably correct despite the many differences.[3] The young man holds a shepherd's crook which is appropriate for Jacob. The second young woman is probably Leah's sister, Rachel, rather than her servant, Zilpah, as has been suggested.[4]

PROVENANCE: Acquired in Leeds by W. Haffety, Scarborough;[5] purchased for the National Gallery at the [W. Haffety] sale, London, 26 March 1926 (lot 119)[6] with the aid of the Claude Phillips Fund.

REFERENCES:
General: B. Nicolson, *Hendrick Terbrugghen*, 1958, No. A40; C. Brown in 1987 Braunschweig Symposium, op. cit., pp. 89–97.

In text:
1. C.B. Collins Baker in BM, vol. 50, 1927, pp. 196ff; A. von Schneider in OH, vol. 44, 1927, p. 268. See also F. Lugt in GBA, 1944, i, p. 346, and C. Brière-Misme, ibid., 1953, vol. 2, pp. 292f.

2. The date is difficult to read. It is given in the 1967 Wallraf-Richartz Museum catalogue (by H. Vey and A. Kersting, pp. 24–5) as 1628. The various alternative readings are discussed there. The present writer considers the correct date to be 1628.

3. For a discussion of alternative subjects of the Cologne painting, see the 1967 catalogue (op. cit., note 2), p. 25. The suggestion of H.F. Secker in the Wallraf-Richartz catalogue of 1927 that the subject is Tobias asking Raguel for the hand of Sarah (Tobit 7: 8–16) is certainly incorrect.

4. Brière-Misme, op. cit., p. 293.

5. Oral information from W. Haffety, 1932.

6. As 'Esau with the Mess of Potage'.

6347 *A Man playing a Lute*   *Plate 48*

Signed, top right: H T Brúgghen. fecit. i624 (HTB in monogram).

Oil on canvas, 100.5 × 78.7 ($39\frac{1}{2}$ × 31).

Cleaned in 1963.

Cross-sections reveal that the painting has a double ground, the lower and thicker one being red-brown ochre, the upper and thinnish one being a mixture of lead-white and charcoal black: it is strikingly similar to that on most of Rembrandt's paintings in the National Gallery (see the discussion of Rembrandt No. 4930 in this catalogue). There are *pentimenti* in the outline of the cap, in the drapery over the right arm and in the ribbon of the right shirt sleeve. The pale blue ribbons of the sleeves have become lighter owing to the deterioration of the cobalt in the smalt pigment.[1]

In the early 1620s, after the return to Utrecht from Rome of Gerrit van Honthorst and Dirck van Baburen, the subject of the half-length single figure in flamboyant dress playing a musical instrument became very popular amongst the Utrecht *Caravaggisti*. Ter Brugghen first treated the subject of half-length musicians in a pair of paintings of flute-playing boys in Cassel.[2] Subsequently he painted numerous pictures of musicians playing bagpipes, bass viols, violins and flutes as well as lutes (Fig. 20), and some holding up a glass of wine.

VERSION/COPY: Canvas, 100.3 × 83.5 cm. Not signed or dated. With Harari and Johns, 1989. It is probably the same painting which was in the Baron Thott collection, Denmark, 1900, and subsequently in the W. Konow collection in Copenhagen (exhibited at the Statens Museum for Kunst, Copenhagen, October 1946, cat. no. 55, as G. van Honthorst). It was considered by Nicolson (who gives the dimensions as 104.5 × 90.5 cm.) to be an autograph replica of No. 6347.

PROVENANCE: Solly Flood collection, Ireland;[4] bought from Flood by James Murnaghan, Dublin, in *c.*1925–30. Purchased from Murnaghan by the National Gallery in 1963.

EXHIBITION: London 1976, No. 19.

REFERENCES:

General: Nicolson, op. cit., A 26.

In text:

1. J. Plesters, 'A Preliminary Note on the Incidence of Discolouration of Smalt in Oil Media', *Studies in Conservation*, 14, 1969, pp. 70–1.

2. Both on canvas, 70 × 55 cm. One signed in full and dated 1621, the other signed in monogram. Cassel catalogue 1929, nos. 179 and 180; Nicolson, op. cit., A 14 and A 15.

3. Nicolson, op. cit., A 43.

4. Nicolson, op. cit.

6483 *The Concert*

Plate 49

Oil on canvas, 99.1 × 116.8 (39 × 46).

X-radiographs (Fig. 21) show a change of composition on the left-hand side.

In this painting, which has strong claim to be ter Brugghen's finest treatment of a secular subject, he has taken a scene favoured by Caravaggio and his Roman followers – a group of flamboyantly dressed musicians seen by candlelight – and treated it in his own distinctive manner, placing the dramatically lit half-length figures against a light background.

Caravaggio's *Musical Party* (New York, Metropolitan Museum)[1] and Bartolommeo Manfredi's *The Concert* (Florence, Uffizi)[2] are amongst the prototypes for this composition: the large-scale half-length figures, their crowding together within the composition and their closeness to the edge of the canvas and the bright, colourful palette, can all be found in No. 6483. Ter Brugghen brings to this existing format an individual fluency in modelling the soft edges of his forms and a remarkable subtlety of palette – which includes light blues, lemon, purple and cerise. Judson[3] pointed out that the painting also displays ter Brugghen's familiarity with Honthorst's musical parties and in particular with the Copenhagen *Musical Party by Candlelight* of 1623.[4] Certainly ter Brugghen was aware of Honthorst's musical groups – and in this respect his *Concert* of 1626 in Leningrad[5] is far closer to Honthorst's compositions – but his treatment of such subjects is very different. Nicolson[6] noted that comparison could also be made with Baburen's *Concert* in Leningrad[7] in which a shadow is thrown by the instrument across the face of the boy on the extreme right.

The precise dating of the painting is discussed at some length by Nicolson.[8] Nicolson had at one time dated the painting very late, that is, *c.*1628/9,[9] believing that ter Brugghen's candlelight scenes were exclusively of the late period. This was shown not to be the case with the discovery of two candlelight scenes dated 1623,[10] and Czobor[11] suggested a redating of No. 6483 to *c.*1623/4. Nicolson acknowledged these arguments and suggested a date of *c.*1626/7.[12] The authors of the Utrecht/Braunschweig exhibition catalogue (op. cit.) argue for a dating of *c.* 1625. The present author prefers a date of *c.*1626 on an analogy with the Leningrad *Concert* which is dated 1626.

PROVENANCE: Somers collection, Eastnor Castle, Ledbury, Herefordshire. There are apparently no early inventories of the collection but the seventeenth-century Dutch paintings are said to have been purchased by Lord Somers (1651–1716), the Lord Chancellor of King William III, in around 1700. He made numerous trips to the Netherlands and presumably bought the paintings there. It is likely therefore that No. 6483 came to England *c.*1700. It passed by descent to the Hon. Mrs E. Hervey-Bathurst, who in 1982 sold the painting to a foreign consortium from which it was purchased by the National Gallery in May 1983 with the aid of a contribution of £500,000 from the National Heritage Memorial Fund and donations from the Pilgrim Trust and the NACF.

EXHIBITIONS: Birmingham 1934, No. 451, as Honthorst;[13] RA 1938, No. 169; Antwerp 1952, Centraal Museum, Utrecht/Museum voor Schone Kunsten, Tentoonstelling, 'Caravaggio en de Nederlanden', No. 82; RA 1952–3, No. 633; Birmingham 1953, No. 109; Manchester 1957, No. 13a; London 1976, No. 20; Utrecht/Braunschweig 1986–7, No. 23; London, British Museum, 'Treasures for the Nation', 1988–9, cat. no. 30.

REFERENCES:

General: Nicolson, op. cit., A 37.

In text:

1. Inv. no. 52.81. Recent (1983) cleaning has revealed the bright tonality of the painting.

2. 1979 cat. P 987. There dated 1610/20.

3. J.R. Judson, *Gerrit van Honthorst*, The Hague, 1956, pp. 68–69.

4. Judson, op. cit., cat. no. 197.

5. Canvas, 102 × 83 cm. Leningrad 1958 cat. no. 276. Nicolson, op. cit., A 38.

6. Nicolson, op. cit., p. 72.

7. Canvas, 99 × 130 cm. Leningrad 1958 cat. no. 772. L. Slatkes, *Dirck van Baburen*, Utrecht, 1965, cat. no. A 26. Slatkes dates the painting to 1623.

8. Nicolson, op. cit., p. 72.

9. B. Nicolson, 'The Rijksmuseum "Incredulity" and Terbrugghen's Chronology', BM, 1956, pp. 109–10 (note 34).

10. The paintings now in Erlau and Raleigh. Nicolson, *Hendrick Terbrugghen*, A 29, B 80.

11. A. Czobor, 'Uber ein unbekanntes Bild des Hendrick Terbrugghen', OH, 1956, p. 230.

12. Nicolson, op. cit., p. 72.

13. It was when the painting was on exhibition in Birmingham in 1934 that N. Pevsner identified it as the work of ter Brugghen. See his review of the exhibition in BM, 1935, p. 30.

PAULUS THEODORUS VAN BRUSSEL, 1754–1795

Flower and fruit painter. Born in Zuid Polsbroek, 16 January 1754. He was a pupil of Jan Augustini (1725–73) in Haarlem and worked in Augustini's *behangsel-fabrijk* (literally, wall-hanging [rather than wallpaper] factory) there and subsequently in those run by Vincent van der Vinne and Hendrick Meijer which were also in Haarlem. Van Brussel's speciality was painting flower pictures for overmantels and overdoors. After his marriage in 1774 he began to concentrate on independent flower and fruit paintings. Later he settled in Amsterdam and died there, 17 March 1795.

REFERENCE: Van Eijnden and van der Willigen, vol. 2, pp. 403–5.

3225 *Flowers in a Vase*   *Plate 50*

In the vase are tulips, poppies, narcissi, peonies and other flowers; roses and a bird's nest containing eggs lie on the ledge below. There are trees in the background.

Signed, left bottom, on the marble ledge: P. T. van Brussel./fecit 1792.

Oil on mahogany, 81.1 × 58.9 ($31\frac{15}{16}$ × $23\frac{3}{16}$).

PROVENANCE: In the William Benoni White sale, London, 23–24 May 1879 (lot 42), bought by Aston (76 gns). W.W. Aston Bequest, 1919.

EXHIBITION: Bath 1953, No. 21.

5174 *Flowers in a Vase*   *Plate 51*

Among the flowers are peonies, roses, iris and tulips. On the ledge is a bird's nest containing eggs. The vase has, in relief, a medallion with an antique head in profile. There is a background of trees.

Signed, bottom right, on the marble slab: P. T. v. Brussel. fecit./1789.

Oil on mahogany, 78.4 × 61.2 (30⅞ × 24⅛).

PROVENANCE: Said to have been in the collection of the King of Holland[1] (presumably meaning William II). Apparently lot 88 of an unidentified British sale of the second half of the nineteenth century;[2] in the possession of Rayner MacConnal, London.[3] Sir Arthur Jackson Bequest, 1940.

REFERENCES:
1. According to the catalogue of an unidentified nineteenth-century sale – see note 2. It is not, however, in C.J. Nieuwenhuys, *Description de la Galerie . . . de S.M. le Roi des Pays-Bas*, 1843, nor in the catalogues of the sales of William II's collection, The Hague, 12–20 August 1850 and 9 sqq. September 1851, and it is possible that Louis Bonaparte (r. 1806–10) is being referred to.
2. On the back of the panel are two cuttings, apparently from the same sale catalogue. The upper one runs: 'P.T. VAN BRUSSEL. / [A SP]LENDID GROUP OF FRUIT AND FLOWERS, elegantly arranged / on a marble slab. *This fine work . . . is signed and dated 1789. Formerly in the Col-* / [*lect*]*ion of the King of Holland*'; the lower one: 'P.T. VAN BRUSSEL. / 88 A FINE BOUQUET OF FLOWERS, elegantly arranged in a sculptural / vase on a marble slab – the companion . . .' The typography shows that these cuttings come from a Christie's sale catalogue of post-1849.
3. MacConnal's label is on the back of the frame.

5800 *Fruit and Flowers*   *Plate 52*

The still life is set against a background of trees.

Signed, below right: P.T. v. Brussel . fecit . 1789.

Oil on mahogany, 78.4 × 61 (30⅞ × 24).

PROVENANCE: Said to have been in the collection of the King of Holland[1] (presumably meaning William II). In the Lt.-Col. W.L. Grant sale, 18 June 1881 (lot 89),[2] bought by Cooling (62 gns); Mrs Gordon Wickham sale, London, 15 July 1926 (lot 132), bought by Parsons[3] (£157); later in the possession of Messrs Leggatt from whom it was bought by Frederick John Nettlefold in 1927;[4] F.J. Nettlefold Gift, 1947.

REFERENCES:
1. In Grant sale catalogue, 1881, but not in C.J. Nieuwenhuys, op. cit., nor in the sales of William II's collection in The Hague, 12 sqq. August 1850 and 9 sqq. September 1851. It is possible that Louis Bonaparte is being referred to.
2. The markings corresponding to this sale are on the back.
3. Letter of 1948 from Messrs Leggatt.
4. Letter from F.J. Nettlefold, 1948, in the National Gallery archives.

WILLEM BUYTEWECH the Younger, 1625–1670

Willem Willemsz. Buytewech, posthumous son of Willem Pietersz. Buytewech (died 1624), was baptised in Rotterdam, 4 January 1625.[1] His father painted genre subjects but in addition he drew and etched both topographical and imagined landscapes.[2] Scarcely anything is known about the son. He is recorded as living in Rotterdam in 1658[3] and was buried there between 20 and 26 April 1670.[4]

Very few works by him are known. Jan Sysmus (writing *c.*1669–78)[5] says he painted Christmas nights and animals ('Karsnagten en beesjes').[6] Naumann[7] has identified six paintings and one drawing by him. Only two are dated, both 1664.[8] Naumann has stressed Buytewech's eclecticism as a landscape painter, pointing out his borrowings from Benjamin Cuyp, Jan Asselijn, Jan Wijnants and others.

REFERENCES:

General: O. Naumann, 'Willem Buytewech the Younger', *Essays in Northern European Art Presented to Egbert Haverkamp-Begemann on his Sixtieth Birthday*, Doornspijk, 1983, pp. 194–8 (with catalogue of works).

In text:
1. OH, 1905, p. 163.
2. E. Haverkamp-Begemann, *Willem Buytewech*, Amsterdam, 1959.

3. OH, 1895, p. 113.
4. According to P. Haverkorn van Rijsewijk in Thieme/Becker, vol. 5, 1911, p. 311.
5. See A. Bredius in OH, 1890, p. 1.
6. OH, 1895, p. 113.
7. Naumann, op. cit.
8. Naumann, op. cit., cat. nos. 3 and 4.

2731 *A Dune Landscape*   Plate 53

Signed faintly in the bottom right corner: w. bujtew( ).

Oil on oak, 25.7 × 34.2 ($10\frac{1}{8}$ × $13\frac{1}{2}$).

The ground and the grain of the wood show through in many places; some wearing in the sky.

At one time ascribed to Jan Wijnants.[1] As Naumann has pointed out, the painting strongly recalls Wijnants' dune landscapes. Probably painted in the 1660s.

PROVENANCE: In the collection of the 2nd Earl of Beverley,[2] the whole of which was bought by John Smith in 1851;[3] bought in the same year by Thomas Baring[4] (died 1873), who bequeathed his collection to his nephew, Thomas Baring, 2nd Baron Northbrook (created Earl of Northbrook, 1876; d.1904). Purchased from the 2nd Earl of Northbrook (out of the Mackerell Fund), 1910.

REFERENCES:

General: Naumann, op. cit., cat. no. 5.
In text:
1. Northbrook catalogue 1889, p. 35, No. 40.

2. Ibid.
3. HdG, vol. 7, W. van de Velde No. 116.
4. Northbrook catalogue, loc. cit.

JAN VAN BIJLERT, 1598–1671

Jan Harmensz. van Bijlert, son of a glass-painter, Harmen van Bijlert. He was born in Utrecht in 1598.[1] He was a pupil, in the first place, of his father and then of Abraham Bloemaert. Afterwards, according to Sandrart, he went to France and thence to Rome.[2] He is the painter 'Giovanni Bilardo, fiamengo', recorded as living in the Via Margutta in Rome in March 1621 and was one of the founder-members of the society of Netherlandish painters there (the *Schildersbent*) in 1623. He made a number of drawings of some of its members at that time.[3] He probably returned to Holland in 1624 and had settled in Utrecht by May 1625, when he married. He entered the Utrecht guild as a master in 1630. In 1628 he presented a painting to St Job's almshouse, Utrecht, and became one of its regents in 1634. (In 1669 he was said to be the longest-serving regent.) He was dean of the Utrecht guild, 1633–5; after the foundation of the Utrecht painters' college (in 1644) he was its dean in 1654, a member of its committee in 1655 and 1666, and dean again in 1667–9. He died in Utrecht, 13 November 1671.

His early work is strongly influenced by Caravaggio and his Roman followers. His earliest dated paintings are from 1624[4] and 1626.[5] Subsequently he came under the influence of the other Utrecht *Caravaggisti*, notably Hendrick ter Brugghen and Gerrit van Honthorst. He painted religious, mythological and Arcadian subjects and genre; he also painted, particularly in his later years, many portraits.

REFERENCES:

General: G.J. Hoogewerff, 'Jan van Bijlert: Schilder van Utrecht (1598–1671)', OH, vol. 80, 1965, pp. 3–33; B. Nicolson, *The International Caravaggesque Movement*, Oxford, 1979, pp. 26–9.

In text:

1. When he married Margaretha Keunig on 15 May 1625 in Utrecht he declared himself to be twenty-seven years of age.

2. Sandrart, *Teutsche Academie*, vol. 2, p. 307.

3. Boymans-van Beuningen Museum, Rotterdam. See, inter al., G. J. Hoogewerff, *De Bentveughels*, 1953, pp. 46–53.

4. Hoogewerff, op. cit., cat. no. 21.

5. Hoogewerff, op. cit., cat. no. 78.

1292 *Portrait of an Elderly Man and Woman, and a Younger Woman, outside a House*

Plate 54

Signed, bottom left: Jv bijlert· fe: (Jv in monogram).

Oil on canvas, 127 × 101 (50 × 39¾).

Hoogewerff[1] describes the younger, standing woman as a maid. She is more likely to be the couple's daughter. With her left hand she grasps the stem of a rose bush while the other woman holds a peach.[2]

No. 1292 probably dates from the 1660s.

PROVENANCE: It was lot 34 in the M.S.B. Bos sale, Amsterdam, 21 February 1888;[3] sold to F. Muller for 680 guilders. Lent by William F. Smithson, Leeds, to an unidentified exhibition at the Leeds Public Art Museum, No. 66.[4] Also said to have been for many years in the collection of William H. Howers of Walthamstow.[5] Bought in 1889 from the trustees of A.W. Thibaudeau, through Messrs Deprez and Gutekunst, London (out of the Clarke Fund).

REFERENCES:

General: Hoogewerff, op. cit., cat. no. 123.

In text:

1. Hoogewerff, op. cit.

2. The iconography of this portrait will be discussed in an article by E. de Jongh in *Mercury* in 1990/1.

3. 'Jan van Bylert: Famille hollandaise. Portratis d'un patricien, de sa femme et de sa fille. La vieille dame est assise, les deux autres figures sont debout et se trouvent sur une terrasse dans leur jardin. Le fond est formé par la façade de leur maison. Signé: J.v. Bylert ft. Fort-belle qualité et conservation parfaite. Toile, hauteur 125, largeur 36 cent.'

4. As a portrait of the artist, his wife and daughter. An undated Leeds Public Art Museum label, so inscribed, and numbered 66, is on the back of the picture.

5. Letter of 1891 from W.H. Howes (in the National Gallery archives).

CABEL *See* ARENT ARENTSZ.

ABRAHAM VAN CALRAET, 1642–1722

Abraham Pietersz. van Calraet; like other members of his family he also spelled his name *Calraat* and, occasionally, *Kalraet*. He was baptised in Dordrecht, 12 October 1642, the eldest son of Pieter Jansz. van Calraet,[1] a wood-carver. Houbraken says that Abraham learned to draw from the sculptors Aemilius (Gillis?) and Samuel Huppe of Dordrecht,[2] and that his brother Barent (1649–1737) was a pupil of Aelbert Cuyp;[3] if the works assigned to Abraham (see below) are in fact his, it is probable that he, too, was Cuyp's pupil. He seems to have spent his life in Dordrecht,[4] where he married in 1680 the daughter of the painter Cornelis Bisschop,[5] and was buried there on 12 June 1722.[6]

According to Houbraken,[7] he painted 'figures and fruit' and was also, like his father, a wood-carver (in 1682, 1697 and 1702 he is described as a painter and in 1687 as a wood-carver).[8]

There are a small number of still-life pictures with fruit, usually including peaches, signed with the initials A.C.; these were formerly accepted as the work of Aelbert Cuyp but the discovery of Abraham van Calraet's signature in full on a still life by the same hand showed that they are his work.[9] There are also numerous small paintings on panel signed A.C., often in minute characters, and representing for the most part stables and riding schools and other scenes with horses and horsemen (among them, cavalry skirmishes),[10] occasionally with views of Dordrecht. These also were at one time assigned to Cuyp to whom many of them are quite close in style. They are, however, clearly by a very able imitator who frequently borrowed freely from Cuyp's compositions but also sometimes imitated Philips Wouwermans; an example of the former is No. 3024 below and of the latter, No. 1851. An interior of a stable by this hand in the Boymans-van Beuningen Museum,[11] signed A.C. (possibly false), has a second signature or inscription: AP(v?)K (AP and v? in monogram) which has been taken to stand for Abraham Pietersz. van Kalraet, and Calraet is now accepted generally as the author of this second group. There exist a few portraits signed in full by Calraet and he is known to have made copies of two by Jan van Ravesteyn (c. 1570–1657).[12]

REFERENCES:

General: A. Bredius in *Kunstchronik*, N.F. vol. 25, 1913–14, cols. 93–94; idem and HdG (*contra*) in *Oude Kunst*, vol. 1, 1915–16, and vol. 2, 1916–17, esp. p. 9; Bredius, *Künstler-Inventare*, vol. 1, 1915, pp. 307–20; HdG in Thieme/Becker, vol. 19, 1926, pp. 482–84; J.G. van Gelder in *Kunsthistorische Mededeelingen*, vol. 1, 1946, pp. 7–8.

In text:

1. OH, 1889, p. 304. Erroneously said by Houbraken to have been born on 7 October 1643 (vol. 3, p. 181).

2. Houbraken, loc. cit.

3. Houbraken, op. cit., p. 292.

4. See Bredius, *Künstler-Inventare*, vol. 1, pp. 317–320.

5. OH, 1889, p. 304.

6. Bredius, *Künstler-Inventare*, vol. 1, p. 320.

7. Op. cit., p. 182.

8. *Künstler-Inventare*, vol. 1, pp. 317–18, and HdG in Thieme/Becker, vol. 19, p. 482.

9. Mauritshuis, The Hague: inv. no. 754, 1977 cat., p. 58.

10. See, for example, a painting in the Rijksmuseum, Amsterdam: 1976 cat., no. A79.

11. Inv. no. 1395, 1962 cat., pp. 35–36. The horse on the right is exactly the same as in a painting in the Hermitage, Leningrad, monogrammed A.C. (see No. 1683, note 2, below).

12. C. Brière-Misme in OH, 1950, pp. 32ff.

1683 *A Brown and White Skewbald Horse with a Saddle beside it*   Plate 55

Signed in the left bottom corner: AC.

Oil on oak, 34.2 × 44.4 ($13\frac{7}{16}$ × $17\frac{7}{16}$).

Like most of Calraet's pictures this was formerly attributed to Cuyp.[1] It is closely related in style to the group of works now accepted as Calraet's. The horse repeats with variations one in the signed *Stable Interior with Two Dapple-Grey Horses* (Fig. 22) in the Boymans-van Beuningen Museum, Rotterdam (see the biographical notice above); in the Boymans Museum picture the colouring of the horse is different and its head is not turned.[2]

PROVENANCE: The picture formed part of the Revd Chauncey Hare Bequest to the South Kensington (now Victoria and Albert) Museum, 1869;[3] on loan to the National Gallery from 1897 onwards.

REFERENCES:

1. HdG, Cuyp No. 547; catalogued as by Cuyp until 1921 (1925–9 as Ascribed to Kalraet).

2. The horse in the Rotterdam picture is repeated exactly in the *Boy with Three Horses* in the Hermitage, Leningrad (HdG, Cuyp No. 563; see van Gelder, op. cit., vol. 1, 1946, p. 8, reproduced p. 7), and in a version of the latter in the Elkins collection, Philadelphia (HdG No. 560; see van Gelder, op. cit., p. 8, note 4).

3. *Catalogue of the National Gallery of British Art at South Kensington*, 1893, part 1, p. 177. 1374–69 (as by A. Cuyp).

1851 *The Interior of a Stable*   Plate 56

Signed near the left edge (level with the head of the old man at the door): AC.

Oil on oak, 39.3 × 57.3 ($15\frac{1}{2}$ × $22\frac{9}{16}$).

Cleaned in 1951. Considerably worn with the grain of the wood showing through in a number of places, especially the sky.

At one time attributed to Aelbert Cuyp.[1]

Painted in imitation of Philips Wouwermans's interiors of stables (cf. Wouwermans No. 879 of this catalogue).

PROVENANCE: In the collection of Miss Susanna Caught by 1895;[2] Miss Susanna Caught Bequest, 1901.

REFERENCES:
1. C.H. Collins Baker in BM, vol. 29, 1916, p. 256, and National Gallery catalogue, 1920 and 1921.
2. As by Philips Wouwermans (letter of 1895 in the National Gallery archives).

3024 *Scene on the Ice outside Dordrecht* *Plate 57*

On the left, in the background, is the Groothoofdspoort and, to the right of it, the Grote Kerk. On the tent, left, is a Dutch flag; a swan is painted on the barrel behind the sleigh in the left foreground.

Signed, bottom left: AC.

Oil on oak, 33.5 × 57.5 ($13\frac{3}{16}$ × $22\frac{5}{8}$).

Dordrecht (Dort) is here seen from the north across the River Maas. The Grote Kerk and the Groothoofd water-gate still stand. The former appears in many of Cuyp's landscapes (cf. Nos. 961 and 962 of this catalogue). The Groothoofdspoort was rebuilt in its present form in 1618. It was damaged in 1692 and the spire was replaced by a dome *c.*1692–4[1] but otherwise remains much as in the present painting.

At one time attributed to Cuyp.[2]

If the picture is to be dated by the costume, it could hardly be later than the 1660s, and would in this case be a fairly early work. It is, however, not impossible that such pastiches of Cuyp were painted at a later period but with the costume of an earlier time. In the present picture the background view of Dordrecht has only slight variations from that in Cuyp's large *View of Dordrecht* in Ascott, Buckinghamshire (National Trust)[3] and may well have been taken from it or a similar picture; for this reason the absence of the Groothoofdspoort dome of 1692–4 does not necessarily provide a *terminus ante quem* here. (The Ascott landscape was probably painted in the 1650s.)

PROVENANCE: In the collection of Baron Huntingfield, Heveningham Hall, Suffolk, by 1907, when it was exhibited at the RA; purchased for the National Gallery at Lord Huntingfield's sale, London, 25 June 1915 (lot 78),[4] 230 gns (out of the Mackerell Fund).

EXHIBITION: RA 1907, No. 45.[5]

REFERENCES:
1. *Voorloopige Lijst der Nederlandsch Monumenten van Geschiedenis en Kunst*, vol. 3, 1915, p. 43; see also J.L. van Dalen, *Geschiedenis van Dordrecht*, vol. 1, 1931, p. 72.
2. Cf. HdG, Cuyp No. 735, and National Gallery catalogue, 1915–21.
3. HdG No. 164. S. Reiss, *Albert Cuyp*, London, 1975, no. 98.
4. As by Cuyp.
5. As by Cuyp.

Attributed to ABRAHAM VAN CALRAET

2548 *A Boy holding a Grey Horse* *Plate 58*

Falsely signed, bottom left: A.c( )yp.

Oil on oak, 36.2 × 32.4 (14¼ × 12¾); made up by false additions on all sides to 38 × 34.5 (15 × 13⅝).

Cleaned in 1959. The sky is worn in several places.

Accepted as a Cuyp by Hofstede de Groot,[1] this painting was described as 'Ascribed to Aelbert Cuyp' in the first edition of this catalogue. MacLaren wrote that 'the man in the right background and the saddlery are much in the manner of Abraham van Calraet', while noting that 'there is no signed painting by him as close as this to Cuyp'. He also noted that the horse repeats that in a painting by Cuyp in the Royal Collection[2] and that this animal reappears with slight variations in a stable interior 'almost certainly by Calraet'.[3]

In the opinion of the present writer, the painting is close enough to paintings signed by Calraet to justify an attribution to him. In particular it is very similar in the handling of both figures and the horse to *The Halt at the Inn*, formerly in the B. de Geus van den Heuvel collection, which is signed with initials.[4]

VERSIONS: A variant, with a castle in the distance, was in an anonymous sale, London, 26 July 1946 (lot 134), bought by Agnew;[5] another, with a dog on the right and a back view of a man in the right background, is in the Wallace Collection, London;[6] a third, with the addition of a man adjusting the saddle, was in the possession of L. de Vries and Co., Berlin, in 1929.[7]

PROVENANCE: Possibly identifiable with one of the following pictures attributed to A. Cuyp: 'A horse and groom' in an anonymous sale (collection of 'a nobleman . . . in Nottinghamshire'), London, 20 sqq. March 1772 (first day, lot 65), bought by M. Phillips (£2); a grey horse with a groom in a landscape in the Hocker collection, Nijmegen, and the Slater sale at Phillips, London, 9 May 1806 (lot 42) bought in.[8] No. 2548 was certainly in the collection of the Earl of Dunmore, Dunmore Park, Stirling, by 1857;[9] Earl of Dunmore sale, London, 13 May 1870 (lot 21), bought in (190 gns). It was in the collection of Viscount Powerscourt by 1878, when it was exhibited at the RA. It was purchased from Agnew in June 1897 by Charles Sedelmeyer, Paris, who sold it to E. Fischof in November 1901.[10] According to HdG[11] it was afterwards in America. In the collection of George Salting, London; Salting Bequest, 1910.

EXHIBITION: RA 1878, No. 268.

REFERENCES:
General: HdG, Cuyp No. 542.
In text:
1. HdG, op. cit.
2. White No. 38.
3. HdG No. 776. Formerly in the Rodolphe Kann collection, Paris. Known to the present writer only from a photograph. Signed A.C. in Calraet's usual form. After leaving the Kann collection, the painting was owned by G. Wildenstein, Paris; in the F. von Gans collection, Frankfurt; in the possession of K.W. Bachstitz, The Hague.
4. Panel, 36 × 57 cm. Signed A.C. B. de Geus van den Heuvel collection sale, Sotheby Mak van Waay,

Amsterdam, 26–7 April 1976, no. 10; Anon. sale, Sotheby's, 9 December 1987 (lot 90).
5. As by Cuyp. Photograph in the National Gallery archives.
6. HdG No. 553. Panel, 40 × 31.8 cm. Falsely signed: A. Cuyp. 1979 Wallace Collection cat. p. 59. Inv. no. P250. In that catalogue it is suggested that it may be by Jacob van Strij but all van Strij's signed works in the style of Cuyp are in an entirely different manner, nearer to No. 2547 (imitator of Cuyp).
7. Previously in the possession of Douwes, Amsterdam.
8. See HdG No. 567a. Lot 42 was 'A Landscape

with a Dapple Grey Horse, Groom &c painted in his best manner'.

9. Waagen, 1857, p. 455.

10. According to a MS note in the copy of C. Sedelmeyer's *Illustrated Catalogue of the 4th Series of 100*

Paintings of Old Masters . . . belonging to the Sedelmeyer Gallery, 1897 (No. 3) in the RKD, transcribed from Sedelmeyer's own copy.

11. HdG, Cuyp No. 542.

JAN VAN DE CAPPELLE, 1626–1679

Jan van de Cappelle; occasionally he spells his name *Capelle* and *Capel* (also *Joannes*).[1] He was baptised in Amsterdam on 25 January 1626;[2] in November 1666 he was said to be about forty-two.[3] His father owned a dye-works and van de Cappelle, who also engaged in this business,[4] was a rich man. His contemporary, Gerbrand van den Eeckhout, described him as self-taught.[5] His style was based in the first place on that of Simon de Vlieger; in the 1680 inventory of van de Cappelle's large collection there are nine paintings and no fewer than 1,300 drawings by de Vlieger, as well as a copy after de Vlieger by him.[6] In addition, he owned sixteen paintings by the marine painter, Jan Porcellis (before 1584–1632), and a copy by him after Porcellis is mentioned. Also in his collection were ten pictures and over 400 drawings by Jan van Goyen, nearly 900 drawings by Hendrick Avercamp, some 500 Rembrandt drawings and many paintings and drawings by Esaias van de Velde, Pieter de Molijn and Hercules Segers (to mention only some of those who seem to have influenced his development). Portraits of him were painted by Rembrandt, Frans Hals and Eeckhout.[7] He acquired Amsterdam citizenship in July 1653,[8] bought a house in the Koestraat in 1661[9] and made a will there in 1666.[10] He was buried in the Nieuwe Kerk in Amsterdam, 22 December 1679.[11]

The number of paintings by him is not large; besides views of estuaries and rivers, invariably with calm waters, there are some forty winter landscapes reminiscent of Aert van der Neer's. His earliest dated painting is of 1645;[12] his latest after 1660.[13] The fact that there is only one dated in the 1660s and probably none thereafter has led to the suggestion that in his later years he devoted himself largely to commerce, like other Dutch painters (e.g. Hobbema and Aert van der Neer). He also made some etchings.

REFERENCES:

General: A. Bredius in OH, 1892, pp. 26–40 and 133–6; HdG, vol. 7; M. Russell, *Jan van de Cappelle 1624/6–79*, Leigh-on-Sea, 1975 (Russell follows HdG's catalogue numbers).

In text:

1. W. Stechow ('Uber das Verhältnis zwischen Signatur und Chronologie bei einigen holländischen Künstlern des 17. Jahrhunderts', *Festschrift Dr Eduard Trautscholdt*, Hamburg, 1965, pp. 111ff) pointed out a link between the form of the signature and the chronology of van de Cappelle's paintings. All the paintings signed I V Capel, he considered, date from before 1650. Between 1650 and 1651 there is a new signature I V Capelle which after 1651 became I V Cappelle. Russell (op. cit., pp. 20–21) discussed Stechow's theory and, although she noted a few ex-

ceptions, found it largely correct. She, however, considered that the signature with two p's is not used before 1652 (see, below, No. 965, for example).

2. Bredius, op. cit., pp. 26ff.

3. Bredius, op. cit., p. 29. Because of this document, his birthdate has been given as *c*.1623/5 or 1624/6. There is, however, absolutely no reason to believe that he was not baptised, as was usual, a few days after his birth.

4. He is, for example, described as a dyer in 1666 (Bredius, op. cit., p. 29).

5. In the Album Amicorum of Jacob Heyblocq, van den Eeckhout wrote (on 29 June 1654) that van de Cappelle was 'bij hem selfs uijt eygen lust geleert' (Russell, op. cit., p. 10).

6. This and the following details about van de Cappelle's collection are taken from the inventory published by Bredius (op. cit., pp. 31–39).

7. Bredius, op. cit., pp. 33 and 35.

8. See note 2.

9. Obreen, vol. 5, p. 12. Previously he had lived in his father's house on the fashionable Keizersgracht.

10. When the will was made the artist was 'lying sick in bed'. This serious illness may be one of the reasons for van de Cappelle's relative inactivity after this time.

11. Bredius, op. cit., p. 31.

12. HdG No. 50: Robarts collection, signed and dated: J V Capel 1645; cf. Russell, pp. 21–22. In the catalogue *Hollandse Schilderkunst: Landschappen 17de Eeuw* (Mauritshuis, The Hague, 1980) F. Duparc gives (on pp 19–20) a list of dated paintings by van de Cappelle, including the newly discovered date of 1651 on *Ships off the Coast* (Mauritshuis, inv. no. 820).

13. Cf. No. 966 below. HdG No. 45 is said to be dated 1671 or 1675. The signature is, however, very difficult to read and the painting may not be authentic.

865 *A Small Vessel in Light Airs, and Another Ashore* Plate 59

On the left, with sails set, is a *smalschip* with a Dutch vane; ashore on the right is a *kaag*.

Signed on the land at the bottom, towards the right: J V Cappelle (rubbed and very faint).

Oil on canvas, 34.8 × 48.1 (13$\frac{3}{4}$ × 18$\frac{15}{16}$).

Cleaned in 1960.

A fairly early work.

PROVENANCE: Apparently in the Ralph Bernal sale, London, 8 May 1824 (lot 28),[1] bought by Seguier (155 gns), possibly for (Sir) Robert Peel (Bart).[2] Purchased with the Peel collection, 1871.

REFERENCES:
General: HdG No. 32; Russell, op. cit., cat. no. 32.
In text:
1. 'V. der Capella   Sea View, Vessels, &c.; the Sun rising in a Mist . . . The effect of Sun in this bijou, is really surprising.'

2. In the copy of the sale catalogue in the National Gallery library there is a contemporary MS note against the lot: 'Seguier/Mr Peel.' The picture is not in the list of Peel paintings in *Le cabinet de l'amateur*, vol. 4, 1845–46, pp. 55ff.

964 *Vessels in Light Airs on a River near a Town* Plate 60

The vessel inshore on the left (a *smalschip*?) has a Dutch vane.

Oil on canvas, 37.5 × 48.6 (14$\frac{3}{4}$ × 19$\frac{1}{8}$).

The church in the right background is not unlike St Lawrence's in Rotterdam.

Probably a work of the late 1640s or early 50s.

PROVENANCE: Possibly the 'River View, with Vessels' exhibited by Wynn Ellis at the BI, 1865, No. 57,[1] but more probably in the William Delafield sale, London, 30 April 1870 (lot 32[2]), bought by Pearce[3] (125 gns). Wynn Ellis Bequest, 1876.

EXHIBITIONS: BI 1865, No. 57(?), Arts Council 1945, No. 2.

REFERENCES:
General: HdG Nos. 33 and (?)137a; Russell, op. cit., cat. no. 33.
In text:
1. This might, however, equally well be the 'River View' lent by Wynn Ellis to the BI in 1858, No. 61 (*not*, as HdG No. 33 states, 1818). That the picture exhibited in 1858 was not National Gallery No. 964 is proved by the description and size given by G.

Scharf in *Artistic and Descriptive Notes on . . . Pictures in the British Institution Exhibition . . . 1858*; it was not among the pictures accepted by the National Gallery and may perhaps be identical with HdG No. 54.

2. 'A River Scene, with fishing boats'; 14¾ × 19 in.
3. Pearce apparently often bought for Wynn Ellis (see Berchem No. 1004, note 3).

965 *A Dutch Yacht firing a Salute as a Barge pulls away, and Many Small Vessels at Anchor* Plate 61

In the centre is a States yacht (*statenjacht*) with Dutch colours and a coat-of-arms on her stern (*d'argent à quatre cotices de gueules, en barres*); she is firing a salute and a trumpeter on board is sounding. The row-barge in the right foreground has a Dutch ensign and one of the men in her bows has the Dutch colours in his hat. In the left foreground is a ferry (*veerpont*) with a yellow and white ensign and a Dutch vane. Most of the surrounding vessels have Dutch vanes.

Signed, bottom left: J V Capelle 1650.

Oil on oak, 85.5 × 114.5 (33⅝ × 45).

Some retouching along the two horizontal panel joins. The paint is thin generally and the grain of the wood shows through in many places.

It has been suggested that the grey-haired man with an order on a blue(?) ribbon in the stern of the barge, right, is Frederik Hendrik Prince of Orange (1584–1647) and that the youth standing in front of him is his son, Prince Willem II (1626–50).[1] These figures, which are very small, are too summarily treated to be recognisable. It seems unlikely that van de Cappelle would have put Prince Frederik Hendrik in a picture of this kind three years after his death unless it depicted some specific historical event, which does not appear to be the case here or in any of the similar scenes painted by van de Cappelle[2] (e.g. Nos. 966 and 4456 below, where the same kind of figure appears).

Russell[3] has asserted that during cleaning some of the painting's original glazes were removed. There is no evidence for this in the condition reports and photographic documentation in the painting's conservation dossier.

PROVENANCE: Perhaps in the Charles Scarisbrick sale, London, 11 sqq. May 1861 (lot 24),[4] bought by Morant (£63). Probably in the Rt. Hon. Edward Ellice sale, London, 17 June 1864 (lot 130), bought by Pearce[5] (510 gns). Wynn Ellis Bequest, 1876.

EXHIBITION: London 1947–8, No. 73.

REFERENCES:
General: HdG Nos. 34 and 1360. Russell, op. cit., cat. no. 34.
In text:
1. G.C.E. Crone, *Nederlandsche jachten, binnenschepen, visschersvaartuigen* etc., 1926, p. 106.
2. A similar suggestion has been made about a van de Cappelle of the same kind in the Rijksmuseum, Amsterdam (No. A453), also dated 1650 (see C.G. 't Hooft in *Bredius Feest-Bundel*, 1915, p. 103); the same objections apply.

3. The painting was cleaned in 1936. Russell, op. cit., cat. no. 34.
4. 'Van der Capella   A grand harbour scene, with a man-of-war firing a salute, a yacht and numerous fishing-boats; figures and horses in a ferry-boat in front.'
5. 'Van der Capella   A Grand River-Scene, with a state-barge, and numerous boats and figures. A very important work.' Pearce apparently often bought for Wynn Ellis (cf. Berchem No. 1004, note 3).

966 *A River Scene with a Dutch Yacht firing a Salute as Two*   Plate 62
Barges pull away

In the right middle distance is a States yacht (*statenjacht*) firing a salute; she has Dutch colours. Closer, in the centre, are two row-barges; the nearer one has a Dutch ensign and the farther one a white ensign with two narrow horizontal stripes of orange. Some of the vessels on the left and around the yacht have blue and white vanes; one on the extreme left has also an orange vane with blue and white stripes and the *pont* on the extreme right has a red and white vane. The men-at-arms standing in the bows of the nearer row-barge have halberds with blue and white tufts and the grey-bearded man seated in the stern has an order on a blue ribbon.

Signed on a mudbank in the foreground, right of centre: J V Cappelle A. 166(?); the last figure is almost obliterated.[1]

Oil on canvas,[2] 93 × 131 (36⅝ × 51⅝).

Cleaned in 1951. Damages along bottom edge and at the lower part of the left edge.

Probably painted in the mid-1660s.

PROVENANCE: In the collection of Wynn Ellis, London, by 1871,[3] when it was exhibited at the RA. Wynn Ellis Bequest, 1876.

EXHIBITION: RA 1871, No. 264.[4]

REFERENCES:
General: HdG No. 35; Russell, op. cit., cat. no. 35.
In text:
1. MacLaren considered that the last digit 'may well be a 5'. In fact, it is impossible to decipher.
2. Not on oak as stated by HdG.
3. It is probably not the van de Cappelle lent by Wynn Ellis to the BI in 1885, No. 86 as 'Sea-Piece', which would more aptly describe No. 967 below.

4. Although described in the exhibition catalogue merely as 'A Seaport', the size given (36 × 52 in.) serves to distinguish it from Nos. 965 and 967 of this catalogue, the other two large van de Cappelles in Wynn Ellis's collection.

967 *A River Scene with a Large Ferry and Numerous Dutch*   Plate 63
Vessels at Anchor

The ferry (*veerpont*) in the foreground, which has in its cargo a cannon, has a red and white striped ensign and a yellow and white flag draped over the side. The passenger vessel on the left (a *wijdschip*) has two blue and white vanes. Towards the right, beyond the ferry, a row-barge with a Dutch ensign is pulling towards the passenger vessel. In the centre middle distance is a States yacht (*statenjacht*) with Dutch colours; a row-barge is just pulling away from her.

Signed on the rudder of the ferry: J V Cappelle.

Oil on canvas, 122 × 154.5 (48 × 60¾).

Cleaned in 1950 and in 1986/7. Somewhat worn; the sky is damaged, especially in a horizontal band 20–30 cm. wide right across the picture on the level of the ships' masts, where much of the paint is missing.

Probably painted in the mid-1660s at about the same time as No. 966 above.

PROVENANCE: It is perhaps the van de Cappelle 'Sea-Piece' exhibited by Wynn Ellis at the BI, 1855, No. 86.[1] Wynn Ellis Bequest, 1876.

EXHIBITIONS: (?)BI 1855, No. 86;[2] London 1976, No. 21.

REFERENCES: General: HdG No. 36; Russell, op. cit., cat. no. 36.
In text: **1.** This might, however, conceivably be van de Cappelle No. 966 above or the 'Calm, with boats and figures' in the Wynn Ellis sale, London, 27 May 1876 (lot 9), later in the Carstanjen collection (HdG No. 54). Nos. 964 and 965 above probably did not enter Wynn Ellis's collection until after 1855.
2. See above, note 1.

2586 A Coast Scene, with a Small Dutch Vessel landing Passengers

Plate 64

The vessel on the left (a *wijdschip*?) has Dutch colours; other vessels have red and white vanes, and one a blue and red.

Oil on oak, 59.5 × 79.2 ($23\frac{7}{16}$ × $31\frac{3}{16}$).

Cleaned in 1972–3.

Probably from the early 1650s.

PROVENANCE: Said to have been in the collection of James Whatman, Vintners, near Maidstone.[1] Apparently at one time in the possession of Agnew.[2] In the collection of George Salting, London, and probably the picture exhibited by him at the BFAC, London, 1906, No. 40.[3] Salting Bequest, 1910.

REFERENCES:
General: HdG No. 37.
In text:
1. It was not in the James Whatman sales, London, 20 February 1882 and 2 July 1887, nor in the Mrs Whatman sale, London, 16 June 1900, but part of the collection was apparently sold privately. **2.** Messrs Agnew's printed label is on the back of the panel. **3.** As 'Scene on the Coast of Holland'.

2588 A Small Dutch Vessel before a Light Breeze

Plate 65

In the centre is a vessel (a *wijdschip*?) with red and white ensign and vanes; a ship with a red and white flag at the main is in the right distance.

Oil on canvas, 44.3 × 55.6 ($17\frac{7}{16}$ × $21\frac{7}{8}$).

Cleaned in 1974. Damaged in several areas in the sky.

Said by Russell[1] to be 'by an unknown follower' of van de Cappelle. However, the present writer believes (as MacLaren did) that it is an authentic work of the late 1640s or early 50s.

ENGRAVING: Engraved by Pierre-François Basan (1723–97).

PROVENANCE: In the collection of Major Corbett, London, by whom exhibited at the RA in 1879. In the [Major Corbett-Winder] sale, London, 25 June 1898 (lot 132),[2] bought by Schaeffer (165 gns). Apparently bought by George Salting in 1901.[3] Salting Bequest, 1910.

EXHIBITION: RA 1879, No. 55.

REFERENCES:
General: HdG Nos. 39 and 120d; Russell, op. cit., cat. no. 39.
In text:
1. Russell, op. cit.
2. Together with an impression of F. Basan's engraving of it.

3. There is a note referring to this picture in one of Salting's notebooks in the National Gallery archives: 'cost £900 in 1901'.

4456 *A River Scene with Many Dutch Vessels Becalmed*   Plate 66

The row-barge in the foreground towards the left has a Dutch ensign, and most of the vessels have Dutch vanes. The farther row-barge, in the centre, has a red and blue striped ensign and the hay vessel in the middle distance towards the right has a red and white vane. The ferry (*veerpont*) in the right foreground has a Dutch flag. In the middle of the group of vessels in the centre middle distance is visible the stern of a States yacht (*statenjacht*). One of the men in the stern of the row-barge in the foreground has an order on a blue ribbon.

Signed at the bottom, towards the left: J. V. Cappelle.

Oil on canvas, 112×153.5 ($44 \times 60\frac{1}{2}$).

Cleaned in 1956–7. There is a large multiple tear near the centre of the sky and a few scattered losses in the lower half of the picture but the general condition is good.

The picture is related both in style and colour to No. 965 above, which is dated 1650.

PROVENANCE: Possibly in the Warnar Wreesman sale, Amsterdam, 11 April 1816 (lot 35),[1] bought by Hulswit (723 guilders). It was purchased from or through Sulley, London, by Lord Revelstoke in November 1909;[2] Lord Revelstoke Bequest, 1929.

EXHIBITION: Brighton 1979, No. 5.

REFERENCES:
General: Russell, op. cit., cat. Addenda No. 1.
In text:
1. (J. van de Capelle) '. . . een stil Water, gestoffeerd met een menigte onderscheidene Vaartuigen, Sloepen met Volk, een Schip met Hooi en Pont. Alles wordt door een treffend zonlicht gedaagd . . .'; on canvas, 47×59 *duim*. HdG (No. 87) identifies the Wreesman sale picture with one in the Christiaan van Tarelink sale, Amsterdam, 18 August 1798 (lot 7), bought by van der Schley (90 guilders). The latter is described in the sale catalogue as 'een stil Water, zeer ryk gestoffeerd met een menigte zoo zeilende als dryvende en stil liggende Vaartuigen; in het midden vertoond zig een Zeiljagt en Roeisloepen met Heeren, verder Hooy-Scheepen en andere, in 't verschiet een Vuurbak; de spiegeling in de water is helder en doorschynend . . .', on canvas, 44×55 *duim*; it cannot therefore be the National Gallery picture which does not show a beacon. On the other hand, the size and description of the Tarelink picture do not agree particularly well with those of the Wreesman one and it may well be a different picture.
2. Letter of 1929 from Lord Revelstoke's executors (in the National Gallery archives).

6406 *Vessels Moored off a Jetty*   Plate 67

Oil on oak, 35.2×42.3 ($13\frac{7}{8} \times 16\frac{5}{8}$).

Cleaned in 1972. The condition is poor. The paint surface is extensively rubbed.

Russell[1] believed the painting to be 'a copy after a lost van de Cappelle composition, probably showing only part of the original painting'. In the present author's view, it is an authentic painting, although considerably damaged.

PROVENANCE: Purchased from M. Colnaghi by W.C. Alexander on 25 February 1886. It passed by descent to the Misses Rachel F. and Jean I. Alexander, who presented it by deed of gift to the National Gallery. It entered the collection in 1972.[2]

EXHIBITIONS: RA 1929, No. 193; Arts Council 1945, No. 3; Paris, Orangerie, 1950, No. 14; London 1972.

REFERENCES:
General: HdG No. 41; Russell, op. cit., cat. no. 41.
In text:
1. Russell, op. cit.

2. A. Smith, 'Presented by the Misses Rachel F. and Jean I. Alexander: Seventeen Paintings for the National Gallery', BM, vol. 114, 1972, pp. 630–34.

PIETER CLAESZ., 1597/8–1660

Still-life painter. Born in Burgsteinfurt (in Westphalia);[1] in a document of September 1640 his age is given as forty-three.[2] He apparently never bore the surname Berchem used by his son, Nicolaes Pietersz. Berchem. Very little is known about him. By May 1617, when he married, he was living in Haarlem,[3] and his son Nicolaes was born there in 1620.[4] His earliest known dated work is of 1621, the latest of 1660. He appears to have continued to live in Haarlem and was buried there on 1 January 1661.[5]

Houbraken[6] says Claesz. painted small still-life pictures. Until the end of the 1620s his pictures are in the style of the older Haarlem still-life painters such as Floris van Dijck (1575–1651) and are mostly of the 'banquet piece' (banketje) type. Thenceforward he painted the semi-monochrome 'breakfast pieces' (ontbijtjes) characteristic of the later school of Haarlem still-life painting, of which he and Willem Claesz. Heda are the founders.

REFERENCES:
General: Bergström, pp. 114–23; Vroom, vol. 1, pp. 23–51, vol. 2, pp. 16–40.
In text:
1. Van der Willigen, p. 76.
2. E.W. Moes in Thieme/Becker, vol. 7, 1912, p. 38.

3. Van der Willigen, p. 76.
4. Van der Willigen, p. 76.
5. Van der Willigen, p. 77.
6. Houbraken, vol. 2, pp. 110–11.

2592 Still Life with Drinking Vessels

Plate 68

On the left is a roemer, in the centre an octagonal pas-glas.

The porcelain is Chinese export, of the Wan-Li period (1573–1619).

Signed on the blade of the knife: 1649 PC (PC in monogram).

Oil on oak, 63.5 × 52.5 (25 × 20⅝).

Cleaned in 1976.

Vroom[1] suggested that the painting may only be a fragment. The composition certainly appears to be truncated on the left and right sides and possibly also at top and bottom. The chipped edges of the paint layer also support the view that the painting has been cut down. There is equal narrow bevelling of the back of the panel on all four sides which suggests that it has been cut down by a similar amount, perhaps as much as 5 cm., at each edge.

PROVENANCE: In the [J. Mash, Ipswich] sale, London, 6 December 1890 (lot 84),[2] bought by Lesser (44 gns). In the collection of George Salting by 1890;[3] Salting Bequest, 1910.

EXHIBITION: London 1976, No. 22.

REFERENCES:
General: Vroom, vol. 2, no. 150.
In text:
1. Vroom, op. cit.
2. As by 'G. Cuyp [sic] Still Life Signed and

dated 1649'. The markings relating to this sale are on the back of the panel.
3. Note in one of Salting's notebooks (in the National Gallery archives).

PIETER CODDE, 1599–1678

Pieter Jacobsz. Codde. He was born in Amsterdam and baptised on 11 December 1599.[1] He married in Amsterdam in 1623 at which time he was described as a painter.[2] In 1630 he bought a house on the Sint Anthonisbreestraat. He moved in literary as well as artistic circles in Amsterdam: in 1627 Elias Herckmans dedicated his tragedy *Tyrus* to Codde and in 1633 the artist's own pastoral love poem was published in the *Hollands Nachtegaelken*.

In 1636, at the time of his separation from his wife, a complete inventory of his possessions was drawn up. After the mid-1640s there are few dated works but Codde does seem to have remained active as a painter. In 1657 he purchased a house on the Keizersgracht. In 1672 he was one of the artists called upon to give their ruling on the authenticity of a group of Italian paintings. He was buried on 12 October 1678 in the Oude Kerk in Amsterdam.[3]

Codde painted small-scale portraits and genre paintings. In 1637 he completed a large militia group, *The Corporalship of Captain Reynier Reael and Lieutenant Cornelis Michielsz. Blaeuw* (Amsterdam, Rijksmuseum) which had been left unfinished by Frans Hals.[4] Codde was influenced in his portraiture by Hals, although he worked on a markedly smaller scale. His genre paintings, many of them of the multi-figured 'merry company' type, are similar in style to those of Anthonie Palamedesz. (1610–73) and Willem Duyster. Duyster may have been his pupil. He also painted a few history pictures, for example, *The Adoration of the Shepherds* of 1645 in the Rijksmuseum.[5]

REFERENCES:
General: Havard, vol. 3, p. 139; C.M. Dozy, 'Pieter Codde, de schilder en de dichter', OH, vol. 2, 1884, pp. 34–67; C. B. Playter, 'Willem Duyster and Pieter Codde: The "Duystere Werelt" of Dutch Genre Painting c. 1625–35', Diss. Harvard University, 1972; I.H. van Eeghen, 'Pieter Codde en Frans Hals', *Maandblad Amstelodamum*, 61, 1974, pp. 137–41.

In text:
1. Dozy, op. cit., pp. 52–53.
2. Dozy, op. cit., p. 53.
3. Dozy, op. cit., p. 65.
4. 1976 cat., C 374.
5. 1976 cat., A 789.

2576 *Portrait of a Man, a Woman and a Boy in a Room* *Plate 69*

In the background is a landscape tapestry and, over the fireplace, a painted landscape. A door at the back on the left is open to reveal a second room in which a chair and a bed can be seen.

Signed at the bottom, towards the left, with a monogram PC. and dated over the doorway: 16—40.

Oil on oak, 48.3 × 65 (19 × 25$\frac{9}{16}$).

There are *pentimenti* in the outlines of the man's right leg.

The landscape over the fireplace is in the style of the Haarlem School of the 1630s (Pieter de Molijn?). Codde painted a number of family groups of this type.[1] There is a very similar one of 1642 in the Rijksmuseum, Amsterdam.[2]

On the RKD mount, Miss L. de Bruyn identified the sitters as Hendricus Meursius and Judith Cotermans and their son,[3] of whom there are engravings by Pontius after Codde.[4] The resemblance, however, is not very close.

PROVENANCE: Apparently in the collection of the 1st Baron Dover (died 1831) in London.[5] In the sale of the 4th Viscount Clifden, London, 6 May 1893 (lot 13), bought in (500 gns) and anonymous sale, London, 13 July 1895 (lot 83), bought by G. Salting (410 gns). In the collection of George Salting, London; Salting Bequest, 1910.

REFERENCES:

1. For a discussion of the contrast between the relaxed pose and expansive gesture of the man and the more formal pose of his wife, see the introduction to the exhibition catalogue (by E. de Jongh), *Portretten van echt en trouw*, Frans Halsmuseum, Haarlem, 1986, p. 15.
2. Panel, 55 × 74 cm. 1976 cat., A 2836.
3. Moes, Nos. 5020 and 1758.
4. Wurzbach, I, p. 310.
5. According to the catalogue of the 1893 Clifden sale, the pictures then sold were from the collection of 'the late Lord Dover, at Whitehall'. The vendor, the 4th Viscount Clifden, was also 3rd Baron Dover, but his father was 2nd Baron Dover only, from 1833 to 1836, before he became the 3rd Viscount Clifden. The Lord Dover referred to in the sale catalogues is, however, almost certainly the grandfather of the 4th Viscount Clifden, who was created Baron Dover in 1831 and died in 1833 before his father, the 2nd Viscount Clifden (cf. Berckheyde No. 1451 of this catalogue, which was in the Clifden sale of May 1895 and certainly came from the collection of the 1st Baron Dover).

2584 *A Seated Woman holding a Mirror* *Plate 70*

Signed on the frame of the landscape: PCodde. Anno 1625 (PC in monogram; the date is faint).

Oil on oak, 38.1 × 33.7 (15 × 13$\frac{1}{4}$).

Cleaned in 1976. Paint losses on either side of the figure along two vertical splits in the panel.

The door was first painted opening out of the room.

The woman's features are not sufficiently individualised for the painting to be a portrait. The object she holds is almost certainly a mirror. A woman looking at herself in a mirror is a traditional symbol of *superbia* (pride)[1] but in this case she does not admire her own features. A closer analogy might be with an emblem showing a woman with a mirror in Roemer Visscher's *Sinnepoppen* (Amsterdam, 1614) with the motto *Ick Geeft Haer Weder* (I conjure her up).[2] The sense of the text beneath is one of *vanitas* and that, too, may be the sense of Codde's painting.

This is apparently Codde's earliest dated work.

PROVENANCE: At one time in the possession of Messrs Agnew; in the collection of George Salting, London; Salting Bequest, 1910.

EXHIBITIONS: London 1976, No. 23; London 1978–9, No. 15.

REFERENCES:

1. An early northern painted example is Jerome Bosch's *Tabletop of the Seven Deadly Sins and the Four Last Things* (Madrid, Prado Museum) from *c.*1485–1500.

2. Emblem no. 30. The text reads: 'Den wereltlijcken handel ende wandel is den aert van de Spieghel niet onghelijck: want in den Spieghel is niet dan een schijn, het dingh dat ghy daer in sien wilt, moet ghy selfs voor u brenghen: wat personagie ghy in de Wereldt spelen wilt, moet ghy in u selfs vormen. Een Sot, een Courtisaen, een Krijchsman, een goet Ghesel, een elen Baes, worden al in den Spieghel ghebootst: maer soo haest zy vertrecken, vergaet haer ghedachtenis, ghelijck of zy daer niet gheweest en hadden: dan een wereldt wijs man schijnt wat deur zijn schriften te willen overschieten: maer het is al wint, ende een handt van Sons.'

CORNELIS VAN HAARLEM, 1562–1638

Cornelis Cornelisz., known as Cornelis van Haarlem. He was born in Haarlem in 1562, according to Carel van Mander, who says he first studied with Pieter Pietersz. in Haarlem and went at the age of seventeen to Rouen and thence to Antwerp, where he was a pupil of Gillis Congnet for a year.[1] He was back in Holland by 1581 and received his first important commission for a group portrait of a Haarlem militia company in 1583 (Haarlem, Frans Halsmuseum). In the second (posthumous) edition of van Mander, 1618,[2] it is stated that shortly after van Mander's return to Haarlem in 1583, van Mander, Hendrick Goltzius and Cornelis van Haarlem 'made an Academy, to study from the life'.

Between 1590 and 1593 he carried out an important municipal commission for four large pictures to decorate the Prinsenhof in Haarlem. Subsequently he received numerous major commissions – for the Civic Guard (1599), the Commanders of the Order of St John (1617 and 1624), the court of the Stadholder in The Hague (1622) and the hospital of the Heilige Geesthuis (1633). From 1613 until 1619, Cornelis served as a regent of the Old Men's Home in Haarlem. From 1626 until 1629 he was a member of the Catholic St Jacob's Guild and in 1630 along with other artists he was involved in the formulation of new regulations for the St Luke's Guild in Haarlem. He died on 11 November 1638.[3]

He painted religious and mythological subjects and portraits, and between 1588 and 1602 produced designs for twenty-two prints. He was a leading figure of Dutch Mannerism. Among his pupils were Gerrit Pietersz., Cornelis Jacobsz. Delff and Cornelis Engelsz. van der Goude.

REFERENCES:

General: For Cornelis's biography, see Pieter van Thiel in exhibition catalogue, Washington/Detroit/Amsterdam, 1980–1, p. 80; idem, 'Cornelis Cornelisz. van Haarlem - his first ten years as a painter, 1582–92', *Netherlandish Mannerism*, Symposium papers (Nationalmuseum, 1984), Stockholm, 1985, pp. 73–84.

In text:
1. Van Mander, fol. 292.
2. Van Mander, in the life of van Mander appended to the end of the volume (p. 11).
3. Van der Willigen, p. 114.

1893 *Two Followers of Cadmus devoured by a Dragon*   *Plate 71*

In the foreground the dismembered corpses of Cadmus's followers in the grasp of the dragon; in the left background Cadmus is attacking the dragon.

Signed, on the stone in the bottom right-hand corner: Cor Corneli . . . fecit 1588.[1]

Oil on canvas (stuck on oak panel), 148.5 × 195.5 (58½ × 77). The picture is on canvas glued to panel: the canvas consists of two pieces stitched vertically up the middle. The left and top edges, and small areas of the bottom edge, of the canvas are ragged and have pieces missing. The panel is made up of five members glued together and strengthened with wooden buttons. The splitting of these joins caused the canvas to tear. There are considerable areas of wearing in the background, in the darks and in the flesh tones. The top left-hand corner – in the area of the outcrop of rock on which there is a tree – has suffered particularly bad damage and is substantially repainted.[2]

Cleaned in 1976–7.

Cadmus, seeking his sister Europa, consulted the Delphic oracle and was ordered to abandon his search; instead he was to follow a cow of a certain kind and build a town where it finally sank from exhaustion. The cow stopped on the site of the future Thebes, and Cadmus, intending to sacrifice it, sent men for water to the neighbouring well of Ares. These men were killed by the guardian of the well, a dragon, son of Ares. Cadmus then killed the dragon and, on the advice of Athena, sowed its teeth into the ground, from which sprang up armed men who slew each other, with the exception of five who became the ancestors of the Thebans (see Ovid's *Metamorphoses*, Book 3, 1–151).

In the first edition of this catalogue the painting was described as 'after Cornelis van Haarlem'. MacLaren noted that it corresponded almost exactly (but reversed) to a composition by Cornelis van Haarlem known only from an engraving of 1588 by Hendrick Goltzius (Fig. 23).[3] He wrote that it was 'only an old copy' differing from the Goltzius engraving in the omission of the head of a man in the top right-hand corner.

In 1961, however, Reznicek suggested that the painting was the original of this composition[4] and at about the same time van Thiel independently came to the same conclusion.[5] Cleaning of the painting in 1976–7 revealed the remains of the signature, the date 1588 and the man's head in the top right-hand corner. The head is forcefully brushed in with brown paint and highlighted on the nose and lips in white. Although the painting is considerably damaged, requiring extensive retouching, No. 1893 is undoubtedly an original of considerable vigour: the dragon's head, for example, is painted with lively brushstrokes and vivid highlights.

In his account of Cornelis van Haarlem's life, van Mander describes a number of paintings he made in the years following his return to Haarlem in 1593. He wrote that 'During the best part of his studies he made an oblong Serpent-biting [*Serpent-bijtinghe langwerpigh*] on a great canvas and another great canvas in a vertical format representing the fall of Lucifer, which two paintings Jacob Rauwart of Amsterdam had from him. Of these two I cannot adequately describe the excellent studies of all the different attitudes of the Nudes and it is a pity that such things cannot be seen in a public place; for at this time he paid a great deal of attention to the art of drawing, of composition, of proportion and other things.'[6] It seems likely that the 'Serpent-biting' referred to by van Mander is No. 1893:[7] Goltzius's print after the painting is dedicated to Jacob Rauwart. Rauwart's collection, sold from the estate of Claes Rauwart in 1612, included seven paintings by Cornelis van Haarlem, but the subject of only one – a *Hercules* – is mentioned in the inventory.[8]

The painting is first certainly recorded in an inventory of the Earl of Northumberland's paintings drawn up by Symon Stone in 1671 (see PROVENANCE).

COPIES: A copy, in the same direction as No. 1893, is in Dresden.[9] A smaller copy in the opposite direction and therefore probably after the Goltzius print is in Vienna.[10] A third was in the K. Köhner and Manster von Markhof sale, Vienna, 8 March 1908, no. 5.[11] The dragon and the two men appear (in the same direction as No. 1893) in a lead plaque by Paulus van Vianen (c.1565/70–1613) in the Umĕleckoprùmyslové Muzeum, Prague.[12]

PROVENANCE: Perhaps in the collection of Jacob Rauwart, Amsterdam, in 1588 and sold from the estate of Claes Rauwart, Amsterdam, 1612;[13] collection of the Earl of Northumberland at Syon House by 1671;[14] presented by the Duke of Northumberland in 1838.[15]

REFERENCES:
General: Christopher Brown, 'A rediscovered painting by Cornelis van Haarlem', BM, vol. 119, 1977, pp. 564–67.
In text:
1. The signature and date, in common with much of the rest of the painting, are badly worn: the date is almost impossible to read with the naked eye but can be made out under strong illumination. In Brown, op. cit., it is incorrectly given as 1585: there can be no doubt that the last digit is, in fact, an 8. See P. van Thiel, *Netherlandish Mannerism,* op. cit., p. 78.
2. The painting, because of its size and delicate condition, was rarely exhibited before its restoration in 1976/7. It was included in the National Gallery's 1929 catalogue in the section 'Pictures withdrawn from exhibition' (p. 414). During the Second World War, the painting remained at the National Gallery and was damaged during the bombing in 1940. Varnish was removed in 1952 but the painting was still obscured by a layer of discoloured varnish when the decision to clean it was made in 1976. The restoration (which included substantial panel work) and cleaning was carried out in the National Gallery's conservation department by Mr A. M. Reeve.

3. Bartsch No. 262; Hollstein, vol. 8, No. 104. It is inscribed in the lower left-hand corner: 'Hasce artis primitias CC [in monogram] Pictor Invent., / simulq. HGoltz. [HG in monogram] sculpt. D. Iacob Raeuwerdo / singulari Picturae alumno, et chalcographiae/admiratori amicitiae ergo D. D. A° 1588', and in the lower margin: 'Dirus Agenoridae laniat socia agmina Serpens, Ultor adest Cadmus paenasq reposcit ab hoste'. Van Thiel discusses this inscription in his article, 'Cornelis Cornelisz. as a draughtsman', *Master Drawing*, 1965, vol. 3, no. 2, pp. 123ff, p. 126 and note 13. In stating that the inscription had been 'previously overlooked', he failed to take account of MacLaren's discussion in the first edition of this catalogue (1960, p. 82, note 2).
4. In the seventeenth thesis accompanying his dissertation, *Hendrick Goltzius als Zeichner*, Utrecht, 1961. He mentioned it subsequently in G. Kauffman, *Die Kunst des 16. Jahrhunderts*, Berlin, 1970, p. 200 and in 'Honthorstiana', NKJ, vol. 23, 1972, p.174 and note 18.
5. His opinion is quoted by A. Mayer-Meintschel, *Gemäldegalerie Alte Meister Katalog I: Niederländische*

Malerei 15. und 16. Jahrhundert, Dresden, 1966, p. 27.
6. 'Doe hy in't alderbeste zijner studie was maeckte hy een Serpent-bijtinghe langwerpigh op eenen grooten doeck en noch eenen grooten doeck in de hooghte wesende den val van Lucifer, dese twee stucken hadde van hem Jacob Ravart t'Amsterdam. Van dese twee en can ick niet volcomlijck ghenoegh schrijven wat utynemende studie in alle de verscheyden Actituden der naeckten te weghe ghebracht is en is jammer dat sulcke dinghen niet in ghemeen plaets te sien en zijn: want hy in desen tijdt sonderlinghe op de Const van teyckenen wel stellen proportie en ander deel seer nouw heeft ghelet.' Karel van Mander, *Schilder-Boeck*, 1604, p. 293.
7. The first meaning of 'serpent' is snake. In his life of Cornelis Engelbrechtsz., van Mander describes the right wing of the triptych now in Leiden (No. 93) as a 'serpent-bijtinghe': its subject is the *Brazen Serpent*. H. Hymans, *Le livre des peintres*, vol. 2, 1885, p. 253 and note 2, translates the phrase (in the life of Cornelis van Haarlem, see above, note 8) as 'serpent d'airain' and identifies the picture with the *Brazen Serpent* of 1597 in Darmstadt. However, in the first edition of this catalogue MacLaren suggested that van Mander may have been referring to the original of the Goltzius print of the *Two Followers of Cadmus*. Both Pieter van Thiel and the present

writer consider that this is the most likely identification.
8. For Rauwart's inventory, see Bredius, *Künstler-Inventare*, vol. 5, pp. 1734ff.
9. Canvas, 164.5 × 205 cm. Inv. no. 851A. Acquired in 1931. See Mayer-Meintschel, op. cit. (note 5), pp. 26–27.
10. Inv. no. 802. Copper, 16 × 22 cm. There are slight changes: there is a rock in place of the severed head in the foreground; Cadmus (in the background) is on horseback and the head of a man in the top left-hand corner is omitted.
11. Panel, 29 × 40 cm. Noted by Pieter van Thiel to be after the print: it is mentioned by Mayer-Meintschel, op. cit., p. 27.
12. J. W. Frederiks, *Dutch Silver*, Amsterdam, 1952, p. 124, No. 68.
13. See above, and note 8.
14. In the section of the inventory, 'Severall Pictures and Peeces at Syon now in the Use of the Rt. Honble the Elder Countesse Dow^r of Northumberland Taken and Appraised by Mr Symon Stone the 10th Day of July 1671'. The first item 'In the lobby' is 'A Picture of Two Men going for water and kill'd by a Draggon', valued at £30.
15. As attributed to Bartholomaus Spranger.

6443 *The Preaching of St John the Baptist* Plate 72

St John is the small figure in the middle background.

Signed and dated, lower right: CvH 1602 (CvH in monogram).

Oil on canvas, 100 × 180 ($39\frac{1}{3}$ × $70\frac{3}{4}$).

Cleaned shortly before its acquisition in 1978.

All four Evangelists describe St John preaching in the Jordan valley to large crowds who came from Jerusalem and the surrounding countryside (Matthew 3: 1–12; Mark 1: 1–8; Luke 3: 1–18; John 1: 15–35). It was a subject often treated by Netherlandish artists of the sixteenth and seventeenth centuries and its popularity may reflect the contemporary debate about open-air sermons by Calvinist preachers.

Van Thiel[1] has suggested identifications for several of the groups and individuals among the 'multitude' who came to hear St John and to be baptised by him. He considers the group in the middle on the far left with exotic head-dresses to be heathens; the seated group eating and drinking in the foreground to be 'those who give themselves over to earthly delights and remain deaf to God's word'; the two men to their right 'are recognisable as priests, probably Ananias and Caiaphas'; the young couple – the young man sporting a feather in his cap, a symbol of vanity, belongs to the Prodigal son type, as depicted elsewhere by Cornelis – 'alludes to careless youth'; while the soldiers on the right are 'the Romans under the leadership of King Herod Antipas who would later have John beheaded'. More tentatively he identified the man in the centre foreground with the distinctive wide-brimmed hat and outstretched left arm as Christ. He argued that Christ's presence refers to the text of John 1: 26 when in reply to a question from the Pharisees as to whether he was the Christ, St John replied: '. . . there standeth one among you, whom ye know not'. Pieter Bruegel the Elder in his painting of 1566 of *St John preaching*[2] includes Christ in reference to this text.

The present writer largely agrees with van Thiel's identifications. The subject gave the opportunity to Netherlandish painters to depict in exotic costume the inhabitants of Judea and the Pharisees and Sadducees mentioned by the Evangelists. The group at the back on the left may simply be intended for Judaeans rather than 'heathens'. The two standing figures in long robes whom van Thiel identifies as priests are presumably intended to refer to the Pharisees and Sadducees: it seems unlikely that they are specifically meant to be Ananias and Caiaphas. Their costumes and those of the other figures such as the woman in the central foreground group who wears a tall, pointed hat would have been taken from costume books. Van Thiel's interpretation of the seated foreground group and the young couple is probably correct. The soldiers (not specifically identified as Romans) are mentioned by St Luke (verse 14). The identification of Christ is far more problematic: in Bruegel's painting, St John gestures directly towards Christ who stands in the largely seated crowd and is quite clearly distinguished from those around him by his light-coloured robe. He is shown bare-headed. The present writer believes it unlikely that Cornelis meant this figure for Christ. This whole group is probably meant to show more Judaeans who are ignoring St John's message.

PROVENANCE: The painting was entirely unrecorded until it was included in an anonymous sale at Phillips, Son and Neale, 14 March 1977 (lot 81); sold to Edward Speelman Ltd for £35,000. Purchased from Speelman in 1978.

EXHIBITION: Washington/Detroit/Amsterdam 1980–1, No. 3.

REFERENCES:
General: Ex. cat., Washington/Detroit/Amsterdam, 1980-1, No. 3.
In text:
1. Van Thiel in Washington/Detroit/Amsterdam, 1980-1, op. cit.

2. Budapest, Szépművészeti Múzeum. Inv. no. 51.2829. 1967 cat., pp.101–3.

AELBERT CUYP, 1620–1691

Aelbert Jacobsz. Cuyp, son of the painter Jacob Gerritsz. Cuyp (1594–1651/2), was baptised in Dordrecht in October 1620. He was a pupil of his father who was primarily a portrait painter. There are two collaborative paintings in which Jacob painted the portraits and Aelbert the landscape in which the figures are placed: both are dated 1641. Aelbert Cuyp's earliest landscapes are in the style of Jan van Goyen's pictures of the later 1630s. His first dated landscape, in Besançon, is from 1639. Subsequently he changed his style under the influence of the Italianising landscape painters of Utrecht, in particular Jan Both who returned to Utrecht from Italy apparently *c.* 1641. Cuyp is not recorded outside Dordrecht but the subjects of paintings and drawings by him show that he travelled extensively in the United Provinces. In 1658 Cuyp married Cornelia Bosman, the wealthy widow of Jan van den Corput, a member of one of Dordrecht's leading families. Cornelia's family had a strong Calvinist tradition – her maternal grandfather was the radical Calvinist theologian Franciscus Gomarus – and in the year after his marriage Cuyp became a deacon of the Reformed Church. He later took on numerous public offices, including being a member of the High Court of South Holland (1679–82). It seems likely that after his marriage he devoted progressively less time to painting.

There are very few dated landscapes by Cuyp and his chronology remains to a certain extent obscure. In addition to landscapes and river scenes, he painted a small number of portraits, some of equestrian subjects, and biblical scenes.

REFERENCES: HdG, vol. 2; Utrecht 1965, cat.; J. G. van Gelder and I. Jost, 'Vroeg contact van Aelbert Cuyp met Utrecht', *Miscellanea J.Q. van Regteren Altena*, Amsterdam, 1969, pp. 100–3; S. Reiss, *Aelbert Cuyp*, London, 1975; Ex. cat., *Aelbert Cuyp en zijn Familie: Schilders te Dordrecht*, Dordrechts Museum, 1978.

53 *A Hilly River Landscape with a Horseman talking to a Shepherdess*

Plate 73

Signed, below right: A: cuyp.

Oil on canvas, 135 × 201.5 (53¼ × 78¾); a further 1.25 cm. of the painted surface is folded over the stretcher on the left edge.

Cleaned in 1947–9 and 1981–2. There is a large damage in the centre above the tower.

Reiss attributed this painting in 1953 to Abraham van Calraet;[1] in 1975 he attributed it to 'Studio of Aelbert Cuyp early 1660s', remarking that 'it seems to stand on the borderline between Cuyp and his imitators'.[2] By contrast, MacLaren described it as 'one of the best and most important works of Cuyp's maturity', tentatively dated to *c.*1655–60. In the view of the present writer there can be no reason to doubt the painting's authenticity: weaknesses in the drawing, notably in the figure of the shepherdess, are entirely consistent with Cuyp's mature style. MacLaren's dating would seem correct (given the difficulties involved in constructing a convincing chronology for Cuyp; see above).

ENGRAVING: Engraved by Peter Mazell.

COPIES: A copy was said to be in the collection of Baron Edmond de Rothschild, Ferrières.[3] A reduced copy (38.5 × 46 cm.; probably nineteenth century) was in the collection of E. van Kovacs-Kanapy, Budapest, in 1928 (as Wouwermans);[4] a reduced copy was in the collection of W. Davies, Mold, in 1936;[5] a later pastiche was in anonymous sale, London, 23 July 1952 (lot 113).[6] A copy by Sarah Setchel (on ivory: 5¾ × 9 in.) was at Sotheby's, 2 March 1966 (lot 64).

PROVENANCE: In the Sir Lawrence Dundas, Bart., sale, London, 29–31 May 1794 (third day, lot 32), bought by [John Julius] Angerstein (195 gns).[7] Purchased with the Angerstein collection, 1824.

EXHIBITION: London 1947–8, No. 5.

REFERENCES:

General: Smith No. 52; HdG No. 426; Reiss, op. cit., No. 143.

In text:
1. BM, vol. 95, 1953, p. 46.
2. Reiss, op. cit.
3. According to a MS note by HdG in his copy of his *Catalogue Raisonné*.
4. Note on the RKD mount of No. 53.

5. Letter in the National Gallery dossier.
6. 39 × 55¾ in. A photograph is in the National Gallery archives.
7. It is presumably the picture mentioned in Joseph Farington's diary, 4 August 1795: 'Mr Angerstein paid Comyns 15 guineas for cleaning the landscape Cuyp' (Farington, vol. 2, p. 373).

797 *Portrait of a Bearded Man* *Plate 74*

Inscribed and signed on the left, below: Ætatis: 56:1649/A: cuÿp. fecit: The second figure of the sitter's age has been painted over a 3 but is certainly original.

Oil on oak, octagonal, 68.9 × 60.2 (27⅛ × 23¹¹⁄₁₆). At the bottom, on the right, is visible a small part only of the cuff of a glove; this suggests that the picture was reduced from a rectangle to an octagon after it was painted. The left side has certainly been trimmed later, since the present edge of the panel cuts through the A of the signature.

Cleaned in 1946–9.

The collar was at first almost twice its present depth.

This portrait is closely related in style to those of Jacob Cuyp.[1] Jacob Cuyp, born in 1594, would have been fifty-six in 1649 and so it is possible that this is a portrait by Aelbert Cuyp of his father.[2] Unfortunately, there is no documented portrait of Jacob Cuyp at around this time. He can be seen as a young man in the background of a group portrait of 1617.[3]

PROVENANCE: In the collection of John Barnard, which passed to Thomas Hankey; Thomas Hankey sale, London, 7–8 June 1799 (first day, lot 22),[4] bought by Admiral William Waldegrave (later Baron Radstock),[5] 10 gns. Said to have been in the collection of [Michael?] Bryan and to be described in his catalogue of 1801 as a self portrait of Cuyp.[6] In the Arthur Champernowne sale, London, 29–30 June 1820 (second day, lot 33), bought by Yates (34 gns); by 1834 in the collection of J. Bulkeley Owen;[7] T. B. Bulkeley Owen sale, London, 30 April 1868 (lot 186),[8] bought by Trant (385 gns). Purchased from C. J. Nieuwenhuys in May 1869.

EXHIBITION: London 1947–8, No. 6.

REFERENCES:

General: Smith No. 176; HdG No. 109.

In text:
1. Cf. J. G. Cuyp's *Portrait of a Man*, painted in the same year, in Budapest (inv. no. 403).
2. This identification was suggested to the present writer by Sir Michael Levey.
3. Dordrecht, Museum Mr Simon van Gijn. Ex. cat. Dordrecht 1978, op. cit., No. 1.
4. The sale catalogue has only the brief description: 'Cuyp A man's portrait.' The identity of this picture with the National Gallery one is supported by an old painted inscription on the back of the panel: J.B./

N:41; these initials are presumably those of John Barnard of London whose collection passed to Thomas Hankey (*vide* the title-page of the Hankey sale, 1799, where Barnard's name is mis-spelled). The Cuyp portrait is not among the paintings in Barnard's collection in London mentioned in *London and its Environs Described*, published by R. and J. Dodsley, 1761, vol. 1, pp. 280ff, nor in *The English Connoisseur*, vol. 1, 1766, pp. 1–7.
5. According to the auctioneer's copy of the catalogue the purchaser was 'Admiral Walgrave'. There was no admiral of this name and the only possible

person is the Hon. William Waldegrave who became a vice-admiral in 1795 and was made 1st Baron Radstock in 1800.

6. National Gallery catalogue, 1870. There does not appear to be a Bryan catalogue of 1801 and no Bryan sale of that year is recorded in Lugt; HdG states that the picture was in the Bryan sale, London, 7–10 May 1804, but this is not so.

7. Smith, loc. cit.

8. The provenance from the Champernowne 1820 sale is mentioned in the Bulkeley Owen sale catalogue.

822 *A Horseman with a Cowherd and Two Boys in a Meadow, and Seven Cows*

Plate 75

Signed at the bottom, towards the right: A. cùÿp.

Oil on canvas, 80 × 106 ($31\frac{1}{2}$ × $41\frac{3}{4}$); the edges have been made up.

Cleaned in 1956.

There are *pentimenti* in the sky above the outlines of the cattle at the back on the right.

Perhaps painted in the later 1650s.

DRAWING: A drawing for the sleeping boy is on a signed sheet of studies in the Rijksprentenkabinet, Amsterdam (Fig. 24).

PROVENANCE: Possibly in the Richard Hulse sale, London, 21–22 March 1806 (second day, lot 83),[1] bought by Birch (430 gns). Sold by Messrs Woodburn,[2] probably to Sir Robert Peel, Bart., in whose collection it was certainly by 1834.[3] Purchased with the Peel collection, 1871.

EXHIBITION: Hull 1961, No. 16.

REFERENCES:
General: Smith No. 102; HdG Nos. 427 and (?)448c.
In text:
1. 'Cuyp   A Landscape with Cattle, and a Farmer on a Grey Horse, conversing with a herdsman.' The horse in the National Gallery picture is dapple grey.
2. Smith, loc. cit.
3. Smith, loc. cit.

823 *A Herdsman with Five Cows by a River*

Plate 76

Signed, bottom right: A: cuyp:

Oil on oak, 45.4 × 74 ($17\frac{7}{8}$ × $29\frac{1}{8}$).

Cleaned in 1960.

MacLaren suggested that it was 'perhaps a work of the mid-1650s'. Reiss dates the painting *c*.1650.

PROVENANCE:[1] Perhaps in the Nogaret sale, 1780: 'Albert Cuyp. Une Marine: on voit à gauche un canot dans lequel sont deux hommes, dont un pêche à la ligne; en pleine mer plusieurs chaloupes; à droite, au bas d'une masse de rochers, cinq boeufs gardés par un pâtre; effect de soleil. Bois. Seize pouces sur vingt-sept.' (1,350 livres: sold to the Vicomte de Choiseul); this is presumably the painting by Cuyp in the 1793 Choiseul-Praslin sale: 'A. CUYP. Six Vaches près de la Meuse ornée de barques, et deux matelots qui s'amusent à pêcher. Bois. Seize pouces et demi sur vingt-neuf (2,350 livres).' Sold in 1822 by John Smith to Joseph Barchard (400 gns);[2] it is perhaps the 'Landscape, with Cattle and Figures' by A. Cuyp exhibited by Joseph Barchard at the BI, 1822 (No. 128).[3] Apparently at one time in the possession of C.J. Nieuwenhuys.[4] Bought by Sir Robert Peel, Bart., by 1834;[5] purchased with the Peel collection, 1871.

EXHIBITION: Norwich Museum Centenary Exhibition, 1925, No. 6.

COPY: A free copy was in the collection of Mrs F. Howard, Taunton, in 1959.[6]

REFERENCES:
General: Smith No. 164; HdG No. 391 (and 325); Reiss, op. cit., no. 88.
In text:
1. Reiss, op. cit., suggested that HdG noted the painting three times under Nos. 325, 328 and 391. No. 823 is certainly 391; it could be No. 325 (Nogaret and Choiseul collections); but cannot be 328 which has quite different dimensions. The Nogaret and Choiseul catalogues are reprinted by C. Blanc, *Le Trésor de la Curiosité*, Paris, 1858 (for these two particular entries see vol. 2, pp. 18 and 164).
2. Smith, loc. cit.
3. But this might equally well be the *Cattle and*

Herdsmen ('The thirsty Herdsman') which also was probably in the Barchard collection by 1822 (Smith No. 142; HdG No. 338). There were no pictures by Cuyp in the [Barchard] sale, London, 6 May 1826.
4. On the back of the panel is an armorial seal. The same seal is on the back of Correggio No. 23, Jan van der Heyden No. 866, Hobbema Nos. 831 and 833, and Willem van de Velde No. 871, of which all but Hobbema No. 833 were certainly at one time in the hands of the dealer Nieuwenhuys.
5. Smith, loc. cit.
6. Correspondence in National Gallery archives.

824   *Ubbergen Castle*   Plate 77

Oil on oak, 32.1 × 54.5 (12⅝ × 21⅜).

Cleaned in 1954.

Ubbergen (Province of Gelderland) is near Nijmegen. The castle seen in the painting was pulled down in 1712 and a house was built on the site.[1] Cuyp has inscribed the name on his preparatory study for the picture (Fig. 25), which is in Vienna.

MacLaren tentatively proposed a date in the mid-50s. Reiss agreed with this dating.

DRAWING: A signed study for this painting, without the figures on the right and with two trees on the left, is in the Albertina, Vienna.[2] In the painting the composition is extended on the right and slightly on the left.

COPY: An old copy on panel (of approximately the same size: 31.6 × 53.3 cm.) was in Dr E.C. Carter's sale, London, 27 October 1950 (lot 17).

PROVENANCE: Said to have been bought in Hoorn from an old clothes man for about 15 pence.[3] D[e] P[reuil] sale, Paris, 25–29 November 1811 (lot 70), bought by Lebrun (6,000 francs); L[apeyrière] sale, Paris, 14 sqq. April 1817 (lot 25), bought by Perignon (8,000 francs). Brought to England by Lafontaine[4] and, according to Smith,[5] bought in at a sale at Phillips's, London, in 1822 for 440 gns.[6] It was sold by Lafontaine to Sir Robert Peel, Bart.,[7] by whom it was exhibited at the BI in 1822. Purchased with the Peel collection, 1871.

EXHIBITIONS: BI 1822, No. 38; London, Tate Gallery, 'Wilson and his Circle Exhibition', 1949, No. 135.

REFERENCES:
General: Smith No. 118; HdG No. 176; Reiss, op. cit., cat. no. 132.
In text:
1. See van der Aa, vol. 11, p. 350.
2. Chalk and wash drawing, 18 × 26.8 cm. Signed, and inscribed by the artist: vbberg(h)en.
3. Smith, loc. cit.
4. Smith, loc. cit.

5. Smith, loc. cit.
6. No Lafontaine sale of 1822 in London is recorded in Lugt. It may have been in an unidentified anonymous sale; if so it must have been early in the year since it was certainly exhibited by Peel at the BI by May 1822.
7. Smith, loc. cit.

961 *A Distant View of Dordrecht, with a Milkmaid and Four Cows, and Other Figures ('The Large Dort')* Plate 78

In the background is Dordrecht (Dort) seen from the south-east; in the centre is the Grote Kerk, and the Vuilpoort is towards the left.

Signed below towards the right: A. cuyp (partially effaced).

Oil on canvas, 157.5 × 197 (62 × 77½).

Cleaned in 1949.

The lower part of the picture is rather worn and the paint surface has been affected in several areas by heat during relining.

The Grote Kerk of Dordrecht appears in a number of Cuyp's landscapes. The tower was begun in 1339; the nave and choir were rebuilt in the second half of the fifteenth century. The Vuilpoort, one of the town's water-gates, was built in 1578 and pulled down in 1864.

The view in the background is repeated almost exactly in *'The Small Dort'* (No. 962 below). A drawing by Cuyp in the British Museum (Fig. 26)[1] shows the same view, including the various windmills, cottages and trees that appear in the background of one or other of these two pictures. The same view is repeated in an engraving in Abraham Rademaker's *Kabinet van Nederlandsche . . . Outheden en Gezichten*, 1725,[2] in which the buildings and trees of the middle distance correspond in detail with those in No. 961 or No. 962. Rademaker's engravings are after the works of earlier artists; the original of this print is not identified but it is described as a view of Dordrecht in 1650.

A view of the Grote Kerk and the Vuilpoort from a slightly different angle can be seen in No. 6405.

MacLaren tentatively dated the painting *c.*1650. Reiss dated it to the late 1640s.

The cow lying on the right and the one standing behind her are seen reversed in an etching by Cuyp.[3] They are repeated, but with the standing cow differently coloured and in a slightly different position, in a landscape with a herdsman and two cows in the Rijksmuseum, Amsterdam,[4] and a landscape with a herdsman and shepherdess and two cows in the Wallraf-Richartz Museum, Cologne.[5] The two cows are repeated, separately, in No. 1289 below; the one lying on the ground reappears in landscapes in the Corcoran Gallery, Washington,[6] and the collection of Sir Nicholas Bacon, Bart.[7] The left half of the background is repeated in a landscape with two horses, probably by Abraham van Calraet, which was sold at Christie's, 27 May 1955 (lot 142).[8]

DRAWING: See above.

PROVENANCE: Possibly to be identified with the 'view of Dort with Figures' by Cuyp, in the [Delahante et al.] sale ('a consignment from Holland'), London, 3 March 1810 (lot 72). No. 961 is said to have been in the Earl of Bristol's collection.[9] It is also said to have been 'purchased at the Coventry sale'[10] but this may be due to confusion with another painting in the Wynn Ellis collection.[11] It was certainly in the sale of [Sir Henry Hervey Bruce, Bart., of Down Hill, Londonderry], London, 30 June 1849 (lot 91),[12] bought by Brown (£735) and in the Thomas B. Brown sale, London, 20 May 1856 (lot 69),[13] bought by Pearce (1,575 gns) probably for Wynn Ellis.[14] Lent by Wynn Ellis to the BI, 1858, No. 72,[15] and the RA, 1871, No. 232.[16] The

'Landscape with Cattle' by Cuyp, lent by Wynn Ellis to the BFAC, 1871, No. 33, was probably a different picture.[17] Wynn Ellis Bequest, 1876.

EXHIBITIONS: BI 1858, No. 72; RA 1871, No. 232.

REFERENCES:
General: HdG Nos. 268e and 368; Reiss, op. cit., cat. no. 83.
In text:
1. Hind, vol. 3, p. 71, No. 17 (pl. 37). Signed: A.C.
2. Vol. 2, No. 134.
3. Hollstein, vol. 5, p. 100.
4. Canvas, 101.5 × 136 cm. 1976 catalogue, A 3754.
5. Canvas, 101.5 × 135 cm. HdG No. 184. 1967 cat. no. 2532.
6. Panel, 48 × 72 cm. HdG No. 424.
7. HdG No. 194.
8. Panel, 38 × 51 cm. Anonymous owner (bought by Cevat for 95 gns).
9. According to the catalogue of the T.B. Brown sale, 1856. It was not in the Earl of Bristol's sale, London, 12 June 1829. HdG lists an Earl of Bristol sale of 1812 (MS list of sales in the RKD) but no copy of the catalogue is known (see Lugt, vol. 1, No. 8161).
10. According to the National Gallery catalogue, 1876; the date of the sale and the name of the purchaser are not given. It was not in any of the Coventry or Lord Coventry sales recorded by Lugt (vol. 1, No. 7703, and vol. 2, Nos. 16003, 17238 and 17380).
11. It may have been confused with the herdsmen and shepherdess with two cows in the Wallraf-Richartz Museum which was also in the Wynn Ellis collection (see the latter part of note 17 below) and had been in Lord Coventry's collection in 1834 (Smith, vol. 5, p. 458, No. 280) although this, too, is untraceable in a Coventry sale. A 'Landscape, Cattle and Figures' by Cuyp was lent by the Earl of Coventry to the BI in 1835 (No. 108). There is a MS note to No. 280 in a copy of Smith's *Catalogue Raisonné*, which may be Smith's own, on p. 458: 'Sold by Mr Briant to Mr Brown who disposed of it in 1852 to Wynn Ellis Esq.ʳ Exhibited in the

BI in 185(?4?6) [last digit is partially erased]'.
12. The picture is identified with National Gallery No. 961 by the description in the Bruce sale catalogue by G. Scharf, *Artistic and Descriptive Notes on . . . Pictures in the British Institution Exhibition*, 1858, p. 28. In a MS addendum to the copy (referred to above in note 11) of Smith's *Catalogue Raisonné* (opposite p. 654 of the Supplement) the picture is described at length. It continues: 'A richly coloured and beautiful picture. Purchased by Mr Brown then apparently in a bad state at the sale of Sir Harvey Bruce Bᵗ at Christie and Manson in 1849 for 700 gns. 5 ft 2 in by 6 ft 6 ins. At the sale of Mr Browns [sic] Phillips, May 1856. Sold for £1,653.15.0. Wynn Ellis Esqʳ.' (See also note 15 below.)
13. As from the collection of the Earl of Bristol; see note 9.
14. Pearce apparently often bought for Wynn Ellis; see Berchem No. 1004 of this catalogue, note 3.
15. See Scharf, loc. cit. Scharf erroneously refers to Waagen, 1854, vol. 2, p. 296; the Wynn Ellis landscape described by Waagen ('Four cows in the foreground; the town of Dort in the distance . . . of his second period') must be National Gallery No. 962 since the present picture cannot have been in the Wynn Ellis collection until after the Brown sale in 1856.
16. As 'Landscape with Cattle, and a View of Dort'; the measurements given in the catalogue show that it is the present picture, not No. 962 below.
17. The size is not given in the exhibition catalogue; the picture exhibited could equally well be No. 962 below, or lot 11 of the Wynn Ellis sale, 17 May 1876 ('A River Scene, with peasants and animals'; bought by Boynton) or lot 156 of that sale (the herdsman and shepherdess with two cows, now in the Wallraf-Richartz Museum, Cologne; HdG No. 184).

962 *A Distant View of Dordrecht, with a Sleeping Herdsman and Five Cows ('The Small Dort')*   Plate 79

In the background is the town of Dordrecht (Dort), with the Grote Kerk in the centre and, to the left, the Vuilpoort.

Signed on the top bar of the fence on the right: A: cuyp:

Oil on oak, 66.4 × 100 (26⅛ × 39⅜).

Cleaned in 1982.

Exactly the same view of Dordrecht appears in the background of '*The Large Dort*' (No. 961 above). The two cows, one standing and one lying, in the centre occur with variations and reversed in an etching attributed to Cuyp.[1] The sleeping cowherd re-appears with slight variations in the *Herdsman with Three Cows* last recorded in the M. G. van Heel collection, Rijssen.[2]

MacLaren dated the painting a little later than No. 961, that is, soon after 1650. Reiss preferred to date it to the late 1640s.

DRAWING: For a drawing of the background see No. 961 above.

COPY: There is a photograph of a copy attributed to Abraham van Strij in the RKD: the painting is noted as in the trade 'before 1940' and no size is given.

PROVENANCE: Probably in Captain Baillie's sale.[3] London, 1–2 February 1771 (first day, lot 68).[4] By 1818 in the collection of Charles Oldfield Bowles, when it was lent to the BI, and still in his collection *c.*1834.[5] It was bought by Wynn Ellis about 1840 for £400, according to Smith;[6] it may be the 'Cattle-piece' lent by Wynn Ellis to the BI, 1853, No. 45,[7] or the 'Landscape with Cattle' lent by him to the BFAC, London, 1871, No. 33.[8] Wynn Ellis Bequest, 1876.

EXHIBITIONS: BI 1818, No. 81; (?)BI 1853, No. 45; (?)BFAC 1871, No. 33.

REFERENCES:
General: Smith Nos. 190(?) and 208. HdG No. 342; Reiss, op. cit., cat. no. 79.
In text:
1. Reproduced in Hollstein, vol. 5, p. 100.
2. Reproduced in the catalogue of the exhibition *Oude Kunst uit Twents particulier bezit*, Almelo (Waaggebouw), 1953, No. 11 and p. 35.
3. According to the catalogue, the sale was of 'pictures selected by Captain Baillie in several tours abroad'.
4. 'A landscape and cattle with view of a town at a distance'; 27 × 36 in.
5. Smith No. 208.
6. According to a MS note in HdG's own copy of his *Catalogue Raisonné* (in the RKD) where it is said to be derived from an annotation in Smith's copy of *his* catalogue. In a copy of Smith's *Catalogue Raisonné* which may be Smith's own, No. 208 is indeed annotated: 'Purchased about 1840 by Wynn Ellis Esqr for £400.' In any case the picture was not in the [Col. Bowles] sale, London, 25 May 1850, and was seen in the Wynn Ellis collection in 1850 or 1851 by Waagen (1854, vol. 2, p. 296); see Cuyp No. 961 above, note 15.
7. and 8. Either description would equally well fit lot 11 or lot 156 of the Wynn Ellis sale, 1876 (see Cuyp No. 961, note 17). On the other hand, the back of the present picture is inscribed in chalk: 45; this may be the BI 1853 numbering.

1289 *Peasants with Four Cows by the River Merwede*   Plate 80

On the left, across the river, is the ruined castle of Merwede.

Signed, bottom right: A. cuyp.

Oil on oak, 38.1 × 50.8 (15 × 20).

Cleaned in 1955.

Merwede Castle (*Huis te Merwede*) lies about a mile to the east of Dordrecht. It was built in the thirteenth century and destroyed in the 1418 siege of Dordrecht or the St Elizabeth flood of 1421. Its ruins, in much the same state as in the seventeenth century, stand on land now reclaimed; they appear in several pictures by Cuyp[1] who made a detailed drawing of the ruins in black chalk and wash.[2]

There is a drawing for the figure on the extreme right (holding a crook) in the Victor de Steurs collection in Vorden (Fig. 27).[3]

The cow farthest to the left occurs in No. 961 above as also, with small variations, that on the extreme right; the former also appears in a *Landscape with a Boy and Two Cows* in the Rijksmuseum.[4] The group of three recumbent cows occurs with slight differences in the *Herdsman with Six Cows near a Palace* in the Bacon collection.[5]

MacLaren tentatively suggested a date in the second half of the 1650s. He noted that it should be considered later than Nos. 961 and 962 above. Reiss dated it to the early 1650s.

ENGRAVING: Line-engraving (in reverse) by F. Vivares, 1754.[6]

COPY: A copy with slight variations (in reverse; probably after Vivares's engraving mentioned above) was in the collection of C. Eastwood, Scotton Grange, in 1897–98.[7] Another copy (in the same direction as No. 1289) was in the collection of G.W. van Aardenze, Dordrecht, in 1949.[8]

PROVENANCE: In the collection of William Herring in 1754.[9] Bought from Morey by John Staniforth Beckett in January 1848;[10] J.S. Beckett Bequest, 1889.

EXHIBITION: London, National Gallery, 'Aelbert Cuyp in British Collections', 1973, No. 9.

REFERENCES:
General: Smith No. 262; HdG Nos. 429 and 446; Reiss, op. cit., cat. no. 90.
In text:
1. For example, HdG No. 291 (National Trust, Ascott); HdG No. 227, Salzburg, Residenzgalerie (Czernin loan; 1970 catalogue, no. 37) which repeats the view of Merwede in No. 1289 almost exactly; HdG No. 74 (and 78), Strasbourg, Art Gallery; HdG No. 172, Montpelier, Musée Fabre; HdG No. 737, collection of the Earl of Yarborough.
2. Paris, Institut Néerlandais, Fondation Custodia. Inv. no. 579. Ex. Dordrecht 1978, op. cit., No. 69.
3. Ex. Dordrecht 1978, op. cit., No. 59.
4. 1976 catalogue, A 3754.
5. HdG No. 194. The only difference is that the head of the nearer cow on the right is there turned farther to the right.
6. Dated 1754 and inscribed: 'THE MORNING. / Engraved from an Original Picture of A. Cuyp. In the Possession of Wm. Herring Esq' Publish'd & Sold by F. Vivares 15th March 1754.'
7. Panel, 22 × 28¾ in. Letters from C. Eastwood and a photograph of the picture are in the National Gallery archives.
8. Ex. Dordrecht 1949, No. 17.
9. See note 4.
10. Letter of 1931 from J.S. Beckett's nephew, Sir Hickman Bacon, Bart. (in the National Gallery archives).

2545 *A River Scene with Distant Windmills*   Plate 81

Signed, in the bottom right corner: A cuÿp. .

Oil on oak, 35.6 × 52.4 (14 × 20⅝).

Cleaned in 1960.

This is an early work in the manner of van Goyen. MacLaren dated the painting to the mid-1640s. Reiss dated it *c*.1642.

On the RKD mount, Miss L. de Bruyn has identified the scene as Beverwyck. While the church profile is similar to that at Beverwyck, it seems unlikely that Cuyp intended to show a precise topographical location.

PROVENANCE: In the collection of Charles Bredel (died 1851);[1] Miss Bredel sale, London, 1 May 1875 (lot 111), bought by Rutley (310 gns). Jean Louis Miéville sale, London, 29 April 1899 (lot 60), bought by

Agnew[2] (410 gns). In the collection of George Salting, London, by 1903, when it was exhibited by him at the RA. Salting Bequest, 1910.

EXHIBITIONS: RA 1903, No. 82; London, National Gallery, 'Aelbert Cuyp in British Collections', 1973, No. 3; London 1976, No. 24.

REFERENCES:
General: HdG Nos. 638, 667 and 677.
In text:
1. According to the Bredel 1875 sale catalogue it was exhibited at the BI in 1840, but it is not traceable in the catalogue of that exhibition nor in any other

BI exhibition. It was seen in the Bredel collection in 1850 or 1851 by Waagen (1854, vol. 2, p. 292).
2. HdG (No. 677) gives Lesser as the purchaser but it was bought by Agnew according to the auctioneer's marked copy of the catalogue.

6405 *The Maas at Dordrecht in a Storm* *Plate 82*

Signed, bottom right: A. cù ÿp.

Oil on oak, 49.8 × 74.4 (19⅝ × 29⁵⁄₁₆).

Cleaned in 1972. There is some damage along a horizontal split in the panel.

Dordrecht, dominated by the profile of the Grote Kerk, is on the right (see Nos. 961 and 962 above).

Storm scenes are very unusual in Cuyp's work. The only known painting to show similar flashes of lightning in the sky is in the Bührle collection in Zurich:[1] it clearly belongs to Cuyp's early, van Goyenesque phase and should be dated to the mid-1640s. There is a painting of a storm at sea with a streak of lightning in the Louvre[2] in which the two boats on the left side of No. 6405 are repeated with very slight variations. The only rain storm at sea is the far less dramatic view of the Maas in Dordrecht in the Wallace Collection[3] which also repeats the two boats on the left. No. 6405 is far more sketchy in technique than either the Louvre or the Wallace Collection painting and its rarity in Cuyp's oeuvre makes it particularly difficult to date. Reiss[4] suggested that it was from the early 1650s (which is also the date he gives to the Wallace Collection painting). The present writer (while conscious of the problems of constructing a chronology for Cuyp) prefers an earlier date, in the second half of the 1640s.

PROVENANCE: Possibly the Earl of Halifax sale, London, 19 April 1782 ('View of Dordrecht in a Storm': sold to Nisbet for £67).[5] Bryan sale, London, 17–18 May 1798 (lot 1798), 'Cuyp: Thunderstorm: a grand and sublime effort of this great artist'; probably in the Baring collection, from which acquired by the Prince Regent; sent from Carlton House to Christie's on 26 May 1814; Anon. sale (Prince of Wales), Christie's, 29 June 1814 (lot 56), bought by Norton. Said to have been in the collection of F. Jorden, on whose death in 1844 it was sold to T. Barber; T. Barber sale, Christie's, 5 May 1862 (lot 54);[6] purchased by Peacock, from whose family bought by P. and D. Colnaghi. Purchased from Colnaghi's by W.C. Alexander, 10 April 1886. Passed by descent to the Misses Rachel F. and Jean I. Alexander, who presented it by deed of gift to the National Gallery; entered the collection in 1972.[7]

EXHIBITIONS: RA 1887, No. 50; RA 1929, No. 291; RA 1952–3, No. 365; Norwich, Castle Museum, 'East Anglia and the Netherlands', 1954, No. 5; London 1972; London 1976, No. 25; Dordrechts Museum, 'Aelbert Cuyp en zijn familie', 1978, No. 28.

REFERENCES:
General: HdG No. 636, No. 167c and (?)167a; Reiss, op. cit., cat. no. 101.
In text:
1. HdG, No. 708; Reiss, op. cit., cat. no. 27.

2. 1979 catalogue (vol. 1: *Ecoles flamande et hollan-daise*), p. 44 (inv. no. 1195). HdG No. 643; Reiss, op. cit., cat. no. 142 (as 'School of Aelbert Cuyp early 1660s').

3. 1979 catalogue, p. 57 (inv. no. P 49). HdG No. 639. Reiss, op. cit., cat. no. 102.

4. Reiss, op. cit., cat. no. 101. In 1953, however,

Reiss had dated the painting *c.*1642–44: BM, vol. 95, 1953, pp. 34 and 46.

5. HdG No. 167a.

6. HdG No. 167c.

7. A. Smith, 'Presented by the Misses Rachel F. and Jean I. Alexander: Seventeen Paintings for the National Gallery', BM, vol. 114, 1972, p. 633.

Imitator of AELBERT CUYP

2547 *A Herdsman with Seven Cows by a River* — Plate 83

Falsely signed near the bottom, left of centre: A cùyp (the last letter nearly effaced).

Oil on oak, 61.4 × 90.8 ($24\frac{3}{16}$ × $35\frac{3}{4}$).

Discoloured by an engrained brown varnish.

Accepted by Hofstede de Groot as by Cuyp.[1] Although its quality is obscured by the present dark varnish, it is clearly far too feeble to be his work and does not appear even to be contemporary with him. Its exact status is not clear. It may be a copy after Cuyp. There does exist, in fact, another picture of identical composition (formerly in the Delessert collection; see VERSIONS) but that, too, is probably not by Cuyp.[2] A small copy or pastiche of an almost identical composition, probably English of the early nineteenth century, is listed below among VERSIONS.

The National Gallery picture could equally well be a deliberate imitation of Cuyp. A landscape closely related to the present composition hangs in the background of *The Scholar* by Abraham van Strij (1753–1826) in the John G. Johnson collection, Philadelphia Museum of Art.[3] Abraham van Strij's brother, Jacob (1756–1815), painted many landscapes in a pastiche of Cuyp's manner and, although none of the signed ones is as close to Cuyp as the present picture, they are not incompatible in style with it.

VERSIONS: A painting on panel of identical design (see above) and approximately the same size was in the Delessert sale, Paris, 13 May 1911 (lot 2),[4] bought by Stettiner for Ernest Cognacq and resold shortly afterwards;[5] it has been confused with the National Gallery picture.[6] A small copy or pastiche of a very closely related composition was in an anonymous sale, London, 15 December 1954 (lot 36).[7] An old copy which shows the composition slightly cut down on all four sides (especially on the left where the section of landscape including the windmill is missing) is in the collection of Mr J. van Trigt, Alkmaar.[8]

PROVENANCE: In the Ralph Bernal sale, London, 8 May 1824 (lot 34), bought by Hill (299 gns), perhaps for M.M. Zachary,[9] by whom it was sold to Frederick Perkins by 1834.[10] It was apparently exhibited by Perkins in Manchester, 1857 (provisional catalogue, No. 816);[11] George Perkins sale, London, 14 June 1890 (lot 4), bought in (950 gns); George Perkins sale, Paris, 3 June 1893 (lot 3), bought by Charles Sedelmeyer (28,000 francs) and sold by him to Rodolphe Kann, Paris, 29 October 1894.[12] It was in the collection of George Salting, London, by 1903, when it was exhibited at the RA. Salting Bequest, 1910.

EXHIBITIONS: Manchester 1857 (provisional catalogue, No. 816);[13] RA 1903, No. 87.

REFERENCES:
General: Smith, Cuyp No. 149; HdG, Cuyp No. 206.

In text:
1. HdG, loc. cit.

2. The Delessert version is known to the present writer only by the reproduction in the 1911 sale catalogue. From this it seems likely to be a copy or imitation of Cuyp by the same hand as the National Gallery picture. HdG, who at one time confused the two versions (see note 6), later believed the Delessert one to be an old copy of No. 2547, which he took to be an original (*Cicerone*, 1911, p. 488; MS note in HdG's own copy of his *Catalogue Raisonné* in the RKD).

3. 1972 cat., p. 84, No. 711.

4. Smith Supplement, Cuyp No. 55. It was in the Comte Perregaux sale, Paris, 8–9 December 1841 (lot 6), bought by Périer (18,100 francs). Smith (Supplement, Cuyp No. 55), writing in 1841 or 1842, says it was bought for Baron Delessert but it does not appear in the *Notice sur la collection de tableaux de MM. Delessert*, 1844, nor in the 1846 edition; furthermore, the Delessert sale catalogue of 1869 (see below) describes it as from the collection of Paul Périer. HdG (Cuyp No. 206) suggests that it may have been in the [Paul Périer] sale, Paris, 16–17 March 1843 but there was no Cuyp in that sale, nor in the Périer sale of 19 December 1846. It was in the Delessert sale, Paris, 15 March 1869 (lot 17), bought in(?). According to a MS note in Sedelmeyer's own copy of his *Catalogue of 100 Paintings of Old Masters . . . belonging to the Sedelmeyer Gallery*, 1894, No. 6 (transcribed in the copy in the RKD), it was afterwards in the collection of Baron Bartholdi, Paris; in any case the same picture was certainly in the Delessert sale of 1911 (see the etching by Bracquemond in GBA, 1869, vol. 1, opposite p. 118, and the reproduction in the 1911 sale catalogue). Smith (Supplement No. 55) describes the Delessert version as showing only six cows; the reproductions mentioned above show that it corresponds exactly to the National Gallery design. The 1869 Delessert sale catalogue states incorrectly that the picture is on can-vas, 59 × 87 cm.; it is in fact on panel, as stated in the 1841 Perregaux sale catalogue (where the size is given as 63 × 89 cm.).

5. For the purchaser at the sale and the subsequent resale see *Cicerone*, 1911, p. 488.

6. In HdG (vol. 4, 1909, Cuyp No. 206) the Perregaux/Delessert picture is confused with the National Gallery version. See also note 2.

7. 8½ × 13¼ in. It was later in the Sir Patrick Donner sale, London, 25 April 1956 (lot 95). A photograph is in the National Gallery archives.

8. Canvas 56.5 × 72.3 cm.

9. See Smith, Cuyp No. 149. The purchaser's name is not marked in the auctioneer's copy of the catalogue. In a copy which apparently belonged to Smith (now at the RKD) it is given as Hill (299 gns) and there is a further note in another, contemporary, hand: 'Now Mr Zacchary's.'

10. According to Smith, Cuyp No. 149. It was not in the M. M. Zachary sale, London, 31 May 1828.

11. According to an MS note to No. 149 in a copy of Smith's *Catalogue Raisonné* which may be Smith's own: 'Exh'd in Arts Treasures, Manchester, 1857.' Although it is in the provisional catalogue (as 'Cows'), it is not in the definitive catalogue, in which appears only the other Cuyp in the Perkins collection (*Landscape with a Rider, a Herdsman and Cows*: HdG 454; Manchester 1857: provisional catalogue, No. 815; definitive catalogue, No. 712. Since Perkins possessed only two Cuyps, this last-named is presumably the picture exhibited at the BI in 1829, 1837 and 1851).

12. According to a MS annotation in Sedelmeyer's own copy of his *Catalogue of 100 Paintings* etc., 1894, No. 4 (cf. note 6). The identity of the Bernal/Perkins/Sedelmeyer picture with the National Gallery one is established by the reproduction in the Sedelmeyer catalogue.

13. See above, note 11.

CORNELIS DECKER, before 1623; died 1678

Cornelis Gerritsz. Decker; little is known about his life. He is first mentioned in 1643, when he appears as a member of the Haarlem guild,[1] but there are dated pictures from 1649[2] onwards. He appears again in the Haarlem guild records in 1661.[3] He was buried in Haarlem, 23 March 1678.[4]

Most of his pictures are landscapes in a style derived from that of Jacob van Ruisdael in his Haarlem period. He is one of a small group of Haarlem followers of Ruisdael, which also includes Salomon Rombouts (active in Haarlem between 1652 and 1660) and Roelof van Vries. Decker also imitated Philips Wouwermans and Jan Wijnants and painted a number of peasant interiors, often of weavers at work.

REFERENCES:
1. Van der Willigen, p. 29.
2. Leipzig, Museum der bildenden Künste. 1979 cat., No. 596 (formerly the date had been read as 1640).

3. Van der Willigen, p. 38.
4. Van der Willigen, p. 117.

1341 *A Cottage among Trees on the Bank of a Stream* Plate 84

Signed at the bottom, right of centre: C.D. 1669.

Oil on canvas, 65.2 × 77.5 ($25\frac{11}{16}$ × $30\frac{1}{2}$).

PROVENANCE: Perhaps bought in Paris by Edward Habich;[1] in his collection at Cassel, and exhibited with pictures from that collection in the Gemäldegalerie, Cassel, 1881–91.[2] It is in the catalogue of the Edward Habich sale, Cassel, 9–10 May 1892 (lot 36) but was bought, together with Nos. 1336–48, by the National Gallery in 1891.

EXHIBITION: Cassel, Gemäldegalerie, 1881–91.[3]

REFERENCES:
1. Habich is said to have bought many of his pictures in Paris; No. 1341 has pieces of a French newspaper on the back.
2. See JKPK, 1881, *Amtliche Berichte*, col. 43, No. 22, and O. Eisenmann, *Führer durch die Kgl.*

Gemäldegalerie zu Cassel, n.d., 5th edition, p. 46 (in both cases the figures are wrongly attributed to Adriaen van Ostade and Adriaen van de Velde).
3. See above, note 2.

DIRCK VAN DELEN, 1604/5–1671

Dirck van Delen (occasionally *Deelen*) was born in Heusden;[1] he is said to have been sixty-six at the time of his death in 1671.[2] He may have been a pupil of Hendrick Aertsz., the painter of architectural fantasies.[3] By 1626 he had settled in Arnemuiden,[4] near Middelburg (Zeeland). He is recorded in the Middelburg painters' guild, 1639–65.[5] He continued to live in Arnemuiden where he became a burgomaster.[6] He visited Antwerp in 1666 in order to collaborate with Theodore Boeyermans (1620–78) on an allegory commissioned by the city's Guild of St Luke.[7] He apparently revisited Antwerp in 1668 or 1669.[8] He died in Arnemuiden, 16 May 1671.[9]

He painted pictures of imaginary architecture,[10] chiefly church interiors and palaces in the northern Renaissance style, in the manner of the younger Hendrick van Steenwyck and continued in this style to the end of his life. The figures in his compositions are quite often painted by other artists, including Dirck Hals, Anthonie Palamedesz., Pieter Codde, Jan Olis.

REFERENCES:
General: T. T. Blade, *The Paintings of Dirck van Delen*, Ann Arbor, 1980. (The documents concerning his life are reviewed – though not significantly added to – on pp. 15–20.)
In text:
1. De Bie, p. 281.
2. Kramm, Supplement, 1864, p. 40.

3. See Jantzen, pp. 66–67.
4. A child of his was baptised in Arnemuiden in 1626, and he acquired citizenship there in 1628 (P. Haverkorn van Rijsewijk, *Notice descriptive des tableaux . . . du Musée de Rotterdam*, 1892, p. 54).
5. Obreen, vol. 6, pp. 177, 188, 191, 196 and 201.
6. OH, vol. 21, 1903, p. 119, and de Bie, loc. cit.

7. Blade, op. cit., cat. no. 97.
8. See *Catalogue du Musée d'Anvers*, 1857, p. 355.
9. According to a later inscription on a painted epitaph to van Delen's three wives, now in Arnemuiden Town Hall (see M. F. Lantsheer and F.

Nagtglas, *Zelandia illustrata*, 1879–85, vol. 1, p. 628).
10. The earliest known dated one is of 1623. Blade, op. cit., cat. no. 1. (Leipzig, Museum der bildenden Künst, Inv. no. 1614).

1010 *An Architectural Fantasy*   *Plate 85*

The fountain in the foreground is surmounted by a small gilt group of Hercules fighting Hydra. The statue in the niche on the extreme left is perhaps intended for Mercury, and the left-hand statue of the two figures in niches, on the left, above, may possibly be Minerva.

Signed, at the foot of the twisted column in the left foreground: D.V. DELEN. F. 1634.

Oil on mahogany, 46.7 × 60.5 ($18\frac{3}{8}$ × $23\frac{13}{16}$).

Cleaned in 1983.

The figures are by another painter, either Anthonie Palamedesz. (1601–73) or Jan Olis. The date was revealed when the painting was cleaned. Blade[1] had dated it to the mid-1630s.

PROVENANCE: In the [Wynn Ellis] sale, London, 6 June 1864 (lot 72),[2] bought in (140 gns). Wynn Ellis Bequest,[3] 1876.

EXHIBITION: London, National Gallery, 'The Capricious View' (travelling exhibition), 1984.

REFERENCES:
General: Jantzen, cat. no. 146; Blade, cat. no. 109.
In text:
1. Blade, op. cit.

2. As by D. van Delen and Gonzales Coques.
3. As by van Delen and Coques.

DELFT SCHOOL, *c.*1660–1665(?)

2552 *An Interior, with a Woman refusing a Glass of Wine offered by a Man*   *Plate 86*

Over the fireplace, part of a painting can be seen. In the top right-hand corner are the forelegs of two horses; below and farther off, half-hidden by sloping ground, is a man with a plumed helmet and a lance and to the left of him, the head of another man; beyond, to the right, are the tops of several lances. To the left of the fireplace the wall is hung with gilt-embossed leather; in the fireplace is a fire-dog, the legs of which are decorated with sea-horses.

Oil on canvas, 117 × 92 ($46\frac{1}{8}$ × $36\frac{1}{4}$). A further 1.6–1.9 cm. of the original canvas, on which the composition is continued, is turned over the edge of the stretcher on the left. A little worn, especially in the shadows. The reflection in the mirror over the chest is badly rubbed in the background part and the face of the man seen in it is worn and, apparently, retouched. The ground of the rug covering the table was probably green originally, and the back of the chair blue; both are now brown.

There are *pentimenti* in the woman's sleeves. The man looking into the mirror may be an afterthought since he has been painted on top of the chest and the reflection in the mirror.[1] However, it is equally likely that this was the artist's usual procedure, as part of the woman's skirt has been painted over the floor tiles.[2]

Gold leaf has been used for the highlights in the fire-dog and in parts of the gilt leather wall-hanging (see also below). The black and white floor tiles do not seem to form a regular pattern.

Too little of the painting over the fireplace can be seen for the subject to be identified with certainty; but Professor R. Fleischer has pointed out (in conversation with the present writer) that it adapts figures from the print of *Abraham liberating his Nephew Lot* by Antonio Tempesta (Bartsch 237). It is unlikely that in choosing this detail the artist meant to give any particular meaning to No. 2552 as a whole.

In 1809, when the painting is first recorded (see PROVENANCE), it was said to be by Pieter de Hooch, an attribution which has been repeated on numerous subsequent occasions;[3] in fact, at no stage in his development did de Hooch paint in this style. The painting has been much discussed at various times: it has been attributed to Jacob Ochtervelt, Samuel van Hoogstraten, Gerbrand van der Eeckhout, Cornelis de Man, Jan van Noordt, Barent Fabritius,[4] Ludolf de Jongh, Eglon van der Neer,[5] and even Johannes Vermeer.[6] In the view of the present writer, none of these attributions stands up to the test of comparison with signed works by any one of these artists. Valentiner[7] considered No. 2552 to be by the same hand as a painting of a man holding a gun at a window,[8] and a view of a terrace seen through a window now in the Chicago Art Institute: he attributed these paintings to Hendrick van der Burch. The facts of van der Burch's life (1627–after 1666), his close personal and professional relationship with Pieter de Hooch and his oeuvre have recently been clarified by Sutton,[9] who rejects the attribution of this group of paintings to van der Burch. Sutton points – as MacLaren had done in the first edition of this catalogue – to similarities in No. 2552 to the work of Carel Fabritius.[10] In the view of the present writer, there is no significant similarity to any of Carel Fabritius's few known works.[11]

No. 2552 appears to be the work of an artist who was active in Delft between 1655 and 1665 or of an artist who was in close contact with those artists. It has obvious analogies with interiors painted by Vermeer and Pieter de Hooch and is also related to experiments in perspective painting associated with the circle of Carel Fabritius. (In this context, it is important to note the handle of an open door in the left foreground and the numerous reflections – of the woman's skirt and the brass fire-dog in the tiled floor and of the man's face in the mirror.) The present writer does not agree with Mac-Laren's argument – on the grounds of costume and the connection with Carel Fabritius, who died in 1654 – that the picture probably dates from before 1655. In fact, it should probably be placed at the very earliest in the first half of the 1660s, that is, a few years after comparable works by de Hooch and Vermeer.

In the 1976 Amsterdam exhibition catalogue (see EXHIBITIONS), the author speculated on the relationships between the figures and the significance of the scene. It was tentatively suggested that on one level the woman's pose may have been intended to suggest a struggle against vice and that the man seen in the mirror, an image of self-knowledge, might stand for the constant need for Christians to be alert to the possibilities of temptation and to fight the good fight. To the present writer these interpretations seem far-fetched.

COPY: A (late?) copy in which the field of the composition has been somewhat reduced at top and bottom and even more on the right, was in an exhibition of pictures for sale at the Château de Grandson, Vaud, Switzerland, June–August 1955 (No. 40).[12] A nineteenth-century(?) copy of approximately the same dimensions is at York House, Twickenham. (It was presented to Richmond Council by Mrs E. M. Profeit.)

PROVENANCE: Pierre Grand-Pré sale, Paris, 16–24 February 1809 (lot 103),[13] bought by Estienne (1,103 francs). According to HdG it was in the collection of the Earl of Shaftesbury, London, from whom it was bought between 1865 and 1870 by a London dealer, Sindor S. Myers; by him it was exchanged for a Turner with Louis Huth, London; by a further exchange it came into the collection of George Salting,[14] possibly in 1876, certainly by 1883.[15] Salting Bequest, 1910.

EXHIBITIONS: London 1947–8, No. 76 (cleaned 1941); Amsterdam 1976, No. 9.

REFERENCES:
General: Smith, P. de Hooch No. 21; HdG, P. de Hooch No. 189.
In text:
1. The front of the chest shows through the man's cloak and the top shows through him in the reflection. Infra-red photographs show that the chest was completed before the man was added; the front was divided into two compartments with arched tops.
2. This can be seen clearly in infra-red photographs.
3. In the Grand-Pré sale (see PROVENANCE). HdG at first (loc. cit.) thought it 'unquestionably' by de Hooch but he is known to have had doubts later.
4. G. Falck in *Tidskrift for Konstvetenskap*, vol. 9, 1924–25, p. 86. O. Naumann has also argued (privately) for this attribution, noting similarities of the reflection in the mirror with the *Self Portrait* of 1650 in Frankfurt and the *Portrait of Willem Leendertsz. van der Helm and his Wife* of 1656 in the Rijksmuseum, Amsterdam. He points to analogies in colour and technique while conceding that this would be an unusual composition for the artist.
5. In the exhibition catalogue, Amsterdam, 1976, p. 63, note 2. The attribution is due to A. Blankert.
6. J. Q. van Regteren Altena, 'Een jeugdwerk van Johannes Vermeer', OH, vol. 75, 1960, pp. 175–94.
7. W. R. Valentiner in *Pantheon*, vol. 3, 1929, pp. 105ff, and in *Klassiker der Kunst: P. de Hooch*, 1930, pp. xxxiii ff.
8. Robinson et al. sale, London, 11 May 1922 (lot 146); later with Sabin, London. Destroyed during the Second World War by bombing in London.
9. P. Sutton, 'Hendrick van der Burch', BM, vol. 122, 1980, pp. 315–26.
10. Sutton, op. cit., pp. 324–25.
11. For Fabritius, see C. Brown, *Carel Fabritius*, Oxford, 1981.
12. Canvas, 95 × 73 cm.; reproduced in the exhibition catalogue, pl. 9. It had been with Kunsthandel Steinmeyer, Lucerne, in April 1926 as Samuel van Hoogstraten; it was with a Hague dealer in 1938 and is presumably the picture in the possession of a Munich dealer some time before 1930 which HdG considered to be probably an original replica but more carelessly painted (see *Klassiker der Kunst: P. de Hooch*, p. 295, note to p. 244).
13. As by P. de Hooch.
14. According to HdG's MS annotation in his own copy of his *Catalogue Raisonné* at the RKD.
15. In one of Salting's notebooks (in the National Gallery archives) is the following note concerning the picture: 'Cost in '76 £1350'; another entry in the same notebook shows that the picture was in his collection by 1883.

OLIVIER VAN DEUREN, 1666–1714

Olivier Pietersz. van Deuren; baptised in Rotterdam, 21 December 1666. A poem addressed to him in 1697 could be taken to imply that he was a pupil or follower of Peter Lely (died 1680), Frans van Mieris the Elder (died 1681) and Caspar Netscher (died 1684). Only two signed works by him are known: *The Hermit in a Grotto* of 1684[1] (Dresden, Gemäldegalerie, cat. 1920, no. 1849) and *A Young Astronomer* dated 1685 (with Christophe Janet, New York, 1978): the latter is comparable with early works of Godfried Schalcken.[2] Van Deuren was a *hoofdman* of the Rotterdam guild in 1697, 1705, 1709 and 1713. He died in Rotterdam in the week of 4–10 February 1714.

REFERENCES:

General: HdG in OH, vol. 18, 1900, pp. 193–98; O. Naumann, *Frans van Mieris*, 2 vols., Doornspijk, 1981, vol. 1, p. 145; vol. 2, pp. 144 (cat. no. C17), 147 (C32), 163 (C99), 164 (C103), 166 (C109).

In text:

1. According to Wurzbach (vol. 1, 1906, p. 401) the date was altered from 1694.

2. Naumann (op. cit.) has made a number of tentative attributions to van Deuren on the basis of the two signed paintings.

2589 *A Young Astronomer*   *Plate 87*

He holds a celestial globe, the stand for which is on the right; in the foreground is a quadrant.

Oil on oak, 15.3 × 12.7 (6 × 5).

On the celestial globe the constellations are shown in the form of animals, figures etc., as was usual at the time. Among those visible are some of the northern and zodiacal constellations; at the top, Draco; on the left, Ursa Major and, below it, Leo; on the right, beneath the encircling brass ring, Bubuleus (Boötes).

The curtain on the right continues to the edges of the painted surface and is perhaps not intended as part of the scene depicted but as a *trompe-l'œil* representation of a curtain over the picture. Simulated curtains of this kind often appear in cabinet paintings of the Leiden School (compare Abraham de Pape's *Tobit and Anna(?)*, No. 1221 of this catalogue).

Hofstede de Groot attributed the painting to Frans van Mieris the Elder;[1] however, the drawing is too weak and the handling too imprecise for van Mieris. MacLaren catalogued the painting as 'Leiden School, second half of the 17th century'. He noted, however, its close similarity to one of only two known signed paintings by the Rotterdam artist, Olivier van Deuren (Fig. 28).[2] He pointed out in addition that the celestial globe in that painting appears to be the same and that the model for the young man may be the same. Naumann has attributed No. 2589 to van Deuren on the basis of similarity to the *Astronomer* of 1685 and in the present author's view there can be no doubt that the two paintings are by the same hand.

PROVENANCE:[3] In the possession of Messrs Agnew, London.[4] In the collection of George Salting, London; Salting Bequest, 1910.

REFERENCES:
1. HdG, Frans van Mieris No. 35.
2. *A Young Astronomer.* Panel, 31 × 25.5 cm. Signed and dated, upper right: O. V. Deuren fecit 1685. HdG as Schalcken No. 101. Collection of J. B. Lebrun; sold to T. Destouches. Destouches sale, Paris, 21 March 1784 (lot 56) (as Schalcken). J. L. Miéville sale, London, 29 April 1899 (lot 29). Mrs Holbrooke sale, Christie's, 17 February 1939 (lot 56). Galerie Heim, Paris. Christophe Janet, New York, 1978.
3. There is an unidentified inventory number – 249/2 – in ink on the reverse of the panel in what seems to be an eighteenth-century hand.
4. Messrs Agnew's label is on the back of the picture.

ARENT(?) DIEPRAEM, 1622(?)–1670(?)

Houbraken's *De Groote Schouburgh*[1] contains an account of a painter, Abraham Diepraem, who is said to have been first a pupil of a glass-painter, then of Hendrick Sorgh in Rotterdam and lastly, after a visit to France, of Adriaen Brouwer whose style his resembled (presumably in Antwerp, where Brouwer seems to have lived from 1631 onwards). Houbraken also says that Abraham Diepraem entered the Dordrecht guild in 1648 and that Matthys Wulfraat (born 1648) was his pupil in Arnhem. Finally, Houbraken adds that he knew him in Dordrecht in 1674 and that he died later in the Rotterdam poorhouse.

The only known archival records about any painter named Diepraem concern the baptism in January 1622 of an *Arent* Diepraem in Rotterdam and his death there in 1670.[2] There are a number of paintings signed A. Diepraem, all scenes of peasant life and more or less in the same style as No. 3534 below, the earliest dated one being of 1648,[3] the latest 1665.[4] These show clearly the influence of Brouwer but if their author was the Arent Diepraem born in 1622 he could hardly have had as his third master Brouwer, who died in 1638. Houbraken was only fourteen at the time he says he knew Diepraem, and it is probable that his statements are, at least in part, erroneous.[5]

REFERENCES:
1. Vol. 3, 1721, pp. 244–7 and 249.
2. P. Haverkorn van Rijsewijk in OH, vol. 10, 1892, pp.250–54.
3. Anon. sale, London, 25 February 1949 (lot 127). The date on the painting in Mainz (Gemäldegalerie, inv. no. 729) has been read as 1644 but this is probably a misreading.
4. Rijksmuseum 1976 cat., no. A1574. The date on a painting in the Princesse de X . . . et al. sale, Paris (Galerie Charpentier), 2 December 1952 (lot 68), has been read as 1677 which may be a misreading for 1667.
5. HdG, *A. Houbraken und seine 'Groote Schouburgh' kritisch beleuchtet,* The Hague, 1893, p. 64.

3534 *A Peasant seated smoking*
Plate 88

Signed on the right, in the centre: A Diepraem.

Oil on oak, 28.5 × 23 (11¼ × 9¹⁄₁₆).

Worn in many places.

The grey and blue jug in the foreground is Rhenish stoneware of the seventeenth century.[1]

In the exhibition catalogue, *Tot Lering en Vermaak*,[2] the author compared a similar scene of a seated peasant smoking with an engraving by Hendrick Barry which bears the inscription: 'Terwyl ik ijvrig rook verinis, kleijn gesneen/Denk ik vast bij mij self; soo vliegt de weerelt heen' (While I am smoking verinis [a type of tobacco], cut up fine,/I think to myself all the time, so the world flies away). If this sense is carried over to No. 3534 it gives it a *vanitas* meaning. As the catalogue also comments, the peasant in a picture of this type is himself intended as the object of humorous ridicule.

VARIANT/COPY: A variant or, more probably, a copy of No. 3534 was lot 22 at Christie's East, New York, 23 March 1984 (Panel, 29 × 20.2 cm.).

PROVENANCE: In the [B. C. Creasy] sale, London, 25 January 1918 (lot 111), bought by Dr J. Seymour Maynard, by whom it was presented (through the NACF) in 1920.

EXHIBITION: London 1978–9, No. 17.

REFERENCES:
1. The same jug can be seen on the floor in a painting by Diepraem in a private collection in New York (Panel, 41.5 × 49 cm. Signed. Formerly with Hoogsteder-Naumann Ltd., New York).
2. Ex. cat. Amsterdam, 1976, pp. 55–57.

G. DONCK, active 1627–1640

Nothing is known about this painter. There are several small genre and portrait paintings, and a *vanitas* allegory, all signed: G. Donck, the earliest dated one being of 1627, the latest of 1640. He is sometimes called Gerard (van) Donck, on insufficient evidence. He apparently engraved or provided the designs for most or all of the illustrations in J. H. Krul's *Eerlycke Tytkorting* (Haarlem, 1634), one of which is inscribed: G. Donck in Venter [sic]. (These engravings were reprinted in J. H. Krul's *De Pampiere Wereld*, Amsterdam, 1644.) The style of his surviving work suggests that Donck may have studied or worked in Amsterdam – there are similarities in his work to that of Pieter Codde – and perhaps Haarlem.

1305 (?)Jan van Hensbeeck and his Wife, Maria Koeck, with an Infant

Plate 89

Signed, towards the bottom left corner, G Donck (GD in monogram).

On the back are the remains of a piece of paper attached to the panel by two seals with the same arms (azure, an eagle displayed).[1]

Oil on oak, 76 × 106.2 (29$\frac{15}{16}$ × 41$\frac{13}{16}$).

Cleaned in 1975.

The evidence for the identification of the sitters is not known. In the Cremer sale of 1886 (see PROVENANCE) the picture was merely described as a family portrait. The present identification was first made in the *Abridged Catalogue: Foreign Schools*, 1891, where the picture is also said to be signed and dated 1636.[2] This date is repeated in the

National Gallery catalogues of 1892 and 1894, but is omitted later[3] and the present writer has been unable to find any date on the picture. Nevertheless the costume is of the 1630s and it is possible that the date and the identification rested on a document now lost. The man's gesture may well refer to his ownership of the estate on which the family is shown. His wife points to a basket of grapes which is a symbol of her fertility ('Thy wife shall be as a fruitful vine . . .' Psalm 128:3).[4] The landscape background seems to be by another hand.

PROVENANCE: J. H. Cremer sale, Amsterdam, 26 October 1886 (lot 21),[5] bought by Goedhart (1,475 guilders). Purchased from S. Richards, 1890.

REFERENCES:
1. These are not the van Hensbeeck arms as given in J. B. Rietstap, *Armorial général*, 1950 ed., vol. 2, p. 929.
2. The entry is apparently the work of Sir Frederick Burton, and appears also in the National Gallery *Annual Report . . . for 1890*, p. 11.
3. The 1898 and 1901 catalogues have a facsimile of the signature; no date is mentioned.
4. See the discussion by D.R. Smith in *Art Bulletin*, vol. 64, 1982, pp. 266–7 (in which the author also suggests, unconvincingly, that Donck knew the *Portrait of a Couple* of 1633 attributed to Rembrandt in the Isabella Stewart Gardner Museum in Boston). For grape symbolism in Dutch portraiture see E. de Jongh, 'Grape symbolism in paintings of the 16th and 17th centuries', *Simiolus*, vol. 7, 1974, pp. 166–91. But see also the powerful rebuttal by J.B. Bedaux, 'Fruit and fertility: Fruit symbolism in Netherlandish portraiture of the 16th and 17th centuries', *Simiolus*, vol. 17, 1987, pp. 150–68. No. 1305 is also discussed in the exhibition catalogue (by E. de Jongh), *Portretten van echt en trouw*, Frans Halsmuseum, Haarlem, 1986, p. 224 (where an unconvincingly elaborate interpretation based on two psalms is proposed).
5. As 'Tableau de famille' by Donck.

GERRIT DOU, 1613–1675

Gerrit Dou, son of a glass-engraver, Douwe Jansz. (His Christian name is sometimes given in the gallicised form, Gerard, in contemporary documents.) He was born in Leiden, 7 April 1613. As a child he was trained by his father as a glass-engraver and subsequently with the copper-engraver Bartholomeus Dolendo and the glass-painter Pieter Couwenhorn; he was a member of the glaziers' guild, 1625–7. In February 1628 he became a pupil of Rembrandt and remained with him until 1631/2. He was one of the first members of the Leiden painters' guild founded in 1648. Among Dou's patrons were Charles II, Queen Christina of Sweden and the Archduke Leopold Wilhelm; he was invited to England by Charles II, but did not go and apparently rarely left Leiden. He was buried in the Pieterskerk there on 9 February 1675.

Dou's highly finished pictures were greatly admired and he was one of the most successful Dutch painters of his time, his reputation extending far beyond Holland itself. He painted portraits and still lifes as well as historical and genre scenes. His pupils included his nephew Dominicus van Tol (*c*.1635–76), Frans van Mieris the Elder, Abraham de Pape, Godfried Schalcken, Matthijs Naiveu (1647–*c*.1721) and Carel de Moor (1656–1738). He was the founder of the school of so-called 'fine painters' (*fijnschilders*) in Leiden which continued into the nineteenth century.

REFERENCES: W. Martin, *Het leven en de werken van Gerrit Dou*, 1901 (revised edition, in French, 1911); HdG, vol. 1; W. Martin, *Klassiker der Kunst: Gerard Dou*, Stuttgart, 1913.

192 *Self Portrait*

Plate 90

Signed on the right, in the centre GDOV (GD in monogram); the signature is worn.

Oil on oak, oval, 18.9 × 14.7 ($7\frac{7}{16}$ × $5\frac{13}{16}$).

The X-radiograph (Fig. 29) shows the portrait to have been painted over another portrait head on a larger scale.

Traditionally, this painting has been considered to be a self portrait.[1] MacLaren, however, rejected the identification, considering that the sitter 'does not have the plump round face and cleft chin of Dou'. He dated it to the 1650s. The present writer believes that it is a (slightly flattering) self portrait of *c*.1635–40, when Dou was in his mid-twenties. The best-documented portrait is an etching by Dou's pupil Godfried Schalcken:[2] though fuller in the face both here and in the self portrait of 1647 in Dresden,[3] there is still a marked resemblance. No. 192 certainly shows the same man as a painting in the Rijksmuseum[4] which is generally accepted to be a self portrait.

ETCHING: By Paul Rajon (as a self portrait of Dou).

COPIES: A copy by Miss Blackmore was in the William Theobald sale, London, 10 May 1851 (lot 2), bought by L. Grundy. Another copy was in Mrs H. McCalmont and others sale, Christie's, 22 October 1943, no. 103 (as Dirk Hals).[5] It was recorded in a private collection in Holland in 1953.[6]

PROVENANCE: Probably in the Pieter Locquet sale, Amsterdam, 22 sqq. September 1783 (lot 76),[7] bought by van Braam Helsdingen (75 guilders); possibly in the Anna Catharina Putnam sale, Amsterdam, 17 August 1803 (lot 23),[8] bought by Roos (180 guilders). Probably in the collection of Paignon Dijonval, Paris, the major part of which was bought by him in Holland, *c*.1731, the rest between then and *c*.1750.[9] His collection was inherited by his grandson, Vicomte de Morel Vindé; No. 192 was certainly in the Paignon Dijonval and Morel Vindé sale, Paris, 17–18 December 1821 (lot 21), bought by Hazard[10] (819 francs). By 1842 it was in the collection of Jeremiah Harman;[11] J. Harman sale, London, 17–18 May 1844 (lot 34),[12] purchased for the National Gallery (125 gns).

REFERENCES:
General: Smith No. 98 and Supplement No. 57; W. Martin, *G. Dou*, op. cit., 1911, No. 53; HdG No. 272; *Klassiker der Kunst:Dou*, 1913, p. 16.
In text:
1. See general references above.
2. Inscribed: G DOV [GD in monogram] Pictor Lugd. Batav./Honoris ergo/Praeceptorem suum delineavit/G. Schalcken. Reproduced in L. Münz, *Rembrandt's Etchings*, 1952, vol. 2, pl. 32c.
3. Panel, 43 × 34.5 cm. Dresden 1982 cat., no. 1704.
4. Panel, 48 × 37 cm. Rijksmuseum 1976 catalogue, no. A 86.
5. Panel, 9 × 7¼ in. Sold to Katz for 9 gns. Said in note in the National Gallery archives to be in poor condition.
6. In the exhibition of seventeenth-century paintings from collections in Gelderland, Arnhem, 1953 (no. 18): identified, without reason, with HdG No. 287 (which itself refers to two or more quite different pictures).

7. G. Dou: 'Het afbeeldzel van deezen beroemden *Konstschilder* in oude *Hollandsche* Kleeding, hy rust met de linkerarm tegen een Stoel aan, en heeft een Pyp in de hand schynende met een vrolyk Gelaat naar iets te zien . . .'; on panel, 8½ × 6 *duim*.
8. G. Dou: 'Het Pourtrait van deezen voortreffelyken Meester, met een fluweele muts op zyn hoofd, om het welke bevallige haarlokken zwieren, verders met een witte Kraag en een bruine Mantel gekleed . . .'; on panel, 7 × 5½ *duim*.
9. See Breenbergh No. 208 of this catalogue, note 5.
10. See also Breenbergh No. 208, notes 6 and 7.
11. Smith Supplement No. 57.
12. The supposed companion portrait of Dou's father in the Paignon Dijonval and Harman sales (HdG No. 291) was painted much earlier and was not with No. 192 in the Locquet sale of 1783.

825 *A Poulterer's Shop* *Plate 91*

On the wall at the back, above the shelves, hangs a painting of which only the right half is visible, possibly a biblical or mythological subject.[1]

Signed on the edge of the sill, below the peahen: GDOV (GD in monogram).

Oil on oak, 58 × 46 (22$\frac{13}{16}$ × 18$\frac{1}{8}$).

Cleaned in 1973.

The bas-relief of children playing with a goat is after a marble bas-relief executed in Rome by François Duquesnoy (1597–1643);[2] there is an ivory plaquette after the same design in the Victoria and Albert Museum.[3] The same relief appears frequently in Dou's pictures from 1651 onwards,[4] sometimes with slight variations, and in one by Willem van Mieris.[5] The old woman is seen in many other paintings by Dou from at least 1647[6] onwards; the old man in the background may be the same model as that in the Rotterdam *Quack* of 1652.[7]

The costume cannot be dated at all closely; for example, the young girl's collar appears in exactly the same form in Dou's paintings as early as 1652[8] and as late as 1672,[9] but the style and colour seem to be those of Dou's later manner (cf., for example, the Buckingham Palace *Grocer's Shop* of 1672).

So-called 'niche' pictures (interiors seen through a window or other aperture), of which this is an example, were popularised by Dou.[10]

ENGRAVING: In *Recueil d'estampes . . . d'après les tableaux du . . . Duc de Choiseul*, 1771, No. 50 (reversed).

PROVENANCE: In the collection of Willem Lormier in The Hague and one of the seventeen pictures sold by him on 27 June 1748 to the Marquis Voyer d'Argenson;[11] apparently still in the latter's collection c.1754.[12] Duc de Choiseul sale, Paris, 6 sqq. April 1772 (lot 14), bought by Brea (17,300 francs); Prince de Conti sale, Paris, 8 sqq. April 1777 (lot 322), bought by Langlier (20,000 francs); Duc de Ch[abot] sale, Paris, 10 sqq. December 1787 (lot 28), bought by Dulac (20,400 francs) for Dupré; Jean-François Coupry Dupré sale, Paris, 21 sqq. February 1811 (lot 14), bought in (26,000 francs). Purchased in Paris by William Beckford, December 1814;[13] exhibited by him at the BI, 1818. In the catalogue of the W. Beckford, Fonthill Abbey, sale announced for 15 October 1822 (lot 111); the sale did not take place, Fonthill Abbey and its contents having been bought by Farquhar;[14] in the Fonthill Abbey sale of 10 sqq. October 1823 (lot 248), bought by John Smith (1,270 gns).[15] In the collection of (Sir) Robert Peel (Bart.) by 1829;[16] purchased with the Peel collection, 1871.

EXHIBITION: BI 1818, No. 27.

REFERENCES:

General: Smith No. 44; W. Martin, *G. Dou*, 1911, No. 141; HdG No. 186; *Klassiker der Kunst: Dou*, 1913, p. 128.

In text:

1. It is described in the Coupry Dupré 1811 sale catalogue as a scene from the life of Christ but it is not possible to distinguish the subject.

2. Marble, 61 × 86 cm. It is in the Galleria Doria Pamphilj in Rome. E. Safarik and G. Torselli, *La Galleria Doria Pamphilj a Roma*, Rome, 1982, p. 33, pl. 37. A copy of Duquesnoy's relief is illustrated in D. Wildenstein, *Chardin*, Paris, 1963, no. 83, fig. 38.

3. M. H. Longhurst, *Victoria and Albert Museum: Catalogue of Carvings in Ivory*, part 2, 1929, p. 73, Nos. 1064–1853; reproduced in M. Fransolet, op. cit., pl. 5. The plaquette corresponds closely to the relief in the picture but has a landscape background.

4. e.g. in HdG Nos. 143, 152, 153, 154, 155, 177, 178, 187, 192, 193, 196, 229 and 270.

5. The Dresden *Game-dealer* of 1699 (HdG No. 204).

6. The earliest dated one is in the Louvre *Grocer's Shop* of 1647 (HdG No. 189; Cat. *Ecoles Flamande et Hollandaise*, 1979, inv. no. 1215).

7. Boymans-van Beuningen Museum, Rotterdam (HdG No. 68).

8. The Rotterdam *Quack* (cf. preceding note).

9. The Buckingham Palace *Grocer's Shop*, dated 1672 (HdG No. 187; White No. 46).

10. His earliest dated one is the Louvre *Grocer's Shop* of 1647 (see note 6 above).

11. It is in Lormier's own MS list of pictures sold by him (now in the library of the RKD): '27 Juny [1748] Marquis dargenson . . . G. Dou-Vrouw, Jongen, haas. = 1950 [guilders].' Martin, loc. cit., gives the date wrongly as 1746.

12. Descamps, vol. 2, p. 223.

13. Letters of 5 and 7 December 1814 from Beckford to Gregorio Franchi (see B. Alexander, *Life at Fonthill*, 1957, pp. 168–69).

14. Cf. [C. Redding], *Memoirs of William Beckford*, 1859, vol. 2, p. 239.

15. Smith, loc. cit.

16. Smith, loc. cit.

968 *Portrait of a Young Woman in a Dark Green Jacket and Black Veil*
Plate 92

Signed on the left, centre: GDOV (GD linked).

Oil on oak, oval, 14.5 × 11.7 ($5\frac{11}{16}$ × $4\frac{5}{8}$).

There are *pentimenti* in the neck of the chemise.

The sitter has been said to be the artist's wife,[1] but Dou never married.[2]

The problems of dating paintings by Dou have been touched upon above (under Nos. 192 and 825). MacLaren believed that this portrait, on grounds of style and costume, should be dated *c*.1655–60. The present writer believes that this is far too late: the relative freedom of handling on a small scale is more characteristic of the earlier years of his career and a date of *c*.1640 would be preferable.

PROVENANCE: In the collection of Robert de Saint-Victor, Rouen;[3] R. de Saint-Victor sale, Paris, 26 November 1822 to 7 January 1823 (lot 95), bought by Mme Hazard (501 francs). According to HdG,[4] No. 968 was in the Paignon Dijonval and Morel Vindé[5] sale, Paris, 17–19 December 1821, but it is not in the sale catalogue. It was in the Fonthill Abbey sale, 10 sqq. October 1823 (lot 220),[6] bought by Townley (29 gns); Henry Fulton sale, London, 20 June 1834 (lot 93), bought by Brind (43 gns). Exhibited at the BI, 1848, lent by Charles Brind; C. Brind sale, London, 12 May 1849 (lot 47), bought by Emery (46 gns). Wynn Ellis Bequest, 1876.

EXHIBITION: BI 1848, No. 27.

REFERENCES:

General: Smith Supplement No. 53; W. Martin, *G. Dou*, 1911, No. 103; HdG No. 364; *Klassiker der Kunst: Dou*, 1913, p. 51.

In text:

1. In the 1823 Fonthill and later sale catalogues.

2. Cf. W. Martin, *G. Dou*, 1911, p. 81.

3. On the back of the panel is a seal: 'Ricquier, notaire à Rouen'. This is presumably the seal of Saint-Victor's notary (Saint-Victor lived in Rouen; see the foreword of his sale catalogue) rather than that of the collector.

4. Loc. cit.

5. For the Paignon Dijonval/Morel Vindé collection, see the provenance of Dou No. 192 above.

6. It is unlikely that it was one of William Beckford's pictures; it is not in the catalogue of the Fonthill Abbey sale announced for 16 October 1822. This sale did not take place, Fonthill and its contents having been bought *en bloc* by Farquhar; in the sale of October 1823 much was included that had never belonged to Beckford (cf. [C. Redding] *Memoirs of W. Beckford*, 1859, vol. 2, pp. 239–40).

4189 *Anna and the Blind Tobit*

Plate 93

Oil on oak, 63.8 × 47.7 (25⅛ × 18¹³⁄₁₆).[1]

Although there is no general wearing, there is thinness in some areas, especially in Tobit's and Anna's headgear, the front of Tobit's robe and the shadows of the still life in the right foreground.

There are *pentimenti* in Tobit's right shoulder, the upper part of Anna's back and the outline of the doorway.

The subject (taken from the Book of Tobit, 2) is identified by Willem van der Leeuw's engraving after the picture (probably contemporary), which bears four Latin verses on Tobit (Fig. 30; see also ENGRAVING).[2]

In the Bell and Watson collections (see PROVENANCE) the picture was attributed to Dou. Holmes,[3] however, published it as a joint work of Rembrandt and Dou partly on the grounds of van der Leeuw's engraving, which is inscribed 'Rembr. van Rijn fecit', and partly for stylistic reasons. MacLaren concurred in this attribution and developed the supporting evidence. Van der Leeuw's engraving corresponds very closely to the National Gallery picture and there can be little doubt that it was made from the painting.[4] Willem van der Leeuw's birth and death dates are not known for certain; he is said to have been born in Antwerp in 1603, to have been a pupil of Pieter Soutman and to have died c.1665(?).[5] Very few engravings by him are known. In addition to that after No. 4189, there are four after Rembrandt[6] and one after Jan Lievens.[7] These five prints are all after paintings of the earlier 1630s, and van der Leeuw does not seem to have been active as an engraver after the 1630s. Two of the five engravings[8] also bear, like that after No. 4189, unpublished verses by Cornelis Gijsbertsz. Plemp and it seems probable that he wrote verses specially for van der Leeuw's engravings;[9] Plemp died in 1638.[10] Thus, MacLaren argued, there are good grounds for assuming that van der Leeuw's print after the present picture was made in the 1630s not long after the latter was painted (its date is discussed below) and that the picture was then considered to be by Rembrandt.

Examination of the painting shows that the execution is too dry and detailed to be Rembrandt's work but is very like that of the young Dou. Holmes,[11] however, believed that some parts of the picture are superior to the rest and too good for Dou; Bode also was inclined to this view.[12] Holmes instanced the heads of Tobit and Anna, the fire and the still life in the right foreground. MacLaren considered that the fire and Tobit's head are different from and superior to the rest. The head he believed was very close to that of Rembrandt's *St Paul* in Nuremberg.[13] MacLaren was also inclined to think that the corrections to the outlines of Tobit's right shoulder and Anna's back, and the ivy seen through the window, might be by Rembrandt, and just possibly some scattered touches elsewhere, for example in the flax held by Anna and Tobit's fur collar. The composition he thought was most probably Rembrandt's; he considered it to be similar to the *Two Scholars Disputing* of 1628 in Melbourne[14] and the figure of Tobit to be related to Rembrandt's drawing of an old man seated, with clasped hands, in Berlin, datable c.1630–1.[15]

For all these reasons MacLaren thought that the picture was painted in Rembrandt's studio, and after his design, by Dou and retouched by Rembrandt.

The present writer, however, does not see any stylistic divergence within the painting: the entire picture is in fact by a single hand and that hand is Dou's. The composition and the individual figures are clearly strongly indebted to Rembrandt: compare, for example, his *Old Man Asleep at the Hearth* of 1629 (Turin, Galleria Sabauda)[16] and his *Prophet Jeremiah mourning over the Destruction of Jerusalem* of 1630 (Amsterdam, Rijksmuseum).[17] There is, however, no need to think that Rembrandt had a direct hand in the design. There are other early paintings by Dou which show figures in similar interiors. Closely comparable examples are *Man writing in an Artist's Studio* (Montreal, private collection),[18] and *Old Woman eating Porridge by a Spinning-wheel* now in a German private collection.[19] The latter uses a model who also appears in paintings by Rembrandt. This group of early interior scenes by Dou – which must pre-date his earliest dated works such as the *Flute-player* of 1636 (Elton Hall, Proby collection)[20] and the *Violinist* of 1637 (Edinburgh, National Gallery of Scotland)[21] – was painted either when he was still in Rembrandt's studio or shortly after Rembrandt left Leiden. No. 4189 should probably be dated *c.*1632–5. The Rembrandt Research Project prefers a dating of 'shortly after 1630'.[22]

The subject of Tobit and Anna was painted several times by both Rembrandt and Dou. Two of Dou's versions, probably a little later than the National Gallery picture, are reminiscent of the present composition, i.e. that in the Louvre[23] and a lost picture known only from Reveil's engraving.[24]

On the evidence of the verses by Plemp beneath van der Leeuw's print, the subject was to be considered an exemplum of piety in prosperity and adversity.[25]

ENGRAVING: Line-engraving in reverse by Willem van der Leeuw, inscribed: 'Rembr. van Rijn inv. WPLeeuw fecit' (WPL in monogram) and 'Paupere sub tecto Tobias perpendit manes/Delicias hominum, et gaudia fluxa pius./Sorteq[ue], divitiae veniunt, et sorte recedunt: O pietas, laus est semper, honorq[ue] tibi./C. G. Plempius.'[26]

COPIES: There is a copy in the J. G. Johnson collection, Philadelphia;[27] another was in an anonymous sale, London, 25 April 1951 (lot 119).[28] Others, with variations, are in the Hofje van Aerden at Leerdam[29] and, in 1936, in the collection of Miss Bridgeman, London.[30] Another copy was with the dealer E. O. Oldenburg, Berlin, 1942;[31] and another, perhaps one of the above, in the collection of D. H. van der Poll, Aarlem, 1958.[32] A drawing after this design was in the collection of Consul Bernhard Limburger of Leipzig (d. 1905).[33] (All these copies are in the same direction as the National Gallery painting.)

PROVENANCE: There was a painting of about the same size, attributed to Rembrandt, of Tobias old and blind and Anna spinning, in the collection of the Unshod Carmelites at the Convent of San Hermenegildo, Madrid, by 1776 (the collection was largely dispersed by 1814) but this was probably of different composition.[34] No. 4189 was in the collection of John Bell, Glasgow; at the John Bell sale at North Park, Glasgow, 1–5 February 1881[35] (lot 357; 50 gns) it was apparently bought by Sir Renny Watson of Braco Castle, Perthshire.[36] On the death of Sir Renny's widow it passed to his cousin's son, Denis Elliot Watson,[37] London, from whom it was purchased in 1926.

REFERENCES:
General: Smith, Rembrandt No. 49; HdG, Rembrandt No. 66 (both in reference to van der Leeuw's engraving only); Bauch No. A6 (as Dou and Rembrandt); Sumowski, *Gemälde*, Dou No. 243; *Rembrandt Corpus*, vol. 1, No. C3.

In text:
1. MacLaren records remains of a false Rembrandt signature (Re.bra) on top of the varnish along the left edge of the beam above the doorway. This is no longer visible even under powerful illumination.

2. Hollstein, No. 4.

3. In BM, vol. 49, 1926, pp. 55–61.

4. The only variations in the print are in the ivy seen through the doorway, and in the top of the arch (which follows the picture before the alteration mentioned above).

5. G. K. Nagler, *Künstler-Lexikon*, vol. 7, 1839, p. 394, says that he was born in Antwerp in 1602 or 1603; J. Immerzeel, *De levens en werken der Hollandsche en Vlaamsche kunstschilders* etc., part 2, 1843, p. 165, gives the date of birth as 1603; both state that he died *c*.1665. He is first described as a pupil of Soutman in F. Basan's *Dictionnaire des graveurs*, 1767, vol. I, p. 266.

6. *David playing before Saul* (Hollstein No. 2). After the painting in Frankfurt (Bredius No. 490); *Bust of a Young Man with Neckerchief and a Feathered Cap* (Hollstein No. 14). After a painting dated 1633 and formerly with Sedelmeyer, Paris (HdG Nos. 431 and (?)838; not in Bredius); *'Mariane'* (Hollstein No. 15; original lost; HdG No. 519 as *c*.1634–36; not in Bredius); *'Liesbeth van Rijn'* (Hollstein No. 16). After a painting dated 1632 in Stockholm (Bredius No. 85).

7. Hollstein No. 6 (as *St Anthony*). H. Schneider, *Jan Lievens*, 2nd ed., 1973, No. 66: *A Capuchin Monk* (Spencer collection, Althorp).

8. Hollstein, Nos. 2 and 6.

9. The verses on the engraving after No. 4189 are to be found in a MS volume written in 1638 by Plemp (but containing work written earlier) in the University Library in Amsterdam. (*Cornelii Giselberti Plempii Amstelodamensis Epigramatum Libri IX Amsterodami manu Auctoris*, lib, 6, epigram 17, p. 113.)

10. See J. F. M. Sterck in NNBW, vol. 6, cols. 1134–35.

11. Loc. cit.

12. Letter of 1926 in the National Gallery archives.

13. Bredius, *Rembrandt*, No. 602.

14. Bredius, *Rembrandt*, No. 423.

15. Benesch, No. 41.

16. Bredius, *Rembrandt*, No. 428 (where its possible attribution to Dou is discussed).

17. Bredius, *Rembrandt*, No. 604.

18. HdG, Dou No. 54. Cat. Philadelphia/Berlin/London, 1984, No. 31.

19. W. Martin, *Klassiker der Kunst: Dou*, pp. 102 and 184. Cat. Philadelphia/Berlin/London, 1984, No. 32.

20. HdG, Dou No. 83.

21. HdG, Dou No. 82.

22. *Rembrandt Corpus*, No. C3, p. 465.

23. HdG, Dou No. 95. (The subject is certainly Tobit and Anna.)

24. HdG, Dou No. 48.

25. See *Rembrandt Corpus*, op. cit.

26. Bartsch, vol. 2, p. 258 (Pièces gravées . . . d'après Rembrandt), No. 43; Hollstein No. 4. A later state of the engraving has the address of Clement de Jonghe (active 1640–70). The print has *manes* instead of *inanes*. This information is given in *Rembrandt Corpus*, op. cit., p. 466 where the inscription is translated thus: Tobit meditates devoutly, beneath his shabby roof,/upon the vanity of human pleasure and the transitoriness of joy./Fate lets riches come and has them go./To you, O piety, be ever praise and honour.

27. Canvas, 66 × 51.4 cm. Falsely signed: R. (catalogue of the J. G. Johnson collection, 1913, vol. 2, No. 482; reproduced p. 335; it is not included in the 1972 catalogue). The only variation from No. 4189 is the addition of a dog at Tobit's feet.

28. Wrongly ascribed to A. de Gelder. Panel, 87.6 × 82.5 cm. The upper edge of the picture runs just above the top of the doorway and the composition has also been cut down to a lesser degree on the other three sides.

29. Panel, 45 × 36 cm. Inscribed in the bottom left corner with a monogram: WCI(?).

30. Canvas, *c*.76.5 × 63.5 cm. The still life is quite different and there is no fire. Acquired by Miss Bridgeman's great-grandfather, Sir R. Gardner, probably about 1840. (The foregoing information is derived from notes in the National Gallery archives made in 1936 by H. Isherwood Kay.)

31. Canvas, 63 × 47 cm.

32. Canvas, 54 × 51 cm.

33. Pen and wash drawing, 16.6 × 14 cm. Inscribed: G^d Douw f. (but certainly not by Dou). Ex colls. R. Willett (1808) and William Esdaile. Reproduced in F. Becker, *Handzeichnungen alter Meister in Privatsammlungen*, Leipzig, 1922, No. 16, as Leiden School, seventeenth century.

34. See A. Ponz, *Viage de España*, vol. 5, 1776, p. 273, and *Boletín de la Sociedad Española de Excursiones*, 1933, pp. 37–39 and 57. In an inventory of 1786 it is described as: 'De Rambran . . . Otro [cuadro] como de 3 quartas de alto y dos de ancho [= *c*.25 × *c*.16½ in.], representa a Tovías, viejo y ciego y a su mujer Ana hilando' (*Boletín*, p. 57) but Ponz, loc. cit., describes it as 'la pintura de Tobías, y su mujer, obra de mucha fuerza, sin otra luz que la de una chimenea, de Rembrandt', which does not closely agree with the present picture.

35. As 'Gerard Douw Interior, old Man and old Woman seated at a window', on panel, 25 × 18½ in.

36. According to D. E. Watson (letter of 1926 in the National Gallery archives), it was bought by Sir R. Watson at a Bell sale in Glasgow; he does not state the year of the sale but Holmes's statement (in the

BM, vol. 44, 1926, p. 55) that it was bought in 1894 is apparently incorrect since the only Bell sale in Glasgow was in 1881, and No. 4189 was certainly in that sale (cf. preceding note).

37. Information from D. E. Watson, 1926 (cf. note 36).

WILLEM VAN DRIELENBURGH, 1632–after 1677

He was baptised in Utrecht on 24 June 1632. He was probably a pupil of Abraham Bloemaert but subsequently was strongly influenced by Jan Both. He married in Utrecht in 1658 and joined the painters' guild in 1666. In 1668 he is recorded for the first time in Dordrecht and for the last time in 1677. Among his pupils in Dordrecht were Arnold Houbraken and Willem Bens.

Few of van Drielenburgh's works are known. He painted a number of Italianate landscapes but most of his known works are landscapes with topographically accurate town views in the background.

REFERENCES: Houbraken, vol. 1, p. 131; vol. 2, p. 147; vol. 3, p. 355; HdG in OH, vol. 13, 1895, p. 36; Thieme/Becker, vol. 9, p. 565; Centraal Museum, Utrecht, 1952 catalogue, p. 33.

Attributed to WILLEM VAN DRIELENBURGH

960 *A Landscape with a View of Dordrecht* Plate 94

The roofs of Dordrecht, seen from the south, are visible above the trees in the distance. In the centre is the Grote Kerk and, just to the left of its tower, the Vuilpoort; on the right is the Groothoofdspoort.

Near the lower edge and slightly right of centre are the remains of a signature: (D?) . . . . . . (h?)[1]

Oil on canvas, 113.5 × 195 ($44\frac{3}{4}$ × $76\frac{3}{4}$).

In fair condition. There are many small losses, especially in the sky and the dark parts of the foreground, and some worn areas in the sky. The horse and its rider have been partially erased at some time and were afterwards painted out. The man in front of the fence in the centre and the man and woman in the right middle distance had also been painted out, the canal on the right had been changed into a meadow with sheep, and a shepherd, sheep and cattle had been added in the right half along the path and in the meadow. Some of the buildings on the right were covered by foliage, and boats had been added in the left distance. (The horse and rider do not seem to be later additions.) All these overpaintings were removed when the picture was cleaned.

Cleaned in 1952–3.

For the Grote Kerk and the Vuilpoort see Cuyp No. 961 of this catalogue; for the Groothoofdspoort see Calraet No. 3024.

Until 1952 the fragmentary signature mentioned above was hidden by repaint and just above it was a false signature: A ( )uyp.[2] Hofstede de Groot accepted the picture as Cuyp's work.[3] The signature is too damaged to read but the first letter would seem to be a D. Van Drielenburgh painted a number of landscapes with topographically accurate town views in the background: the best known is his signed view of the Wittevrouwenpoort in Utrecht (Fig. 31) which in the treatment of figures and of the buildings has significant similarities to No. 960.

Van Drielenburgh is first recorded in Dordrecht in 1668 which is probably too late for the present painting which would not seem to date from after 1660.

PROVENANCE: Wynn Ellis Bequest, 1876.

REFERENCES:

1. This signature is in light buff on the dark grey of the foreground. The lower edge of the picture is much damaged and the paint has flaked off in the area of the signature, leaving the canvas exposed. The first letter is probably D but might conceivably be R. One other letter is visible, to the right of the damage. It is indistinct but could be a lower case h or m.

2. This false signature was in rather clumsy letters and otherwise unlike genuine Cuyp signatures; it is noted in the 1920 National Gallery catalogue as mutilated. It was removed in 1952.
3. HdG, Cuyp No. 428.

WILLEM DROST, active 1652–after 1663

Very little is known about the circumstances of Willem Drost's life. Houbraken,[1] who does not give his Christian name, merely says 'Drost' was a pupil of Rembrandt and lived for a long time in Rome where he was friendly with Johann Carl Loth (1632–98) and Jan van der Meer of Utrecht (c.1640?–after 1692). It has been surmised that he was the Willem Drost who witnessed an inventory in Rotterdam on 23 December 1680.[2] His pictures are signed Drost but one has Wilhelmus Drost;[3] which has led to the suggestion that he might have been of German origin.[4]

His earliest work is an etching of 1652: there are dated paintings between 1653 and 1663. His dated paintings of 1653 and 1654 are related to Rembrandt's work of the early 1650s and substantiate Houbraken's statement that Drost was his pupil. He presumably left for Italy in the mid-1650s and a number of history paintings attributed to him – notably the *Mercury and Argus* in Dresden[5] – and his Uffizi *Self Portrait*[6] show the strong influence of Loth and the Venetian painters Gianbattista Langetti and Antonio Zanchi. His latest painting, a portrait of Hillegonda van Beuningen of 1663,[7] reveals the influence of Bartholomeus van der Helst.

REFERENCES:

General: Sumowski, *Gemälde*, vol. 1, pp. 608–51.
In text:
1. Houbraken, vol. 3, p. 61.

2. Bredius, *Künstler-Inventare*, vol. 5, p. 1626. His profession is not stated.
3. The portrait of a man in the Metropolitan

Museum, New York (Sumowski, *Gemälde*, No. 335).
4. W. R. Valentiner, 'Willem Drost', *Art Quarterly*, vol. 2, 1939, p. 300.

5. Sumowski, *Gemälde*, No. 314.
6. Sumowski, *Gemälde*, No. 341.
7. Sumowski, *Gemälde*, No. 342.

Attributed to WILLEM DROST

237 *Portrait of a Young Woman with her Hands Folded on a Book*   *Plate 95*

Falsely signed near the sitter's right elbow: Rembrandt/f1666. The signature and date are much worn and the last letter of the former runs into the woman's sleeve.

Oil on canvas, 66 × 58.5 (26 × 23).

Cross-sections reveal that this painting has a double ground – red-brown ochre directly on the canvas and a greyish layer of lead white and charcoal black on top – found in many of the National Gallery's Rembrandts (see the discussion of Rembrandt No. 4930 in this catalogue).

The black dress is somewhat worn and an earlier outline of her right cheek has at some time been partly uncovered and later retouched; this repaint encroaches a little on the cheek.

PENTIMENTI: The outline of her right cheek has been altered (see above) and her shoulders were originally higher. There are apparently also alterations in the outline of her right upper arm, the top and back of her head and the kerchief she is holding. The lower part of her right cuff is an afterthought.

Traditionally this painting was attributed to Rembrandt.[1] The signature, however, is patently false[2] and the handling is too formless for Rembrandt, especially the left hand, the back of the head and the earrings; cleaning tests made in 1954 showed that these weaknesses are even greater than appears through the present brown varnish. Mac-Laren attributed the painting to Drost, pointing to similarities with Drost's few secure works, in particular the portrait of a man in the Metropolitan Museum, New York,[3] and the companion portrait of a woman in the Bredius Museum in The Hague (Fig. 32),[4] both of 1653. He suggested that No. 237 should be dated a little earlier. Bauch[5] commented that the painting's poor condition made any judgement impossible; Gerson[6] supported MacLaren's attribution; Sumowski[7] does not include the painting in his catalogue of Drost's work. The present writer believes that there are sufficient similarities with Drost's signed paintings of 1653 and 1654 to justify the attribution.

COPY: A (nineteenth-century?) copy is in the collection of the Hon. Mrs J. White Flete.

PROVENANCE: Smith has confused this picture with one in the Jean de Jullienne sale, Paris, 30 March–22 May 1767 (lot 132), 1,155 francs.[8] The present picture was in the collection of N. W. Ridley Colborne (later Lord Colborne) by 1829, when it was exhibited at the BI. Lord Colborne Bequest, 1854.

EXHIBITIONS: BI 1829, No. 73;[9] BI 1844, No. 10; BI 1851, No. 9.

REFERENCES:

1. Smith, Rembrandt No. 501; Bode and HdG, No. 499; *Klassiker der Kunst: Rembrandt: Des Meisters Gemälde*, 1909, p. 508; HdG, Rembrandt No. 855; Bredius, *Rembrandt*, first edition, 1935, p. 399.
2. As well as being in suspect handwriting, it seems to be on top of old damage.
3. Sumowski, *Gemälde*, No. 335.
4. Sumowski, *Gemälde*, No. 336.
5. Bauch, pp. VIII and 48.
6. Bredius, *Rembrandt*, 3rd ed., 1969, revised by H. Gerson, No. 399, p. 581. Gerson noted that, with MacLaren but unlike Bauch, 'I see only minor restorations in this school picture'.
7. Sumowski, *Gemälde*, op. cit.
8. Smith No. 501. Smith's description and the price he states as paid for the picture at the sale prove that he was referring to lot 132: 'Un très beau & bon Tableau peint sur bois, qui porte 25 pouces 3 lignes de haut, sur 19 pouces 3 lignes de large. Il représente un Portrait de femme vue de face & à mi-corps, elle est assise, les mains l'une dans l'autre; son habillement est noir garni d'hermine; sa coëffure est composée d'une cornette blanche, elle porte au col une fraise.' In any case no other painting in the Jullienne sale can possibly be identified with the National Gallery picture.
9. Although the BI catalogue merely describes it as 'Rembrandt Portrait of a Lady', its identity with the National Gallery picture is proved by the painting of the interior of the BI in 1829 by John Scarlett Davis which shows it on the walls of the Institution (collection of Lt.-Col. A. Heywood Lonsdale, Shavington; reproduced in *Connoisseur*, vol. 33, 1912, p. 215).

HENDRICK DUBBELS, 1621–1707

Hendrick Jacobsz. Dubbels. He was baptised in the Oude Kerk, Amsterdam, on 2 May 1621.[1] He was probably (between about 1635 and 1638) a pupil of Abraham de Verwer. There are documents of 1641, 1651 (his first marriage: he is said to be living in the Haarlemmerstraat), 1656 (his second marriage), 1663 (in which he is described as a shopkeeper), 1664, 1665 (again described as a shopkeeper, he was made bankrupt), 1688 (named as a member of the Amsterdam guild) and 1691, which record his presence in Amsterdam. On 20 October 1707 he was buried in the Nieuwe Zuids chapel in Amsterdam.

Dubbels's earliest work is apparently a signed drawing of 1641 and his earliest painting is a moonlit seascape of 1645. He painted marine pictures – seascapes, views on inland waters and beach scenes – and a few winter landscapes (in the style of Jan van de Cappelle; the earliest is dated 1655). He had close contacts with Ludolf Bakhuizen in the late 1650s and the 1660s. He was an eclectic artist, being also influenced by the style of the van de Veldes (in the years before they left for London in 1672) and later by that of Abraham Storck.

REFERENCES: General: Bredius, *Künstler-Inventare*, vol. 6, pp. 1879–85; A. Bredius, OH, 1885, p. 151.
In text: 1. The present writer is grateful to Ulrike Middendorf (Münster) for archival material (notably the dates of baptism and burial) which considerably supplements that discovered by Bredius.

2587 *A Dutch Yacht and Other Vessels Becalmed near the Shore*

Plate 96

On the right is a States yacht (*statenjacht*) with Dutch colours. In the left distance are anchored a man-of-war, broadside on, with a red and white vane, and another States yacht with Dutch colours, stern on, firing a salute.

Oil on canvas, 48.3 × 48.1 (19 × 18$\frac{15}{16}$).

Cleaned in 1957. The rigging is slightly worn. There is a prominent craquelure.

Attributed to Jan van de Cappelle by Hofstede de Groot.[1] It is in fact a characteristic work of Dubbels, in which he shows the influence of the younger van de Velde rather than that of van de Cappelle.[2]

PROVENANCE: In the collection of S. Herman de Zoete, Hayes, by 1884, when exhibited at the RA; S. H. de Zoete sale, London, 8–9 May 1885 (lot 213),[3] bought by Agnew[4] (380 gns). Exhibited by James Knowles at the RA; Sir James Knowles sale, London, 27–29 May 1908 (lot 419), bought by Colnaghi and Co. (1,050 gns) for George Salting. Salting Bequest, 1910.

EXHIBITIONS: RA 1844, No. 109;[5] RA 1895, No. 61.[6]

REFERENCES:
1. See HdG, Cappelle No. 38.
2. Compare, for example, the signed painting of a calm sea in the Rijksmuseum: 1976 catalogue, no. A 687.
3. The picture appears in the sale catalogue as by J. van de Cappelle but was apparently sold as by W. van de Velde since the latter's name is substi-tuted in manuscript in the auctioneer's copy of the catalogue.
4. HdG, loc. cit., gives Knowles as the purchaser, but the auctioneer's copy of the catalogue has Agnew.
5. As by van de Cappelle.
6. As by van de Cappelle.

KAREL DUJARDIN, *c.*1622–1678

He was probably born in Amsterdam and may have been the son of the painter Guilliam du Gardin (born 1597), a member of the du Gardyn family of Amsterdam's regent class. Guilliam's only signed painting, *The Finding of Moses* (Amsterdam, Rijksmuseum),[1] is a pre-Rembrandtist composition with echoes of Pieter Lastman and Jacob Pynas. In May 1672, Dujardin is said to be about fifty.[2] He may have learned the rudiments of painting in his father's studio but according to Houbraken[3] he was a pupil of Nicolaes Berchem in Haarlem. He was probably in Italy at some time between 1640 and 1650; Brochhagen[4] dates his stay in Italy around 1646/7. Houbraken[5] says that in Rome he was a member of the *Schildersbent*, the Netherlandish artists' society, where he was given the name *Bokkebaart* (goat's beard). In 1650 a Carel du Gardin 'coopman' was in Amsterdam preparing to visit France.[6] According to Houbraken,[7] Dujardin married in Lyons, a popular stopping point for Netherlandish painters on the way to and from Italy. By September 1652 Dujardin was back in Amsterdam where he made a will.[8] He was still living there in 1655[9] but in October 1656 was a member of *Pictura*, the newly founded painters' fraternity in The Hague.[10] He is mentioned again in the records of *Pictura* in 1657 and 1658 but in May 1659 is said to have gone to live in Amsterdam.[11] He apparently stayed in the city until 1675;[12] he painted a group portrait of the governors of the Amsterdam house of correction in 1669.[13] He went to Italy, probably for the second time, in 1675.[14] He visited Tangier in North Africa in October 1675.[15] In Italy he stayed largely in Rome.[16] He was in Rome in 1678[17] but died in Venice in November of that year.[18]

The largest single part of Dujardin's oeuvre is his idealised Italianate landscapes in

Berchem's manner; his work, however, is remarkably varied. In the years 1654–6 he painted landscapes with animals close in style to those of Paulus Potter. He also painted animal and genre scenes, *bambocciate*, history paintings (some – as No. 6296 of this catalogue – on a monumental scale) and portraits. There are dated paintings of every year from 1650 onwards. He also made about fifty etchings of landscapes and animals.

REFERENCES:

General: HdG, vol. 9, 1926; E. Brochhagen, 'Karel Dujardin, Ein Betrag zum Italianismus in Holland im 17. Jahrhundert', Diss. Cologne, 1958; ex. cat. Utrecht 1965, pp. 195ff; L. Salerno, *Landscape Painters of the Seventeenth Century in Rome*, Rome, 1977, vol. 2, pp. 738ff.

In text:

1. 1976 cat., A 1572.
2. OH, vol. 4, 1886, p. 279.
3. Houbraken, vol. 3, p. 56.
4. Brochhagen, op. cit., pp. 3ff. There is an extended discussion of the question of Dujardin's visit to Italy in the 1640s in ex. cat. Utrecht, 1965, op. cit., p. 196, note 3.
5. Houbraken, vol. 2, p. 352, and vol. 3, pp. 56 and 218.
6. Bredius in OH, vol. 24, 1906, pp. 223–24: Carel du Gardin (sic) is said to be a 'coopman, staende op sijn vertreck omme te gaen naar Parijs'. The identification is not certain but Brochhagen (op. cit., p. 3) claims that the self-portrait drawing in Berlin, signed 'Du jardin fecit Paris', belongs stylistically to this period and that some paintings apparently of this period show the influence of Sebastian Bourdon (pp. 25ff and 105ff).
7. Houbraken, vol. 3, p. 56.
8. Bredius in OH, vol. 8, 1890, p. 233.
9. OH, 1885, p. 157.
10. Obreen, vol. 4, p. 60.
11. Obreen, vol. 4, p. 127.
12. He is last documented in Amsterdam in February and November 1674 (OH, 1890, p. 233). According, however, to Bredius (OH, 1906, p. 224), there are Italian drawings by Dujardin dated 1674 (cf. Brochhagen, op. cit., p. 7, note 52).
13. Rijksmuseum, Amsterdam, 1976 cat., no. C4.
14. He was still in Amsterdam in November 1674 (see above, note 12); there is a landscape signed by him 'K. Du Jardin Fec. Roma 1675' (Antwerp, Museum voor Schone Kunsten; 1958 cat., no. 965; HdG no. 255 as dated 1674).
15. His visit to Tangier, in the company of his friend from Amsterdam, Jan Reynst, was discussed for the first time in ex. cat. Utrecht 1965, op. cit.
16. Houbraken, vol. 3, pp. 59–60.
17. There is a painting, *The Riding School*, signed and dated Roma 1678, in Dublin, National Gallery of Ireland (Dublin, *Dutch Paintings*, pp. 38–9, No. 544). HdG No. 274; ex. cat. Utrecht 1965, op. cit., no. 132.
18. Houbraken, vol. 3, p. 60.

826 Farm Animals in the Shade of a Tree, with a Boy and a Sleeping Herdswoman

Plate 97

Signed in the bottom right corner: · K · DU · JARDIN · fe/1656 (the N reversed).

Oil on canvas, 34.6 × 39.7 (13⅝ × 15⅝).

The influence of Paulus Potter is very marked in this picture.

PROVENANCE: In the collection of the Duc de Praslin;[1] Choiseul-Praslin sale, Paris, 18 sqq. February 1793 (lot 78), bought by Boucher (15,200 francs); Robit sale, Paris, 11 sqq. May 1801 (lot 52), bought by Lafontaine (9,020 francs), probably for Bryan who brought it to England[2] and exhibited it for sale with other pictures from the Robit collection in London, November 1801–May 1802 (No. 31). Sold to Sir Simon H. Clarke, Bart., who exhibited it at the BI, 1818; BI, 1837, lent by Lady Clarke. Sir Simon H. Clarke sale, London, 8–10 May 1840 (lot 51), bought by Seguier (930 gns), probably for Sir Robert Peel, Bart., in whose collection it certainly was by 1842.[3] Purchased with the Peel collection, 1871.

EXHIBITIONS: BI 1818, No. 30; BI 1837, No. 155.

REFERENCES:
General: Smith No. 43 and Supplement No. 11; HdG No. 64.
In text:
1. See pp. iv–v of the foreword to the Choiseul-Praslin 1793 sale catalogue.
2. Buchanan, vol. 2, pp. 36 and 48–49.

3. Smith, Supplement No. 11. A MS note in a copy of Smith's catalogue, which may be his own, reads (vol. 5, p. 247, No. 43): 'Sold with the Coll[n] of Sir S Clarke at Christie and Co. in 1840 for 930[gs] Bo[t] by Sir Rob[t] Peel Bar[t].'

827 *A Woman and a Boy with Animals at a Ford* Plate 98

Signed on the left, on the lower part of the rock: K · DU · JARDIN/fe/1657 (the N is reversed).

Oil on canvas, 37.7 × 43.5 (14$\frac{7}{8}$ × 17$\frac{1}{8}$); the painted surface made up by later additions at each side to a width of 44.5 cm. (these additions are covered by the frame).

Cleaned in 1970.

The woman and the mule are repeated in reverse, in an etching by Dujardin.[1]

PROVENANCE: Possibly in the collection of Pieter Leendert de Neufville by 1752.[2] In the Chevalier de C[lesne] sale, Paris, 4–7 December 1786 (lot 35), bought by Le Brun (4,000 francs); Alexis Delahante sale, London, 14 July 1821 (lot 120),[3] 430 gns.[4] Exhibited at the BI, 1822, lent by Joseph Barchard. In the collection of Sir Robert Peel, Bart., by 1834;[5] purchased with the Peel collection, 1871.

EXHIBITION: BI 1822, No. 32.

REFERENCES:
General: Smith No. 41; HdG No. 185.
In text:
1. Hollstein, vol. 6, B27; signed, top left, but not dated. Noted by Brochhagen, op. cit., p. 41, note 169.
2. 'Een Landschapje daar een Vrouwtje in 't water gaat met eenige Beesjes door C. du Jardin.' 1 voet 1$\frac{1}{2}$ duim × 1 voet 5 duim (Hoet, vol. 2, p. 514). This picture was not in the P. Leendert de Neufville sale, Amsterdam, 19 June 1765 (cf. Terwesten, pp. 468–77), and does not figure in HdG's catalogue of Dujardin's works.

3. 'Landscape, Cattle and Figures.' There is a MS note (made before 1830) in the copy of the Delahante sale catalogue in the RKD: 'Now in the Colln./of Mr Peel figures passing a Brook/among them is a Boy making water.'
4. A MS note at the end of Sir Abraham Hume's copy of the Delahante sale catalogue (now in the Courtauld Institute Library) states: 'Mostly bt. in.' HdG mistakenly gives the name of the purchaser as Phillips; this was the name of the auctioneer.
5. Smith, loc. cit.

828 *A Woman with Cattle and Sheep in an Italian Landscape* Plate 99

Signed, bottom right: K · D · J ·

Oil on copper,[1] 22.6 × 29.4 (8$\frac{7}{8}$ × 11$\frac{9}{16}$).

Cleaned in 1981.

MacLaren considered this to be 'probably a work of the early 1650s'. Brochhagen[2] preferred to date it *c.*1646/7, that is, at the beginning of Dujardin's first visit to Italy.

PROVENANCE: Jacobus Willemsen sale, Middelburg, 16–17 August 1780 (lot 3). In the collection of Robert de Saint-Victor, Rouen; Robert de Saint-Victor sale, Paris, 7 sqq. January 1823 (lot 149), bought by Emmerson (2,120 francs). In the collection of Sir Robert Peel, Bart., by 1834.[3] Purchased with the Peel collection, 1871.

REFERENCES:
General: Smith No. 75; HdG No. 65.
In text:
1. The copper panel has been prepared for painting
with a thin layer of tin.

2. Brochhagen, op. cit., p. 18.
3. Smith, loc. cit.

985 *Sheep and Goats*

Plate 100

Signed, bottom left: K DV IARDIN f 1673 (very small; the N reversed).

Oil on copper, 18 × 20.9 ($7\frac{1}{8}$ × $8\frac{1}{4}$).

Dujardin etched this composition in 1655.[1]

PROVENANCE: Probably in the Charles Scarisbrick sale, London, 11 sqq. May 1861 (lot 12),[2] bought by Pearce[3] (51 gns). Wynn Ellis Bequest, 1876.

REFERENCES:
General: HdG No. 66.
In text:
1. Hollstein, vol. 6, B33. Noted by Brochhagen, op. cit., p. 97.

2. (K. Dujardin) 'A small landscape with sheep and goats'.
3. Pearce seems to have bought frequently for Wynn Ellis (cf. Berchem No. 1004, note 3).

1680 *Portrait of a Young Man (Self Portrait?)*

Plate 101

Oil on canvas, 62 × 52.5 ($24\frac{1}{2}$ × $20\frac{5}{8}$).

Cleaned in 1981–2. A false signature, on the left, at shoulder level, was removed during cleaning. There are some paint losses along the top edge and some parts of the face and collar are worn.

X-radiographs (Fig. 33) of the painting show beneath the visible head another head facing in the opposite direction, turned a quarter to the right. Analysis of the panel layers reveals the presence of a third head apparently between these two.[1] The X-radiograph also reveals that the shape of the collar has been altered.

The portrait was first described as a self portrait in 1899.[2] There is a drawing by Dujardin in the British Museum[3] signed and dated 1658, which may show the same man somewhat older: the pose in that drawing supports the traditional identification of it as a self portrait, although he looks younger than Dujardin's age of thirty-six or thirty-seven in 1658.

There is a drawing by Jan Stolker (1724–85)[4] which according to the inscription is a copy after a portrait of Dujardin by Ferdinand Bol painted in 1658.[5] It is inscribed *Aetatis 23* which if this repeats an original inscription on a portrait by Bol rules out Dujardin who was about thirty-six at that time. The head and shoulders in Stolker's drawing correspond exactly (in reverse) with the bust engraved in Houbraken's *Groote Schouburgh* as a likeness of Dujardin.[6] The man in Stolker's drawing does not appear to be the same man – both are dated 1658 – as in the British Museum drawing.

In short, there is no authenticated likeness of Dujardin and the weight of evidence makes it unlikely that No. 1680 is a self portrait.[7] A number of other paintings have been identified as self portraits of Dujardin – among these paintings in the Louvre,[8] Hanover,[9] Philadelphia[10] – but each seems to show a different man and none resembles the sitter in No. 1680 or the drawings discussed above. A portrait in the Rijksmuseum,[11] however, may show the same man as in Stolker's drawing.

Brochhagen[12] considers that the painting (which he believed to be a self portrait) was painted c.1655/6 in Amsterdam, shortly before the artist moved to The Hague.

COPY: A copy by Ferdinand Roybet (1840–1920) was in Anon. sale, Sotheby's, 31 July 1974 (lot 266) (£200: bought by Cutler).[13]

PROVENANCE: In the [M. H. Colnaghi] sale, London, 4 March 1899 (lot 26), bought by Horace Buttery (165 gns), from whom it was purchased in the same year.

REFERENCES:
General: HdG No. 395.
In text:
1. For a full discussion of the X-radiograph and the paint analysis, see J. Dunkerton and A. Roy, 'Interpretation of the X-ray of du Jardin's "Portrait of a Young Man"', *National Gallery Technical Bulletin*, vol. 6, 1982, pp. 19–25.
2. In the catalogue of the Colnaghi sale of 1899.
3. Hind, vol. 3, p. 123 (no. 1), pl. 65. The way in which the sitter's left arm is drawn, with the hand hidden, suggests it may be a self portrait drawn from a reflection in a mirror.
4. Discussed and illustrated by M. N. Benisovich, 'Notes sur Jan Stolker (1724–1785)', OH, vol. 61, 1946, fig. 1, pp. 185–88. At that time the drawing was in a private collection, New York.
5. A. Blankert (*Ferdinand Bol*, Doornspijk, 1982; cat. no. R140) does not consider the drawing to record an original by Bol.
6. Engraved by Jacob Houbraken in Houbraken, vol. 3, pl. D, opposite p. 40.
7. Brochhagen, op. cit., devotes an excursus (pp. 135–37) to the whole question of Dujardin's self portraits. He considers Stolker's drawing to record a

lost Bol portrait of Dujardin. On this basis he accepts as self portraits (pp. 105–10) the portrait formerly in Berlin and dated 1652 (HdG No. 388; destroyed during the Second World War); a drawing in the Kupferstichkabinett, Berlin-Dahlem, signed 'K. du Jardin fe. Paris' (inv. no. 6697); No. 1680 (as having been painted in Amsterdam c.1655/6); a portrait in the Louvre of 1657 (1979 cat. no. 140, as 'Portrait of a Man, formerly Self Portrait'); the British Museum drawing of 1658 (see above, note 3); and the painting in the Rijksmuseum (HdG No. 370; 1976 cat. no. A190).
8. HdG No. 372; see above, note 7.
9. Dated 1666; 1954 catalogue no. 89; HdG No. 371. Discussed by Brochhagen, op. cit., p. 113 (as *Portrait of a Man*).
10. HdG No. 373. Johnson collection, Philadelphia Museum of Art; 1972 cat. no. 609 (as formerly attributed to Dujardin). The attribution to Dujardin is rejected by Brochhagen, op. cit., p. 109, note 371.
11. See above, note 6.
12. Brochhagen, op. cit., p. 107; see above, note 7.
13. Canvas, 62 × 52 cm.

6296 *The Conversion of St Paul*   Plate 102

St Paul is in the right foreground; one of the cherubs above on the left holds a torch and (?) an olive branch.

Signed, bottom left: K du IARDIN. fe/1662 (the N is reversed).

Oil on canvas, 186.5 × 134.5 (73$\frac{1}{2}$ × 53).

Cleaned in 1959. There is some wearing in the sky. There is patchy discoloration in the brilliant blue cloak of the saint. This is due to deterioration of the smalt used as a drier for ultramarine in oil medium.[1]

Brochhagen[2] has noted that the composition is based on a print by Antonio Tempesta (Fig. 34),[3] whose work was widely circulated in the Netherlands and was influential on a number of Dutch artists, among them Rembrandt and Bol. There is certainly a striking resemblance between the most prominent horse on the left in No. 6296 and St Paul's horse in the print, and there is a similarity between the pose of the bearded and helmeted rider and his horse in the middle ground on the right of No. 6296 and the rider in the foreground on the right of the print. The screaming soldier on the left in No. 6296 can be paralleled in various soldiers in the Tempesta print. The prominent flag is similar to that held by the rider in the right foreground of Tempesta's print. Otherwise the compositions are very different, not least in No. 6296 being upright in format and Tempesta's print being oblong. Certain dissimilarities point up the unusual iconographic features of No. 6296.[4] In the print the fallen St Paul occupies a prominent central position while Christ can be seen in the clouds delivering the rebuke 'Saule, Saule quid me persequeris'. In No. 6296, St Paul is presumably the turbaned figure seen from behind on the right while Christ is represented by the cherubs.

The Conversion of St Paul was very rarely represented in the Netherlands in the seventeenth century.[5] Both the subject and the size of the painting point to its being a commissioned painting and it is possible that it was commissioned by the family of Jan François d'Orvielle in whose sale it was in Amsterdam in 1705. There is a painting by Dujardin similar in size and in the scale of the figures, said to show St Paul healing the sick at Lystra and to have formerly borne the date 1663.[6]

The figure of a bearded man, naked but for a loincloth, lying in the left middle ground is reminiscent of river gods in Italian High Renaissance prints such as Marcantonio's *Judgement of Paris*.

PROVENANCE: Jan François d'Orvielle sale, Amsterdam, 15 July 1705 (lot 60), 440 guilders;[7] anonymous sale, Amsterdam, 15 May 1708 (lot 8), 190 guilders;[8] J. H. Troost van Groenendoelen sale, Amsterdam, 29 sqq. August 1774 (lot 3), 855 guilders. According to Smith it was in an anonymous sale at Foster's, London, in 1834 and was bought in (£200).[9] Edward Solly sale, London, 31 May 1837 (lot 82),[10] bought by Talbot (96 gns). In the collection of Christopher Rice Mansel Talbot at Margam Castle, Port Talbot, which passed to Miss Emily Charlotte Talbot (d. 1918); Margam Castle sale, 29 October 1941 (lot 384), bought for Mrs van der Elst (50 gns); in the catalogue of Mrs Violet van der Elst's sale, London, 11 March 1959 (lot 224) but withdrawn before the sale. Presented by Mrs Violet van der Elst, July 1959.

REFERENCES:
General: Smith, Supplement No. 1; HdG No. 25.
In text:
1. J. Plesters, 'A Preliminary Note on the Incidence of Discolouration of Smalt in Oil Media', *Studies in Conservation*, 14, 1969, p. 71.
2. Brochhagen, op. cit., p. 73.
3. Bartsch, vol. 35, B496.
4. For the iconography of the Conversion of St Paul, see E. von Dobschütz in *Repertorium für Kunstwissenschaft*, 1929, pp. 87ff; W. Friedländer, *Caravaggio Studies*, 1955, pp. 3ff; S. Hohenstein, 'Die Ikonographie der Bekehrung Pauli', unpublished dissertation, Frankfurt, 1956.
5. It was treated at least four times by Benjamin Cuyp (Vienna, Gemäldegalerie der Akademie der bildenden Künste: cat. 1961, no. 53; Zurich, Kunsthaus, Ruzicka collection: cat. 1949/50, no. 7; sale, Van Maru and Bignell, The Hague, 3 March 1967,

no. 56; sale, Mak van Waay, Amsterdam, 14 April 1942, no. 5), once by Aelbert Cuyp (ex-Wetzlar collection, Amsterdam; sale, Sotheby Mak van Waay, Amsterdam, 9 June 1977, No. 66, now private collection, New York) and once by Saloman van Ruysdael (W. Stechow, *Salmon van Ruysdael*, second edition, Berlin, 1975, cat. no. 120A). The subject was treated far more frequently in Flanders by the Rubens studio, Frans Francken the Younger and a number of the Frankenthal landscapists.
6. Canvas, 179 × 139 cm. Brochhagen, op. cit., pp. 67 and 69. Sold at Christie's, 11 December 1987, lot 29 (£310,000).
7. Hoet, vol. 1, p. 84.
8. Hoet, vol. 1, p. 121.
9. Smith, op. cit. It is not traceable in any of the anonymous sales at Foster's in 1834 listed in Lugt.
10. As from the 'D'Orville' collection, Amsterdam.

DUTCH SCHOOL, *c.*1635–1640

3725 *Portrait of a Young Man in Black* *Plate 103*

On the right is a small crowned Cupid(?) seated on a flaming heart which he seems to be piercing with an arrow; below this device is an inscription: Sic puer ille manet.

Oil on canvas, 73.8 × 58.2 (29$\frac{1}{16}$ × 22$\frac{15}{16}$).

In the Townshend collection (see PROVENANCE) the sitter was called Lucius Cary, Viscount Falkland. Lord Falkland was born in 1609 or 1610 and succeeded his father as 2nd Viscount in 1633. He played a prominent part in the events leading up to the Civil War and died for the royalist cause at the battle of Newbury in 1643. The man here, however, bears no resemblance to the portrait in the collection of the Duke of Devonshire,[1] which was identified as the 2nd Viscount Falkland by 1707.[2]

Judging by the costume, this portrait is of the second half of the 1630s, in any case not later than the first years of the 1640s. It was once catalogued as 'Anglo-Dutch', presumably because of a superficial resemblance to some of Cornelius Johnson's works of the 1630s, but it seems much more likely on stylistic grounds that it was painted in Holland. The lack of individuality in the style and the unsatisfactory condition of the painting make attribution to any specific artist too speculative; it is perhaps the work of a minor painter associated with the school of The Hague.

PROVENANCE: In the collection of the 6th Marquess Townshend, Raynham Hall, Norfolk; in his sale, London, 5–7 March 1904 (lot 13),[3] bought by J. G. Griffiths (70 gns). John G. Griffiths Bequest, 1923.

REFERENCES:
1. Formerly attributed to van Dyck and later, by Cust to Hanneman. Reproduced in M. Rooses, *Vijftig Meesterwerken van A. van Dyck*, 1900, between pp. 104 and 105.
2. The Duke of Devonshire's picture was engraved (in reverse) by M. van der Gucht as a portrait of the 2nd Viscount Falkland in *The Works of Mr Abraham Cowley*, 10th edition, 1707, vol. 1, opposite p. 6.
3. As Lucius, Viscount Falkland; author unknown. The picture is not identifiable in the 1810 manuscript list of paintings at Raynham published in J. Durham, *The Collection of Pictures at Raynham Hall*, 1926.

DUTCH SCHOOL, *c.*1640–1645

145 *Portrait of a Man* *Plate 104*

Oil on oak, 31.1 × 24.3 (12$\frac{1}{4}$ × 9$\frac{9}{16}$).

The bitumen craquelure visible on the background and parts of the face appears to be in the areas of retouching, not in the original paint.

At one time attributed to Bartholomeus van der Helst;[1] Hofstede de Groot rightly pointed out that it has nothing to do with him.[2] The costume is of the 1640s, probably the earlier half. Although there is no reason to suppose it is not a seventeenth-century work, the very inferior quality and small size suggest that it may be a copy, perhaps after some painter of the Amsterdam school.

PROVENANCE: Lt.-Col. John Harvey Ollney Bequest,[3] 1837. On loan to the National Gallery of Scotland, 1862–1927.

REFERENCES:
1. National Gallery catalogue, 1838–61.
2. In OH, vol. 11, 1893, p. 131; J. J. de Gelder, *B. van der Helst*, 1921, No. 195, as doubtful.
3. As by Rembrandt.

DUTCH SCHOOL, *c.*1640–1645

2546 *Portrait of a Seated Woman and a Girl in a Landscape*   Plate 105

Oil on canvas, 92.7 × 68.3 (36½ × 26⅞).

There is a *pentimento* in the outline of the woman's right shoulder.

It is not by Aelbert Cuyp or Jacob Gerritsz. Cuyp[1] to whom it has been attributed in the past. The child's costume could date from as early as the late 1630s but hardly later than 1645.[2]

The landscape may well be by a different hand.

ETCHING: Etched by C. L. Kratké, 1893.[3]

PROVENANCE: An old woman seated, with a little child beside her, attributed to Cuyp (without initial), was in an anonymous sale, Amsterdam, 22 sqq. June 1814 (lot 32 of the paintings).[4] No. 2546 was in the M. M. Zachary sale, London, 31 May 1828 (lot 59), bought by [Frederick] Perkins (30 gns). In the George Perkins sale, London, 14 June 1890 (lot 5), bought in (£525); George Perkins sale, Paris, 3 June 1893 (lot 4), bought in (6,500 francs); George Perkins sale, London, 29 February 1896 (lot 27), bought by Colnaghi (380 gns). Apparently acquired by George Salting, London, in 1896.[5] Salting Bequest, 1910.

REFERENCES:
1. In the catalogue of the 1893 Perkins sale (cf. PROVENANCE).
2. The woman's collar is in a much earlier fashion.
3. In the Perkins 1893 sale catalogue.
4. 'Een zittende bejaarde Vrouw, nevens haar een Kindje in oud Hollandsche Kleeding door Cuyp'; HdG No. 136a.
5. In one of Salting's notebooks in the National Gallery archives is the following annotation against this picture: 'cost 440 in '96'.

DUTCH SCHOOL, *c*.1640–1650

6414 *A Man and a Woman* Plate 106

Oil on oak, 40.3 × 27.2 ($15\frac{7}{8}$ × $10\frac{3}{4}$).

Some wearing in the sky.

Formerly attributed to Thomas de Keyser.[1] It is not by de Keyser but may have been painted in Amsterdam in the 1640s. It is not by any of the leading artists at work in the city at that time.

PROVENANCE: Bought by W. C. Alexander from P. and D. Colnaghi, July 1886.[2] Passed by descent to the Misses Rachel F. and Jean I. Alexander, who presented it by deed of gift to the National Gallery; entered the collection in 1972.[3]

EXHIBITIONS: RA 1952-3, No. 525; London 1972.

REFERENCES:
1. When bought by W. C. Alexander in 1886 (see PROVENANCE) and exhibited at the RA in 1952-3 (see EXHIBITIONS).
2. According to notes made by W. C. Alexander: 'Came from America. Bt. of P. D. Colnaghi. July 14, 1886.'
3. A. Smith, 'Presented by the Misses Rachel F. and Jean I. Alexander: Seventeen Paintings for the National Gallery', BM, vol. 114, 1972, pp. 630–34.

DUTCH SCHOOL, 1647

140 *Portrait of a Lady with a Fan* Plate 107

In the top left corner is a lozenge-shaped escutcheon: *de gueules, à deux lions adossés d'or*; inscribed below this: Anno 1647.

On the back of the panel is painted an inscription, now illegible, and a date: 1652; the date at least appears old, possibly seventeenth century.

Oil on oak, 84.8 × 69.9 ($33\frac{3}{8}$ × $27\frac{1}{2}$).

The grain of the wood is prominent in some places, especially the face.

The arms are apparently those of the Gillon family, Barons of Basseghem (near Bruges).[1] Judging by the shape of the escutcheon the sitter is an unmarried lady or a widow.

The picture has been attributed to Bartholomeus van der Helst;[2] there seems to be no direct stylistic connection with him but it may be a work of an Amsterdam painter.

PROVENANCE: Lt.-Col. John Harvey Ollney Bequest, 1837. On loan to the McLean Museum, Greenock, 1904-25.

REFERENCES:
1. J. B. Rietstap, *Armorial Général*, Lyons, 1950 (réédition originale), vol. 2, p. 777.
2. National Gallery catalogue, 1838–1901 and 1915–25.

Imitator of the mid-17th-century DUTCH SCHOOL

1343 *A Company of Amsterdam Militiamen* *Plate 108*

The arms of Amsterdam are on the standard borne by the man towards the left.

There are illegible traces of a partially erased signature or inscription by the right foot of the man seated on the steps to the right.

Oil on canvas, 75 × 133 (29½ × 52⅜); at top and bottom a further 2.5 cm. of the painted surface is folded over the edge of the stretcher and 2 cm. at each side, so that the original painted surface measured at least 80 × 137 (31½ × 54).

There is a *pentimento* in the left side of the gable of the house on the right.

Before the first edition of this catalogue (1960), this painting was described as seventeenth-century Dutch.[1] W. del Court and J. Six suggested that it is a copy of the *Militia Company of Hendrik Speigel* by Jacob Adriaensz. Backer (1608–51), painted for the Kloveniersdoelen in Amsterdam in 1638, of which no trace now remains.[2] K. Bauch[3] believed it could have nothing to do with the lost Backer group and thought it more probably a rejected sketch for the *Celebration of the Peace of Münster* which Govert Flinck was commissioned to paint in 1648.

Microchemical investigation has proved that the picture is certainly nineteenth century and probably post-1850.[4] It is, therefore, either a copy of a lost seventeenth-century work or a fake. The composition is not related in any way to the large *Celebration* group which Flinck painted in 1648 (now in the Rijksmuseum)[5] but there is a very superficial resemblance to Flinck's manner of the later 1640s (and also to that of Frans Hals) and the costume is in the style of those years. Nevertheless, it is difficult to believe that this inept composition and its spurious-looking background are after an original by Flinck or any other painter of the period, and it seems more likely to be a purely modern invention, possibly painted with Flinck's 1648 painting in mind.

PROVENANCE: In the collection of Edward Habich in Cassel. It appears in the catalogue of the Habich sale, Cassel, 9–10 May 1892 (lot 54),[6] but was purchased from Habich, together with National Gallery Nos. 1336–48, in 1891.

REFERENCES:
1. National Gallery catalogue, 1892–98 and 1915–29.
2. In OH, vol. 21, 1903, p. 80.
3. K. Bauch, *Jakob Adriaensz. Backer*, 1926, p. 100, note.
4. Samples of unretouched original paint from the sky and the right stocking of the man on the extreme left were examined in the National Gallery laboratory in 1951 and found to contain Prussian blue and opaque chromium-oxide green respectively. Prussian blue was not made until sometime between 1704–7; it seems to have been well known as a pigment in the second half of the eighteenth century

(see R. J. Gettens and G. L. Stout, *Painting Materials, A Short Encyclopaedia*, 1942, pp. 149ff, and R. D. Harley, *Artists' Pigments c.1600–1835*, 2nd edition 1982, p. 71). Chromium-oxide green (opaque) was known as a chemical compound as early as 1809 but was apparently not available as an artist's pigment before the 1840s (see Harley, op. cit., p. 86).
5. Rijksmuseum 1976 catalogue, No. C1; signed and dated 1648.
6. Catalogued as by G. Flinck but according to the accompanying text more probably of the Haarlem School (see also p.xii of the foreword of the sale catalogue).

125

WILLEM DUYSTER, 1599–1635

Willem Cornelisz. Duyster. He was baptised in the Oude Kerk in Amsterdam on 30 August 1599. In 1620 his family moved to a house in the Koningstraat known as *De Duystere Werelt* (The Dark World): it gave Duyster his adopted surname. The name appears for the first time in a document of 1625[1] concerning a quarrel between Duyster and Pieter Codde which took place at Meerhuysen, a country house rented by Barent van Someren (*c.*1572–1632), a painter, dealer and innkeeper, who was also a patron of Adriaen Brouwer. On 5 September 1631 Duyster married Margrieta Kick, sister of the Amsterdam genre painter Simon Kick, in a double ceremony which also united Simon Kick and Duyster's youngest sister, Styntge.[2] After the wedding both couples moved into *De Duystere Werelt*. Duyster died in an outbreak of plague and was buried in the Zuiderkerk on 31 January 1635.[3]

Nothing is known of Duyster's training. It has been suggested that he was a pupil of Pieter Codde but this may not be the case as the artists were contemporaries. It appears more likely that Barent van Someren or the portrait painter Cornelis van der Voort (*c.*1576–1624) taught both Duyster and Codde. Duyster painted small-scale portraits and genre scenes: in his *De Lof der Schilderkonst* (1642), Philips Angel praised his skill in the painting of silk.[4]

REFERENCES:

General: C. B. Playter, 'Willem Duyster and Pieter Codde: The "Duystere Werelt" of Dutch Genre Painting *c.*1625–35,' Diss., Harvard University, 1972.

In text:

1. OH, 1888, p. 191.

2. OH, 1888, pp. 191–93.

3. OH, 1888, p. 193.

4. P. Angel, *De Lof der Schilderkonst*, Leiden, 1642, p. 55.

1386 *Soldiers fighting over Booty in a Barn*   *Plate 109*

Signed on a package at the feet of the man second from the left: DVYSTER and on a bale next to the package: WCD (in monogram).

Oil on oak, 37.6 × 57 ($14\frac{3}{4}$ × $22\frac{7}{16}$).

Probably to be dated *c.*1623–24.

Duyster's treatment of this subject – unique in his oeuvre – is presumably intended to be satirical. There was both a literary and a visual tradition of the satirical treatment of soldiers. These particular mercenaries dressed in silks and velvets, quite unsuitable for a real theatre of war, squabble over booty. The soldier on the left taking aim with his firelock is in the correct position as shown by Jacob de Gheyn in his *Wappenhandelinghe van Roers, Musquetten ende Spiesen* (Amsterdam, 1608).

COPIES: There is an exact copy in the Dresden Gallery[1] and another, rather inferior, in the Nationalmuseum, Stockholm.[2] A third copy was with the art dealer Galerie Internationale (Maas), The Hague, 1961.[3]

PROVENANCE: Nos. 1386 and 1387 (below) are said to have been brought to England by Colonel Wolfgang William Romer (son of Matthias Römer of Düsseldorf, who was the Elector Palatine's ambassador in The Hague) when he accompanied William III here in 1688;[4] he died in 1713.[5] They were in the collection of his descendant, John Romer, and were inherited by the latter's grandson, Romer Williams,[6] from whom purchased in 1893.

EXHIBITION: London 1978–9, No. 26.

REFERENCES:
1. Dresden 1930 catalogue, No. 1548. Oak, 39.5 × 58.5 cm. This copy repeats the WCD monogram on the bale, and the package is inscribed: DVSter.
2. Stockholm 1958 catalogue, No. 403. On wood, 39 × 55 cm. There is the same monogram on the bale; the package is inscribed: WDVSter.

3. Panel, 52.5 × 74 cm.
4. According to a letter from Romer Williams quoted by Arthur Smith (letter of 1893 in the National Gallery archives).
5 Cf. DNB, vol. 17, pp. 184–85.
6. See note 4.

1387 *Two Men playing Tric-trac, with a Woman scoring*   Plate 110

The woman is keeping score with a piece of chalk on the side of the board. The table is covered with a Turkey rug.

Signed on the border of the table rug: WC.DVYSTER. (WC in monogram).

Oil on oak, 41 × 67.6 ($16\frac{1}{8}$ × $26\frac{5}{8}$).

Cleaned in 1982–3.

There is a *pentimento* in the area of the head and shoulder of the man filling his pipe. There may originally have been a different figure in this position.

The cast-iron stove partially visible on the right is of a kind in use in Holland in the seventeenth century;[1] the figures in relief on the front of it may be part of an Adoration of the Kings.

Probably to be dated c.1625–30.

A very similar painting by Duyster of tric-trac players in the Rijksmuseum has been related to Netherlandish traditions of representing gambling scenes as symbolic of idleness and of mortality.[2]

PROVENANCE: See No. 1386 above.

EXHIBITIONS: London 1976, No. 33; London 1978–9, No. 16.

REFERENCES:
1. Two very similar iron stoves, with different decoration and of somewhat later date, are reproduced in K. Sluyterman, *Huisraad en binnenhuis in Nederland in vroegere eeuwen*, 2nd ed., 1925, figs. 141–44.

2. Rijksmuseum 1976 cat., A1427; This interpretation is proposed in Amsterdam, 1976, cat. no. 22.

GERBRAND VAN DEN EECKHOUT, 1621–1674

Gerbrand Jansz. van den Eeckhout, son of a goldsmith, Jan Pietersz. van den Eeckhout, was born in Amsterdam, 19 August 1621.[1] According to Houbraken he was a pupil of Rembrandt (presumably in the later 1630s) of whom he was a 'great friend'.[2] He lived all his life in Amsterdam: he is recorded as having valued paintings there in 1659, 1669 and 1672. He made a number of etchings and designed pattern books for goldsmiths and silversmiths, among them Jan Lutma and Paulus van Vianen. Van den Eeckhout was also a poet: in 1657 he composed a poem in praise of his friend, the landscape painter Willem Schellinks. He was buried in the Oude Zijds chapel in the city on 29 September 1674.[3]

In his religious pictures, particularly the early ones, he is closely dependent on Rembrandt, but in the early 1650s he painted genre interiors which foreshadow those of Pieter de Hooch and almost from the beginning his portraits are much nearer to the more conventional Amsterdam style. He also painted a few landscapes: the only dated one is from 1663.[4]

REFERENCES:
General: R. Roy, 'Studien zu Gerbrand van den Eeckhout', Diss., University of Vienna, 1972. Sumowski, *Gemälde*, vol.2, pp. 719ff.
In text:
1. Houbraken, vol. 2, 1719, p. 100.
2. Houbraken, vol. 1, 1718, p. 174.
3. OH, 1885, p. 141; according to Houbraken, vol. 2, p. 101, he died on 22 September.
4. Sumowski, *Gemälde*, vol. 2, cat. no. 546.

1459 *Four Officers of the Amsterdam Coopers' and Wine-rackers' Guild*   Plate 111

In the background is a painting of St Matthias holding an axe; on its frame are carved the implements of the cooper's trade (including a cooper's adze and broad axe). To the left, part of a wall-map is visible. On the table, between an inkstand and an open book, are a seal and a document inscribed in the right bottom corner: 'Philips [sic] vandr Neer. Jan vanden (. . .)khout/Tomas hendrick Jan Hendrick' (this inscription, which is worn and faint in parts, is certainly original but the same four names were all at first written about 2 cm. farther to the left and afterwards were painted out by the artist).[1] The impression of the seal attached to the document shows a draped figure, presumably St Matthias, with the lettering around the edge: KVYPERS EN WYNVERL.

Signed on the left, behind the dog; G. V. Eeckhout.fc/Ao 1657.

Oil on canvas, 163 × 197 (64⅛ × 77½).

Cross-sections reveal that this painting has a double ground – red-brown ochre directly on the canvas and a greyish layer of lead white and charcoal black above of a type found in many of the Rembrandts in the National Gallery (see No. 4930 in this catalogue).

Cleaned in 1976. Some damage at the top edge where the picture was at one time turned over a smaller stretcher.

A. Staring[2] pointed out that the tools carved on the picture frame in the background are those of the cooper, and that the men portrayed must be members of the coopers' guild, to which the wine-rackers (*wijnverlaters*) were admitted.[3] The inscription on the impression of the seal, KVYPERS EN WYNVERL[aters] proves that his suggestion is correct. The saint in the background picture is not St Matthew, as Staring supposed, but St Matthias who was patron saint of, among others, the coopers; he holds one of his customary emblems, an axe (in this case a cooper's broad axe similar to that carved on the picture frame), and the crown above it presumably indicates his martyrdom.

The four names on the document (see above) are obviously those of the sitters, who cannot now be identified individually. Although the first three letters of the second surname are now obliterated, the whole name can be read clearly in the overpainted earlier inscription as *Jan vanden Eeckhout*. It has been supposed[4] that this is the painter's father, Jan Pietersz. van den Eeckhout, who was born in August 1584 and could, therefore, only be the old man on the left. This man, however, has no more than a very superficial resemblance to the certain portrait of Jan Pietersz. painted by his son in 1651[5] and in any case Jan Pietersz., who could hardly have been a member of the coopers' guild since he was a goldsmith, died in 1652 before the present picture was painted.[6]

Staring's suggestion[7] that the Jan van Eeckhout of the National Gallery picture is the painter's brother, Jan Jansz. van den Eeckhout (1619–69), is obviously right; although almost all the records of the Coopers' and Wine-rackers' Guild in Amsterdam have been lost, it is known that he was an officer of it at least in 1664.[8] Jan Jansz. was thirty-seven or thirty-eight when this portrait group was made and he must be one of the three younger men here. Staring thought he was most likely to be the one to the extreme right on the grounds that this man looks more like a vintner than a mere cooper.[9] But although Jan Jansz. was described as a *wijnkooper* (vintner) at the time of his death,[10] it is most improbable that he was one, at least until after 1664, since the wine-rackers were greatly inferior in status to the vintners, who in any case had their own guild. Indeed the man on the right and the older one on the left, who are the most prominent figures, are more probably coopers, who played the leading part in the guild.

Eeckhout painted a portrait of four other officers of the same guild in 1673.[11]

Schatborn has associated a drawing of a group portrait by van den Eeckhout[12] with No. 1459. The composition, however, is not very close in detail and, according to Sumowski,[13] the drawing should be dated significantly later than the painting, c.1665–70.

PROVENANCE: Apparently purchased from Héris of Brussels in 1823 by the 2nd Earl of Clancarty (died 1837);[14] in the Clancarty collection in Garbally, Co. Galway, Ireland.[15] In the sale of the 2nd Earl's collection, London, 12 March 1892 (lot 24),[16] bought by Martin Colnaghi (450 gns) by whom it was sold to the National Gallery in 1895.

EXHIBITION: London 1976, No. 36.

REFERENCES:

General: Roy, op. cit., cat. no. 126; Sumowski, *Gemälde*, vol. 2, cat. no. 542.

In text:

1. Parts of the earlier inscription can be seen with the naked eye; more are visible in an infra-red photograph taken in 1953.
2. A. Staring in OH, vol. 63, 1948, p. 187.
3. The function of the *wijnverlater* is to draw off the fermented wine from the lees into a fresh barrel (cf. H. Hexham and D. Manly, *Dictionarium ofte Woor-* den-Boeck etc., 1672; 'Wijnverlater, Drawer of Wine from a foul vessel into a cleane'); in modern English the process is known as racking. The nature of the wine-rackers' craft explains their incorporation into the Coopers' Guild.

4. Catalogue of the exhibition, London, 1929, No. 137.
5. Signed and dated 1651 and inscribed: AEtatis 67; it bears the Eeckhout coat-of-arms. In the collection of the Hubrecht family, Doorn, by whom it was

inherited from the van den Eeckhout family. Sumowski, *Gemälde*, vol. 2, cat. no. 525. Another portrait of Jan Pietersz. by his son, dated 1644, is no. 520 in Sumowski's catalogue.

6. *Algemeen Nederlandsch Familieblad*, vol. 1, 1883–84, Nos. 104 and 105; OH, vol. 3, 1885, p. 141; Staring, op. cit., p. 181.

7. Staring, op. cit., pp. 188–89.

8. Information given by the Amsterdam archivist to Staring, op. cit., p. 187.

9. Staring, op. cit., p. 188.

10. OH, vol. 3, 1885, p. 141.

11. Amsterdam, Historisch Museum (Inv. no. B5402); on loan from RBK, The Hague (NK2378). Sumowski, *Gemälde*, vol. 2., cat. no. 543. In the background is a statue of St Matthias; on the ground are some of the cooper's tools that

appear on the frame in the background of the National Gallery picture.

12. The drawing is in the Rijksprentenkabinet, Amsterdam, inv. no. A308; Rijksmuseum, *Hollandse Genre-Tekeningen*, 1973, cat. no. 32.

13. Sumowski, *Zeichnungen*, vol. 3, no. 776*.

14. The catalogue of the Clancarty sale, 12 March 1892, merely says 'Purchased from Heris, 1823'; according to the title-page, the collection of pictures in this sale was formed by the 2nd Earl during his residence as Ambassador in Brussels and in The Hague from 1813 to 1823. 'Heris' is presumably the dealer Héris of Brussels.

15. See the title-page of the Clancarty 1892 sale catalogue.

16. As *The Wine Contract*.

ALLART VAN EVERDINGEN, 1621–1675

Allart Pietersz. van Everdingen, brother of Cesar van Everdingen; baptised in Alkmaar, 18 June 1621.[1] According to Houbraken[2] he was a pupil [presumably in Utrecht] of Roelandt Savery who died in 1639 and then of Pieter de Molijn in Haarlem. He was in Scandinavia – the eastern coast of Norway and western Sweden – in 1644.[3] He had returned to the Netherlands by February 1645 when he married in Haarlem. He entered the guild there in October of that year; he is recorded in Haarlem in 1646–8 and 1651. He moved to Amsterdam in 1652,[4] where he acquired citizenship in 1657. He lived in the Conincxstraat but subsequently moved (after 1663) to the Bantammerstraat.[5] He was buried in the Oude Kerk on 8 November 1675.

Everdingen's earliest work is a seascape of 1640 in the manner of Jan Porcellis. However, after his visit to Scandinavia in 1644, he introduced a new type of landscape into Dutch painting: rocky mountainous scenes with torrents or waterfalls, based on those he had drawn there. Most of his pictures are landscapes of this kind and are probably the source of Jacob van Ruisdael's interest in this sort of view. He continued to paint seascapes: Ludolf Bakhuizen was his pupil. His many etchings are mostly of mountain torrents but include a series of fifty-seven illustrations to Reynard the Fox. He was also active as an art dealer.[6]

REFERENCES:

General: Alice I. Davies, *Allart van Everdingen*, New York/London, 1978.

In text:

1. For the biographical details of Everdingen's life, see Davies, op. cit., pp. 28–43.

2. Houbraken, vol. 2, 1719, p. 95.

3. Davies, op. cit., p. 35.

4. Davies, op. cit., p. 37.

5. Davies, op. cit., p. 38.

6. Davies, op. cit., pp. 41–43.

1701 *A Rocky Landscape with a Saw-mill by a Torrent*   Plate 112

Signed, bottom right: A V EVERDINGEN.

Oil on oak, 44.8 × 60.3 (17⅝ × 23¾).

Davies[1] dates the painting towards the end of Everdingen's career, *c*.1670.

PROVENANCE: Samuel Rogers sale, London, 28 April–10 May 1856 (lot 562),[2] bought by Emery (21 gns); William Rendall sale, London, 24 March 1891 (lot 21),[3] bought by Smart (£1 10s). Presented by George H. Boughton, RA, in 1900.

REFERENCES:
General: Davies, op. cit., no. 117.
In text:
1. Davies, op. cit., p. 209.
2. The identification of No. 1701 with the only Everdingen in the Rogers sale rests on a statement by the donor (letter of 1900 in the National Gallery archives). It is not in the catalogue of Rogers' pictures given in Mrs Jameson, *Companion to the . . . Private Galleries . . . in London*, 1844, pp. 383–413.
3. The markings corresponding to this sale are on the back of the picture.

CESAR VAN EVERDINGEN, *c.* 1617–1678

Cesar Pietersz. van Everdingen; in his later years he sometimes signed himself *Cesar Bo[v]etius van Everdingen*. He was a native of Alkmaar. In February 1637 he is said to be twenty 'or thereabouts'; in July 1661 he declared his age to be forty-four and later in the same month he said he was forty, but since he entered the Alkmaar guild in 1632 the last statement is obviously incorrect. He was the brother of the landscape painter, Allart van Everdingen (born in 1621; see above). According to Houbraken[1] he was a pupil of Jan van Bronchorst (1603–61); his style is related to that of the Haarlem 'Classicists' (e.g. Pieter de Grebber) rather than to the Utrecht *Caravaggisti*. In 1641 he painted a portrait of Alkmaar militiamen and in 1643–5 decorated the doors of a new organ designed by Jacob van Campen for the Grote Kerk, a commission which took him for a time to Amersfoort; he was still in Alkmaar late in 1647. In the following year he was living in Haarlem, and entered the guild there in 1651. He made several pictures for the Oranjezaal in the Huis ten Bosch near The Hague between 1648 and 1650. In 1655 and 1656 he was dean of the Haarlem guild. He had apparently returned to Alkmaar by 1657 (he painted group portraits of the Alkmaar militiamen in 1657 and 1659, and *Lycurgus* for the town hall in 1662). He seems to have spent the rest of his life in Alkmaar (but was in Amsterdam in 1661) and was buried there on 13 October 1678.

He painted history subjects, militia pieces and single portraits: in his *Diogenes searching for an Honest Man* (1652) in the Mauritshuis[2] he skilfully combined history painting and portraiture.

REFERENCES:
General: Van der Willigen, pp. 126f; Obreen, vol. 1, pp. 141ff, and vol. 2, p. 35.
In text:
1. Vol. 2, p. 94.
2. 1977 cat., no. 39.

Attributed to CESAR VAN EVERDINGEN

3315 *Portrait of a Dutch Commander(?)* *Plate 113*

He wears a sword belt of gold braid and has a commander's baton in his right hand. In the background is visible part of a bridge over a river, flanked by two round towers beside which is a third, larger tower.

Falsely signed,[1] bottom left: G. Honthorst f./1651.

Oil on canvas, 120 × 86.5 (47¼ × 34⅛).

Wearing throughout, especially in the flesh and hair: numerous retouchings.

The bridge and towers in the background appear to be a reminiscence of the Castel Sant'Angelo.

The Honthorst signature is certainly false and there is nothing in this style by him (or by his brother Willem, who also signed pictures G. Honthorst). J. Bruyn[2] has tentatively put forward the name of Cesar van Everdingen as the author. The poor condition (and disfiguring varnish) makes a firm attribution difficult but there are distinct similarities of style between No. 3315 and certain of Everdingen's portraits, in particular the *Wollebrandt Geleynsz. de Jongh* in the Stedelijk Museum in Alkmaar[3] and the *Albert Capelman* in the Sint Salvator-hof in Leiden,[4] both of which are dated 1648; the date 1651 on No. 3315 may be correct.

The sitter presumably wished to commemorate a stay in Rome by the inclusion of what seems to be the Castel Sant'Angelo.

PROVENANCE: Presented by an anonymous donor in 1918.

REFERENCES:
1. The clumsy signature and date are hardly worn although the immediately adjacent paint is; under magnification (× 10) they appear to run over cracks in the underlying grey background.
2. Letter of 1954.
3. Alkmaar catalogue, 1932, No. 22 and pl. 3. Inscribed on a paper on the table: Ma(·) W'G·DJ/54 1648. It is sometimes stated that this picture was painted in 1674; it was apparently paid for only in that year (according to C. W. Bruinvels in OH, vol. 27, 1909, p. 118) but the date on the picture is fully confirmed by the costume.
4. Inscribed and signed: AETA:46/AN 1648/CVE (in monogram). It was formerly on loan to the Lakenhal Museum, Leiden (1949 catalogue, No.98). Withdrawn in 1951.

BARENT FABRITIUS, 1624–1673

Barent Pietersz., a younger brother of Carel Fabritius, was baptised on 16 November 1624 in Midden-Beemster[1] (in North Holland, between Amsterdam and Hoorn). In his early days he was sometimes called, and signed himself, *Barent Maes* or *Maesse[n]*[2] (i.e. Maeszoon); this is from the name of his mother, Barbertje Barentsdr. van der Maes;[3] by 1650 he had adopted the same cognomen, Fabritius, as his brother Carel (like Carel, he was described as a *timmerman* in 1641).[4] He was living in Midden-Beemster in May 1641;[5] in April 1643 he was in Amsterdam;[6] his name appears on a list of parishioners of the Reformed Church in Midden-Beemster drawn up in June 1643.[7] He was said to be an inhabitant of Amsterdam when he married in Midden-Beemster in August 1652.[8] He may possibly have been also in Delft at some time since the woman he married was described as living there[9] and his brother, Carel, was in Delft from at least 1650 until his death in 1654; there is, however, no documentary evidence of Barent's presence there. He seems to have lived in Midden-Beemster for a time: children of his were baptised there in April 1653 and April 1655.[10] He was presumably in Leiden in 1656 since his portrait of the Leiden architect, Willem van der Helm, is dated in that year.[11] In January 1657 he rented a house in Leiden;[12] he entered the Leiden guild in May 1658 and paid dues again in October 1658 but according to the guild records he left Leiden, apparently in 1658 or 1659;[13] in 1661 he painted five pictures for the Lutheran church in Leiden.[14] He appears in a register of Midden-Beemster church members in 1665/6;[15] in 1669 he painted the cupola of a house near Midden-Beemster.[16] He was afterwards in Amsterdam, where he was buried in the Leidse Kerkhof on 20 October 1673.[17]

His earliest known certain work is the presumed self portrait of 1650 in Frankfurt which derives from Rembrandt's style of the late 1640s. It is unlikely that he was a pupil of Rembrandt; the 'Fabritius' who was working in Rembrandt's studio at the same time as Samuel van Hoogstraten was undoubtedly his brother Carel (see the biographical notice on pages 135–6). The Rotterdam *Slaughtered Ox* was apparently painted partly under the influence of Carel and has parallels also with the early style of Nicolaes Maes (it was probably painted in the early 1650s and has been supposed to be dated 1652 but the last two figures are illegible). The *Peter in the House of Cornelius* in Braunschweig, dated 1653, shows in addition the influence of Gerbrand van den Eeckhout (which is visible also in works of the 1660s).

REFERENCES:

General: D. Pont, *Barent Fabritius*, Utrecht, 1958; W. A. Liedtke, 'The Three "Parables" by Barent Fabritius with a chronological list of his paintings dating from 1660 onward', BM, vol. 119, 1977, pp. 316–27; Sumowski, *Gemälde*, vol. 2, pp. 910ff. In text:
1. A. Bredius in OH, 1920, p. 131.
2. H. F. Wijnman in OH, 1931, pp. 114 and 116.
3. Wijnman, op. cit., p. 111.
4. and 5. Wijnman, op. cit., p. 108.
6. OH, 1890, p. 226 and Wijnman, op. cit., p. 114.
7. Wijnman, op. cit., p. 116.

8. 9. and 10. Bredius, op. cit., p. 132.
11. Rijksmuseum, Amsterdam, 1976 cat., no. A1304
12. Obreen, vol. 5, p. 218 (note).
13. Obreen, vol. 5, pp. 218–19.
14. Only three are known today: Rijksmuseum, Amsterdam, 1976 cat., nos. A2958, 2959, 2960; for an account of this commission see Liedtke, op. cit.
15. Wijnman, op. cit., p. 132, note 1.
16. *Onze Kunst*, 1928, p. 88.
17. OH, 1921, p. 63.

1338 *The Adoration of the Shepherds*   Plate 114

The Virgin kneels on the left beside the manger; behind her stands St Joseph.

Signed on the lower part of the manger, in the shadow: (·). Fab(·)it(·)u(·)/ 1667.

Oil on canvas, 66 × 61 (26 × 24).

Cleaned in 1959. Worn in some areas.

At one time attributed to Carel Fabritius.[1] The composition is derived from Rembrandt's treatments of this subject, notably those of 1646 in Munich and No. 47 in this catalogue.[2]

DRAWING: A composition study of an *Adoration of the Shepherds*, attributed to Barent Fabritius in the Boymans-van Beuningen Museum, Rotterdam,[3] is related (though not closely) to No. 1338.

PROVENANCE: A 'Birth of Christ, by Fabritius' was in the Cornelis Wittert, Heer van Valkenburg sale, Rotterdam, 11 April 1731 (lot 73), 30 guilders.[4] In the collection of Edward Habich, Cassel, and exhibited with other Habich pictures at the Gemäldegalerie, Cassel, 1881–91.[5] It appears in the catalogue of the Edward Habich sale, Cassel, 9–10 May 1892 (lot 49), but was purchased from Habich, together with Nos. 1336–48, in 1891.

EXHIBITION: Cassel, Gemäldegalerie, 1881–91.

REFERENCES:
General: Pont, op. cit., cat. no. 15; Liedtke, op. cit., cat. no. 15; Sumowski, op. cit., cat. no. 573.
In text:
1. On the back of the picture is a label inscribed: 'N: 196 / Carl Fabritzius.'
2. Bredius, *Rembrandt*, Nos. 574 and 575.
3. Pen and brown ink, red chalk and watercolour. 244 × 242 mm. Inv. no. R72. Pont, op. cit., cat. no. 3; discussed on pp. 90–91. He dates the drawing to *c*.1647–50. Sumowski (*Zeichnungen*, vol. 4, no. 848*) discusses the drawing at length. He rejects Haverkamp-Begemann's idea that it is preparatory to No. 1338 and so should be dated *c*.1660–67 (ex. cat. *Rembrandt after Three Hundred Years*, Chicago, Art Institute, 1969, no. 170), preferring to place it in the first half of the 1650s. He notes that Rembrandt's etching of *The Adoration of the Shepherds* of *c*.1654 (B45) was another model available to the artist. J. Giltaij, *The Drawings by Rembrandt and his school in the Museum Boymans-van Beuningen*, Rotterdam, 1988, No. 69 (conceivably influenced by the etching and so from the second half of the 1650s).
4. 'De Geboorte van Christus, door Fabritius' (see Hoet, vol. 1, p. 370).
5. See JKPK, 1881, *Amtliche Berichte*, col. 91, No. 8.

1339 *The Naming of St John the Baptist*   Plate 115

The infant St John lies in a cradle, at the foot of which sits St Elizabeth; St Zacharias is seated on the right, writing the infant's name on a tablet. The woman with a halo, standing in the centre background, is presumably the Virgin.

Oil on canvas, 36.8 × 48 (14½ × 18⅞); this includes a repainted strip about one centimetre wide around all the edges which may not be part of the original painted surface.

A pronounced craquelure and many small retouchings, especially in the heads. The best-preserved area is the child standing in the centre. St Zacharias's foot has been painted over the cradle.

For the birth and naming of St John see Luke 1: 59–63.

The woman with a halo (see above) is presumably intended for the Virgin although she had apparently left St Elizabeth's house before the birth of St John (see Luke 1: 56–7).

Probably painted *c*.1650–5 (cf. *Peter in the House of Cornelius* in Braunschweig, signed and dated 1653). Pont[1] dates the painting *c*.1655 and Sumowski *c*.1653.[2]

There is another painting of the same subject by Barent Fabritius, signed and dated 166(.), in Frankfurt;[3] it is of different composition but the figure of St Zacharias is similar to that in the present picture.

DRAWINGS: There are two related drawings of this subject by Barent Fabritius. The one in the Staatsgalerie, Stuttgart,[4] is closer in composition: more of the room and more figures are shown, but the principal foreground groups are strikingly similar. The other, in the Albertina,[5] has few points of strict compositional similarity: the room and the figure groups have been re-arranged. MacLaren suggested that the Albertina drawing might possibly have been made in connection with studies for No. 1339 but Pont[6] related it to the Frankfurt painting of the same subject.[7] Sumowski[8] discusses both drawings, considering them to be derivations from, rather than studies for, No. 1339 and the Frankfurt painting. He considers them both to be from *c*.1665–70.

PROVENANCE: A *Birth of St John Baptist* by 'Fabritius' was in the George Bruyn sale, Amsterdam, 16 March 1724 (lot 86), 30 guilders.[9] No. 1339 was in the Edward Habich collection, Cassel, and exhibited with other Habich pictures in the Gemäldegalerie, Cassel, 1881–91.[10] It appears in the catalogue of the Edward Habich sale, Cassel, 9–10 May 1892 (lot 48), but was purchased from Habich, together with Nos. 1336–48, in 1891.

REFERENCES:
General: Pont, op. cit., cat. no. 12; Sumowski, *Gemälde*, vol. 2, cat. no. 552.
In text:
1. Pont, op. cit., cat. no. 12.
2. Sumowski, *Gemälde*, vol. 2, cat. no. 552.
3. Pont, op. cit., cat. no. 13; Sumowski, *Gemälde*, vol. 2, cat. no. 575 (as 1669).
4. Inv. no. 64/1325; Sumowski, *Zeichnungen*, vol. 4, no. 852.
5. Inv. no. 9553; Pont, op. cit., cat. no. 22; Sumowski, *Zeichnungen*, vol. 4, no. 853.

6. Pont, op. cit., cat. no. 22.
7. Pont, op. cit., cat. no. 13.
8. Op. cit., notes 2 and 3.
9. See Hoet, vol. 1, p. 303: 'De Geboorte van Johannes den Dooper, door Fabritius'. Wijnman (OH, vol. 48, 1931, p. 140) supposes this to refer to Carel Fabritius.
10. See JKPK, 1881, *Amtliche Berichte*, col. 91, No. 7.

CAREL FABRITIUS, 1622–1654

Carel (Carolus) Pietersz., son of a schoolmaster, Pieter Carelsz., was baptised in Midden-Beemster, 27 February 1622.[1] He adopted (by 1641) the cognomen Fabritius[2] which had also been used by his father. The same surname was used by his brothers, Barent and Johannes (1636–after 1693). He may at first have studied painting with his father, who painted in his spare time according to documents of 1620.[3] He is certainly the 'Fabritius', whose Christian name is not mentioned, who was a pupil of Rembrandt at the same time as Samuel van Hoogstraten.[4] This must have been after 1640 since Hoogstraten did not enter Rembrandt's studio before 1641 (see the biographical notice on pages 203–4). In May 1641, Carel Fabritius was in Midden-Beemster and then described as a *timmerman* (carpenter);[5] he was married there in September 1641.[6] He probably entered Rembrandt's studio soon after and remained there until 1643.[7] His earliest known certain work, *The Raising of Lazarus* in Warsaw, shows his acquaintance with Rembrandt's so-called *Night Watch*, finished in 1642. He is recorded again in Midden-Beemster in June 1643 and in April 1646.[8] He may have continued to live in Beemster but from time to time probably visited Amsterdam which is less than fifteen miles away. His betrothal to his second wife is recorded in Midden-Beemster in August 1650 but both he and his future wife are then said to be living in Delft.[9] He seems to have remained in Delft for the rest of his life; he is recorded there in May 1651,[10] was inscribed in the Delft guild in October 1652,[11] was living there in February and August 1653.[12] In July 1654 he was paid for painting two coats-of-arms of Delft.[13] He died there on 12 October 1654 as the result of his injuries in the explosion of the powder magazine[14] (cf. E. van der Poel, No. 1061). A few months after his death his widow described him as a 'painter of H.H. the Prince of Orange';[15] there is no other evidence that he ever worked for the prince.

Very little of Fabritius's work has survived. The earliest paintings by or attributable to him, in particular the Warsaw *Lazarus*, are closely dependent on Rembrandt, yet the *Abraham de Potter* of 1648(or 9) in the Rijksmuseum shows that he soon developed an individual style.

It is probable that he attracted the attention of his contemporaries particularly by illusionistic perspective pictures.[16] There is evidence that he made wall-paintings of this kind in Delft;[17] no such paintings have survived and the only known perspective painting certainly by him is the little *View in Delft*, No. 3714 below. Fabritius's only recorded pupil is Mathias Spoors who perished in the 1654 explosion.[18]

REFERENCES:

General: HdG, vol. 1, 1908 (German edition, 1907); Bredius in OH, 1920, pp. 129–37; H. F. Wijnman in OH, 1931, pp. 100–41; K. E. Schuurman, *Carel Fabritius* [1947]; C. Brown, *Carel Fabritius: Complete Edition with a Catalogue Raisonné*, Oxford, 1981; Sumowski, *Gemälde*, vol. 2, pp. 979ff.

In text:

1. Wijnman, op. cit., p. 106.
2. Brown, op. cit., pp. 15–16.
3. Bredius, op. cit., p. 130; Brown, op. cit., p. 14.
4. Hoogstraten, p. 11. It is clear from Hoogstraten's other references to 'Fabritius' that he is referring to Carel, not Barent (see *Inleyding* etc., pp. 274 and 308).
5. Wijnman, op. cit., p. 108; Brown, op. cit., pp. 15, 146.

6. Bredius, op. cit., p. 132; Brown, op. cit., pp. 15–16, 147.
7. Brown, op. cit., pp. 16–17.
8. Brown, op. cit., pp. 18–19, 147–48.
9. Bredius, p. 132; Brown, op. cit., pp. 22, 148–49.
10. OH, 1910, p. 187; Brown, op. cit., pp. 149–50.
11. Obreen, vol. 1, p. 54; Brown, op. cit., p. 150.
12. OH, 1890, pp. 227–28; Brown, op. cit., pp. 150–51.
13. OH, 1910, p. 188; Brown, op. cit., p. 151.
14. Van Bleyswijck, vol. 2, p. 852.
15. OH, 1890, p. 228; Brown, op. cit., p. 152.
16. Cf. van Bleyswijck, op. cit., p. 852, and Hoogstraten, pp. 274 and 308.
17. OH, 1910, p. 187; cf. Hoogstraten, p. 274.
18. Van Bleyswijck, op. cit., p. 852.

3714 *A View in Delft, with a Musical Instrument Seller's Stall*

Plate 116

In the centre is the Nieuwe Kerk and just to the left of it, in the distance, the town hall; on the right are the houses of the Vrouwenrecht.[1]

On the left is, apparently, the booth of a musical instrument vendor with, in the foreground, a viola da gamba and, against the wall, a lute.

Signed on the wall on the left: c. FABRITIVS./1652.

Oil on canvas, 15.5 × 31.6 ($6\frac{1}{16}$ × $12\frac{7}{16}$), stuck on walnut, 15.5 × 31.7 ($6\frac{1}{8}$ × $12\frac{1}{2}$). The edges of the canvas had been cut before it was stuck on the panel, and do not correspond to the edges of the latter. There is a further millimetre of painted canvas turned over the edge of the panel on the right.

Some wearing in most areas.

The view is taken from the corner of the Oude Langendijk and Oosteinde, looking roughly north-west. The Nieuwe Kerk and the town hall exist in much the same state, but the latter now has on the tower a spire added in the nineteenth century. The canal along the south side of the Nieuwe Kerk is the Oude Langendijk (now filled in). The second house from the right (in the Vrouwenrecht) has survived, the rest have been rebuilt.

The function and method of display of No. 3714 have been the subject of much discussion.[2] Its exaggerated perspective and the cutting-off of the foreshortened viola da gamba are the two principal features which lend support to the suggestion, first made by Richardson,[3] that the painting formed part of a perspective box or peepshow. On an analogy with the perspective box in the Detroit Institute of Arts which is attributed to Samuel van Hoogstraten, Richardson argued that the back of the box was originally V-shaped, but Martin[4] preferred a curved back, an arrangement supported by Schuurman.[5] There are four documents which support the contention that Fabritius, whose interest in perspective and illusionism is commented on by his early biographers, made perspective boxes.[6] Liedtke[7] has considered the various possible dispositions of the painting within a perspective box, concluding with his own original suggestion that it was curved against the back of a triangular peepshow. His proposal to mount it in a semi-cylindrical support does seem to correct the perspectival distortions of the architectural elements in the painting – the lack of prominence accorded to the Nieuwe Kerk, the angle of the houses of the Vrouwenrecht, etc. No truly comparable box survives and any reconstruction must remain hypothetical.

Wheelock[8] has discussed the way in which Fabritius painted No. 3714, suggesting that he made use of a double concave lens in accordance with recent developments in optics and perspectival theory. In order to demonstrate his thesis he had photographs of the site in Delft taken through such a lens. The present writer is not persuaded that such a device was employed and believes that Fabritius could have painted No. 3714 using traditional perspective procedures and empirical observation. Wheelock also argued that the painting was displayed flat and that it is a fragment. As has been stated above, the present writer prefers the curved format within a triangular box proposed by Liedtke and does not believe that the painting has been significantly cut down. The composition is satisfactory as it is; the edges were probably crudely trimmed at the time when the canvas was stuck down on the walnut panel.

Martin's suggestion[9] that No. 3714 may have been a study for a mural is unacceptable, as is Holmes's notion[10] that Fabritius was here influenced by Chinese compositions through the medium of Delft pottery. The present writer cannot agree with Liedtke's interpretations of particular elements within the painting:[11] for him the viola da gamba and the church present a 'worldly–spiritual contrast' and the swan is a *memento mori*. Nor is Wheelock's[12] reading of the infra-red photograph of the painting acceptable. He has written that 'in the left . . . major changes are apparent. The seated figure and the trellis behind him are later additions to the composition. Fabritius initially painted a somewhat smaller scaled standing figure gazing over the vista. His head was at the level of the protruding sign, directly above the present figure.' It may well be that Fabritius added the seated man and the trellis after painting the wall and the other principal features of the left-hand side of the composition: this would be a quite usual procedure. However, the infra-red photograph does not present irrefutable evidence of this. Nor can a standing man gazing over a vista be identified. There are, apparently, small changes in this area but only of detail.

COPY: A copy on panel was in the 'Delfts Verleden' exhibition, Delft, 1946, No. 6, lent by Jacob Mees, Rotterdam.

PROVENANCE: Bought in Naples in 1836.[13] Lent by Sir William Eden, Bart., to the National Loan Exhibition, Grafton Galleries, 1909–10. Purchased from his son, Sir Thomas Eden, Bart., by the NACF and presented to the National Gallery, 1922.

EXHIBITIONS: London, Grafton Galleries, National Loan Exhibition, 1909–10, No. 52; London, NACF, 1945–6, No. 46; London 1976, No. 40.

REFERENCES:

General: HdG No. 4; Brown, op. cit., cat. no. 5; Sumowski, *Gemälde*, vol. 2, cat. no. 605.

In text:

1. This entry is essentially a shortened version of that in the present writer's monograph on the artist, op. cit. The various arguments are given at greater length there. (The painting is also discussed by J. Elkins, '*Das Nüsslein beisset auf, ihr Künstler!*' *Curvilinear perspective in seventeenth-century Dutch art*, OH, 102, 1988, pp. 268–70, 274–6.)

2. See Brown, op. cit.

3. E. P. Richardson, 'Samuel van Hoogstraten and Carel Fabritius', *Art in America*, vol. 25, 1937, pp. 141–52.

4. W. Martin, *De Hollandsche Schilderkunst in de zeventiende eeuw: Rembrandt en zijn tijd*, 2nd ed., Amsterdam, 1942, pp. 392–3

5. Schuurman, op. cit., p. 53.

6. Brown, op. cit., p. 124.

7. W. A. Liedtke, 'The View in Delft by Carel Fabritius', BM, vol. 118, 1976, pp. 61–73.

8. A. K. Wheelock Jnr., 'Carel Fabritius: Perspective and Optics in Delft', NKJ, vol. 24, 1973, pp. 63–83.

9. Martin, op. cit.

10. C. Holmes, 'Honthorst, Fabritius and De Witte', BM, vol. 42, 1923, pp. 87–88.

11. Liedtke, op. cit.

12. Wheelock, op. cit.

13. On the back of the panel is a label inscribed: 'Bought at Naples/1836'. (This is partly on top of a painted inscription: 'Sr W. Eden. 35.')

4042 *A Young Man in a Fur Cap and a Cuirass (Self Portrait?)* Plate 117

He wears a steel breastplate and backplate.

Signed, bottom right: c.fabritius./.1654.

Oil on canvas, 70.5 × 61.5 (27¾ × 24¼).

The ground is a light cream colour: analysis has shown it to be a mixture of lead white and calcium carbonate. (It is quite unlike the double ground found in many of the paintings by Rembrandt in the National Gallery: cf. No. 4930 in this catalogue.)

Cleaned in 1976. Some wearing in the sky and in the shadowed side of the face.

No documented portrait of Carel Fabritius is known. However, the present picture has been generally accepted as a likeness of him. It certainly represents the same man as the bust portrait in the Boymans-van Beuningen Museum, Rotterdam (Fig. 35).[1]

The directness of the gaze and the unconventionality of dress and pose in both paintings support their identification as self portraits.[2] In the Rotterdam portrait which can be dated c.1648–50[3] Fabritius shows himself against a background of crumbling plasterwork with long, tousled hair, open-necked shirt and working smock. In No. 4042 he makes use of a self-portrait type familiar from the work of Rembrandt and his pupils. Rembrandt had painted a number of self portraits wearing a breastplate or gorget in the late 1620s and 1630s.[4] Thereafter this became a popular self-portrait type among his pupils: one example is an etching of 1645 by Ferdinand Bol.[5] However, while he is clearly aware of these precedents, Fabritius chooses a quite original background, placing himself starkly against a cloudy sky.

Sumowski has published a portrait of a woman, apparently signed by Fabritius and dated 1654, as a pendant to No. 4042.[6] He suggested that the sitter was Fabritius's second wife, Agatha van Pruyssen. In the opinion of the present writer, the painting is not by Fabritius.[7]

PROVENANCE: An undescribed portrait of Carel Fabritius was in the inventory of Catharina Scharckens, widow of Cornelis Smout, Amsterdam, 7 December 1654.[8] The National Gallery picture was bought in Bruges from 'Mareneff' (presumably Marneffe) by George Rimington of Tynefield, Penrith, for 400 francs.[9] The purchase is said to have been made about 1824 and the picture brought to Tynefield about 1830.[10] (A 'guerrier au teint basane' by 'Fabricius', without initial, was in the P. J. de Marneffe sale, Brussels, 24 sqq. May 1830 (lot 118),[11] bought by Burton[12] for 60 francs, but this was of completely different size according to the sale catalogue.) It passed to George Rimmington's youngest son, Reginald, whose wife bequeathed it to her niece, who in turn left it, c.1910, to her son, T. A. Brewerton of Manchester,[13] T. A. Brewerton sale, London, 12 December 1924 (lot 135), bought for the National Gallery out of the Claude Phillips Fund.

EXHIBITION: London 1976, No. 41.

REFERENCES:
General: Brown, op. cit., cat. no. 6; Sumowski, *Gemälde*, vol. 2, cat. no. 609.
In text:
1. Brown, op. cit., cat. no. 4.

2. See discussion in Brown, op. cit., pp. 38–39, 44–45.
3. Brown, op. cit., cat. no. 4.
4. Bredius, Nos. 6, 20, 22 [dated 1634], 23.

5. Hollstein No. 12 (dated 1645).

6. Canvas, 66 × 57 cm. Hanover, Niedersächsische Landesgalerie. W. Sumowski, 'Zu einem Gemälde von Carel Fabritius', *Pantheon*, vol. 26, 1968, pp. 278–83; Sumowski, op. cit., cat. no. 608.

7. Brown, op. cit., cat. no. R21 (Rejected Attributions section of *Catalogue Raisonné*). In 1987 the present writer studied the painting under excellent laboratory conditions in Hanover. This confirmed his opinion that it is not by Fabritius.

8. 'Het conterfeitsel van Carel Fabritsius' (see OH, vol. 8, 1890, p. 229).

9. According to an undated entry in a MS list of his pictures made by George Rimington, which in 1924 was in the possession of his grandson, George Arthur Rimington. In this list the picture is called 'Grumbo' [sic!]. (See *Penrith Observer*, 23 December 1924.)

10. According to *Penrith Observer*, loc. cit.

11. 'Fabricius Un guerrier au teint basanné [sic], fier d'expression, fier de touche, fier de ton; on dirait un Rembrandt.' Canvas, 40 × 33 *pouces*.

12. The name of the purchaser has been checked in the marked copies of the sale catalogue in the library of the Musées Royaux des Beaux-Arts, Brussels, and the RKD.

13. See the catalogue of the Brewerton sale and *Penrith Observer*, 23 December 1924.

PAULUS CONSTANTIJN LA FARGUE
See LA FARGUE

GOVERT FLINCK, 1615–1660

Govert Teunisz. (Anthonisz.) Flinck was born in Cleves on 25 January 1615. Houbraken[1] says he was sent to Leeuwarden in Friesland to study with Lambert Jacobsz. and afterwards went with Jacob Backer (his fellow-pupil) to Amsterdam probably in 1631 or 1632 where he studied with Rembrandt.[2] There are dated paintings from 1636 onwards. He settled in Amsterdam. Flinck had considerable success as a portraitist and received many public commissions both for portraits and for historical and other subjects. In 1642 he painted a portrait group of Amsterdam musketeers, in 1645 the large *Militia Company of Captain Albert Bas* and in 1648 the great picture of the militia banquet in celebration of the Peace of Münster (all in the Rijksmuseum, Amsterdam). He did not acquire citizenship until 24 January 1652. In 1656 he painted *Solomon praying for Wisdom* for the new town hall in Amsterdam, for which he was paid 1,000 guilders, and about this time he painted for the same location a *Marcus Curius Dentatus*, for which he received 1,500 guilders.[3] In November 1659 he was commissioned to produce twelve more compositions for the town hall at 1,000 guilders each: eight of the struggle between the Batavians and the Romans, and four of Roman and biblical heroes.[4] He executed four of the compositions provisionally in a watercolour medium (one of which, overpainted in oil by Jurriaen Ovens in 1662, was substituted for Rembrandt's painting of the same subject) but died shortly afterwards in Amsterdam, 2 February 1660.

His early works, both portraits and subject pieces, are very much in the style of Rembrandt. In the early 1640s he began to abandon this manner and model himself more on Bartholomeus van der Helst and van Dyck, who was then beginning to be fashionable, and devoted most of his time to portraiture. He became one of the leading painters of Amsterdam and received the lion's share of the town hall commissions. Flinck was a friend of the poet Joost van den Vondel who wrote a number of eulogistic poems about his work and dubbed him the 'Kleefsche Apelles'.

REFERENCES:
General: D. C. Meijer in OH, 1889, pp. 45–60; HdG in Thieme/Becker, vol. 12, 1916, pp. 97–100; J. W. von Moltke, *Govaert Flinck 1615–60*, Amsterdam, 1965; Sumowski, *Gemälde*, vol. 2, pp. 998ff.
In text:
1. *De Groote Schouburgh*, vol. 2, 1719, pp. 20–21.

2. Von Moltke, op. cit., p. 10, suggests that Flinck did not move to Amsterdam until 1633.
3. Meijer, op. cit., pp. 58–59.
4. Houbraken, pp. 24–25.

4068 *Self Portrait aged Twenty-four*   *Plate 118*

Signed on the right, towards the bottom: G.flinck/1639. The name has been partly erased and was at one time covered by a false Rembrandt signature[1] which was removed when the picture was cleaned in 1925.

Oil on oak, 65.8 × 54.4 ($25\frac{7}{8}$ × $21\frac{7}{16}$).

MacLaren identified the painting as a portrait of Rembrandt aged about thirty-three. This identification was accepted by von Moltke.[2] Although the sitter modelled his appearance on that of Rembrandt and although the painting is in a profoundly Rembrandtesque style, the features are clearly not Rembrandt's when they are compared, for example, to the self portrait of 1638 or 1639 in the Norton Simon Museum in Pasadena.[3] It was de Bruyn Kops who made the correct identification of the sitter as Flinck himself on an analogy with a portrait engraving by Blootelingh (Fig. 36) and a self portrait in the 1648 Militia piece.[4]

PROVENANCE: This is probably identical with the bust portrait of Rembrandt by Flinck, of the same size, which was in the collection of Graf von Schönborn, in Pommersfelden by 1857,[5] in the Schönborn (Pommersfelden) sale, Paris, 17 sqq. May 1867 (lot 30),[6] bought by Milberg (260 francs), and in the E. Hardy sale, Frankfurt, 14 October 1878 (lot 49),[7] 420 marks. No. 4068 was in the Dame Florence Emily Fernor-Hesketh sale, London, 6 March 1925 (lot 137),[8] bought by Permain (250 gns) for Ayerst H. Buttery, by whom it was presented in the same month.

REFERENCES:
General: Von Moltke, op. cit., cat. no. 226; Sumowski, *Gemälde*, vol. 2, cat. no. 666.
In text:
1. If the picture is identical with that in the Pommersfelden and Hardy sales (see PROVENANCE), the false Rembrandt signature was added after 1878.
2. Von Moltke, op. cit., pp. 21–22, and cat. no. 226.
3. Bredius, *Rembrandt*, cat. no. 32.
4. C. J. de Bruyn Kops, 'Vergeten zelfportretten van Govert Flinck en Bartholomeus van der Helst', *Bulletin van het Rijksmuseum*, 1965, no. 1, pp. 25–29.

5. According to the Schönborn sale catalogue of 1867, this picture is No. 426 of the Pommersfelden catalogue of 1857 attributed to Rembrandt. It may be the Rembrandt *Portrait of a Man* mentioned in J. Heller, *Die Gräflich Schönborn'sche Gemälde Sammlung . . . in Pommersfelden*, 1845, p. 29.
6. As signed below, on the right: Flinck; on wood, 70 × 55 cm. Bust portrait.
7. As by Flinck and from the Pommersfelden collection.
8. As by Rembrandt.

JACOB DE GHEYN III (JACOB DE GHEYN the Younger), c.1596–1641

His father married in April 1595 and he himself was probably born in 1596 (certainly by 1599) in Haarlem or Leiden.[1] He was the grandson of a glass-painter and miniaturist, Jacob de Gheyn I (1537/8–81), and son of the engraver and painter, Jacob de Gheyn II (1565–1629). He lived from an early age in The Hague where his father had settled by 1603; his earliest dated works are prints of 1614 after Tempesta. In 1618 he was in London with Constantijn Huygens and in 1620 he went to Sweden carrying prints and drawings by his father. Huygens lamented in c.1630 that de Gheyn, who was the sole heir of a wealthy father, had practically ceased artistic activity. He was in The Hague until c.1633; by October 1634 he had settled in Utrecht, where he became a canon of St Mary's. He died in Utrecht, 4 or 5 June 1641.

Relatively few paintings can be attributed to him with any degree of certainty[2] but van Regteren Altena's catalogue of his drawings contains more than a hundred items.[3] He also made etchings. His paintings - notably a series of octagonal canvases of the *Evangelists*[4] - display the influence of the Utrecht *Caravaggisti* and Jacob Jordaens. He was an early patron of Rembrandt and Lievens.

REFERENCES:
General: I. Q. van Regteren Altena, *Jacques de Gheyn: Three Generations*, 3 vols., The Hague, 1983 (Jacob de Gheyn III's career is discussed in vol. 1, pp. 115ff, and his paintings and drawings catalogued in vol. 2).

In text:
1. Van Regteren Altena, op. cit., vol. 1, pp. 40–41.
2. Van Regteren Altena, op. cit., vol. 2, cat. III P.
3. Van Regteren Altena, op. cit., vol. 2, cat. III.
4. Van Regteren Altena, op. cit., vol. 2, cat. III P, nos. 2–5.

After JACOB DE GHEYN III

3590 *St Paul seated reading*   *Plate 119*

Oil on canvas, 120.2 × 96.8 ($47\frac{7}{8}$ × $38\frac{3}{8}$).

Considerably worn and with a pronounced craquelure. Two large damages on the shoulder and a number of smaller holes elsewhere.

The composition corresponds with slight variations to an etching (in the same direction) by Jacob de Gheyn III (Fig. 37),[1] the main differences being that in the etching there is a step in the foreground, to which is affixed a *cartellino* inscribed: S.PAVLVS., and the stone on which the saint's foot rests is there wedge-shaped. When compared to Jacob de Gheyn III's *Evangelists*,[2] No. 3590 seems to be a contemporary copy, although van Regteren Altena thought that it could possibly be an original.[3] It is more likely to have been made from the etching than from a lost painting since it is in the same direction as the print but in the opposite direction from the drawing in Budapest[4] from which the etching appears to have been made.

DRAWING: A drawing of this composition is mentioned above.

ETCHING: Jacob de Gheyn III's etching of this composition is discussed above.

PROVENANCE: In the possession of Percy Ravenscroft, Tunbridge Wells,[5] from whom purchased (out of the Florence Fund) in 1921.

REFERENCES:

1. Hollstein, vol. 7, no. 21. Inscribed below: 'Conversus Paulus, Zelosus, vt antè magister,/Explicat obscuri mystica sensa libri.' There is a companion etching of St Peter. Although these two etchings bear a monogram IDG which was also used by Jacob de Gheyn II, their author is established beyond doubt by comparison with the Seven Wise Men of Greece series of 1616, the title-page of which describes him as *Jacopus Gheynius junior*.
2. Van Regteren Altena, op. cit., vol. 2, cat. III P, nos. 2–5.
3. Van Regteren Altena, op. cit., vol. 2, cat. III P,

no. 8 as ?Jacques de Gheyn III. He commented that 'if the work is by the same artist [as the etching] it would have been a first attempt at oil-painting, showing some shortcomings due to his inexperience'.
4. Museum of Fine Arts, Budapest (inv. no. 1513). Van Regteren Altena, op. cit., vol. 2, cat. III, no. 5. The drawing corresponds very closely (in reverse) to the etching but the point of the sword is not broken off as it is in the print and the *cartellino* and inscription are lacking.
5. As by Zurbarán.

JAN VAN GOYEN, 1596–1656

Jan Josephsz. van Goyen (until about 1627 he frequently spelled his name *Goein*); born in Leiden, 13 January 1596. According to Orlers,[1] from 1606 onwards he was a pupil successively of the Leiden painters Coenraet van Schilperoort, Isaac Claesz. van Swanenburgh and Jan Arentsz. de Man, and the glass-painter Cornelis Cornelisz. Clock;[2] then for two years of a Willem Gerritsz. in Hoorn.[3] Orlers says he came back to Leiden and worked on his own, then when about nineteen travelled in France for a year and, after his return, spent a year in Haarlem as the pupil of Esaias van de Velde. He married in Leiden in 1618 and is mentioned in documents there throughout the 1620s. In 1629 he sold a house in Leiden to Jan Porcellis, the marine painter. Orlers says he went to The Hague in 1631; he was still in Leiden in November of that year, when he sold a house, but settled probably shortly afterwards in The Hague, of which he acquired citizenship in March 1634. He is said to have lost heavily in the 'tulipmania' of 1636/7. At some time in 1634 he was painting in Haarlem in the house of Isaac van Ruisdael, the brother of Salomon van Ruysdael. He was a *hoofdman* of The Hague guild in 1638 and 1640. In 1649 his daughter married Jan Steen. In 1651 he painted for the Burgomasters' room in The Hague town hall a panoramic view of the town for which he received 650 guilders. He died in The Hague, 27 April 1656.

The only one of his masters whose influence is traceable in van Goyen's early works (his first known dated picture is of 1620) is Esaias van de Velde, and until 1626 van Goyen's landscape style is closely dependent on him. His early marine paintings reveal the influence of Jan Porcellis. Immediately afterwards he began to paint in the new Haarlem landscape style of which he, Pieter de Molijn and Salomon van Ruysdael are the principal exponents.

Van Goyen was extremely prolific: the standard catalogue of his work lists more than 800 drawings and 1,200 paintings. He travelled extensively in the Netherlands and in Germany.

REFERENCES:
General: HdG, vol. 8, 1927 (German edition, 1923); H.-U. Beck, *Jan van Goyen 1596–1656: Ein Oeuvre-verzeichnis*, 2 vols., Amsterdam, 1972.
In text:
1. J. J. Orlers, *Beschrijvinge der Stadt Leyden*, Leiden, 1641, pp. 373–74.
2. Orlers names this teacher of van Goyen as Hen-

drick Clock but no artist of this name is recorded and he probably confused him with Cornelis Clock (1561–1629).
3. This artist is entirely unknown: see B. J. A. Renckens, 'Jan van Goyen en zijn Noordhollandse leermeester', OH, vol. 66, 1951, pp. 23–24.

151 *A River Landscape* *Plate 120*

Signed on the nearer boat in the right foreground: VGOYEN 1645 (VG linked).

Oil on oak, 66 × 96.5 (26 × 38).

MacLaren identified the scene as Overschie in the Province of South Holland: it is on the River Schie, about three miles north-west of Rotterdam. The identification was based on comparison with a drawing in the 'Bredius Sketchbook' (now in the collection of J. O. Kronig, Monaco).[1] Beck, however, has rejected this identification[2] and is followed in this by the present writer.

The difficulty presented by the identification of the scene as Overschie is – as Mac-Laren conceded – the shape of the church spire. There can be no doubt that the spire had on top of it a small, open cupola surmounted by a weather vane which gave it a bulbous appearance at the top. This can be clearly seen in an engraving of 1667[3] and had apparently been unchanged since the sixteenth century.[4] The spire is plain in the drawings, both of which are inscribed *Oudeschie* – an old name for Overschie[5] – and in No. 151 and its variants (listed below). There are, however, three paintings by van Goyen showing the church with just such a spire as that on the church in Overschie.[6] If Beck is correct and these paintings show Overschie, No. 151 cannot represent the same place.

VERSIONS: There are a number of similar river landscapes with prominent churches by van Goyen. A smaller variant, dated 1648, is in the Argenti collection in London;[7] another, signed and dated 1645, was with Knoedler in London in 1923;[8] another, signed and illegibly dated but probably also of the 1640s, was in an anonymous sale in Berlin, 19–23 November 1927 (lot 108);[9] another, signed and dated 1651, is in the Corcoran Gallery of Art, Washington D.C.[10]

PROVENANCE: Mrs S. F. Hodges Bequest, 1852.[11]

REFERENCES:
General: HdG No. 561; Beck, op. cit., No. 509.
In text:
1. The sketchbook is No. 845 in Beck's catalogue of van Goyen's drawings (Beck, op. cit., vol. 1). The relevant cat. nos. are 845/55 and 845/57. The same author has published this sketchbook in full: H. U. Beck, *Ein Skizzenbuch von Jan van Goyen*, The Hague, 1966.

2. Beck, op. cit., vol. 2, No. 509.
3. Van Bleyswijck, opposite p. 92. The church was destroyed by fire in 1899: see G. C. Helbers, *Overschie in den loop van tien eeuwen*, 1929, p. 140.
4. Helbers, op. cit., pp. 132–40.
5. Beck believes these inscriptions to be by a later hand and so not necessarily reliable. (Beck, op. cit., vol. 1, p. 268.) Overschie was formerly also known

as Ouderschie, Ouwerschie and Oldschie: see van der Aa, vol. 3, p. 758.

6. Beck, op. cit., vol. 2, Nos. 263 (dated 1651: Rijksmuseum Twenthe, Enschede; inv. no. 411), 505 (dated 1645: Earl of Wemyss and March, Gosford House, East Lothian), 529 (with A. Brod, London, 1972).

7. Beck, op. cit., vol. 2, No. 534. The suggestion made in the catalogue of the BFAC exhibition, London, 1938–39, No. 69, that this painting shows Tienhoven on the River Lek in South Holland is

incorrect. The church there was quite different, as can be seen in the engraving in Rademaker, vol. 2, No. 188.

8. Beck, op. cit., vol. 2, No. 507.

9. Panel, 45 × 69 cm.; reproduced in the sale catalogue, pl. 21. Not recorded by Beck.

10. Inv. no. 26.96; Beck, op. cit., vol. 2, No. 552.

11. The painting was not catalogued until 1892; until then its inventory number, 151, referred to a *Leda* (Style of Mola) which was renumbered 151A.

1327 *A Scene on the Ice outside Dordrecht* *Plate 121*

In the right foreground is the Riedijk water-gate. In the left distance, across the frozen Merwede river, are the ruins of Merwede castle.

Signed on the back of the sleigh in the centre foreground: VGOYEN 1642 (VG linked).

Oil on canvas, 117.5 × 151 ($46\frac{1}{4}$ × $59\frac{1}{2}$).

Cleaned in 1950. The sky is very badly worn throughout and has been almost entirely overpainted. This overpainting was not removed when the painting was cleaned. There is a large damage immediately below the kneeling figure at the bottom right. In the right bottom corner van Goyen has painted out a group composed of a man and a seated woman with a baby and, above it, a boat; the squatting man is painted on top of the latter.

The Riedijk or Rietdijk water-gate (*Rietdijksche Poort*) stood at the eastern end of Dordrecht; it was built in 1590 and demolished *c*.1830. Merwede castle (Huis te Merwede) was built in the thirteenth century and ruined in 1418 or 1421; it still exists in much the same state as in the present painting but now stands on reclaimed land. It appears also in a number of pictures by Cuyp (e.g. No. 1289 of the present catalogue). Van Goyen drew and painted many views of Dordrecht and its vicinity.

PROVENANCE: In Baron Haldon's sale, London, 28 February 1891 (lot 30), bought by Colnaghi (290 gns), from whom purchased (out of the Lewis Fund) in 1891.

ENGRAVING: P. J. Arendzen.

REFERENCES:
HdG No. 46; Beck, op. cit., No. 63.

2578 *A Windmill by a River* *Plate 122*

Signed, bottom left: VG 1642 (VG linked).

Oil on oak, 29.4 × 36.3 ($11\frac{9}{16}$ × $14\frac{5}{16}$).

Cleaned in 1978.

PROVENANCE: Robert Prioleau Roupell sale, London, 25 June 1887 (lot 20), bought by Martin Colnaghi (55 gns) for George Salting.[1] George Salting Bequest, 1910.

EXHIBITIONS: London, Thomas Agnew and Sons, 1910, No. 103; London 1986, No. 47.

REFERENCES:
General: HdG No. 835; Beck op, cit., No. 975.
In text: **1.** Note in one of Salting's notebooks in the National Gallery archives.

2579 *A Scene on the Ice by a Drinking Booth; A Village in the Distance*   *Plate 123*

Signed, bottom left: VG 1645 (VG linked).

Oil on oak, 25.2 × 34 ($9\frac{15}{16}$ × $13\frac{3}{8}$).

Cleaned in 1950–1.

PROVENANCE: Robert Prioleau Roupell sale, London, 25 June 1887 (lot 23), bought by Salting (110 gns). George Salting Bequest, 1910.

EXHIBITIONS: London, Thomas Agnew and Sons, 1910, No. 123; Leiden, Stedelijk Museum De Lakenhal; Arnhem, Gemeentemuseum, 1960, 'Jan van Goyen', No. 32.

REFERENCES:
HdG No. 1166 (with the description of a different picture); Beck, op. cit., No. 71.

2580 *A River Scene, with Fishermen laying a Net*   *Plate 124*

Signed on the rowing boat, left: VG 1638 (VG linked).

Oil on oak, 31.1 × 25.8 ($12\frac{1}{4}$ × $10\frac{3}{16}$).

The church with a square tower in the centre distance may be meant for the Grote Kerk in Dordrecht (cf. Cuyp No. 961, etc.).

PROVENANCE: Robert Prioleau Roupell sale, London, 25 June 1887 (lot 22), bought by Colnaghi (145 gns) for George Salting.[1] Salting Bequest, 1910.

EXHIBITION: London, Thomas Agnew and Sons, 1910, No. 79.

REFERENCES:
General: HdG No. 1043; Beck, op. cit., No. 168.
In text: **1.** Note in one of Salting's notebooks in the National Gallery archives.

6154 *A River Scene, with a Hut on an Island*   *Plate 125*

Signed on the boat in the left foreground: VG (linked).

Oil on oak, 37 × 33 ($14\frac{9}{16}$ × 13).

Cleaned in 1970.

The style is apparently of the early 1640s. No. 6155 below is the companion piece.

COPY:[1] Panel, 25.3 × 31.7 cm. Falsely signed: VG. Lord Clinton sale, London, 19 July 1950 (lot 50) (£220, W. Sabin); Wildenstein, London, 1955.

PROVENANCE: Robert Prioleau Roupell sale, London, 25 June 1887[2] (lot 16), bought by Colnaghi (£168). In the collection of Samuel S. Joseph, London; collection of Mrs E. Joseph, London; sold in May 1911 to Colnaghi, London; Knoedler, London, 1914; in the collection of Mrs Charles S. Carstairs, Paris (d. 1949); Mrs Carstairs Bequest, 1952.

EXHIBITIONS: RA 1891, No. 49; BFAC 1900, No. 14.

REFERENCES:
General: HdG No. 89; Beck, op. cit., No. 208.
In text:
1. Beck, op. cit., vol. 2, No. 208 I.
2. The markings corresponding to this sale are on the back of the panel.

6155 *A River Scene with Fishermen hauling a Net*   *Plate 126*

On the land in the far distance is a windmill, centre, and a church, right.

Signed on the boat in the left foreground: VG (linked).

Oil on oak, 37 × 33 ($14\frac{9}{16}$ × 13).

Cleaned in 1970.

Like its companion piece, No. 6154 above, probably of the early 1640s.

COPIES: (a)[1] Panel, 25.3 × 31.7 cm. Falsely signed: VG. Lord Clinton sale, London, 19 July 1950 (lot 51) (£300, Rosendaal). Collection Sidney Blumstein, London, 1970. (b)[2] by Johannes Schoeff. Signed and dated 1651. Panel, 45 × 70 cm. Collection H. W. Campe, Leipzig; sale of the Vieweg collection from Braunschweig, Berlin, 18 March 1930 (No. 5).

PROVENANCE: Robert Prioleau Roupell sale, London, 25 June 1887 (lot 18),[3] bought by Colnaghi (130 gns). In the collection of Samuel S. Joseph, London; collection of Mrs E. Joseph, London; sold in May 1911 to Colnaghi; Knoedler, London, 1914. In the collection of Mrs Charles S. Carstairs, Paris (d. 1949). Mrs Carstairs Bequest, 1952.

EXHIBITIONS: RA 1891, No. 54; BFAC 1900, No. 13.

REFERENCES:
General: HdG No. 88; Beck, op. cit., No. 209.
In text:
1. Beck, op. cit., vol. 2, No. 209 I.
2. Beck, op. cit., vol. 2, No. 209 II.
3. As 'A River Scene with a church and windmill, fishing boats, and fishermen drawing in a net. Signed. $14\frac{1}{2}$ in. by 13 in.' Identification with the Roupell sale picture is further supported by the fact that the companion piece, No. 6154 above, was certainly in that sale.

6423 *An Estuary with Fishing Boats and Two Frigates*   *Plate 127*

Oil on oak, 49.5 × 69.1 ($19\frac{3}{8}$ × $27\frac{1}{8}$).

Cleaned in 1973.

The painting is not signed or dated: stylistically it clearly belongs to a group of marine pictures from the last few years of van Goyen's life. There is a closely comparable painting of 1656 in the Städelsches Kunstinstitut in Frankfurt (Fig. 38).[1]

PROVENANCE: Possibly in the Erbstein and Montfoort sale, Paris, 15 January 1835 (lot 12), 241 francs. Collection of Sir Herbert Cook, Doughty House, Richmond.[2] With Agnew's, 1946. Purchased from Agnew's by Sir John Heathcoat Amory, Bart., who bequeathed the painting to the National Gallery in 1972, with a life interest to Lady Amory who renounced this in 1973.

EXHIBITIONS: London, Agnew's, November-December 1946, No. 16; London 1976, No. 46.

REFERENCES:
General: HdG No. 1062; Beck, op. cit., No. 920.
In text:
1. Panel, 39.5 × 54.3 cm. Signed, bottom left: VG 1656. Frankfurt, Städelsches Kunstinstitut, inv. no. 1071. Beck, op. cit., No. 898.
2. Doughty House catalogue, 1914, No. 261.

6464   *The Mouth of an Estuary with a Gateway*   *Plate 128*

Signed and dated on the side of the nearer, large boat left of centre: VG 1649.

Oil on oak, 33.2 × 47.6 (13¼ × 19¾).

The twin-towered building on the left would seem to be a water-gate, which stood at the entrances to many Dutch towns. This particular building has not, however, been identified. Not apparently known to either Hofstede de Groot or Beck.

PROVENANCE: Collection of Rudolph Ernst Brandt (d. 1962); presented by Mrs Alice Bleecker, 1981.

Attributed to JAN VAN GOYEN

137   *A Cottage on a Heath*   *Plate 129*

Signed on the bank in the foreground: VG.

Oil on oak, 39.7 × 60.5 (15⁷⁄₁₆ × 23¹³⁄₁₆).

Cleaned in 1958. The sky is worn. Prior to cleaning there was the figure of a man in a broad-brimmed hat holding a net in the centre foreground. This was found to be a later addition and was removed. There is a vigorous and extensive underdrawing which shows through the paint in many places.

Catalogued by MacLaren as 'Ascribed to van Goyen'. He considered that the foreground and left distance are so formless and carelessly painted as to suggest this is the work of a contemporary imitator. The attribution to van Goyen was rejected by Beck in his catalogue.[1] In a letter (1986) to the present writer he comments, however, that cleaning and the removal of the foreground figure have much improved the appearance of the painting and that 'it might be by van Goyen of about 1629, but one of his weaker works'. He compares it with *A Rider and a Man with a Basket* of 1629 in Frankfurt.[2] The present writer believes that it is probably an authentic work of about 1629 by van Goyen. The monogram appears to be authentic.

PROVENANCE: Lt.-Col. John Harvey Ollney Bequest, 1837.

REFERENCES:
General: HdG, Goyen No. 332.
In text: **1.** In the index tabulating his catalogue numbers with those of HdG, he notes that the painting is by an unidentified imitator or follower.
2. Frankfurt, Städelsches Kunstinstitut. Inv. no. 1271. Beck, op. cit., No. 1077.

Imitator of JAN VAN GOYEN

2577 *Sailing Vessels on a River in a Breeze* Plate 130

Formerly signed falsely, bottom right: 1651./J. Van Goyen ft.; since cleaning only traces of the date remain.

Oil on oak, 37.1 × 53.1 (14⅝ × 20⅞).

Cleaned in 1958.

Previously attributed to van Goyen but certainly only an imitation in the style of his later works.[1] The attribution to van Goyen is rejected by Beck.[2]

PROVENANCE: George Salting Bequest, 1910.

REFERENCES:
General: HdG No. 1042.
In text:
1. Such as Mauritshuis No. 624 (HdG No. 1033; Beck, op. cit., cat. no. 821), signed and dated 1655.
2. In the index tabulating his catalogue numbers with those of HdG, he notes that the painting is by an unidentified imitator or follower.

JORIS VAN DER HAAGEN, *c.*1615–1669

He was the son of the painter Abraham van der Haagen (1587–1639), who worked in Arnhem but by whom no work is known today. Abraham had moved from Dordrecht to Arnhem by 1617 and it is not known exactly where or when Joris was born. He was presumably trained in his father's workshop in Arnhem. In 1640 Joris is recorded in The Hague: he married there two years later and in 1643 joined the guild. In 1644 he became a citizen of The Hague: like his friend, the architect and painter Pieter Post, he lived on the Veerkade. In 1653 he was a *hoofdman* of the guild. In 1656 he was one of the founder members of the painters' confraternity, *Pictura*. In 1650 and 1657 he is recorded in Amsterdam. Van der Haagen died in The Hague on 20 May 1669 and was buried in the Kloosterkerk.

He was a landscape painter who specialised in the representation of thickly wooded countryside but he is probably best known for his topographical drawings and paintings of towns and individual houses and castles. He travelled widely in the Nether-

149

lands: there are drawings and paintings of Holland, Gelderland, Cleves and Limburg. He collaborated with figure and animal painters, among them Ludolph de Jongh and Dirck Wijntrack. Two of his sons, Cornelis and Jacobus, were painters.

REFERENCES: General: J. K. van der Haagen, *De Schilders Van der Haagen en hun werk*, Voorburg, 1932 (with a *catalogue raisonné* of Joris van der Haagen's paintings and drawings).

901 *A River Landscape*   *Plate 131*

Oil on canvas, 109 × 209 (43 × 50¾).

Cleaned in 1966.

The painting is unsigned. MacLaren attributed it to Jan Looten (*c.*1618–*c.*1680?), an Amsterdam landscape painter who moved to England. There are similarities to signed paintings by Looten of heavily wooded landscapes such as *The Path in the Woods* in the Rijksmuseum.[1] However, in an annotation on the mount of the photograph in the RKD, Dr Nieuwstraten has attributed No. 901 to Joris van der Haagen and this is far more convincing. Van der Haagen is known as a topographical painter and draughts-man but he also painted wooded landscapes. A strikingly similar painting by van der Haagen (Fig. 39), with a prominent foreground tree with a gnarled and twisted trunk as in No. 901 (but on the right rather than the left), was in the S. del Monte sale at Sotheby's, 24 June 1959:[2] it is signed clearly in the bottom right-hand corner. For the detailed painting of the plants in the foreground and of the branches and foliage comparison should also be made with the signed painting in the Bredius Museum, The Hague,[3] and a signed painting in Copenhagen.[4]

PROVENANCE: Mrs Jewer Henry Jewer Bequest, 1873.

REFERENCES:
In text:
1. 1976 cat. A48 (Figures by Jan Lingelbach).
2. Canvas, 45 × 48¼ in.
3. Panel, 49.5 × 60 cm. Signed, lower left. Inv. no. 49–1946. A. Blankert, *Museum Bredius: Catalogus van*

de Schilderijen en Tekeningen, The Hague, 1978, cat. no. 64.
4. Canvas, 178 × 210 cm. Statens Museum for Kunst, inv. no. 358. Van der Haagen, op. cit., no. 28.

CORNELIS VAN HAARLEM *See* CORNELIS

JOHANNES CORNELIS HACCOU, 1798–1839

Born 18 April 1798 in Middelburg, where he was a pupil of Johannes Hermanus Koekkoek (1778–1851). After travelling in Switzerland, France and Germany, he settled in London. He exhibited at the Royal Academy in 1836; died in London, 21 January 1839.

He painted winter landscapes and river views with sheep in both oil and watercolour.

3683 *A Road by a Cottage*   *Plate 132*

Signed at the bottom, towards the right: J.C.H 1819 (the last letter of the signature may be intended for HC in monogram).

Oil on oak, 23.8 × 32.9 (9⅜ × 13).

PROVENANCE: In the collection of William Thomas Blinco, London; W. T. Blinco Bequest, 1922.

JAN HACKAERT, 1628/9–after 1685

Jan (also *Johannes, Joannes, Joan*) *Jansz. Hackaert*; born in Amsterdam;[1] in January 1667 he is said to be thirty-eight.[2] Little is known of his life. He travelled in Switzerland[3] (there are books of drawings of Swiss views by him bearing dates from July 1653 to July 1656) and possibly also in Italy.[4] He returned to settle in Amsterdam where, according to Houbraken,[5] he was a friend of Adriaen van de Velde, who sometimes painted the figures and animals in his pictures (as did also Jan Lingelbach, Nicolaes Berchem – for example No. 829 below – and others). There are a few dated paintings between 1657 and 1685. He is usually said to have died in Amsterdam about 1699 but the grounds for this statement are not known.[6]

He painted mostly Italianate landscapes; these and his less frequent views in woods (for example No. 829 below) seem to derive in the first place from Jan Both. He also made some landscape etchings.

REFERENCES:
General: HdG; ex. cat. Utrecht 1965.
In text:
1. In an album of drawings by Hackaert are several signed: 'Johannes Hackaert Amstelodamensis' (HdG, p. 1); see also Houbraken, vol. 3, 1721, p. 46.
2. According to Bredius (mentioned in Thieme/Becker, vol. 15, 1922, p. 407).
3. Houbraken, op. cit., p. 46.
4. Some of his paintings and drawings seem to be of Italian views, and one of the former shows the lake of Zurich (Amsterdam, Rijksmuseum; 1976 cat., A 1709).
5. Op. cit., p. 48.
6. A. Bredius, *Les chefs-d'oeuvre du Musée Royal d'Amsterdam*, [1891], p. 58, says Hackaert died in Amsterdam in 1699 'according to Houbraken', but there is no mention of his death in *De Groote Schouburgh*. In Thieme/Becker, loc. cit., he is said to have died *c.*1700.

JAN HACKAERT and
NICOLAES BERCHEM

829 *A Stag Hunt in a Forest* *Plate 133*

Signed at the bottom, towards the left: NBerchem f. (NB in monogram) and inscribed above and to the left of the signature: MonSeron.[1]

Oil on canvas, 99.7 × 120 (39¼ × 47¼); the picture surface has been increased at a later date to 100.3 × 122.2 (39½ × 48⅛).

Cleaned in 1966.

Nicolaes Berchem, whose signature appears on the picture, painted the figures and animals only; these were put in on top of the landscape.[2] The meaning of the inscription is not clear. It seems to be in handwriting different from Berchem's signature but there is no reason to suppose that it is not contemporary with it. At one time it must have been taken for a painter's name (presumably Moucheron), since an F (presumably for *Fecit*) had been added later; this came away when the old brown varnish was removed from the area of the inscription. No painter of this or similar name is recorded and, in any case, the landscape is without doubt by Hackaert (cf., for example, the signed landscapes of a similar kind in the Wallace Collection[3] and the Rijksmuseum).[4] It is possible that *Monsieur Seron* is intended, and that this was the name of the person for whom the picture was painted; no collector of this name, however, is recorded.

Probably painted *c.*1660.

PROVENANCE: HdG identifies this picture with one of similar description in the Jan Danser Nijman sale, Amsterdam, 16–17 August 1797 (lot 350), bought by Roos (250 florins),[5] but according to the sale catalogue that picture was by Hackaert and [Willem] Schellinks. The present picture was certainly in the collection of the Prince of Wales who probably acquired it before December 1806; it was at Carlton House in 1816 and was given in exchange for two pictures to Lafontaine, 10 July 1819.[6] It was in an anonymous [Varroc and Lafontaine] sale, Paris, 28 May sqq. 1821 (lot 38),[7] bought by Laneuville (5,320 francs). Lent by Earl Granville to the BI in 1835 and 1844; Earl Granville sale, London, 21 June 1845 (lot 15), bought by Nieuwenhuys (650 gns) for Sir Robert Peel, Bart.[8] Purchased with the Peel collection, 1871.

EXHIBITIONS: BI 1835, No. 120; BI 1844, No. 21.

REFERENCES:
General: Smith Supplement, Hackaert No.1; HdG No. 18.
In text:
1. This is legible in an infra-red photograph.
2. The underlying foliage shows through the horsemen in the left bottom corner (this is particularly clear in infra-red photographs).
3. Wallace Collection, London: 1979 cat., P 121. HdG No. 41 (figures by Adriaen van de Velde).
4. Rijksmuseum, Amsterdam; 1976 cat., no. A 131. HdG No. 33.
5. 'In een Boomryk Landschap met een klaare Waterbeek, vertoont zich een Harte-Jagt, met Heeren en een Dame te paard, verder Jagers met

Honden . . . door Hackert en Schellings'; on canvas, 42 × 50 *duim*.
6. The picture is not in the records of the Prince's acquisitions kept from 31 December 1806 on; it only appears in the Carlton House inventory of 1816 (No. 120) with the addition of the following note: 'Sold to Mr Lafountain in Exchange for 2 Pictures . . . July 10th 1819.'
7. The description in the sale catalogue tallies but the size is given erroneously as 56 × 46 *pouces*.
8. According to a MS note by Smith in a copy of the *Catalogue Raisonné* said to be his own (HdG, loc. cit.).

DIRCK HALS, 1591–1656

Younger brother of Frans Hals; baptised in Haarlem, 19 March 1591.[1] From 1618 to 1626 he was a member of De Wijngaertranken, the rhetoricians' chamber (*rederijkercamer*) to which Frans Hals also belonged. He seems to have lived mostly in Haarlem, but is recorded in Leiden in 1641–2 and 1648–9 and was perhaps there in the intervening years.[2] He was buried in Haarlem, 17 May 1656.[3]

His style was based in the first place on that of his brother with whom, according to Houbraken, he studied. He and Willem Buytewech the Elder of Rotterdam (1591/2–1624), whose work his strongly resembles, specialised in so-called 'merry company' scenes such as No. 1074. With his brother he was praised by Samuel Ampzing in 1628.[4]

REFERENCES:

1. E. W. Moes, *Frans Hals*, 1909, p. 7.
2. Bredius in OH, vol. 41, 1923–24, pp. 60–61.
3. Van der Willigen, p. 149.

4. S. Ampzing, *Beschryvinge ende Lof der Stad Haerlem*, Haarlem, 1628, p. 371 ('Wat supv're beeldekens weet Dirk ons niet te geven!').

1074 *A Party of Young Men and Women at a Table*   *Plate 134*

In the left background is a map; on the wall on the right a partly visible painting of the Taking of Christ.

Signed on the lintel of the door: DHALS · AN° 1626 (DH in monogram).

Oil on oak, 28 × 38.8 (11 × 15¼).

Compositionally merry company scenes (*geselschapjes*) such as this one developed from biblical subjects such as the Prodigal Son feasting and Mankind before the Flood.[1] When they were engraved, admonitory verses condemning the foolish and extravagant behaviour which is depicted were added to them. There is, for example, a print by Cornelis Kittensteyn[2] reproducing a painting by Dirck Hals very similar to No. 1074 with such an inscription. It seems most likely that at least some contemporaries would have viewed these paintings in this sense.

There are two similar paintings by Dirck Hals, also dated 1626, in San Francisco (Palace of the Legion of Honor) and the Hermitage, Leningrad.

COPY: A copy was sold in Brussels in 1953[3] and a second (possibly the same painting) was with the art dealer F. Pallamar, Vienna, in 1973.[4]

PROVENANCE: On the back of the panel is inscribed a name: 'T. V. Crimpen'. Purchased from Edward C. Hill in 1879.

EXHIBITIONS: London, 1976, No. 47; London 1978–9, No. 5.

REFERENCES:

1. For this development, see E. Haverkamp-Begemann, *Willem Buytewech*, Amsterdam, 1959, p. 26ff.
2. The print is illustrated in E. de Jongh, *Zinne- en minnebeelden in de schilderkunst van de zeventiende eeuw*, 1967, pl. 2 and discussed on pp. 6–8.
3. Panel, 27 × 37 cm. Signed above the door. Sale, Brussels (Palais des Beaux-Arts), 24 June 1953, No. 21.
4. Panel, 28.5 × 39 cm. Signed above the door. Art dealer van Diemen-Lilienfeld, New York; sale, Spik, Bad Kissingen, 7 June 1963 (lot 197); F. Pallamar, Vienna, ex. 1973, No. 11.

153

FRANS HALS, c.1580/5–1666

The place and date of his birth are the subject of dispute. He was most probably born in Antwerp, of which he is stated to be a native in various documents of 1611–28,[1] but a later source says Mechelen (Malines).[2] As to the date of birth: Houbraken quotes a manuscript note, almost certainly by Vincent Laurensz. van der Vinne (1629–1702), a pupil of Hals, to the effect that Hals was eighty-five or eighty-six when he died in 1666,[3] in which case he would have been born within the years 1579 to 1581. Yet according to a note written in 1679 by Mathias Scheits, a Hamburg painter who had been a pupil of Wouwermans in Haarlem, Hals was ninety or not much less when he died 'in 1665 or 1666';[4] Weyerman gives 1584 as the year of Hals's birth.[5]

Hals's parents, who came from Malines,[6] had settled in Haarlem by March 1591 (when his brother Dirck was born there – see the biographical notice on page 153) and he lived there for the rest of his life. He was, it is reliably claimed,[7] a pupil of Carel van Mander, who left Haarlem in 1603.[8] He joined the Haarlem Guild of St Luke in 1610. His earliest dated work, the *Portrait of Jacobus Zaffius* in the Frans Halsmuseum in Haarlem, is of 1611. In 1616 he painted a militia company banquet, the first of a series of large group portraits of Haarlem musketeers; there are others of the years 1627, 1633 and 1639. In August 1616 he was said to be in Antwerp[9] but was in Haarlem in November of that year.[10]   Although he received many commissions for portraits from the regent class in Haarlem, he had money difficulties from 1616 onwards. In 1633 he was commissioned to paint a militia group portrait in Amsterdam (for which he was to be paid 960 guilders) but left it unfinished,[11] and it was completed in 1637 by Pieter Codde.[12] In 1641 he painted the regents of the Haarlem hospital; in 1644 he was an officer of the Haarlem guild.[13] Hals's financial difficulties worsened and from 1662 onwards he had to accept relief from the city council.[14] In 1664 he painted group portraits of the regents and regentesses of the Haarlem almshouse. He died in Haarlem and was buried there, 1 September 1666.[15]

Five of Hals's sons were artists: Harmen (1611–69), Frans the Younger (1618–69), Reynier (1627–72), Nicholaes (1628–86), and Jan (active c.1635–1674). According to Houbraken, Hals had a number of apprentices, among them his brother Dirck, Adriaen Brouwer, Adriaen van Ostade and Philips Wouwermans. Judith Leyster, Pieter van Roestraten, and Jan Miense Molenaer may also have studied with him.

The standard modern catalogue of his work (by Slive) contains about 220 authentic works: of these, four-fifths are portraits. He also painted some genre scenes and a handful of religious subjects. There are no known drawings or prints by Hals.

REFERENCES:
General: HdG, vol. 3; S. Slive, *Frans Hals*, 3 vols., London, 1970–74; C. Grimm, *Frans Hals*, Berlin, 1972; Washington/London/Haarlem 1989–90.
In text:
1. Van der Willigen, p. 140.
2. and 3. Houbraken, vol. 1, 1718, pp. 95 and 325, quoting a note apparently by Vincent Laurensz. van

der Vinne on the back of the notification of Hals's burial (*begrafenis-briefje*).
4. Published by C. Vosmer in *Kunstkronijk*, vol. 13, 1871, p. 12.
5. Weyerman, vol. 1, 1729, p. 352.
6. Bredius in OH, vol. 32, 1914, p. 216.
7. and 8. See the life of van Mander [p. 13] appended

to the second (posthumous) edition of his *Schilder-Boeck* (1618).

9. and **10.** Bredius in OH, vol. 41, 1923–24, pp. 20 and 21.

11. Bredius in OH, vol. 31, 1913, pp. 81–84.

12. According to a note made in 1653 by Gerrit Schaep (P. Scheltema, *Aemstel's Oudheid*, vol. 7, 1885, p. 134); cf. OH, vol. 3, 1885, p. 122.

13. Van der Willigen, p. 145.

14. Van der Willigen, pp. 147–48, and OH, 1923–24, pp. 28–30.

15. According to van der Vinne's note (see Notes 2 and 3 above) Hals was buried on 29 August 1666, but a document published by van der Willigen (pp. 148–49) shows that a grave was opened in St Bavo for Hals on 1 September 1666.

1021 *Portrait of a Middle-aged Woman with Hands Folded*   Plate 135

Signed on the left: FH (in monogram).

Oil on canvas, 61.4 × 47 ($24\frac{3}{8}$ × $18\frac{3}{8}$).

Probably cut down at least at the sides and the bottom.

The picture was at one time mounted on a smaller stretcher (which was not necessarily the original one).[1]

The sitter has been called the wife of the man in No. 1251 below and the portrait consequently dated 1633.[2] There is, however, no reason to suppose that the two pictures are companion pieces; their known provenance differs, the present portrait may originally have been larger than No. 1251 and also seems a little later in style. Grimm[3] suggests that the painting may be a pendant to a *Portrait of a Man holding a Book* in the collection of Saul Steinberg, New York (Slive, op. cit., cat. no. 143). That painting is slightly larger than No. 1021 (66 × 48.5 cm.) and perhaps a little later in date. The costume of the sitter in No. 1021 is of the earlier 1630s but was often worn at a later date by older women (cf. Hals No. 2285).

     Slive[4] dates the painting to the late 1630s, noting its similarity to the *Portrait of a Woman*[5] of 1639 in the Museum voor Schone Kunsten in Ghent.

PROVENANCE: Purchased (out of the Lewis Fund) from F. A. Keogh, 1876.

EXHIBITION: London 1976, No. 50.

REFERENCES:
General: HdG No. 381; Slive, op. cit., cat. no. 131; Grimm, op. cit., cat. no. 103.
In text:
1. Old stretcher marks show that at some time the picture surface was reduced to *c.*59.5 × 44 cm.

2. W. R. Valentiner, *Klassiker der Kunst: Frans Hals*, 1921, Stuttgart-Berlin, p. 106.
3. Grimm, op. cit.: as *c.*1639/40.
4. Slive, op. cit.
5. Slive, op. cit., cat. no. 136.

1251 *Portrait of a Man in his Thirties*   Plate 136

Signed on the right, centre: FH (in monogram) and inscribed below this: AETAT SVAE 3(.) AN° 1633.

Oil on canvas, 64.8 × 50.2 ($25\frac{1}{2}$ × $19\frac{3}{4}$).

Cut down on the right where the present edge of the canvas runs through the first figure of the sitter's age.[1]

Cleaned in 1970.

Incorrectly supposed by Valentiner to be the pendant to No. 1021[2] (which is in fact significantly later in date). It is not a self portrait, as Hofstede de Groot believed.[3]

PROVENANCE: In the collection of Decimus Burton by 1875, when it was exhibited at the RA. By the wish of Decimus Burton presented by his niece, Miss Emily Jane Wood, in 1888.

EXHIBITION: RA 1875, No. 237.[4]

REFERENCES:
General: HdG Nos. 148l and 281; Slive, op. cit., cat. no. 81; Grimm, op. cit., cat. no. 59.
In text:
1. Although mutilated this figure is certainly a 3; it is at present covered by the frame.

2. See above, under No. 1021. Valentiner, op. cit., p. 106.
3. HdG No. 148l.
4. As a portrait of the painter.

2285 *A Family Group in a Landscape*   *Plate 137*

Oil on canvas, 148.5 × 251 (58½ × 98¾). It is most probable that the canvas has been cut down at top and bottom.[1]

The ground is cream coloured: it is lead-white tinted with yellow-brown ochre pigment. The discoloration in the sky has been caused by the deterioration of the smalt pigment.[2]

Cleaned in 1962. Scattered losses in the sky and along the bottom edge.

The sitters have not been identified.[3]

The costume here is that of the second half of the 1640s (except for that of the oldest woman, which is an earlier mode, c.1630–5); the style of the picture is that of the late 1640s.[4] The landscape background is clearly by another hand.[5] Slive attributed it to Pieter de Molijn, while Jan Briels has suggested Reyer Claesz. Suycker (c.1590–1653/5). MacLaren considered that the 'baby held by the girl on the left is distinctly inferior to the rest of the figures and may be by an assistant'. For the present writer (as for Slive) there is nothing in the way the baby is painted which is inconsistent with Hals's style of the late 1640s.

Grimm has unconvincingly attributed the painting to Frans Hals the Younger.[6]

PROVENANCE: Perhaps to be identified with the 'Family Piece, containing 10 Figures' by F. Hals in the Buckingham House sale, London, 24–25 February 1763 (first day, lot 69),[7] 25½ gns. In the collection of Lord Talbot de Malahide, Malahide Castle, near Dublin, from whom it was purchased in 1908.

EXHIBITION: Haarlem, Frans Halsmuseum, 'Frans Hals', 1962, No. 57.

REFERENCES:
General: HdG No. 439; Slive, op. cit., cat. no. 176.
In text:
1. Besides the appearance of having been cut down in height, there are the marks of an earlier stretcher along the sides but not at the top and the bottom edges. Slive notes that comparison with the family portrait by Hals in the Thyssen-Bornemisza collection (Slive, op. cit., cat. no. 177), which is of a similar date, suggests that a rather wide strip – c.15 cm. – has been cut from the top edge.

2. J. Plesters, 'A Preliminary Note on the Incidence of Discolouration of Smalt in Oil Media', *Studies in Conservation*, 14, 1969, pp. 66–67.
3. Slive, op. cit., reviews the various unsatisfactory identifications which have been proposed.
4. Slive, op. cit., dates it *c*.1648.
5. The landscape background seems to have been painted in after the completion of the figures: see, for example, the outlines of the two standing boys, especially the one towards the right.
6. C. Grimm, 'Frans Hals und seine "Schule" ', *Münchner Jahrbuch der Bildenden Kunst*, vol. 22, 1971, pp. 163 (cat. no. 18), 168; Grimm, op. cit., p. 215.
7. The National Gallery picture is the only known Hals family group with ten figures.

2528 *Portrait of a Man holding Gloves*   Plate 138

Oil on canvas, 78.5 × 67.3 (30$\frac{7}{8}$ × 26$\frac{1}{2}$).

Worn both in the figure and the background; a large tear runs from the sitter's right eye vertically into his black coat.

Cleaned in 1941.

Dated by MacLaren to the mid-1640s which he considered would agree with the date of the costume. Slive agreed with this dating, noting that the animation of the light passages related the painting to Hals's *Portrait of an Artist* of 1644 in Chicago.[1]
    Grimm unconvincingly attributed the portrait to Jan Hals.[2]

PROVENANCE: This picture and the *Portrait of a Woman with a Fan* (No. 2529 below) are said to have been in London in the possession of a dealer Joseph Flack, apparently in the mid-1860s.[3] It was in the H. W. Cholmley sale, London, 1 February 1902 (lot 40), bought by Agnew (£3,780) who sold it in the same year to George Salting.[4] Salting Bequest, 1910.

EXHIBITION: London 1947–8, No. 58.

REFERENCES:
General: HdG No. 289; Slive, op. cit., cat. no. 163.
In text:
1. Slive, op. cit., cat. no. 164.
2. C. Grimm, 'Frans Hals und seine "Schule" ', *Münchner Jahrbuch der Bildenden Kunst*, 1971, p. 156 (cat. no. 14), pp. 158–59; Grimm, op. cit., p. 215.

3. W. S. Spanton, *An Art Student and his Teachers in the Sixties*, 1927, p. 33. It should be noted that the two pictures can hardly be companion pieces and were certainly separated at least between 1889 and 1902.
4. According to a note in one of Salting's notebooks in the National Gallery archives.

2529 *Portrait of a Woman with a Fan*   Plate 139

Oil on canvas, 79.8 × 59 (31$\frac{3}{8}$ × 23$\frac{3}{16}$).

Cleaned in 1988.

MacLaren noted that the costume is very like that of the woman in the *Portrait of a Man, Woman and Boy* by Codde (No. 2576 in this catalogue) which is dated 1640; in his view this date would agree also with the style of the painting. Slive[1] concurred in this dating.
    Grimm[2] has unconvincingly attributed the painting to Frans Hals the Younger.

EXHIBITIONS: RA 1891, No. 127; Washington/London/Haarlem 1989–90, No. 53.

PROVENANCE: This picture and No. 2528 above are said to have been in the possession of a London dealer, Joseph Flack, apparently in the mid-1860s.[3] No. 2529 was in the Revd Robert Gwilt sale, London, 13 July

1889 (lot 78), bought by Agnew (£1,680) and sold to George Salting in the same month.[4] George Salting Bequest, 1910.

REFERENCES:

General: HdG No. 385; Slive, op. cit., cat. no. 141.
In text:
1. Slive, op. cit., cat. no. 141.
2. C. Grimm, 'Frans Hals und seine "'Schule'' ',
Münchner Jahrbuch der Bildenden Kunst, vol. 22, 1971,

p. 162 (cat. no. 10); Grimm, op. cit., p. 214.
3. W. S. Spanton, *An Art Student and his Teachers in the Sixties*, 1927, p. 33.
4. Note in one of Salting's notebooks in the National Gallery archives.

6411 *Portrait of Jean de la Chambre at the Age of Thirty-three*

Plate 140

Inscribed, upper left: 1638· and beneath, aet 33·

Oil on panel, 20.6 × 16.8 (8⅛ × 6⅝).

Jean de la Chambre the Elder (1605/6–68) was the Master of the French School in the Ursulasteeg in Haarlem.[1] He was a distinguished calligrapher and this portrait was the *modello* for an engraving by Suyderhoef (Fig. 40)[2] which served as the frontispiece to a collection of six of his own engraved examples of his calligraphic skill. Like the painting, Suyderhoef's engraving bears the date 1638 and is inscribed, lower right: F. Hals pinxit/J. S. Hoef Sculpsit. The inscription below gives the title and date of de la Chambre's book: Verscheyden geschriften, geschreven ende int Koper gesneden,/door Jean de la Chambre, liefhebber ende beminder der / pennen, tot Haarlem. Anno 1638.

De la Chambre's portrait was painted probably in 1666 by Jan de Braij.[3] This, too, was engraved for the frontispiece of a volume of examples of his calligraphic work.

Grimm[4] incorrectly suggested that No. 6411 is a copy after Suyderhoef's engraving.

COPIES: Panel, 27 × 21 cm. Inscribed, upper left, 1638, aet 33. With Silverman, New York, 1937 (?identical with a copy noted by HdG No. 164); A (?nineteenth-century) drawing (wash, white highlights: 19.1 × 15.3 cm.)[5] after the painting (or print) is in the collection of Arthur Rosenauer, Vienna.

PROVENANCE: Sale, Amsterdam, 1 April 1883, lot 74 (90 guilders to Roos); C. Wertheimer, London; P. and D. Colnaghi, London, from whom purchased by W. C. Alexander, London, 16 March 1892 (£650); by descent to the Misses Rachel F. and Jean I. Alexander. Alexander Gift, 1972.[6]

EXHIBITIONS: BFAC 1900, No. 45; RA 1952–3, No. 108; King's Lynn, Guildhall of St George, 'Seventeenth Century Dutch Pictures', 1958, No. 1; London 1972; London 1976, No. 51; Washington/London/Haarlem 1989–90, No. 50.

REFERENCES:

General: HdG No. 164; Slive, op. cit., cat. no. 122; Grimm A25b.
In text:
1. His birth date is calculated from the inscription on No. 6411. De la Chambre was confirmed as a member of the French Protestant Church on 26 February 1628. He married twice, in Haarlem: on 11 December 1633 Anthonetta Boddens, by whom he had a son, Jacques (baptised 29 December 1634) and a daughter, Marie (baptised 18 October 1635); on 22 November 1639 Maria van Pouch(?k)e by whom he had two daughters, Maria (baptised 31 March 1641),

Hester (baptised 21 December 1642) and a son, Jean (baptised 9 February 1648). This son, Jean de la Chambre the Younger, succeeded his father as Master of the French School. He died on 24 June 1685: at the house in the Ursulasteeg a sale was held of his goods and chattels on 12–13 March 1686. It included paintings and his father's copper plates. His widow, Catharina Kint, placed advertisements in the *Haarlemer Courant* of 30 June 1685 and 7 March 1686 for the sale of the schoolhouse and its contents. It is described as new and solidly built, with a schoolroom and a dining hall big enough to hold sixty to seventy children, with several rooms for boarders. (The present writer is grateful to Frederik van Kretschmar for the archival information about the de la Chambre family.)

2. Hollstein No. 64.

3. J. von Moltke, 'Jan de Bray', *Marburger Jahrbuch für Kunstwissenschaft*, vols. 11–12, 1938–39, pp. 421–523, No. 47. Canvas, 83 × 69 cm., inscribed: Aetatis suae 62 and said to be dated 1662 (in fact ?1666). Six sale, Amsterdam, 10 July 1923 (lot 101); Lady I. M. Peyronnet Browne et al. sale, Christie's, 12 March 1948 (lot 135: to de Boer). The engraving is

listed as No. 48 in von Moltke's catalogue. It is inscribed: J. D. Bray pinxit. P. Holsteyn sculpt. The inscription beneath reads: Verscheijde ghescriften op d'Italiaensche maniere geschreven/Door Jean de la Chambre Françoysche Schoolm./Tot Haerlem Anno 1666.

4. Grimm, op. cit., p. 203.

5. Noted by Slive, op. cit.

6. A. Smith, 'Presented by the Misses Rachel F. and Jean I. Alexander: Seventeen Paintings for the National Gallery', BM, vol. 114, 1972, p. 634.

6413 *Portrait of a Woman (Marie Larp?)* *Plate 141*

Oil on canvas, 83.4 × 68.1 (32⅛ × 26¹³⁄₁₆).

When it was included in the Oultremont sale in Brussels in 1889 the painting was described as a portrait of 'Maria Larp'. With it was a portrait of a man, said to be its pair, identified as 'Pieter Tjarck'.[1] That portrait, which today is in the Los Angeles County Museum, is not in fact the pendant to No. 6413. Although it is to be dated to the same period of Hals's career, that is c.1635–8, the differences in the mouldings of their simulated oval frames make it clear that they were not intended to be a pair.[2]

The identification of the sitter in No. 6413 as Marie Larp apparently depends on a label probably in an eighteenth-century hand pasted to the stretcher. It reads: 'Mademoiselle Marie Larp fille/de Nicolas Larp et de/Mademoiselle ★ ★ ★ de/Wanemburg . . .' A marriage between a Pieter Dircksz. and a Maria Claesdr. on 11 February 1634 is recorded in the Haarlem archives. Pieter's date of death is unknown but in 1646 a Maritgen Claesdr. Larp is mentioned as the widow of Pieter Dircksz. *verwer* (dyer of silk and cloth). She married Leonart van Bosvelt, a lawyer, on 7 February 1648 and was again mentioned as a widow in February 1653. She was buried in the choir of St Bavo's in Haarlem in the week of 9–15 November 1675. She and Pieter Tjarck had one son, Nicolaes Pietersz. Tjarck. There are no documented portraits of Marie Larp or Pieter Tjarck.[3]

COPIES: Paper mounted on panel, 18.7 × 13.7 cm. London, E. Bottenweiser; exhibited Haarlem, Frans Halsmuseum, 'Frans Hals Tentoonstelling . . .', 1937, No. 61 (as from the R. Koenigs collection, Haarlem).[4] Canvas, 85 × 71 cm., the portrait without the painted oval. With the dealer D. Katz, Dieren, 1939. Probably a modern copy.[5]

PROVENANCE: Collection of the Comte d'Oultremont; Comte d'Oultremont sale, Brussels, 27 June 1889, lot 4 (bought Arnold and Tripp); Arnold and Tripp, Paris; purchased from Colnaghi, London, March 1891, for £1,750 by W. C. Alexander; by descent to the Misses Rachel F. and Jean I. Alexander. Alexander Gift, 1972.[6]

EXHIBITIONS: Brussels, 'Exposition néerlandaise des beaux-arts', 1882; London, 'Second National Loan Exhibition',1913–14, No. 66; RA 1938, No. 135; RA 1952–3, No. 56; London 1972.

REFERENCES:
General: HdG No. 232 (incorrectly as on panel); Slive, op. cit., cat. no. 112; Grimm, op. cit., No. 75 (as painted in 1635).

In text:
1. Slive, op. cit., cat. no. 108.
2. Both this dating and the observation that the

paintings do not constitute a pair are made in Slive, op. cit. The present writer is in agreement.

3. This information from documents in the Haarlem archives is taken from Slive, op. cit., cat. nos. 108 and 112. Slive there acknowledges the assistance of J. Temminck of the Haarlem Municipal Archives. The full references are given in Slive.

4. Valentiner published this small oil sketch as a preparatory study in his 1921 *Klassiker der Kunst* volume (No. 139, right). As it was a pendant of a small study of the *Portrait of a Man* at Woburn Abbey

(Slive, op. cit., cat. no. 111) he proposed that these paintings were companion pieces. However, he rejected this idea in the 1923 edition of the *Klassiker*. Neither painting is by Hals.

5. According to a note in the Witt Library this painting was in the Lyndhurst collection and had been stolen from Belgium between 1939 and 1945.

6. A. Smith, 'Presented by the Misses Rachel F. and Jean I. Alexander: Seventeen Painting for the National Gallery', BM, vol. 114, 1972, p. 634.

6458 *Young Man holding a Skull (Vanitas)* Plate 142

Oil on canvas, 92.2 × 80.8 (36¼ × 34½).

Cleaned in 1980.

The painting is a *vanitas*; the skull held by the boy is a reminder of the transience of life and the certainty of death. As such it belongs to a tradition showing young men holding skulls which goes back at least as far as Lucas van Leyden's engraving of 1516.[1] The boy's costume is of an extravagant kind favoured by the Dutch *Caravaggisti* in their allegorical and genre subjects.[2]

Hofstede de Groot described it as Hamlet[3] but this identification is entirely fanciful.

The painting has been dated by Slive to c.1626–8[4] and by Grimm[5] to c.1626–7.

A *vanitas* by Frans Hals is cited in the inventory of the painter Pieter Codde (Amsterdam, 5 February 1636) but there is no way of knowing whether or not this was No. 6458.[6] Plietzsch[7] incorrectly attributed the painting to Judith Leyster.

COPY/COPIES: Slive[8] suggested that a small panel which was lot 175 in the K. van Winkel sale, Rotterdam, 20 October 1791 – 'Een Jong Manspersoon met een Doodshoofd in zij hand, hoog 8, breed 6 duim, op paneel' – might be a copy of No. 6458 or perhaps a preparatory study for it. In an unpublished note in the RKD,[9] HdG noted 'a little copy of the so-called Hamlet' (which could be the same painting) at the Galerie Locarno in Paris, December 1928.

EXHIBITIONS: Dublin, National Gallery of Ireland, 1896; Haarlem, Frans Halsmuseum, 'Frans Hals Tentoonstelling', 1937, No. 93; RA 1928, No. 132; RA 1952–3, No. 102; Haarlem, Frans Halsmuseum, Frans Hals Exhibition, 1962, No. 18; San Francisco/Toledo/Boston 1966–7, No. 17; London 1976, No. 49; Washington/London/Haarlem 1989–90, No. 29.

PROVENANCE: According to the Elton Hall catalogue[10] it was purchased for Sir James Stuart, Bart., by the painter Andrew Geddes; it passed to his daughter, Mrs Woodcock, 1849; and then to her son, the Revd E. Woodcock, 1875; was inherited by his sister, Mrs Stuart Johnson, 1893; and purchased from her by the 5th Earl of Carysfort, Glenhart Castle, Ireland, in 1895 through Messrs Lawrie, London, for £3,800. By descent to Sir Richard Proby, Bart., MC; it was purchased from the Trustees of the Elton Heirloom Settlement under private treaty sale arrangements in 1980.

REFERENCES:
General: HdG No. 102; Slive, op. cit., cat. no. 61; Grimm, op. cit., cat. no. 26.
In text:
1. There is, for example, a drawing by Hendrick Goltzius of 1614 inscribed *Quis evadit/Nemo* (Pier-

pont Morgan Library, New York: inv. no. III, 145) and two drawings by Jan Muller, one inscribed *Cognita mori* (E. K. J. Reznicek, 'Jan Harmensz. Muller als Tekenaar', NKJ, vol. 7, 1956, p. 115, no. 24, fig. 24 and p. 116, no. 26, fig. 25).

160

2. For a similar costume (though without the elaborate feather in the beret) see ter Brugghen No. 6483 in this catalogue.

3. HdG, loc. cit.

4. Slive, loc. cit.

5. Grimm, op. cit., p. 200.

6. HdG, loc. cit.

7. E. Plietzsch, 'Austellung holländischer Gemälde in der Londoner Akademie', *Kunstchronik*, vol. 6, 1953, p. 123.

8. Slive, op. cit.

9. Slive, loc. cit.

10. T. Borenius and J. V. Hodgson, *A Catalogue of the Pictures at Elton Hall*, London, 1924, p. 29, No. 24.

GERRIT WILLEMSZ. HEDA, active 1637; before 1702

Gerrit Willemsz. Heda. Son of the still-life painter, Willem Claesz. Heda. Practically nothing is known about him. He was in his father's studio in 1642 in Haarlem (presumably as an assistant rather than a pupil);[1] there are dated pictures of 1637–47. He is noted by Vincent Laurensz. van der Vinne (1658–1729) as having died during the lifetime of the latter's father who died in July 1702.[2] His father incurred the expense of a grave opened in 1649 and this has been probably incorrectly taken (by Vroom) to refer to the burial of Gerrit Heda.

He painted still life in close imitation of his father. Some paintings signed HEDA may be by him or done in collaboration. Later, however, he signed 'Jonge Heda' or Gerrit Heda.

REFERENCES:
General: Bergström, pp. 136–40; Vroom, vol. 1, pp. 166–76 and vol. 2, pp. 56–65.
In text:
1. Van der Willigen, p. 156.
2. See Bredius, *Künstler-Inventare*, vol. 6, 1919, pp. 2214 and 2216 (No. 63).

Attributed to GERRIT WILLEMSZ. HEDA

6336 *Still Life with a Nautilus Cup*   Plate 143

Still life with a nautilus cup, glasses, books and food on a table; a curtain on the right.

Oil on oak, 84.6 × 99.5 ($33\frac{5}{16}$ × $39\frac{3}{16}$).

The curtain originally hung slightly lower falling behind the *roemer*, as can be seen in an infra-red photograph.

When the painting was acquired, its attribution was to Pieter Claesz.[1] The elaborate composition and the coarse technique make this attribution untenable.

It is close in style to the work of Gerrit Heda who imitated his father but whose technique was cruder and compositions more cluttered. It should be compared, for example, to a signed painting of 1644.[2]

PROVENANCE: Bequeathed to the National Gallery by C. D. Rotch, 1962.

REFERENCES:
1. *National Gallery Acquisitions 1953–1962*, 1962, p. 18.
2. Vroom, vol. 2, no. 293. Panel, 63.5 × 78 cm. Signed: . . . t Heda. Present whereabouts unknown.

WILLEM CLAESZ. HEDA, 1593/4–1680/2

His birthdate has been calculated on the basis of a portrait of him at the age of eighty-four by Jan de Bray which is dated 1678. In 1631 he entered the Haarlem guild as a master. In 1637 he first served as a *hoofdman*: he served as a *hoofdman* on a number of other occasions and later held various other offices in the guild. His son Gerrit Willemsz. was a close imitator.

He devoted himself almost exclusively[1] to still life and with Pieter Claesz. developed in Haarlem the so-called 'monochromatic' style of still life.

REFERENCES:
General: Bergström, pp. 123–34; Vroom, vol. 1, pp. 53–78, vol. 2, pp. 65–80.
In text:
1. For a drawing of John the Baptist, a religious painting and portraits attributed to Heda, see H. E. van Gelder, *W. Heda, A. van Beyeren, W. Kalf*, Amsterdam, n.d. (1941), pp. 12–13.

1469 *Still Life: Pewter and Silver Vessels and a Crab*   Plate 144

Oil on oak, 54.2 × 73.8 ($21\frac{5}{16}$ × $29\frac{1}{16}$).

Attributed by MacLaren to Gerrit Heda[1] but more probably by his father. Gerrit painted in a style closely based on that of his father. The attribution[2] depends on its similarity to indisputable works by Willem Heda such as the painting in the Oppenheimer collection in Sweden which is signed; it is dated by Vroom to 1636.[3] No. 1469 was probably painted at about the same time, that is, in the mid-1630s.

PROVENANCE: Apparently in the collection of Arthur Kay, Glasgow, by 1893 and passed from him to Henry J. Pfungst,[4] by whom it was presented in 1896.

REFERENCES:
General: Vroom, cat. no. 371.
In text:
1. For the first time in the National Gallery catalogue of 1913 it was said to be signed: HEDA 1644, but no trace can now be found of either signature or date. (Vroom, op. cit., repeats this incorrect information.)
2. It was attributed to Gerrit Heda by HdG already in 1893, if it is the picture then seen by him in the Arthur Kay collection, as seems probable (see OH, 1893, p. 224).
3. Vroom, cat. no. 355.
4. See A. Kay, *Treasure Trove in Art*, 1939, p. 60; HdG saw an *ontbijtje* attributed to Willem Heda in Kay's collection in 1893 (see note 2).

5787 *Still Life with a Lobster* Plate 145

On the left is a *pas-glas*; in the centre a *roemer*.

Signed on the edge of the white cloth, in the centre, below the knife-handle:
· HEDA · F · 165( )

There is a merchant's or guild cipher on the hanging corner of the cloth, centre, below.

Oil on canvas, 114 × 103 (45 × 40½).

Cleaned in 1976. Background worn and retouched.

Attributed by MacLaren to Gerrit Heda, the son of Willem, who painted in a style closely modelled on that of his father. There are, however, closely comparable signed paintings by Willem Heda of 1656 in Houston[1] and Budapest.[2]

PROVENANCE: In the possession of J. Scully, London; anonymous sale, London, 4 July 1919 (lot 65),[3] bought by Agnew (240 gns) by whom sold to Cremetti.[4] Sold by Paul Cremetti, London, in 1927 to Frederick John Nettlefold, by whom presented in 1947.[5]

REFERENCES:
1. Vroom, cat. no. 382.
2. Vroom, cat. no. 383.
3. As by P. de Ring. The signature and date were at some time overpainted and the painting said to be by Pieter de Ring (c.1615–60), the ring in the shadow of the dish on the left being taken for a rebus of his name, a form of signature he sometimes used. The overpainting was removed in 1950.
4. Letter of 1948 from Messrs Agnew (in the National Gallery archives).
5. As by P. de Ring.

DAVID DAVIDSZ. DE HEEM, active 1668

A 'David Davidsz. de Heem, painter', was a member of the painters' college in Utrecht in 1668;[1] no other fact is known about him. Since he had both the same patronymic and the same family name as Jan Davidsz. de Heem, it seems more than likely that he was a brother. Jan Davidsz., the best known of the family of still-life and flower painters, was born in Utrecht in 1605 or 1606[2] and it has been suggested that because David Davidsz. is not recorded in a guild until 1668 he must have been so much younger that this relationship is impossible. The argument carries little weight as the records of the Utrecht guild and the later painters' college are certainly incomplete and in any case David Davidsz., like Jan Davidsz., may very well have been inscribed as a master first in some other town. (Jan Davidsz. de Heem was working in Leiden from before December 1626 to after February 1631;[3] he settled in Antwerp and entered the guild there in 1635/6[4] but it is reasonable to suppose that he may have been admitted as a master earlier somewhere else. Although the records show he was often absent from Antwerp after 1658, the first known mention of him in the Utrecht painters' college is in 1669.[5] In 1672 he returned from Utrecht to Antwerp where he died between October 1683 and May 1684.[6])

There exists a small number of still-life and flower paintings signed D. De Heem and

D. D. Heem. They have been variously ascribed to Jan Davidsz.'s father, David de Heem the Elder (1570?–1632), to the David Davidsz. de Heem mentioned above and to David Cornelisz. de Heem (1663–1718 or later?) whose father was Cornelisz. Jansz. de Heem, a son of Jan Davidsz. It is clear that the pictures in question are not all by the same painter. Among them can be distinguished a small group obviously by the same hand as No. 2582 below: to this belong a still life in the Rijksmuseum, Amsterdam,[7] and another in the Brussels Museum,[8] a fruit piece in the Ashmolean Museum, Oxford,[9] a garland of flowers in the Landesmuseum in Darmstadt,[10] a flower piece with the art dealer Katz in London in 1961,[11] and a still life in Copenhagen.[12] These are very close in style to some of Jan Davidsz.'s simpler works and also to those of Cornelis de Heem (1631–95). They can scarcely be by the eldest David since they are dependent on the type of still life developed by Jan Davidsz. after he settled in Antwerp,[13] when the eldest de Heem was most probably already dead. The pictures in Oxford and Darmstadt have a form of signature with a flourish below identical, except for the first initial, with that of Cornelis de Heem. This could possibly be taken as an indication that they, and the rest of the group, are by Cornelis's son, David Cornelisz., were it not that their style would be old-fashioned for a painter who cannot have been active much before the middle of the 1680s. It is much more likely that David Cornelisz. was the author of the D. de Heem flower pieces in a later style (and greatly inferior to those listed above) in the Aachen Museum[14] and formerly in the Gemeentemuseum in The Hague.[15]

To resume: the group of pictures under discussion must be the work of a painter very close to Jan Davidsz. and a member of the same family. There is no D. de Heem recorded other than those already mentioned and of them the David Davidsz. active in 1668 is the one most likely to have been the author of the group.

REFERENCES:

1. Kramm, vol. 3, 1859, p. 652.
2. and 3. OH, 1886, p. 214.
4. P. Rombouts and T. Lerius, *De Liggeren . . . der Antwerpsche Sint Lucasgilde*, vol. 2 [1876], pp. 71 and 77.
5. Kramm, op. cit., p. 654, and Muller, p. 33.
6. F. J. van den Branden, *Geschiedenis der Antwerpsche schilderschool*, 1883, pp. 869ff.
7. Rijksmuseum, cat. 1976 A2566; signed: D DE HEEM f.
8. 1949 catalogue, No. 205; signed: D. DE HEEM.
9. Signed: D DE HEEM; [J. G. van Gelder], *Catalogue of the . . . Dutch and Flemish Still-life Pictures bequeathed by Daisy Linda Ward*, 1950, No. 33.
10. 1914 catalogue, No. 287; signed: D DE HEEM.
11. Photo in RKD.
12. Canvas, 54 × 41 cm., inv. no. 86.
13. For Jan Davidsz.'s pre-Antwerp style see Bergström, pp. 192–95.
14. 1932 catalogue, No. 189; signed: D d Heem.
15. 1935 catalogue, No. 201; signed: D DE HEEM. Sold by the Gemeentemuseum: with Nystad, The Hague, 1960.

Attributed to DAVID DAVIDSZ. DE HEEM

2582 *Still Life: A Glass of Wine, Oysters, Fruit and Flowers*

Plate 146

Signed in the bottom right corner: D.DE HEEM (DE in monogram).

Oil on oak, 33.7 × 24.2 (13¼ × 9⁹⁄₁₆).

F. Meijer (RKD) has suggested to the present writer that, despite the signature, No. 2582 is closer in style to Cornelis de Heem than to David Davidsz. de Heem: he considers that it resembles the Cornelis de Heem in the Ward Bequest at the Ashmolean Museum, Oxford, more closely than the David de Heem in the same collection,[1] for example. He considers No. 2582 to be the work of a contemporary follower or imitator of Cornelis de Heem.

There seems, however, no reason to doubt that the first letter of the signature is a D and the present writer prefers to retain MacLaren's attribution to David Davidsz. de Heem, which is discussed in the biographical notice above.

PROVENANCE: In the William Theobald sale, London, 10 May 1851 (lot 43),[2] bought by Clarke (£21); probably in the collection of Capt. Charles Spencer Ricketts, RN;[3] in the [George Bonnor, of Brighton] sale, London, 2 sqq. July 1895 (lot 660),[4] bought by Lesser (76 gns). In the collection of George Salting, London. Salting Bequest, 1910.

REFERENCES:

1. They are nos. 32 and 33 respectively of van Gelder's catalogue of the Ward collection (see note 9 of the biographical notice above).
2. As by de Heem (without initial). The markings corresponding to this sale are on the back of the panel.

3. According to the catalogue of the [Bonnor] sale of 2 sqq. July 1895, the greater part of the pictures then sold had formed part of the collection of 'the late Capt. Charles Spencer Ricketts, RN'.
4. As by J. de Heem. The markings for this sale are on the back.

BARTHOLOMEUS VAN DER HELST, 1613–1670

Bartholomeus (also *Bartel*) van der Helst, son of Lodewijk van der Helst, an innkeeper, was a native of Haarlem.[1] According to Cornelis de Bie he was born in 1613;[2] in the betrothal document of April 1636 his age is given as twenty-four,[3] in 1653 he is said to be thirty-nine[4] and in 1658 about forty-three.[5] His early pictures (the first known dated one is of 1637) suggest he was a pupil of Nicolaes Eliasz. (1591?–1654/6) in Amsterdam. He married in 1636 in Amsterdam where he is often recorded subsequently. He was buried in Amsterdam, 16 December 1670.[6]

Van der Helst was the most fashionable Dutch portrait painter of his time from about the mid-1640s onwards and painted a number of guild and militia group portraits. He also painted a few subject pictures. There are many portraits bearing his signature; the variations of execution and quality sometimes discernible between signed portraits even of the same year suggest that he employed assistants (in 1652 a pupil, Marcus Waltusz., contracted to paint for him ten hours daily for a year[7]). His son Lodewijk (born in 1642) followed his style in portraiture and many contemporary painters were influenced by him (e.g. Ferdinand Bol, Govert Flinck).

REFERENCES :
General: J. J. de Gelder, *Bartholomeus van der Helst*, Rotterdam, 1921.
In text:
1. According to a document of 1636 (de Gelder, op. cit., p. 138).
2. De Bie, p. 283.

3. De Gelder, op. cit., p. 138.
4. De Gelder, op. cit., p. 142.
5. De Gelder, op. cit., p. 143.
6. De Gelder, op. cit., p. 146.
7. De Gelder, op. cit., pp. 21 and 142.

1248 *Portrait of a Girl in Pale Blue with an Ostrich Feather Fan*

Plate 147

Signed top left: B. vander.helst/1645.

Oil on canvas, 75.4 × 65.3 ($29\frac{11}{16}$ × $25\frac{11}{16}$).

Cleaned in 1958–9.

The sitter was at one time said to be a member of the Braganza family.[1]

PROVENANCE: The picture is said[2] to have been in the William Beckford collection, Fonthill Abbey, and has been identified[3] with one in the second Fonthill Abbey sale, 14 October 1823 (lot 219),[4] 6½ gns. It was certainly in the collection of Joseph Everett, Heytesbury, by 1857;[5] Col. Everett sale, London, 12 May 1888 (lot 31),[6] £189, purchased for the National Gallery (out of the Clarke Fund).

REFERENCES:
General: De Gelder, op. cit., No. 804.
In text:
1. On the back of the lining is a label with early nineteenth-century lettering: 'One of the Bragansa/ family./B. Vander Helst./a/1645.'
2. National Gallery catalogue 1889–1913.
3. National Gallery catalogue 1915–29.
4. In the sale catalogue as 'Vanderhelst Portrait of a Lady'. It is unlikely that this was one of William Beckford's pictures; it is not in the catalogue of the

William Beckford sale, Fonthill Abbey, announced for 16 October 1822. This sale did not take place, Fonthill and its contents having been bought by Farquhar (cf. [C. Redding], *Memoirs of W. Beckford*, 1859, vol. 2, p. 239). The contents were included in the sale of October 1823 but (according to Redding, op. cit., p. 240) much was included in this sale that had never belonged to Beckford.
5. Waagen, 1857, p. 391.
6. As a lady of the Braganza family.

1937 *Portrait of a Lady in Black Satin with a Fan*

Plate 148

Signed, top right: b van der helst f1644.

Oil on oak, 104.6 × 76 ($41\frac{3}{16}$ × $29\frac{7}{8}$).

Cleaned in 1976. Cleaning revealed that the background had been entirely repainted concealing the signature and date and obscuring the outlines of the skirt.

In the nineteenth century the picture was attributed to van der Helst,[1] Nicolaes Maes[2] and Rembrandt.[3] It was reattributed to van der Helst by Bredius.[4]

PROVENANCE: In the collection of Louisa, Lady Ashburton, by 1871, when it was exhibited at the RA;[5]

exhibited at the RA, 1904,[6] lent by her executor, the Marquess of Northampton, from whom it was purchased in 1904.

EXHIBITIONS: RA 1871, No. 143; RA 1904, No. 77; Arts Council 1945, No. 9; London 1976, No. 54.

REFERENCES:
General: de Gelder, op. cit., Nos. 555 and 750 and pl. 11.
In text:
1. On the back of the panel there was formerly a cutting, most probably from a mid-nineteenth-century sale catalogue: 'VANDER HELST.' (now in the National Gallery archives).

2. In the catalogue of the RA exhibition of 1871.
3. In the catalogue of the RA exhibition of 1904.
4. See de Gelder, op. cit., No. 750.
5. Cf. note 2.
6. Cf. note 3.

4691 *Portrait of a Man in Black holding a Glove*   *Plate 149*

Inscribed at the bottom, on the left: An° 1641.

Oil on canvas, 113.5 × 80.2 ($44\frac{11}{16}$ × $31\frac{9}{16}$).

Cleaned in 1951. Some wearing in the background.

Van der Helst had a number of assistants even at this early stage in his career and this portrait, which is significantly weaker than Nos. 1248 and 1937, may include some studio participation.

PROVENANCE: Possibly in the collection of George Salting, London, in 1889.[1] It was purchased from Agnew by Sir Edward Stern, Bart., before winter 1904, when it was exhibited at the BFAC. It was bequeathed to the National Gallery by Sir Edward Stern in 1933 with a life interest to Lady Stern; ceded to the Gallery by Lady Stern in 1946.

EXHIBITIONS: BFAC 1904, No. 40; RA 1938–9, No. 140.

REFERENCES:
General: de Gelder, op. cit., No. 483.
In text:
1. In one of Salting's notebooks in the National Gallery archives there is the following note, apparently made in 1889, of a picture then in his collection: 'V. der Helst(?)/portrait of a Gentleman/blk lace and cloth dress/white collar and sleeves-/right arm akimbo, left hand/holds glove./dated A° 1641'; earlier and later attributions to 'Jansen', J. Ovens and Nicolaes Eliasz. have been deleted. The whole note has later been crossed out, and the picture was not among those bequeathed by Salting to the National Gallery in 1909.

WYBRAND HENDRIKS, 1744–1831

Born 24 June 1744 in Amsterdam, where he studied at the city drawing school and worked in a wallpaper manufactory. He married in Amsterdam in 1775 and settled in Haarlem, where he became a member of the painters' guild in 1776. In the same year he travelled to England in the company of Hendrick Meyer. Between 1782 and 1785 he lived in Ede in Gelderland but returned in 1785 to Haarlem, as director of the Drawing Academy and curator of the Teylers Foundation, where he died on 28 January 1831.

He painted in oils and watercolour portraits, peasant scenes, landscape, topographical views, flower pieces and still life, and also made drawings after paintings by old masters (e.g. Frans Hals).

REFERENCE: I. Q. van Regteren Altena et al., *Wybrand Hendricks* (exhibition catalogue), Teylers Museum, Haarlem, 1972.

1015 *Fruit, Flowers and Dead Birds* Plate 150

Grapes, peaches, plums, a pineapple, etc. and flowers; on the slab below are a lapwing and two other dead birds.

Signed below, in the centre of the marble slab: W^d Hendriks,

Oil on canvas, 67.7 × 54.6 ($26\frac{5}{8}$ × $21\frac{1}{2}$).

It is a deliberate imitation of the work of Jan van Os and until 1954 bore a false van Os signature.[1]

PROVENANCE: In the Wynn Ellis collection, London.[2] Wynn Ellis Bequest, 1876.

REFERENCES:
1. J van Os fecit.
2. As by Jan van Os.

JAN VAN DER HEYDEN, 1637–1712

Jan Jansz. van der Heyden; he usually signs himself *Heyde* or *Heyden*, occasionally *Heijde(n)* or *Heide(n)*. He was born in Gorkum (Gorinchem). His family had moved to Amsterdam by 1650. Houbraken says that he was the pupil of a glass-painter. He lived in Amsterdam but the views in some of his pictures show that he visited various parts of Holland, Flanders and the Rhineland. From the end of the 1660s he was also engaged in projects to improve street-lighting and fire-fighting. He died in Amsterdam, 28 March 1712.

In addition to town views he painted a few landscapes and still lifes.

REFERENCES: HdG, vol. 8; H. Wagner, *Jan van der Heyden*, Amsterdam/Haarlem, 1971; L. de Vries, *Jan van der Heyden*, Amsterdam, 1984.

866 A View in Cologne

Plate 151

In the centre background is the unfinished cathedral.

Signed in the lower left corner: J V.D.H.

Oil on oak, 33.1 × 42.9 (13 × 16⅞).

The building of Cologne Cathedral began in the middle of the thirteenth century, continued through the fourteenth and fifteenth centuries and was discontinued in the mid-sixteenth century; it was completed in 1842–80.[1] In van der Heyden's picture the cathedral is seen from the west. In the centre distance is the choir, completed *c.*1320; across the west end of it is the enclosing wall with a balustrade which was erected on its completion. To the right of it, nearer the spectator, is the southern tower of the west front. This tower had reached the stage in which it is seen here by *c.*1450 and remained in the same state until 1868. The large crane on top of it was in position already by the second half of the fifteenth century (it appears in a woodcut of 1479[2] and in the view of Cologne on Memlinc's *Shrine of St Ursula* in Bruges, painted in 1489) and remained a Cologne landmark for 400 years until its removal in 1868.[3]

The low edifice just to the left of the south-west tower, partly hiding the wall across the end of the choir, is the east wall of the north-west tower which was apparently built at some time between 1450 and 1550.

The street running into the left background is the Trankgasse; that on the right alongside the garden wall is Unter fetten Hennen; both disappeared when the cathedral was disengaged from surrounding buildings at the end of the last century.

The large house with a walled garden in front of the south-west tower is the deanery, later the palace of the suffragan bishop of Cologne;[4] it was extensively remodelled in the years following 1658 during the reign of Bishop Franz Egon von Fürstenberg: it was at that time that the ornate, stepped façade was built.[5] Its previous appearance can be seen in a drawing by Lambert Doomer (which probably dates from shortly before 1658).[6] The deanery was pulled down in 1892.[7] The house with a steep roof and Gothic windows just beyond the buildings along the end of the deanery garden is perhaps the cathedral vicarage which stood in this position;[8] its garden, as here, ran along the north side of the cathedral.

It is not possible now to determine the degree of topographical accuracy in this picture; unlike his contemporary, Gerrit Berckheyde, van der Heyden was apt to introduce extraneous elements into his views (compare No. 994 below) and some of the architectural detail of the cathedral is certainly incorrect. Nevertheless the general disposition of the buildings and the streets agrees with old views and plans of the cathedral and its vicinity.[9] Of the cathedral itself, the choir seems more or less accurately reproduced but the tracery of the windows in its west wall is wrong.[10] The north side of the south-west tower is approximately correct (except for the window tracery) and also the crane, but the western side is inaccurate.[11] The fragment of the north-west tower corresponds fairly well with old views of it but it is doubtful if it ever had the blind arcade shown here at the top.[12] Judging by old plans the deanery and its garden were approximately of the form seen in the picture but the gable with pinnacles in the centre of the façade seems to be an invention of the painter. In van der Heyden's later versions of this view (see below) there are small variations in the details of the cathedral and considerable variations in the deanery, while all the remaining buildings are entirely different; it seems reasonable to suppose that all these divergences are the consequence of the painter's imagination. (There is a fanciful view in the Academy in Vienna[13] in which van der Heyden has arbitrarily changed the location of the south-west tower and the deanery in relation to the body of the cathedral.)

The authorship of the figures in van der Heyden's pictures has been a matter of dispute and it is reasonable to accept Hofstede de Groot's suggestion that those in the style of Adriaen van de Velde in pictures painted after the latter's death in 1672 are, in fact, by van der Heyden himself. In No. 866 the figures are certainly very close to van de Velde's and in view of its probable date (see below) they may well be his work.

The National Gallery picture is the best of van der Heyden's various versions of this view and it seems likely that it is the earliest. The costume in it and the Leningrad version is probably of the first half of the 1660s but is exactly the same in both pictures and therefore gives no indication of which is the earlier. The detail in the Leningrad picture, however, is much less delicate; also, the façade of the deanery is more or less the same as that in the Wallace Collection which is certainly later (the costume of two of the figures in the latter cannot be before the late 1660s) and in the still later version in the Manchester City Art Gallery (1684). It is rather unlikely that in these later variants van der Heyden would have reverted to an earlier form of the façade, as would be the case if the Leningrad view were prior to the National Gallery one.

VERSIONS:[14] A slightly smaller variant is in the Hermitage Museum, Leningrad,[15] in which the cathedral varies only in minor details, but the deanery has a different façade and all the other buildings are completely different (except for those in the distance just to the left of the cathedral). Another variant is in the Wallace Collection, London;[16] in this much of the lesser architectural detail of the cathedral is omitted, the façade of the deanery agrees more or less with that in the Leningrad version and the remaining buildings are taken entirely from those of either the Leningrad or the National Gallery versions. There is a slightly simplified repetition of the Wallace Collection picture, with different figures and dated 1684, in the Manchester City Art Gallery.[17] A further variant, very small, in which the south-west tower of the cathedral has been omitted, the façade of the deanery is again different and without buildings in the foreground, right and left, was in the Becker collection, Dortmund.[18]

PROVENANCE: Two, or possibly three, undescribed *Views in Cologne* by van der Heyden were in the Petronella de la Court sale, Amsterdam, 19 October 1707;[19] another was in the Hendrik Schut sale, Rotterdam, 8 April 1739 (lot 25), 51 guilders.[20] The present picture was in the Veuve Johan Philip de Monté sale, Rotterdam, 4–5 July 1825 (lot 3), bought in (4,000 guilders) and purchased later in 1825 by Messrs Nieuwenhuys;[21] [Joseph Barchard] sale, London, 6 May 1826 (lot 9),[22] bought by Nieuwenhuys (415 gns). In the collection of Sir Robert Peel, Bart., by 1834;[23] purchased with the Peel collection, 1871.

EXHIBITION: London 1974.

REFERENCES:
General: Smith No. 98; HdG Nos. 84 and 92a; Wagner, op. cit., cat. no. 50.
In text:
1. The details of the construction of Cologne Cathedral are taken from P. Clemen, *Der Dom zu Köln (Kunstdenkmäler der Rheinprovinz)*, 1937.

2. In W. Rolevinck's *Fasciculus temporum*, Cologne, 1479; reproduced in Clemen, op. cit., p. 5.
3. It appears in a photograph of c.1865 reproduced in Clemen, op. cit., fig. 45.
4. See the copy of an early nineteenth-century plan reproduced in Clemen, op. cit., fig. 22.

5. See discussion of the building in W. Schulz, *Lambert Doomer: Sämtliche Zeichnungen*, Berlin, 1974, pp. 24, 91.

6. Rotterdam, Museum Boymans-van Beuningen, Prentenkabinet MB 171. See Schulz, op. cit., cat. no. 212.

7. Clemen, op. cit., p. 395.

8. See note 4.

9. See note 4.

10. See the drawing of *c.*1665 reproduced in Clemen, op. cit., fig. 12 (also figs. 15, 16 and 30).

11. See esp. figs. 31, 33 and 70 in Clemen, op. cit.

12. See figs. 10, 31 and 70 in Clemen, op. cit.

13. Wagner, op. cit., cat. no. 52.

14. Versions and variants are in Wagner's catalogue as nos. 45, 46, 47, 48, 49, 51, 52. MacLaren believed that Wagner's cat. no. 49 is a copy with slight variations of no. 47 (ex-Becker collection, Dortmund). The present writer has not seen the painting.

15. Wagner, op. cit., cat. no. 51.

16. Inv. no. P195; Wagner, op. cit., cat. no. 45.

17. Wagner, op. cit., cat. no. 46.

18. Wagner, op. cit., cat. no. 47: sold at Sotheby's, 11 July 1973 (lot 50) to Speelman, £42,000. Private collection, London.

19. Lots 20 and 31 are described as 'Een Keuls Gezigtje'; lot 21 merely as the companion to lot 20 (see Hoet, vol. 1, pp. 105 and 106). HdG without justification identifies lots 20 and 21 with his Nos. 83 and 88.

20. '. . . een Gezigt te Keulen, door vander Heyden' (Hoet, vol. 1, p. 573).

21. Nieuwenhuys, pp. 136–37. Nieuwenhuys's seal is on the back of the panel (cf. Cuyp No. 823, note 4).

22. As from the Monté collection.

23. Smith No. 98 and Nieuwenhuys, loc. cit.

992 *An Architectural Fantasy* *Plate 152*

Signed on a block of stone to the left of the tree in the right foreground: I·vD. Heijde.

Oil on oak, 51.8 × 64.5 (20⅜ × 25⅜).

This is an imaginary view, probably with details taken from actual buildings. The arch in the centre background may be a reminiscence of one of the seventeenth-century gates of Amsterdam; it does not, however, resemble any of them closely.[1]

The figures have been attributed to Adriaen van de Velde,[2] probably correctly.

Probably painted in the late 1660s.

COPY: A copy is said to have been in an anonymous sale, Amsterdam, 27–29 June 1905 (lot 59).[3]

PROVENANCE: It has been suggested,[4] without very good reason, that this might possibly be the *Scene in Rome* by van der Heyden in the collection of the Elector Palatine Johann Wilhelm in Düsseldorf in 1716.[5] It was in the Jan Gildemeester Jansz. sale, Amsterdam, 11 sqq. June 1800 (lot 71), bought by W. Reijers (1,150 guilders). In the Wynn Ellis collection, London, apparently by 1850 or 1851.[6] Wynn Ellis Bequest, 1876.

REFERENCES:
General: Smith No. 65; HdG No. 279; Wagner, op. cit., cat. no. 119.[7]
In text:
1. None of these still exists but they are reproduced in contemporary engravings and paintings.

2. HdG, loc. cit.; also in the catalogue of the Gildemeester sale (see PROVENANCE). Wagner, op. cit., also attributes the figures to Adriaen van de Velde. She discusses the painting in her text on p. 40, describing it as 'ein echtes "Capriccio"'.

3. Canvas, 38 × 48 cm. According to HdG, loc. cit., this was a copy of the National Gallery picture but judging by the description in the sale catalogue it was at most a copy of a variant.

4. HdG No. 283a.

5. See van Gool, vol. 2, p. 561; HdG (No. 283a) notes that it could equally well be identified with one or other of his Nos. 278, 285 or 290.

6. It is probably the van der Heyden mentioned by Waagen in the Wynn Ellis collection in 1850 or 1851 (1854, vol. 2, p. 298): 'A view of buildings, with figures by Adrian Van de Velde; of first rate quality in its sunny truth and beauty of treatment, but not attractive in composition'; this would fit No. 992 better than No. 994 below, the only other possible candidate.

7. Wagner incorrectly transcribed the signature.

993 *A Farm among Trees* *Plate 153*

Oil on oak, 22.1 × 28.8 ($8\frac{11}{16}$ × $11\frac{5}{16}$).

Cleaned in 1975.

PROVENANCE: In the collection of Wynn Ellis, London.[1] Wynn Ellis Bequest, 1876.

REFERENCES:
General: HdG No. 302; Wagner, op. cit., cat. no. 184.
In text:
1. It is not among the pictures in the Wynn Ellis collection in 1850–51 mentioned by Waagen, 1854, vol. 2, pp. 293–98.

994 *An Imaginary View of Nijenrode Castle and the Sacristy* *Plate 154* *of Utrecht Cathedral*

On the left is the east end of the sacristy of Utrecht Cathedral; part of Nijenrode Castle is in the background.

Signed on a buttress, left centre: VHeijde. (VH in monogram).

Oil on oak, 52.9 × 41.4 ($20\frac{13}{16}$ × $16\frac{1}{4}$).

Nijenrode Castle is in Breukelen on the Vecht river, some seven miles from Utrecht; since the time of this painting it has been much altered by restoration. Van der Heyden introduced it into several pictures.[1]

The sacristy of Utrecht Cathedral has also been altered by restoration; the wall in front no longer exists and the subsidiary building on the left between the buttress of the choir and the windows of the sacristy has gone, and the window tracery is different. That van der Heyden's view reproduces the building more or less accurately as it was in his time is proved by a late eighteenth-century drawing of the cathedral from the north-east,[2] which shows this part of the building with only slight differences from the painting.[3] The only liberty the painter has taken is to represent the sacristy as built of brick instead of stone.

Probably painted in the late 1660s.

PROVENANCE: Possibly in the Isack Clockener sale, Amsterdam, 15 January 1759 (lot 17): 'Een gezicht agter de Vecht, ziende op het Huis Nieuwenrode, met een Kerk op de voorgronde . . . door J. van der Heide. 23 × 18 *duim*.' Probably lot 70 of the [Wynn Ellis] sale, London, 6 June 1864, which was bought in (160 gns).[4] Wynn Ellis Bequest, 1876.

REFERENCES:
General: HdG No. 157; Wagner, op. cit., cat. no. 145.
In text:
1. Wagner, op. cit., cat. nos. 141, 142, 143, 144, 146.
2. Gemeente Archief, Utrecht (No. 1329).
3. The only difference of any importance is that the drawing shows a balustrade above the window of the sacristy.

4. 'J. van der Heyden. A view in a Dutch town, with a church, and figures in an open place before a mansion.' It is not among the pictures in the Wynn Ellis collection in 1850–51 mentioned by Waagen, 1854, vol. 2, pp. 293–98 (cf. Heyden No. 992, note 6).

1914 *The Huis ten Bosch at The Hague*   *Plate 155*

Signed on a stone, bottom left: IVDH.

Oil on oak, 21.6 × 28.6 (8½ × 11¼).

Cleaned in 1976. Some wearing in the sky.

The Huis ten Bosch (i.e. the house in the wood), which contains the painted Oran-jezaal, is in the Haagse Bos about one and a half miles east of The Hague. It was built in 1645–52 for Amalia van Solms, wife of the Stadholder, Prince Frederik Hendrik of Orange, to the designs of Pieter Post.[1] There are several views of the Huis ten Bosch by van der Heyden;[2] the present one shows the back of the building[3] (the south or garden side). The building is here seen in its original state;[4] among other alterations an outer staircase has since been built on this side, the dome has been changed and the wings added in 1734–7. The statues and the lattice obelisks are no longer there.

The figures, which have been painted in after the completion of the rest of the picture, have been wrongly attributed to Eglon van der Neer;[5] they are almost certainly by van der Heyden himself.

Probably painted in the late 1660s or early 1670s.

VERSION: Another, larger, version of the same view, seen from a little farther away, is in the Metropolitan Museum, New York.[6]

PROVENANCE: It may be the view of the Huis ten Bosch from the rear, with the garden, of the same size and on panel, which was in the following sales (but this might equally well be the view from the south-west, with a pavilion in the foreground, in the Kunsthalle in Hamburg[7]): anon. sale, Amsterdam, 20 March 1764 (lot 14), bought by Odon (with pendant, 153 guilders); N——— sale, Leiden, 1 June 1765 (lot 36),[8] bought by de Zwart (with pendant, 100 guilders); Jacob van Zaanen sale, The Hague, 16 November 1767 (lot 24, with pendant),[9] 40 guilders; anon. sale, Amsterdam, 26 sqq. April 1769 (lot 31); C. Ploos van Amstel sale, Amsterdam, 3 sqq. March 1800 (lot 10), bought by J. P. van der Schley (with pendant, 300 guilders); Johannes van de Putten sale, Amsterdam, 22 sqq. May 1810 (lot 36, with pendant), bought by de Gruyter (258 guilders). Nos. 1914 and 1915 (below) are said to have come from the collection of Desenfans [presumably the dealer, Noel Joseph Desenfans, who died in 1807] into that of the Carmichael-Smyth family.[10] It certainly belonged to Major-General Sir James Carmichael-Smyth, Bart. (d. 1838);[11] exhibited at the RA, 1873, lent by Sir James Robert Carmichael, Bart.;[12] and 1902, lent by Sir James Morse Carmichael, Bart., by whom it was bequeathed to the National Gallery in the same year.

EXHIBITIONS: RA 1873, No. 89; RA 1902, No. 198; London 1976, No. 57; Apeldoorn, Rijksmuseum Paleis Het Loo; London, Christie's, 'The Anglo-Dutch Garden in the Age of William and Mary', 1988–9, cat. no. 18b.

REFERENCES:

General: HdG No. 75; Wagner, op. cit., cat. no. 133.

In text:

1. See D. F. Slothouwer, *De Paleizen van Frederik Hendrik*, 1946, pp. 179ff.

2. For other views of the Huis ten Bosch and its gardens by van der Heyden, see Wagner, cat. nos. 134, 135, 136, 137, 138, 139 and 152.

3. Not, as HdG (No. 75) states, the front (cf. the reproductions in Slothouwer, op. cit., pp. 191 and 193, figs. 64 and 65).

4. See Slothouwer, op. cit., p. 193, fig. 65.

5. In the catalogues of the RA exhibitions of 1873 and 1902 (see EXHIBITIONS).

6. Wagner, op. cit., cat. no. 134.

7. Wagner, op. cit., cat. no. 136.

8. Terwesten, p. 448. The pendant, a view of the Huis ten Bosch from the side, was lot 37 of this sale.

9. Terwesten, p. 653. The measurements of the picture and its pendant in this sale are given in Terwesten as 11 *duim* high by 8½ wide but they have probably been inverted in error.

10. Letter of 1901 from Sir James M. Carmichael (in the National Gallery archives). It is not identifiable

in any of the following Desenfans sales: 11–14 May 1785; 8 sqq. April 1786; 8 sqq. June 1786 (by private contract); 13–17 June 1786; 24–28 February 1795; 16–18 March 1802; nor is it in Noel Desenfans's *Descriptive Catalogue . . . of some Pictures . . . purchased for*

. . . the late King of Poland which will be exhibited in 1802, 1801.

11. His card is stuck on the back of the panel.

12. He had changed his surname from Carmichael-Smyth in 1841.

1915 *A Square before a Church* *Plate 156*

Signed, bottom left, on the base of the round tower: JVH. 1678. (VH in monogram).[1]

Oil on oak, 21.8 × 28.9 ($8\frac{9}{16}$ × $11\frac{3}{8}$).

This view was previously described as Dutch, but the architecture of the church in the centre is German. It is typical of the flamboyant Gothic of the mid-sixteenth century in Franconia, Braunschweig and the neighbourhood of Cologne. The building on the left is more Dutch in character but is somewhat improbable architecturally and the view, as is often the case with van der Heyden, is probably a fantasy made up of elements from different places (cf. No. 994 above). Wagner[2] suggests that the building seen on the far side of the square is a reminiscence of St Gereon in Cologne. The similarity is not striking.

The figures have been attributed to Adriaen van de Velde;[3] he was dead when this picture was painted and in any case there is no reason to suppose they are not by van der Heyden.

PROVENANCE: Together with No. 1914 above, said to have come from the 'collection' of Desenfans [presumably the dealer, Noel Joseph Desenfans, who died in 1807] into that of the Carmichael-Smyth family.[4] It certainly belonged to Major-General Sir James Carmichael-Smyth, Bart. (d. 1838);[5] exhibited at the RA, 1873, lent by Sir James Robert Carmichael, Bart.,[6] and 1902, lent by Sir James Morse Carmichael, Bart., by whom it was bequeathed to the National Gallery in the same year.

EXHIBITIONS: RA 1873, No. 90; RA 1902, No. 193.

REFERENCES:
General: HdG No. 158; Wagner, op. cit., cat. no. 120.[7]
In text:
1. HdG says the last figure is illegible. It is, however, quite clearly 1678.
2. Wagner, op. cit.
3. In the catalogues of the RA exhibitions of 1873 and 1902.
4. Letter of 1901 from Sir James M. Carmichael (in the National Gallery archives). It is not identifiable in any of the following Desenfans sales: 11–14 May 1785; 8 sqq. April 1786; 8 sqq. June 1786 (by private contract); 13–17 June 1786; 24–28 February 1795; 16–18 March 1802; nor is it in Noel Desenfans' *Descriptive Catalogue . . . of some Pictures . . . purchased for . . . the late King of Poland which will be exhibited in 1802*, 1801.
5. His card is stuck on the back of the panel.
6. He had changed his name from Carmichael-Smyth in 1841.
7. Wagner incorrectly transcribes the signature.

MEINDERT HOBBEMA, 1638–1709

Meindert (also *Meijndert*) *Lubbertsz.*, son of Lubbert Meyn(d)ertsz.; baptised in Amsterdam, 31 October 1638.[1] As a young man he adopted the surname Hobbema which does not appear ever to have been used by the father. In July 1660, Jacob van Ruisdael testified that Hobbema, then living in Amsterdam, had been his apprentice for 'some years'[2] (presumably in Amsterdam, where Ruisdael had settled by June 1657).[3] Hobbema at times imitated Ruisdael closely, and as late as 1664 his compositions are sometimes based on Ruisdael's. In 1668 Hobbema became one of the wine-gaugers of the Amsterdam octroi,[4] a post he held until the end of his life.[5] It was at one time thought that he gave up painting after 1668; there are, however, several pictures with later dates (see Nos. 830 and 831 below), some of them among his best works. Nevertheless it seems clear that his painting activity was greatly reduced. Hobbema always lived in Amsterdam; in 1689, however, he appears to have visited South Holland and Overijssel (see No. 830 below). He died in Amsterdam, 7 December 1709.[6]

REFERENCES:

General: HdG, vol. 4; J. Rosenberg in *Jahrbuch der Preussischen Kunstsammlungen*, 1927, pp. 139–51. Most of Hobbema's pictures are reproduced in G. Broulhiet's *M. Hobbema*, 1938 (the text of which is unreliable). W. Stechow, 'The Early Years of Hobbema', *Art Quarterly*, 1959, pp. 3–18; Stechow, pp. 76–80.

In text:
1. Bredius in OH, vol. 33, 1915, p. 198.
2. Bredius, op. cit., p. 194.
3. H. F. Wijnman in OH, vol. 49, 1932, p. 176.
4. OH, vol. 3, 1885, p. 151.
5. and 6. OH, vol. 1, 1883, p. 82.

685 *A Woody Landscape with a Road by a Cottage*   *Plate 157*

Signed at the bottom, in the centre: M. hobbema.

Oil on oak, 60.4 × 84.3 (23¾ × 33³⁄₁₆).

Cleaned in 1960. Some wearing in the sky.

There is a version of this design dated 1665 in the Ruzicka collection in the Kunsthaus, Zurich.[1] Gerson[2] has suggested that this variant is the preliminary version of the larger composition of the same date formerly in the Meyer collection, London[3] (of which, as he points out, the *Cottages and a Church among Trees* in the Metropolitan Museum, New York,[4] is a later development). The National Gallery version of this composition is, however, very much closer to the Zurich picture than either of the two last-mentioned larger pictures; it is of the same size and, like the Zurich version, has something of the character of a sketch. The only important differences are that in the latter there are cottages and a few trees in the left distance in place of the belt of trees in No. 685, and a small hut has been added in the right foreground. Both these features occur also in the Meyer picture and it is logical to suppose that the Zurich version represents a stage between the National Gallery landscape and the fully developed composition. The priority of the National Gallery design is further supported by the style: the closing of the vista on the left and the less animated contours of the foliage (especially of the clump of trees in the centre) are more in the manner of Hobbema's earlier works under the influence of Ruisdael (cf. No. 2570 below). Nevertheless, although No. 685 must be earlier than the Zurich version, the difference in date cannot be very great.

VERSIONS: Versions of this composition in the Ruzicka collection, Kunsthaus, Zurich, and formerly in the Percy B. Meyer collection, London, are discussed above.

PROVENANCE: In the J. M. Raikes sale, London, 6 June 1829 (lot 39), bought by Thomas Emmerson or Woodin[5] (222 gns). By 1835 it was in the collection of Comte Perregaux, Paris;[6] Comte Perregaux sale, Paris, 8–9 December 1841 (lot 13), bought by Mennechet and Leroy (23,000 francs), according to Smith,[7] for the Prince [Auguste] d'Arenberg.[8] It was brought to England by Farrer.[9] Purchased from G. H. Phillips in 1862.

REFERENCES:
General: Smith No. 73 and Supplement No. 29; HdG No. 160.
In text:
1. On panel, 60.5 × 84.5 cm. Signed: m hobbema/ f 1665. HdG No. 223.
2. H. Gerson in *Kunsthistorische Mededeelingen*, 1947, pp. 43–46.
3. Canvas, 96.5 × 122 cm. Signed: m hobbema 1665. HdG Nos. 61c and 228c; exhibited at the RA, 1952 (No. 344); Percy B. Meyer sale, London, 16 March 1956 (lot 52). Reproduced by Gerson, op. cit., p. 44. A copy was in a Brussels sale, 15 March 1926 (lot 22), reproduced in the sale catalogue.

4. Panel, 76 × 107 cm. HdG No. 44. Reproduced in Gerson, op. cit., p. 45.
5. According to Smith, No. 73, it was bought by Emmerson; the auctioneer's copy of the catalogue gives Woodin as the purchaser.
6. Smith No. 73.
7. Smith Supplement No. 29.
8. It is not in W. Bürger, *La Galerie d'Arenberg à Bruxelles*, 1859.
9. According to the National Gallery catalogue, 1863.

830 *The Avenue, Middelharnis*   Plate 158

In the distance the village and church of Middelharnis are seen to the left of the avenue; to the right of it are ships' masts and a beacon.

Signed at the bottom, towards the right (on the reflection of the bank in the ditch): M: hobbema/f 1689.

Oil on canvas, 103.5 × 141 ($40\frac{3}{4}$ × $55\frac{1}{2}$).

The sky is considerably worn. The best preserved area is to the right of the nearest right-hand tree.

Cleaned in 1951 at which time the sky was found to be extensively damaged and repainted. Old varnish and some discoloured retouchings were removed and the sky was extensively restored. In 1972 scientific analysis revealed that synthetic ultramarine and chrome yellow from an early nineteenth-century restoration were still present in the sky and the painting was cleaned again but not all of the 1951 restoration was removed. This gave the painting an unsatisfactory appearance and therefore in 1980–1 the 1951 restoration was entirely removed and the damages in the sky retouched.

X-radiographs (Fig. 41) made in 1980 revealed that Hobbema had originally placed another tree on either side of the avenue in the foreground and subsequently painted them out. A reasonable hypothesis to account for the poor state of preservation of the sky (the landscape and trees are very well preserved) is that by the early nineteenth century the two painted-out foreground trees had begun to show through the paint of the sky and that a restorer at that time attempted to remove the sky in order to reveal the trees fully. This would account for the very severe wearing which begins at the line of the horizon and is worst on either side of the avenue.

Cross-sections revealed that the ground was of an unusually intense orange-brown colour. Optical microscopy and laser microspectrography analysis identified the ground as ferric oxide, so that it is probably one of the yellow-brown hydrated oxides, which differ in hue considerably depending on the geological source. Yellow ochre is one form. Medium analysis by gas chromatography showed the medium to be linseed oil, like that of the paint layers, but with a much lower proportion of medium to pigment. Some ochre pigments have a high oil absorption (about twice that of lead white) and it could be that initially too little oil was used to bind the pigment particles of the ground firmly to each other and to the paint layers above. This may explain why the orange-brown ground was found to be slightly more vulnerable to cleaning solvents than the paint layers above. It also may explain the reluctance of past restorers to remove previous retouchings completely.

The blue pigment in the sky is smalt which has become darker and more transparent with time, the orange-brown ground beneath reducing the blue colour to some extent. The green paint is in every case not based on the use of a green pigment but mixtures of blue and yellow, azurite and yellow lake. There has probably been some fading of the yellow, resulting in a lighter and bluer shade of green than originally intended.

The village of Middelharnis lies on the north coast of the island of Over Flakee (Province of South Holland) in the mouth of the Maas. It is here seen from the south-east, from a point on the Boomgaardweg (now the Steene Weg). The view has changed little and Hobbema's painting is remarkably accurate.[1] The church (St Michael's) was built in the second half of the fifteenth century. It still stands but the brick balustrade on the tower was replaced by another, in stone, in 1778 and the spire with the bulbous top was removed by the French in 1811 to make room for a semaphore (Middelharnis being on the semaphore route from The Hague to Paris); the brickwork of the tower has since been partly covered with stone.[2] Just visible beyond the east end of the church is the tower of the town hall built in 1639. The barn (which, with its high roof, may be a madder kiln) in the middle distance survived until about 1879.[3]

In the belief that Hobbema gave up painting soon after 1668 (cf. the biographical notice above), Hofstede de Groot[4] supposed the third figure of the date to be a mutilated 6; he also thought it improbable that such a picture could have been produced as late as 1689 when Dutch painting was in its decadence. Although the top of the third figure is smudged, there is, *pace* Hofstede de Groot, no doubt whatsoever that it is an 8; this has been made even clearer by recent cleaning and confirmed by infra-red photography.[5] Nor is there any reason for supposing that the signature and date are not authentic; they conform to Hobbema's usual calligraphy and resisted the action of the solvents used when the picture was cleaned. The placing of the signature on the reflection in the water cannot be considered suspicious since it is paralleled in other works by Hobbema (and also in some of Ruisdael's paintings). In any case the date of the picture has been put beyond doubt by external evidence. Ulbo Mijs[6] proved by means of contemporary documents in the Middelharnis archives that the beacon visible in the picture in the distance towards the right was not erected until 1682 (on the East Dyke). He also found less conclusive additional evidence in support of the later date in the avenue of trees along the Boomgaardweg, which was not planted until 1664, and in the trees in the south and south-east part of the churchyard (noticeably shorter than those on the north) planted in place of others cut down in 1666; he suggested reasonably that neither could have been as tall as those in the picture by 1669.

There is no documentary evidence that Hobbema travelled in South Holland in the 1680s and he may have painted the picture from drawings made earlier. It should be noted, nevertheless, that there is a view of Deventer[7] (in the Province of Gelderland) the date on which has been read as 1689 and he may have been travelling around the Netherlands at this period. The fact that *The Avenue* came from a collection in Sommelsdijk, the neighbouring village to Middelharnis (see PROVENANCE), suggests that it may have been commissioned by a local patron.

Rosenberg[8] suggested that Jacob van Ruisdael's *Grainfield* in the Metropolitan Museum, New York, was the formal source for Hobbema's composition, while Stechow[9] also mentioned a Flemish painting in the Rijksmuseum[10] and a picture by Cuyp in the Wallace Collection[11] in this context. However, when an image is so clearly topographically accurate to a considerable degree, it hardly seems necessary to undertake an exhaustive search for its compositional prototypes in the works of earlier landscape painters.

COPY: A reduced copy by Adrianus van der Koogh (1796–1831), made in 1822,[12] is in the council-chamber of the town hall in Middelharnis (cf. PROVENANCE).

PROVENANCE: The picture was in the collection of Theodorus Kruislander (d. 1782), clerk of the Council of Sommelsdijk, near Middelharnis, and is said to have been bought from Kruislander's estate in 1783 by the Middelharnis council for the town hall[13] but HdG has very acceptably suggested that it was bought for them at the sale of Kruislander's possessions (in Sommelsdijk?), 15–22 October 1782 (lot 31) for 25 guilders 10 stuivers by L. Kolff (a Lambertus Kolff was the head of Middelharnis council in 1782[14]). It remained in Middelharnis town hall until 1822 when it was exchanged for a view of the village of Renkum and a copy of *The Avenue*, both by Adrianus van der Koogh of Dordrecht. It was purchased from Adrianus van der Koogh by the art dealer Arnoldus Lamme for 800 guilders.[15] He sold the painting to Heer Rom Pot for 2,500 guilders. Later Pot's entire collection was purchased (in 1824?) by Charles Galli and taken to Edinburgh, 1826 (No. 23);[16] James Stuart of Dunean sale, Edinburgh, 9–11 February 1829 (lot 120),[17] 195 gns. It was afterwards brought to London and cleaned, and was sold by Ewing for £800.[18] It was in the collection of Sir Robert Peel, Bart., by 1834,[19] and exhibited at the BI, 1835. Purchased with the Peel collection, 1871.

EXHIBITIONS: BI 1835, No. 19; Amsterdam, Rijksmuseum; Boston, Museum of Fine Arts; Philadelphia, Museum of Art, 'Masters of 17th-Century Dutch Landscape Painting', 1987–8, cat. no. 47.

REFERENCES:
General: Smith No. 88; HdG No. 13.
In text:
1. Cf. the photograph taken from the same viewpoint and reproduced by K. Blokhuis in *Oude Kunst*, vol. 3, 1917–18, p. 279. (There is an engraving of apparently the same view in Rademaker, vol. 1, No. 116, erroneously described as a view of Voorschooten.)

2. See Blokhuis, op. cit., pp. 280–82.
3. Blokhuis, op. cit., p. 278.
4. HdG in *De Nederlandsche Spectator*, 1893, p. 62, and *Catalogue Raisonné*, vol. 4, pp. 350–1 and No. 13.
5. The date was already noted as 1689 in 1823 (in the inscription of that date which hangs in the town hall at Middelharnis; cf. note 12). Smith, loc. cit., also

gives the date as 1689 but doubts its authenticity (vol. 6, p. 113) for reasons similar to HdG's.

6. The researches of Ulbo J. Mijs (burgomaster of Middelharnis, 1891–1917) were published by C. G. 't Hooft in *De Amsterdammer*, No. 947, 18 August 1895, pp. 5–6.

7. *A Watermill in a Village near a Church* (actually a view of the Bergkerk and Bergpoort at Deventer) in the Sutherland collection (HdG No. 77). The date was formerly read as 1657 (e.g. Smith No. 51 and Waagen, 1854, vol. 2, p. 50) but Broulhiet and Mac-Laren read it as 1689. The most recent catalogue of the National Gallery of Scotland (Shorter Catalogue, Edinburgh, 1970, p. 46) prefers to record the signature and date: M. Hobbema f. 16 ….

8. JKPK, 48, 1927, p. 151.

9. Stechow, pp. 32–33.

10. 1976 cat., A2699. Attributed to Sebastian Vrancx.

11. 1979 cat., p. 51. The Avenue at Meerdervoort, Dordrecht.

12. *c.*64 × 87 cm. The minute of the Middelharnis council's resolution of 8 May 1822 approving the exchange of *The Avenue* against a copy by van der Koogh and another picture (see PROVENANCE) states explicitly that the copy is yet to be made ('een door hem te maken copie'); it had been painted by the end of the year since the inscription of 1823 hanging between the two pictures in the Middelharnis town hall shows that the exchange was affected in 1822. (The resolution of 1822 was published by Ulbo J. Mijs in *De Nieuwe Rotterdamsche Courant*, 17 January 1893, and the inscription of 1823 by HdG in *De Nederlandsche Spectator*, 1893, pp. 61–62; both were republished by Blokhuis, op. cit., pp. 283–84.)

13. According to the Middelharnis council's resolution of 8 May 1822 and the inscription of 1823 in the Middelharnis town hall (see preceding note).

14. HdG in *De Nederlandsche Spectator*, 1893, p. 62. No detailed catalogue of this sale is known, but HdG points out that in a record of the buyers and prices at the sale (preserved in the Rijksarchief) the painting that fetched the highest price was lot 31, which was bought by L. Kolff, presumably the Lambertus Kolff who was the head of the Middelharnis council in 1782 or 1783 (and again at the time of the exchange in 1822).

15. The details of this transaction were unknown to Smith who simply states (op. cit.) that the painting was sold privately in Dordrecht and then bought by 'Van der Pots' (sic). There is in the National Gallery archives a letter of 1893 written by Ary Johannes Lamme, first director of the Boymans Museum in Rotterdam, concerning his father's purchase and re-sale of the painting. (This letter was generously presented to the National Gallery by his great-granddaughter, Mevrouw O. C. D. Idenburg-Siegenbeek van Henkelom in 1963.)

16. 'Landscape View in the Island over Flackee. [sic]. - Minderhout Hobbima.'

17. As 'View in Holland Hobbema'. Smith (No. 88) states incorrectly that it was in an Edinburgh sale of 1828. As J. Pope-Hennessy has already noted (BM, vol. 74, 1939, p. 67), *The Avenue* was seen before the sale by Sir Walter Scott and described in a letter to the Duke of Buccleuch (see *The Letters of Sir Walter Scott, 1828–31*, edited by H. J. C. Grierson, 1936, pp. 121–22).

18. Smith No. 88.

19. Nieuwenhuys, p. 143.

831 *The Ruins of Brederode Castle*   *Plate 159*

Signed below a fallen tree, bottom right: m. Hobbema./f·i67i·[1]

Oil on canvas, 82 × 106 (32$\frac{1}{4}$ × 41$\frac{3}{4}$).

Cleaned in 1951.

Brederode Castle in Santpoort, about three miles north of Haarlem, was built in the thirteenth century and finally destroyed in 1573.[2] The ruins and the moat still exist in much the same state as in the present picture, though restored.[3] Towards the left is the north-west tower, in the centre the north-east tower and on the right, almost hidden by the grass and trees growing over it, the base of the south-west tower. Behind the latter, in the distance, are the remains of the barbican.

The figures, both in the background and in the left foreground, are by Hobbema himself but the ducks in the centre foreground are probably by another hand, perhaps Dirck Wijntrack (before 1625–78).[4]

Another view of Brederode Castle attributed to Hobbema was in the Berg (and others) sale, Parke Bernet, New York, 15 April 1953 (lot 17).[5]

PROVENANCE: In the collection of W. Kops or H. Kopps, Haarlem.[6] There is an unconfirmed statement by Smith that it was sold by the Kopps family to Thomas Emmerson in 1816, together with Vermeer's *View of Delft*,[7] on condition that both passed through the sale of the family's effects, and that at the sale in Amsterdam in 1816 the Hobbema was bought for 7,500 guilders by a Dutchman.[8] Both were certainly in the S. J. Stinstra (of Harlingen) sale, Amsterdam, 22 May 1822, the Hobbema being lot 74, bought by Brondgeest (7,000 guilders); it was bought by C. J. Nieuwenhuys in 1825 (for 22,300 francs).[9] Later(?) in the possession of H. J. Héris of Brussels.[10] By 1834 it was in the collection of Sir Robert Peel, Bart.;[11] purchased with the Peel collection, 1871.

EXHIBITIONS: BI 1840, No. 26; Arts Council 1945, No. 12; London, Whitechapel Art Gallery, 'Five Centuries of European Painting', 1948, No. 22.

REFERENCES:
General: Smith No. 59; HdG No. 6.
In text:
1. This signature had been overpainted and was uncovered when the painting was cleaned in 1951; a false signature (M hobbema ft/1667) in the bottom left-hand corner was removed at that time. The false signature must have been added and the true one overpainted before 1835, since Smith (loc. cit.) says the picture is dated 1667. Most of the false signature was removed in 1951 but some traces are still visible, especially of the date.
2. See *Voorloopige Lijst der Nederlandsche Monumenten van Geschiedenis en Kunst*, vol. 5, part i, p. 332.
3. The two paintings by J. van Ruisdael described as views of Brederode Castle by HdG (Nos. 38 and 39) are of two entirely different ruins. There are, however, accurate views of Brederode by Berchem: HdG No. 284 (a replica of this painting, unrecorded by HdG, signed and dated 1679: canvas, 74 × 116 cm. was sold at Lempertz, Cologne, 2 June 1943; lot 4); and No. 399.
4. Smith, loc. cit., attributed the figures in the painting to Lingelbach and the birds to Dirck Wijntrack. The figures are not by Lingelbach but there are instances of collaboration between Wijnants and Wijntrack in which the animals are similar to those

in No. 831: for example, a painting which was lot 142, Sir Foster Cunliffe sale, Sotheby's, 1 February 1950 (canvas, 76 by 65 in.) which is signed by both artists and dated 1654.
5. Panel, 18 × 23½ in.
6. According to C. J. Nieuwenhuys (p. 143), who owned the picture later, it had belonged to 'W. Kops, Haarlem'; Smith, loc. cit., says the 'Kopps' family and HdG, loc. cit., 'H. Kopps'.
7. Now in the Mauritshuis.
8. Smith, loc. cit. The 1816 sale mentioned by him has not been traced and there is no Kops or Kopps sale recorded at this period in Lugt, vol. 1. The likelihood that Smith was mistaken is increased by the fact that he says Vermeer's *View of Delft* was bought at this 1816 sale for 3,700 guilders by William II of Holland, which is certainly wrong. (It was bought by the Dutch government at the Stinstra sale in 1822 (lot 122); cf. PROVENANCE.)
9. Nieuwenhuys, loc. cit. Nieuwenhuys's seal is on the back of the panel (cf. Cuyp No. 823, note 4).
10. H. J. Héris, *Notice Raisonné sur la vie et les ouvrages de Meindert Hobbema*, 1854, p. 11; according to Héris it once bore a false Jan Wijnants signature.
11. Nieuwenhuys, loc. cit.

832 *The Watermills at Singraven near Denekamp* Plate 160

Signed, bottom right: m hobb( )ma.

Oil on oak, 60 × 84.5 (23⅝ × 33¼).

Cleaned in 1978.

Denekamp[1] is north-east of Enschede close to the border between Overijssel and Germany. Hobbema painted the picturesque group of watermills that belonged to the manor house in Singraven from the south-south-east. The river is the Dinkel. The watermills still stand at Singraven largely unchanged.

Hobbema painted at least one other view of the watermills at Singraven.[2] They had also been painted by Jacob van Ruisdael;[3] Ruisdael presumably visited Singraven in 1650 and 1651 during the same trip on which he visited Bentheim Castle[4] which is only thirteen kilometres from Singraven.

Probably painted c.1665–70 (cf. the *Woody Landscape with a Large Pool* in the Allen Memorial Art Museum, Oberlin, dated 1668).[5]

VERSION: A pastiche was in a Paris collection c.1938.[6]

PROVENANCE: Bought from Vaillant of Amsterdam in 1824 by John Smith, who sold it to Sir Robert Peel, Bart.[7] Purchased with the Peel collection, 1871.

EXHIBITIONS: BI 1832, No. 49; Enschede, Rijksmuseum Twenthe, 'Oost-Nederland model, Landschappen, stads- en dorpsgezichten 17de–19de eeuw', 1980, No. 15.

REFERENCES:
General: Smith No. 61; HdG No. 76.
In text:
1. The identification was made by K. Döhemann and W. H. Dingeldein, *Singraven. De Geschiedenis van een Twentsche Haverzate*, vol. 3, Brussels, 1934, pp. 135–49; see also, ex. cat., *Oost-Nederland model, Landschappen, stads- en dorpsgezichten 17de–19de eeuw*, Enschede, Rijksmuseum Twenthe, 1980, No. 15 (pp. 62 and 77).
2. Louvre, Paris. HdG No. 89. Broulhiet, op. cit., No. 441.

3. Formerly in the E. Habich collection, Cassel. HdG No. 170. Discussed in the catalogue of the exhibition, The Hague/Cambridge, Mass., 1981–2, p. 79.
4. For the Bentheim Castle paintings see the ex. cat., The Hague/Cambridge, Mass., 1981–2, pp. 51ff.
5. HdG No. 218; Oberlin, inv. no. 44.52. Oberlin catalogue 1967, pp. 74–75.
6. Panel, 54.5 × 77.5 cm. Broulhiet, op. cit., No. 221.
7. Smith, loc. cit.

833 *A Stream by a Wood* *Plate 161*

Oil on oak, 31.4 × 40.1 ($12\frac{3}{8}$ × $15\frac{13}{16}$).

Cleaned in 1974.

This is a study for the composition elaborated in a larger picture in the Boymans-van Beuningen Museum, Rotterdam (Fig. 42),[1] which follows this design fairly closely but has in addition a road with figures and a distant horizon on the left. Both were probably painted c.1663 (cf. the landscapes dated 1663 in the Beit collection[2] and in the National Gallery of Art, Washington[3]).

PROVENANCE: Apparently at one time in the possession of Nieuwenhuys.[4] In the [Joseph Barchard] sale, London, 6 May 1826 (lot 13), bought by Sir Robert Peel, Bart., 198 gns. Purchased with the Peel collection, 1871.

REFERENCES:
1. 1972 cat. no. 1306. Panel, 76.4 × 110 cm.; signed. HdG No. 138. A pastiche of the Rotterdam picture was in the S. Borchard sale, New York, 9 January 1947 (lot 41); reproduced in the sale catalogue and in Broulhiet, op. cit., p. 359, No. 521.
2. HdG No. 136.
3. HdG No. 171. Inv. No. 1937.1.61.

4. On the back of the panel is Nieuwenhuys's seal. The same seal is on the back of Correggio No. 23, Cuyp No. 823, van der Heyden No. 866, Hobbema No. 831 and W. van de Velde No. 871, of which all but Cuyp No. 823 were certainly at some time in his possession.

995 *A Woody Landscape with a Cottage on the right*   *Plate 162*

Oil on canvas, 99.5 × 130.5 (39⅛ × 51⅜).

Cleaned in 1973–4.

There are three other versions of this design. Judging by the development of the composition, the earliest seems to be the picture in the National Gallery of Art, Washington (Fig. 43).[1] Probably a little later is the comparatively small version now in the Mauritshuis[2] which agrees closely with the Washington picture. A final development is the large landscape in the Robarts collection.[3] No. 995 is perhaps of about 1665 (cf. the *Village among Trees* dated 1665 in the Frick Collection, New York[4]); the two smaller versions can be very little earlier, the Robarts one is probably a little later.

COPY: There was a (?seventeenth-century) copy of the landscape (the figures are replaced by a man on a horse talking to a standing man) in the collection of Dr G. Holland, Frankfurt-am-Main, in 1964 (photo in RKD: no dimensions given).

PROVENANCE: In the collection of William Leader by 1824, when it was exhibited at the BI; apparently still in his collection in Putney *c*.1835.[5] Probably in the collection of Wynn Ellis, London, by 1850 or 1851;[6] perhaps exhibited at the BI, 1853.[7] Wynn Ellis Bequest, 1876.

EXHIBITIONS: BI 1824, No. 121;(?) BI 1853, No. 67; London 1976, No. 58.

REFERENCES:
General: Smith No. 63; HdG No. 162.
In text:
1. HdG No. 181. Canvas, 96.5 × 108 cm., signed. National Gallery of Art, Washington, No. 1942.9.30 (Widener gift, 1942).
2. HdG No. 184. Panel, 53.5 × 71 cm.; signed. Ex-Heywood-Lonsdale collection.
3. HdG No. 114. Canvas, 89 × 105.5 cm.; signed. Exhibited at the RA, 1952–3, No. 346.
4. Inv. no. 02.1.73. HdG No. 42. Frick Collection catalogue, 1968, vol. 1, pp. 222–4.
5. Smith, loc. cit.
6. It is presumably the Hobbema seen in that collection by Waagen, 1854, vol. 2, p. 297, No. 1: 'A landscape, of peculiarly clear chiaroscuro; gleams of sunshine in the foreground and middle distance. Of delicate execution.' It should be noted, however, that the picture described by Waagen might possibly be one of the three paintings attributed to Hobbema in the Wynn Ellis sale, London, 27 May 1876; lot 40: 'A Landscape with peasants'; lot 41: 'A Woody Landscape, with Cottages and Peasants'; lot 42: 'A Woody Landscape, with peasants'. There is a MS note in a copy of Smith's *Catalogue Raisonné* said to have been his own: 'Now in possession of Wynn Ellis Esqʳᵉ.'
7. 'Hobbema: Landscape, Summer.' Lent by W. Ellis.

2570 *Cottages in a Wood*   *Plate 163*

Signed, bottom right: m. hobbema.

Oil on oak, 52.1 × 68 (20½ × 26¾).

Cleaned in 1974.

Probably painted *c*.1660.

PROVENANCE: HdG[1] suggests that this may be the Hobbema landscape of the same size in the Jonkheer Menno Baron van Coehoorn sale, Amsterdam, 19 sqq. October 1801 (lot 27),[2] bought by Coclers (1,710 guilders). By 1835 it was in the collection of Henry Philip Hope,[3] London (d. 1839); inherited by his nephew, Henry Thomas Hope of Deepdene[4] (d. 1862), whose widow bequeathed it with the rest of the Hope collection to her grandson, Lord Henry Francis Pelham-Clinton-Hope, in 1887; exhibited at the South

Kensington (now Victoria and Albert) Museum, 1891–97,[5] with the rest of the collection, a part of which was sold by Lord Francis to Asher Wertheimer, London, in 1898.[6] In the collection of George Salting, London. Salting Bequest, 1910.

REFERENCES:

General: Smith No. 98; HdG Nos. 36a, 233 and (?)51.

In text:

1. HdG No. 51.

2. 'Een extra fraay en natuurlyk Landschap met zwaare Boomen, Boerewoningen en Beelden'; panel, 20½ × 26 *duim*.

3. Smith, loc. cit. (For the earlier history of the

Hope collection, see the PROVENANCE of Potter No. 2583 of this catalogue.)

4. Cf. Waagen, 1854, vol. 2, p. 122.

5. *Catalogue of Pictures . . . lent to South Kensington Museum by Lord Francis Pelham Clinton-Hope*, 1891, No. 36.

6. See the Introduction to *The Hope Collection*, 1898.

2571 *A Road winding past Cottages in a Wood*   Plate 164

Oil on oak, 61.3 × 84.5 (24⅛ × 33¼).

Probably of about the same date as the *Woody Landscape with a Lady and a Gentleman on Horseback* of 1667 in the Fitzwilliam Museum, Cambridge,[1] and the *Woody Landscape with Travellers and Beggars* of 1668 in the collection of HM the Queen.[2]

PROVENANCE: In the collection of the Hon. William Pole-Tylney-Long-Wellesley (later 4th Earl of Mornington) in Brussels by 1842;[3] Earl of Mornington sale, Ixelles, 15–18 June 1846 (lot 7),[4] bought by Nieuwenhuys (20,600 francs). It was in the collection of Joseph Barchard by 1847, when it was exhibited at the BI. [F. Barchard of Horsted Place, Uckfield] sale, London, 3 May 1902 (lot 104), bought by Agnew (9,200 gns). In the collection of George Salting, London. Salting Bequest, 1910.

EXHIBITION: BI 1847, No. 47.

REFERENCES:

General: Smith Supplement No. 7; HdG Nos. 127a and 234.

In text:

1. HdG No. 118. Fitzwilliam Museum catalogue, 1960, no. 49

2. HdG No. 78; White No. 67.

3. Smith, loc. cit. Although the catalogue of the Mornington sale of 1846 (cf. PROVENANCE) describes the collection of which the present picture formed a part as the property of 'Lord Wellesley,

Comte de Mornington', it is clear that this refers not to the 3rd Earl, William Wellesley-Pole, but to the 4th (who succeeded his father in 1845), since Smith, loc. cit., calls him 'Hon. Long Wellesley' and it was the 4th Earl who took the additional surnames Tylney-Long (in 1812).

4. The size is given in the sale catalogue as 60 × 75 cm. but the description and support agree with No. 2571.

6138 *A View of the Haarlem Lock and the Herring-Packers'*   Plate 165
Tower, Amsterdam

The topography is discussed in detail below.

On some of the ships' masts in the centre background are Dutch flags. The hands of the clock on the tower stand at five minutes to five.

Signed near the stern of the boat in the foreground towards the left: m hobb( )ma (very faint; the last three letters are barely visible in ordinary light).[1]

183

Oil on canvas, 77 × 98 (30$\frac{1}{4}$ × 38$\frac{5}{8}$).

There is wearing in the covers of the pulley blocks each side of the lock, the dark parts of which have almost disappeared.[2] The craquelure is prominent in some areas of the sky and trees on the right.

There are *pentimenti* in the spire of the tower and the outlines of the trees; the roof farthest to the right was apparently at first higher.

The Haarlem Lock (Haarlemmersluis) and the Herring-Packers' Tower (Haaringpak-kerstoren) are here seen from the south-west. The view is taken from the west side of the Singel canal at its junction with the Brouwersgracht, the end of which is in the left foreground. In the centre is the Haarlem Lock, the reconstructed walls of which still stand; the lock is no longer in use and the drawbridge has been replaced by a permanent one. In the left background can be seen the corner of the Haarlemmerdijk (now the Haarlemmerstraat). In the centre background are the masts of shipping in the former open harbour in the IJ. On the right, beyond the lock-keeper, is the beginning of the Nieuwendijk.

None of the buildings seen in the painting has survived. The Herring-Packers' Tower, originally the Holy Cross Tower (Heilige Kruistoren), stood detached at the water's edge on the corner of the Singel and the Buitenkant (now Prins Hendrikskade). It was part of the town fortifications built at the end of the fifteenth century; its spire was added at the beginning of the seventeenth century. It took its later name from the adjoining herring-packery and its weather-vane was a herring (visible in the picture). The spire was replaced by a cupola in 1813 and the whole tower was pulled down in 1829.[3]

Miss van Eeghen[4] has demonstrated that this picture shows the view as it was before 1662 at the latest, and most probably before 1661. In 1662 the little low house on the corner of the Nieuwendijk (here only partly visible just above the two men working the lock gates) was replaced by a tall house with a necked gable. This later house, dated on the façade: ANNO 1662, can be seen in a painting of the same view by Jan Ekels the Elder (dated 1767) in the Amsterdam Historical Museum.[5] At the end of 1660 or the beginning of 1661 the buildings of the new fish market were erected on the west bank of the northern end of the Singel canal,[6] i.e. beyond the left side of the lock in the picture; there appears to be no sign of them here (it is unlikely that the low dark shape just beyond the left half of the lock in Hobbema's view has anything to do with the new market buildings, which remained on this spot until the second quarter of the nineteenth century).

Although the picture shows the view before the alterations of 1661–2, it does not necessarily follow that it was painted previously; it would not be out of keeping with the practice of seventeenth-century Dutch view painters to base a composition on a drawing made years earlier, even if the scene had since changed. The problem of dating in the present case is complicated by lack of any comparable works. Hobbema's earliest paintings – of 1658 and 1659 – are river landscapes.[7] There are dated landscapes from 1660 onwards. No. 6138 would seem to date from *c.*1663–5.

It is perhaps worth noting that Hobbema, who apparently settled in Amsterdam some years before 1660,[8] was living in the Haarlemmerdijk, the corner of which appears in the present picture, by November 1668.[9]

Hobbema painted several views of actual places (e.g. Nos. 830, 831 and 832 above) but this is the only true 'townscape' by him known to exist. There is no reason to suppose that the buildings here are not his work; they are handled in exactly the same manner as the cottages in his wooded landscapes.

COPY: A copy is in the collection of Mevrouw P. E. 't Hooft-Spakler, Amsterdam.[10]

PROVENANCE: It has been suggested[11] that the present picture is identical with the 'View along the Singel towards the Haarlem Lock and the Herring Packers' Tower' attributed to Jacob van Ruisdael in the sales of Catharina Backer, widow of Allard de la Court van der Voort, Leiden, 8 and 9 September 1766 (lot 163),[12] bought by Verbeek (320 guilders) and Jan Danser Nijman, Amsterdam, 16 and 17 August 1797 (lot 225),[13] bought by C. S. Roos (400 guilders). No. 6138 was certainly in the following sales:[14] Pieter de Smeth van Alphen sale, Amsterdam, 1 and 2 August 1810 (lot 41), bought by J. de Vries (bought in), 1,000 guilders; Henry Croese sale, Amsterdam, 18 September 1811 (lot 31), bought by de Vries (bought in), 600 guilders; sale of paintings from the Croese collection et al., Amsterdam, 20 July 1812 (lot 18), bought by Gruijter (455 guilders). It was in the [T. G. Campbell] sale, London, 25 June 1831 (lot 90), bought by Nieuwenhuys (213 gns);[15] [C. J.] Nieuwenhuys sale, London, 10 and 11 May 1833 (lot 68),[16] bought by Reeve (bought in?), 405 gns;[17] apparently also at one time in the possession of A. Brondgeest.[18] It was in the collection of Baron J. G. Verstolk van Soelen, The Hague, by 1834;[19] his whole collection was sold in 1846 to Thomas Baring, S. Jones Lloyd, Humphrey St John Mildmay and Chaplin,[20] the Hobbema being among those pictures which fell to Mildmay (who died in 1853). Lent by his son, Henry Bingham Mildmay, to the RA, 1876; H. B. Mildmay sale, London, 24 June 1893 (lot 23),[21] bought by Dr J. P. Richter (£2,310). By autumn 1921 it was in the possession of A. J. Sulley, London,[22] who sold it in May 1923 to Alfred Mildmay (son of H. B. Mildmay), from whom it passed to his sister, Miss Beatrice Mildmay, London. Miss Beatrice Mildmay Bequest, 1953.

EXHIBITION: RA 1876, No. 149.

REFERENCES:
General: Smith No. 28; HdG No. 3 (and Ruisdael No. 14?).
In text:
1. The doubts expressed about the genuineness of the signature by Miss I. H. van Eeghen (in OH, vol. 48, 1953, p. 125) are groundless. The fact that it is not mentioned in the Mildmay 1893 sale catalogue is of no significance; this catalogue also omits mention of the signatures of lots 36, 71, 76, 86 and 88, all of which are in fact signed. It is worn and faint and could scarcely be seen before the picture was cleaned; this would account also for the misattribution of the picture in certain nineteenth-century sales (see PROVENANCE).
2. It has been suggested that the picture is not in a good state of preservation (I. H. van Eeghen, op. cit., p. 126, note 13). Although the shadows of the covers of the pair of pulleys each side of the lock are almost entirely worn away, the damage elsewhere is negligible. The paint is well preserved, even the delicate rigging of the ships in the centre distance being intact.
3. For the Herring-Packers' Tower, see Zeven eeuwen Amsterdam, edited by A. E. D'Ailly, [1942

onwards], vol. 3, p. 138. A view of the tower by Thomas Heeremans, signed and dated 1676, was in an anonymous sale, Sotheby's, 27 April 1960 (lot 151). A view of the tower from the west by Johannes Storck, dated 1687, was in an anonymous sale, Christie's, 10 July 1953 (lot 112), and one from the east by Abraham Storck, also of 1687, was in the Lady Keppel sale, Sotheby's, 28 November 1956 (lot 117). It appears with an open cupola in a watercolour drawing made in 1816 by Gerrit Lamberts (reproduced in Zeven eeuwen Amsterdam, vol. 3, p. 184) and in a painting of 1826 by Johannes Jelgerhuis in the Rijksmuseum, Amsterdam (1976 catalogue, No. A1053).
4. I. H. van Eeghen in OH, vol. 68, 1953. pp. 120–26.
5. A. Blankert, Amsterdams Historisch Museum: Schilderijen daterend van voor 1800, Amsterdam, 1975–9, No. 133, p. 100. Reproduced by van Eeghen, op. cit., p. 123. Documents in the Amsterdam city archives confirm that the later house was built in 1662 (see van Eeghen, op. cit., p. 124).
6. The new fish market was built in 1661 according to the so-called third edition of M. Fokkens's Bes-

chrijvingh der wijdt-vermaarde Koop-stadt Amstelredam, 1664, p. 771, but it may have been begun by the end of the previous year; the market stalls were already leased by 1 May 1661 (see van Eeghen, op. cit. p. 124). See, for example, the view of the Singel by J. Storck (undated but possibly of 1689) [Kisch sale, Sotheby's, 16 July 1958 (lot 43)].

7. W. Stechow, 'The Early Years of Hobbema', op. cit., pp. 3–10.

8. OH, vol. 30, 1915, p. 194.

9. GB-A, 1864, i, p. 222.

10. On canvas, 79 × 100 cm. In an anonymous sale. Frederick Muller, Amsterdam, 30 November 1909 (lot 107), as by J. Beerstraaten, bought by August Jansen, Amsterdam; after Jansen's death it came into the possession of J. Goudstikker, Amsterdam, who sold it in 1919 or 1920 to C. G. 't Hooft, Amsterdam (cf. van Eeghen, op. cit., p. 123); Historical Exhibition, Amsterdam, 1925, No. 420. Reproduced in the Amsterdam 30 November 1909 sale catalogue, and the Amsterdam 1925 exhibition catalogue. It agrees in detail with the original except for the weather-vane, which in the copy is a cock. Since the well-known herring weather-vane remained in position on the tower until the demolition of 1829 (it can be seen in Jelgerhuis's painting of 1826 mentioned in note 3), it is conceivable that this rather pedestrian copy may be nineteenth century.

11. K. E. Simon, *Jacob van Ruisdael*, 1927, p. 73, and in *Zeitschrift für Kunstgeschichte*, 1940, p. 210.

12. 'J. Ruysdael. De Haarlemmer-sluis en Haaring-pakkerstoren te Amsterdam'; 29¾ × 38 *duim*.

13. 'Jacob Ruysdael Een Gezicht, ziende langs de Cingel na de Haarlemmersluis en Haringpakkers-Tooren te Amsterdam; met verscheide stoffagie ...'; on canvas, 29 × 38 *duim*.

14. Miss van Eeghen has suggested (op. cit., p. 125, note 5) that, as the National Gallery picture and the copy in the 't Hooft collection are of almost the same size, it is not always possible to say whether the items in the nineteenth-century sales mentioned in the PROVENANCE refer to the original or the copy. In fact, however, the picture in the Croese sales of 1811 and 1812 is identified in the catalogues of those sales

as lot 41 of the Smeth van Alphen sale and Smith, who certainly knew the picture (then belonging to Baron Verstolk van Soelen; see Smith No. 28), identifies it with that of the Smeth van Alphen, T. G. Campbell and Nieuwenhuys sales. The Nieuwenhuys 1833 sale catalogue mentions that it came from the Smeth van Alphen sale. Subsidiary evidence that the picture in the sales mentioned was the original is proved by the prices paid. (The identity of the National Gallery picture with that in the Mildmay collection in the nineteenth century is proved by the RA 1876 label and Mildmay 1893 sale markings on the back.)

15. As 'Storck View of one of the Towers and part of the City of Amsterdam, with figures'. Storck's name is deleted in the auctioneer's marked copy of the catalogue of this (anonymous) sale which gives the same vendor, purchaser and price paid for this lot as Smith does (loc. cit.).

16. As by Hobbema and from the Smeth van Alphen sale.

17. The auctioneer's marked copy of the sale catalogue names Reeve as the purchaser of lot 68; according to Smith, loc. cit., the lot was bought in (both give the same purchase price).

18. The lining canvas is inscribed in ink: 'A. Brondgeest'. It is not known when the picture was in his possession but he is known to have bought a number of pictures for Baron Verstolk (see note 7 to P. Koninck No. 4251 of this catalogue).

19. Nieuwenhuys, p. 140.

20. See Northbrook catalogue, pp. ix–x and 199. MS note in copy of Smith's *Catalogue Raisonné* said to have been his own: 'Purchased by Messrs Baring Lloyd and Co. 1848 [sic]. Now in the possession of Hump[y] S[t] J Mildmay Esqr.'

21. See the copy of his *Catalogue Raisonné* at the RKD; HdG, who saw the picture when in Sulley's possession, adds that Sulley bought it from the purchaser at the Mildmay sale [presumably not Richter who probably bought it for someone else].

22. A copy of A. J. Sulley's receipt, kindly communicated by Messrs Baring Bros., is in the National Gallery archives.

MELCHIOR D'HONDECOETER, 1636–1695

Melchior (also *Melgior*) d' (or *de*) Hondecoeter. Born in Utrecht in 1636, according to Houbraken;[1] grandson of the landscape painter, Gillis de Hondecoeter, and son and pupil of the landscape and bird painter, Gysbert de Hondecoeter (died 1653). He apparently also studied with his uncle, Jan Baptist Weenix, to whose influence is due the decorative, Italianate element in his style. No. 1222 below and similar pictures show that at one time he imitated Otto Marseus van Schrieck (1619/20–78; in Amsterdam from 1657). He was working in The Hague by 1659; in 1662 he was a *hoofdman* of the painters' confraternity there. By 1663, when he married, he had settled in Amsterdam, where he apparently remained for the rest of his life, and where he died on 3 April 1695.

Almost all his paintings are of birds. There are a number of dated pictures from 1668 onwards, but little evolution of style is apparent. He had many imitators, perhaps the most interesting of whom is the Antwerp painter Peter Casteels (1684–1749).

REFERENCES:
General: Obreen, vol. 4, pp. 75, 83, 120, 130–31;   In text:
Bredius, *Künstler-Inventare*, vol. 4, pp. 1210ff.   **1.** Vol. 3, p. 68.

202 *A Cock, Hens and Chicks*   *Plate 166*

Above left are a pigeon and a finch.

Oil on canvas, 85.5 × 110 ($33\frac{5}{8}$ × $43\frac{1}{4}$).

Cleaned in 1951.

The style is close to that of the *Cock with Hens and Chicks* in the Kunsthalle, Karlsruhe,[1] which is signed and dated 1668, and in which the chick in the left foreground is repeated.

PROVENANCE: Richard Simmons Bequest, 1847.

REFERENCE: **1.** Karlsruhe 1966 catalogue, No. 344.

1222 *Birds, Butterflies and a Frog among Plants and Fungi*   *Plate 167*

Above, centre, is a bullfinch and three more are below.

Over a hole in the tree-trunk, above, centre, are the remains of a signature: M · ( )/ 1668. To the right of the M is a series of small holes, presumably where the rest of the name has been scratched off.

Oil on canvas (irregular edges), 68.3 × 56.8 ($26\frac{7}{8}$ × $22\frac{3}{8}$); a further centimetre of the original painted surface is at present folded over the edges of the stretcher on all sides.

At one time ascribed to Otto Marseus van Schrieck (1619/20–78),[1] whose compositions it much resembles. Later attributed to Melchior d'Hondecoeter by Bredius (who,

however, read the signature incorrectly as M.d'H).[2] In the 1915 and subsequent catalogues the fragmentary signature was wrongly given as Mi( ) and the picture ascribed
to Abraham Mignon (1640–79). There is certainly no letter immediately after the M
and although the dot which follows it could conceivably have been that over an i,
neither in style nor in subject does it resemble Mignon's work. The correctness of
Bredius's attribution to Hondecoeter is proved by a painting in the Rijksmuseum[3] in
identical style, which is not only signed, but repeats exactly, although differently
arranged, the birds and tree and most of all the butterflies and fungi. Further, the
surviving M is very like that of Hondecoeter's usual signature, in which it is sometimes
followed by a single dot, as here.

The National Gallery picture and those belonging to the Cassel[4] and Schwerin[5]
Museums, also of 1668, are among the earliest known dated works by Hondecoeter.[6]
The others show already his fully developed style, but No. 1222 and the Rijksmuseum
variant are clearly based on the style of Marseus, who was closely imitated by several of
his contemporaries.[7]

VARIANT: A painting in the Rijksmuseum composed of the same elements is mentioned above.

PROVENANCE: A painting of wild plants, fungi and birds by Hondecoeter, of about the same size as No. 1222,
was in the collection of Willem Lormier in The Hague by 1752[8] and in the Willem Lormier sale, The Hague,
4 sqq. July 1763 (lot 110), bought by Balden (88 guilders). No. 1222 was possibly in French possession in
mid-nineteenth century or later.[9] Presented by J. Whitworth Shaw, 1886.

REFERENCES:

1. Presented as by Marseus and so catalogued, 1888
and 1889.
2. According to a correction slip in the National
Gallery, *Descriptive and Historical Catalogue: Foreign
Schools*, 1889, opp. p. 260. Catalogued 1890–1913 as
by Hondecoeter.
3. Rijksmuseum 1976 catalogue, A169: canvas,
66 × 52.5 cm.; signed on the tree-trunk: M de
hondec.
4. Cassel 1929 catalogue, No. 380.
5. Staatliches Museum, Schwerin, *Holländische und
flämische Malerei des 17. Jahrhunderts*, 1982, No. 141.
Canvas, 102 × 128 cm. Signed: M d hondecoeter
A 1668.
6. The signature and date – 1661 – on the *Still Life*

with *Fish* in Braunschweig was questioned by Mac-
Laren, but Klessmann (*Herzog Anton Ulrich-Museum,
Braunschweig: Die Holländischen Gemälde*, Braunschweig, 1983, p. 97) rejects such doubts. The painting shows the powerful influence of Jan Baptist
Weenix.
7. For example the signed painting by Abraham Begeijn (*c.*1630) in Braunschweig (Klessmann, op. cit.,
No. 382, p. 20).
8. Hoet, vol. 2, p. 425; 'Wilde kruyden, Champin-
jons en Vogels', on canvas, 2 *voet* 2¼ *duim* high by
1 *v.* 10 *d.* wide.
9. Pasted round the edges of the stretcher and the
paintings are pieces of mid-nineteenth-century
French printed forms.

GERRIT VAN HONTHORST, 1592–1656

Gerrit van Honthorst; known in Italy as *Gherardo della Notte* or *delle Notti*. Born in
Utrecht, on 4 November 1592.[1] Both his grandfather and his father were artists: the
former, Gerrit Huyghen, was dean of the Utrecht guild in 1579 and the latter, Herman
Gerritsz., was a painter of tapestry cartoons. He was a pupil of Abraham Bloemaert in
Utrecht.[2] Afterwards he went to Rome; this may have been as early as 1610 but the
date is far from certain.[3] Among his patrons there were Marchese Vincenzo Giustiniani

(in whose palace he lived for a long time, according to Sandrart),[4] Cardinal Scipione Borghese and the Grand Duke of Tuscany. In Rome he developed a style based in the first place on that of Caravaggio (died July 1610) and his Roman followers; his earliest dated work is a drawing of 1616 after Caravaggio's *Martyrdom of St Peter* in S. Maria del Popolo. He seems to have made a considerable reputation in Rome and a number of pictures were commissioned from him for churches there and in the vicinity. The *Beheading of St John the Baptist* in S. Maria della Scala was apparently painted in 1617–18;[5] the *Virgin and Child with Saints* in Albano is dated 1618. Honthorst was still in Rome in January 1619;[6] by October 1620 he was back again in Holland and married that month in Utrecht.[7] He became a member of the Utrecht guild in 1622[8] and was its dean in 1625, 1626, 1628 and 1629.[9] In Holland he painted few religious pictures and turned to classical and Arcadian subjects and, even more, to genre and portraits, in which the influence of some of his Utrecht contemporaries is also discernible. His fame was soon widespread; when Sandrart came to study with him about 1625 he had twenty-five pupils, each of whom paid him a hundred guilders a year.[10] He was invited to England by Charles I: he came to London in spring 1628[11] and in the six months he was here painted the large *Mercury presenting the Liberal Arts to Apollo and Diana* (which includes portraits of the king and queen) at Hampton Court, and various royal portraits, for which he was given 4,000 florins, a life pension of £100 and various costly presents.[12] He returned to Holland in December 1628.[13] In 1635 he sent to Denmark the first of a long series of classical and historical pictures commissioned by King Christian IV.[14] From about this time until 1652 he lived mainly in The Hague (he was inscribed in The Hague guild in May 1637[15]); he was painter to the Stadholder[16] and produced allegorical paintings for the Stadholder's palaces at Rijswijk and Honselaersdijk and large numbers of portraits of the prince and his family and court personages.[17] In 1649 and 1650 he painted some of the decorations of the Oranjezaal in the Huis ten Bosch.[18] During his years in The Hague, the Queen of Bohemia (see below, No. 6362) and her daughters were among his pupils. From 1652 onwards he lived in Utrecht,[19] where he died, 27 April 1656.[20]

Honthorst was one of the few Dutch painters of his day who was an international figure. He was one of the principal channels, though not the earliest, through which Caravaggio's innovations reached Holland and he popularised candle-light scenes. His portraits, on the other hand, are much nearer to the conventional style of the earlier Dutch court painters such as Michiel van Miereveld. Much of his later work appears to have been executed with the aid of assistants. His brother Willem (1594–1666) painted portraits in the same manner (and also signed G. Honthorst, which has caused some confusion). Among his pupils were Jan van Bronchorst and Joachim van Sandrart, whose *Teutsche Academie* of 1675 gives the fullest early account of Honthorst's career.

REFERENCES:

General: G. J. Hoogewerff in *Onze Kunst*, 1917, pp. 37ff; idem, *Gerrit van Honthorst*, 1924; A. von Schneider, *Caravaggio und die Niederländer*, 1933, pp. 21–31 and 134–36; J. R. Judson, *Gerrit van Honthorst*, 1959; H. Braun, 'Gerard und Willem van Honthorst', Diss., Göttingen, 1966; B. Nicolson, *The International Caravaggesque Movement*, Oxford, 1979, pp. 57–61.

In text:

1. He has previously been thought to have been born in 1590 on the evidence of an entry in the burial register. However, an epigram on a self-portrait print gives his birthdate as 1592 as does Sandrart. Archival evidence concerning his family confirms this date. For an extended discussion, see Braun, op. cit., p. 15, note 1.

2. See Sir Dudley Carleton's letter to the Earl of Arundel, June 1621 (W. N. Sainsbury, *Original Unpublished Papers Illustrative of the Life of Sir P. P. Rubens* etc., 1859, pp. 290–91); see also the title of Pieter de Jode's print after a self portrait, published in 1649 by Jan Meyssens in Antwerp (*Images de divers hommes d'esprit sublime* etc.) and reprinted in de Bie, p. 165; also Sandrart, *Teutsche Academie*, vol. 2, p. 303.

3. See Judson, op. cit., p. 11.

4. Loc. cit.

5. E. Borsook in BM, vol. 96, 1954, p. 271.

6. E. Borsook, loc. cit.

7. Judson, op. cit.

8. Muller, p. 16.

9. Muller, p. 128.

10. Sandrart, loc. cit.

11. See Gerbier's letter of April 1628 (W. H. Carpenter, *Pictorial Notices* etc., 1844, p. 180).

12. Sandrart, op. cit., pp. 303–4; O. Millar in BM, vol. 96, 1954, pp. 36–39.

13. Millar, op. cit.

14. Judson, op. cit., pp. 117ff.

15. Obreen, vol. 5, p. 98.

16. See the inscription on the print of 1649 mentioned in note 2 and Hoogstraten, p. 234.

17. Many payments for paintings commissioned by Prince Frederik Hendrik are recorded in the years 1637–50 (Kramm, Supplement, pp. 83–84).

18. See J. G. van Gelder, NKJ, 1949, pp. 151–54.

19. De Vries, Bredius and Muller, loc. cit.

20. Kramm, op. cit., p. 83.

3679 *Christ before the High Priest* *Plate 168*

Christ stands before the High Priest, who is seated at a table; behind him are soldiers in Roman costume.

On the back of the lining canvas is the cipher of the Duke of Lucca (C.L. surmounted by a crown).

Oil on canvas, 272 × 183 (106 × 72).

Cleaned in 1969. Some wearing especially in the shadows of Christ's robe.

The subject was described by Joachim von Sandrart,[1] who was Honthorst's pupil about 1625, as *Christ before Pilate*; this has been repeated by many subsequent writers. Nevertheless, although the accounts of Christ's trials given in the Gospels differ considerably,[2] all make it evident that Christ appeared before Pilate in daytime, while from three of them (Matthew, Mark and John)[3] it emerges that he was taken before the high priest at night. It seems reasonably certain, therefore, that the subject here is Christ before the high priest. A greater difficulty is the identity of the latter. Annas had been deposed by the Romans and his place taken by his son-in-law, Caiaphas, but he seems to have been regarded by the Jews as having equal authority with Caiaphas.[4] Mark and Luke do not name the high priest; Matthew says that Christ was tried before the high priest Caiaphas. John states that Christ was tried by Annas (whom he describes as high priest) and although he says afterwards that Annas afterwards sent Christ to the high priest Caiaphas, he does not mention an interrogation by the latter. It seems possible, however, that the two men standing apart from the rest beside the high priest in this picture are intended for the two false witnesses of Matthew's account[5] (the number is not specified in any of the other Gospels); if so, the judge would be meant to represent Caiaphas.

According to Sandrart the picture was painted in Rome for Marchese [Vincenzo] Giustiniani, in whose house Honthorst lived.[6] Honthorst went to Rome perhaps about 1610; he was still there in January 1619[7] but had returned to Utrecht before mid-October 1620.[8] The picture probably belongs to the later part of his stay in Rome: Judson[9] dates it *c.*1617, that is shortly before the *Beheading of St John the Baptist* of 1618 in S. Maria della Scala, Rome. It became one of the more celebrated paintings in Rome and numerous copies were made of it (see below).

It was also influential: for example, a derivation, showing the figures in half length, was painted by Matthias Stomer;[10] and a second, showing the figures in full length, with Christ's head turned slightly towards the spectator, was drawn by Raymond de Lafage (*c.*1650–84).[11]

ENGRAVINGS: Engraved by Pietro Fontana (1762–1837); Girolamo Carattoni, 1812;[12] S. Morelli, 1816.[13]

COPIES: Copies are in the Hermitage, Leningrad;[14] Bordeaux Cathedral;[15] collection of Marchese Luigi Cappelli, Aquila;[16] S. Croce in Gerusalemme, Rome;[17] S. Andrea della Valle, Rome;[18] Kunsthistorisches Museum, Vienna;[19] Rouen Museum;[20] Academia de S. Fernando, Madrid;[21] R. St G. Walker collection, New York (before 1932);[22] Lord Barrymore sale, Sotheby's, 21 June 1933 (lot 20).[23] (This painting is mentioned by Waagen, 1854, vol. 4, p. 413: 'Christ before Pilate by candlelight . . . both good pictures'.); sale, Brussels (Nackers), 12 February 1964 (lot 153).[24] (In this copy an arch has been added behind the principal figures through which can be seen, on the right, the group of soldiers and on the left at the top an old woman leaning from a window holding a lighted candle. She gazes at the face of Christ.); sale, Mrs F. Marsham, Christie's, 1 May 1964 (lot 85), 70 gns;[25] anon. sale, Christie's, 5 May 1972 (lot 54);[26] Gregorio Sella collection, Turin, 1983.[27] A three-quarter-length copy was at the S. Hartveld Gallery, Antwerp, *c.*1939. A small late copy was in a Turin private collection in 1947;[28] a fragment of a reduced copy is in the Rheims Museum.[29] A half-length copy was in an anon. sale, Christie's, 7 March 1969 (lot 25), 50 gns.[30] Other possible versions or copies were in the J. A. Snijers sale, Antwerp, 10 October 1842 (lot 13); William Young Ottley sale, London, 4 March 1837 (lot 85),[31] bought by Jackson; Lord Northwick sale, 26 July sqq. 1859 (lot 403),[32] bought by Moore. There is a drawing after the National Gallery picture by Nikolaus Mosmann (*c.*1727–87) in the British Museum Printroom.[33]

PROVENANCE: Painted for the Marchese Vincenzo Giustiniani, Rome (see above) and in the Giustiniani Palace, Rome, until 1804[34] when it was bought by Lucien Bonaparte.[35] Sold in 1820 by Lucien Bonaparte to Maria Luisa, Duchess of Lucca[36] (Queen of Etruria; died 1824); in the Royal Palace in Lucca.[37] Exhibited for sale with the collection of her son, Carlo Lodovico, Duke of Lucca, at the Society of Painters in Water-Colours, London, July 1840,[38] and bought then or shortly afterwards by the 2nd Duke of Sutherland.[39] In the Sutherland collection at Stafford House, London;[40] 4th Duke of Sutherland sale, London, 11 July 1913 (lot 108),[41] bought by Jones Bros., London (65 gns). Purchased from the Art Collectors' Association in 1922.[42]

EXHIBITION: London, Society of Painters in Water-Colours, July 1840, No. 3.

REFERENCES:
General: Judson, op. cit., cat. no. 44; Braun, op. cit., cat. no. 13.
In text:
1. Sandrart, *Teutsche Academie*, pp. 172–73.
2. See Matthew 26: 57–66, and 27: 1–14; Mark 14: 53–64, and 15: 1–5; Luke 22: 54–71, and 23: 1–11; John 18: 13–38, and 19: 9–11.
3. Matthew 26: 57 (contrast 26: 60); Mark 14: 53 (contrast 15: 1); John 18: 13 (contrast 18: 28). Luke says that Christ was taken to the house of the high priest (at night) but mentions only an interrogation on the following day.

4. Cf. Luke 3: 2. John also calls both Annas and Caiaphas 'high priest' (John 18: 19 and 24).
5. Matthew 26: 60.
6. According to Sandrart, loc. cit.
7. and 8. See p. 179.
9. Judson, op. cit., pp. 24ff.
10. Canvas, 149.8 × 204 cm. G. Bourne-May sale, Christie's, 14 July 1978 (lot 124), as Honthorst (£8,000 to J. Weitzner).
11. The pen and wash drawing, which is in the collection of Emile Wolf, New York, is inscribed: LAFAGE invenit.

12. In *Choix de gravures . . . de la Galerie de Lucien Bonaparte*, 1812, No. 10, pl. 49.

13. S. Morelli, *La Pittura Comparata*, 1816, p. 208, pl. 52.

14. Hermitage catalogue, vol. 2, 1901, No. 746 (as *Christ before Caiaphas*). 272 × 185 cm. From the Godoy sale, Paris, 1831.

15. It can be seen in a reproduction of the interior of the cathedral in P. Brun, *La Cathédrale St André de Bordeaux*, 1952 (frontispiece).

16. See G. J. Hoogewerff, *Honthorst*, 1924, p. 11. From the Palazzo Pignatelli, Naples.

17. Hoogewerff (loc. cit. and in Thieme/Becker vol. 17, p. 447) conjectured that this was the picture painted for Marchese Giustiniani; this is disproved by the provenance of the National Gallery picture. A. von Schneider (*Caravaggio und die Niederländer*, 1933, p. 135) calls it a copy.

18. See Hoogewerff, loc. cit.

19. Vienna 1884 catalogue, No. 923; 267 × 167 cm. Engraved by J. Hyrtl. Shelves with books have been added in the left background.

20. 234 × 195 cm.

21. No. 229. With arched top and slight variations; inscribed: CONTEMPLA EN /MI HVMILDAD.

22. A photograph is in the National Gallery archives.

23. Canvas, 56½ × 75½ in.

24. Canvas, 120 × 80 cm.

25. 88½ × 63¾ in.

26. Paper laid down on panel, 48.3 × 41.9 cm.

27. Canvas, 240 × 180 cm. Said by M. Sella to have been in his family for about 200 years and brought to Turin from Savoy (photo in National Gallery dossier).

28. 42 × 30.5 cm.

29. Rheims 1881 catalogue, p. 47, No. 1; on canvas, 58 × 72 cm. In the Rheims Museum by 1794.

30. Panel, 33½ × 43½ in. (as North Italian School).

31. 'Honthorst Christ before Caiaphas; with brilliant effect of candlelight.'

32. (G. Honthorst) 'Jesus bound, brought before Caiaphas'. It is described by Waagen (1854, vol. 3, p. 206) as 'Christ before Pilate; a most remarkable picture for the effect of light for which [Honthorst] is so distinguished'.

33. Black chalk; signed and inscribed in the lower margin: 'Gherardo della Notte pinxit. Nicolaus Mosman del.', and, in another hand: 'In the Giustiniani Palace in Rome'. It is one of a series of drawings made by Mosmann in Rome.

34. See F. Titi, *Descrizione delle Pitture . . . esposte al pubblico in Roma*, 1763, p. 149; M. Vasi, *Itinerario . . . di Roma*, 1791 ed., vol. 2, p. 426; F. W. B. von Ramdohr, *Ueber Mahlerei . . . in Rom*, 1787, vol. 3, p. 38; J. Forsyth, *Remarks on Antiquities . . . in Italy in the Years 1802 and 1803*, 1816 (2nd ed.), p. 195; etc.

35. Buchanan, vol. 2, p. 154.

36. See *Kunst-Blatt*, Tübingen, 1820, p. 160 (18 May).

37. It is not in T. Trenta, *Guida de Forestiere per la Città . . . di Lucca*, 1820, but appears in the edition revised by A. Mazzarosa, 1829, pp. 86–87.

38. Incorrectly stated in the catalogue to have been bought by the Queen of Etruria from the Giustiniani family.

39. According to the catalogue of the Lucca pictures exhibited for sale in London in 1840 (p. 20, note), the Honthorst was then already sold; the buyer's name is not given. The picture was at Stafford House by 1844 (see Mrs Jameson, *Companion to Private Galleries in London*, 1844, p. 189).

40. See Jameson, loc. cit., and Waagen, 1854, vol. 2, p. 70.

41. As *Christ before Caiaphas*. The markings relating to this sale are on the back of the stretcher.

42. In the National Gallery archives is a letter dated 2 October 1979 from Mr R. H. Ward, who was the manager of the Art Collectors' Association in 1922. He recalls that No. 3679 'was purchased by my eldest brother A. G. Holzappel Ward at Fosters Auction Rooms Pall Mall for £14. It was on the floor wrapped around the stretcher and I had it put together and offered it to the National Gallery who purchased it from me for £250. Sir Ch[arles] Holmes told me shortly afterwards that he had been reproached for buying a poor picture.' (In fact, the correspondence between Mr Ward and Sir Charles Holmes at the time of the painting's purchase reveals that the price was reduced to £200.)

4503 *St Sebastian* *Plate 169*

Signed, below left: GvHonthorst. fe (GvH in monogram).

Oil on canvas, 101 × 117 (39¾ × 46).

Cleaned in 1976.

Probably painted shortly after Honthorst's return to Utrecht. Judson[1] dates it *c*.1623.

The subject of St Sebastian had often been treated in the North. Memlinc[2] had shown him, for example, tied to a tree while archers shoot at him. In the print by Lucas van Leyden,[3] Sebastian stands alone full length pierced by arrows, a format which had gained wide circulation in a print by Mantegna.[4]

Honthorst's conception of a half-length figure slumped into a seated position, pierced by arrows, is original. It was adapted and developed by other Utrecht *Caravaggisti*, notably Jan van Bijlert[5] in 1624 and Hendrick ter Brugghen[6] in 1625. Both showed St Sebastian's wound being tended by St Irene.

VERSIONS OR COPIES: Unsigned replicas or copies are in Schloss Schleissheim near Munich,[7] and in private possession at Aix-en-Provence[8] (formerly), Antwerp[9] (1936) and Zurich[10] (1946). An old reduced copy on panel belonged to Miss G. Openshaw, London, in 1932–35.[11] A copy was in an anonymous sale, Sotheby's, 21 May 1969 (lot 113).[12]

PROVENANCE: Possibly the 'St Sebastian pierced with Arrows – in a Landscape' by Honthorst, of about the same size, which was in an anonymous sale at Phillips', London, 27–28 July 1832 (lot 138),[13] 30 gns. It is said to have been bought from a collection near Bristol *c*.1928 by Mrs Mabel Berryman,[14] in whose possession it certainly was by November 1928,[15] and from whom it was purchased in 1930.

EXHIBITIONS: London 1976, No. 59; Utrecht, Centraal Museum, and Braunschweig, Herzog Anton Ulrich-Museum, 'Nieuw Licht op de Gouden Eeuw: Hendrick ter Brugghen en tijdgenoten', 1986–7, No. 61.

REFERENCES:
General: Judson, op. cit., cat. no. 68.
In text:
1. Judson, op. cit., p. 88.
2. Brussels, Musée Royale des Beaux-Arts.
3. Hollstein, vol. 10, p. 137.
4. Bartsch, No. 10.
5. Vienna, Galerie Harrach, 1926 cat. no. 68; G. J. Hoogewerff, 'Jan van Bijlert, Schilder van Utrecht (1578–1671)', OH, vol. 80, 1965, pp. 2–33, cat. no. 21.
6. Allen Art Museum, Oberlin, Ohio, inv. no. 53.256; 1967 cat., pp. 148–50.
7. Bayerische Staatsgemälde Sammlungen, Munich, inv. no. 621/2937 as Jan van Bijlert; on loan to Schleissheim. Schleissheim Gallery catalogue, 1914, No. 1236, as in the style of Caravaggio. Canvas, 108 × 140 cm., including later additions at the sides and top.
8. According to G. Isarlo (*Caravage et le caravagisme européen*, 1941, p. 133) who apparently attributes

this copy to Louis Finson (Finsonius). Said to be from the collection of Cardinal Grimaldi, Archbishop of Aix. Canvas, 100 × 130 cm.
9. Letter of 1936 in the National Gallery archives.
10. Reproduced in *Pro Arte*, 1944, p. 527. This picture was in the collection of Dr Fritz Haussmann, Berlin, in 1930 (letter in the National Gallery archives) and is perhaps the picture that was in the possession of Asscher and Welcker, London, 1932 (according to a note by H. Isherwood Kay in the Gallery archives).
11. A photograph is in the National Gallery archives.
12. Panel, 28 × 23½ in. (£80 to Koetser).
13. According to the sale catalogue, it measured 90 × 114 cm.
14. According to the National Gallery Director's Report for 1930.
15. When the picture was sent to London for sale (note in the National Gallery archives).

6362 *Elizabeth Stuart, Queen of Bohemia*   *Plate 170*

Signed, centre right, on the balustrade: G Honthorst. 1642 (GH in monogram) and inscribed, centre left, on the balustrade (by a later hand): Queen of Bohemia.

Oil on canvas, 205.1 × 130.8 (80¾ × 51½).

The sitter, known as 'The Winter Queen' (1569–1662), was the daughter of James I. She married Frederick V, Elector Palatine, in 1613 in London and then returned with him to Heidelberg. Frederick, a Protestant, was elected King of Bohemia in 1619 but in the following year he was defeated at the battle of the White Mountain and in 1621 Frederick and Elizabeth went into exile in Holland. Frederick died in 1632 and Elizabeth and her children remained in exile in The Hague. In 1648 her eldest surviving son, Charles Louis, was restored to the Palatinate. Elizabeth eventually returned to England in 1661 after the restoration of her nephew, Charles II, but died only nine months after her return.[1]

Michiel van Miereveld and Gerrit von Honthorst were the portrait painters most favoured by the exiled Palatinate family. Honthorst was especially favoured by Elizabeth; he gave drawing lessons to her and her daughters and even made the impoverished queen a loan of 35,000 guilders in 1651. There are numerous portraits of Frederick, Elizabeth and their children by Honthorst. In the sequence of the many portraits he painted of Elizabeth, No. 6362 is of especial interest as the prime version of a new type of formal portrait of the queen. It was painted ten years after the death of her husband (and may have been commissioned to mark this anniversary) and shows her as a still grieving widow. She wears black with very few pieces of jewellery, notably the pearl earrings which had been given to her by Frederick. The black ribbon on her right arm also refers to her widowhood. The queen is shown holding a stem on which there are two roses: one hangs down while the other is upright and healthy. This conventional symbolism refers to her widowhood. The fact that she holds the roses by the thorny stem may, too, refer to the popular metaphor for the pain of love, *geen rosje zonder doornen* (no roses without thorns), and so to her widowhood. An emblem with this theme can be found, for example, in Otto Vaenius's *Amorum Emblemata* (Antwerp, 1608) in which a winged cupid is shown holding a rose by the stem.[2] In this context of conventional symbolism referring to the queen's widowhood the dog can be taken to refer to fidelity. It is also worth noting two other new features of this portrait when it is compared to earlier ones of Elizabeth by Honthorst: she is seen for the first time in the open air and she sports a new style of coiffure, without the fringe which she had previously worn.

A constant supporter of 'The Winter Queen' was William Craven, 1st Earl of Craven (1606–97), who had fought in the campaigns of the 1630s to restore Frederick to his throne. He returned to England with Charles II in 1660 and it was at his invitation (rather than that of her nephew) that Elizabeth returned to London in 1661. She died in Craven's house in Drury Lane. She apparently bequeathed her collection of family portraits to her son, Prince Rupert, and he, on his death in 1681, bequeathed them to Craven.[3] This full length was presumably among the paintings left by Rupert to Craven, although there are no inventories of Combe Abbey, the seat of the Craven family, before 1769. It is presumably the 'Queen of Bohemia, full-length, by Honthorst' listed in that inventory[4] and the portrait of 'his [that is, Frederick V's] queen, dressed in black, and with a melancholy look' seen by Thomas Pennant at Combe in 1783.[5]

Although not the most copied portrait of 'The Winter Queen' – that was probably the Miereveld portrait of 1623[6] – there is one apparently autograph version (see VER-

SION) and many variants of No. 6362. Among the latter are, for example, the head and shoulders portraits in the collection of the Duke of Atholl[7] and the National Portrait Gallery,[8] the half length in the Historisches Museum, Hanover,[9] and the heads in the Oranje Nassau Museum, Delft,[10] and at Ashdown House.[11]

VERSION: There is an unsigned version (probably a replica) in the collection of Prince Ernst August of Hanover.[12] A number of variants are discussed above.

PROVENANCE: Probably in the collection of the sitter, Wassenaer Hof, The Hague and London; probably bequeathed by her to her son Prince Rupert of the Palatinate; probably bequeathed by him to the 1st Earl Craven, Combe Abbey, Warwickshire, 1681;[13] probably the portrait of Elizabeth in the 1769 Combe Abbey inventory (see above) and seen there by Pennant in 1783 (see above); certainly 'no. 189 whole length portrait of the Queen of Bohemia in a black dress. (Signed and dated 1642) G. Honthorst' in the 1866 Combe Abbey inventory;[14] bequeathed to the National Gallery by Cornelia, Lady Craven, in 1965. On loan to the National Portrait Gallery, 1965–85.

EXHIBITIONS: RA 1952–3, No. 276; London, National Portrait Gallery, 'The Winter Queen', 1963, No. 58.

REFERENCES:

General: G. H. Hoogewerff, *Gerrit von Honthorst*, The Hague, 1924, p. 14; Braun, op. cit., cat. no. 110.

In text:
1. See C. Oman, *Elizabeth of Bohemia*, 1938.
2. See E. de Jongh. *Zinne- en minne-beelden in de schilderkunst van de zeventiende eeuw*, 1967, p. 27.
3. For this information (and for much else in this catalogue entry, particularly concerning provenance and variants) the present writer is indebted to Mr W.-J. Hoogsteder, who is currently preparing a study of portraits of 'The Winter Queen' and her family.
4. This reference to the 1769 inventory was provided by Mr W.-J. Hoogsteder.
5. T. Pennant, *The Journey from Chester to London*, Dublin, 1783, p. 184.
6. It was engraved by Delff.
7. Panel, 76.3 × 63.5 cm. (oval).
8. Panel, 66.5 × 54.6 cm. D. Piper, *Catalogue of Seventeenth-century Portraits in the National Portrait Gallery 1625–1714*, Cambridge, 1963, pp. 118/19.
9. Panel, 74.3 × 62.5 cm. Wearing a crown.
10. Panel, 74 × 95.5 cm. (in a painted oval).

11. Canvas, 72.5 × 60 cm. Signed and dated 1650. Ex-Combe Abbey collection. National Trust, Ashdown House, inv. no. 6.
12. Canvas, 106.8 × 86.6 cm. From the collection of the Electress Sophia of Hanover, daughter of 'The Winter Queen'. It was exhibited in Heidelberg in 1963 in the exhibition 'England und Kurpfalz', cat. no. 30.
13. George Vertue saw the paintings at Combe Abbey in 1732: 'at Lord Cravens Combe Abby near Coventry. a large Gallery Many pictures. & old paintings in a great number. Many of the Royal Bohemian Family. Suppos Honthorst.' ('G. Vertue, Notebooks', vol. IV, *Walpole Society*, vol. 24, 1935/6, p. 46.)
14. It is also in the 1916 Inventory, p. 95, no. 189. Estimated at £400: 'The Queen of Bohemia, in black dress with slashed sleeves, lace collar, wearing pearl necklace, standing in a garden, with pillar at side, and plucking a rose with her right hand, a dog jumping up at her feet – full length – signed – and dated. 80 in. × 54 in.' (Inventory drawn up by Tom Cox, 21 King Street).

PIETER DE HOOCH, 1629–1684

Pieter Hendricksz. de Hooch, son of Hendrick Hendricksz. de Hooch, a mason, was baptised in Rotterdam, 20 December 1629.[1] In his earlier days he often spelled his name de Hooch; later he also used the spelling d[e] Hoogh. According to Houbraken[2] he was a pupil of Nicolaes Berchem at the same time as Jacob Ochtervelt; this was presumably in Haarlem (see the biographical notice of Berchem, pages 19–20). He is first mentioned as a resident of Delft in August 1652. In May and July 1653 he is mentioned in the service of Justus de la Grange, a cloth-merchant who lived in Delft and in and about Leiden; he is described both as a servant (*dienaar*) and painter, and in 1655 La Grange had in his collection eleven paintings by him. De Hooch was said to be living in Rotterdam in April 1654, when he was betrothed to Anna (Jannetge) van der Burch of Delft who was probably the sister of the painter Hendrick van der Burch;[3] he married her in Delft in May 1654 and in September 1655 he was inscribed in the Delft guild. Children of his were baptised in Delft in February 1655 and November 1656 and he is recorded as a member of the guild there again in 1656 and 1657. De Hooch had moved to Amsterdam by 15 April 1661 when he was present at the baptism of his daughter Diewertje in the Westerkerk. He may have been there by May 1660 when his wife is recorded there at a baptism in the same church. However, No. 794 is dated 166( ) and shows part of the old town wall in Delft; it may have been painted in Delft or shortly after the move to Amsterdam. A date of *c*.1660 for the move to Amsterdam is acceptable.

The burial records of de Hooch's children record that in 1663 and 1665 he was living in Amsterdam on the Regulierspad and the Engelspad respectively. By May 1668 he had moved to the more prosperous Konijnenstraat. In 1670 de Hooch testified in the law suit brought by Adriana van Heusden, widow of the Amsterdam notary Joris de Wijs, against the painter Emanuel de Witte (see No. 3682 of this catalogue). Two years later the last of the painter's seven children was baptised. From then until his death we have no documents concerning him. He was buried in the Sint Anthonis Kerkhof in Amsterdam on 24 March 1684 as coming from the *Dolhuys* (bedlam).

His earliest paintings seem to be those (some are signed but none dated) in the style of the Haarlem and Amsterdam guardroom painters (Codde, Duyster, etc.) but there are no dated paintings before 1658. The pictures of that year and those painted immediately before and after are in the new Delft style of the 1650s. This is characterised by simple, domestic subjects, carefully constructed interior spaces and the subtle use of light to illuminate them. Carel Fabritius and Nicolaes Maes (in Dordrecht) may have been influential in the development of this style which finds its finest expression in the work of de Hooch's Delft period and of Vermeer. After his move to Amsterdam, de Hooch's style gradually changed. The interiors he shows in his genre paintings and his portraits became richer and more elaborate and his technique becomes progressively coarser; his late paintings often (as in No. 3047 of 1677) contain clumsy figure drawing and a coarse palette.

REFERENCES:
General: HdG, vol. 1, 1908 (German edition, 1907); P. Sutton, *Pieter de Hooch*, Oxford, 1980.
In text:
1. De Hooch's baptismal record and all the other documents referred to here are given in Sutton, op. cit., pp. 145–47.

2. Houbraken, vol. 2, p. 35.
3. For van der Burch, see P. Sutton, 'Hendrick van der Burch', BM, vol. 122, 1980, pp. 315–25.

794 *A Woman and her Maid in a Courtyard*

Plate 171

Signed, bottom right: P.D.H./166( ); the date is discussed below.

Oil on canvas, 73.7 × 62.6 (29 × 24⅝).

Cleaned in 1958. There are some inexplicable patches of blue in the front of the servant's skirt which seem to be original; it does not seem likely that the whole of her skirt was once blue. Some of the leaves behind the servant have turned blue.

PENTIMENTI: On the right, above the present roofs, there was at first another roof, seen from the side; it shows faintly through the sky. The roof of the outhouse in the right foreground was originally higher. The door on the left in the distant wall was apparently at first above the arbour. There are also *pentimenti* in the outlines of the head and right side of the servant.

The suggestion that the wall at the end of the garden is the old town wall of Delft[1] is almost certainly right. This wall no longer exists but in the seventeenth century the gardens of the houses on the west side of Oude Delft were bounded by the town wall, which stood on a higher level as in the picture. That de Hooch was well acquainted with this quarter of Delft is shown by several of his pictures. The Hieronymusdale Cloister, the tablet from whose portal appears in No. 835 below, was in precisely this area and the view of the Stadhuis and the Nieuwe Kerk in the background of the Buckingham Palace *Courtyard*[2] is taken from a point in Oude Delft only a few yards from the house in whose garden the tablet still is.

The view here is almost certainly a fanciful one composed of actual elements, as is usually the case with de Hooch. The same summer-house against a similar wall appears in the *Family Group* in the Vienna Academy,[3] in which the tower of the Nieuwe Kerk in Delft can be seen in the background. The same piece of wall and summer-house occur also in the *Courtyard* in the National Gallery of Art, Washington,[4] which has, too, the identical pump that appears in the present picture, but in a different position.

The picture formerly bore the date 1665. This reading had often been doubted since the picture is very much closer in style to the dated works of 1658 than to the *Good Housewife* of 1663 in the Rijksmuseum[5] and no dated works of the intervening years were previously known. Valentiner[6] supposed the date had been changed and that originally it had been 1655 or 1656. Removal of brownish varnish and repaint has shown that although the date had at some time been strengthened in places by retouching,[7] the first three figures are certainly original. The last figure, a 5, was found to be in the same darker paint as the retouchings on the other figures and as it was obviously false it was removed. Beneath it was found a minute portion of the original last figure, unfortunately too small to give any indication of what the figure was.

The picture is very close in style to the dated works of 1658 (e.g. No. 835 below) and a date of *c.*1660/1 is acceptable. It seems likely that it was painted in Delft, but could date from shortly after the painter's move to Amsterdam. De Hooch is also recorded as having visited Delft in 1663,[8] but this would seem too late for the present painting.

PROVENANCE: In 1833 it was for sale in Amsterdam, according to Smith.[9] It was in the Comte Perregaux sale,

197

Paris, 8–9 December 1841 (lot 14), bought by Paillet (12,700 francs), according to Smith for Baron Delessert, in whose collection it certainly was by 1842;[10] Delessert sale, Paris, 15 sqq. March 1869 (lot 37), 42,000 francs, bought for the National Gallery.

EXHIBITION: London 1976, No. 61.

REFERENCES:

General: Smith No. 37 and Supplement No. 29; HdG No. 290; Sutton, op. cit., cat. no. 44.

In text:

1. W. R. Valentiner, *Klassiker der Kunst: P. de Hooch*, 1930, p. 270, note to p. 38.

2. White No. 84. Sutton, op. cit., cat. no. 36.

3. HdG No. 321; Sutton, op. cit., cat. no. 24.

4. HdG No. 294; Sutton, op. cit., cat. no. 39.

5. HdG No. 25; Sutton, op. cit., cat. no. 52.

6. Valentiner, op. cit., p. 270, note to p. 38. There are no grounds whatsoever for his supposition that

there was another number beyond the fourth one and that the present third and fourth numbers were originally second and third.

7. The signature had also been strengthened in places but is certainly original.

8. Sutton, op. cit., document no. 39.

9. Smith No. 37.

10. Smith Supplement No. 29. It is No. 57 of the *Notice sur la collection de tableaux de MM. Delessert*, 1844.

834 *An Interior, with a Woman drinking with Two Men, and a Maidservant* — Plate 172

In the right background, over the fireplace, is a painting of the Virgin kneeling before St Anne, with an older woman on the left and three cherubs above (see below). In the left background is a map of Holland and Flanders, inscribed above, in the centre: OCEANUS.

Signed on the side of the table on the extreme left: P D H ·

Oil on canvas, 73.7 × 64.6 (29 × $25\frac{7}{16}$).

PENTIMENTI: To the left of the woman on the right a white-bearded man has been painted out by the artist; infra-red photography shows that the man seated in profile had at first a wide-brimmed hat; other alterations are visible in his right hand, the left shirt sleeve of the man behind the table and the apron of the woman on the left.

At least some of the figures have been painted after the completion of the architectural background: the tiled floor shows through the skirt of the woman on the right and the cloak of the man in profile. The upper part of the chimney is painted on top of the wooden ceiling and the table on the left on top of the woman's skirt and the floor.

The picture above the fireplace perhaps represents the Education of the Virgin. A strikingly similar painting hangs in the Esterhazy Chapel in Ering in South Bavaria.[1] It appears to be a Flemish early seventeenth-century picture. The map on the far wall has been tentatively identified as an early state of the map of the Seventeen Provinces of the Netherlands published by Huyck Allart (active *c.*1650–75).[2]

The young woman is used as a model in a number of other paintings of de Hooch's earlier years, for example in No. 835, in the *Courtyards* in the Hermitage, Leningrad,[3] and Buckingham Palace.[4] Valentiner[5] has conjectured that she is Jannetge van der Burch, whom de Hooch married in 1654, but there is nothing except the frequency of her appearance to support this.

Probably painted in Delft in about 1658: it is very close in style to No. 835, below.

As was first noted in the van Leyden sale catalogue,[6] the man on the far side of the table may be pretending to play the violin. The painting was known in the nineteenth century as *La Chanson Joyeuse* because the girl with her back to the viewer was thought to be singing.[7]

COPY: A small watercolour pastiche by Hercules Brabazon Brabazon (1821–1906) is in the Tate Gallery.[8]

EXHIBITIONS: London 1976, No. 60; Philadelphia/Berlin/London 1984, No. 51.

PROVENANCE: It has been suggested[9] that this picture is the *Interior with Figures*, of about the same size, in the David Jetswaart sale, Amsterdam, 22 April 1749 (lot 197),[10] bought by Jetswaart (bought in?; 70 guilders) but the description is too vague to support the identification. It was certainly in the van Leyden of Amsterdam sale, Paris, 5 sqq. November 1804 (lot 43), bought by Paillet (5,500 francs) and was bought with other pictures from Comte de Pourtalès, Paris, by Emmerson and Smith in 1826 and sold to Sir Robert Peel, Bart.[11] Purchased with the Peel collection, 1871.

REFERENCES:

General: Smith No. 49; HdG No. 183; Sutton, op. cit., cat. no. 29.

In text:

1. It was brought to the present writer's attention by Mr A. Laing. It is reproduced in Sutton, op. cit., fig. 38. In the van Leyden sale catalogue, 1804, the painting over the mantelpiece was said to be by Bol.

2. This identification was made by Dr J. Welu. He is cited by Sutton, op. cit.

3. Sutton, op. cit., cat. no. 46.

4. White No. 84. Sutton, op. cit., cat. no. 36.

5. Valentiner, op. cit., p. 272, note to p. 43.

6. See PROVENANCE.

7. Havard, p. 183.

8. No. 3043; *Souvenir of De Hoogh*, 22 × 17 cm.

9. HdG No. 183 and in OH, vol. 10, 1892, p. 183.

10. 'Een Binnekamer met Beelden en Bywerk, van denzelven [P. de Hooch], konstig of het van Metzu was'; 2 *voet* 5 *duim* × 2 *v.* 1 *d.* (Hoet, vol. 2, p. 251, wrongly as lot 189). HdG (see preceding note), who took the reference from Hoet, loc. cit., erroneously attributed this item to the Sebastiaan Heemskerck sale, Amsterdam, 31 March 1749, but the catalogue of that sale ends on p. 237 of Hoet and the Jetswaart sale begins on p. 238.

11. Smith No. 49.

835 *The Courtyard of a House in Delft*   Plate 173

The tablet above the arch has the following legend carved in Gothic letters: (· it?) (· ·) (·) te ·hyronimusdale / wil(t?) (t?) ntie tsamhey(t?) / begheven w(· ·)t w(y?) mu(·) n / eerst dalle wijlle wy w(· ·)rden / verheven anno 1614.

Signed left, at the base of the archway: P·D·H·/An° 1658· (An° in monogram).

Oil on canvas, 73.5 × 60 ($28\frac{15}{16}$ × $23\frac{5}{8}$).

Cleaned in 1954–5.

Cross-sections revealed a single pale fawn or buff ground of moderate thickness which on analysis proved to consist of lead white with an admixture of chalk (calcium carbonate) coloured by sparsely scattered particles of brown and yellowish ochre and charcoal black. The use of a lightish fawn ground shows some affinity with Vermeer's technique, although his canvases usually have two layers of lightly tinted ground each based on lead white. There is a close similarity with the light-coloured ground of No. 4042: Carel Fabritius, *A Young Man in a Fur Cap and a Cuirass*, which was also found to be a mixture of lead white and chalk containing ochre and charcoal particles. The detection of aluminium in the blue-green of the grass in the bottom right-hand corner implies the use of a yellow lake pigment. Yellow lakes (the so-called 'Dutch Pink' or

'Schietgeel') are probably the most light-fugitive of all pigments used in the artist's palette. It seems likely, therefore, that the foliage in No. 835 was originally much greener than it is now, the yellow component having faded, leaving the blue (azurite) unchanged. It also seems likely that the blue of the sky has both faded and discoloured, since the blue pigment is smalt, though the small proportion of smalt suggests that it was never an intense blue. Examination of the blue skirt of the woman under magnification reveals that this is also smalt, of a deeper blue and larger particle size. With an increase in the refractive index of the medium with age the smalt paint is likely to have become more translucent, and does appear so in the picture, and very likely duller and paler in tone.

The stone tablet seen above the archway was originally over the entrance to the Hieronymusdale Cloister in Delft, which was on the Oude Delft canal, opposite the end of the Nieuwstraat. The tablet has survived and is now set in the wall of the garden behind No. 157, Oude Delft. The legend on the actual tablet is: 'dit·is·in· sint·hieronimus·daelle / wildt·v·tot·pacientie·en·lijdt- / saemheijt·begeeven / wandt·wij· muetten·eerst daellē / willen·wij·worden·verheeūen·1614.'[1] ('This is in St Jerome's vale, if you wish to retire to patience and meekness. For we must first descend if we wish to be raised.')

In the variant of the same date in the Byng collection (Fig. 44) the legend on the tablet, although it does not follow the original exactly,[2] is nevertheless nearer to it than that on the National Gallery version, especially in the division of the lines (Figs. 45a and b). This, together with the improved disposition of the figures in the National Gallery picture, suggests that the latter may be the later version of the two.

Four other pictures by de Hooch bear the same date as No. 835;[3] no earlier dated works by him are known (see also the biographical notice on pages 195–6).

See No. 834 above for other pictures in which the young woman appears. The same child served as model in the Byng picture.

VERSION: A variant of this composition, also signed and dated 1658, with different figures and variations in the architecture, is in the collection of the Hon. Julian Byng.[4] A replica of the Byng version, with very slight variations, was imported from Holland by Chaplin in 1839, according to Smith.[5]

COPIES: A copy was sold at Christie's, 12 May 1961 (lot 183);[6] another was in a private collection in Holland in 1939;[7] another was in the van den Eeckhout sale, Paris, 9 March 1861 (lot 47);[8] a drawn copy by J. Buys (1724–1801) was in the Ploos van Amstel sale in Amsterdam, 3 March 1800, no. 30 (sold to de Graat for 61 guilders); a drawn copy by C. Buys (1745–1826) was in the Engleberts sale, Amsterdam, 14 December 1807, no. 3 (bought by de Vries). There was a drawing by Jan Stolker (1729–85) in the de Jongh sale, Rotterdam, 26 March 1810, no. 4: 'naar P. de Hooge. Hironymus Dale, een oud gestigt te Delft, breeder op de achterzijde van de teekening omschreven'. This drawing was later sold at a sale in Rotterdam on 4 June 1828, no. 7. It could be a copy of No. 835 or of the variant in the Byng collection.

PROVENANCE: In the Pieter de Smeth van Alphen sale, Amsterdam, 1–2 August 1810 (lot 46),[9] probably bought by Yperen for Backer[10] (2,075 guilders); bought in 1825 from Backer's widow, Mme J(?) W(?) Backer of Amsterdam, by W. Brondgeest (10,750 guilders) for W. Emmerson,[11] who sold it to Sir Robert Peel, Bart., before 1833.[12] Purchased with the Peel collection, 1871.

REFERENCES:

General: Smith No. 50; HdG No. 291; Sutton, op. cit., cat. no. 34.

In text:

1. The inscription was transcribed on the spot by MacLaren in 1955.

2. It is as follows: dit is in sint elle / wil tot pa (· ·) entie en lydt / sa (be?) he / w (· ·) dt wij m ten (· · · · ·) d (· · · · ·) / willen wy·w (· ·) (·) 1614.

3. Sutton, op. cit., cat. nos. 26, 27, 28, 30.

4. Canvas on panel, 66.5 × 56.5 cm. Signed and dated left centre on pier: P.D.H./1658; Sutton, op. cit., cat. no. 33. At the present time (1989) the painting is on loan to the Fitzwilliam Museum, Cambridge.

5. See Smith Supplement No. 15; earlier in the Koopman collection in Utrecht. HdG (No. 299) suggests that it is probably to be identified with his No. 295 (Washington, National Gallery of Art; from the Alfred de Rothschild collection) but that is an entirely different composition, while the picture mentioned by Smith is said by him to be a 'duplicate' of the Byng version 'with some trifling variations in the details'.

6. Canvas, 72 × 57 cm.

7. Photo in RKD: no support or dimensions given.

8. Noted in C. Brière-Misme's unpublished papers in the RKD.

9. (P. de Hooch) 'Op eene Binnenplaats ziet men eene Vrouw en Kind, kommende van eenen steenen Trap, en terzijde in eenen Gang of Doorloop eene andere Vrouw, gaande naar eene tweede opene Plaats'; canvas, 26 × 23 *duim*.

10. The marked copies of the Smeth van Alphen sale catalogue at the Victoria and Albert Museum, London, and the RKD, give van Yperen as the purchaser; a MS list in the RKD of buyers and prices at this sale has Backer. Smith, loc. cit., says it was bought by Backer.

11. There was formerly on the back of the stretcher a label inscribed: 'Ce chef d'oeuvre de l'école hollandaise a été acheté par moi soussigné pour comte [sic] de monsieur W. Emmerson de Londres de Madame la douairière J(?) W(?) B[ac]ker à Amsterdam pour dix mille sept cents cinquante florins d'Hollande y compris le comptage. Amsterdam 12 Juillet 1825 W. Brondgeest' (transcribed by H. Isherwood Kay; this label was apparently destroyed when the picture was attached to a new stretcher in 1938). See also Nieuwenhuys, p. 156.

12. Smith, loc. cit.

3047 *A Musical Party in a Courtyard*   *Plate 174*

The woman on the left is playing a viola. On the left-hand house across the canal is a tablet inscribed: 1620.

Signed above the arch: P:d Hoogh·1677·

Oil on canvas, 83.5 × 68.5 ($32\frac{7}{8}$ × 27); irregular edges.

Cleaned in 1974. The sky is extensively worn: the tree above the arch had been extended to conceal damage in this area. This was removed when the painting was cleaned. There is wearing in the dark areas elsewhere, especially in the hat of the seated man. There are also scattered losses throughout.

The houses seen across the canal are probably not accurate renderings of actual buildings, but the one dated 1620 is in the style of Hendrik de Keyser and is reminiscent of the 'Huis met de Hoofden' on the Keizersgracht in Amsterdam, built in 1622 (perhaps by Hendrik's son, Pieter de Keyser);[1] other very similar houses were formerly at Nos. 52 and 54, Keizersgracht.[2]

The carpet has been identified as of the Herat type.[3]

COPY: A very inferior old copy was in an anonymous sale, London, 22 January 1954 (lot 127).

PROVENANCE: In the collection of Jonkheer Johan Steengracht van Oostkappelle in The Hague by 1833;[4] Jonkheer Hendrik Adolf Steengracht van Duivenvoorde sale, Paris, 9 June 1913 (lot 33), bought in (84,000 francs); sold by order of the Steengracht executor in the R. Peltzer et al. sale, Amsterdam, 26–27 May 1914 (lot 323), bought by Goudstikker of Amsterdam (21,000 guilders), from whom it was purchased (out of the Temple-West Fund) in 1916.

EXHIBITIONS: Rotterdam, Goudstikker, Kunstkring, 1915, No. 20, and The Hague, Pulchri Studios, 1915, No. 22; London 1974; London 1976, No. 62.

REFERENCES:
General: Smith No. 35; HdG No. 122; Sutton, op. cit., cat. no. 134.
In text:
1. Reproduced in *Zeven Eeuwen Amsterdam*, vol. 3, n.d., p. 213. G. Roosegaarde Bisschop pointed out this resemblance.

2. They are engraved in Caspar Philip's *Verzameling van alle de huizen en prachtige gebouwen langs de Keizers en Heere-grachten der Stadt Amsteldam*, etc., 1768–71.
3. J. Mills, *Carpets in Pictures* (Themes and Painters in the National Gallery), London, 1975, p. 34.
4. Smith, loc. cit.

3881 *A Man with Dead Birds, and Other Figures, in a Stable* Plate 175

In the centre of the leaded glass partition above the woman is a kneeling figure (the Virgin?) in coloured glass.

Oil on oak, 53.5 × 49.7 ($21\frac{1}{16}$ × $19\frac{9}{16}$).

At one time attributed to Jan Baptist Weenix and said to be signed;[1] later said to be signed: P.H.D. [sic].[2] There is no stylistic reason for supposing any part of the picture (e.g. the dead game) is by Weenix. It is, however, closely related in style to youthful works by de Hooch, such as the signed *Backgammon Players* in Dublin.[3]

Probably painted in the mid-1650s.

Fleischer[4] has identified the painting as lot 51 in the O. W. J. Berg sale in Amsterdam, 7–8 July 1825: 'Eene Stal, van binnen, op den voorgrond ligt een gekwetst man, welke door den heelmeester verbonden wordt, nevens hen staat eene vrouw met een Kind, achterwaarts door eene openstaande deur komt een heer in; door P. de Hooge. Paneel, h. 5p. 3d., br. 5p.' ('A stable interior, in the foreground lies a wounded man who is being bandaged by a surgeon, beside them stands a woman with a child, at the rear a gentleman enters through an open door; by P. de Hooge. Panel, h. 53 cm., w. 50 cm.')

Infra-red and X-ray photographs (Fig. 46)[5] reveal that the dog and the dead game have been painted over the figure of a wounded man lying on the ground, his head supported by a sack or pillow. The seated man on the left is attending a wound just below the knee on the inner side of the man's right leg. The yellow jacket hanging over the edge of the stall at the right belongs to the wounded man. Later in his career de Hooch painted a strikingly similar scene of a man attending a wounded soldier in a barn with a woman holding a child looking on.[6] The overpainting of the dog and dead game (done presumably to make the painting more saleable) must have been done between 1825 and 1900 when it was attributed to J. B. Weenix (because of the presence of the game) in the de Falbe sale.[7]

PROVENANCE: Probably in the O. W. J. Berg sale, Amsterdam, 7–8 July, 1825, lot 51 (bought by Regemorter, 38 guilders). In the Madame de Falbe sale, London, 19 May 1900 (lot 141),[8] bought by A. H. Buttery (85 gns) and sold by him to C. Fleischmann, June 1900.[9] Exhibited in Leiden, 1906 as lent by C. Fleischmann (his name was changed later to Ashcroft). In the anonymous [Ashcroft] collection exhibited at Agnew's, London, June 1915. Presented by F. N. and O. S. Ashcroft, in memory of their parents, on the occasion of the National Gallery Centenary, 1924.

EXHIBITIONS: Leiden, Stedelijk Museum De Lakenhal, 'Tentoonstelling van Schilderijen en Teekeningen van

Rembrandt en Schilderijen van andere Leidsche Meesters der zeventiende eeuw', 1906, No. 21;[10] London, Agnew's, anon. [Ashcroft] collection, 1915, No. 45.[11]

REFERENCES:

General: HdG No. 269; Sutton, op. cit., cat. no. 14. In text:

1. In the catalogue of the de Falbe sale, 1900 (see PROVENANCE).

2. In the catalogue of the Agnew exhibition of June 1915 (see PROVENANCE). There are some marks on the lower part of the cloth beneath the dead birds which may have been taken for letters but are in fact purely fortuitous.

3. Signed: P de hooch. Sutton, op. cit., cat. no. 12.

4. R. E. Fleischer, 'An Altered Painting by Pieter de Hooch', OH, vol. 90, 1976, pp. 108–14.

5. Reproduced in Fleischer, op. cit., plates 3 and 4.

6. Present location unknown. Sutton, op. cit., cat.

no. 80. Fleischer, op. cit., dates this painting to the early or mid-1650s, but Sutton (following Valentiner) is correct to date it to much later in the artist's career, c.1667.

7. See PROVENANCE.

8. As by J. B. Weenix. The identity of the de Falbe picture with No. 3881 is proved by an entry in Messrs Buttery's records (letter of 1953 from Horace A. Buttery in the National Gallery archives).

9. As by de Hooch and J. B. Weenix (letter from Horace A. Buttery – cf. preceding note).

10. As by P. de Hooch.

11. As by P. de Hooch.

SAMUEL VAN HOOGSTRATEN, 1627–1678

Samuel Dircksz. van Hoogstraten; born in Dordrecht, 2 August 1627.[1] According to his own account, he was first a pupil of his father, Dirck van Hoogstraten, and after the latter's death [in December 1640[2]] of Rembrandt in Amsterdam;[3] among his fellow-pupils in Rembrandt's studio were 'Fabritius' [certainly Carel, not Barent[4]], Abraham Furnerius (born c.1628), and Constantijn van Renesse.[5] By April 1648 he had returned to Dordrecht.[6] In May 1651 he travelled to Vienna where he was patronised by the emperor.[7] In 1652 he was in Rome;[8] he returned to Vienna (in the same year?) and was almost certainly there in 1653.[9] He was back in Dordrecht apparently before November 1654, married there in 1656[10] and seems to have continued there until he left for London, which was before September 1662.[11] He was still in London at the time of the Great Fire, September 1666.[12] Probably soon afterwards he returned to Holland and appears to have lived in The Hague since he was inscribed in January 1668 in the books of *Pictura*, the painters' confraternity there,[13] and is recorded there in September 1671.[14] He finally settled in Dordrecht where he was one of the two Provosts of the Mint by 1673.[15] In the following years he was writing his *Inleyding tot de Hooge Schoole der Schilderkonst*, which was published in 1678; he died in Dordrecht on 19 October of the same year.[16]

He painted genre, portraits, architectural fantasies and religious subjects; also (according to Houbraken, who was his pupil) landscapes, marines, animals, flowers and still life.[17] His early work is in a Rembrandtesque style but he soon abandoned this. Houbraken speaks of his great interest in *trompe-l'oeil* painting[18] and he also made perspective experiments such as the peepshow catalogued below; his preoccupation with such matters is paralleled in the work of Carel Fabritius who was in Rembrandt's studio at the same time (see above). Hoogstraten was already painting illusionist pictures when he was in Vienna in 1651. At a later date his genre pictures show the influence of Pieter de Hooch.

REFERENCES:

General: G. H. Veth in OH, vol. 7, 1889, pp. 129–48; Sumowski, *Gemälde*, vol. 2, pp. 1286 ff.

In text:

1. Veth, op. cit., pp. 129–30.
2. OH, 1886, p. 275.
3. Hoogstraten, p. 257.
4. See the biographical note, pp. 135–6.
5. Hoogstraten, p. 95.
6. Veth, op. cit., p. 131.
7. Veth, op. cit., pp. 132–33; Hoogstraten, p. 356.
8. Hoogstraten, p. 169.
9. There are pictures by him dated 1652 and 1653 in the former Imperial collection at the Kunsthistorisches Museum, Vienna (Inv. Nos. 1752 and 378).
10. Veth, op. cit., p. 134.
11. In a document of September 1662 he is said to have gone to London (Veth, op. cit., p. 136).
12. Hoogstraten, p. 266.
13. Obreen, vol. 5, p. 138.
14. Veth, op. cit., p. 138; see also Houbraken, vol. 2, p. 156.
15. Veth, op. cit., pp. 139–40.
16. Veth, op. cit., p. 130, note 2, and p. 141.
17. and **18.** Houbraken, p. 157.

3832 A Peepshow with Views of the Interior of a Dutch House

Plates 176(a–i)

A rectangular box; the interior is painted on three sides, as well as the top and bottom; the sixth side is open. Originally light would have entered the box from this side, perhaps through specially treated paper stretched across it: the box would have been placed close to a window or illumination provided by a candle. There are peep-holes in the two shorter sides.

EXTERIOR: On the top, painted in an anamorphic projection, are Venus and the infant Cupid in bed. On one of the short sides an artist is making a drawing of the Muse Urania, at whom a winged putto behind him is pointing; in the centre a *cartellino* inscribed: Amoris Causa. On the long side a putto with crown and sceptre (as infant Pluto?) pours bags of gold and silver coins from a cornucopia; behind is a painter before an easel on which is a portrait of a woman; inscribed on the *cartellino*: Lucri Causa. On the other short side a man is seated painting at an easel; a winged putto has placed a gold chain around his neck and is crowning him with a laurel wreath; to the left a *cartellino* inscribed: Gloriæ Causa.

INTERIOR: The inside shows two views of the interior of a house, painted to be viewed through the peep-holes. On the left-hand side (i.e. the left of a spectator looking into the interior through the open side) there is, to the left of a door, a painting of Minerva(?) surrounded by many figures; over the door is St Peter liberated from prison by an angel; to the right, Christ blessing children. On the long side, between two doors, is an engraved half-length portrait of a man in an oval with a decorative border, a female nude each side, a child with a coat-of-arms above and a simulated inscription below. Above the door to the right of this (and partly painted on the top of the box) is a picture of a rocky landscape. Seen through the same door is a room in which there is another landscape painting and in a farther room there is a stained-glass window with a standing figure holding a (?)Cross and, above, a coat-of-arms. On the right-hand side of the box is a door with a view into a room in which are pictures of the contest of Apollo and Marsyas before King Midas and (?)Christ bearing the Cross; to the right of the door is an engraving of St Christopher with the infant Christ on his shoulders; above the door (but painted on the roof of the box) is a landscape.

Signed on a letter on the floor of the box: A Monsieur/Mon(s?) S: de Hoogstraten/a/ . . .d( )echt.

The box is of wood. Exterior measurements: 58 high, 88 wide, 60.5 deep ($22\frac{7}{8} \times 35\frac{3}{8} \times 25$). Interior measurements: 54.5 high, 80 wide, 53 deep ($21\frac{1}{2} \times 31\frac{1}{2} \times 20\frac{7}{8}$).

Cleaned and restored in 1984–7.[1]

Exterior: The top is much worn and scratched, the two short sides are somewhat damaged and the long side is in fair condition. The black paint on the mouldings and around the peep-holes is largely worn away.

Interior: The floor is considerably worn. The inscription on the letter is worn and partly missing. There are *pentimenti* around the legs of the chair in the back left corner; the seat of the chair bearing the letter was once longer.

The panel of the short side on the left has a narrow strip of new wood let in along a horizontal split running the entire width of the panel below the peep-hole.

The paintings on the exterior of the three sides illustrate the three incentives of the painter mentioned by Seneca,[2] Love of art, Wealth and Fame, which form the subjects of the last three chapters in Hoogstraten's book on painting, *Inleyding tot de Hooge Schoole der Schilderkonst: anders de Zichtbaere Werelt*, published in 1678.[3] Each of the nine parts of the book is dedicated to one of the Muses and is prefaced by an etched plate of the appropriate one. The ninth and last part is dedicated to the Muse of Astronomy, Urania, who figures as the painter's inspiration towards the sublime; she appears here in the painting symbolising Love of art. The artist shown painting for money is making a likeness of a woman, since portraiture was not considered a worthy form of art. In the scene illustrating Fame the putto has placed a gold chain around the painter's neck; in the *Inleyding*, Hoogstraten says that painters are sometimes rewarded with gold chains, and mentions the one given to him when a young man by Emperor Ferdinand III.[4]

Illusionistic perspective pictures and various other forms of *trompe l'oeil* were painted by a number of Dutch artists during the third quarter of the seventeenth century.[5] It is probable that this renewed preoccupation with the problems of perspective was due to some extent to Carel Fabritius, and Hoogstraten was a fellow-pupil of Carel's in Rembrandt's studio (see the biographical notice on pages 203–4). Hoogstraten's interest in perspective and *trompe l'oeil* is well known; Houbraken, who had been his pupil, describes among other such things by him peepshows of interiors,[6] and Hoogstraten himself mentions the 'wonderlijke perspectyfkas' as one of the triumphs of the art of perspective.[7] Perspective boxes were probably first developed in Italy in the fifteenth century; some sixteenth-century ones have been preserved.[8] Of those made in Holland in the second half of the seventeenth century, only six are known to have survived.[9] In 1656 John Evelyn saw (in London) a 'triangular' one with a view of the interior of the Grote Kerk in Haarlem.[10] A triangular one is in the Bredius Museum in The Hague[11] and three others are in the National Museum in Copenhagen;[12] a pentagonal one, dated 1663, is in the Detroit Institute of Arts.[13] A perspective box by Job Berckheyde (1630–93) is mentioned in an inventory of 1704.[14]

The paintings on the outside have been thought the work of an assistant.[15] Cleaning has revealed that this is not the case.

Because of the connection of the subjects on the exterior with the last three chapters in the *Inleyding*, Mme Brière-Misme[16] supposes the peepshow to have been painted in the period immediately before the publication of the book in 1678 (the year of Hoogstraten's death). It seems likely, however, that the outside of the box was painted at the same time as the inside, which was probably executed long before 1678. The interior is similar in style to the *Perspective View in a House*, in Dyrham Park (near Bath), dated 1662,[17] but it is less dry and seems a little earlier. The last word of the inscription on the letter in the interior of the box was obviously *Dordrecht* and suggests that it was painted while Hoogstraten was still living there, i.e. between 1654 and September 1662.[18] A date in the later 1650s is the most acceptable.

PROVENANCE: Possibly in the [F. Halford] sale, London, 6 July 1861 (lot 126A),[19] bought in (£4.15.0). It was in the collection of Sir Henry H. Howorth, London, from 1893.[20] Sir H. H. Howorth sale, London, 14 December 1923 (lot 97), bought by R. Langton Douglas (270 gns). Presented by Sir Robert and Lady Witt (through the NACF) in 1924.

EXHIBITIONS: London, Royal Society, 9 May 1900; BFAC, Winter 1908;[21] London, Royal Society, 15 June 1921, No. 6; London, NACF, 1945–6, No. 113; Birmingham 1950, No. 31; London 1976, No. 63.

REFERENCES:
General: Sumowski, *Gemälde*, vol. 2, nos. 887–93; C. Brown, D. Bomford, J. Plesters and J. Mills, 'Samuel van Hoogstraten: Perspective and Painting', *National Gallery Technical Bulletin*, vol. 11, 1987, pp. 66–85.
In text:
1. For a detailed discussion of the restoration of the peepshow, its perspective scheme, construction, materials and techniques, and paint medium, see Brown et al., op. cit.
2. *De beneficiis*, book 2, chapter 33 (see the 1672 Amsterdam edition of his work, *L. Annaei Senecae Opera*, vol. 1, p. 649).
3. *Inleyding* etc., pp. 345ff (book 9, chapters 4–6).
4. *Inleyding* etc., p. 353.
5. S. Koslow, '*De wonderlijke Perspectyfkas*: An Aspect of Seventeenth-century Dutch Painting', OH, vol. 82, 1967, pp. 33–56.
6. Houbraken, vol. 2, p. 158: '. . . Prespectiven in Kamers (waar toe dan een gat in den muur buiten het vertrek om door te zien gemaakt werd) . . .'
7. *Inleyding* etc., pp. 274–75.
8. See W. Born in *Connoisseur*, vol. 107, 1941, p. 161.
9. They are all catalogued in the article by Koslow, op. cit., note 5.
10. See *The Diary of John Evelyn*, edited by E. S. de Beer, 1955, vol. 3, p. 165 (5 February 1656).

11. See C. Misme in GB-A, 1925, i, pp. 156ff. A. Blankert, *Museum Bredius: Catalogus van de schilderijen en tekeningen*, The Hague, 1978, cat. no. 57 (as 'omgeving P. Janssens Elinga').
12. One represents the interior of a Protestant church, another a Catholic church and the third a domestic interior.
13. See E. P. Richardson in *Art in America*, 1937, pp. 141ff. See Sumowski, *Gemälde*, vol. 2, under no. 887 (as workshop of Hoogstraten, with extensive bibliography).
14. Bredius, *Künstler-Inventare*, vol. 1, p. 37.
15. Misme, op. cit., p. 160.
16. Misme, op. cit., pp. 161–62.
17. Sumowski, *Gemälde*, vol. 2, no. 895.
18. In the Dordrecht records Hoogstraten and his wife are noted in September 1662 as 'vertrokken na Londen' (see G. H. Veth in OH, vol. 7, 1889, p. 136); he remained in London until after September 1666 (Veth, op. cit., p. 137, and *Inleyding* etc., p. 266).
19. 'Hoogstraten A Perspective Box. Admirably painted with interior Views by Hoogstraten, and signed by him – and a case.'
20. According to an undated typescript [of 1924?] in the National Gallery archives.
21. See p. 23 of the exhibition catalogue.

JOHAN VAN HUCHTENBURG, 1647–1733

Also signed himself *Hugtenburgh* and *Hughtenburgh*. Baptised 20 November 1647 in Haarlem.[1] Probably the pupil of Thomas Wijck, whose son Jan was his friend;[2] also influenced by Berchem and Philips Wouwermans. Houbraken says he went to Rome *c*.1667;[3] Huchtenburg himself says that from 1667 onwards he worked for the Gobelins tapestry factory under Adam Frans van der Meulen.[4] By 1670 he had returned to Haarlem;[5] he was in Amsterdam in 1676, 1679 and 1681/2.[6] Later he painted a series of battle scenes for Prince Eugene of Savoy. He was inscribed in The Hague guild, 1719;[7] he died in Amsterdam, 1733.[8]

REFERENCES:

1. Thieme/Becker, vol. 18, 1925.
2. and 3. Houbraken, vol. 3, p. 251.
4. In the 'Avis du Peintre' in *Batailles gagnées par le Prince Eugene . . . Dépeintes et gravées . . . par Jean Huchtenburg*, 1725.

5. Van der Willigen, 1870, p. 185.
6. Mauritshuis catalogue, 1914.
7. Obreen, vol. 5, p. 142.
8. Van Gool, vol. 2, pp. 413–14.

211 *A Battle*   *Plate 177*

Oil on canvas (stuck on oak panel), 42.8 × 58.3 ($16\frac{7}{8}$ × $22\frac{15}{16}$).

Cleaned in 1951.

Although unsigned, the painting has always been attributed to Huchtenburg and is certainly by him. For comparison see, for example, the signed *Cavalry Attack* in the Rijksmuseum.[1]

PROVENANCE: Brought from Paris by Bryan and exhibited for sale with pictures from the Robit and other Paris collections, in London, November 1801–May 1802, No. 177.[2] Presumably the Huchtenburg 'Battle' bought by Simmons at the John Webb sale, London, 30–31 May 1821 (lot 92), 70 gns. Richard Simmons Bequest, 1847.

REFERENCES:
1. 1976 cat., A184.
2. This provenance is first mentioned in the 1859 National Gallery catalogue.

JAN VAN HUYSUM, 1682–1749

He was born in Amsterdam, 15 April 1682,[1] and according to Houbraken[2] was a pupil of his father, Justus van Huysum the Elder (1659–1716), who was primarily a flower painter. Jan van Huysum married in Amsterdam in 1704 and appears to have spent the rest of his life there.[3] The earliest known dated picture is apparently of 1702[4] and the latest of 1743.[5] He died in Amsterdam, 8 February 1749.[6]

He painted some idealised landscapes but the bulk of his work consists of paintings of flowers and fruit; these brought him considerable fame in his lifetime even outside Holland and he was among the most highly-paid painters of his time. According to van Gool[7] he refused to have pupils, except, for a short while, Margaretha Haverman. His younger brother Jacob (1686–1740) imitated him and he had very many later imitators, especially in the second half of the eighteenth century and the earlier part of the nineteenth, for example Wybrand Hendriks, Jan van Os, Paul Theodoor van Brussel (all represented in the National Gallery), Jacob Linthorst (1745–1815), Gerard van Spaendonck (1746–1822) and Willem van Leen (1753–1825). One of his latest imitators was G. J. J. van Os, who died in 1861 (see No. 3226 of this catalogue).

REFERENCES:

General: HdG, vol. 10, 1928; M. H. Grant, *Jan van Huysum*, 1954; C. White, *The Drawings of Jan van Huysum*, Leigh-on-Sea, 1964.
In text:
1. Van Gool, vol. 2, pp. 13–14.
2. Houbraken, vol. 3, p. 387.
3. Bredius, *Künstler-Inventare*, vol. 4, pp. 1198–200.
4. A flower piece signed and dated 1702 was in the

Baron de C. sale, Paris, 20 December 1913, lot 40. Another of 1706 is in the Kunsthalle, Hamburg.
5. Schwerin, Staatliches Museum, *Holländische und Flämische Malerei des 17. Jahrhunderts*, 1982, no. 164. (Inv. no. 418). Purchased from the artist in 1744.
6. Van Gool, p. 27.
7. Van Gool, pp. 31–32.

796 *Flowers in a Terracotta Vase, and Fruit*   Plate 178

In the vase, which is decorated with putti in low relief, are pink, red and pale mauve peonies, poppies, blue iris, African marigolds, apple blossom, narcissi, marigolds, red and white tulips, pale blue and white jacinths, white and yellow roses, ranunculus and auriculas. At the foot of the vase are pink roses, red and white carnations and blue convolvulus, with black and white grapes, peaches and a chaffinch's nest. Most of the flowers are larger than the natural size.

Signed on the ledge, bottom left: Jan Van Huijsum / fecit 1736 / en. 1737.

Oil on canvas (shaped top), 133.5 × 91.5 (52½ × 36). The bottom edge of the canvas has been shaped in a similar manner to the arch at the top. A shallow curve in the centre of the bottom edge has been filled and retouched to make the present horizontal edge.

Cleaned in 1970.

The blue colour of the leaves is accentuated by the fading of some yellow pigment.

As often in van Huysum's pictures, the flowers are of different seasons. It seems that he sometimes delayed the completion of a painting until a particular flower was in bloom.[1] This is presumably the reason for the double dates that appear on some of his flower pieces,[2] for example the present one which is among the largest and most elaborate of his works in this genre.

COPY: A copy (canvas, 34 × 127 cm.) was at Sotheby's, 13 May 1970 (lot 31), bought in; and again at Sotheby's, 26 May 1971 (lot 153), bought by Moulemestre, £540.

PROVENANCE: This is possibly the picture of similar size and description in the Gerret Braamcamp collection, Amsterdam, in 1752[3] and the Gerret Braamcamp sale, Amsterdam, 31 July sqq. 1771 (lot 89), bought by Fouquet (800 guilders). It was in the Adriaan Palthe sale, Spaarndam, 10 August 1774 (lot 1), bought by J. Yver (4,050 guilders); Nicolaas Nieuhoff sale, Amsterdam, 14 sqq. April 1777 (lot 78), bought by Gildemeester (3,375 florins); Jan Gildemeester Jansz. sale, Amsterdam, 11 sqq. June 1800 (lot 90),[4] bought by Labouchère (990 florins). It is possibly the 'Fruit and Flowers' exhibited at the BI, 1823, No. 98, by William Wells, in whose collection at Redleaf it certainly was by 1835,[5] or the 'Flowers in a Vase' lent by him to the

BI, 1840, No. 125, but these descriptions would fit equally well the only other Huysum in his collection.[6] No. 796 was certainly in the William Wells sale, London, 12–13 May 1848 (lot 120), bought by Darby[7] (400 gns); [Abraham Darby] sale, London, 8 June 1867 (lot 80), bought by Newman (380 gns). Purchased from C. J. Nieuwenhuys in May 1869.

EXHIBITIONS: BI 1823, No. 98(?); BI 1840, No. 125(?); Bath 1953, No. 8; RA 1954–5, No. 212.

REFERENCES:

General: Smith Nos. 20 and 43; HdG No. 175; Grant, op. cit., No. 135.

In text:

1. In a letter of July 1742, van Huysum informs the agent of the Duke of Mecklenburg that he would have already finished the flower piece on which he was then engaged had he been able to find a yellow rose the previous year (see OH, vol. 18, 1900, p. 141).

2. For example, HdG Nos. 51, 182 (dated: 1727/ 1728 afgemaekt), 203 (dated: 1732 en 1733) and 231.

3. 'Een vaas met Bloemen, door *Jan van Huysum* (het vaas door J. de Wit), h.4 *v[oet]*. 8 en een half *d[uim]*., br. 3*v*. 9*d*. D[oek].' = 52½ × 42 in. [an Amsterdam *voet* = 11 *duim*] [Hoet, vol. 2, p. 503; C. Bille, *De Tempel der Kunst of het Kabinet van den Heer Braamcamp*, Amsterdam, 1961, pp. 21–22 (no. 89)].

4. HdG (No. 175) suggests that No. 796 was perhaps in the George Watson Taylor sale, London, 13–14 June 1823. There were only two Huysums in that sale, i.e. lots 62 and 63. Lot 63 was a fruit piece which passed later to the Marquess of Westminster's collection (HdG No. 208). Lot 62 was described as 'A Vase of Flowers . . . on a yellow ground' and according to the sale catalogue was from the Gil-

demeester collection [presumably lot 87 of the 1800 sale, despite HdG's assertion (No. 93) to the contrary], but this was a much smaller picture than No. 796 (80 × 59 cm.), on panel and dated 1734. (It was later in the collection of William II of Holland – see Smith No. 15 and C. J. Nieuwenhuys, *Description de la Collection . . . [du] Prince d'Orange*, 1837, pp. 92–93; William II sale, The Hague, 12 sqq. August 1850, lot 100.)

5. Smith No. 20.

6. i.e. lot 39 of the Wells sale, 1848: 'A Vase of Flowers – upright – 20 in. × 25 in.'; it was bought by Darby. The 1929 catalogue suggested that this was No. 1001 below, but it was apparently the picture (on canvas, 23 × 19½ in.) in the collection of Mrs F. M. Cope Darby which passed to Mrs MacGregor in 1935 (according to notes made in 1936 by H. Isherwood Kay, in the National Gallery archives).

7. A MS note by Smith on p. 469 in a copy of the *Catalogue Raisonné* said to be his own names the purchaser as F. Darby ['Coll. of ditto [W. Wells] dec*d* 1848. (Christie) £420. F. Darby Esq']; in the auctioneer's copy of the sale catalogue at Christie's the purchaser is given as Darby, without initials.

1001 *Hollyhocks and Other Flowers in a Vase*

Plate 179

Signed, bottom right: Jan Van Huijsum fe.[1]

Oil on canvas, 62.1 × 52.3 (24 $\frac{7}{16}$ × 20 $\frac{9}{16}$).

Cleaned in 1946–9.

This picture must belong to the earlier half of van Huysum's career, i.e. before the early 1720s when he began to paint the more elaborate and artificial flower pieces, light in tone and on light backgrounds, such as No. 796 above.

VERSION: A signed repetition with slight variations is in the Gallery of the Vienna Academy.[2]

PROVENANCE: It has been suggested[3] that No. 1001 was in the William Wells (of Redleaf) sale, London, 12–13 May 1848 (lot 30), bought by Darby; but this was a different picture.[4] It was in the Wynn Ellis collection, London. Wynn Ellis Bequest, 1876.

EXHIBITIONS: London 1947–8, No. 4; RA 1954–5, No. 168.

REFERENCES:
General: HdG No. 124; Grant, op. cit., No. 85.
In text:
1. The letters *ct* had been added later to the *fe* of the signature; these were found to be false and were removed in 1949.
2. Canvas, 63 × 53 cm.; signed, lower right. Acquired in 1821. HdG No. 119; inv. no. 677; 1961 cat. no. 176.
3. In the National Gallery catalogue, 1915–29.
4. This picture was apparently in the collection of Mrs F. M. Cope Darby until 1935 (see Huysum No. 796, note 6).

Style of JAN VAN HUYSUM

3165 *Flowers in a Stone Vase*   *Plate 180*

Poppies, convolvuluses, roses, etc.

Falsely signed on the pedestal, towards the right: Jan. Van Huijsum.[1]

Oil on canvas, octagonal, 88.3 × 77.2 ($34\frac{3}{4}$ × $30\frac{3}{8}$); the four corners are later additions.[2]

The drawing is too weak for van Huysum, the execution too clumsy, and the signature is certainly false. The composition and the comparatively light background are dependent on van Huysum's style of *c.*1710–20; the handling suggests rather some connection with the followers of Willem van Aelst.

PROVENANCE: Probably in the collection of a Mr Saunders; bought in 1874, apparently from Saunders's grandson, John Field, by Dr W. D. Wilkes of Salisbury (died *c.*1897).[3] Dr W. D. Wilkes Bequest, 1917.

REFERENCES:
General: Grant, op. cit., No. 221.
In text:
1. Under magnification the 'signature' can be seen to be painted on top of old wearing in places and it continues into the right bottom corner, which is a later addition.
2. An X-radiograph of the right bottom corner shows that the corners were added after the picture was lined.
3. Letter of 1917 (quoting one of 1874 from John Field to Dr Wilkes) in the National Gallery archives.

JOZEF ISRAËLS, 1824–1911

He was born in Groningen on 27 January 1824. He attended the French school until he was fifteen and from September 1835 onwards he had drawing and painting lessons at the Academie Minerva under van Wicheren and Cornelis Buys. In 1842 he entered the Amsterdam studio of Jan Adam Kruseman and also attended evening classes given by Jan Willem Pieneman at the Amsterdamse Academie. In 1845 he went to Paris where he studied with François Edouard Picot. He returned to Holland in 1847, settling in Amsterdam. He had his first great success in 1850 with the large canvas, *Ophelia*. In 1853 he was back in Paris and in 1862 visited London where his *Fishermen carrying a Drowned Man* (No. 2732) attracted enthusiastic attention at the International

Exhibition. In 1871 Israëls settled in The Hague. From the 1860s onwards he travelled widely in Europe. Israëls achieved great contemporary success: he received numerous honours and decorations and in 1910 his work was the subject of a *Mostra individuale* at the Venice Biennale. He died in Scheveningen on 12 August 1911 and was buried with great ceremony in the Jewish cemetery in The Hague.

After a number of early academic paintings, Israëls (following stays in Zandvoort in 1855 and Katwijk in 1856) became fascinated by the lives of poor fishermen, and these fishing communities, as well as aspects of Jewish life, were important sources of inspiration for his paintings and watercolours.

REFERENCE: Ex. cat., Paris/London/The Hague, 1983, pp. 187ff.

2713 *An Old Man writing by Candlelight* ('The Philosopher')

Plate 181

Signed, bottom left: Jozef Israëls.

Oil on canvas (not lined), 65 × 54.6 ($25\frac{9}{16}$ × $21\frac{1}{2}$).

Wide cracks throughout due to paint shrinkage, revealing the light-coloured ground.

The picture is referred to as 'The Philosopher' by J. C. J. Drucker,[1] who owned it in the painter's lifetime; this may be the title given it by Israëls who was a friend of Drucker and stayed with him in London.[2] It is perhaps a work of the later 1880s or 1890s.

PROVENANCE: It is perhaps 'The Philosopher' in the Jozef Israëls exhibition at the Goupil Gallery, London, 1897, No. 5; the owner is not stated but some of the pictures in this exhibition were apparently lent by private owners. It was in the collection of J. C. J. Drucker, London, who lent it to the National Gallery from March 1907 until June 1910, when he presented it. Transferred to the Tate Gallery, c.1920;[3] transferred back to the National Gallery in 1956.

EXHIBITION: London, Ben Uri Gallery, June-July 1949, No. 1.

REFERENCES:
1. Letter of 25 February 1907 from Drucker in the National Gallery archives.
2. He was staying with him in May 1903 (letter of 1914 from Drucker in the National Gallery archives).
3. Tate Gallery Modern Foreign Schools catalogue, 1926–34.

2732 *Fishermen carrying a Drowned Man* ('The Shipwrecked')

Plate 182

A woman behind the central group is pointing to a wreck on a reef.

Signed, bottom left: Jozef Israëls.

Oil on canvas, 129 × 244 ($50\frac{3}{4}$ × 96).

Cleaned in 1981–2.

The picture was called 'Le naufragé' when exhibited by Israëls in Paris 1861 and 'The Shipwrecked' when shown in London in 1862. It is said to have been painted in 1861;[1]

if so, it must have been finished by May of that year since the Salon opened in that month. According to Zilcken[2] it was painted in Amsterdam from studies made on the North Sea coast in Zandvoort, a fishing village where Israëls spent several months. It had considerable success when exhibited in London in 1862.

The cataloguers of the 1983 Hague School exhibition (see below) stress Israëls' indebtedness in this case to French prototypes, in particular to paintings by Courbet such as the *Burial at Ornans* of 1849/50 and *Return from the Fair* of 1850/1 as well as Jules Breton's *La Plantation d'un Calvaire* which was exhibited in Antwerp and Paris in 1858–9.

VERSIONS: A small version, perhaps a study for No. 2732, was in the Eugene Cremetti sale, 1 June 1923 (lot 111);[3] it is perhaps the version in the possession of Barbizon House, London, in 1919. Further versions were sold at F. Muller, Amsterdam, 29 November 1921 (lot 8);[4] at Heerlem (Hommes), 3 December 1962 (lot 199);[5] and at Sotheby Mak van Waay, Amsterdam, 15 April 1975 (lot 85).[6] Another is recorded in a private collection in Rijswijk (Z. H.) in 1968.[7] A signed wash drawing, perhaps a compositional sketch, is in the Aberdeen Art Gallery.[8]

PROVENANCE: It was apparently bought in 1862 by Gambart and sold to Arthur J. Lewis,[9] and purchased shortly afterwards by Alexander Young, London.[10] Alexander Young sale, London, 30 June sqq. 1910 (lot 302), 4,600 gns, bought by his widow who presented it to the National Gallery, in fulfilment of the wish of Alexander Young, in the same year. Transferred to the Tate Gallery, c.1920;[11] transferred back to the National Gallery in 1956.

EXHIBITIONS: Paris, Salon, 1861, No. 1596; South Kensington, London International exhibition, 1862 (Foreign Division, No. 1253);[12] Glasgow 1888, No. 74; London, Dowdeswell Galleries, April–May 1889, No. 124; London, Hanover Gallery, J. Israëls Exhibition, [c.1890?], No. 18;[13] perhaps in a loan exhibition at the Grafton Galleries, January–March 1896, No. 15;[14] London, Guildhall, 1903, No. 11; London, French Gallery, 1909, No. 18; London, Ben Uri Art Gallery, June–July 1949, No. 2; Paris/London/The Hague 1983, No. 29.

REFERENCES:
1. National Gallery catalogue, 1913.
2. P. Zilcken, *Peintres hollandais modernes*, 1893, p. 45.
3. 46 × 86 cm. As from the James Staats Forbes collection and exhibited at the Scottish National Gallery.
4. Oil on canvas, laid on panel, 34.5 × 45 cm.
5. Oil on canvas, 70 × 107 cm., ill. in sale catalogue.
6. Oil on canvas, 45.5 × 86.5 cm., ill. in sale catalogue.
7. Noted in Paris/London/The Hague, 1983, op. cit., No. 29.
8. Paper, 19.6 × 34.3 cm. Presented by Sir George Reid, 1913.
9. *Studio*, vol. 33, 1906–7, p. 294, as bought in 1862 by Arthur J. Lewis; *Art Journal*, 1910, p. 310, as bought by Gambart, who sold it to Arthur Lewis. See also the preface to the catalogue of the Israëls exhibition at the Goupil Gallery, 1897.
10. According to P. Zilcken, *Jozef Israëls*, Bergamo, 1910, p. 43.
11. Tate Gallery Modern Foreign Schools catalogue, 1926–34.
12. 'The Drowned Fisherman'; the lender is not specified but Alexander Young is listed among the lenders.
13. As 'The Shipwrecked'.
14. 'Drowned Fisherman'; the lender's name is not given.

CORNELI(U)S JANSON or JANSSENS (properly JOHNSON, or JONSON VAN CEULEN): *See* the catalogue of the British School (under JOHNSON)

WILLEM KALF, 1619–1693

He was born in Rotterdam. His teacher is unknown: Houbraken[1] says it was Hendrick Pot of Haarlem and Bergström[2] has suggested François Ryckhals of Middelburg (who was in Dordrecht in 1633 and 1634). Kalf is known to have been in Paris in 1641 when he met the Flemish painters Philip Vleughels and Jean-Michel Picart. He may have arrived in Paris in 1639 or 1640; he was back in Rotterdam by 1646.

In 1651 Kalf married the gifted Cornelia Pluvier[3] (she was a calligrapher, glass-engraver, poetess and musician) in Hoorn. The couple had settled in Amsterdam by 1653: Kalf was praised by the poet Jan Vos as one of the city's leading painters in the following year.[4] Kalf remained in Amsterdam until his death.

Kalf painted a number of barn interiors – the dated ones are from 1642–4[5] – but subsequently specialised in still lifes. He is particularly associated with the development of the lavish still-life displays incorporating rich vessels, glassware and carpets as well as exotic food known as *pronkstilleven*.

REFERENCES:
General: L. Grisebach, *Willem Kalf*, Berlin, 1974.
In text:
1. Houbraken, vol. 2, pp. 171–72.
2. Bergström, p. 275.
3. Grisebach, op. cit., pp. 199–206.
4. Grisebach, op. cit., pp. 21–22.

5. Grisebach, op. cit., cat. nos. 20, 36, 52, 53. Recently in the catalogue of an exhibition 'A Prosperous Past' (see under No. 6444) Segal has published a painting (now in the Carter collection, Los Angeles) he believes to be dated 1639.

6444 *Still Life with the Drinking-horn of the St Sebastian Archers' Guild, Lobster and Glasses*   Plate 183

Signed, lower left: W. Kalf.

Oil on canvas, 86.4 × 102.2 (34 × 40¼).

The drinking-horn of the St Sebastian Archers' Guild which is the centrepiece of this composition is today in the Amsterdam Historisch Museum (Fig. 47).[1] It is dated 1565.[2] It is a buffalo-horn in a silver mount. The foot is a silver tree-trunk to which St Sebastian is bound; a soldier stands on either side of him. On the silver band to which the foot is attached, there is a lion holding a shield bearing the arms of the city of Amsterdam. In this painting and in the upright variant of it (see below)[3] Kalf's representation of the horn varies in detail from the original, noticeably in the position of the two soldiers on either side of the saint. The drinking-horn also appears (more faithfully represented) in Bartholomeus van der Helst's *Four Regents of the St Sebastian Archers' Guild* of 1653 in the Rijksmuseum[4] and in two figure scenes by Metsu.[5]

In the variant which is in an upright format[6] the composition is extended at the bottom. The chair on the left (only three tacks can be made out with difficulty in No. 6444) can be seen clearly and more of the cherub supporting the table (in the upright version Kalf has turned him to face the viewer directly) and the table carpet can be seen. Similar arrangements of glasses, silver, lobster and fruit can be found in other still lifes by Kalf.[7]

213

Grisebach dates No. 6444 (and the upright version) to the early 1650s,[8] with which the present writer concurs. It is strikingly similar in technique (and in particular details) to, for example, the *Still Life with Porcelain Jug, Roemer and Fruit* of 1653 in the Alte Pinakothek, Munich.[9]

VERSIONS AND COPIES: An autograph version,[10] in an upright format, is discussed above. It was in the collection of Dr K. Lilienfeld in New York in about 1935. Its present whereabouts is unknown. A copy said to be by Barent van der Meer was in the C. Th. F. Thurkow collection, The Hague, in 1941.[11] A second copy, attributed to Juriaan van Streeck but probably significantly later in date, was in the collection of Mrs Carla Rava in Reggio Emilia in 1978.[12]

PROVENANCE: Either No. 6444 or the autograph version discussed above (under VERSIONS AND COPIES) was presumably the painting recorded in the inventory of the Amsterdam wine dealer Arnout Stevens (28 January 1706): 'de horen met meerder stil leven van Willem Kalf f. 100.'[13] This painting was sold shortly afterwards at auction: Amsterdam, 31 March 1706, lot 1: 'Een Kapitael stuk, van Willem Kalf (zynde een stil leven) daer in de Drinkhoren, 't beste van hem bekent f. 155.'[14] No. 6444 was in the collection of William Newall, London, around 1860. Bequeathed to the National Gallery by his descendant, Robert Sterling Newall, in 1978.

EXHIBITIONS: RA 1938, No. 191; London 1976, No. 64; Delft, Stedelijk Museum Het Prinsenhof; Cambridge, Mass., Fogg Art Museum; Fort Worth, Kimbell Art Museum, 1988/9, 'A Prosperous Past: The Sumptuous Still Life in the Netherlands 1600–1700', cat. no. 54.

REFERENCES:

General: Grisebach, op. cit., cat. no. 77.

In text:

1. It is catalogued in the Rijksmuseum silver catalogue, 1952, no. 40.

2. J. W. Fredericks, *Dutch Silver*, 1961, vol. 4, no. 2.

3. Grisebach, op. cit., cat. no. 78. Canvas, 128 × 106 cm.

4. 1976, cat.C3. The painting bears the date 1657 over 1653. There is a smaller version of the painting dated 1653 in the Louvre (cat.1979, no. 1332). Although known as a guild, the St Sebastian archers' guild was in fact part of the city's civic guard.

5. *The Oyster Eaters*, Hermitage, Leningrad (HdG 174); *Girl playing a Lute*, Gemäldegalerie, Cassel (HdG 146).

6. See note 3.

7. Grisebach, op. cit., cat. nos. 73, 74, 75, 76.

8. Grisebach, op. cit., p. 155. He also notes the influence of still lifes of this type by Kalf on a still life of 1656 by Simon Luttichuys.

9. Grisebach, op. cit., cat. no. 72. Alte Pinakothek 1983 cat., p. 268. Inv. no. 10763.

10. See note 3.

11. Canvas, 80 × 98 cm. Note in RKD quoted by Grisebach, op. cit., cat. no. 77a.

12. Photograph in the National Gallery archives.

13. Gemeentearchief Amsterdam, N.A.A., no. 4642, folios 493–94. Quoted by Grisebach, op. cit., cat. no. 77.

14. Hoet, 1, pp. 85–87.

ABRAHAM VAN KALRAET *See* CALRAET

THOMAS DE KEYSER, 1596/7–1667

Thomas Hendricksz. de Keyser, son of the Amsterdam architect and sculptor, Hendrick de Keyser (1565–1621). He was a native of Amsterdam and in June 1626 was said to be twenty-nine.[1] From January 1616 he was a pupil of his father for two years. His earliest surviving dated work is *The Officers of the Surgeons' Guild* of 1619 (Amsterdam, Historisch Museum).[2] He married in Amsterdam in 1626. In 1627 he painted two group portraits[3] which show him having moved away from the stiff, formal arrangement of *The Officers of the Surgeons' Guild* to a far more informal, relaxed composition. He apparently entered the Amsterdam stonemasons' guild in 1640; from then on he was also active as a stone merchant and painted less. In 1662 he was appointed stonemason to the town of Amsterdam. He always lived in Amsterdam and was buried there in the Zuiderkerk on 7 June 1667.

De Keyser originally based his style on that of Cornelis van der Voort (1576–1624) and Nicolaes Eliasz. (1591/2–1654/6). Until Rembrandt's arrival in Amsterdam in 1631 or 1632 he and Nicolaes Eliasz. were the most favoured Amsterdam portrait painters. Although he painted some life-size portraits, including guild and militia groups, he popularised small whole-length likenesses and in his later years introduced a new type, that of small equestrian portraits. Besides portraits he also painted religious and mythological subjects.

REFERENCES:

General: R. Oldenbourg, *Thomas de Keysers Tätigkeit als Maler*, 1911. A. J. Adams, *The Paintings of Thomas de Keyser (1596/7–1667): A Study of Portraiture in Seventeenth-Century Amsterdam* (Harvard University thesis, 1985), 4 vols., Ann Arbor, 1987.
In text:
1. According to the entry in the Marriage Register when he married on 5 July 1626. (All the documents concerning de Keyser are published by Adams, op. cit., vol. 2, pp. 490–528.)

2. Adams, op. cit., cat. no. 1. 1975 cat., No. A7352.
3. *The Syndics of the Amsterdam Goldsmiths Guild*, 1627: Toledo, Ohio, Museum of Art, Acq. no. 60.11; *The Syndics of the Amsterdam Goldsmiths Guild*, 1627: formerly Musée des Beaux-Arts, Strasbourg (destroyed 1944). These portraits may show the outgoing and incoming syndics in 1627 and 1628. Adams, op. cit., cat. nos. 17 and 18.

212 *Portrait of Constantijn Huygens and his (?)Clerk*   *Plate 184*

In the background hangs a tapestry with many figures, apparently representing St Francis before the Sultan; in the centre of its upper border is a coat-of-arms: '*aux 1 & 4 d'argent au pal d'azur; aux 2 & 3 de gueules à deux lions léopardés d'argent*' (see below). Above the fireplace is a painting of a vessel in a rough sea, in the style of Jan Porcellis, and below it a small bust portrait of a man.

On the table, which is covered by a Turkey carpet, are a pair of terrestrial and celestial globes, a *chitarrone*, books, an ink-pot, a paper with architectural plans, a pair of compasses and a chronometer.

Signed on the front of the chimney-piece: TDK AN 1627 (TDK in monogram); very faint.

Oil on oak, 92.4 × 69.3 (36$\frac{3}{8}$ × 27$\frac{1}{4}$).

Cleaned in 1964. There is some wearing in the darks.

Constantijn Huygens the Elder, lord of Zuylichem, was born on 4 September 1596 in The Hague. He was secretary to the Dutch embassy in Venice, 1620, and London,

1621–4, and was knighted by King James I in 1622. He was appointed secretary to the Stadholder, Prince Frederik Hendrik of Orange, in 1625, and after the latter's death in 1647 to his son and successor, Prince Willem II. When Willem II died in 1650 he continued as adviser to the Prince Frederik Hendrik's widow, Amalia van Solms, and was often entrusted with the affairs of the House of Orange. Finally, he was first councillor and *reekenmeester* to the Stadholder-King William III, until his death in The Hague in 1687.[1] He had very considerable and varied talents and was particularly interested in the fine arts. He worked with the architect, Pieter Post, on the plans for his own house in The Hague.

The identity of the sitter was established by F. Schmidt-Degener[2] and is put beyond doubt by comparison with the many authenticated portraits of Constantijn the Elder, for example Willem Delff's engraving of 1625 after Michiel Miereveld,[3] Paul Pontius's engraving in the *Iconographie* after a portrait by van Dyck probably painted in 1632,[4] and Adriaen Hanneman's composite portrait, finished in 1639, in the Mauritshuis in The Hague.[5] Further, the arms of the tapestry are obviously intended for those of Constantijn Huygens, who quartered the Huygens arms with those of Bacx:[6] '*aux 1 & 4 d'argent à deux pals d'azur* (= Huygens); *aux 2 & 3 d'argent au chef de gueules chargé d'un lion, léopardé du champ*' (= Bacx).[7] They are rendered inaccurately in the picture; the nature of the principal differences – one pale instead of two in the Huygens quarters and two lions instead of one in those of Bacx – suggests that the painter confused his instructions. In any case it will be noted that, unlike the rest of the accessories, the coat-of-arms is rather carelessly painted.

The *chitarrone* and the globes are clearly references to Huygens's interest in music and astronomy. The plans on the sheet of paper are architectural drawings and, together with the compasses, are intended to illustrate Huygens's studies in this art (see above). Huygens is shown spurred in reference to the knighthood conferred on him by James I five years earlier. The identity of the young man with Huygens is not known. A 1785 inventory describes him as Huygens's clerk or page (see PROVENANCE).

De Keyser is not known to have been in The Hague, where Huygens lived, and it seems highly probable that Huygens sat for this portrait in Amsterdam; it appears from his diary that he was staying there for most of the time between 22 February and 27 April 1627.[8] Indeed the present picture may very well be 'my portrait painted shortly before my wedding' (which took place on 6 April 1627) about which he wrote some Latin verses on 31 July 1627, but without naming the painter.[9] This suggestion has been disputed[10] on the grounds that in these verses Huygens cites as evidence of his great joy the unwrinkled brow in the portrait whereas this is not visible in de Keyser's picture since he is wearing a hat, but Huygens may well have used the expression figuratively. (The portrait mentioned in Huygens's lines of 1627 cannot be, in any case, that painted by Lievens, probably in 1626 or 1627, in the Rijksmuseum, for that shows Huygens with a serious, almost melancholy countenance.[11])

PROVENANCE: It is most probably the full-length portrait of Constantijn Huygens with his clerk or page which was in the inventory of possessions of Huygens's last direct descendant, Susanna Louisa Huygens, widow of Baron Willem van Wassenaer van Ruyven, who died in The Hague in December 1785.[12]

It was in the collection of Anna Maria Ebeling (wife of Jonkheer Paul Iwan Hogguer) who died in 1812 and in the sale of her collection in Amsterdam, 18 sqq. August 1817 (lot 37), bought by Coclers (275 guilders); John Webb sale, London, 30–31 May 1821 (lot 145), bought by Simmons[13] (100 gns). Richard Simmons Bequest, 1847.

EXHIBITIONS: London 1976, No. 65; The Hague 1979, No. 18.

REFERENCES:
General: Oldenbourg, op. cit., No. 79 and pl. 8; F. Schmidt-Degener in *Onze Kunst*, vol. 27, 1915, pp. 113ff; H. E. van Gelder, *Ikonographie van Constantijn Huygens en de zijnen*, The Hague, 1957, No. 6; Adams, op. cit: no. 13 (with full bibliography).

In text:
1. See inter al., NNBW, vol. 1, cols. 1186ff; F. Bachrach, *Sir Constantine Huygens and Britain*, Leiden, 1962.
2. Loc. cit.
3. Reproduced in OH, vol. 32, 1914, between pp. 222 and 223, and in Hollstein, vol. 5, p. 172.
4. F. Wibiral, *L'Iconographie d'Antoine van Dyck*, No. 53. The original of this engraving is presumably the portrait painted by van Dyck in January 1632 which is mentioned in Huygens's diary (J. H. W. Unger, *Dagboek van Constantyn Huygens*, 1885, p. 20).
5. Mauritshuis catalogue, 1977, No. 241.
6. The Bacx arms are derived from his paternal grandmother, Geertrui Bacx.
7. See J. B. Rietstap, *Armorial général*, 1950 reprint, vol. 2, p. 1013. In 1642 Huygens's arms were altered by the addition of an augmentation: *d'azur à une fleur-de-lis d'or*.
8. Unger, op. cit., p. 12.
9. 'In effigiem meam paulo ante nuptias pictam' (*Momenta desultoria*, 1644, p. 68); he put these verses into Dutch, 2 August 1627: 'Op mijn afbeelding korts voor mijnen Trou-dagh gemaeckt, uyt mijn Latijnsch' (*Koren-Bloemen*, 1658, vol. 17, p. 1076; *De gedichten van Constantyn Huygens*, edited by J. A. Worp, vol. 2, 1893, pp. 235–36).
10. By C. Brière-Misme in OH, vol. 53, 1936, p. 198.
11. Published by Brière-Misme, op. cit., pp. 193–200. See also ex. cat. Braunschweig, Herzog Anton Ulrich-Museum, *Jan Lievens, ein Maler im Schatten Rembrandts*, 1979, No. 17. The portrait (which is on loan from the Douai Museum; Rijksmuseum 1976 cat. no. C1467) is almost certainly the Lievens portrait about which Huygens wrote a quatrain on 5 April 1632 ('In effigiem meam manu I. Liuii. Picturae nec lingua deest, ne fallere, nec vox; Hugenii facies haec meditantis erat' etc.) and about which he wrote in his autobiography that many had found the face too pensive ('cogitabundus'; see J. A. Worp in OH, vol. 9, 1891, pp. 129–30). Although the quatrain was written in 1632 (5 April) and the autobiography 1629–(?)31, Worp has produced good reasons for believing that the portrait then referred to was painted in 1626–27 (op. cit., p. 129, note; so also Mme Brière-Misme, op. cit., pp. 196–98). The passages quoted by Worp show that Lievens's portrait cannot be the subject of Huygens's verses of 1627.
12. It is the eighteenth item in the inventory, which contains no less than eleven other portraits (and a print) of Constantijn Huygens the Elder: 'Dezelve [Huygens] ten voeten uit met zijn klerk of knegt' (this inventory was published by E. W. Moes in OH, vol. 14, 1896, pp. 176–84; the identification is due to Schmidt-Degener, loc. cit. It was not in Susanna Huygens's sale in The Hague, 22 May 1786).
13. Although this lot is described in the sale catalogue as 'A. Cuyp Christopher Columbus in his Study', in the marked copy at the RKD, the painter's name is crossed out and 'De Keyser' substituted in a contemporary hand. Further, Simmons purchased six more pictures at the Webb Gallery (i.e. Huchtenburg No. 211 of this catalogue, G. Herp No. 203 and probably F. Guardi No. 210).

WILLEM KOEKKOEK, 1839–1895

He was born in Amsterdam on 13 January 1839. He was a pupil of his father, Hermanus Koekkoek (1815–82). The Koekkoeks were a dynasty of painters: Willem's grandfather (Johannes Hermanus), uncles (Barend Cornelis and Marinus Adrianus), brothers (Johannes Hermanus Barend, Barend Hendrick, Hermanus II and Johannes) were all painters and two of Willem's sons, Hermanus Willem and Marinus Adrianus II, also became painters.

After stays in The Hague and Utrecht, he returned to Amsterdam in 1880 and in 1885 settled in Nieuwer-Amstel (today known as Amstelveen). In 1888 he visited London. He died in Nieuwer-Amstel on 29 January 1895.

Willem Koekkoek specialised in the painting of town views and street scenes loosely based on those of the seventeenth-century painter Jan van der Heyden. Koekkoek preferred picturesque effects to topographical accuracy.

REFERENCE: Scheen, p. 278.

6472 *A View of Oudewater*   *Plate 185*

Signed, lower left: W KoeKKoeK (WK in monogram).

Oil on canvas, 84.4 × 64.8 ($33\frac{1}{4}$ × $25\frac{1}{2}$).

The small town of Oudewater[1] is on the river Ijssel between Gouda and Utrecht. It is dominated by the distinctive outline of the clock tower of the Grote Kerk (Church of St Michael):[2] the church was built in the late thirteenth and early fourteenth centuries and the clock tower erected in 1601. Koekkoek painted a number of views of Oudewater:[3] his views of streets in the old town are picturesque rather than strictly topographically accurate. One of his views of the town is apparently dated 1867[4] and No. 6472 probably dates from around the same time.

PROVENANCE: Bequeathed by Miss J. M. Hawkins Turner, London, 1982.

REFERENCES:
1. The identification of the town of Oudewater was made by L. G. van der Klooster of the topographical section of the RKD for whose help the present writer is most grateful.
2. Compare, for example, the view of Oudewater in an engraving of 1745 by H. de Winter in R. Boitet, *Beschryvinge der Stad Oudewater*, 1747, p. 30.
3. For example: a very similar view of Oudewater by Willem Koekkoek (canvas, 35 × 50 cm.) was in the exhibition, 'The Dutch Romantic School', D. Vanderker Gallery, London, 19 February–17 March 1962, No. 12 (illustrated in the catalogue). See also note 4 below.
4. Canvas, 22 × 29 in. With M. Newman Ltd., London, 1947 (illustrated in an advertisement in *Connoisseur*, September 1947, p. 11 as 'Near Amsterdam').

PHILIPS KONINCK, 1619–1688

Philips Aertsz. Koninck (he also signs *Koning, Conninckx*). Born in Amsterdam, 5 November 1619. In 1639 he was the pupil of his elder brother, Jacob (1614/15–after 1690), in Rotterdam and married there in January 1641. In the banns for the marriage he is described as 'Philips Koninck van A[msterdam]'. He had returned to Amsterdam by 1653 and is frequently mentioned in documents there in the following years. He was buried in Amsterdam on 6 October 1688.

According to Houbraken,[1] he was a pupil of Rembrandt; although this is not certain, his earlier work shows considerable Rembrandtesque elements; his landscapes are also clearly influenced by the panoramic views of Hercules Segers. In his own time he seems to have been chiefly known as a painter of genre and portraits (the earliest dated 1642) rather than landscapes, of which some seventy have survived. Although there are a number of dated landscapes from 1647 or 1648 until 1676, they do not have a continuous stylistic development, and the chronology of the undated ones remains unclear.

REFERENCES:
General: H. Gerson, *Philips Koninck*, 1936 (reprint 1980).
In text: **1.** Vol. 2, p. 53.

836 *An Extensive Landscape with a Hawking Party*   Plate 186

Oil on canvas, 132.5 × 160.5 ($52\frac{1}{4}$ × $63\frac{1}{8}$). Reduced on the right, where a right arm with a stick and part of the right leg of a man are visible at the edge of the canvas (just below the cottage and to the right of the dog at present covered by the frame); the rest has been cut off.

Cleaned in 1942.

The figures are very close to those of Johannes Lingelbach (who frequently painted the figures in others' landscapes) and are almost certainly by him. Gerson[1] maintains that Koninck painted the figures in his own landscapes, but often took those of other painters as a model; he instances the present picture. The figures in Koninck's subject pieces, however, are very weak and it is hard to believe that he could have imitated so deceptively both Lingelbach and Adriaen van de Velde (see No. 4251 below), to take only two examples. (It is worth noting that in both these instances the figures have been painted in after the landscape was finished.) Moreover, there are a number of Koninck's landscapes in which the figures seem much more likely to be by the same hand as the landscape, for example No. 6398 (dated 1655) and that at Glasgow University;[2] the figures in all these are in the same style and are different from and inferior to those in the present picture and No. 4251.

It is probably a fairly late work but, if the figures are by Lingelbach, must have been painted before November 1674, the date of the latter's death.

COPIES: A reduced copy (eighteenth century?) is in the Mauritshuis in The Hague.[3] Another (nineteenth century?) reduced copy with slight variations was in the Viscount Scarsdale sale, London, 18 July 1930 (lot 100).[4]

PROVENANCE: In the [Smeth et al.] sale, Paris, 16–20 April 1811 (lot 81), bought by Lerouge (1,800 francs); Villers sale, Paris, 30 March–1 April 1812 (lot 42[5]), bought by Francillon (2,001 francs). Probably in the Thomas Emmerson sale, London, 1–2 May 1829 (lot 63[6]), 50 gns. Apparently in the collection of Dr Fletcher, Gloucester, by 1836;[7] Ralph Fletcher sale, London, 9 June 1838 (lot 71), bought for Edmund Higginson (£588) and in his collection at Saltmarsh;[8] Edmund Higginson sale, London. 4–6 June 1846 (lot 217), bought by Emmerson (£1,050) for Sir Robert Peel, Bart.[9] It was in the collection of Sir Robert Peel, Bart.;[10] purchased with the Peel collection, 1871.

EXHIBITION: London 1947–8, No. 71.

REFERENCES:

General: Gerson, op. cit., No. 31 and pl. 16.

In text:

1. Gerson, op. cit., p. 38, note 75.

2. Gerson, op. cit., No. 23. *Glasgow University's Pictures*, Colnaghi, London, 1973, cat. no. 16.

3. Mauritshuis catalogue, 1977, No. 80. On canvas, 64 × 78 cm. In this copy, which has not been cut down, the man with a hawk and three dogs in the middle distance just below the coach has been omitted, as also the arm and leg of a man on the right edge and the dog near by, and the two figures outside the cottage on the left. Bought from Héris of Brussels, 1830.

4. On canvas, 62 × 77.5 cm. The dog and the arm and leg of the man on the extreme right are omitted, also the child behind the washerwoman and some of the dogs with the falconers; there are a number of simplifications of detail. (Exhibited at the RA, 1902, No. 138, lent by Charles Newton Robinson; [F. C. Grein] sale, London, 12 May 1906, lot 129, bought by Cohen, 205 gns.)

5. According to the catalogue of the Villers sale, 1812, the picture had previously been in a Lebrun sale; this presumably refers to the [Smeth et al.] sale, 1811, the auctioneer for which was Lebrun.

6. 'P. de Koning A Landscape and Figures, a bird's eye view in Holland with Travellers halting, and Figures passing along a road by Lingelback.'

7. Smith, vol. 7, 1836, p. 248.

8. H. Artaria, *A Descriptive Catalogue of the Gallery of Edmund Higginson Esq., of Saltmarsh Castle*, 1841, pp. 59–60.

9. MS note on p. 248 of volume 7 (in a copy of the *Catalogue Raisonné* said to be Smith's own), referring to Dr Fletcher's picture: 'Sold in sale of Dr Fletcher's pictures at Christie and Co., June 1838 bought by Edm^d Higginson Esqre again put up to auction with the whole Collection of E. H. Esqr June 1846 and sold for £1,050.0.0. bought by Mr. Emmerson for the R^t Honble Sir Robt Peel Bt.'

10. Waagen, 1854, vol. 1, p. 411.

4251 *An Extensive Landscape with Houses in a Wood and a Distant Town*   Plate 187

Oil on canvas, 101.5 × 146.5 (39$\frac{7}{8}$ × 57$\frac{3}{4}$).

The condition is obscured by the brown ingrained varnish which now covers the picture, but the dark parts seem to be very worn and the sky, in parts at least, is much worn and retouched.[1] There is repaint along a considerable part of the horizon in the left half.

Previously described as a view in Gelderland but the existence of variants (see below) suggests the view is imaginary.

The old attribution of the figures to Adriaen van de Velde[2] is almost certainly correct. (There is a note on the authorship of the figures in Koninck's landscapes in the entry for No. 836 above.) Although a little more freely painted than those in van de Velde's own landscapes, both figures and animals are very close in style to his, especially those outside the inn in the centre.

This is considered by Gerson[3] a characteristic late work, related stylistically to the Rijksmuseum landscape of 1676,[4] but before the mid–1670s. It is certainly close in style to the Rijksmuseum picture, but if, as seems to be the case, the figures are by Adriaen van de Velde, the picture must be before 1672 since he died in January of that year.

It is one of a group of variations of the same design, the others (apparently of the same period) being in the Michaelis collection in the Old Town House, Cape Town,[5] and the Pushkin Museum, Moscow.[6]

PROVENANCE: In the collection of Sir Charles Bagot by 1834, when it was exhibited at the BI; Sir Charles Bagot sale, London, 18 June 1836 (lot 35), bought by A. Brondgeest (137 gns), probably for Baron J. G.

Verstolk van Soelen of The Hague;[7] it was in the latter's collection which was sold *en bloc* to Thomas Baring, Humphrey Mildmay, Samuel Jones Loyd (Lord Overstone) and Chaplin in 1846.[8] The present picture fell to Thomas Baring, who exhibited it at the BI in 1850. Baring, who died in 1873, left his collection of paintings to his nephew, 2nd Baron Northbrook (later 1st Earl of Northbrook).[9] Purchased from the 2nd Earl of Northbrook in 1927 (with the aid of gifts from the Benson family and the NACF).

EXHIBITIONS: BI 1834, No. 100; BI 1850, No. 47; London, Agnew's Loan Exhibition, 1925, No. 14; London 1947–8, No. 72.[10]

REFERENCES:

General: Gerson, op. cit., No. 32.

In text:

1. See also the catalogue of the Cleaned Pictures Exhibition, London, 1948, No. 72.

2. The attribution is made already in the catalogues of the 1834 BI exhibition and the 1836 Bagot sale.

3. Gerson, op. cit., pp. 39–40.

4. Gerson, op. cit., No. 2; Rijksmuseum cat. 1976, A206.

5. Canvas, 90.8 × 110.5. Gerson, op. cit., No. 25. D. Bax, *Catalogue of the Michaelis Collection (The Old Town House, Cape Town)*, Cape Town, 1981, No. 41.

6. Canvas, 131 × 161 cm. Pushkin Museum catalogue, 1957, No. 989. Gerson, op. cit., No. 43.

7. Albert Brondgeest (whose name is inscribed on the back of the lining) bought a number of pictures for Baron Verstolk (e.g. Smith, Cuyp No. 216; Smith, van der Heyden No. 84; Smith Supplement, Metsu No. 29; see also Smith, vol. 9, p. 574). See also Hobbema No. 6138 of this catalogue.

8. See Northbrook catalogue, pp. ix–x and 199.

9. See Northbrook catalogue, p. ix (see also p. 50, No. 64).

10. Exhibited with the varnish removed from a small area in the sky; this has since been covered again.

6398 *An Extensive Landscape with a Road by a River*   *Plate 188*

Signed, lower right: P koninck 1655

Oil on canvas, 137.4 × 167.3 ($54\frac{1}{8}$ × 66).

The figures are by Koninck himself. The painting is one of a pair; both are of exceptional quality. The other, also signed and dated 1655, is still in the Gage collection at Firle Place.[1]

PROVENANCE: E. Hooft (widow of Wouter Valckenier) auction, Amsterdam, 31 August 1796, lot 21 (sold for 200 guilders to Achtienhoven). In the collection of Earl Granville. Lord Granville sale, 21 June 1845 (lot 17): bought for £565 by W. H. Grenfell, London, who was created Baron Desborough in 1905; on his death it passed to his daughter, the Viscountess Gage. Acquired from the collection of Lady Gage under the terms of the 1956 Finance Act, 1971.

EXHIBITIONS: BI 1844, No. 68; RA 1878, No. 257; RA 1952–3, No. 271; London 1976, No. 66.

REFERENCES:

General: Gerson, op. cit., No. 57.

In text: 1. Gerson, op. cit., No. 56; Washington, National Gallery of Art, *The Treasure Houses of Britain*, 1985–6, cat. no. 322.

6408 *An Extensive Landscape with a Town in the Middle Distance*

Plate 189

Signed, bottom right, in monogram: PK.

Oil on canvas, 43.7 × 53.5 ($17\frac{1}{8}$ × $21\frac{1}{16}$).

Slight wearing throughout.

Gerson suggests that this is a late work, *c*.1665–8.[1]

PROVENANCE: Mansfield sale, Amsterdam, 13 August 1806, lot 89 (as by Ph. Koninck and Adr. van de Velde: bought by van Iperen). Purchased from P. and D. Colnaghi, 6 December 1905, by W. C. Alexander. Passed by descent to the Misses Rachel F. and Jean I. Alexander, who presented it by deed of gift to the National Gallery; entered the collection in 1972.[2]

EXHIBITIONS: RA 1929, No. 163; Manchester 1929, No. 1; London 1972.

REFERENCES:
General: Gerson, op. cit., No. 35.
In text:
1. Gerson, op. cit., p. 35.

2. A, Smith, 'Presented by the Misses Rachel F. and Jean I. Alexander: Seventeen Paintings for the National Gallery', BM, vol. 114, 1972, p. 633.

PAULUS CONSTANTIJN LA FARGUE, 1729–1782

Paulus Constantijn La Fargue, landscape and topographical painter, was baptised in The Hague, 5 January 1729. He worked chiefly in The Hague, where he entered the painters' confraternity *Pictura* in 1761, and he is mentioned as a pupil of The Hague Academy in 1768. His works record his visits to cities and villages, mainly in Zuid-Holland. He was the most prolific member of a family of topographical artists which also included his brothers Jacob Elias, Isaac Louis, Karel and his sister Maria Margaretha. As well as paintings, he made topographical watercolours and series of etchings and book illustrations.

REFERENCES: The Hague, Gemeentemuseum, *Den Haag in de Prinkentijd, gezien door de Familie La Fargue*, 1973–4; Scheen.

1918 *The Grote Markt at The Hague*

Plate 190

On the extreme left is the Groot Boterhuis; beyond the houses in the centre are the tower and, farther to the right, the choir of the Grote or St Jacob Kerk. On the wall of the Boterhuis are various sale bills; those to the left of the tree are inscribed respectively: 'HUIS/en/ERVE; (') HOS (S?)/V(....)/O(....); VERKOOP VAN HIACIN'; those to the right of the tree: 'VERK; HUIS/en/ERVE'. Over the east door of the Boterhuis are carved the arms of The Hague, with butter barrels beside them. The door of the house immediately to the right of the Boterhuis has an inscription above it: 'STADS A (B?)'. Over a window of the house on the extreme right is an inscription (interrupted by the trunk of a tree): 'B I B (I?) U M'.

Signed at the bottom, near the centre: P.C. la Fargue Pinx 1760.

Oil on mahogany, 57.6 × 75.9 (22$\frac{11}{16}$ × 29$\frac{7}{8}$).

Cleaned in 1959.

The market square (Grote Markt) is seen from the Prinsengracht, looking towards the north. The building at the corner on the left, which still stands, is the former butter market (Groot Boterhuis, also called the Boterwaag) built in the 1650s by the city architect Bartholomeus van Bassen. Most of the other houses have been rebuilt and the fountain or pump in the middle of the square has gone. The spire on the tower of the Grote or St Jacob Kerk is that erected in the sixteenth century. It was replaced in the nineteenth century but today has a reconstruction of the original spire. The street leading northwards to the St Jacob Kerk is the Schoolstraat; at the end of it, on the right, was the former location of the fish market.

DRAWINGS: Several drawings and watercolours of the same place were made by Jacob Elias La Fargue (1735–76?) from more or less the same point of view, but without the crowd and the stalls. One, catalogued as by P. C. La Fargue, but signed J. E. La Fargue, entitled *Gesigt van de Groote of Wekelijksche Groenmarkt in 's Hage*, is in the Fodor collection (Amsterdams Historisch Museum). Another, *De weeklijkse of Grote Markt van 's-Gravenhage*, is in the Municipal Archives of The Hague, where the most important collection of drawings of the La Fargue family is to be found.

PROVENANCE: Purchased (out of the Lewis Fund) from the Hon. C. Sclater-Booth, 1903.

EXHIBITION: The Hague, Gemeentemuseum, 'Den Haag in de Prinkentijd, gezien door de Familie La Fargue', 1973–4, No. 15.

JAN DE LAGOOR, active 1645–1659

Little is known about his life. He entered the Haarlem guild in 1645 and was a *hoofdman* in 1649; an inventory of his possessions was made in Amsterdam – he was living on the Oude Schans – in December 1659 when he became insolvent.

There are signed and dated paintings of 1649[1] and 1654[2] and signed etchings, all of woody landscapes. Lagoor's early work shows the influence of Cornelis Vroom and it has been suggested that he was a pupil of Vroom. Later Lagoor became a close follower of Jacob van Ruisdael.

REFERENCES:
General: G. Keyes, 'Jan de Lagoor', *Tableau*, vol. 1, 1979, pp. 36–44 (with checklist).
In text:
1. Keyes, op. cit., No. 27. With Alan Jacobs, London, 1976.
2. Keyes, op. cit., No. 37. *View of Beverwijck,* Leger Galleries, London, 1972.

1008 *A Woody Landscape with a Stag Hunt* Plate 191

Signed at the bottom, towards the left: JD Lag... f. (JD in monogram). All but the monogram is badly worn, and had been partly overpainted with a false Potter signature (P. Potter.f.1651[1]). Most of this false signature was removed in 1953.

Oil on canvas, 112 × 148.5 (44⅛ × 58½).

Formerly attributed to Paulus Potter,[2] and later to his father, Pieter Simonsz. Potter[3] (c.1597–1652), on account of the false signature. Although the original signature is damaged it is certainly that of Jan de Lagoor. The signature is very close to that on a *Woody Landscape* in a private collection in London.[4]

Probably painted in the late 1640s.[5]

PROVENANCE: It has been suggested[6] that No. 1008 is the P. Potter 'Woody Landscape with Deer' in the Hastings Elwyn sale, London, 23 May 1806 (lot 11), £85, but there is nothing to support this suggestion. It was certainly in the Wynn Ellis collection by 1850 or 1851.[7] Wynn Ellis Bequest, 1876.

REFERENCES:
General: Keyes, op. cit., No. 20.
In text:
1. The first P of the false signature and apparently the f were made out of the original signature; Potter and the date were false.
2. When in the Wynn Ellis collection (cf. note 7).
3. National Gallery catalogue, 1877–1929.
4. Keyes, op. cit., No. 21. Ex-Spencer-Churchill collection.

5. It is apparently comparable in date to the 1649 *Woody Landscape*, for which see note 1 of the biographical notice.
6. National Gallery catalogue, 1915–29.
7. Waagen, 1854, vol. 2, p. 296, as by Paulus Potter and dated 1656.

PIETER LASTMAN, c.1583–1633

Pieter Pietersz. Lastman, son of Pieter Zeegersz.; he and his brother Nicolaes adopted the surname Lastman. He was probably born in Amsterdam;[1] in November 1619 he is stated to be about thirty-six.[2] Carel van Mander says he studied with Gerrit Pietersz. Sweelinck.[3] He went to Italy, probably by 1603 and certainly by 1604 (according to Carel van Mander,[4] whose dedication of this part of his book is dated July 1604, Lastman was then in Italy). He worked in Rome; Elsheimer and Caravaggio seem to have been the principal influences on the formation of his style. He was back in Amsterdam possibly by 1605,[5] certainly by March 1607,[6] and appears to have lived there for the rest of his life. There are dated paintings every few years from 1606[7] until 1631.[8] Lastman was a Catholic. He was buried in Amsterdam, 4 April 1633.[9]

He achieved great contemporary success and his work was praised by the poets Rodenburgh and Vondel. He received a commission from King Christian IV of Denmark for a series of paintings for Frederiksborg Palace.

Lastman was one of the most influential painters of his time in Holland; his two most important pupils were Jan Lievens and Rembrandt. His pictures are mostly of religious or mythological subjects.

REFERENCES:
General: K. Freise, *Pieter Lastman*, 1911. A. Tümpel in *The Pre-Rembrandtists*, catalogue of an exhibition held at the E. B. Crocker Art Gallery, Sacramento, 1974, pp. 47–61.

In text:
1. Cf. C. Vosmaer, *Rembrandt*, 1877, p. 68.
2. OH, 1886, p. 7.
3. Van Mander, fol. 293 v.

4. Loc. cit.

5. Freise, op. cit., pp. 7–8.

6. OH, 1885, p. 46, and 1886, p. 7.

7. *The Adoration of the Magi*, Národní Galerie, Prague.

8. *The Triumph of Joseph*, M. H. de Young Memorial Museum, San Francisco.

9. OH, 1886, p. 18.

6272 *Juno discovering Jupiter with Io*   *Plate 192*

On the left Juno, with crown and sceptre, descends to earth with her peacocks. On the right is Jupiter with Io in the form of a white heifer; a drapery is being cast over her by the winged Cupid and Deceit (a masked man with a fox's pelt about him). Cupid's bow lies on the ground with its string loosed.

Signed, top right: Pietro La∫tman/fecit A° 1618.

Oil on oak, 54.3 × 77.8 ($21\frac{3}{8}$ × $30\frac{5}{8}$).

Cleaned in 1957.

There are numerous versions of the story of Io. The account best known in later times is that in Ovid's *Metamorphoses* (Book I, 583ff). Io, daughter of Inachus, was seduced by Jupiter. Juno, looking down from the sky, saw the dark cloud he had spread to entrap Io and descended to earth to look for him. Jupiter, hoping to deceive her, had turned Io into a beautiful heifer but Juno made him give it to her and put it in the charge of Argus the hundred-eyed. At the orders of Jupiter, Mercury lulled Argus to sleep and killed him. Juno then caused Io to wander into Egypt; finally, however, she let Jupiter change her back into human form.

In verses 612–16 Ovid describes how Juno, having discovered Jupiter with the heifer, pretends not to know that the latter is Io and asks where it comes from and to whom it belongs; Jupiter says it was born of the earth, whereupon Juno asks for it as a gift. The gestures and expressions of the principal actors in Lastman's picture, especially Juno's, fit these lines so well that it is tempting to suppose the painter had Ovid's text in mind. On the other hand, the two secondary figures do not occur in Ovid. The winged child is obviously Love; the other figure is Deceit (the mask and the fox's skin are among Deceit's most usual attributes). Lastman presumably introduced these allegorical figures as appropriate to the action rather than having a particular text in mind.[2]

After the death of Argus, Juno took his eyes to decorate the tail of the peacock; Lastman correctly shows the birds here without the 'eyes'.

PROVENANCE: In an anonymous sale, London, 3 May 1957 (lot 152), bought by Doward (155 gns).[1] Presented by Julius Weitzner, June 1957.

EXHIBITION: London 1976, No. 67.

REFERENCES:

1. As 'Mercury and Argus with Juno'.

2. See discussion in E.J. Sluijter, *De 'Heydensche Fabulen' in de Noordnederlandse Schilderkunst circa 1590–1670*, Leiden 1986, pp. 55, 394.

JUDITH LEYSTER, 1609–1660

Judith Jansdr. Leyster; on occasion she signed herself *Judita Leystar* (see also below). She was the daughter of Jan Willemsz., a brewer from Antwerp, who appears to have taken his surname from his brewery in Haarlem, the 'Ley-starre'.[1] She was baptised in Haarlem, 28 July 1609.[2] She is already mentioned in 1627 as painting in Haarlem.[3] In 1628 her parents were living in Vreeland,[4] some ten miles from Utrecht, and some of her early works show clearly the influence of the Utrecht *Caravaggisti*, in particular Hendrick ter Brugghen. Her parents had moved to Zaandam (near Haarlem) by September 1629[5] and she may have become a pupil of Frans Hals in Haarlem at about that time; in any case her earliest known dated paintings, of 1629 and 1631, are very much in his manner and it seems likely that she was the 'Judith Jans[dr.]' who was a witness at the baptism of one of Hals's children in Haarlem in November 1631.[6] She was a member of the Haarlem guild by 1633,[7] and in 1635 had three pupils there.[8] In June 1636 she married the painter Jan Molenaer in Heemstede (near Haarlem);[9] in 1637 they were living in Amsterdam and remained there until 1648 when they bought a house in Heemstede where they lived for the most part thereafter.[10] She was buried in Heemstede, 10 February 1660.[11]

She painted mostly genre scenes but there are also some portraits by her and one or two still-life and flower paintings; pictures of birds by her are listed in the 1668 inventory of her husband's estate.[12] After 1630 she came under the influence of the Haarlem painters of small genre pictures, such as Dirck Hals and, a little later, her husband. There are no works by her dated later than 1652. She executed a number of watercolours of tulips: two, in a Tulip Book in the Frans Halsmuseum, Haarlem, are dated 1643. In the signatures on her pictures her surname is usually in the form of L followed by a star; see No. 5417 below.

REFERENCES:

General: J. Harms in OH, 1927, *passim*; H. F. Wijnman, OH, 1932, pp. 62–65. F. F. Hofrichter, 'Judith Leyster 1609–1660', diss., Rutgers University, 1979 [idem, *Judith Leyster*, Doornspijk, 1989].
In text:
1. Bredius, *Künstler-Inventare*, vol. 1, p. 9.
2. Wijnman, op. cit., p. 63.
3. In Samuel Ampzing's *Beschryvinge ende Lof der Stadt Haerlem*, p. 370; although published in 1628 the foreword is dated 1 February 1627.
4. and **5.** Wijnman, op. cit., p. 65.

6. Van der Willigen, p. 140.
7. Van der Willigen, p. 202 and Errata.
8. OH, 1917, pp. 71–73.
9. Wijnman, op. cit., p. 63. The banns were read on 11 May; the wedding took place on 1 June.
10. See the biographical note on Molenaer, p. 271. They bought a house in Amsterdam in 1655 (Bredius, op. cit., p. 17).
11. Van der Willigen, p. 202.
12. Bredius, op. cit., pp. 4, 5 and 7.

5417 *A Boy and a Girl with a Cat and (?)an Eel* Plate 193

Signed on the right, above the girl's shoulder: iudiyh [sic] followed by a star (worn and faint, the star barely visible).

Oil on oak, 59.4 × 48.8 ($23\frac{3}{8}$ × $19\frac{3}{16}$).

Cleaned in 1981–2. Considerable paint loss along the vertical join in the centre of the panel.

PENTIMENTI: The X-radiograph (Fig. 48) reveals a number of significant changes. The girl at first had a kerchief instead of a ruff around her neck with the ends crossed over her chest. Two other positions for the cat were attempted and the boy's shoulder was originally slightly higher. There were small alterations to his scarf.

MacLaren made two suggestions about the meaning of the painting. He thought it might illustrate a Dutch proverb or saying, such as 'to hold an eel by its tail'. The proverb in its entirety is 'to hold an eel by its tail does not mean you have caught it'. He also noted similarities to an engraving by Cornelis Danckerts of *Two Children with a Cat*, the verses beneath which refer to freedom from care.[1] (Hofrichter[2] has recently pointed out that this print is after a work by Leyster.) Each interpretation, however, accounts for only one of the animals in the painting. Hofrichter[3] prefers to relate the painting to an emblem in Guillaume de la Perrière's *Le théâtre des bons engins auquel sont contenu cent emblèmes moraulx*, of which a Dutch edition had appeared in 1554.[4] It shows a man who holds an eel in his right hand and a woman's left hand in his left. The text comments on the woman's fickleness and infidelity and notes that maintaining a woman's love is like 'holding an eel by its tail'. The children, Hofrichter suggests, mock adult behaviour, a familiar conceit in Dutch genre paintings. In Hofrichter 1989 (op. cit.) it is proposed that the creature is a slow-worm (*anguis fragilis*)]. For the present writer none of these explanations is entirely satisfactory and a particular text or saying remains to be discovered.

Judith Leyster often signed her pictures with J or L followed by a star, a punning reference to her surname.[5] The spelling of her Christian name here is apparently unique on a painting.[6] In an Amsterdam inventory of 1642[7] is recorded: 'Een schilderij synde twee lachenden tronyen met een catien soo groot als 't leven en naer het leven geschildert door Judith Molenaer.' ('A painting of two people laughing with a cat life-size and painted from the life by Judith Molenaer.') It is possible that this is No. 5417. A date in the late 1630s or early 1640s would be acceptable.[8]

PROVENANCE: In the [John Hotchkis] sale, London, 8 July 1910 (lot 30),[9] bought by Rutley (Reynolds Gallery, London), 720 gns; Mrs Holbrooke sale, London, 17 February 1939 (lot 98), bought by Vicars (920 gns). C. F. Leach Bequest, 1943.

EXHIBITION: London 1978–9, No. 25.

REFERENCES:

General: Hofrichter, op. cit., cat. no. 22 [idem, 1989 op. cit., cat. no. 44].

In text:

1. 'Seght my of hy,/of weesens schyn,/Die lacht is blyt/Verbercht geen pyn' (Hollstein, No. 79). The print is inscribed 'F HALS pinxit' but is in fact after Leyster (see Hofrichter, op. cit.).

2. and 3. Hofrichter, op. cit.

4. *Tpalays der Geleender Ingienen*, Amsterdam, 1554. Emblem no. 88.

5. *Leidstar* (in seventeenth-century Dutch *leydt-sterre* or *ley-ster*) = lodestar; it was the name of the inn in Haarlem from which Judith Leyster's father, a brewer, took his name.

6. In documents of 1655 and 1659 she uses the form *Judita* (see Bredius, *Künstler-Inventare*, vol. 1, pp. 17 and 22). This and similar signatures (with the date 1643) appear on two pages of a Tulip Book in the Frans Halsmuseum, Haarlem (see Hofrichter, op. cit., cat. nos. L20 and L21).

7. Bredius, op. cit., p. 14.

8. Hofrichter, op. cit., p. 63.

9. The markings corresponding to this sale are on the back of the picture.

JAN LIEVENS, 1607–1674

Jan Lievens, son of Lieven Hendricx, embroiderer from Ghent. (Although the usual spelling *Lievens* is used here, it should be noted that the name is patronymic, i.e. Lievenszoon. *Lievensz.* and *Lievenss*[*en*] are generally used in contemporary references.)

He was born in Leiden, 24 October 1607, according to Orlers,[1] who says he became a pupil of Joris van Schooten of Leiden when about eight and at about the age of ten went to study with Pieter Lastman in Amsterdam for some two years, returning then to Leiden where he subsequently worked on his own. He is recorded there in 1624, 1626 and 1629;[2] in 1626–7 he painted a portrait of Constantijn Huygens, the Stadholder's secretary.[3] In the later 1620s and until about 1631 he appears to have been closely associated with Rembrandt and they may have worked together at times; their works at this period are often difficult to distinguish.[4] According to Orlers,[5] Lievens went in 1631 to England where he stayed for about three years and painted the royal family and many great persons, and thence to Antwerp. He was, however, still in Leiden in February 1632[6] and must have left for England shortly after. Van der Doort's inventory of the Royal Collection confirms Orlers's account of royal commissions.[7] He had settled in Antwerp by 1635, when he entered the guild there.[8] In Antwerp he was acquainted with Adriaen Brouwer and Jan Davidsz. de Heem, who witnessed a contract for him in May 1636.[9] He continued to live in Antwerp and in December 1638 married there,[10] but was in Holland for a time in 1639;[11] in 1639–40 he painted a *Scipio Africanus* for the town hall of Leiden, for which he was paid 1,500 guilders.[12] In December 1640 he acquired Antwerp citizenship; a son of his was baptised in Antwerp in July 1642 and another, Jan Andrea, in January 1644.[13] By March 1644, however, he was in Amsterdam (then apparently living with Jan Molenaer)[14] and is recorded there until June 1653.[15] In 1650 he painted a large picture of five Muses for the Huis ten Bosch near The Hague. He lived in The Hague 1654–8[16] and was among the founders of *Pictura*, the painters' confraternity there, in October 1656,[17] in which year he painted a large composition of *Quintus Fabius Maximus and his Son* for the new town hall in Amsterdam.[18] He paid his dues to *Pictura* in 1661[19] although by March 1659 he was once more living in Amsterdam, where he continued until October 1669.[20] In 1661 he was commissioned to paint for the town hall of Amsterdam an episode in the struggle of the Batavians against the Romans.[21] In 1664 he painted an allegorical picture of War for the chamber of the provincial assembly of Holland in The Hague;[22] in 1666 a *Mathematician* for the Rijnlandshuis in Leiden;[23] and in 1669–70 an allegorical picture of Justice for the same building.[24] He rented a house in The Hague in March 1670 for a year[25] and was living there throughout 1671[26] but was in Leiden in September of that year.[27] In February 1674 he took a house in Amsterdam,[28] where he died on 4 June 1674.[29]

Lievens was a precocious artist; according to Orlers, he was painting independently in 1621 when he was fourteen. His earliest known works are broadly painted large-scale figures representing the Four Elements. Subsequently he painted small-scale religious scenes, very similar to those of Rembrandt's Leiden period. At the English court he came under the powerful influence of van Dyck and subsequently both his portraiture and his history painting reveal the almost overwhelming impression that van Dyck made on the young Dutch artist. Lievens was a history painter and portraitist; after his return to Holland he largely concerned himself with portraits and with official commissions for historical and allegorical subjects on a monumental scale. In his later years Lievens evolved an individual landscape style based in the first place on those of Rubens and Brouwer. His landscape drawings are highly original and he also made many etchings and some woodcuts (including one *chiaroscuro* print).

REFERENCES:

General: H. Schneider, *Jan Lievens, sein Leben und seine Werken*, 2nd ed., revised by R. E. O. Ekkart, Amsterdam, 1973; *Jan Lievens, ein Maler im Schatten Rembrandts*, exhibition catalogue, Braunschweig, 1979; Sumowski, *Gemälde*, vol. 3.

In text:

1. J. Orlers, *Beschrijvinge der Stadt Leyden*, 2nd ed., 1641, pp. 375f; quoted in Schneider, op. cit., pp. 293–94.

2. Schneider, op. cit., p. 3.

3. See T. de Keyser, No. 212 of this catalogue, note 11.

4. On the subject of Rembrandt's and Lievens's early works, see J. Bialostocki in *Jan Lievens, ein Maler im Schatten Rembrandts*, op. cit., pp. 13–20.

5. Op. cit., p. 377.

6. Bredius, *Künstler-Inventare*, vol. 1, p. 195.

7. Ed. O. Millar, 'Abraham van Doort's catalogue of the Collections of Charles I', *Walpole Society*, vol. 37, 1958–60, London, 1960, pp. 146, 161. For Lievens's stay in England, see also C. Brown, 'Jan Lievens in Leiden and London', BM, vol. 125, 1983, pp. 663–71.

8. P. Rombouts and T. van Lerius, *De Liggeren . . . der Antwerpsche Sint Lucasgilde*, vol. 2, [1876], p. 61, and F. J. van den Branden, *Geschiedenis der Antwerpsche Schilderschool*, 1883, p. 863.

9. and 10. Van den Branden, op. cit., p. 865.

11. He was in Leiden in August 1639 (Bredius, op. cit., vol. 1, p. 196) and his portrait drawing of Constantijn Huygens, engraved by L. Vorsterman, must have been made in the summer of 1639, probably in The Hague.

12. Schneider, op. cit., No. 106.

13. Van den Branden, op. cit., pp. 865–66.

14. Obreen, vol. 7, pp. 293–94.

15. Bredius, op. cit., vol. 1, pp. 196–98.

16. Bredius, op. cit., vol. 1, pp. 198–99.

17. Obreen, vol. 4, p. 59.

18. Schneider, op. cit., No. 102.

19. Obreen, vol. 5, p. 131.

20. Bredius, op. cit., vol. 1, pp. 199–208.

21. Bredius, op. cit., vol. 1, pp. 199–200, and Schneider, op. cit., No. 99.

22. Schneider, op. cit., No. 86.

23. Schneider, op. cit., No. 117.

24. Schneider, op. cit., No. 112.

25. Bredius, op. cit., vol. 1, p. 208.

26. Bredius, op. cit., vol. 1, p. 212 and vol. 7, p. 141.

27. Bredius, op. cit., vol. 1, pp. 210–11.

28. Bredius, op. cit., vol. 1, p. 213.

29. Loc. cit. He was buried 8 June 1674 (Bredius, vol. 7, p. 142).

72 *A Landscape with Tobias and the Angel* Plate 194

Oil on oak, 56.9 × 88.5 (22⅜ × 34¹³⁄₁₆).

On the back of the panel is the brand of the Antwerp panelmakers' guild.

Cleaned in 1952–3. Pronounced craquelure in the darks.

For the subject, see the Book of Tobit 6: 1–3.

Ascribed to Rembrandt since the middle of the eighteenth century; an attribution accepted by Hofstede de Groot.[1] The attribution to Lievens proposed by W. Drost[2] was accepted by H. Schneider.[3]

The brand on the back (Fig. 49) makes it likely that the picture was painted in Antwerp. The influence of Brouwer's landscapes is evident here but, as Drost[4] has pointed out, the handling is too pastose for him; nor is there any comparable work by his Flemish followers. On the other hand, a small group of landscapes showing the influence of Rubens and, more especially, of Brouwer can be ascribed with some confidence to Lievens on the basis of comparison with the background of the National Gallery *Self Portrait* (No. 2864) and a landscape in Berlin with a contemporary inscription or signature on the back.[5] The present picture is certainly by the same hand.

Lievens was in Antwerp from 1635 until early in 1644; No. 72 was probably painted in Lievens's last years in Antwerp.

COPY: A copy was made by Mrs Long, 1814.[6]

PROVENANCE: In a [Dr Robert] Bragge sale, London(?), 1749 [1748 O.S.],[7] second day, lot 63, bought by Barnard (9 gns);[8] in the collection of John Barnard at Berkeley Square, c.1761.[9] Possibly in the Duke of Argyll sale, London, 25–26 May 1798 (lot 136).[10] It was later in the possession of Thomas Emmerson;[11] by April 1814[12] it was in the collection of Revd William Holwell Carr, who lent it to the BI, 1815. Holwell Carr Bequest, 1831.

EXHIBITION: BI 1815, No. 26.

REFERENCES:
General: Smith, Rembrandt No. 43; HdG, Rembrandt No. 68a; Schneider, op. cit., No. 305; Sumowski, op. cit., No. 1308.
In text:
1. HdG, Rembrandt No. 68a (as c.1655).
2. W. Drost, *Barockmalerei in den germanischen Ländern*, 1926, p. 166.
3. Op. cit., pp. 61–62. Schneider thought the picture had been retouched in the eighteenth century, probably by Sir Joshua Reynolds. Cleaning has shown that this was not the case and in any case the picture was not in Reynolds's collection as he supposes; it has been confused with a landscape in Glasgow (HdG, Rembrandt No. 68).
4. Loc. cit.
5. It is inscribed on the back in ·a contemporary hand: Jan lievens and I.L. It was included in the Braunschweig exhibition as cat. no. 41. See that catalogue entry and nos. 42, 43, 45, 46, 47 and 48; and the introductory essay by S. Jacob, 'Zur En-

twicklung der Landschaftsmalerei von Jan Lievens', pp. 21–26. (The dating of the painted landscapes proposed in the catalogue is, however, problematic: see C. Brown, BM, vol. 121, 1979, pp. 741–46.)
6. See Farington, vol. 13, p. 4479 (3 April 1814): 'The Revd Holwell Carr overtook me on my way back & told me of an extraordinary picture, – a Landscape by Rembrandt, which He had purchased. He said He had lent it to Mrs. Long and was told she had made a good copy from it.' The Mrs Long referred to by Farington is presumably Amelia Hume, an amateur landscape painter, who married in 1793 Charles Long (afterwards Baron Farnborough).
7. This sale is known only from a copy in vol. 1 (pp. 211ff) of two MS volumes of extracts from eighteenth-century sale catalogues in the Victoria and Albert Museum Library (pressmark R.C.S. 1 and 2); the day and month of the sale are not given.
8. 'A Landskip, Tobit [sic] and the Angel Rembrandt. 9.9. [bought by] Mr Barnard.'

9. Smith, loc. cit.; *London and its Environs Described*, published by R. and J. Dodsley, 1761, vol. 1, p. 827: 'A fine landskip with Tobit [sic] and the Angel, near three feet wide [by Rembrandt]'. (It has been pointed out by C. F. Bell that the materials for Dodsley's *London* were collected somewhat before 1761 [see T. Borenius, *Pictures . . . in the Library of Christ Church, Oxford*, 1916, p. 13, note].)

10. '*Rembrandt* A Landscape, with the story of Tobit – a charming cabinet piece.'

11. Smith, loc. cit.

12. See Farington, loc. cit.

1095 *Portrait of Anna Maria van Schurman* Plate 195

Signed on the left, below centre: I.L./1649.

Inscribed by a later hand, above left: Anna Maria Schurman [sic].

Oil on canvas, 87 × 68.6 (34¼ × 27); original edges on all sides. The canvas has not been lined.

Worn and, in the darks, retouched.

There is a *pentimento* in the outline of the jacket on the right.

Anna Maria van Schurman (1607–78), Dutch poetess and scholar, was born in Cologne. At an early age she came to live in Utrecht and, while still young, became famous for her erudition. In 1668 she left Utrecht to follow the religious teacher, Jean de la Badie, and died in the Labadist community in Wiewerd. She was celebrated in her lifetime for her learning and accomplishments and was visited by and corresponded with scholars from all parts of Europe. She also drew, etched, and engraved on glass.[1]

There are many certain portraits, and some self portraits, of Anna Maria van Schurman.[2] The head (including the coiffure) in the present portrait is closely related to that of the self-portrait bust in pastel in the Museum in Franeker[3] and one may have served directly or indirectly as a model for the other.

ENGRAVING: The present picture or a variant was engraved (in reverse) by Jonas Suyderhoef (d. 1686).[4]

PROVENANCE: Brought from Holland, probably by Sir Hans Sloane,[5] and bequeathed with the rest of his collection to the nation in 1753. Presented by the Trustees of the British Museum, 1880.

REFERENCES:

General: Schneider, op. cit., No. 258; van Hall, No. 1907, 17; Sumowski, op. cit., No. 129.

In text:

1. See NNBW, vol. 1, cols. 1465–66.

2. For example, etched self portrait, signed and dated 1640 (catalogue of the Centraal Museum, Utrecht, 1952, No. 988); frontispiece of *Nobilissimae virginis Annae Mariae a Schurman Opuscula hebraea, graeca, latina, gallica, prosaica et metrica*, Leiden, 1648; engraving after Cornelis Jonson van Ceulen (Cornelius Johnson, died 1661/2) by C. van Dalen (catalogue of the Centraal Museum, Utrecht, 1952, No. 873 and pl. 142); engraving of 1657 by Steven van Lamsweerde (Utrecht catalogue, 1952, No. 883).

3. Reproduced in A. Staring, *Kunsthistorische Verkenningen*, 1948, pl. 47. It was given to the town of Franeker by a descendant of Anna Maria.

4. J. Wussin, *J. Suyderhoef*, 1861, No. 78. Suyderhoef's engraving is inscribed: 'ANNA MARIA A SCHURMAN. Joannes Liuius pinxit. Jonas Suyderhoef sculpsit' (with four lines of Latin verse by Daniel Heinsius). The head and bust are the same as in the National Gallery picture, but only one hand (the nearer) is shown, placed upon the book, and there are no writing implements on the table, nor is the fringe of the table-covering visible.

5. In a MS inventory of the Sloane collection in the British Museum it is No. 274, noted as 'brought from Holland'.

2864 *Self Portrait*

Plate 196

Signed in the centre of the wall, left: IL (barely visible).

Oil on canvas, 96.2 × 77 ($37\frac{7}{8}$ × $30\frac{5}{16}$).

Cleaned in 1970. There is a tear through the neck and the hair. Wearing in the sky and pronounced craquelure in dark areas have been reduced by retouching.

There is a *pentimento* of a column at the left edge.

Cross-sections reveal that the canvas was prepared with a double ground: beneath, a thin greyish-white granular layer of lead white with carbon black and yellow-brown ochre, and on top, a thick granular brown layer, a mixture of brown ochre pigment with lead white and a few grains of a red-brown opaque ochre similar to light red.

The identification rests in the first place on the inscription on a copy made in 1792 by Aert Schouman, who owned the portrait (see below). It is confirmed by comparison with Lucas Vorsterman's engraved portrait after a lost study by van Dyck in the *Iconographie*,[1] the features in which agree well enough allowing for the difference in the sitter's age (Vorsterman's prototype was presumably made by van Dyck when Lievens was in London *c*.1632–4).

Schneider[2] rightly stresses the influence of van Dyck in this portrait and places it in Lievens's Antwerp period (1634–44). MacLaren felt that the sitter's age made it likely that it was painted either towards the end of that time or shortly after Lievens's return to Amsterdam. The authors of the Braunschweig exhibition catalogue,[3] however, were inclined to date it to Lievens's first years in Antwerp, between 1635 and 1638 (the year of his marriage). Sumowski[4] considers it to be from the late 1630s. The present writer considers a dating of *c*.1638 most likely: the technique is similar to other paintings of the early Antwerp years, such as the *Miserly Couple surprised by Death* of 1638,[5] and the sitter is perfectly consistent with the appearance of a man in his early thirties.

COPY: There is a summary watercolour copy made in 1792 by Aert Schouman in the van Regteren Altena collection, Amsterdam.[6]

PROVENANCE: A self portrait of Lievens was in the inventory of Susanna van Sonnervelt, widow of Simon Middelgeest, The Hague, 1696;[7] a *Portrait of Jan Lievens* was in the Salomon Arensklauw [and Cornelis Troost's] sale, Amsterdam, 16 March 1750 (lot 102).[8] The National Gallery picture has been identified with a *Portrait of a Man* by Lievens in the Baron de Banckheim sale, Paris, 12 April 1747 (lot 103),[9] but there seems to be no particular reason for connecting them. No. 2864 belonged to Aert Schouman (1710–92), The Hague, and was presented by him, 25 April 1792, to The Hague painters' confraternity, *Pictura*,[10] of which Schouman had been dean. It was in the possession of Gooden, London, in 1896,[11] and afterwards in the collection of Charles Fairfax Murray, London, by whom it was presented in 1912.

EXHIBITION: Braunschweig, Herzog Anton Ulrich-Museum, 'Jan Lievens: ein Maler im Schatten Rembrandts', 1979, No. 33.

REFERENCES:

General: Schneider, op. cit., no. 248; van Hall, No. 1271, 6; Braunschweig ex. cat., op. cit., No. 33; Sumowski, op. cit., No. 1289.
In text:
1. M. Mauquoy-Hendrickx, *L'Iconographie d'An-* *toine van Dyck*, Brussels, 1956, No. 85. Inscribed: IOANNES LIVENS PICTOR HVMANARVM FIGVRARVM MAIORVM LVGDVNI BATTAVORVM.
2. Op. cit., No. 248 and p. 69.
3. Braunschweig ex. cat., op. cit., No. 33.

4. Sumowski, op. cit.

5. Panel, 77 × 90 cm. Signed, lower right: I LIVYUS FECIT 1638. Collection of Lady Teresa Agnew, Melbury House. Braunschweig ex. cat., op. cit., No. 34.

6. Watercolour on paper, 17.8 × 13.4 cm. Inscribed on the reverse by Schouman: 'Dese origineele schildery present gedaan aan de Kamer van der Heeren Regent der Academie in Schravenhage in den Jaare 1792. A. Schouman' and 'dit geteekent naar een origineel portret van Jan Lievens door hem selve geschildert in de manier van zijn meester Rembrandt. A. Schouman 1792.' The mount of the

drawing is inscribed: 'Dit is het laaste schilderwerk van myn Oom Aart Schouman. Zynde den 5 July 1792 Overleden   N:L: Penning.'

7. No. 54: 'Het pourtrait van Jan Lievensz door hem selffs gedaen' (Bredius, *Künstler-Inventare*, vol. 1, p. 219; Schneider, op. cit., No. 246a).

8. Schneider, op. cit., No. 248.

9. 'Un Portrait d'homme de Jean Lievens'; 3 *pieds* × 2 *pieds* 3 *pouces* (= *c.*76.5 × 70.5 cm.).

10. Obreen, vol. 4, p. 213, and OH, vol. 19, 1901, pp. 239–40.

11. According to Schneider, op. cit., No. 248.

JAN LINGELBACH, 1622–1674

Baptised in Frankfurt, 10 October 1622. By 1634 his family had settled in Amsterdam, where his father, David, ran the Nieuwe Doolhof, a successful pleasure garden. The identity of Lingelbach's teacher is unknown. According to Houbraken, he left Amsterdam for France in 1642 and two years later he travelled to Rome where he stayed until 1650. This account is supported by the few surviving documents: Lingelbach is recorded in 1647 and 1648 as living in Rome on the Strada Paolina delli Greci and the following year on the nearby Horto di Napoli. In Rome, Lingelbach came under the powerful influence of the style of Pieter van Laer, *Il Bamboccio*, who had given his nickname to a new type of small-scale genre painting representing Italian street life - the *bambocciate*. Although van Laer had returned to Haarlem by 1639, a number of artists, among them the Fleming Jan Miel (1599–1664) and the native Roman Michelangelo Cerquozzi (1602–60), continued to work in his style. So closely did Lingelbach follow van Laer's style at this time that there has been considerable confusion about the attribution of individual paintings.

According to Houbraken, Lingelbach left Rome on 8 May 1650, to return to Amsterdam; however, no documents record his presence in the city until 1653, when he married and was granted citizenship. He lived in Amsterdam for the rest of his life and was buried in the city's Old Lutheran Church.

After his return to Holland, Lingelbach was increasingly influenced by the work of the successful and prolific Philips Wouwermans, in particular by his landscapes containing figures at work or on horseback. He also painted Italianate landscapes and seaports in the manner of Jan Baptist Weenix and his son, Jan Weenix. Lingelbach collaborated with a number of artists, painting figures in landscapes by, among others, Jan Hackaert, Philips Koninck (see No. 836 in this catalogue), Frederick de Moucheron and Jan Wijnants.

REFERENCES: C. Burger-Wegener, 'Johannes Lingelbach 1622–1674', Diss., Berlin, 1976; T. Kren, 'Jan Lingelbach in Rome', *The J. Paul Getty Museum Journal*, vol. 10, 1982, pp. 45–62.

837 *Peasants loading a Hay Cart*   *Plate 197*

Signed, bottom left: J: lingelbach/1664.

Oil on canvas, 70 × 88.7 (27$\frac{5}{16}$ × 34$\frac{15}{16}$).

Lingelbach is here imitating Philips Wouwermans. A similar painting (dated 1665) was in the art trade in London[1] and another is in Schwerin.[2]

PROVENANCE: Probably at one time in the possession of John Smith, London.[3] Marquess of Bute sale, London, 7–8 June 1822 (second day, lot 53), bought by (Sir) Robert Peel (Bart.), 106 gns; purchased with the Peel collection, 1871.

REFERENCES:
General: Burger-Wegener, op. cit., No. 155.
In text:
1. Burger-Wegener, op. cit., No. 156. Duits, London.

2. Burger-Wegener, op. cit., No. 157; Schwerin, Staatliches Museum, *Holländische und Flämische Malerei des 17. Jahrhunderts,* 1982, no. 204 (inv. no. 145).
3. His printed trade label is on the back.

See also PHILIPS KONINCK No. 836;
JAN WIJNANTS No. 883

LODEWIJCK VAN LUDICK, 1629 – before 1697

He was baptised in Amsterdam on 11 November 1629. He married in 1657. In 1672 he was one of a number of artists (Vermeer was another) who were asked to adjudicate in a dispute over the authenticity of a group of paintings sold by Hendrick van Uylenburch to the Elector of Brandenburg. Van Ludick's father, who had the same name, was a merchant and art dealer who was acquainted with a number of artists, of whom Rembrandt was one.[1]

Van Ludick was a landscape painter in the manner of Jan Both.

REFERENCE: 1. Houbraken, vol. 1, p. 344, mentions a *David and Bathsheba* painted for van Ludick by Salomon Koninck.

1007 *A River between Rocky Cliffs, with a*   *Plate 198*
Waterfall on the left

Falsely signed in the bottom right corner: P(·) W (a later addition, and much worn).[1]

Oil on canvas, 53.5 × 66.4 (21$\frac{1}{16}$ × 26$\frac{1}{8}$).

MacLaren attributed this painting to Abraham Begeijn on the grounds of its similarity to two pictures in the Statens Museum for Kunst, Copenhagen. It had formerly been attributed to Johannes Wils. Albert Blankert, in an annotation on the mount of the photograph in the RKD, attributed No. 1007 to van Ludick and his signed paintings are far closer in style. No. 1007 is strikingly similar in composition and treatment, for example, to a signed painting in the National Museum, Warsaw (Fig. 50).[2] There are also two signed paintings by van Ludick in the Alte Pinakothek, Munich.

PROVENANCE: Probably at one time in the possession of Nieuwenhuys;[3] most probably to be identified with lot 75 of the [Wynn Ellis] sale, London, 6 June 1864, which was bought in (155 gns).[4] Wynn Ellis Bequest, 1876.

REFERENCES:
1. The false signature is an imitation of the usual one of Philips Wouwermans.
2. Canvas, 42 × 56.8. Inv. no. 35790 National Museum in Warsaw. *Catalogue of Paintings, Foreign Schools*, Warsaw, 1969, no. 700.
3. On the back of the panel is the impression of an armorial seal, which, although mostly obliterated, can be identified as from the same seal as those on the backs of several pictures in the National Gallery which were certainly in the possession of Nieuwenhuys (see Cuyp No. 823, note 4).
4. 'J. Asselyn and P. Wouvermans. An Italian River-scene, with a castle on a height; and a mounted cavalier and lady in the foreground.'

GERRIT LUNDENS, 1622 – after September 1683

He was baptised in Amsterdam, 27 September 1622, and is recorded there frequently 1643–83. He is last mentioned on 27 September 1683. Nothing is known of his training. He was presumably active in Amsterdam throughout his working life.

He painted genre scenes such as *The Country Wedding* of 1649 (present whereabouts unknown: see No. 289 below, note 14) and miniature portraits (such as the pendant portraits of a young man and a woman dated 1650 in the Rijksmuseum).[1] He was commissioned to paint small-scale copies of militia company portraits (see No. 289 below).

REFERENCES:
General: Bredius, *Künstler-Inventare*, vol. 3, pp. 966–73.
In text: 1. Rijksmuseum 1976 cat. nos. A4337, A4338.

289 The Company of Captain Banning Cocq and Lieutenant Willem van Ruytenburch ('The Nightwatch')

Plate 199

In the foreground are the company's captain, Frans Banning Cocq (in black), and his lieutenant, Willem van Ruytenburch (in pale yellow). In the background the company's colours (blue and orange with the arms of Amsterdam in the centre) are carried by the ensign, Jan Visscher Cornelisen.

On the back of the panel is a piece of paper inscribed in an eighteenth- or early nineteenth-century hand[1] with the supposed names of sixteen of the men in the picture: 'Naamen / van de / Hooftofficiers en Gemeenen. / Frans Banning Cock Heer van Purmerland & / Ilpendam. Capitein. / Willem van Ruijtenburg van Vlaardingen / Heere van Vlaardingen Leijtenant / Jan Visscher, Vaandrig / Rombout Kemp en / Reijnier Engel, Sergianten / Barent Harmense / Jan Adriaan Kijser / Hendrick Willemse / Jan Ockerze / Jan Melessen Bronkhorst / Harmen Jacob Verraken / Jacob Dirkse de Boog / Jan van der Hard / Johan Schellinger / Jan Bringman / Jan van Kampoort, Tamboer.'

Oil on oak. The panel measures 66.8–67 × 85.4–85.8 ($26\frac{5}{16}$–$26\frac{3}{8}$ × $33\frac{5}{8}$–$33\frac{3}{4}$); the top and left edges are irregular. The picture is painted up to the edges at top and bottom; along the left edge a strip 2–5 mm. wide has been left unpainted, and 5–7 mm. along the right edge.

Cleaned in 1958.

This is a greatly reduced copy of Rembrandt's so-called *Nightwatch* in the Rijksmuseum, Amsterdam (Fig. 51).[2]

Rembrandt was commissioned to paint a group portrait of the militia company of musketeers under the company of Captain Frans Banning Cocq; the picture was finished in 1642. He received 1,600 guilders for it; his sitters paid an average of a hundred guilders each, the sum varying with the degree of prominence in the portrait. It was hung in the Great Room of the Amsterdam musketeers' place of assembly (the Kloveniersdoelen) together with militia groups by other painters and remained there until 1715, when it was removed to the town hall. According to the contemporary description in the genealogical and family album kept by Banning Cocq, the picture shows him directing Lieutenant van Ruytenburch to order the company to march out.[3]

The National Gallery copy follows the design of the *Nightwatch* closely in most particulars but shows an extension of the composition on all sides. The two men and a child behind a parapet on the extreme left in No. 289 no longer appear in the *Nightwatch* which has been reduced (see below); the left edge of the canvas now runs through the back of the sergeant seated on the parapet and the forearm of the running boy below him. The National Gallery copy also shows more of the drummer on the right; in the *Nightwatch* the edge of the picture is just behind his ear and cuts through the back of the helmet of the man beyond him. In the copy there is a space between Banning Cocq's right foot and the bottom of the picture; the upper edge is some way above the top of the arch instead of cutting into it as in the *Nightwatch*. An elaborately framed cartouche inscribed with militiamen's names which hangs on the right side of the arch in the *Nightwatch* is not seen in the copy.

The same variations (except for the top edge) occur in a summary watercolour copy in Banning Cocq's album;[4] this drawing attributed to Jacob Colijns[5] appears to have been made before the latter's death in 1655.[6] A watercolour drawing of 1779 by Jacob Cats in the Rijksmuseum[7] shows once more the same differences and agrees in almost every detail with the National Gallery copy. An engraving of 1797 by L. A. Claessens[8] is also of this design but omits the head of the child seen behind the parapet; on the other hand it includes the cartouche on the right of the arch (without its inscription) and follows the *Nightwatch* in a few minor details.

It is now generally accepted that the present picture and the drawing in the Banning Cocq album show the composition in the form in which Rembrandt left it and confirm

Jan van Dijk's statement that it was cut down to fit between two doors.[9] This mutilation presumably took place in 1715, in which year the original was transferred from the Kloveniersdoelen to the Small War Council Chamber at the town hall in Amsterdam[10] (now the Royal Palace), and certainly before 1758 when it is mentioned by van Dijk as being there in its present state. A drawing said to be of 1762 and by Hendrik Pothoven[11] shows the *Nightwatch* in the reduced form.

It follows that Jacob Cats's drawing of 1779 must have been taken from a copy of the original before it was mutilated; so also Claessens's print of 1797, despite its engraved title which states that it is after the picture in the town hall.[12] The cartouche with the sitters' names in the *Nightwatch*, lacking in the National Gallery copy and the Banning Cocq drawing, is not by Rembrandt but was added later.

The National Gallery copy has long been attributed to Gerrit Lundens. This ascription was based primarily on the assumption that the picture is to be identified with one in the van der Lip sale of 1712 (see PROVENANCE) described in the sale catalogue as 'Het Doele Stuk, daar in komt Capiteyn Benning Kok, met zijn Burgerij, door Gerard Lundens, uytvoerig geschildert, 't best van hem bekent';[13] the size and support are not given. Glück, who accepted the attribution to Lundens, thought No. 289 might be datable before 1649, the date on a *Country Wedding* by him which seems to be a reminiscence of the *Nightwatch* composition.[14]

MacLaren unnecessarily doubted the traditional attribution to Lundens. It is confirmed, as Haverkamp-Begemann has shown, by comparison with three signed and dated (1650) miniature portraits in the Rijksmuseum. In addition, his relationship with the Amsterdam militia is confirmed by his portrait of Reier Pietersz. Elias with musket and slowmatch, formerly in the Boymans Museum (destroyed by fire in 1864: 64 × 47 cm., signed but not dated, described in *Beschrijving Boymans*, 1862, No. 192). The commission presumably came from Banning Cocq himself. This is supported by the provenance (see below), by the fact that the drawing in his album is undoubtedly a copy after the Lundens copy (note in particular the similarity of the disposition of lances in the right background: Lundens had simplified the arrangement for the purposes of a small-scale copy and the watercolourist followed); and by the fact that Banning Cocq also owned a copy of a second group portrait that included him. The latter, the *Governors of the Handboogsdoelen*, now in the Louvre, is probably also by Lundens.[15]

PROVENANCE: A painting of a militia company was in the inventory made in Amsterdam in 1691 of the estate of Catharina Hooft, widow of Cornelis de Graeff[16] (Frans Banning Cocq was related to the Hooft and de Graeff families[17]); this picture is presumably the militia company by Gerrit Lundens listed in the inventory of Pieter de Graeff, Amsterdam, 1709[18] (the size is not given in either case). No. 289 was almost certainly in the Pieter van der Lip sale, Amsterdam, 14 June 1712 (lot 27), 263 guilders (see above). A picture supposed to be Rembrandt's *modello* for the *Nightwatch*, on panel and exactly the same size as No. 289, belonged to Heer Boendermaker in 1758[19] and was in Vrouw Theodore Beondermaker's sale, Amsterdam, 30 March 1768 (lot 1),[20] bought by Foucquet (2,580 guilders). It seems likely that No. 289 is the reduction of the *Nightwatch* on panel which, ascribed to Rembrandt, was in the Randon de Boisset sale, Paris, 27 February sqq. 1777 (lot 51),[21] bought by Lafitte (7,030 francs), and afterwards in the Counts d'Orsay and Hohenzollern sale, Paris, 20 March 1810 (lot 100),[22] when it was said to have been withdrawn.[23] It seems likely that No. 289 is the copy (on panel, about 25 × 32 in.) which according to Smith[24] was in the possession of George Gillow (who is said to have imported it into England[25]) and by 1836 belonged to [John?] William Brett. No. 289 was in the collection of the Revd Thomas Halford, London, and was bequeathed by him, 1857. On loan to the Rijksmuseum, Amsterdam, since 1958.

REFERENCES:

1. This inscription was written after 1758 since it repeats, with only slight variations, the faulty and incomplete list of sitters given in Jan van Dijk's *Kunst- en Historie-Kundige Beschryving van alle de Schilderyen op het Stadhuis van Amsterdam* etc., published in that year (p. 59 of the 1790 edition). The names in van Dijk and the MS list differ considerably from those on the cartouche in Rembrandt's painting in the Rijksmuseum (see the main text). This now bears eighteen names, as follows: 'Frans Banning Cocq / heer van purmerlant en Ilpendam / Capiteijn / Willem van Ruijtenburch van Vlaerding / heer van Vlaerdingen Le(ij?)tenant / Jan Visscher Cornelisen Vaendrich / Rombout Kemp Sergeant / Reijnier Engelen Sergeant / Barent Harmansen / Jan adriaensen Keyser / Elbert Willemsen / Jan Clasen Leijdeckers / Ian Ockersen / Jan Pietersen bronchorst / Harman Iacobsen wormskerck / Jacob Dircksen de Roy / Jan vander heede / Walich Schellingwou / Jan brugman / Claes van Cruysbergen / Paulus Schoonhoven.' For a comprehensive modern discussion of Rembrandt's painting and the identification of the sitters, see E. Haverkamp-Begemann, *Rembrandt: The Nightwatch*, Princeton, 1982.

2. Canvas, 363 × 438 cm.; signed and dated 1642. Rijksmuseum, 1976, cat. no. C5. HdG No. 926; Bauch No. 537; Bredius, *Rembrandt*, No. 410. The best modern account of the painting (with all previous literature) is Haverkamp-Begemann, op. cit. For the most recent restoration of the painting, see *Bulletin van het Rijksmuseum*, vol. 24, Nos. 1 and 2, 1976, pp. 1–119.

3. The page opposite the drawing of the *Nightwatch* in Banning Cocq's album is inscribed: 'Schets van de Schilderije op de groote Sael van/de Cleveniers Doelen, daerinne de Jonge/Heer van Purmerlandt, als Capiteijn, geeft/last aen sijnen Lieutenant de Heer van/Vlaerdingen, om sijn Compaignie Burgers/te doen marcheren.' There is little doubt that both copy and description were made before Banning Cocq's death in January 1655. The album, which belongs to the de Graeff family (cf. PROVENANCE), is on loan to the Rijksmuseum. See also note 4.

4. The drawing measures 14.5 × 19 cm.

5. For the attribution to Colijns, see Haverkamp-Begemann, op. cit., pp. 24–25, esp. note 8.

6. Frans Banning Cocq died 1 January 1655.

7. Rijksprentenkabinet, 33.3 × 42.5 cm. Signed on the reverse: Jacob Cats fec^t A°/1779, naar het schilderij van Rembrand van Rheyn.

8. Subject size, 46.5 × 61.5 cm. Inscribed below:

'Rembrand van Ryn pinx L. A. Claessens Sculp 1797/Amsterdamsche Gewapende Burgery 1642./ Gegraveerd naer de Origineele Schildery/Berustende op het Stadhuis van Amsterdam', followed by an incomplete list of the sitters derived from that in van Dijk (see note 1). The inscription ends: 'a Amsterdam chez L.A. Claessens et C. S. Roos.'

9. Jan van Dijk, op. cit., p. 61 (3rd ed., 1790, p. 61): '. . . 't is te beklagen dat dit stuk zoo veel is afgenomen om tussen de twee deuren te kunnen plaatsen, want op de rechter hand hebben noch twee Beelden, en op de linker heeft den Tamboer geheel gestaan, 't welk te zien is aan het egte Model thans in handen van den Heer *Boendermaker*.'

10. The resolution concerning the removal and cleaning of the picture is dated 23 May 1715.

11. Anon. sale, Amsterdam (at R. W. P. de Vries), 18–20 February 1933 (lot 1034); reproduced in the sale catalogue, pl. 17. 43 × 54 cm.

12. See note 8. Claessens's print may have been based in the first place on Cats's drawing of 1779 and later corrected to agree with the *Nightwatch* in some particulars.

13. See Hoet, vol. 1, p. 147.

14. G. Glück, *Niederländische Gemälde aus der Sammlung . . . Alexander Tritsch in Wien*, 1907, p. 18. Haverkamp-Begemann, op. cit., accepts the attribution to Lundens and follows Glück in placing the painting before *The Country Wedding* of 1649 on the grounds that it influenced the unusual composition of that picture.

15. Canvas laid down on panel, 50 × 67 cm. 1979 cat. Inv. No. 1332 (Van der Helst). For the attribution to Lundens see Haverkamp-Begemann, op. cit., pp. 25–6, note 12.

16. 'Een schilderye, verbeeldende een Corporaelschap borgerye'; valued at 63 guilders (see A. Bredius in OH, vol. 30, 1912, p. 197).

17. D. C. Meijer in OH, vol. 4, 1886, p. 199.

18. 'Een schilderij van een Compagnie burgers van Gerard Lundens (Bredius, op. cit., p. 199). The arguments for identifying this with No. 289 are given in Bredius, op. cit., pp. 197–200.

19. See J. van Dijk, loc. cit. (quoted in note 9).

20. Panel, 26½ × 33½ *duim*. As by Rembrandt; more than 25 figures. 'Dit . . . Schildery is dezelfde Ordinantie, gelyk als Rembrandt geschildert heeft . . . hangende in de Kleyne Krygsraad Kamer, op het Stadhuis . . . Jan van Dyk, Beschrijving van alle de Schilderyen op het Stadhuis van Amsterdam . . . Pag. 60 [sic] maakt . . . ook gewag van dit voorgemelde Schildery.'

21. As by Rembrandt. 'Les Arquebusiers. Ce tableau est le petit du grand que l'on voit à Amsterdam; il est composé de vingt-six figures . . .'; wood, 2 *pieds 6 lignes* × 2 *pieds 7 pouces*.
22. As by Rembrandt; on wood. The sale catalogue identifies it with lot 51 of the Randon de Boisset sale.
23. D. C. Meijer, op. cit., p. 205.
24. Smith, Rembrandt No. 140.
25. According to a note made by Sir Charles Eastlake in the National Gallery manuscript catalogue in 1857. (Burton Fredericksen has brought to the attention of the present writer [letter of 1990] the undated [but probably *c.* 1850] catalogue of an exhibition held in the Assembly Rooms, Bath, in which No. 289 was cat. no. 72 [as by Rembrandt]. The catalogue entry confirms that the painting was in the Randon de Boisset collection; bought by Lafitte; owned by 'M. Kalkbrenner, the celebrated composer, who sold it to Mr Gillow for £7,000 sterling, of whose widow it was purchased'. The name of the current owner is not mentioned. The catalogue is in the Bath Reference Library.)

NICOLAES MAES, 1634–1693

Born in Dordrecht; the date often given, 1632, is derived from Houbraken[1] but a document in the Dordrecht archives makes it certain that he was in fact born in January 1634.[2] Houbraken says Maes learned drawing from a mediocre master ('een gemeen Meester') and painting from Rembrandt. Maes was probably with Rembrandt around 1650; he was back in Dordrecht by late in 1653[3] and stayed until 1673, when he settled in Amsterdam.[4] According to Houbraken he made a journey to Antwerp to see the pictures of Rubens, van Dyck and others, and visited artists, among them Jordaens (who died 1678). This journey probably took place in the mid-1660s. He was buried in Amsterdam, 24 December 1693.[5]

Houbraken's remark that Maes soon abandoned Rembrandt's way of painting is confirmed by his surviving pictures. Several religious subjects in a strongly Rembrandtesque style have been attributed to him (see No. 757 below); and Maes' earliest dated painting is *The Dismissal of Hagar* of 1653 (New York, Metropolitan Museum).[6] However, by 1654 he was painting small domestic interiors in an individual style like Nos. 153, 159 and 207 below. Maes continued to paint genre scenes in this style until 1659; he had begun to paint portraits by 1656[7] and from 1660 onwards he confined himself to portraiture. According to Houbraken his portraits were in great demand; there are several hundred in existence, many of the later ones on a small scale.

REFERENCES:
General: HdG, vol. 6, 1916; Bredius in OH, vol. 41, 1923–4, pp. 207–14; W. R. Valentiner, *Nicolaes Maes*, 1924; Sumowski, *Gemälde*, vol. 3.
In text:
1. Houbraken, vol. 2, pp. 273 ff.
2. W. Martin, *De Hollandsche schilderkunst in de zeventiende eeuw*, 1942 ed., vol. 2, p. 512, note 325.
3. He was betrothed in Dordrecht 28 December 1653 and married there 13 January 1654 (G. H. Veth in OH, vol. 8, 1890, p. 127).
4. Veth, op. cit., p. 134; see also Bredius, op. cit., pp. 211–13.
5. Veth, op cit., p. 135 (and note 2); see also Houbraken, pp. 274–5. Bredius (op. cit., p. 213) gives 24 *November* as the date of burial.
6. Canvas, 87.9 × 69.9. Inv. no. 1971–73. Sumowski, op. cit., No. 1315.
7. Sumowski, op. cit., Nos. 1388 and 1389.

153 *A Little Girl rocking a Cradle*

Plate 200

Signed, bottom right: N. MAE (MAE in monogram); the present edge of the panel runs through the signature.

Oil on oak, 40.4 × 32.6 ($15\frac{15}{16}$ × $12\frac{7}{8}$). The truncated signature shows that at least 5 mm. has been cut off the right side.[1]

Worn and retouched.

One of a group of genre pictures painted in Dordrecht *c.*1654–9 (cf. No. 159 below). It may have formerly borne the date, 1655, on the section which has been cut off at the right edge.[2]

PROVENANCE: Possibly in the second collection of François Tronchin, Geneva, by 1780.[3] Lent by Lord Farnborough to the BI, 1828. Lord Farnborough Bequest, 1838.

EXHIBITION: BI 1828, No. 88.

REFERENCES:
General: Smith No. 23 and Supplement No. 19; HdG No. 87; Sumowski, op. cit., No. 1336.
In text:
1. The same edge of the panel also runs through the first letter of an old painted inscription on the back of the panel: (N?) maes/38. On the missing section was presumably the date, 1655, recorded in the Tronchin catalogue of 1780 (see below, note 3) if this painting can be identified with that item.
2. According to the Tronchin catalogue of 1780 (see below, note 3).
3. The size varies slightly but the description accords clearly with a Maes owned by Tronchin: François Tronchin, *Catalogue des tableaux de mon Cabinet*, Geneva, 1780, p. 44: 'Nicolaes Maes. Un enfant dormant dans un berceau d'osier, bercé par

une petite fille assise à côté du berceau. Près d'eux est une grande table couverte d'un tapis de Turquie, sur laquelle est un livre ouvert, et un pot de grès bleu et blanc. B.h. 19°. 5°°. l. 17°. 3°°. Les portraits de ce maître, élève de Rembrandt, ne sont pas rares; mais il a fait très-peu de tableaux. Celui-ci est de la couleur la plus vigoureuse et du plus grand effet. Les détails sont la nature même. Il est peint en 1655.'
This painting is recorded in the Tronchin catalogue of 1798 on p. 92 (*Catalogue raisonné du Cabinet de tableaux de feu Monseiur François Tronchin des Délices, ancien Conseiller d'Etat de la République de Genève. Fait par lui-même*, Geneva, 1798). Tronchin sale, Paris, 23 March 1801, lot 108: bought by Bonnemaison, 255 francs; Ralph Bernal sale, London, 1824: £73.10s.

159 *A Woman scraping Parsnips, with a Child standing by her*

Plate 201

Signed, bottom right: N. MAES 1655 (MAE in monogram).

Oil on oak, 35.6 × 29.8 (14 × $11\frac{3}{4}$).

There is some wearing in the shadows.

DRAWINGS: There are two studies of the woman scraping a parsnip (Figs. 52 and 53)[1] which appear to be preparatory to this painting.

COPY: A copy[2] was in the Dr Casimir Wurster (of Strasbourg) sale, Cologne, 15 June 1896 (lot 175).[3]

PROVENANCE: [Juriaans] sale, Amsterdam, 28 August 1817 (lot 33), bought by de Vries (430 guilders). Exhibited at the BI, 1821, lent by Sir Charles Long (later Baron Farnborough). Lord Farnborough Bequest, 1838.

EXHIBITIONS: BI 1821, No. 62; Arts Council 1945, No. 17; Birmingham 1950, No. 38; London 1976, No. 69; London 1978–9, No. 19.

REFERENCES:
General: Smith No. 24; HdG No. 29; Sumowski, *Gemälde*, No. 1333.

In text:

1. Both drawings were from a scrapbook which until 1922 was in the collection of the Earl of Dalhousie (Lugt 717a). It apparently contained a substantial number of early drawings by Maes. They are Nos. 1771 and 1772 in Sumowski, *Drawings*. No. 1772 shows a woman who is very close in pose to the woman scraping parsnips in No. 159. It is now in the Institut Néerlandais (Brush and brown ink; verso: red chalk, 12.4 × 8.4 cm.) On the reverse is a sketch of a listening woman on a staircase closely related to *The Eavesdropper* of 1656 in the Wallace Collection. The second ex-Dalhousie collection drawing (Pen and ink with brown wash, 9.8 × 8.4 cm.: Sumowski, op. cit., No. 1771) also shows a woman peeling a vegetable in her lap, although the pose is less close to No. 159. The drawing is today in the collection of Ian Woodner, New York.

2. According to HdG, loc. cit.

3. On canvas, 34 × 28 cm.

207 *Interior with a Sleeping Maid and her Mistress ('The Idle Servant')*

Plate 202

Signed, bottom right: N. MAES. i655. (MAE in monogram).

Oil on oak, 70 × 53.3 ($27\frac{9}{16}$ × 21).

There is wearing in the darks.

In a number of his genre paintings of the second half of the 1650s Maes employed the device of a figure looking out of the composition directly at the spectator. Here the housewife draws attention to the maid who has fallen asleep over her work, allowing the cat to steal a fowl. The maid's pose – her head to one side, resting on her hand – is traditional for the deadly sin of Acedia (idleness).[1] Vermeer uses the same pose for his *Sleeping Maid* (New York, Metropolitan Museum).[2] However, despite this reference to Acedia, it is difficult to believe that the smiling housewife is puritanically condemning a mortal sin. It seems rather to be an amused comment on the fallibility of servants: it calls to mind a popular saying recorded by Johan de Brune – 'Een Keuckenmeyt moet d'eene ooghe, naer de panne, en d'ander, naer de Katte hebben' (A kitchenmaid must keep one eye on the pan and the other on the cat).[3]

MacLaren claimed that this was the earliest dated genre painting of this type with a view into a farther room. He connected it with contemporary Delft paintings with perspective effects, concluding, however, that the exact nature of the relationship is obscure. The present writer would stress that although there are superficial similarities between the work of Maes and that of de Hooch, Carel Fabritius and Vermeer, there is no documentary evidence of Maes' presence in Delft and it is unlikely that his influence played a major role in the evolution of the genre scenes of the Delft School.

ENGRAVING: Mezzotint by Thomas G. Lupton before 1833.[4]

COPY: Sir J. Harrowing sale, Christie's, 27 July 1962, lot 23; Anon. sale, Christie's, 31 January 1964, lot 162.[5]

PROVENANCE: Purchased in Leiden by Dr Sanderus; acquired from him in Amsterdam in 1823 by C. J. Nieuwenhuys and taken to Paris where he sold it for 3,000 francs.[6] Brought to England by John Smith and in the collection of Richard Simmons by 1833.[7] Richard Simmons Bequest, 1847.

EXHIBITIONS: Amsterdam 1976, No. 33. London 1978–9, No. 23.

REFERENCES:

General: Smith No. 16; HdG No. 100; Sumowski, *Gemälde*, No. 1352.

In text:

1. The iconography of the painting is discussed at length in the catalogue of the exhibition, *Tot Lering en Vermaak*, Amsterdam, Rijksmuseum, 1976, No. 33. There Philips Galle's print of *c*.1600 of *Acedia* is illustrated (pl. 33a) showing the same pose as in No. 207.

2. Inv. no. 14.40.611.

3. Johan de Brune, *Banket-werk van goede gedagten*, vol. 2, Middelburg, 1660, p. 385.

4. Smith, loc. cit.

5. Canvas, 23 × 19½ in. (1962) sold to Young for 24 gns; (1964) sold to Pro Arte for 30 gns.

6. Nieuwenhuys, p. 288, footnote.

7. Smith, loc. cit.

757 *Christ blessing the Children* Plate 203

A slate, on which there are unintelligible scribbles, hangs at the side of the child in the centre.

Oil on canvas, 206 × 154 (81 × 60⅝); this does not include a strip *c*.14 cm. wide which has been added later along the top (this is hidden under the frame). The picture has also been added to at the right edge to a depth of about 3 cm. (This is also hidden under the frame.) There is an original seam across the painting about half-way down.

Cleaned in 1968. There is a *pentimento* in Christ's left sleeve.

The subject (from Matthew 19, Mark 10, etc.: 'Suffer the little children to come unto me') was represented by Rembrandt in *The Hundred Guilder Print* of *c*.1642–5[1] and by a considerable number of his pupils in addition to Maes. It was painted by Govert Flinck, Jurriaen Ovens and Jacob de Wet and drawn by Samuel van Hoogstraten.[2] It was also treated by many Dutch artists outside the Rembrandt circle.[3]

The attribution of this painting has been the subject of much debate. In the eighteenth and nineteenth centuries it was thought to be a Rembrandt: from 1880 onwards it was catalogued as a School painting and it has been attributed to no fewer than eight Rembrandt pupils – Leendert Cornelisz. van Beyeren,[4] Gerbrand van den Eeckhout,[5] Barent Fabritius,[6] Carel Fabritius,[7] Aert de Gelder,[8] Nicolaes Maes,[9] Jurriaen Ovens[10] and Jan Victors.[11] However, the attribution to Maes which was cogently argued by MacLaren (following Hind) has generally been accepted in the recent literature.[12]

Maes was in Rembrandt's studio in Amsterdam in the late 1640s and early 1650s. He had returned to his native Dordrecht by late in 1653: his earliest dated painting is *The Dismissal of Hagar* (New York, Metropolitan Museum of Art) of 1653.[13] This is on a relatively small scale and, given the difference in subject–matter, is consistent in size, style and palette with the genre paintings of the second half of the 1650s, the earliest of which is dated 1654. The attribution of No. 757 to Maes must imply a date of 1652/3, that is, while he was still in Rembrandt's studio or had just left it. A number of other large-scale history paintings have been attributed to this period of Maes' activity: the only acceptable one is *The Sacrifice of Isaac* (Milwaukee, Bader collection).[14]

The attribution of No. 757 to the young Maes rests on three arguments: the existence of a number of drawings, apparently preparatory to the painting, which have been attributed convincingly to Maes; the characteristically restrained palette of creams, browns and blacks; and the similarity to *The Dismissal of Hagar* of 1653 and *The Sacrifice of Isaac* which has been attributed to Maes in *c.*1655–8.

It was Hind[15] who first published a drawing in the British Museum as a compositional sketch for the painting: Sumowski[16] has discussed this drawing, its verso and a compositional drawing in pen and wash in the Rijksmuseum. In the view of the present writer, both drawings are undoubtedly the work of Maes. In the Amsterdam drawing (Fig. 54), Christ is standing and both his pose and the group of figures are loosely based on *The Hundred Guilder Print*. In the London drawing (Fig. 55), which is presumably later, he is seated and the crowded group of figures is closer in detail to the painting. The verso contains studies of a mother with her children. In addition, there are a number of looser pen and wash drawings of *Christ blessing the Children* from the Rembrandt workshop which have also been associated with No. 757: the present writer agrees with Sumowski[17] that these are by another hand and that an attribution to Samuel van Hoogstraten is likely. Sumowski[18] believes that Maes worked from the drawings by van Hoogstraten when developing the composition of No. 757. This is highly speculative.

As for the other two arguments, the painting's dark palette of browns and blacks with the heads strikingly highlighted is entirely consistent with a work by a member of Rembrandt's studio of the early 1650s and with Maes' work of that date (in as far as it can be reconstructed). Although No. 757 is significantly larger than *The Sacrifice of Isaac* and *The Dismissal of Hagar* there are similarities in the stocky figure types and in the tight handling of details of dress.

To summarise: No. 757 is probably the work of Nicolaes Maes painted in *c.*1652/3, while he was still in Rembrandt's studio or just after he left it. It pre-dates his return to Dordrecht late in 1653. In its ambitious scale (which he was never to attempt again), its subject–matter, palette and technique, it reflects Maes' profound absorption of Rembrandt's history painting style.

The young man in the extreme left of the painting seems to be a portrait. The character of the head and the way in which it is awkwardly squeezed into the picture space supports the idea that it is a self portrait. Sumowski[19] has published a drawing and a painting as self portraits of the young Maes ('the [drawn] portrait dates from the end of the 1640s') and there are some similarities to the head of the young man in No. 757.

ENGRAVING AND ETCHING.: Engraved by Carl Ernst Christoph Hess, 1812;[20] etched by Léopold Flameng, 1866.[21]

DRAWINGS: Compositional drawings in the British Museum and the Rijksmuseum, Amsterdam, are discussed above.

COPY: An old copy is in the depot of the Residenz in Würzburg; in this the composition has been extended slightly at the sides and a tree-stump has been added in the right foreground.[22]

PROVENANCE: It has been suggested by Bredius that this is the life-size *Christ blessing the Children*, whose author is not named, which was with an *Ecce Homo* in an inventory of pictures belonging to Maria van Rommerswael, widow of Godschalck van der Hulst, in Dordrecht, 1674.[23] No. 757 was apparently in the collection of Graf von Schönborn in Vienna by 1746;[24] it was bought from the Schönborn-Buchheim collection in Vienna by Barthold Suermondt of Aachen, March 1866,[25] and sold by him to the National Gallery in July 1866.

REFERENCES:

General: Smith, Rembrandt No. 81 (described from Hess's engraving); Sumowski, *Gemälde*, No. 1312 (with full bibliography).

In text:

1. Hollstein B 74.
2. (a) Flinck: present whereabouts unknown: in 1859 in the collection of Graf A. Stolberg, Söder; see J. W. von Moltke, *Govaert Flinck 1615–1660*, 1965, p. 233, No. 45. (b) Ovens: present whereabouts unknown: a painting by Ovens of this subject was listed in the catalogue of the Earl of Arundel's sale, Amsterdam, 26 September 1684, lot 19 (Hoet, vol. 1, p. 2). See H. Schmidt, *Jürgen Ovens, Sein Leben und seine Werke*, 1922, p. 147, No. 42. (c) De Wet: Signed. Rijksmuseum, Amsterdam, 1976 cat., A1530. (d) Drawings by Samuel van Hoogstraten: see Sumowski, *Drawings*, vol. 5, Nos. 1171–4.
3. A. Pigler, *Barockthemen*, vol. 1, Budapest, 1974, pp. 301–3.
4. The attribution to van Beyeren was made by Bredius solely on the grounds that he was a Rembrandt pupil in 1637 and that a large painting of the subject of the *Ecce Homo* was in the 1649 inventory of his estate. See Bredius, *Künstler-Inventare*, vol. 1, pp. 228, 250; and BM, vol. 43, 1923, p. 104; in fact, the only known signed painting by van Beyeren, a bust portrait of a young man, is quite different in style: see Sumowski, *Gemälde*, vol. 1, pp. 280–1.
5. The attribution to Gerbrand van den Eeckhout was made in Bode and HdG, vol. 7, p. 233, note i (cf. G. Redford, *Art Sales*, 1888, vol. 1, p. 22); the picture is quite unlike van den Eeckhout's small-scale, multi-figured religious scenes (for which see Sumowski, *Gemälde*, vol. 2, pp. 719ff).
6. The attribution to Barent Fabritius seems to have originated with Frimmel (T. von Frimmel, *Kleine Galeriestudien*, N.F., vol. 3, 1896, p. 9) but was argued in detail by Münz (L. Münz in *Die graphischen Künste*, N.F., vol. 2, 1937, pp. 151–6). Münz rejected the attribution to Maes which is based in the first place on the connection with the British Museum drawing. He believed that a drawing in Weimar, which he attributed to Barent Fabritius, is closer to the composition of No. 757 and also that the young man on the extreme left is the same person as in the presumed self portrait of Barent Fabritius, dated 1650, in Frankfurt (for a discussion of this painting see under Carel Fabritius No. 4042 of this catalogue). Münz's arguments were convincingly rejected by Valentiner (in *Art Quarterly*, vol. 2, 1939, p. 325, note 8) and – in a perceptive extended discus-

sion of the painting – by Pont (D. Pont, *Barent Fabritius 1624–73*, Utrecht, 1958, pp. 155–6).

7. The attribution to Carel Fabritius was made by Holmes (C. J. Holmes in the BM, vol. 6, 1904–5, p. 330): it is quite unlike his only large-scale history painting, *The Raising of Lazarus* in Warsaw (see C. Brown, *Carel Fabritius*, Oxford, 1981, cat. no. 1).
8. The attribution to Aert de Gelder was made by D. van Fossen ('Aert de Gelder: An Attribution for the *Christ blessing the Children* in London', *Art Quarterly*, vol. 33, 1970, pp. 134–46); van Fossen's argument involved attributing the preparatory drawings in London and Amsterdam to de Gelder, which is entirely unacceptable. His comparison of details of No. 757 with de Gelder's *Jacob's Dream* (Winterthur, Reinhart Collection) and *The Rest on the Flight* (Boston, Museum of Fine Arts) were unconvincing.
9. The attribution to Maes was first made tentatively by Hind (vol. 1, p. 50, no. 144). It was strongly supported by Valentiner (BM, vol. 43, 1923, p. 22 and in idem, *Nicolaes Maes*, 1924, p. 38) and eventually accepted by Bredius (contested by Bredius in BM, vol. 43, 1923, p. 104 and OH, vol. 41, 1923–4, p. 207; accepted by him in BM, vol. 46, 1925, p. 143). HdG, who noted the painting's close stylistic relationship to Maes (HdG, vol. 6, p. 459, note 31) and to Barent Fabritius (Thieme/Becker, vol. 11, p. 171), was unable to accept Maes as the artist (*Repertorium für Kunstwissenschaft*, vol. 50, 1929, pp. 144–5). The attribution was, however, argued strongly by MacLaren and subsequently supported by, among others, Rosenberg and Slive (J. Rosenberg, S. Slive and E. H. ter Kuile, *Dutch Art and Architecture 1600 to 1800*, Harmondsworth, 1966, p. 96); Sumowski ('"Christus segnet die Kinder": Bemerkungen zu einem Frühwerk von Nicolaes Maes', *Festschrift für Heinz Ladendorf*, Cologne/Vienna, 1970, pp. 41–9 and Sumowski, *Gemälde*, op. cit.); and Robinson (W. Robinson, 'The Sacrifice of Isaac', an unpublished painting by Nicolaes Maes', BM, vol. 126, 1984, p. 540, note 1). Sumowski's article is the most detailed and important modern study of the painting and the related drawings. The attribution to Maes is accepted there (see below).
10. Wurzbach (vol. 2, p. 294) identified the painting with a lost picture of the subject in the Arundel sale of 1684 (see note 2b). It is quite unlike Ovens' religious paintings.
11. The ascription to Jan Victors was made in the 1925 National Gallery catalogue and need not be seriously considered.

12. See note 9 above.

13. Inv. no. 1971.73. J. Walsh, 'The Earliest Dated Painting by Nicolaes Maes', *Metropolitan Museum Journal*, vol. 6, 1972, pp. 105–14. On p. 113 Walsh expressed his doubts that either Maes or Aert de Gelder is the artist of No. 757.

14. For *The Sacrifice of Isaac* see Robinson, op. cit. (note 9). HdG (*Monatshefte für Kunstwissenschaft*, vol. 3, 1910, p. 116) suggested that No. 757 is by the same hand as a *Christ before Pilate* in Budapest (Museum of Fine Arts; 1967 cat. no. 229 – as Maes) and a *Mocking of Christ* in the Hermitage (1948 catalogue, vol. 2, p. 265, No. 6242 as School of Rembrandt; on the mount of the RKD photograph, Karel van der Pluym and Reynier van Gherwen are suggested. The latter seems more likely). Bredius also believed No. 757 to be by the same hand as the Budapest painting and proposed Leendert van Beyeren as the artist of both (for the reference to this attribution see note 4 above). In the view of the present writer neither is in fact by the same hand as No. 757. For a number of other paintings attributed to Maes in the years around 1653 which cannot be his work, see Robinson, op. cit., p. 540, note 1.

15. See note 9 above.

16. Sumowski, 1970, op. cit. (note 9); and Sumowski, *Drawings*, vol. 8, Nos. 1759 (recto of the sheet in the British Museum: no inventory number); 1760 (Amsterdam, Rijksprentenkabinet, inv. no. 1957:156 [This drawing comes from the collection of an eighteenth-century Dordrecht painter, Matthys Balen]); 1762 (verso of the British Museum drawing). In his 1970 article, Sumowski relates a red chalk study of a young girl to No. 757 but in his catalogue of Maes drawings in volume 8 of his *Drawings* this sheet is No. 1768a and is related to a painting of a *Slaughtered Pig*. In this volume he publishes a further drawing (No. 1761), a verso of a landscape drawing in Lille (Musée des Beaux Arts, inv. no. 1030) as a further preparatory study for No. 757. In the view of the present writer there is not sufficient similarity to the composition of No. 757 or indeed to those of either the London or Amsterdam drawings to justify this assertion (although there can be no doubt that the drawing is by Maes): it is not even clear that *Christ blessing the Children* is the true subject of this drawing.

17. Sumowski, 1970, op. cit. (note 9). See also Sumowski, *Drawings*, vol. 5, Nos. 1171–4.

18. Sumowski, 1970, op. cit. (note 9). He repeated this view in *Drawings*, vol. 8, No. 1760: '. . . above all, the influence of Samuel van Hoogstraten is manifest. The composition is based on the *Christ blessing the Children* (No. 1171) in Bremen, whereas details (the mother behind Christ, the column) correspond to the version in the Goethe collection in Weimar (No. 1174).'

19. Sumowski, *Drawings*, vol. 8, No. 1758 (Rotterdam, Museum Boymans-van Beuningen, inv. no. MB 237). Sumowski's identification of this drawing as a self portrait by Maes is problematic as is his identification (following Bauch) of a painting in the Museo de Arte Cataluña in Barcelona (canvas, 116 × 85 cm. Sumowski's Fig. 99) as another self portrait of Maes. The present writer considers the Barcelona portrait to be by Willem Drost.

20. As by Rembrandt and in the collection of Graf Franz von Schönborn in Vienna.

21. In GB-A, 1866, vol. 2, p. 254, and *Zeitschrift für bildende Künste*, vol. 1, 1866, opp. p. 192.

22. Canvas, 225 × 180 cm. A photograph is in the National Gallery archives (kindly provided by Professor K. Gerstenberg).

23. Bredius in BM, vol. 46, 1925, p. 143, and Bredius, *Künstler-Inventare*, vol. 4, p. 1375.

24. According to T. von Frimmel, loc. cit. (note 6).

25. Attached to the back of the stretcher is the following document: 'Aus der Erlaucht gräflich Schönborn- / Buchheim'schen Gemäldegalerie / in Wien dem Herrn B. Suermondt / in Aachen überliessen. / Wien den 2. Marz 1866. / Dr Eduard G(runitzer?) / gräflicher Rath.'

1277 *Portrait of an Elderly Man in a Black Robe* {Plate 204}

Signed on the right, centre: .N: MAES. Ao. 1666.

Oil on canvas, 89.5 × 71.4 ($35\frac{1}{4}$ × $28\frac{1}{8}$).

A tear runs up from the lower edge between the sitters' hands.

Hofstede de Groot[1] mentions another portrait by Maes of the same sitter, signed and dated 1665, in the Johnson collection, Washington.

PROVENANCE: Presented by Sir Theodore Martin, KCB, in 1888.

REFERENCES: General: HdG No. 333. In text: 1. HdG No. 374.

2581 *Portrait of Jan de Reus* *Plate 205*

Oil on canvas, 79 × 62.5 (31⅛ × 24⅝); irregular edges.

Cleaned in 1959.

There is a *pentimento* in the neck of the shirt.

Jan (Johan) de Reus, silk merchant of Rotterdam, was born *c.*1600 and died in 1685. He was a member of the Rotterdam town council often from 1629 onwards and burgomaster eight times between 1652 and 1673. He was a director of the Dutch East India Company from 1658.[1]

The sitter was at one time thought to be the scientist Anthonie van Leeuwenhoek (1632–1723);[2] authentic portraits of van Leeuwenhoek show that this is impossible.[3] The correct identification is established[4] by a copy of the National Gallery picture painted by Pieter van der Werff (1655–1722).[5] This copy (Fig. 56) is one of a series of portraits of directors of the Dutch East India Company made for the Rotterdam Chamber of the Company which are now in the Rijksmuseum;[6] the identification of the sitters is traditional.

The present portrait is obviously later in style than No. 1277 above and was probably painted in the 1670s; this would agree also with the apparent age of the sitter and the costume.

VERSION AND COPY: A variant is in the Historical Museum, Rotterdam.[7] A copy of the National Gallery picture, by Pieter van der Werff, is mentioned above.

PROVENANCE: In the Sir Hugh Hume Campbell, Bart., sale, London, 16 June 1894 (lot 41), bought by George Salting (130 gns). Salting Bequest, 1910.

REFERENCES:
General: HdG No. 202.
In text:
1. See NNBW, vol. 2, col. 1200.
2. He was apparently first called van Leeuwenhoek in the National Gallery catalogue of 1911; in the catalogue of the Campbell sale, 1894 (see PROVENANCE) he was not identified. The variant (see VERSION AND COPY) was already described as a portrait of van Leeuwenhoek in 1914 (see note 7).
3. e.g. the portrait by Jan Verkolje, dated 1686, in the Rijksmuseum, Amsterdam (1976 cat. no. A957) which was engraved as van Leeuwenhoek in 1687 by Abraham de Blois.
4. The sitter was first identified as Jan de Reus in 1935, apparently by C. J. K. van Aalst (letter in the National Gallery archives); the same identification was made independently by S. J. Gudlaugsson in *Kunsthistorische Mededeelingen*, 1946, pp. 31–2.
5. Rijksmuseum 1976 catalogue, No. A4505. Oval,

on canvas, 82 × 68 cm. This copy agrees exactly with the National Gallery picture, but the right hand has been omitted.
6. For this series of portraits see the 1976 Rijksmuseum catalogue, pp. 706ff.
7. HdG No. 202a. On canvas, 28 × 24 in. In the Rotterdam version the sitter has no skull cap, his robe is dark red with a yellow lining instead of black trimmed with brown fur and he is holding it with his left hand instead of his right. The provenance of the Rotterdam picture is: Major-General Sterling sale, London, 29 April 1914 (lot 119); [Hugh Blaker] sale, London, 10 July 1914 (lot 106) bought in; [Hugh Blaker] sale, London, 18 February 1927 (lot 50), bought by F. Partridge (in all three sales the sitter was called A. van Leeuwenhoek); presented by Dr C. J. K. van Aalst to the Rotterdam Historical Museum in 1935.

2954 *Portrait of a Man in a Black Wig*

Plate 206

Oil on canvas, 47.6 × 38.7 (18¾ × 15¼).

Formerly attributed to Caspar Netscher, presumably by association with Netscher's *Portrait of a Lady and a Girl with Oranges* (No. 2953 of this catalogue). These two portraits are not, however, companions[1] and the present one is clearly not by Netscher but by Maes, who painted many similar small portraits in his later years; it is probably from the later 1670s or early 80s.

PROVENANCE: In the collection of Mrs Sara Austen (died *c.*1891), London, and bequeathed by her to Sir Austen Henry Layard.[2] Sir A. H. Layard collection, London; Layard Bequest, 1913.

REFERENCES:
1. The scale is different and No. 2953 is not in a painted oval.
2. According to Major A. A. M. Layard (affidavit of 1914 in the National Gallery archives).

JACOB MARIS, 1837–1899

Jacob Hendricus Maris. Born in The Hague, 25 August 1837, the eldest son of Mattheus Maris and Hendrika Bloemert; of their five children all three sons, Jacob, Matthijs and Willem became artists. In 1849 Jacob became a pupil of Johannes Stroebel and a year later took lessons at the Haagse Academie from Jacobus van den Berg. Subsequently he was a pupil of Huib van Hove and moved with him to Antwerp in 1854. In Antwerp he attended evening classes given at the Academy by Nicaise de Keyser. He was joined there by Matthijs; the two brothers shared a studio and painted pictures together for the American market. They were joined by their friend Alma Tadema who took a room in the same house.

In 1857 Jacob returned to The Hague and in the following year shared a studio with Matthijs. In 1861 they travelled in Germany, Switzerland and France. In 1865 Jacob moved to Paris where he remained until 1871. He worked for some months in the studio of Ernest Hebert whose style he imitated in a series of paintings of Italian peasant girls. After his return to The Hague in 1871, where he had a studio on the Noordwest Binnensingel, Jacob moved increasingly towards landscape. He also painted an impressive series of townscapes. He died on 7 August 1899 on a visit to Carlsbad.

He had only one pupil, Willem de Zwart (1862–1931).

REFERENCE: Ex. cat. Paris/London/The Hague, 1983, pp. 201 ff.

2709 A Young Woman nursing a Baby   *Plate 207*

Signed, bottom left: J. Maris ft 1868

Oil on mahogany, 29.1 × 22.8 (11$\frac{7}{16}$ × 8$\frac{15}{16}$).

The woman's right breast was originally uncovered and has been overpainted later, perhaps not by Maris.[1]

This picture was painted when the artist was living in Paris; according to J. Veth[2] it represents Maris' wife. Maris married Catharina Hendrika Horn in 1867; their first child, Guillaume, was born in Paris on 23 April 1868 and died there on 31 March 1869.[3]

DRAWING: A pencil study for the picture (with the woman's breast uncovered), squared for transfer, was in the possession of the Maris family.[4]

PROVENANCE: Exhibited at the French Gallery, London, 1868–9, No. 5.[5] Bought from a dealer by Obach and Co., London,[6] who sold it, probably in 1898, to J. C. J. Drucker, London.[7] It is possibly the 'Mrs Maris and Child' which was in a loan exhibition at Tooth's, London, in January 1899 (No. 104); the lender is not recorded. It was lent by Drucker to the Jacob Maris Memorial Exhibition in Amsterdam, 1899, the Rijksmuseum, Amsterdam, 1904–7,[8] and the National Gallery, 1907–10; presented by him in 1910. Transferred to the Tate Gallery c.1920;[9] transferred back to the National Gallery in 1956.

EXHIBITIONS (see also under PROVENANCE): Amsterdam Arti et Amicitiae Society, Jacob Maris Memorial Exhibition, 1899, No. 2.[10]

REFERENCES:
1. The overpainting, which is certainly later than the rest of the picture, was done before 1907 since it appears in the reproduction in D. Croal Thomson, *The Brothers Maris*, 1907, pl. J4. The breast is uncovered in the preparatory study (see DRAWING).
2. J. Veth, *Portretstudies en Silhouetten*, [1908], pp. 166–7.
3. The dates of the child's birth and death were discovered in the archives of the 18^e *arrondissement* by Miss A. Hoogendoorn (letter of 1955 in the National Gallery archives).
4. According to J. Veth, loc. cit.
5. As 'Young Mother'.
6. Letter of 1 April 1915 from Messrs Colnaghi and Obach (in the National Gallery archives).
7. Letter of 15 September 1914 from J. C. J. Drucker (in the National Gallery archives).
8. It is in the 1905 Rijksmuseum catalogue, No. 1519b.
9. Tate Gallery Modern Foreign Schools catalogues, 1926–34.
10. As 'Jonge moeder'.

2710 A Drawbridge in a Dutch Town   *Plate 208*

Signed, bottom right: J Maris

Oil on canvas (not lined), 30.2 × 22.7 (11$\frac{7}{8}$ × 8$\frac{15}{16}$).

Said to have been painted in 1875;[1] there is a watercolour version of this date (see VERSION).

ETCHING: Etched by (Charles Louis) Philippe Zilcken.[2]

VERSION: A watercolour version of this composition, dated 1875, is in the Rijksmuseum, Amsterdam (Fig. 57).[3]

PROVENANCE: In the collection of R. T. Hamilton Bruce, Edinburgh; Hamilton Bruce sale, London, 16 May 1903 (lot 45) bought by J. C. J. Drucker (£441). Lent by Drucker to the Rijksmuseum, Amsterdam, 1904–7,[4] and to the National Gallery, 1907–10; presented by him in 1910. Transferred to the Tate Gallery in 1934;[5] transferred back to the National Gallery in 1956.

REFERENCES:
1. Catalogue of the Rijksmuseum, Amsterdam, 1905, No. 1519f.
2. A. J. Godoy, *Jacob Maris: Twelve Landscapes etched by Ph. Zilcken*, Amsterdam, 1890 [No. 8].
3. 28 × 21.5 cm. Signed and dated bottom right: J. Maris 1875. Bequeathed to the State of the Netherlands by Mrs A. E. Reich-Hohwü; on loan to the Rijksmuseum. Exhibited in Paris/London/The Hague, 1983, cat. no. 53.
4. See note 1.
5. Although not transferred until 1934 it appears in the Tate Gallery Modern Foreign Schools catalogues, 1926–34.

3261 A Girl feeding a Bird in a Cage

Plate 209

Signed, bottom right: J Maris f.

Oil on mahogany, 32.6 × 20.8 ($12\frac{13}{16}$ × $8\frac{3}{16}$). A strip about 5 mm. wide has been left unpainted at each side, about 3 mm. at top and bottom.

Probably painted during the artist's stay in Paris. It is very similar in style to No. 5568 below, dated 1867, in which the model for the girl is perhaps the same, and it may be the picture exhibited by the artist in London in 1868 (see PROVENANCE).

PROVENANCE: It is perhaps 'The pet Bird' by J. Maris in the fifteenth annual exhibition of pictures ('The Contributions of Artists of the French and Flemish Schools') at the French Gallery, London, 1868, No. 100; possibly the 'Girl feeding Bird' exhibited at Liverpool, 1886, No. 750, lent by Arthur Earle. It is presumably the 'Feeding the Bird' in a loan exhibition at the Grafton Galleries, London, January–March 1896, No. 124;[1] possibly 'The pet Bird' in the Modern Dutch Artists Exhibition at the French Gallery, 1896, No. 19.[2] It was in the collection of James Staats Forbes, London, by 1898, when it was exhibited as 'The pet Bird' in the Jacob Maris exhibition at the Goupil Gallery, London. James Staats Forbes died in April 1904; the picture was lent by his executors to the Royal Hibernian Academy Winter Exhibition, Dublin, 1904–5[3] and the National Museum, Dublin, 1905. Acquired c.1905 by (Sir) Hugh Percy Lane and lent to the Municipal Gallery, Dublin, 1908–13 (No. 165);[4] deposited with other pictures at the National Gallery in 1913 by Sir Hugh Lane (d. May 1915); Sir Hugh Lane Bequest, 1917. Transferred to the Tate Gallery, 1920;[5] transferred back to the National Gallery in 1956.

EXHIBITIONS: (See also under PROVENANCE) London, Goupil Gallery, 'Jacob Maris', 1898, No. 20; Preston, Guild Art Exhibition, September–December, 1902, No. 45;[6] London, Guildhall, Dutch School Exhibition, 1903, No. 31;[7] Dublin, Royal Hibernian Academy, Winter Exhibition, 1904–5, No. 125; Dublin, National Museum, 1905, No. 78.

REFERENCES:
1. and **2.** The names of the lenders to these exhibitions are not given in the catalogues.
3. As 'Feeding the Bird'.
4. As 'Feeding the Bird'. See also T. Bodkin, *Hugh Lane and his Pictures*, 1932, caption to pl. 42 (1956 edition, pl. 43).
5. Tate Gallery Modern Foreign Schools catalogues, 1926–34.
6. As 'Feeding the Bird'.
7. As 'The Birdcage'.

4262 *A Beach*   *Plate 210*

Signed, bottom left: J Maris

Oil on canvas (not lined), 42.5 × 54.5 (16¾ × 21½).

Probably painted in the late 1870s or 1880s.

PROVENANCE: In the possession of E. J. van Wisselingh and Co., Amsterdam, and included in their Jacob Maris exhibition, 1898, No. 3.[1] Presented by Mrs R. M. Dunlop to the Tate Gallery, 1927;[2] transferred to the National Gallery in 1956.

REFERENCES:
1. As 'Strand'. Reproduced in the exhibition catalogue; the plate cuts off a strip along each of the edges.
2. Tate Gallery Modern Foreign Schools catalogues, 1928 and 1934.

4269 *A Windmill and Houses beside Water: Stormy Sky*   *Plate 211*

Signed, bottom right: J Maris

Oil on canvas (not lined), 48.3 × 59.5 (19 × 23⅜).

Probably painted in the 1880s.

PROVENANCE: In the Ch. L. de Hèle collection, Brussels; de Hèle sale, Amsterdam, 13 June 1911 (lot 10),[1] bought by Arthur Tooth and Sons, London (5,000 guilders). Presented by Mrs R. M. Dunlop to the Tate Gallery, 1927;[2] transferred to the National Gallery in 1956.

REFERENCES:
1. As 'La Tourmente'. Reproduced in the sale catalogue.
2. Tate Gallery Modern Foreign Schools catalogues, 1928 and 1934.

4399 *Three Windmills*   *Plate 212*

Signed, bottom right: J Maris 80

Oil on canvas, 33.7 × 41.3 (13¼ × 16¼).

ETCHING: Etched by (Charles Louis) Philippe Zilcken.[1]

PROVENANCE: In the possession of the Goupil Gallery, London;[2] it is presumably 'The Three Windmills' exhibited there in June–July 1888, No. 3, November 1899, No. 5 and October–November 1901, No. 46. It is possibly 'The Three Mills' in the Spring exhibition at Arthur Tooth and Sons, London, 1902, No. 81.[3] It is said to have been in the collection of C. Frank Stoop by 1908 or 1909;[4] presented by C. Frank Stoop to the Tate Gallery, 1928;[5] transferred to the National Gallery in 1956.

REFERENCES:
1. A. J. Godoy, *Jacob Maris: Twelve Landscapes etched by Ph. Zilcken*, Amsterdam, 1890 [No. 12]; GB-A, 1900, vol. 1, p. 153.
2. On the back is the printed label of 'William Marchant and Co., The Goupil Gallery' (W. S. Marchant took over the Goupil Gallery from Boussod, Valadon and Co. in August 1901; see *The Year's Art*, 1902, p. 118).

3. The picture cannot be traced as Messrs Tooth's records were partially destroyed in the last war (letter of 12 March 1958 from Messrs Tooth).
4. According to a note in the National Gallery archives derived from information supplied orally by Herr Käsbach, 1952.
5. Tate Gallery Modern Foreign Schools catalogues, 1928 and 1934.

5568 *A Girl seated outside a House*

Plate 213

Signed, bottom right: J. Maris fc (*or* ft)/67

Oil on mahogany, 32.7 × 20.9 (12$\frac{7}{8}$ × 8$\frac{3}{16}$).

The church seen in the background is in Montigny-sur-Loing and appears in a view of that town by Jacob Maris, dated 1870, in the Boymans-van Beuningen Museum, Rotterdam.[1]

The girl is perhaps the same as that in No. 3261 above, which is of the same period.

The picture was bequeathed in 1944 under the title 'Vespers' but the girl appears to be trimming her hat with flowers rather than praying.

PROVENANCE: A picture by J. Maris was exhibited as 'Vespers' (see above) at Obach and Co., London, June 1906, No. 35, and another (or the same?) at the French Gallery, London, 1910, No. 47.[2] No. 5568 is said to have been bought at a sale at Christie's by Frank Claughton Mathews,[3] in whose memory it was bequeathed to the Tate Gallery by his widow, Mrs Mary James Mathews, 1944. Transferred to the National Gallery in 1956.

REFERENCES:
1. 1972 cat. no. 1489; Paris/London/The Hague, 1983, cat. no. 48.
2. A review reprinted at the back of the illustrated catalogue of this exhibition mentions 'Vespers (47)

in . . . which a little Dutch girl appears'.
3. According to Mrs Fox (letter of 1953 in the Tate Gallery archives).

MATTHIJS MARIS, 1839–1917

Matthias Maris – later called *Matthijs* or *Thijs* – was born in The Hague on 17 August 1839, the second son of Mattheus Maris and Hendrika Bloemert. His brothers, Jacob and Willem, were also painters. In 1851 he became a pupil of Cornelis Elink Sterk; from 1852 until 1855 he attended classes at the Haagse Academie; in 1854 he worked in the studio of Louis Meijer. Soon after he joined his brother Jacob in Antwerp and studied at the Academy under Nicaise de Keyser. After three years in Antwerp Matthijs returned to The Hague, where he shared a studio with Jacob. In 1861 the two brothers travelled to Germany, Switzerland (where the castle, cathedral and timbered houses of Lausanne made a particularly strong impression on him) and France. Matthijs had little success in The Hague and moved to Paris in 1869. E. J. van Wisselingh, who worked for the Parisian art dealer Goupil, bought paintings from him, as did Daniel Cottier, a Scottish art dealer working in London. In 1875 van Wisselingh went to work for Cottier in London and in 1877 Matthijs was also persuaded by Cottier to come to live in London. Matthijs lived in Cottier's house until 1887: he remained in London until his death. In his later years in London Matthijs, who was supported financially by van Wisselingh, produced very few works. They are dreamy grey landscapes and veiled figures which show the influence of the Pre-Raphaelites and Burne-Jones. He died in London on 22 August 1917.

REFERENCE: Ex. cat., Paris/London/The Hague, 1983, pp. 217–25.

2874 *Men unloading Carts, Montmartre* *Plate 214*

Signed, bottom right: M. M. 70.

Oil on canvas (not lined), 23.2 × 30.5 (9⅛ × 12).

Another view of the Montmartre quarry by Matthijs Maris, in the Burrell Collection, Glasgow,[1] is dated 1872; two others, in the Budapest Museum,[2] and in the Gemeente-museum, The Hague,[3] are undated but were probably painted at about that time.

Following his brother Jacob's return to The Hague in 1871, Matthijs had moved to new lodgings in Montmartre.

PROVENANCE: In the Messrs Murrieta sale, London, 14–16 May 1892 (lot 83),[4] 105 gns, bought by Boussod, Valadon and Co. (The Goupil Gallery, London), who sold it to James Staats Forbes, London.[5] J. Staats Forbes died in April 1904; the picture was lent by his executors to the Royal Hibernian Academy, Dublin, 1904, No. 127,[6] and the National Museum, Dublin, 1905, No. 73.[7] Bought from Forbes' executors by A. Preyer of The Hague;[8] perhaps the *Gravel Pit* by M. Maris exhibited with paintings belonging to A. Preyer at the Kunstkring, Rotterdam, August–September 1905, No. 44.[9] Sold by Preyer in February 1907 to J. C. J. Drucker, London,[10] who lent it to the National Gallery in June 1911 and presented it in May 1912. Transferred to the Tate Gallery in 1934;[11] transferred back to the National Gallery in 1956.

EXHIBITIONS (See also above under PROVENANCE): London, International Society of Sculptors, Painters and Gravers Exhibition, October–December 1901, No. 109;[12] Dublin, Royal Hibernian Academy, 1904, No. 127; Dublin, National Museum, 1905, No. 73; London, Grafton Galleries, J. Staats Forbes Collection Exhibition, 1905, No. 208.[13]

REFERENCES:
1. Canvas, 36.7 × 58.5 cm.; signed: M. M. 72. Reproduced in D. Croal Thomson, *The Brothers Maris*, 1907, pl. M8, and in the catalogue of the French Gallery exhibition, London, 1909, No. 2. Erroneously reproduced as in a Canadian collection by H. E. van Gelder, *Matthijs Maris*, [1939], p. 30.
2. Panel, 24.3 × 34.3 cm.; signed: M. M.
3. Canvas, 55 × 46 cm.; signed, bottom left, M. M.; 1962 cat. no. 210; Paris/London/The Hague, 1983, cat. no. 74.
4. As 'Unloading Carts'.
5. According to J. C. J. Drucker (letter of 15 September 1914 in the National Gallery archives).

6. and 7. As 'The Stone Quarry'.
8. According to J. C. J. Drucker (see note 5).
9. As 'Grintgroeve' (i.e. gravel pit).
10. See note 5; see also Bosboom No. 2712, notes 13 and 14.
11. It appears in the Tate Gallery Modern Foreign Schools catalogues, 1926–34, as at the National Gallery.
12. As 'The Gravel Pit'; reproduced in the exhibition catalogue.
13. As 'Gravel Pit'.

WILLEM MARIS, 1844–1910

Wenzel Maris – later called *Willem* – was born in The Hague on 18 February 1844; the youngest son of Mattheus Maris and Hendrika Bloemert. His elder brothers, Jacob and Matthijs, were also painters. He was taught by his brothers and the animal painter Pieter Stortenbeker; he also attended evening classes at the Haagse Academie. In 1862 he met Anton Mauve, who became a lifelong friend, in Oosterbeek. In the following year he shared a studio with his brothers in The Hague. In 1865 he travelled along the Rhine; in 1867 he went to Paris to attend Jacob's wedding; and in 1871 he travelled to Norway. Apart from these trips and a few excursions in the Netherlands and Belgium, he remained in or near The Hague.

In 1876 Willem founded the Hollandsche Teeken-Maatschappij (Dutch Drawing Society) with Anton Mauve and Hendrick Mesdag.

In his paintings and his watercolours he treats the same subjects: cattle in a meadow or by a pool and ducks beside water. He died in The Hague on 10 October 1910.

In 1880 George Hendrick Breitner was his pupil for a year.

REFERENCE: Ex. cat., Paris/London/The Hague, 1983, pp. 227–31.

2875 *Ducks alighting on a Pool*   *Plate 215*

Signed, bottom right: W. Maris. fc. (*or* fe).

Oil on canvas, 32.4 × 20.3 (12¾ × 8); the sides are cut irregularly.

Willem Maris painted a number of similar pictures of ducks.[1] He had a duck pond near his house at Voorburg and there drew and painted them in oil and watercolours.

PROVENANCE: Lent to the National Gallery by J. C. J. Drucker, London in June 1911 and presented in May 1912. Transferred to the Tate Gallery in 1920;[2] transferred back to the National Gallery, 1956.

REFERENCES:
1. e.g. D. Croal Thomson, *The Brothers Maris*, 1907, pls. W2, W5 and W9.
2. In the Tate Gallery Modern Foreign Schools catalogues, 1926–34.

GABRIEL METSU, 1629–1667

Gabriel Metsu, son of Jacques Metsue, a painter of Flemish origin (who died in March 1629[1]). He spelled his name also *Metzu* (occasionally) and *Metsue* or *Metzue* (more rarely). He was born in Leiden;[2] it can be deduced that he was probably born in January 1629 from the following facts: (1) in October 1657 he is said to be twenty-seven[3] and in April 1658 his age is given as twenty-eight (i.e. born in 1629 or 1630);[4] (2) in January 1654 he is described as 'voljaerde',[5] i.e. over twenty-five. According to Houbraken, he was a pupil of Gerrit Dou. In 1644 his name appears on a notarised list of artists who wanted to form a guild of St Luke in Leiden; he was one of the founder members of the Leiden guild in March 1648.[6] He paid his dues to the guild again in 1649 and 1650; at some time after 1650 (probably 1651) he is noted in the guild records as having left Leiden[7] but in January 1654 he is recorded as living in Leiden.[8] He was living on the Prinsengracht in Amsterdam by July 1657;[9] he married Isabella de Wolff from Enkhuizen, daughter of the painter Maria de Wolff-de Grebber, in Amsterdam on 12 April 1658 and is recorded there also in 1664.[10] He was buried in the Nieuwe Kerk in Amsterdam, 24 October 1667.[11]

From a total oeuvre of about 150 paintings, only nineteen are dated. Given the range of styles, subject-matter and techniques in Metsu's work, the establishment of a convincing chronology is difficult. His earliest dated painting, *A Young Woman spooling Thread* of 1643 (Leningrad, Hermitage), shows little relationship to the work of Dou. Metsu was an eclectic artist and his work shows at different times the influences of Jan Steen, Nicolaes Knüpfer, Dou and ter Borch. Most of Metsu's pictures are genre scenes, but he also painted religious subjects (his *Noli Me Tangere* in Vienna is dated 1667) as well as a few portraits, still lifes and game pieces. According to Houbraken, Michiel van Musscher was a pupil of Metsu in Amsterdam in 1665.

REFERENCES:

General: Bredius in OH, 1907, pp. 197–203; HdG, vol. 1; Catalogue of the exhibition, *Gabriel Metsu*, Stedelijk Museum De Lakenhal, Leiden, 1966; S. J. Gudlaugsson, 'Kanttekeningen bij de ontwikkeling van Metsu', OH, vol. 83, 1968, pp. 14–44; F. W. Robinson, *Gabriel Metsu (1629–1667): A Study of his Place in Dutch Genre Painting of the Golden Age*, New York, 1974 (see also the review by A. K. Wheelock Jnr. in *Art Bulletin*, vol. 58, 1976, pp. 456–9).

In text:

1. Bredius, op. cit., p. 198.
2. According to the entry in the Amsterdam marriage register, 1658 (Kramm, vol. 4, p. 1106).
3. Bredius, op. cit., p. 202.
4. Kramm, loc. cit.
5. Bredius, op. cit., p. 201.
6. Obreen, vol. 5, p. 206.
7. Loc. cit.
8. Bredius, op. cit., p. 201.
9. Bredius, op. cit., p. 202.
10. OH, 1883, pp. 78–9.
11. OH, 1883, p. 80.

838 *A Woman seated at a Table and a Man*   *Plate 216*
 tuning a Violin

The woman holds a sheet of music; on the table before her is a viola da gamba. Beside the fireplace is a carved figure of Atlas.

Signed, below the window, left: G·Metsu (of the G only the tail remains).[1]

Oil on canvas, 43 × 37.5 ($16\frac{15}{16}$ × $14\frac{3}{4}$).

Gudlaugsson[2] stressed the influence of interiors by ter Borch, notably a painting of 1658 in Schwerin,[3] and considered the painting to date from '1658 at the latest'. MacLaren related it to a painting of 1661 in Dresden, and Robinson[4] placed it 'in the 50s'. The present writer agrees with Gudlaugsson that a date *c.*1658 is acceptable.

COPIES: A copy is in the National Loan Collection.[5] A copy[6] in reverse (presumably after the engraving), with an open book added in the right foreground with a false Frans van Mieris signature, was in a sale in Rotterdam (van Marle, de Sille en Baan), 19 December 1956, lot 62. Another[7] with the same composition (i.e. in reverse, with a book added in the right foreground) was in the R. Lindsay and others sale, Sotheby's, 4 November 1964, lot 111 as Dutch *c.*1800. A close copy of the engraving is, according to the mount of a photograph in the RKD, in a private collection in West Germany as E. van der Neer.[8] An early nineteenth-century free copy,[9] close in style to Abraham van Strij, was with the Seventeenth Century Gallery, London, in 1919 as R. Brakenburg(?).

ENGRAVING: Engraved in reverse in 1771 when in the Choiseul collection.[10]

PROVENANCE: Duc de Choiseul sale, Paris, 6 sqq. April 1772 (lot 20), bought by Vicomte de Choiseul (6,800 francs); Choiseul-Praslin sale, Paris, 18 sqq. February 1793 (lot 63), bought by Paillet (6,051 francs); Pierre Fouquet Junr sale, Amsterdam, 13 sqq. April 1801 (lot 42), bought by C. S. Roos (670 guilders); Paillet and Coclers sale, Paris, 26 sqq. August 1801 (lot 10), bought in, 3,150 francs;[11] Solirène sale, Paris, 11 sqq. March 1812 (lot 60), bought by Lebrun (4,030 francs). In the collection of Prince de Talleyrand, Paris, apparently by 1814;[12] it is in the catalogue of the [Prince de Talleyrand] sale, Paris, announced for 9 July 1817 (lot 20) but the sale did not take place, the whole collection having been bought by William Buchanan who brought it to England.[13] The present picture was sold by Buchanan to John Webb, London, from whom it passed into the collection of Sébastien Erard, Paris,[14] and was afterwards bought by John Smith.[15] Perhaps lent by (Sir) Robert Peel (Bart.) to the BI, 1823 (No. 75)[16] or 1824 (No. 77);[17] in any case it was in his collection by 1833.[18] Purchased with the Peel collection, 1871.

EXHIBITIONS: BI 1823, No. 75(?); BI 1824, No. 77(?); Arts Council 1945, No. 18.

REFERENCES:
General: Smith No. 31; HdG No. 154.
In text:
1. The signature is very faint.
2. Gudlaugsson, op. cit., pp. 26–7, 41.
3. Canvas, 78.5 × 74.5. Gudlaugsson, op. cit., cat. No. 112. Staatliches Museum Schwerin, *Höllandische und flämische Malerei des 17. Jahrhunderts*, 1982, No. 335.
4. Robinson, op. cit., p. 38.
5. Canvas, 44.4 × 37.5 cm. Cannon Hall Museum, Barnsley, *The William Harvey Collection of Dutch and Flemish Paintings*, n.d., No. 21 (as Metsu). The National Loan Collection is presently (1989) at the Cooper Art Gallery, Barnsley.
6. Panel, 24 × 18 cm.
7. Panel, 25.5 × 20 cm. As the property of Mrs H. D. Felton.
8. Panel, 47.5 × 37 cm. (Photograph from N. Antonowicz, Frankfurt-am-Main.)

9. Photograph in RKD: Cooper, London, neg. no. 437.
10. In *Recueil d'estampes . . . d'après les tableaux du Cabinet . . . Choiseul*, 1771, No. 90.
11. Smith No. 31, incorrectly as Anon. sale, 1802.
12. See p. i of the catalogue of the Talleyrand sale announced for 9 July 1817.
13. Buchanan, vol. 2, pp. 305ff.
14. Buchanan, vol. 2, p. 329.
15. Smith No. 31.
16. 'Metzu   An Interior, with a Lady and Gentleman in conversation.' Smith (No. 31) says that the present picture was exhibited at the BI in 1823, and there was no other Metsu lent to the exhibition that year, but the description fits better Metsu No. 839 below.
17. 'Metzu   A Musical Party'; this might equally well be Metsu No. 839 below.
18. Smith No. 31.

839 *A Man and a Woman seated by a Virginal*   Plate 217

In the left background, partly covered by a curtain, is a painting of a Twelfth Night feast; in the centre a landscape apparently in the style of Jacob van Ruisdael. The woman holds a sheet of music; on the table, right, is a violin.

The lid of the virginal is inscribed: IN · TE · D[O]MINE · SPERAVI · NON · CONF[UN]DAR · Ī AETERNV̄ (the F of CONF[UN]DAR has been later changed into I). The inside of the keyboard cover is inscribed: OMNIS · [SPIRITUS LAUDE]T · DOMINVM.

Signed, top right: G. Metsu

Oil on oak, 38.4 × 32.2 ($15\frac{1}{8}$ × $12\frac{11}{16}$).

The inscriptions on the virginal are taken from the Psalms (Vulgate: 30.2, and 70.1; cl. 6). The same virginal (with slight variations) with the same inscriptions occurs in other paintings by Metsu;[1] the second inscription is on a virginal of 1620, made by Andries Rucker the Elder of Antwerp, in the Musée Instrumental du Conservatoire in Brussels,[2] which also has a printed paper of very similar design on the front (see also the harpsichord in Steen No. 856 of this catalogue).

The figure seen on the right of the painting hanging in the left background and partially covered by a curtain is the king in the traditional celebration of the Twelfth Night feast (6 January); there is a painting by Metsu of this subject in Munich (Fig. 58)[3] which has a very similar figure on the left-hand side. Here, however, the composition is reversed and the scale of the painting and size of the figures differ from the Munich picture. The Munich painting is a relatively early work, probably painted in the first half of the 1650s.[4]

Gudlaugsson[5] dated the painting 'shortly after 1660' and Robinson[6] placed it in Metsu's later Amsterdam years as among his last works. The present writer considers that a date of c. 1665 is acceptable.

PROVENANCE: It is improbable that the present picture is to be identified, as HdG suggested,[7] with that in the Lambert Witsen sale, Amsterdam, 25 May 1746 (lot 5), bought by Quinkhard (615 guilders), since the woman there is said to be in a satin dress, which is not the case here.[8] It was in the [Michael] Bryan sale, London, 17–19 May 1798, 3rd day, lot 28 (150 gns); later in the collection of Lord Radstock.[9] Perhaps lent by (Sir) Robert Peel (Bart.) to the BI, 1823 (No. 75)[10] or 1824 (No. 77);[11] in any case it was in his collection by 1833.[12] Purchased with the Peel collection, 1871.

EXHIBITIONS: BI 1823, No. 75(?); BI 1824 No. 77(?), Leiden, Stedelijk Museum De Lakenhal, 'Gabriel Metsu', 1966, No. 31; London 1976, No. 71; London 1978–9, No. 9.

REFERENCES:
General: Smith, No. 97; HdG Nos. 155 and (?)162d.
In text:
1. *A Man and a Woman at a Virginal* in the Wernher collection, Luton Hoo (HdG No. 159), *A Woman at a Virginal* in the W. van der Vorm collection in the Museum Boymans-van Beuningen, Rotterdam (HdG No. 160), and *The Concert* in the Hermitage, Leningrad (HdG No. 151).
2. See B. Nicolson, *Vermeer's Lady at the Virginals*, 1946, p. 4 and pl. 15.
3. Munich, Alte Pinakothek, 1983 cat., No. 871.
4. This is the dating suggested in the Munich catalogue (op. cit., note 3) with which Robinson (op. cit., p. 23) and the present writer agree. Gudlaugsson (op. cit., p. 40) preferred c. 1657.
5. Gudlaugsson, op. cit., p. 41.
6. Robinson, op. cit., p. 61.
7. HdG No. 162d.
8. 'Een Juffer met een satyne kleed aan, die met een Heer Musiceert . . . door Gabriël Metsu'; 1 *voet* 4½

duim × 1 *v.* 1d. (see also Hoet, vol. 2, p. 186, where the lot number is incorrectly given as 4). HdG (No. 162d) suggests that the Witsen sale picture may be either the present picture or the so-called *Duet* at Upton House (National Trust: Viscount Bearsted collection).
9. Smith, loc. cit. It was not in the Admiral Lord Radstock sales, London, 19 April 1823, and 12–13 May 1826.
10. 'Metsu An Interior, with a Lady and Gentleman in conversation.' This, the only Metsu lent to the BI in 1823, has previously been identified with Metsu No. 838 above, which Smith (No. 31) says was exhibited there in that year, but the description seems closer to the present picture.
11. 'Metsu A Musical Party'; this might equally well be Metsu No. 838 above. Smith does not mention that the present picture was ever exhibited at the BI. (See also preceding note.)
12. Smith No. 97.

970 *Two Men with a Sleeping Woman*   *Plate 218*

Among the objects on the table are playing cards, an inn-keeper's slate and chalk, a pipe and a closed backgammon board.

At the bottom of the slate on the table are the worn remains of a signature: G M(et?)(. .).[1]

Oil on oak, 37.1 × 32.4 (14⅝ × 12¾).

Cleaned in 1957. Considerable wearing throughout, especially in the area of the woman's face.

Judging from the presence of the slate, the setting is probably a tavern. The sleeping woman, the innkeeper's wife or a serving maid, has been drinking and smoking. Female drunkenness was a subject both of amusement and moral admonition in seventeenth-century Dutch genre painting.[2]

Gudlaugsson[3] and Robinson[4] both date the painting to the late 1650s, and the present writer concurs with this dating.

PROVENANCE: Probably in the collection of the Greffiers Fagel (The Hague?) 1752;[5] certainly in the Greffiers Fagel (of Holland) sale, London, 22–23 May 1801 (2nd day, lot 48),[6] bought by Willett (158 gns); John W. Willett sale, London, 31 May–2 June 1813 (lot 103),[7] 113 gns. By 1833 it was in the collection of Daniel Wade Acraman, Bristol;[8] Daniel Wade Acraman sale, Clifton (Bristol), 22–24 August 1842 (lot 148), bought by Brown (£210). In the collection of Wynn Ellis, London, by 1850 or 1851.[9] Wynn Ellis Bequest, 1876.

EXHIBITION: RA 1871, No. 222.

REFERENCES:

General: Smith No. 55 and Supplement, p. 818, No. 42; HdG No. 197.
In text:
1. The signature had at some time been altered by retouching to G METZU; the false part was removed when the picture was cleaned in 1957.
2. See, for example, Jan Steen's *The Effects of Intemperance*, No. 6442 of this catalogue; and the print by Hendrick Bary with the biblical inscription *De Wijn is een spotter* (illustrated and discussed in the exhibition catalogue, *Tot Lering en Vermaak*,

Amsterdam, Rijksmuseum, 1976, No. 65).
3. Gudlaugsson, op. cit., p. 41.
4. Robinson, op. cit., p. 38.
5. 'Een slapende Vrouw door G. *Metzu*' (Hoet, vol. 2, p. 410); also Descamps, vol. 2, p. 242: 'une belle dormeuse'. There was no other Metsu in the Fagel sale, 1801, which answered this description.
6. 'Metzu   The Sleeping Female disturbed.'
7. As from the Fagel collection.
8. Smith No. 55.
9. Seen there by Waagen (1854, vol. 2, p. 295).

2590 *An Old Woman with a Book at a Window*   Plate 219

At the top of the paper hanging over the ledge is a line of inscription so damaged as to be illegible; on the paper, beneath this inscription, is an initial D.

Signed below in the centre: G. Metsu

Oil on canvas, 31.6 × 27.3 ($12\frac{7}{16}$ × $10\frac{3}{4}$).

Some wearing throughout.

This type of subject is derived from Dou's so-called 'niche' paintings. Dated to 'shortly after 1660' by Gudlaugsson,[1] presumably on an analogy with the closely comparable *Hunter in a Niche* in the Mauritshuis which is dated 1661.[2] Robinson[3] apparently believed it to be earlier – from the mid-1650s – and compared it with another 'niche' painting, *The Public Notary* of 1655.[4] The present writer prefers a dating of *c.*1660.

It has been suggested[5] that this painting is a pair to *The Apothecary* in the Louvre.[6] The dimensions, however, are significantly different and a description of 1766[7] of the pendant to *The Apothecary* when it was in the Braamcamp collection makes it clear that No. 2590 (which was also in the Braamcamp collection) was not the pendant.

PROVENANCE: Probably in the Pieter van Lip sale, Amsterdam, 14 June 1712 (lot 15), 83 guilders.[8] In the collection of Gerret Braamcamp, Amsterdam, by 1752;[9] Gerret Braamcamp sale, Amsterdam, 31 July sqq. 1771 (lot 129), bought by Pieter Locquet (1,095 guilders). In the collection of Maria Hoofman, Haarlem, by 1833[10] and still there in 1842;[11] by 1851 in the collection of the 2nd Baron Ashburton, London;[12] sold with the Ashburton collection to Agnew and others in August 1907. In the collection of George Salting, London; Salting Bequest, 1910.

EXHIBITIONS: RA 1871, No. 184; RA 1890, No. 64.

REFERENCES:

General: Smith No. 24 and Supplement No. 39; HdG No. 211.

In text:

1. Gudlaugsson, op. cit., p. 41.

2. Mauritshuis, The Hague: 1977 cat., inv. no. 93. HdG No. 207.

3. Robinson, op. cit., p. 31.

4. Robinson, op. cit., pl. 37; Paris, art market, 1960. Not in HdG.

5. C. Bille, *De Tempel der Kunst of het Kabinet van der Heer Braamcamp*, Amsterdam, 1961, No. 129, p. 105.

6. Panel, 27 × 23.5 cm. Signed. Inv. no. 1463.

7. J. F. Bastide, *Temple des Arts*, 1766, p. 101. The pendant to The Apothecary is described as: 'Femme tenant un couteau et un lièvre écorché, à côté d'elle un coq mort pend à l'arbre. Le pendant est un vieillard assis, tenant sur ses genoux un livre qu'il est occupé à feuilleter. Il paraît être un Medecin de Village; car l'on voit auprès de lui une Bouteille, un Pot à onguent et un Pilon. Le fond est une Bibliothèque. Ces deux morceaux sont précieusement peints et

d'une touche large.' (The present writer is grateful to J. Foucart for this reference.)

8. (G. Metsu) 'Een Lesent Vrouwtje, in een Nisje' (Hoet, vol. 1, p. 147).

9. (G. Metsu) 'Een oud Wyfje in een Nisje met bywerk', canvas, 1 *voet* 1 *duim* × 1 *voet* (in this case the Amsterdam *voet* of 11 *duim*); see Hoet, vol. 2, p. 506.

10. Smith No. 24 (incorrectly described but corrected in Supplement No. 39). Maria Hoofman apparently inherited the paintings from her father J. Hoofman (d. 1799). Many of the paintings in the collection were bought by C. J. Nieuwenhuys.

11. Smith Supplement No. 39. It was not in the Mlle M. Hoofman sale, Haarlem, 2 sqq. June 1846 as HdG suggests (loc. cit.).

12. Waagen, 1854, vol. 2, p. 104. The collection was formed by Alexander Baring, 1st Baron Ashburton, who died in 1848, but some pictures were added by the 2nd Baron.

2591 *The Interior of a Smithy*

Plate 220

In the windows above the entrance there is painted glass.

Signed on the right, centre (on the window frame): GMetsu (GM in monogram).

Oil on canvas, 65.4 × 73.3 ($25\frac{3}{4}$ × $28\frac{7}{8}$).

Cleaned in 1983–4.

In his earlier years, before about 1655, Metsu painted several pictures showing the interiors of smithies: a painting last recorded in the Schönlank sale of 1896 depicts *Venus and Amor at Vulcan's Forge*;[1] the Stockholm painting, *Woman weeping in a Blacksmith's Shop*, illustrates a popular saying or a literary text;[2] *The Armourer*, in the Rijksmuseum,[3] like No. 2591, shows a craftsman at work. The National Gallery picture seems to be in a more developed style than any of these. MacLaren considered it to be later than the Boston Museum *Usurer* of 1654[4] but thought that it could not be after about 1658 and may well be a product of his later Leiden days. Gudlaugsson[5] dated the painting *c.*1657; Robinson[6] to about 1659; and Sutton[7] to 'mid to late 1650s'. The present writer considers *c.*1657 to be acceptable.

The painting, with its meticulous depiction of the tools of the smith's trade, belongs to a tradition of depicting trades and occupations; among others, Quiringh van Brekelenkam, Pieter Quast, Cornelis Beelt, Paulus Potter and Philips Wouwermans depicted smiths and farriers.[8] Gudlaugsson commented on the 'Brekelenkam-like' composition (cf. No. 2549 of this catalogue).[9]

COPY: An old copy is in the RBK (No. NK2870).[10]

PROVENANCE: In the Abraham Delfos et al. sale, The Hague, 10 June 1807 (lot 71); Baroness van Leyden sale, Warmond Castle, near Leiden, 31 July 1816 (lot 25), bought by Coclers (100 guilders); Anon. sale, Christie's, 26 June 1824 (lot 38),[11] bought in (245 gns).[12] Revd W. Jones Thomas (of Llanthomas Hayon, Breconshire) sale, London, 10 July 1886 (lot 164), bought by Salting (£399). George Salting Bequest, 1910.

EXHIBITIONS: Leiden, Stedelijk Museum De Lakenhal, 'Gabriel Metsu', 1966, No. 38; London 1978–9, No. 2; Philadelphia/Berlin/London 1984, No. 70.

REFERENCES:
General: Smith No. 75; HdG No. 220.
In text:
1. HdG No. 18; reproduced in the catalogue of the Schönlank sale, Cologne, 28 April 1896 (lot 117). Panel 37 × 33 cm. Although the picture is signed in full, the reproduction in the sale catalogue suggests that this may be a copy of an early Metsu rather than an original; in this connection it is perhaps worth noting that, unlike Metsu's other paintings of smithies, it is of small dimensions.
2. Nationalmuseum, Stockholm, 1958 cat., inv. no. 512. HdG No. 17. Canvas, 107 × 121 cm. Signed. J. B. F. van Gils, 'De Stockholmer Smidse van Gabriel Metsu', OH, vol. 60, 1943, pp. 68–70, identified the subject as an illustration of the saying 'to write a debt in the chimney'. It has recently been suggested (by P. Sutton in the exhibition catalogue, Philadelphia/Berlin/London, 1984, pp. 248–9) that it could illustrate an episode from a poem by Adriaen van de Venne.
3. Rijksmuseum, Amsterdam: 1976 cat., A2156. Canvas, 101 × 85 cm. Signed. HdG No. 219.
4. Boston, Museum of Fine Arts. Inv. no. 89.501. HdG No. 56.

5. Gudlaugsson, op. cit., p. 41.
6. Robinson, op. cit., p. 50.
7. Op. cit., p. 248.
8. See Sutton, op. cit., p. 249.
9. Gudlaugsson, op. cit., p. 23, note 17.
10. This is apparently the painting (Canvas, 64 × 71 cm.) which was bought by van den Berch (of Leiden) at the [J. A. Bennet] sale, Leiden, 1–7 April 1829, lot 56 (of the paintings), and subsequently in the van den Berch van Heemstede sale, Amsterdam, 7 July 1903, lot 155.
11. 'Gabriel Metzu The Discovery of Charles II. in his flight, by the Blacksmith, who is pausing before he strikes the hot iron; and is regarding the King with a keen inquiring eye. The Horse seems alive; and the shop is filled with all imaginable implements and tools suited to the business . . .' The identity of this picture with that in the van Leyden sale is confirmed by Smith (loc. cit.).
12. The auctioneer's marked copy of the sale catalogue gives Carleton as the purchaser but the form of the entry shows that this lot was, in fact, bought in at 245 gns.

5225 *A Young Woman seated drawing* — Plate 221

On the table, beneath a bust of a woman, is visible part of an engraving of *Christ at the Column*.

Oil on oak, 36.3 × 30.7 ($14\frac{5}{16}$ × $12\frac{1}{16}$).

Apparently worn and retouched, especially in the darks.[1]

The engraving is Lucas Vorsterman's print after Gerard Seghers' *Christ at the Column before the Flagellation* in St Michael's, Ghent (Fig. 59).[2] The same engraving and bust (reminiscent of the style of Duquesnoy) appear in the *Self Portrait standing at a Window* by Metsu in the collection of HM the Queen;[3] the bust alone in *The Letter-writer* in the Wallace Collection[4] and the *Artist painting a Woman playing a Cello* in a private collection in Los Angeles.[5]

MacLaren and Gudlaugsson[6] believed the painting to be from the late 1650s; Robinson[7] said that the palette was of the 1650s. A date in the second half of the 1650s is acceptable.

COPIES: Copies, probably of No. 5225, were in the [Lenglier] sale, Paris, 6 sqq. April 1789 (lot 151),[8] bought by Colmer (26 francs) and the [Herman ten Kate] sale, Amsterdam, 10–11 June 1801 (lot 124),[9] bought by Rijnders (66 guilders). A late copy, with variations, was in an anonymous sale, London, 4 November 1949 (lot 147);[10] a copy of the woman alone (reversed; probably from an engraving) was in an anonymous sale, London, 9 July 1948 (lot 118).[11] A copy, in reverse, was in an anonymous sale, Sotheby's, New York, 16 March 1979, lot 47.[12]

ENGRAVINGS: Mezzotint by Wallerant Vaillant (1623–77);[13] engravings by Robert(?) Brichet, 1781 (in reverse)[14] and J. Pelletier.[15]

PROVENANCE: In the inventory of Petronella de La Court (widow of Adam Oortmans), 16 August 1707, 'Een tekenaressie van Metzu' (Amsterdam, Gemeentearchief N.A.A. 5338, FF. 553–639); her sale Amsterdam, 19 October 1707 (lot 47),[16] 56 guilders; Abraham du Pré and Petronella Oortmans sale, Amsterdam, 19 May 1729 (lot 3), 260 guilders.[17] Possibly in the Jaques de Roore sale, The Hague, 4 sqq. September 1747 (lot 87),[18] bought by David Jetswaart (138 guilders). In the inventory of Jeronimus Tonneman, 12 July 1752, '35. Een juffertje dat zit en teekend van den zelven [Metsu]' (Amsterdam, Gemeentearchief N.A.A. 10747, akte 521); in his sale, Amsterdam, 21 sqq. October 1754 (lot 15),[19] bought by Fouquet (610 guilders); [Pieter Leendert de] N[eufville] sale, Amsterdam, 19 June 1765 (lot 63),[20] bought by Jan Matthias Kok (1,050 guilders) for van de Velde; Frans van de Velde sale, Amsterdam, 7 September 1774 (lot 67),[21] bought by Fouquet (2,100 guilders). Bought in Holland c.1777 from 'Grampry' by Poullain;[22] Poullain sale, Paris, 15 sqq. March 1780 (lot 52 bis), bought by Paillet (5,000 francs); Comte de Merle sale, Paris, 1–4 March 1784 (lot 56), bought by Julliot (4,800 francs). [Prince Galitzin][23] sale, Paris, 28 February sqq. 1825 (lot 24), bought by de Lahante (6,600 francs) by whom it was brought to England;[24] in the collection of Alexander Baring (later 1st Baron Ashburton) by 1833.[25] When exhibited at the RA in 1871 and 1890, lent by Lord Ashburton; presumably among the Ashburton pictures sold to Agnew and others in August 1907. In the collection of Alfred Charles de Rothschild (d. 1918) and bequeathed by him to the Countess of Carnarvon; Countess of Carnarvon sale, London, 22 May 1925 (lot 77), bought by Martin (2,100 gns). By 1932 in the collection of the 1st Viscount Rothermere[26] and presented by him, 1940.

EXHIBITIONS: RA 1871, No. 190; RA 1890, No. 116; Leiden, Stedelijk Museum De Lakenhal, 'Gabriel Metsu', 1966, No. 15; London 1976, No. 70.

REFERENCES:

General: Smith No. 41; HdG No. 29.

In text:

1. The picture is already noted as 'usé et repeint' in a contemporary MS annotation in the National Gallery copy of the [Galitzin] sale catalogue of 1825 (see PROVENANCE).

2 Vorsterman's print is fig. 47b in A. von Schneider, *Caravaggio und die Niederländer*, 1933.

3. White No. 102. HdG No. 208.

4. 1979 cat. P240. HdG No. 186.

5. Victor Rothschild sale, London, 19 sqq. April 1937 (lot 10). Art market, London, 1949. In 1966 said to be in the collection of Judge Lucius P. Green, Los Angeles (Leiden ex. cat., 1966, op. cit., p. 63).

6. Gudlaugsson, op. cit., p. 40.

7. Robinson, op. cit., p. 48.

8. 'D'après Metsu. L'intérieur d'une chambre où l'on voit une femme cherchant à prendre le trait d'un enfant sculpté placé sur une table qui est devant elle'; canvas, 8 × 8 *pouces*.

9. As after Metsu: 'Anna Maria Schuurman, zittende te Tekenen, naar een pleister Kop, aanheffende een rood satyn Kleed, met een bonte Rand . . .'; panel, 14½ × 11½ *duim*.

10. Panel, 35.5 × 29 cm. In this copy Vorsterman's

engraving is replaced by a print (in reverse) after Adriaen van der Werff's *Rest on the Flight into Egypt*, probably P. van Bleeck's mezzotint of 1748 (see No. 3909 of this catalogue). There are also a number of other changes, including the addition of an oval *Portrait of a Man* on the wall above the woman's head.

11. As by W. van Mieris. Panel, 28 × 23 cm.

12. Panel, 39.5 × 29 cm. Signed, falsely.

13. J. E. Wessely, *Wallerant Vaillant*, 2nd ed., 1881, No. 151 and p. 95.

14. In *Collection de cent-vingt estampes . . . d'après les tableaux . . . de M. Poullain. . .*, 1781, No. 56.

15. As 'La Hollandaise studieuse' according to Wessely, op. cit., note to No. 151.

16. 'Een Tekenares, van Gerbrand [sic] Metzu' (Hoet, vol. I, p. 107, erroneously as lot 44).

17. 'Een Vrouwtje in haer Teekenkamer, dat Teekent naar 't Pleyster, door Gabriel Metzu' (Hoet, vol. I, p. 341).

18. 'Een Vrouwtje dat in een Kamer zit te teekenen, door Gabr. Metzu . . .'; 12½ × 1(.)½ *duim*. In view of the size, this may equally well be HdG No. 30.

19. '. . . een Juffertje dat zit en teekend, door den zelven' [Metsu]; 14 × 11½ *duim*. The Tonneman provenance is mentioned in the Leendert de Neufville and

Frans van de Velde sale catalogues.

20. '. . . het bekende Tekenaarstertje, door Gabriel Metzu'; panel, 14 × 12 *duim*; as from the Tonneman collection (Terwesten, p. 473).

21. As from the Tonneman collection. The description in the van de Velde sale catalogue agrees in detail with the National Gallery picture.

22. According to the Poullain sale catalogue, 1780.

23. Prince Galitzin was the vendor of some if not all of the pictures in this anonymous sale; a seal with his arms is on the back of the present picture (see also G. ter Borch No. 864 and C. Netscher No. 845 of this catalogue).

24. and **25.** Smith, loc. cit.

26. P. G. Konody, *Works of Art in the Collection of Viscount Rothermere*, 1932, pl. 51.

MICHIEL VAN MIEREVELD, 1567–1641

Michiel Jansz. van Miereveld or *Mierevelt* (he used both forms) was born in Delft, 1 May 1567, according to Carel van Mander.[1] Van Mander says he studied for a little while with Willem Willemsz., then with 'Augustijn' in Delft and finally, when about fourteen, with Anthonie van Blocklandt in Utrecht, with whom he stayed two and a quarter years; and that at the death of Blocklandt [in 1583] he returned to Delft and devoted himself to portraiture.[2] He married in Delft in 1589[3] and was inscribed in the guild there before 1613.[4] He was much employed at the Stadholder's court in The Hague and became a member of The Hague guild in 1625[5] yet apparently lived chiefly in Delft where he remarried in 1633;[6] he died there on 27 June 1641.[7]

He was a very successful portrait painter, producing a large number of portraits, many of members of the house of Nassau and the court; there are numerous repetitions, often the work of pupils, among whom were his sons Pieter (1596–1623) and Jan (1604–33). Many of his portraits were reproduced by contemporary engravers, mostly by Willem Jacobsz. Delff, his son-in-law.

REFERENCES:

1. *Het Schilder Boeck*, 1604, fol. 301r.
2. Van Mander, loc. cit.
3. Havard, vol. 1, p. 28.
4. Obreen, vol. 1, p. 4.

5. Obreen, vol. 3, p. 263.
6. Havard, vol. 1, p. 30.
7. OH, 1903, p. 4.

2292 *Portrait of a Woman*   *Plate 222*

Signed just above her left shoulder: F(?) 1618/M Mierevelt (the signature much worn and faint).

On the back is a fragment of paper with the remains of an inscription: Cad(. .) rello/ . . . rta (·) (p?)rello.

Oil on oak, 61.6 × 50.5 (24¼ × 19⅞).

PROVENANCE: In the collection of George Fielder by 1878;[1] George Fielder Bequest, 1908.

EXHIBITION: Guildford, Surrey Art Loan Exhibition, 1884, No. 77.[2]

REFERENCES:

1. It is mentioned in his will of 1878.

2. As by C. Janssen.

FRANS VAN MIERIS the Elder, 1635–1681

Frans Jansz. van Mieris, son of a goldsmith, was born in Leiden, 16 April 1635.[1] He was first apprenticed as a goldsmith to his cousin Willem Fransz.; by 1650 he had become a pupil (in Leiden) of Abraham van Toorenvliet, a glass-painter; then for some years he was apprenticed to Gerrit Dou; subsequently to Abraham van den Tempel and, finally, once more to Dou, who called him 'the Prince of his pupils'.[2] The earliest dated pictures are of 1657 (Glasgow[3] and Vienna[4]). He entered the Leiden guild on 14 May 1658[5] and was a *hoofdman*, 1663 and 1664, and a *deken*, 1665.[6] Van Mieris spent his whole life in Leiden and was extensively patronised by the town's leading citizens. He also received important commissions from Grand Duke Cosimo III de' Medici and the Archduke Leopold Wilhelm who tried unsuccessfully to bring him to Vienna as court painter. Despite these successes, notarial records indicate that in the 1660s and 1670s van Mieris was frequently in debt; they also confirm Houbraken's claim that the painter was a habitual drunkard. He died in Leiden on 12 March 1681[7] and was buried in the Pieterskerk.

Van Mieris was the most important of Dou's pupils and one of the principal members of the Leiden school of 'fine painters'. In subject and style his work derives in the first place from Dou. Most of his works are small genre scenes and portraits; there are also religious, classical and literary subjects. Many of the later Leiden 'fine painters' seem to follow him rather than Dou. He was imitated by his sons, Jan and Willem, and his grandson, Frans van Mieris the Younger (1689–1763), worked in the same tradition. Another pupil was the Leiden genre and portrait painter, Carel de Moor.

REFERENCES:
General: HdG, vol. 10; O. Naumann, *Frans van Mieris the Elder*, 2 vols., Doornspijk, 1981.
In text:
1. Houbraken, vol. 3, p. 2.
2. Loc. cit., pp. 2–3. Houbraken erroneously calls van den Tempel 'Adriaan' instead of Abraham.

3. Naumann, op. cit., cat. no. II 20.
4. Naumann, op. cit., cat. no. I 20.
5. Obreen, vol. 5, p. 220.
6. Obreen, vol. 5, pp. 246–7.
7. Houbraken, op. cit., p. 11.

840 *A Woman in a Red Jacket feeding a Parrot*   *Plate 223*

In the background, now barely visible, are (to the left) a bed with dark-green damask curtains and (to the right) an open door with foliage round the edges.

Oil on copper, 22.5 × 17.3 ($8\frac{7}{8}$ × 7).

The best and probably the original version of this design is the picture, signed and dated 1663, in a private collection in England (Fig. 60).[1] No. 840 is an exact repetition of this, probably a little later in date, and slightly inferior to it. There are many copies of the composition (see below).

Naumann has suggested that the composition represents Taste in a series of the Five Senses.[2]

VERSIONS AND COPIES: The best of all the extant versions is discussed above. A version, which was recorded as early as 1722 and may well have been autograph, was in Dresden[3] until its destruction during the Second World War. There is another version, probably an old copy, in the Royal Collection.[4] There is a copy in the Musée de la Ville, Alès;[5] another (with variations: the bird is in the cage) is in the Musée des Beaux-Arts, Mulhouse.[6] Further copies were in the Schuvaloff collection in Leningrad in 1928[7] and in the Cook collection in Richmond.[8] In addition, two copies are recorded by Parthey[9] and another was seen by HdG with the London dealer, E. Bolton, in 1926.[10] There are also the following sale catalogue items which are not firmly identified with any of the above: Prince de Conti sale, Paris, Remy, 8 April–6 June 1777, lot 410;[11] Johan van der Linden van Slingelandt sale, Dordrecht, 22 August 1785, lot 263 (430 guilders to van der Meij);[12] Choiseul-Praslin sale, Paris, 18 February 1793, lot 68 (9,451 francs);[13] Anon. sale, London, Phillips, 28 February 1799, lot 41;[14] Catton sale, London, Greenwood, 11 March 1802, lot 76;[15] Anon. sale, London, Edwards, 25 May 1808, lot 54;[16] Anon. sale, Rotterdam, 6 June 1810, lot 12;[17] Dr Franck sale, Christie's, 25 May 1843, lot 87 (12 gns to Emery);[18] Anon. sale, Antwerp, 15 April 1884, lot 70;[19] Albert Lehmann sale, Paris, Galerie Georges Petit, 12 June 1925, lot 264;[20] 'Z' et al. sale, Zurich, Stori, 26 November 1927, lot 162;[21] Earl of Jersey and others sale, Christie's, 15 August 1944, lot 16 (as ter Borch);[22] Anon. sale, Christie's, 15 July 1949, lot 16 (as ter Borch: 14 gns to Leaver);[23] Anon. sale, Christie's, 9 November 1951, lot 149 (26 gns to Malaise);[24] Anon. sale, Sotheby's, 17 June 1959, lot 99 (£20 to Kroning);[25] Anon. sale, Stockholm, 12–16 November 1968, lot 662.[26] There is a pastiche which includes the figure of the woman in the Museum of Fine Arts in Boston.[27] A number of drawn copies are listed by Naumann.[28]

PROVENANCE: (It is difficult to disentangle the provenance of the National Gallery picture from those of other versions and copies. Smith gives the provenance of the present version as from the Gaignat, Choiseul-Praslin, Talleyrand and Beckford sales but this is partially wrong.[29])

No. 840 was probably the version in the collection of L. J. Gaignat by 1760[30] and in the L. J. Gaignat sale, Paris, 14 sqq. February 1769 (lot 46),[31] bought by Remy (3,100 francs). According to Smith[32] it was in the collection of the Prince de Talleyrand and thence bought privately in 1817 (it is not in the catalogue of the sale announced for 9 July 1817 nor in the list of pictures bought from the Talleyrand collection by Buchanan in 1817).[33] In the collection of William Beckford, Fonthill Abbey; it is in the catalogue of the Fonthill Abbey sale announced for 15 October 1822 (lot 105) which did not take place, Fonthill Abbey and its contents having been bought by Farquhar;[34] in the Fonthill Abbey sale of 10 sqq. October 1823 (lot 200)[35] bought by S. T. Howe[36] (305 gns), probably for (Sir) Robert Peel (Bart.),[37] in whose collection it certainly was by 1829.[38] Purchased with the Peel collection, 1871.

REFERENCES:

General: Smith No. 29; HdG No. 210; Naumann, op. cit., No. II 54.

In text:

1. HdG No. 213; Naumann op. cit., No. I 54. Panel, 22.5 × 17.5 cm. The signature and date, F van Mieris Fect Anno 1663, once clearly visible in the upper left, is now indistinct. The painting was in the Bavarian Royal Collection: it was listed in the Schleissheim inventory of 1748 (p. 4 recto) and later in the catalogues of the Alte Pinakothek, Munich. It was sold in 1936 to the Amsterdam dealer, D. A. Hoogendijk. Subsequently it was in the collection of Mr and Mrs David Birnbaum in New York. It was in the Mrs Charles E. Dunlop sale, Parke-Bernet, New York, 3 December 1975, lot 304 (bought Speelman). Collection of Lord Samuel, Wych Cross; Collection of Lady Samuel, London. (Not among the paintings bequeathed to the Corporation of the City of London by Lord Samuel in 1987 [see ex. cat. *The Harold Samuel Collection*, London, Barbican Art Gallery, 1988].) The painting was engraved by J. S. Klauber (1789) and Johannes Bürger and etched by N. Strixner and J. Wölffle.

2. Naumann, op. cit., vol. 1, p. 66.

3. Panel, 22.5 × 17.5 cm. HdG under No. 210 (as a copy). Naumann, op. cit., 54e. In Dresden inventory of 1722 (No. A340); 1920 Dresden catalogue, No. 1754 (as a copy). The painting was first doubted by Woermann in the 1899 Dresden catalogue: he believed it to be an old copy of the original, then in Munich (see note 1, above) but too hard in technique to be autograph. The photograph, however, shows a painting of very considerable quality (illustrated in Naumann, op. cit., as Fig. C54e).

4. Panel, 22.9 × 17.8 cm. HdG No. 212. White No. 113. Naumann, op. cit., 54b. Bought by King George IV in 1816.

5. Panel, 23 × 19.5 cm. Inv. no. 43 (as Willem van Mieris). Naumann, op. cit., No. 54r. Photo in RKD.

6. Panel, 26 × 21 cm. Inv. no. 54 (as a copy). Naumann, op. cit., No. 54v.

7. HdG under No. 210 (as a copy); Naumann, op. cit., No. 54i.

8. Panel, 21.5 × 17.8 cm. Naumann, op. cit., No. 54f (fig. C54f). J. O. Kronig, *Catalogue of the Paintings at Doughty House*, vol. 2, 1914, No. 286.

The painting was later in the sale J. Goudstikker et al., Berlin, Lange, 12 March 1941, lot 61 (pl. 37).

9. Naumann, op. cit., No. 54p, 54q. G. Parthey, *Deutscher Bildersaal: Verzeichnis der in Deutschland vorhandenen Oelbilder verstorbener Maler aller Schulen . . .*, 2 vols., Berlin, 1863–4: vol. 2, p. 134, No. 2; 'Koblenz, Casino – Frau in rother Jacke mit einem grünen Papageien spielend, angeblich die Frau des Malers'; vol. 2, p. 130, No. 2: 'Löwenberg, Hohenzollern-Hechingen – Ein Mädchen mit einem Papageien. Original in München.'

10. Copper. Naumann, op. cit., No. 54x. HdG Fiches, RKD: 'Zittend vrouwtje in 't rood, haar papagaai, die links op een stok zit, voerend. Op koper met heel leelijke barsten.'

11. *6 pouces 6 lignes × 5 pouces* (17.6 × 13.5 cm.): 'De Mieris, composé d'une femme qui donne à manger à un oiseau. Sold to Paillet.' Naumann, op. cit., No. 54y.

12. Panel, 8¾ × 6¼ *duim* (22.5 × 16.1 cm.). Smith, under No. 29; HdG, under No. 212. Both Smith and HdG believed that this was the Royal Collection painting (see above, and note 4); MacLaren, however, pointed out that the description in the van Slingelandt sale catalogue describes the colour of the woman's jacket as *paars* (violet) whereas it is red. This may be the same painting as in the Choiseul-Praslin sale of 1793 (note 13) and the Anon. sale, Rotterdam, of 1810 (note 17).

13. Panel, 8 × 6 *pouces* (21.7 × 16.2 cm.). Smith (No. 29) and HdG (under No. 210) believed that this referred to No. 840. MacLaren, however, pointed out that the support, dimensions and description in the Praslin catalogue differ. The woman in the Praslin catalogue lot is said to be wearing 'un large manteau de lit, de velours pourpre, bordé d'hermine'. This may be the painting in the van Slingelandt sale of 1785 (note 12) and in the Anon. sale, Rotterdam, of 1810 (note 17).

14. 'Mieris. Woman and parrot . . . equal to Ger. Douw.' Naumann, op. cit., No. 54l.

15. 'Mieris. A Lady and a Parrot.' Naumann, op. cit., No. 54m.

16. 'Mieris. A woman feeding a parrot, a very fine and scarce cabinet picture, in its pristine state.' Plate 5 in the catalogue. Naumann, op. cit., No. 54o.

17. Panel, 8 × 6 *duim* (20.6 × 15.4 cm.). HdG (under No. 210) suggested that this was the Royal Collection painting but the jacket worn by the woman is described in the sale catalogue as *paars* (violet), not red. This may be the painting in the van Slingelandt sale of 1785 (note 12) and in the Choiseul-Praslin sale of 1793 (note 13). Naumann, op. cit., No. 54d.

18. 'Mieris. A Lady in a red corset, and yellow satin gown, playing with a parrot.' (Size and support not stated.) A. Graves, *Art Sales*, vol. 2, 1821, p. 220. Naumann, op. cit., No. 51k.

19. Canvas, 30 × 25 cm. Naumann, op. cit., No. 54w.

20. Panel, 24.5 × 19.5 cm. In the sale catalogue the painting was given this provenance: 'Coll. Chevalier de Cosson; English collection; A. Hulot sale, Paris, 9 May 1892, lot 29 (700 francs).' Photo in Witt and Fogg Art Reference Library. Apparently a poor copy. Naumann, op. cit., No. 54h.

21. Copper, 57 × 48 cm. Reproduced in sale catalogue. Poor copy; greatly enlarged. Naumann, op. cit., No. 54t.

22. Panel, 36.8 × 29.2 cm. Photo in RKD. With variations (framed by stone arch and ledge; no bag on woman's lap). Apparently a nineteenth-century copy. Naumann, op. cit., No. 54s.

23. Panel, 14½ × 11½ in. Naumann, op. cit., No. 54j.

24. Copper, 22.9 × 17.8 cm. This painting, apparently a poor nineteenth-century copy, was subsequently in these sales: Anon. sale, Christie's, 28 March 1952, lot 86 (as Willem van Mieris: 32 gns to Waters); Anon. sale, Christie's, 23 April 1954, lot 14 (18 gns to Ryan); Anon. sale, Christie's, 29 October 1954, lot 38 (14 gns to de Henvil). Naumann, op. cit., No. 54g.

25. Panel, 22.9 × 23 cm. Photo in RKD: poor copy. Naumann, op. cit., No. 54n.

26. Plate 17 in the catalogue: apparently a poor copy. Naumann, op. cit., No. 54n.

27. Panel, 27.5 × 21.5 cm. Inv. no. 74.a6. The painting also contains the figure of the black servant from *A Young Lady before a Mirror* (Berlin-Dahlem, Gemäldegalerie: 1978 cat., No. 838). Naumann, op. cit., No. 54z.

28. Naumann, op. cit., p. 69 (cat. no. 54).

29. Smith No. 29. See also note 12.

30. See Descamps, vol. 3, p. 20.

31. As on copper, 8 *pouces × 6 pouces 6 lignes*. There is a sketch of lot 46 in the reproduction of the sale catalogue in *Catalogues de ventes . . . illustrés par Gabriel de Saint-Aubin*, vol. 11, 1921.

32. Smith No. 29.

33. See Buchanan, vol. 2, pp. 308 and 316–48.

34. See [C. Redding], *Memoirs of W. Beckford*, 1859, vol. 2, p. 239.

35. The 1822 and 1823 Fonthill sale catalogues give the provenance wrongly as ex-Choiseul-Praslin (see note 13).

36. According to G. Redford, *Art Sales*, 1888, vol. 2, p. 309.

37. A copy of the sale catalogue in the Victoria and Albert Museum Library with contemporary annotations gives 'Hon. R. Peel' as the purchaser.

38. Smith No. 29.

1415 *Portrait of the Artist's Wife, Cunera van der Cock* Plate 224

The original part of the picture consists of an oval of vellum(?), 11.1 × 8.2 (4⅜ × 3¼).[1] At some time before 1800 (possibly before 1768) this oval was inlaid in the present oak panel, which measures 16 × 13.3 (6⁵⁄₁₆ × 5¼).[2] The lower part of the jacket and the fur trimming of the sleeve, which lie outside the original oval, are clearly later and probably not by van Mieris;[3] the upper part of the jacket has been in part retouched to match this addition. The original background of the oval has presumably been overpainted to match that of the addition.

Cunera Cornelisdr. van der Cock (1629 or 1639–1700) married Frans van Mieris in 1657.[4] The sitter was long thought to be Anna Maria van Schurman (1607–78)[5] but bears no resemblance to authentic portraits of the latter such as that by Jan Lievens (No. 1095 of the present catalogue). A small oval bust portrait in Munich, clearly of the same woman as in the National Gallery portrait, is the companion to the self portrait of van Mieris in the same collection; both are dated 1662.[6] Van Mieris often used his wife as a model in genre scenes.[7] Hofstede de Groot catalogued No. 1415 as by Dou.[8] MacLaren correctly attributed it to van Mieris and noted its similarity in style to the *Doctor's Visit* of 1657 in Glasgow.[9] Naumann[10] dated No. 1415 to the late 1650s. A date of *c.*1657–8 is acceptable.[11] The *Self Portrait* of van Mieris in East Berlin (Fig. 61),[12] an oval panel of similar dimensions, may well be a pair to No. 1415.

ENGRAVING: Said to be engraved by Samuel Gottlob Kuetner, 1773.[13]

PROVENANCE: Possibly in the Josua van Belle sale, Rotterdam, 6 September 1730, lot 63;[14] possibly the small portrait of a woman which was apparently in the collection of Willem Lormier, The Hague, *c.*1752[15] (W. Lormier sale, The Hague, 4 July 1763, lot 68,[16] bought by Yver, 120 guilders) and in the collection of Gottfried Winkler, Leipzig, by 1768 (still there in 1773).[17] The National Gallery picture was certainly in the Cornelis Ploos van Amstel sale, Amsterdam, 3 sqq. March 1800 (lot 20 of the paintings), bought by van der Schley (71 guilders); Anon. sale ('a foreign collector'), Amsterdam, 16 sqq. June 1802 (lot 38), bought by Coclers (75 florins); possibly in the Comte F. de Robiano sale, Brussels, 1 sqq. May 1837 (lot 151),[18] bought by Godde(?), 180 francs. (The Lormier/Winkler painting was in the Duval sale, Phillips, 12–13 May 1846 [lot 98, as Douw(sic)], bought by Paley [£29.8s].) It was in the [Mrs Wallis] sale, London, 28 March 1893 (lot 147),[19] bought by Horace Buttery (£63), from whom purchased in June 1894.

REFERENCES:
General: HdG, Dou Nos. 365 and (?)85c; Naumann, op. cit., No. 30.
In text:
1. It is not possible to see the material of the original support but X-radiographs show that it is not metal and probably not wood; certain undulations of the surface suggest that it may be vellum. There are a number of oval portraits by van Mieris of the same size, e.g. those in Munich and East Berlin mentioned later in the main text.
2. The size of the picture is given as 6 × 5 *duim* in the catalogue of the Ploos van Amstel sale of 1800 (see PROVENANCE); that in the Winkler collection, 1768, with which No. 1415 has been identified, measured 7½ × 6 *Zoll*, i.e. about 7½ × 6 in. (see note 17). Running in a semicircle across the upper part of the picture surface is a raised line; it continues down the

right side parallel to, and about a centimetre from, the right edge. This led HdG (loc. cit.) to suppose that the original oval had first been made into a picture with a rounded top and later enlarged again to the present rectangular shape (see also the following note). X-radiographs show that this raised line exists only in the paint or the varnish and that the only addition made to the original oval was when it was inlaid in the rectangular oak panel.
3. HdG (Dou No. 365) thought that the additional portion was the work of the painter of the original oval. Quite apart from the difference and inferiority of execution, the shortness of the jacket sleeve suggests that the addition was made at least five years later since jackets of this kind had three-quarter length sleeves reaching to the elbow until the later 1660s.

4. The banns were published on 15 March 1657 (document transcribed in full in Naumann, op. cit., vol. 1, p. 164).

5. On the back of the panel is a bookplate with the Ploos van Amstel arms (*fascé d'or et de sable, de huit pièces; au sautoir échiqueté d'argent et de gueules, brochant sur le tout*) inscribed in an eighteenth-century hand: '+ Pourtret / van de geleerde en kuns(. . .) / Juffr Anna Maria / Schuurman. / gebooren (te?) Utrecht 1607 / gestorven 1678. / Geschildert door Gerard Douw / gebooren te Leyden 1613 / Discipil van Rembrand.' The same identification is made in the catalogues of the Ploos van Amstel and anonymous 1802 Amsterdam sales (see PROVENANCE).

6. 1983 cat., Nos. 627, 628. HdG, Nos. 247 and 258. Naumann, op. cit., cat. nos. 41, 42. These two portraits were already described as the elder Frans van Mieris and his wife by van Gool, vol. 2, p. 563.

7. Naumann, op. cit., vol. 1, pp. 127–8.

8. HdG, Dou No. 365. The attribution to Dou was revived in 1960 by Plietzch (E. Plietzch, *Holländische und Flämische Maler des XVII Jahrhunderts*, Leipzig, 1960, p. 38).

9. Naumann, op. cit., cat. no. II20.

10. Naumann, op. cit., vol. 1, pp. 64–5.

11. Blankert (Blankert et al., *Vermeer*, New York, 1988, p. 120) also dates No. 1415 as *c.* 1658. He suggests it as a possible source for the composition of Vermeer's *Woman with a Pearl Earring* (The Hague, Mauritshuis).

12. Staatliche Museen zu Berlin, Gemäldegalerie: *Holländische und Flämische Gemälde*, Berlin, 1976, No. 834. Panel, oval, 12.3 × 9.6 cm. Naumann, op. cit., cat. no. 29. This self portrait may be the painting mentioned in the van Belle sale of 1730.

13. When in the Winkler collection (see note 17).

14. Hoet, vol. 1, p. 356: 'Twee kleine Stukjes,

zynde Miris en zijn Vrouw, door hem zelfs geschildert in 't ovael.'

15. 'Gerard Dou . . . Een Vrouwtje in 't bont'; panel, 7 × 6 *duim* (see Hoet, vol. 2, p. 421).

16. Identical description and size as in note 15.

17. HdG (Dou No. 365) identifies the National Gallery picture with one in the Winkler collection engraved by S. G. Kuetner in 1773. The present writer has not been able to see an impression of this print and cannot verify whether it is in fact after No. 1415. According to HdG the picture is mentioned in the Winkler collection in 1768; this presumably refers to A. F. Oever's *Historische Erklaerungen der Gemaelde welche Herr Gottfried Winkler in Leipzig gesammelt*, 1768, and the only possible item in this catalogue is No. 320: 'Gerard Douw . . . Die Büste einer jungen Frau, fast in Profil zur Linken gewandt. Ihr glatt aufgekämmtes Haar ist auf dem Hinterkopfe mit einem weissen Häubchen bedeckt, ihr Ohr mit einer Perl geschmücket und ihr braungestreiftes Wams mit Pelze verbrämet. Sie war sonst im Cabinette des Herrn de Lormier im Haag'; wood, 7½ × 6 *Zoll* (*c.* 19 × 15 cm.). This description does not fit the National Gallery picture. The only picture in the Lormier collection to which it could refer is that mentioned in the PROVENANCE, the description of which is very vague (see note 15 above).

18. 'Dow, Gérard Autre portrait de jeune fille vêtue d'un casaquin rouge brun garni d'hermine'; panel, 15 × 12 cm. Although the Robiano picture is described as 'ceintré' and No. 1415 has a rectangular top, there is a semicircular mark across the top of the latter (see note 2) and it may once have been in a frame with a round top; this would explain the remark in the Robiano sale catalogue.

19. As by Dou.

1874 *Self Portrait of the Artist, with a Cittern* Plate 225

Inscribed on the lower part of the stonework: ÆTAT 38$\frac{4}{13}$/A° D^{om} 1674 (see Fig. 62).

Oil on canvas, 17.5 × 14 (6$\frac{7}{8}$ × 5$\frac{1}{2}$).

Some wearing in the hair and in the darks.

The identity of the sitter is established by the self-portrait drawing, signed and dated 1667, in the British Museum (Fig. 63),[1] the identification of which is certain.[2] The date of the present portrait, 13 April 1674, is three days before van Mieris' thirty-ninth birthday.[3]

The artist is wearing an archaic type of dress. Gudlaugsson[4] has suggested that similar costumes, which occur quite often in works of the Leiden painters, were based on the 'Spanish' or 'Italian' costumes worn by actors of the *commedia dell'arte* (see also No. 2952 below, After F. van Mieris).

VERSIONS AND COPIES: A number of versions are listed in early sale catalogues: Comte de Vence sale, Paris, Remy, 9 February 1761, lot 106;[5] Frans van Mieris the Younger sale, Leiden, Pieter van der Eyck, 7 May 1764, lot 248 (270 guilders to Capello);[6] Menageot sale, Paris (Clariot; Paillet), 17 March 1778, lot 217;[7] 'Deux Amateurs' sale, Leiden, 26 August 1788, lot 83 (9½ guilders to Hoefman);[8] Dubois sale, Paris, Lebrun, 31 March 1784, lot 36 (241 francs: to Saubert).[9] A second grisaille version: Bicker van Zwieten sale, The Hague, 12 April 1741, lot 62.[10] An oval copy by Arie de Vois, in grey wash on paper, is in the printroom of Leiden University.[11]

PROVENANCE: No. 1874 is possibly the self portrait of van Mieris in 'Italian' costume, playing the lute, which was in the collection of Diego Duarte, Antwerp in 1682.[12] It was in the collection of General Sir John May by 1847;[13] May Bequest, 1854.

EXHIBITION: London 1976, No. 72.

REFERENCES:

General: Naumann, op. cit., cat. no. 96.
In text:
1. Hind, vol. 3, p. 144, No. 4.
2. It was mezzotinted as a self portrait of Frans van Mieris I by Abraham Blooteling (Hollstein No. 185). It was etched as a portrait of F. van Mieris I by his pupil, Carel de Moor (Hollstein No. 3). Further, the British Museum drawing or a monochrome repetition of it appears in the Frans van Mieris the Younger's painting (dated 1742) of the three generations of the van Mieris family (Stedelijk Museum De Lakenhal, Leiden; 1983 cat., No. 311).
3. Frans van Mieris the Elder was born on 16 April 1635 (Houbraken, vol. 3, p. 2).
4. S. J. Gudlaugsson, *The Comedians in the work of Jan Steen and his contemporaries*, Soest, 1975, *passim*.
5. Panel, 6½ × 5 *pouces* (17.6 × 13.5 cm.): 'FRAN-COIS MIERIS. Le Portrait de Mieris, ce Tableau colé sur bois . . . On ne scait si l'on peut assurer que ce Tableau peint par Francois Mieris, les Connoisseurs geront comme bon leur semblera (145 francs).' (Descamps, vol. 3, p. 20.) This may be the painting subsequently in the collection of the Count D'Angiviller in Paris in 1793: 'Un portrait de Mieris, peint par lui-même, jouant de la guitare dans sa bordure.' (see M. Furcy-Raynaud, *Les tableaux et objets d'art saisis chez les émigrés et condamnés et envoyés au musée central*, Archives de l'art français, 4, 1912, p. 250, no. 12). It was apparently in the Louvre in 1815: *Notice des tableaux exposés dans la galerie du musée*, Paris, 1815, p. 51, No. 428: 'Francois Mieris jouant de la guitare.' Naumann, op. cit., No. 96h (and 96f, 96g).
6. Panel, 7¾ × 6 *duimen*: 'Een Man die een lind [sic: for luit] stelt, zittende voor een tafel met veel bywerk, konstig geschildert door den ouden Frans van Mieris. hoog 7¾, breed 6 duimen.' This painting was subsequently lot 43, in the Pieter van Capello sale, Amsterdam, J. M. Cok, 6 May 1767: 'MIERIS de Oude. Een overheerlyk Cabinet-Stukje, verbeel-

dende een deftige Musikant, halver lyf, zyn Luyt stellende, en ziende over zyn linker schouder, waar in de hartstogt, aangaande het attrappeeren des toons wonderlyk wel geobserveert is' (206 guilders to Fouquet) (Terwesten, p. 589). HdG (under No. 243). Naumann, op. cit., No. 96b.
7. 9 *pouces* × 6 *pouces*, 6 *lignes* (24.4 × 17.6 cm.): 'Francois Mieris. Le Portrait de ce Peintre peint par lui-même, vu à mi-corps, la tête de trois quarts, & adjusté à l'Espagnole; il est apuyé contre un piédestal, sur lequel est un verre & un chapeau garni de plumes blanches.'
8. Panel, 8 × 7 *duimen* (21 × 18.2 cm.): 'Frans MIERIS, den Ouden. Het Pourtrait van deze grote Konstenaar in 't Grauw Geschildert 1674 den 13 April, oud 38 Jaar, zo als blykt op de rand van een Steenen Pilaster, war op men ziet een Liquerglas en zyn Schilders Muts verciert met Pluimen, hy is op zyn Spaans gekleet, in de Achtergrond is een Landschap.' This painting was lot 84 in the J. E. Grave et al. sale, Amsterdam, 5 May 1806: 'Een Model in het grauw geschildert, zynde het Pourtret van F. van Mieris, door F. VAN MIERIS' (12 guilders to Roos). HdG No. 251. Naumann, op. cit., No. 96c.
9. Canvas, 7 × 5 *pouces* (17.8 × 12.7 cm.): 'F. MIERIS. Le portrait de ce Peintre à mi-corps, & vu par le dos, la tête tournée sur l'épaule droite, tenant une guitarre, & vêtu de différens satins, le tout dans le costume espagnol: en avant est un socle de pierre où il paroît accoté, & sur lequel est posé un verre à demi rempli de vin & un bonnet de velours garni de plumes, près duquel on lit son age de trente huit ans, peint en 1674.' This painting was subsequently lot 18 in the Calonne Angelot sale, Paris, Lebrun, 11 May 1789, No. 18 (description identical to that in the 1784 sale catalogue: sold for 501 francs to Rousseau). Smith No. 45 (Calonne sale); HdG No. 250 (Calonne sale). Naumann, op. cit., No. 96a.
10. Panel(?), 7 × 5¾ *duimen* (18 × 14.5 cm.). Hoet,

vol. 2, p. 16, No. 62: 'Het Pourtrait van den Ouden Miris, met een Tafel en Roemer met Wyn door den zelven, in 't graauw, h. 7, br. 5 en drie vierde d[uimen].' Lot 63 in this sale was a pendant portrait of the artist's wife: 'Zyn Vrouw, door denzelven, zynde een weerga, mede in 't graauw, h. en br. als voren' (the pair: 30 guilders to Rottermondt). This painting was probably lot 60 in the E. van Dishoek sale, The Hague, 9 June 1745: Hoet, vol. 2, p. 172: 'Den oude F. Mieris zyn Pourtrait, speelende op een Loyt, h. 6 d[uimen], br. 8 d[uimen] (105 guilders).' This may be the version which was in the first collection of François Tronchin. 1765 catalogue, No. 80: 'Un Musicien tête nuë, vêtu à l'antique avec une fraise, jouant de la guitarre: son bonnet & une verre à moitié plein à côté de lui sur la table. B. 6 *pouces* 10 *lignes* de hauteur, 5 *pouces* 6 *lignes* de largeur' (Exhibition catalogue, *De Genève à l'Ermitage; Les collections de François Tronchin*, Musée Rath, Geneva, 1974, cat. no. 160). This painting was purchased from Tron-

chin by Empress Catherine II in Geneva in 1770. It is in the Hermitage catalogues of 1774 (Munich: No. 717), 1838 (No. 39), 1863, 1909 (A. Somof: p. 234, No. 919 as signed FvM); and was in the Museum's collection until 1929. Naumann, op. cit., No. 96d.

11. 16.5 × 12.5 cm. Signed: Aetat 38 4/13/A DVois 1674 (the DV in monogram). Naumann, op. cit., under cat. no. 96, p. 108.

12. In the inventory of Duarte's pictures, dated 12 July 1682 (No. 90): 'Van Mieris Een cleynder syn conterfeytsel tien op sen Italiaens gekleet spelende op een Luyt', valued at 170 florins, see Naumann, op. cit., vol. 1, p. 188; according to MacLaren, Muller (*De Oude Tijd*, 1870, p. 400) erroneously described the collection as being in Amsterdam but it apparently never left Antwerp.

13. It was bequeathed (with Nos. 44, 1858 and 1879) in 1847 with a life-interest to Lady May, and ceded by her to the National Gallery in 1854.

After FRANS VAN MIERIS the Elder

2952 *An Old Fiddler at a Window*   Plate 226

In the background is a woman writing on a slate.

Inscribed below the window: M. D C. LX.

Oil on oak. The panel measures 28.9 × 22.9 (11⅜ × 9); the ground has been left uncovered for about 5 mm. at each side and 2–3 mm. at the top.

The man is wearing late sixteenth-century dress; such archaic costume seems to have been associated with stage and musical performers (cf. F. van Mieris No. 1874 above).

A copy, perhaps of much later date, of a picture, signed and dated 1660, which was last recorded with Knoedler and Co., New York, in 1946 (Fig. 64).[1] It differs from the original, and from the other copies mentioned below, in having a vine about the window instead of ivy.

Naumann has suggested that a painting of an *Old Woman with a Lobster*, known only in a copy,[2] was a pendant to the original of this composition.

VERSIONS AND COPIES: The original of this design is mentioned above. Other versions and copies are in the Pushkin Museum, Moscow;[3] the Herzog Anton Ulrich-Museum, Braunschweig;[4] the Nationalmuseum, Stockholm;[5] the Musée des Beaux-Arts, Dijon;[6] and in the collection of the Rt. Hon. A. R. G. Gordon, Delmont, Killyleagh, Co. Down, Northern Ireland.[7] A copy in the collection of the Brodie of Brodie, Brodie Castle, Morayshire, Scotland[8] has substantial variations (a plate and a peeled lemon in place of the shrimps, and with changes in the ivy). There was a copy with the dealer Jules Porgès in Paris in 1921[9] and copies are also recorded in the following sales: J. van Loon sale, Delft, 18 July 1736, lot 9 (68 guilders);[10] Anon. sale, Amsterdam, 15 April 1739, lot 6 (40 guilders);[11] Humble sale, Farebrother, London, 3 February 1804, lot 58;[12] Miss James et al. sale, London, 20 June 1891, lot 83;[13] Charles T. Yerkes sale, American Art

Galleries, New York, 5 April 1910, lot 62;[14] Diane et al. sale, Christie's, 3 August 1940, lot 141 (5 gns to Gibbons);[15] Duke of Buccleuch sale, Christie's, 1 February 1946, lot 93 (£210 to Slatter);[16] Anon. sale, J. de Mul, Palais des Beaux-Arts, Brussels, 22 October 1951, lot 170;[17] Anon. sale, Drouot, Paris, 31 October 1957;[18] Basingstoke Town Hall et al. sale, Sotheby's, 24 February 1965, lot 66 (£35 to Verney);[19] Anon. sale, Christie's, 24 January 1969, lot 38 (80 gns to Proarte);[20] Anon. sale, Sotheby's, 10 April 1974, lot 23 (£820 to P. Putz).[21]

PROVENANCE: In the collection of Sir Austen Henry Layard (died 1894); Layard Bequest, 1913.

REFERENCES:

General: HdG No. 153 (as copy); Naumann, op. cit., No. 33e (as copy).

In text:

1. Panel, 28.1 × 21 cm. HdG No. 153. Naumann, op. cit., cat. no. 33. The painting's provenance (to 1946) is given in full by Naumann.

2. The copy is on copper, 29.8 × 22.2 cm. It is last recorded in the Leon Lilienfeld sale, Parke-Bernet, New York, 17 May 1972, lot 35 (as School of Frans van Mieris): HdG No. 51; Naumann, op. cit., No. 34.

3. Panel, 29.6 × 22 cm. Signed, beneath the violin: F. van Mieris. Pushkin Museum, 1961 catalogue, No. 637. HdG No. 135 (1c). Naumann, op. cit., cat. no. 33a (with full history). Naumann believes that it 'may well be an authentic replica'.

4. Panel, 29.5 × 22 cm. R. Klessmann, Herzog Anton Ulrich-Museum, Braunschweig, *Die Holländischen Gemälde*, 1983, No. 735 (as copy). Naumann, op. cit., cat. no. 33b (with full history).

5. Panel, 28 × 23 cm. Stockholm 1958 cat. no. 397 (as copy). HdG under No. 153. Naumann, op. cit., cat. no. 33d.

6. Photo in RKD. In 1954 on loan or a gift to Dijon. Substantial variations – no niche, woman omitted, table covered with rug and with glass and pipe resting on it. Naumann, op. cit., cat. no. 33g.

7. Panel, 27 × 22 cm. Naumann, op. cit., cat. no. 33i.

8. 1938 catalogue, No. 94. Photo in Witt Library. Naumann, op. cit., cat. no. 33f.

9. RKD Fiches; seen by HdG in 1921 (a copy). Naumann, op. cit., No. 33n.

10. HdG (No. 114) considered that this painting (support unknown, but presumably panel: 31.7 × 23 cm.) was also included in the following sales: Count van Fraula sale, Brussels, 21 July 1738, lot 136 (64 francs); Anon. sale, Amsterdam, 15 April 1739, lot 6 (40 guilders); Bicker van Zwieten sale, The Hague, 12 April 1741, lot 61 (27 guilders to De Waart); Gerard Bicker van Zwieten sale, The Hague, 4 April 1755, lot 26 (44 guilders); and (?)Anon. sale, Amsterdam, 27 February 1760, lot 9. Although these items do describe the composition, it is possible that they refer to more than one version. Naumann, op. cit., cat. no. 33j.

11. Hoet, vol. 1, p. 576: 'Een Man met een Meyd, Fiool en een Wyngaard, door denzelven [F van Mieris].' Naumann, op. cit., cat. no. 33p.

12. 'MIERIS: Violin player, highly finished.' Naumann, op. cit., cat. no. 33s.

13. As ex-Anderson collection. Naumann, op. cit., cat. no. 33l.

14. Copper, 25.4 × 19 cm. Reproduced in catalogue. Naumann, op. cit., cat. no. 33m.

15. 29.2 × 21 cm. 'Mieris: A Man in Contemplation.' Naumann, op. cit., cat. no. 33t.

16. Panel, 29.2 × 21.6 cm. According to the sale catalogue this painting was in the Cauwerven sale (1765), the Nogaret sale (1780) and the Hope collection. It was later in Anon. sale, Christie's, 28 March 1952, lot 100 (90 gns to Hallsborough). Photo in RKD. Naumann, op. cit., cat. no. 33k.

17. ?Panel, 30 × 22 cm. Naumann, op. cit., cat. no. 33r.

18. 29.5 × 21.7 cm. Reproduced in catalogue. Naumann, op. cit., cat. no. 33q.

19. Panel, 28 × 20.3 cm. Naumann, op. cit., cat. no. 33o.

20. Panel, 29.2 × 21.5 cm. Perhaps the same painting as in note 12, above. Naumann, op. cit., cat. no. 33n.

21. Panel, 30.5 × 22 cm. Naumann, op. cit., cat. no. 33c.

WILLEM VAN MIERIS, 1662–1747

Born in Leiden, 3 June 1662, second son of Frans van Mieris the Elder. According to Johan van Gool, his only teacher was his father, who died when Willem was eighteen;[1] throughout his life he painted in his father's style. He became a member of the Leiden guild in June 1683[2] and always lived in Leiden. He was dean of the guild in 1699.[3] Towards the end of his life he went blind[4] (there are dated pictures of every year, 1682–1736, but no certain ones later). He died in Leiden, 27 January 1747.[5]

As well as paintings of genre subjects (especially shop scenes), religious, mythological and literary subjects, and portraits, he made numerous copies of his father's pictures for his patron, Allard de la Court van der Voort of Leiden, and also designed ornamental vases with figures in relief.[6] His son, Frans van Mieris the Younger, painted in the same style.

REFERENCES:

General: Van Gool, vol. 1, pp. 191–203; HdG, vol. 10; Naumann, *Frans van Mieris the Elder*, Doornspijk, 1981, vol. 1, pp. 13–15.

In text:

1. Van Gool, p. 191.
2. Obreen, vol. 5, p. 238.

3. Obreen, vol. 5, p. 256.
4. and 5. Van Gool, p. 201.
6. Cf. van Gool, pp. 196–7. For this aspect of his activity see C. W. Fock, 'Willem van Mieris als ontwerper en boetseerder van tuinvazen', OH, vol. 87, 1973, pp. 27–48.

841 *A Woman and a Fish-pedlar in a Kitchen*   Plate 227

On the sill are two ducks, a basket of snipe, and fish; hanging on the right, a pheasant and two rabbits. In the right foreground is a white and tortoiseshell cat. In the left background porcelain is displayed on a wooden *theerak*.

Signed along the top edge on the left: W. van Mieris. Fc Anno 1713.

Oil on oak, 49.5 × 41 (19½ × 16⅛).

The bas-relief of tritons and nereids is a variant of a *Triumph of Galatea* relief which appears in several paintings by Willem van Mieris.[1]

ENGRAVING: Engraved by J. Burnet.

PROVENANCE: Probably in the Graaf van Wassenaar Obdam sale, The Hague, 19 August 1750 (lot 55),[2] bought by van der Hoek (500 guilders). Said to have been brought from Brussels to England by West, a dealer.[3] In the Sir Simon Clarke, Bart., and George Hibbert sale, London, 14–15 May 1802 (2nd day, lot 62), bought by Seguier[4] (350 gns). Lent by John Dent to the BI in 1815 and 1824; John Dent sale, London, 28 April 1827 (lot 98), bought by Smith (370 gns)[5] for (Sir) Robert Peel (Bart.).[6] Purchased with the Peel collection, 1871.

EXHIBITIONS: BI 1815, No. 122; BI 1824, No. 68; Rotterdam, Museum Boymans-van Beuningen, 'Thema Thee: De Geschiedenis van de Thee en het Theegebruik in Nederland', 1978, No. 4; Washington/London/Haarlem 1989–90, No. 23.

REFERENCES:

General: Smith Nos. 2(?) and 45; HdG No. 164.

In text:

1. e.g. *A Man with Pipe and Glass at a Window*, dated 1701 (HdG No. 274a; Henry Doetsch sale, London,

22 June 1895, lot 436; reproduced in the sale catalogue); *An Apothecary's Shop* (HdG No. 157; John Walter sale, Sotheby's, 13 February 1946, lot 100; reproduced in the sale catalogue); *Joseph and*

Potiphar's Wife (Karlsruhe Gallery; HdG No. 6); cf. also HdG No. 259.

2. (W. van Mieris) 'Een Boer, die Visch verkoopt aen een Vrou, met veel bywerk, in een Keuken', 19 × 16 *duim*. Hoet, vol. 2, p. 294, gives the lot number wrongly as 56.

3. HdG No. 164.

4. HdG (No. 164) gives Dent as the purchaser, but the correct name is given in Messrs Christie's copy of the sale catalogue.

5. Smith No. 45.

6. According to a contemporary MS annotation in the National Gallery's copy of the sale catalogue.

JAN MOLENAER, *c.* 1610–1668

Jan Miense Molenaer; he signs documents *Jan* or *Johannes Molenaer*, occasionally with the addition of the patronymic *Miense(n)* (= Mienszoon). He was born in Haarlem;[1] in a document of November 1637 he is said to be about twenty-seven.[2] There are dated paintings from 1629 onwards. He was living in Haarlem in 1636[3] and in June of that year he married the painter Judith Leyster in Heemstede, near Haarlem.[4] By November 1637 he was living in Amsterdam[5] and is recorded there several times until 1644 (in which year Jan Lievens appears to have been living in his house) and seems to have continued in Amsterdam until 1648;[6] in October of that year he bought a house in Heemstede[7] and thenceforward lived mostly there and in Haarlem.[8] (He bought a house on the Voetboogstraat in Amsterdam in January 1655 and was living there from May 1655 until October 1656.[9]) He was buried in Haarlem, 19 September 1668.[10]

Apart from a few portraits and religious pictures his work (often signed with a monogram, IMR, IMOR or JMR) consists entirely of genre subjects. His earlier paintings are connected in style with Frans Hals although there is no documentary evidence of his having been a pupil of Hals. His style is also similar to that of Judith Leyster. He later imitated Adriaen van Ostade's interiors.

REFERENCES:
General: Bredius in Obreen, vol. 7, pp. 289–304; W. Bode and Bredius in JKPK, 1890, pp. 65–78; Bredius, *Künstler-Inventare*, vol. 1, pp. 1–26, and vol. 7, pp. 154–61.

In text:
1. According to Theodoor Schrevelius, *Harlemias*, 1648, p. 384.

2. *Künstler-Inventare*, vol. 1, p. 11.

3. *Künstler-Inventare*, vol. 1, pp. 9–10.

4. H. F. Wijnman in OH, 1932, p. 63.

5. *Künstler-Inventare*, vol. 1, p. 11.

6. Obreen, vol. 7, pp. 289–94, and *Künstler-Inventare*, vol. 1, pp. 11–13.

7. Obreen, vol. 7, p. 294.

8. *Künstler-Inventare*, vol. 1, pp. 14ff, and vol. 7, pp. 156–60.

9. *Künstler-Inventare*, vol. 1, pp. 17 and 19.

10. Van der Willigen, p. 225.

1293 *A Young Man playing a Theorbo and a Young Woman playing a Cittern*

Plate 228

Signed on the foot-warmer: (I?) MR (in monogram; faint).

Oil on canvas, 68 × 84 (26¾ × 33).

Cleaned in 1976.

The portrait of a bearded man in armour with an orange sash (right background), in the style of Michiel van Miereveld, is probably of Prince Frederik Hendrik of Orange (1584–1647) who became Stadholder in 1625.[1]

Probably painted in the early 1630s; compare, for example, with *The Dentist* of 1630 (Braunschweig)[2] and *The Painter's Studio* of 1631 (East Berlin).[3] A young couple playing a duet can stand for the harmony of true love in Dutch genre painting.[4]

PROVENANCE: Purchased from Messrs Colnaghi (out of the Clarke Fund) in 1889.

EXHIBITIONS: London 1976, No. 73; London 1978–9, No. 8.

REFERENCES:
1. Cf. Willem Delff's engraving of 1632–3 after Miereveld's portrait of him (Hollstein, vol. 5, no. 62). For an implausible interpretation of No. 1293 as a political allegory, see N. Salmon, 'Political iconography in a painting by Jan Miense Molenaer', *Mercury*, 4, 1986, pp. 23–38.
2. R. Klessmann, Herzog Anton Ulrich-Museum, Braunschweig, *Die Holländischen Gemälde*, 1983, No. 668.
3. Staatliche Museen zu Berlin, Gemäldegalerie: 1976 cat. no. 873.
4. See, for example, the exhibition catalogue, *Tot Lering en Vermaak*, Amsterdam, Rijksmuseum, 1976, No. 45.

5416 *Two Boys and a Girl making Music*   Plate 229

The boy on the right is playing on a *rommelpot*, the one on the left a violin. The girl wears a gorget and beats an accompaniment with spoons on a morion. Against the wall, right is a *kolf* club.

Signed on the end of the box, bottom left: I MR/1629 (MR in monogram).[1]

Oil on canvas, 68.3 × 84.5 (26⅞ × 33¼). (MacLaren suggested that the canvas might have been slightly cut down at the sides, and, less so, at the bottom, but the 'squeezing' of elements of the composition at the edges of the canvas is entirely consistent with other paintings by Molenaer and there is no physical evidence for its reduction.)

Cleaned in 1964.

Molenaer often treated the subject of children playing musical instruments: they are presumably intended as evocations of the carefree time of childhood.[2] There is, for example, a very similar group of four music-making children in a painting in the collection of the Rijksdienst Beeldende Kunst.[3]

The painting was once attributed to 'the Lenains',[4] the falsified signature appearing to be theirs.

COPIES: An exact copy is in the Evelyn collection in Stonor Park.[5] A variant copy was in the J. and R. Wanamaker sale, Parke Bernet, New York, 2 November 1939, lot 35.[6]

PROVENANCE: Bought from H. Phillips in 1826 by Charles Bredel (d. 1851); Miss Bredel sale, London, 1 May 1875 (lot 105), bought by Agnew (470 gns). Sir Robert Loder, Bart., sale, London, 29 May 1908 (lot 531), bought by A. Wertheimer (1,270 gns), and passed in the same year into the collection of Adolf Hirsch. Lent to the Lenain Exhibition, BFAC, 1910, by Leonard Hirsch; Henry Hirsch sale, London, 12 June 1931 (lot 11), bought by Leyman (1,800 gns). C. F. Leach Bequest, 1943.

EXHIBITION: BFAC, Lenain Exhibition, 1910, No. 36.

REFERENCES:

1. The I and R had been painted out and the M altered so that the signature read N/1692. This was a deliberate falsification so that the painting would be passed off as by 'the Lenains' (see note 3 below). These alterations were removed in 1963/4. The signature and date as revealed by the removal of the alterations are repeated exactly in the Evelyn collection copy (see COPIES).

2. M. F. Durantini, *The Child in Seventeenth-Century Dutch Painting* (Ann Arbor, 1983), pp. 292–6), discusses No. 5416, unconvincingly suggesting that the children's music-making would be regarded by contemporaries as a 'dubious activity' and one to be condemned.

3. Canvas laid onto panel, 52.2 × 69.9 cm. Inv. no. NK 2696.

4. Waagen, 1854, vol. 2, p. 291, and in the Loder and Hirsch sale catalogues (see PROVENANCE). It was reproduced by the Arundel Society, 1908, No. 18, as by the Lenains, but the accompanying caption notes the resemblance to Molenaer's work; see also the catalogue of the BFAC exhibition, 1910, p. 18. There is an old inscription on the back of the stretcher: Le Nain, En 1629.

5. On panel, $22\frac{3}{4}$ × 32 in. (sight edge size). In the John Evelyn exhibition at the Victoria and Albert Museum, 1953–4, as having been in the collection of John Evelyn (1620–1706) but the grounds for this belief are not known.

6. Canvas, 67 × 87.6 cm. From the Galerie Sedelmeyer, Paris. The composition is extended to the right to include a window and with domestic implements hanging on the back wall. Photo in RKD.

FREDERICK DE MOUCHERON, 1633–1686

Frederick de Moucheron (he occasionally signs also *Frederico* or *Frederiko de Moucheron*) was born in Emden in 1633 according to Houbraken;[1] this date is supported by a document of July 1659 where his age is given as twenty-five.[2] Houbraken says he was a pupil of Jan Asselijn [presumably in Amsterdam; Asselijn died in 1652] and worked for several years in France. In 1656 he was in Paris and in Lyons. After a short stay in Antwerp, he returned to Amsterdam where he married in July 1659;[3] a daughter of his was baptised there in 1662.[4] In April 1671 he was in Rotterdam but was then described as a resident of Amsterdam.[5] In 1678 or 1679 he completed some paintings left unfinished by Willem Schellincks at his death (Nicolaes Berchem added the figures).[6] He was buried in Amsterdam, 5 January 1686.[7]

His landscapes are usually Italianate scenes reminiscent of Jan Both and Adam Pynacker. His master Jan Asselijn was an influence on his early work. Houbraken mentions that Adriaen van de Velde often painted the figures in his landscapes, as for instance in No. 842 below. Frederick de Moucheron also painted game and fish still lifes.

REFERENCES:

General: Ex. cat., Utrecht 1965, pp. 219ff.

In text:

1. *De Groote Schouburgh*, vol. 2, p. 327.

2. OH, 1885, p. 231.

3. Ibid.

4. Ibid.

5. OH, 1890, p. 208.

6. OH, 1883, p. 157.

7. Wurzbach, vol. 2, p. 199.

842 *Figures in an Italian Garden with Fountains and Statuary* *Plate 230*

Signed, bottom left: Moucheron.f.

Oil on canvas, 73.7 × 93.2 (29 × $36\frac{11}{16}$).

Cleaned in 1974.

A *Landscape with Narcissus* of 1668 in the Thurkow collection in The Hague[1] is very close to No. 842 in the painting of the statuary and the foliage. No. 842 should therefore be dated *c.*1668.

The figures in the right foreground and the dog are quite different from those in No. 1352 below. They are in the style of Adriaen van de Velde and most probably by him (cf. A. van de Velde No. 869 of this catalogue). Those in the left background are apparently by the same hand.

PROVENANCE: In the collection of Sir Robert Peel, Bart., by 1845.[2] Purchased with the Peel collection, 1871.

EXHIBITIONS: London, National Gallery, 'The Working of the National Gallery', 1974, cat. pl. no. 43 (exhibited partially cleaned); London 1982, cat. p. 27.

REFERENCES:
1. Utrecht 1965, cat. no. 139. The similarity of the landscape is noted by Blankert, the author of the Utrecht catalogue.
2. It is among the Peel pictures listed in *Le Cabinet de l'amateur*, 1845–6, p. 61, No. 23.

1352 *A Landscape with Classical Ruins* *Plate 231*

Signed, above left, on the architrave: F DE MOUCHERON (worn).

Oil on canvas, 71 × 65.2 ($27\frac{15}{16}$ × $25\frac{5}{8}$).

Cleaned in 1981–2. Extensive wearing in the sky.

Blankert[1] noted the close similarities between this painting, and in particular the classical views in the left background, and Jan Asselijn's *Shepherd and Shepherdess amidst Ruins* in Dresden.[2] He noted de Moucheron's more schematic treatment of the architecture and more decorative account of the landscape. It should be considered a relatively early work, painted shortly after his return to Amsterdam, i.e. *c.*1660.

PROVENANCE: In the Charles William Harrison Pickering sale, London, 11 June 1881 (lot 151),[3] bought by Goldstein (5 gns). Richard W. Cooper Bequest, 1892.

EXHIBITION: London 1982, cat. p. 28.

REFERENCES:
1. Utrecht 1965, cat. no. 139, note 6.
2. Dresden 1912, cat. no. 1593. A. C. Steland-Stief, *Jan Asselijn*, Amsterdam, 1971, cat. no. 53. A copy with variations of the Dresden painting is in the Herzog Anton Ulrich-Museum, Braunschweig (*Die* *Holländischen Gemälde*, 1983, no. 336 as 'Asselyn-Umkreis'; Steland-Stief, op. cit., no. 274 as a copy).
3. The markings relating to this sale are on the back of the picture.

AERT VAN DER NEER, 1603/4–1677

His Christian name is generally given as *Aert* but he also signs himself *Aernout*. In May 1642 he is said to be about thirty-eight;[1] in July 1647 his age is given as forty-three;[2] and so forth. According to Houbraken,[3] van der Neer was the *mayoor* (steward) of a family in Gorinchem (Gorkum) in his earlier days and did not devote himself wholly to painting until he moved to Amsterdam in about 1630. His earliest known dated picture is of 1632.[4] He had settled in Amsterdam before 1634; his son Eglon Hendrik van der Neer may have been born there in that year[5] and another son, Jan, was born there in 1637 or 1638.[6] Aert van der Neer is certainly recorded in Amsterdam in March 1640.[7] He continued to live in Amsterdam and kept an inn there in the years 1659–62; in December 1662 he was declared bankrupt.[8] He died in Amsterdam, 9 November 1677.[9]

In Gorinchem, van der Neer came into contact with the landscape painters Joachim and Raphael Camphuysen[10] and his early work was influenced by them, particularly by Raphael who was born in Gorinchem in 1597 or 1598 and had moved to Amsterdam by 1626; Raphael was a witness at the baptism of one of van der Neer's children in Amsterdam in 1642.[11] Van der Neer painted moonlit landscapes, winter scenes, landscapes at dawn and dusk and nocturnal fires. Two of his sons, Eglon Hendrick and Jan, were trained by him and became painters. Eglon Hendrick became a genre and history painter: Jan (1637/8–65) imitated his father's work.

REFERENCES:
General: Bredius in OH, 1900, pp. 69–82; HdG, vol. 7; F. Bachmann, *Aert van der Neer 1603/04–1677*, Bremen, 1982 (this is not a catalogue raisonné, but a study of the artist).
In text:
1. and **2.** Bredius, op. cit., p. 71.
3. Houbraken, vol. 3, p. 172.
4. *Figures in an Interior.* Panel, 47.5 × 39 cm. Signed and dated on the reverse. Liberec (Czechoslovakia), Gemäldegalerie, Inv. no. D667. This genre painting is entirely unlike van der Neer's later work. See H. Seifertová-Korecká in OH, vol. 77, 1962, pp. 57–8, and Bachmann, op. cit., pp. 18–19 (which states that

the painting is now in the Národní Galerie, Prague).
5. See the biographical notice on p. 280.
6. Bredius, op. cit., pp. 70–1.
7. OH, 1885, p. 234.
8. Bredius, op. cit., pp. 71–5.
9. Bredius, op. cit., p. 75.
10. W. Liedtke has recently suggested that van der Neer was the brother-in-law of Joachim and Raphael Camphuysen (Ex. cat. *Liechtenstein: The Princely Collections*, Metropolitan Museum of Art, New York, 1985, p. 255).
11. As note 9.

152 *An Evening View near a Village, with a Man and a Milkmaid*

Plate 232

Signed, bottom left, on a tree trunk: AV DN f (AV DN in two monograms). Formerly signed falsely on the milkmaid's pail: A. Cuyp; this was removed when the picture was cleaned.

Oil on canvas, 121.5 × 162.5 (47¾ × 64).

Cleaned in 1956. Some wearing in the sky.

At one time the figures were thought to be the work of Aelbert Cuyp[1] but they are clearly by van der Neer and the Cuyp 'signature', which was unlike authentic ones, had certainly been added later.

MacLaren suggested that 'the picture may be of *c*.1650–5'. Bachmann[2] preferred a dating in the late 1640s.

VERSION: A repetition or copy was in the collection of Lt.-Col. W. Ewart Dittman, 1950.

ENGRAVING: Engraved in outline by Parboni, *c*.1812.[3]

PROVENANCE: In the collection of Lucien Bonaparte by 1812;[4] together with the rest of the collection brought to England, and exhibited by Buchanan for sale by private contract, London, 6 February sqq. 1815, No. 8; in the Lucien Bonaparte sale, London, 14–16 May 1816 (lot 169), bought in and afterwards purchased privately by the Chevalier Sébastien Erard;[5] in the Erard collection, Château de la Muette, Passy; S. Erard sale, Paris, 23 April sqq. 1832 (lot 101), bought in (25,900 francs); S. Erard sale, London, 22 June 1833 (lot 41), bought by Séguier (770 gns), probably for Lord Farnborough in whose collection it certainly was by 1834.[6] Lord Farnborough Bequest, 1838.

EXHIBITION: BI 1837, No. 16.

REFERENCES:
General: HdG No. 45.
In text:
1. In the catalogues of the Bonaparte and Erard catalogues, and the National Gallery catalogue prior to 1913.
2. Bachmann, op. cit., p. 62.
3. In *Galerie...Lucien Bonaparte*, 1812, p. 21 (No. 11.)

4. Cf. note 3.
5. Buchanan, vol. 2, p. 287. It is No. 101 of the *Catalogue des tableaux . . . de M. le Chevalier Erard*, 1831.
6. It was bought at the 1833 Erard sale by Lord Farnborough according to Nieuwenhys (p. 167).

239 *A River near a Town, by Moonlight* Plate 233

A vessel on the extreme left has a vane with the Dutch colours.

Signed, bottom left: AV DN (in two monograms).

Oil on oak, 30.3 × 48.4 ($11\frac{15}{16}$ × $19\frac{1}{16}$).

The grain of the wood shows through in many places in the sky.

MacLaren considered it to be 'probably a work of the middle 1640s'. Bachmann[1] preferred a dating in the 1650s.

VERSIONS: A signed variant was in the K– (of The Hague) et al. sale, Amsterdam, 25 April 1911 (lot 82), 4,600 guilders.[2] Another, apparently unsigned, is in the City Art Gallery, Leeds.[3]

COPY: There is a copy in the Thyssen-Bornemisza collection, Lugano.[4]

PROVENANCE: Robert Heathcote sale, London, 5–6 April 1805 (lot 33), bought by Harris (80 gns) and sold by him to N. Ridley-Colborne;[5] lent by Lord Colborne to the BI, 1840. Lord Colborne Bequest, 1854.

EXHIBITION: BI 1840, No. 89.

REFERENCES:
General: HdG No. 221.
In text:
1. Bachmann, op. cit., p. 113.
2. HdG No. 138. On panel, 30.5 × 46 cm. Reproduced in the sale catalogue.

3. Panel, 30.5 × 48.5 cm. Inv. no. 26.28/55.
4. Panel, 29.8 × 45.8 cm.; 1986 cat., No. 230.
5. Contemporary MS note in the National Gallery copy of the Heathcote sale catalogue.

732 A View along a River near a Village at Evening Plate 234

The arms of Amsterdam are on the stern of the *trekjacht* in the foreground, which has a Dutch flag and an orange and white vane. On the façade of the house or inn farthest to the left are three red bottles.

Signed on the lee-board of the barge in the foreground: AV DN (in two monograms).

Oil on canvas, 133.5 × 167.5 (52½ × 66).

This is one of van der Neer's largest paintings.[1] Hofstede de Groot[2] suggested it might be the picture of the same size by van der Neer, said to represent an evening view near the bridge in Maarssen, which appeared in two eighteenth-century sales in Leiden (see PROVENANCE). Maarssen is on the River Vecht about five miles from Utrecht. The National Gallery picture does not agree at all with the engraved view of Maarssen in Daniel Stopendael's *Zegepraalende Vecht* of 1719,[3] nor can the place be identified with any of the other views in that book. Van der Neer seems to have rarely depicted actual places but it is quite possible that the present view is an idealised reminiscence of the Vecht, which had many comparable reaches lined with houses.[4] or (less probably) of the River Amstel.[5]

MacLaren considered this painting to be a work of the 1660s. This was principally on the grounds of the costume of the figures, especially that of the man on the left bending forward, which he dated to *c*.1660–5. Bachmann[6] also noted that the costume of the man on the left was of the so-called *rhyngrave* type which was first worn after 1660. However, he dated the landscape to *c*.1645, believing that the figures were added subsequently by another hand. The figures had previously been attributed to Lingelbach[7] but in MacLaren's view, both they and the animals were by van der Neer himself. The present writer is entirely in agreement with MacLaren, that is, that the painting is the work of van der Neer alone and that it should be dated in the 1660s.

PROVENANCE: Perhaps the picture mentioned above, which was in the [van Haeften] sale, Leiden, 15 June 1764 (lot 8),[8] bought by van der Eyk (17 guilders), and the Pieter van der Eyk sale, Leiden, 28 November 1769 (lot 45),[9] bought by Adriaanse (102 guilders). No. 732 was in the collection of the Earl of Shaftesbury, London, by 1857,[10] and was purchased from him in 1864.

REFERENCES:

General: HdG Nos. 46 and (?) 15aa.

In text:

1. HdG lists only two others of this size (Nos. 29 and 98) and three a little larger (Nos. 106, 435 and 544).

2. Loc. cit.

3. Daniel Stoependael, *De Zegepraalende Vecht, Vertoonende verscheidene Gesichten van Lustplaatsen . . . Beginnende van Uitrecht en met Muyden besluytende*, 1719, No. 10.

4. See Stoependael, op. cit., *passim*.

5. There is nothing very similar among the engraved views on the River Amstel in A. Rademak-

er's *Hollands Arcadia of de vermaarde Rivier den Amstel*, 1730.

6. Bachmann, op. cit., p. 49.

7. HdG No. 46, op. cit.

8. 'Een Gezigt van Maarsen in 't vallen van den avond, door A. van der Neer' (size and support not given).

9. A. van der Neer: 'Een Kapitaal Schildery, verbeeldende een Avontstont: zynde het Gezigt aan de Brug te Maarsen, met Vaartuigen en andere Stoffagie'; on canvas, 51 × 64 *duim*.

10. Waagen, 1857, p. 166.

969 *A Frozen River by a Town at Evening*   *Plate 235*

Signed at the bottom, left of centre: AV DN (in two monograms).

Oil on oak, 26.4 × 40.5 ($10\frac{3}{8}$ × $15\frac{15}{16}$).

Cleaned in 1969. Cleaning revealed that the lower half of the squatting man in the right foreground had been overpainted.

MacLaren considered that it was 'probably painted in the mid-40s'. Stechow[1] noted that this was too early: he compared it to a painting which he believed to be dated 1665.[2] Bachmann,[3] however, considered this date to be false. On grounds of style, he (following Stechow) dates No. 969 to the mid-1660s, which seems correct to the present writer.

PROVENANCE: Wynn Ellis Bequest, 1876.

EXHIBITION: London 1976, No. 74.

REFERENCES:
General: HdG No. 502.
In text:
1. Stechow, p. 94 and note 41.

2. HdG No. 575. HdG gives the date as 1662 but Stechow (p. 93) said it 'can clearly be read 1665'.
3. Bachmann, op. cit., p. 137 and note 158.

1288 *A Frozen River near a Village, with*   *Plate 236*
Golfers and Skaters

Signed on a rock just above the head of the man in the left bottom corner: AV DN (in two monograms); faint.

Oil on canvas, 39.5 × 53 ($15\frac{9}{16}$ × $20\frac{7}{8}$).

Cleaned in 1959.

MacLaren considered that this was 'probably a work of the later 1640s'. Bachmann[1] agreed with this dating, noting its similarity in style to a painting of 1649 in Prague.[2]

PROVENANCE: Sold by Rutley to John Staniforth Beckett, 10 December 1853;[3] J. S. Beckett Bequest, 1889.

REFERENCES:
General: HdG No. 503.
In text:
1. Bachmann, op. cit., p. 66.
2. Panel, 42 × 70 cm. HdG No. 76. Bachmann,

op. cit., p. 65.
3. Letter of 1931 from Sir Hickman Bacon, Bart., nephew of J. S. Beckett (in the National Gallery archives).

2283 *A Landscape with a River at Evening*   *Plate 237*

Signed, bottom centre: AV DN (in two monograms).

Oil on canvas, 79 × 65.1 ($31\frac{1}{8}$ × $25\frac{5}{8}$).

The time of day represented has sometimes been supposed to be dawn, but it seems more likely that late evening is intended.

MacLaren considered that it was 'probably painted in the early 1650s'. Bachmann[1] noted its close similarity to a painting in the Boymans-van Beuningen Museum, Rotterdam,[2] and dated both paintings to the late 1640s.

PROVENANCE: Ramsay Richard Reinagle sale, London, 27–9 June 1832 (lot 204), bought by Bevan (75 gns); lent by Robert Cooper Lee Bevan to the BI in 1856 and the RA in 1886. R. C. L. Bevan died in 1890; the picture was in the [Bevan?] sale, London, 6 April 1892 (lot 158),[3] bought by Martin H. Colnaghi (400 gns) who lent it to the RA in 1893, the Guildhall, London, in 1895 and Whitechapel Art Gallery in 1904. Martin H. Colnaghi Bequest, 1908.

EXHIBITIONS: BI 1856, No. 126; RA 1886, No. 88; RA 1893, No. 94; London, Guildhall, 1895, No. 96; London, Whitechapel Art Gallery, 1904, No. 305; Arts Council 1945, No. 22.

REFERENCES :
General: HdG No. 47.
In text:
1. Bachmann, op. cit., p. 73. Stechow (p. 178) praised the painting but did not date it with any precision. He placed it after the 'relatively earlier works in the fully developed style': he apparently considered that 'the fully developed style' began c.1646.
2. Panel, 60 × 49.5 cm. 1977 cat., inv. no. 2509. HdG No. 311.
3. As 'Van der Neer A Moonlight, exhibited at

Burlington House, 1866' [sic]. According to the catalogue of this anonymous sale (at Foster's) 'Lots 139 to 168 removed from a country Mansion were collected by a Gentleman early in the present century.' Frank Simpson, who generously provided the references to this and the Reinagle sales, pointed out that among other pictures from the same source sold anonymously at Foster's on 25 May 1892 was a Wilson *Thames at Isleworth* that can be identified with lot 54 of the Reinagle sale of 27 sqq. June 1832 bought by 'Bevan'.

2534 *A River Landscape with a Village* *Plate 238*

Signed, bottom right (false?): AV N (AV in monogram).

Oil on oak, 28.4 × 43.2 ($11\frac{13}{16}$ × 17).

MacLaren considered it to be 'perhaps painted c.1645–50'. Bachmann[1] has related it to a group of paintings which he dated to shortly after 1642.

PROVENANCE: Probably bought from Sulley by George Salting in June 1904.[2] Salting Bequest, 1910.

REFERENCES :
General: HdG No. 48.
In text:
1. Bachmann, op. cit., pp. 39–40. The related paintings are in Rotterdam (Boymans-van Beuningen Museum: 1972 cat., inv. no. 1584; not in HdG), Amsterdam (Rijksmuseum: 1976 cat. no. C192: HdG No. 19), the Thyssen collection, Lugano (1981 cat., no. 234) and on the art market (HdG No. 137). Bachmann considered that all these stylistically related paintings date from shortly after the 1642 *Landscape with a Hunter* in

Frankfurt (Städelsches Kunstinstitut; 1971 cat., inv. no. 1090). HdG (No. 32) gave the date incorrectly as 1652 and this has been followed by more recent publications, even the 1971 museum catalogue. Stechow (p. 56 and note 30) was the first to read the date correctly as 1642.
2. If it is the picture referred to in a Salting notebook of October 1900 onwards (in the National Gallery archives): 'Aart v. der Neer, small river-scene on a sunny/evening, luminous with fleecy clouds. (cost 400)/ (bt June 1904 from Sulley).'

2536 *A Village by a River in Moonlight* *Plate 239*

Signed (probably falsely), bottom left: AV DN (in two monograms).

Oil on oak, 19.7 × 28.3 ($7\frac{3}{4}$ × $11\frac{1}{8}$).

There is a narrow black line round the edges.

Some trees have been painted out by the artist to the right of the tallest tree on the left.

MacLaren considered that it was 'perhaps painted in the middle 1640s'.

PROVENANCE: In the collection of George Salting, London; Salting Bequest, 1910.

REFERENCE: HdG No. 222.

2537 *An Evening Landscape with a Horse and Cart by a Stream*

Plate 240

Oil on canvas, 52.3 × 63.5 (20$\frac{9}{16}$ × 25).

MacLaren considered that it was 'possibly painted in the late 1640s or early 50s'.

PROVENANCE: Alexis-Joseph Febvre sale, Paris, 17 sqq. April 1882 (lot 77), bought by de Beurnonville (6,000 francs); Baron de B[eurnonville] sale, Paris, 21–22 May 1883 (lot 72), 4,000 francs. In the collection of George Salting, London. Salting Bequest, 1910.

REFERENCE: HdG No. 49.

EGLON HENDRIK VAN DER NEER, 1634(?)–1703

The son of Aert van der Neer, he was born in Amsterdam in 1643 according to Houbraken but this is obviously too late and may well be a misprint for 1634, since Houbraken says elsewhere that van der Neer died in May 1703 and that he went on painting up to his seventieth year. Houbraken relates that van der Neer was a pupil of his father and of Jacob van Loo, and afterwards went to France where he was painter to the Dutch governor of Orange from the age of nineteen for three or four years. He had returned to Holland by 1659 and married in February of that year in Rotterdam, but at that time he was said to be living in Amsterdam and a child of his was baptised in Amsterdam in February 1660. Until 1679 he seems to have lived chiefly in Rotterdam, although he also spent some time in Amsterdam and The Hague, and he became a member of *Pictura*, The Hague painters' confraternity, in 1670. His wife died in 1677. He was in Amsterdam in December 1678 to act as a witness at the wedding of the still-life painter Willem van Aelst. In 1679–89 he lived in Brussels; in 1681 he married there Marie Duchatel, a miniaturist, daughter of the artist François Duchatel. On 18 July 1687, van der Neer was appointed court painter to Charles II of Spain. In August 1689, however, he is recorded in Amsterdam and he may not have ever gone to Spain. In the following year he succeeded Johann Spilberg, who had died in August 1690, as court painter to the Elector Palatine, Johann Wilhelm, in Düsseldorf. In 1697 he married for the third time there: his wife was Adriana Spilberg, the daughter of his predecessor and widow of the painter Willem Breekvelt. Van der Neer lived in Düsseldorf from 1690 until his death on 3 May 1703.

There are dated pictures of most years from 1662 to 1702; besides genre paintings there are portraits in the style of Caspar Netscher, landscapes and history paintings.

Houbraken mentions only one pupil, Adriaen van der Werff: this must have been *c.*1671–6 in Rotterdam.[1]

REFERENCES:
General: HdG, vol. 5. For the biographical data see Houbraken, vol. 3, pp. 172–5; Obreen, vol. 4, p. 153; OH, vol. 3, 1885, pp. 58 and 234, vol. 8, 1890, p. 208, and vol. 18, 1900, p. 75; Rotterdam catalogue, 1892.
In text: **1.** B. Gaehtgens, *Adriaen van der Werff 1659-1722*, Munich, 1987, pp. 42–5.

2535 Judith (*Portrait of a Woman as Judith?*)   *Plate 241*

In the bed in the left background is the body of Holofernes; on the right, Judith's maid is putting his head in a bag.

Signed on the blade of the sword in Judith's hand: E. Vander Neer fe (or fc). The signature is worn in places and retouched.

Oil on oak, 32 × 24.6 ($12\frac{5}{8}$ × $9\frac{11}{16}$).

The subject is taken from the apocryphal Book of Judith, 8 (see especially verses 9 and 10). It was treated by a number of sixteenth- and seventeenth-century Netherlandish artists,[1] among them Maerten de Vos, Hendrick Goltzius, Rubens and Jan de Bray.[2] In this painting, the prominence of the figure of Judith, the portrait character of her face and the subsidiary position of the maid and the head of Holofernes make it likely that this is intended as a portrait of a woman as Judith.

MacLaren considered that the painting 'may well be of the 1670s or early 80s'. The figure of Judith is comparable to that of the female lute player in a painting of 1678 in Munich.[3] A dating of *c.*1678 for No. 2535 would therefore be acceptable.

COPY: A copy is in a private collection near Karlsruhe in West Germany.[4]

PROVENANCE: This or a very similar picture was in the Destouches sale, Paris, 1 germinal (21 March) sqq. 1794 (lot 53), bought by Paillet (501 francs). No. 2535 is said to have been in the Baumgaertner collection;[5] it was in an anonymous sale ('collection of a lady removed from Warwickshire') at Christie's, 27 January 1838 (lot 134), bought by Dr Franck (44 gns); in the Franck collection, London; Dr Franck sale, London, 25 March 1843 (lot 100),[6] bought by Farrer (38 gns). In the Sir Frederick Martin Williams, Bart., sale, London, 28–9 April 1880 (lot 410),[7] bought by George Salting (80 gns). Salting Bequest, 1910.

EXHIBITION: Amsterdam 1989–90, No. 28.

REFERENCES:
General: Smith No. 15; HdG No. 12.
In text:
1. A. Pigler, *Barockthemen*, Budapest, 1974, vol. 1, p. 196.
2. Prints record the compositions by de Vos, Goltzius and Rubens: see Pigler, op. cit., note 1. Jan de Bray's painting which shows Judith raising her sword above a sleeping Holofernes is in the Rijksmuseum: 1976 cat. no. A2353. It is dated 1659.
3. Alte Pinakothek, Munich, 1983 cat., no. 204. Panel, 42.5 × 36.7 cm. Signed on the base of the pilaster in the background: E. vander. Neer. fe. 1678.
4. Panel, 32 × 25 cm. Photograph (from the Karlsruhe Museum) in the RKD.
5. The catalogue of the Franck sale, 1843 (see PROVENANCE), a cutting of the relevant part of which is stuck on the back of No. 2535, says that it came 'from M. Baumgaertner's collection'. It was not in the Baumgaertner of Leipzig (deceased) sale, London, 4 December 1830.
6. See note 5.
7. As from the Baumgaertner collection.

CASPAR NETSCHER, 1635/6(?)–1684

The birth date formerly given, 1639, was taken from Houbraken,[1] who says that Netscher was born in Heidelberg (and was the son of Johannes Netscher, a sculptor from Stuttgart); earlier he says Prague.[2] Roger de Piles in the *Abrégé* (written in Holland in 1692–7) says Netscher was born in Prague and was forty-eight when he died in The Hague in 1684.[3] Houbraken also gives 1684 (15 January) as the date of Netscher's death;[4] if the rest of de Piles' statement is correct, Netscher must have been born in 1635 or 1636.[5] According to Houbraken, Netscher was taken as a child to Arnhem where he was a pupil of a painter, Herman Coster, and afterwards studied with Gerard ter Borch in Deventer[6] (there is a copy of a painting by ter Borch signed by Netscher and dated 1655 in the museum in Gotha).[7] He left for Rome in 1658 or 1659 (Houbraken says at the age of twenty-one) but got no farther than Bordeaux, where he married in November 1659.[8] He was probably still there in 1661 (J. van Gool[9] says that Netscher's eldest son, Theodorus, was born in Bordeaux in that year); he had returned to Holland by October 1662, when he paid his entry into *Pictura*, the painters' confraternity in The Hague.[10] From then on he lived in The Hague. He soon had a considerable reputation, especially as a portraitist of the aristocracy. He was invited to England by Charles II;[11] according to Vertue[12] he came here for a short while about 1668; both de Piles[13] and Houbraken,[14] however, say he declined the invitation and there can be little doubt that his portraits of English people, as of other foreigners, were painted when the sitters were in Holland.[15] (In any case many of the portraits supposedly of English and French sitters are misidentified.) He died in The Hague, 15 January 1684.[16]

Until the later part of the 60s he often painted, besides portraits, genre pictures and also some religious and classical subjects; the earlier ones are related stylistically to ter Borch and Metsu, the later ones to Frans van Mieris the Elder. In the 70s and 80s he devoted himself almost entirely to portraiture; his portraits, of which there is a large number,[17] are invariably small. They were strongly influenced in style by van Dyck and his followers in The Hague, Adriaen Hanneman and Jan Mytens. They had considerable influence on Dutch portraiture in the latter part of the century and even afterwards. Among Netscher's closest imitators is his son, Constantijn (1668–1723).

REFERENCES:

General: Bredius in OH, vol. 5, 1887, pp. 263ff; HdG, vol. 5, 1913 (German edition, 1912).

In text:

1. Houbraken, vol. 3, p. 92.
2. Op. cit., vol. 1, p. 6.
3. *Abrégé de la vie des peintres*, 1699, pp. 452 and 455.
4. Op. cit., vol. 3, p. 96.
5. HdG, *Arnold Houbraken und seine 'Groote Schouburgh'*, 1893, p. 317.
6. Op. cit., vol. 3, pp. 93–4.
7. Canvas, 79 × 66 cm. Signed: C. Netscher Fecit 1655. Gotha Museum, 1890 cat. no. 298. (S. J. Gudlaugsson, *Gerard ter Borch*, The Hague, 1960, vol. 2, cat. no. 110 IIa and plate XII, no. 1.)

8. Houbraken, op. cit., vol. 3, pp. 94–5.
9. Van Gool, vol. 1, 1750, p. 172.
10. Obreen, vol. 4, p. 150, and vol. 5, p. 131.
11. Houbraken, op. cit., vol. 3, p. 95.
12. Notebook of 1725–31 (*Walpole Society*, vol. 20, 1932, p. 53).
13. Op. cit., p. 455.
14. Op. cit., vol. 3, p. 92.
15. See p. 288, note 4.
16. Houbraken, op. cit., vol. 3, p. 96.
17. For the mass production techniques of both Caspar and Constantijn Netscher, see A. Blankert, 'Invul-portretten door Caspar en Constantyn Netscher', OH, vol. 81, 1966, pp. 263–9.

843 *Two Boys blowing Bubbles* ('*Homo Bulla*')   *Plate 242*

On the sill is a silver dish with the figures of a nude man and woman embracing. The boy in the background is blowing bubbles from a shell held in his left hand.

Inscribed along the bottom: A° 1670. G. Net∫cher. This inscription is rather clumsy and almost certainly a later addition, since it has apparently been painted over cracks in the brown paint.[1]

Oil on oak, 31.2 × 24.6 ($12\frac{5}{16}$ × $9\frac{11}{16}$).

The silver dish repeats exactly the design of the bowl of a small *tazza* by Adam van Vianen, signed and dated 1618, in the Rijksmuseum.[2]

    Although the signature and date are fairly surely later additions (apart from the physical evidence mentioned above, Caspar Netscher rarely if ever spelled his first name with a G), the picture is certainly by Netscher and both style and costume agree very well with those of *c.*1670; the inscription may, therefore, have been copied from a genuine one formerly on the picture.[3]

    Children blowing bubbles are often a symbol of the transience of human life: the subject, which has a classical origin, is known as the *homo bulla*.[4] In the Netherlands in the sixteenth century the subject was represented in a clearly symbolic manner: a putto seated or resting on a skull blowing bubbles in, for example, prints by Christoffel van Sichem[5] and Hendrick Goltzius.[6] Netscher treats the same subject, but in place of putti employs children in contemporary dress. In this context the elaborate *tazza* and the rare shells, which were enthusiastically collected in Holland in the seventeenth century, stand for the futility of worldly possessions.

    Netscher painted a number of other versions of the *homo bulla* subject, among them, single figures within a niche[7] and a girl and a boy behind a stone parapet.[8]

ENGRAVING: Engraved (in reverse) by Mme Lingée.[9]

VERSIONS AND COPIES: A possible replica or copy, on canvas, was in the J. Christiaanze sale, Amsterdam, 17 November 1779 (lot 89),[10] bought by Lammers (22 guilders, with pendant). A copy was in the Frau Sandor von Longay (Budapest) and others sale, Vienna, 2 May 1918, lot 120.[11] An old copy was in Anon. sale at Sotheby's, 9 June 1937, lot 29 (to Hulme for £6 10 shillings);[12] another copy (?) is in the collection of Chr. Moltke, Bregentved Castle, Denmark.[13] A good quality old copy was in Anon. sale, Christie's, 11 April 1975, lot 43 (2,000 gns).[14]

PROVENANCE: Probably in the three following sales: Adriaan Bout sale, The Hague, 11 sqq. August 1733 (lot 60),[15] bought by da Costa (205 florins); Ferdinand, Count of Plettenberg and Wittem sale, Amsterdam, 2 April 1738 (lot 63),[16] bought by W. Lormier[17] (125 florins); Willem Lormier sale, The Hague, 4 sqq. July 1763 (lot 192),[18] bought by Voet (310 florins). Randon de Boisset sale, Paris, 27 February sqq. 1777 (lot 142), bought by Poullain (1,598 francs); Poullain sale, Paris, 15 March sqq. 1780 (lot 75), bought by the Duchesse de Grammont[19] (2,399 francs). It was in an anonymous sale by J. B. P. Le Brun, Paris, 14–16 April 1784 (supplement, lot 164), bought by Le Brun (?bought in; 1,205 francs); [C. A. de Calonne] sale, Paris, 21–30 April 1788 (lot 114), bought by Le Brun the Elder (1,675 francs); Le Brun sale, Paris, 11–30 April 1791 (lot 141), bought by Constantin[20] (1,600 francs); [Le Rouge or de Catelan] sale, Paris, 16 January 1816 (lot 15), bought by Robichon for the Duc de Berry(?), 3,810 francs.[21] In any case in the collection of the Duchesse de Berry, Paris, by 1833;[22] exhibited with the Berry collection for sale by private contract in London, April 1834 (No. 47) and bought by Sir Robert Peel, Bart.,[23] who exhibited it at the BI, 1835. Purchased with the Peel collection, 1871.

EXHIBITIONS: BI 1835, No. 92; London 1976, No. 75; London 1978–9, No. 18.

REFERENCES:

General: Smith No. 14 and Supplement No. 11; HdG No. 149.

In text:

1. This is visible under magnification × 30.

2. *Catalogus van Goud en Zilverwerken*, 2nd ed., 1952, No. 91; J. W. Frederiks, *Dutch Silver*, 1952, No. 53L. For a discussion of the appearance of silverware by Adam van Vianen in paintings see J. R. ter Molen in *Apollo*, vol. 110, 1979, pp. 482–9, and in the exhibition catalogue, *Zeldzaam Zilver uit de Gouden Eeuw: De Utrechtse edelsmeden Van Vianen*, Centraal Museum, Utrecht, 1984–85.

3. There is no visible trace of an earlier signature below the present one. The Randon de Boisset sale catalogue of 1777 is the first to mention the date 1670.

4. For the *homo bulla* theme, see W. Stechow, 'Homo Bulla', *Art Bulletin*, vol. 20, 1983, pp. 227–8; E. Snoep-Reitsma, 'Chardin and the Bourgeois Ideals of his Time', NKJ, vol. 24, 1973, pp. 147–243; and ex. cat., *Tot Lering en Vermaak*, Rijksmuseum, Amsterdam, 1976, No. 4.

5. The print by van Sichem is illustrated in ex. cat., op. cit. (note 4), plate 4a.

6. The Goltzius print, inscribed 'Quis Evadet?', is dated 1594. Hollstein No. 110.

7. Panel, 15.24 × 12.7 cm. Bacon collection. Raveningham Hall, Norwich. HdG No. 65a(?); a different composition: Panel, 22.8 × 17.8 cm. Anon, sale, Christie's, New York, 10 January 1980, lot 238a, $18,000.

8. Panel, 26.6 × 20.3 cm. HdG No. 150. With J. Kraus, Paris, 1976; Christie's, New York, 5 June 1983, lot 137 (bought in); Sotheby's, New York, 14 January 1988. The Linda and Gerald Guterman Collection, lot 27 (with full provenance) (sold for $46,750).

9. In *Collection de Cent-vingt Estampes . . . d'après les Tableaux . . . de M. Poullain*, 1781, No. 63.

10. (Caspar Netscher) 'Een Nisje, waar in men ziet verbeeld twee Jongelingen, de een Bellen blaazende, en de andere dezelven in zyn Muts of Hoed schynende te zullen ontfangen . . .', on canvas, 13½ × 10½ *duim*.

11. Photo in RKD.

12. 33 × 26.6 cm. Support not given.

13. 31 × 25 cm. Reproduced in Winkel and Magnussen's *Kunst i privat Eje*, vol. 3, 1945, p. 5 (attributed to Frans van Mieris I).

14. Panel, 33 × 26.7 cm. (as Caspar Netscher). Without the inscription on No. 843.

15. 'Een dito [i.e. by Caspar Netscher] Speelende Kindertjes, Blaasjens makende', 10 × 8 *duim* (Hoet, vol. 1, p. 389).

16. 'Twee Kindertjes, zynde Belle blasertjes, van den Ouden Netscher', 1 *voet* 1 *duim* × 9½ *duim*.

17. According to HdG (loc. cit.). It appears in Hoet's catalogue of William Lormier's collection in The Hague (op. cit., vol. 2, p. 433): 'Twee belle blasende Jongens' (as by Netscher), 1 *voet* × 9½ *duim*.

18. (Caspar Netscher), 'Twee Belle blasende Jongens'; on panel, 9½ *duim* × 1 *voet*.

19. According to C. Blanc (*Trésor de la curiosité*, 1858, vol. 2, pp. 11–12) the purchaser was Boileau; the marked catalogue in the RKD gives the Duchesse de Grammont, and it was certainly in her collection by 1781 (see *Collection de Cent-vingt Estampes ...d'après les Tableaux...de M. Poullain*, 1781, p. 12.

20. Blanc, op. cit., vol. 2, pp. 134–5.

21. The marked copy of the [Le Rouge] sale, Paris, 16 January 1816, in the library of the RKD gives the Duc de Berry as the purchaser. Blanc, op. cit., vol. 2, p. 303, has Robichon.

22. Smith No. 14. A seal with the arms of the Dukes of Berry is on the back of the panel.

23. Smith Supplement No. 11.

844 *A Lady teaching a Child to read, and a Child playing with a Dog ('La Maîtresse d'école')* Plate 243

On the wall behind is a reduced version or copy of Rubens' *Brazen Serpent* (Fig. 65),[1] and on the right a map. In the right foreground is a coloured broadsheet.

Oil on oak, 45.1 × 37 ($17\frac{3}{4}$ × $14\frac{9}{16}$).

Worn in the darks and the background.

PENTIMENTI: Underneath the cap hanging on the wall, right, a map(?) has been painted out by the artist; other *pentimenti* are in the upper part of the outline of the mirror, top left, and in the lower half of the broadsheet, bottom right.

Netscher intends a deliberate contrast between the child – a girl – who is being helped with her reading by her mother and the other child – a boy – who prefers to play with the dog and with the knucklebone and top which lie on the ground. The broadsheet with its large, brightly coloured and crudely printed illustrations contrasts with the book being read by the girl. The two children stand for industry and idleness. There is a similar painting by Netscher in the Rijksmuseum, Amsterdam (Fig. 66):[2] it also shows a mother and two children. The mother combs the boy's hair, a familiar illustration of *moederzorg* (maternal care), while the girl admires herself in a mirror and represents vanity. Once again, a contrast between a dutiful and wilful child is intended.[3] The paintings have the same dimensions and may well have constituted a pair. The style and the costume of both paintings indicate a date in the 1670s.

ENGRAVING: Line-engraving (reversed) by Robert de Launay, *c.*1806–8.[4]

COPIES: A copy was in the collection of Dr Radema, The Hague, 1925. A copy was in the von Gemmingen and others sale, Berlin, P. Cassirer, 23 November 1927, lot 26.[5]

PROVENANCE: In the collection of Philippe, Duc d'Orléans (the Regent) at the Palais-Royal, Paris,[6] which was formed in the quarter of a century before the duke's death in 1723.[7] It remained at the Palais-Royal until the Flemish and Dutch paintings of the collection were sold by his great-grandson ('Philippe-Egalité') in 1791 or 1792 to Thomas Moore Slade, acting on behalf of Lord Kinnaird, Mr Morland and Mr Hammersley.[8] These paintings were brought to England in 1792, and No. 844 was exhibited with them for sale by private contract in London, April–June 1793, No. 7. It was presumably sold before May 1795 since it is not among the remaining Flemish and Dutch pictures from the Orléans collection then exhibited for sale in London. By 1824 it was in the collection of (Sir) Robert Peel (Bart.) by whom it was lent to the BI in that year. Purchased with the Peel collection, 1871.

EXHIBITIONS: BI 1824, No. 73; London 1978–9, No. 20; Amsterdam 1989–90, No. 33.

REFERENCES:
General: Smith No. 35; HdG No. 96.
In text:
1. The original of this composition is Rubens No. 59 in the National Gallery.
2. Panel, 44.5 × 38 cm. Signed: C. Netscher Fec. Rijksmuseum, 1976 cat. A293. It was purchased by the Rijksmuseum with the Kabinet van Heteren Gevers, The Hague – Rotterdam, 1809.
3. For more elaborate interpretations of the paintings and particular elements within them (notably the copy of Rubens' *Brazen Serpent* and the spinning tops) see E. Snoep-Reitsma, 'Chardin and the Bourgeois Ideals of his Time', NKJ, vol. 24, 1973, pp. 195, 206, 239 (note 131); ex. cat., *Tot Lering en*

Vermaak, Rijksmuseum, Amsterdam, 1976, No. 49; ex. cat., London 1978–9, No. 20.
4. In *Galerie du Palais Royal*, vol. 3, 1808, No. 40.
5. Canvas, 45 × 37 cm. Illustrated in catalogue. Photograph in RKD.
6. Dubois de Saint-Gelais, *Description des tableaux du Palais Royal*, 1727, pp. 162–3. No. 844 cannot, therefore, be the *Mother with Two Children* by Netscher in the Adriaan Bout sale, The Hague, 11 August 1733 (lot 59), as HdG (loc. cit.) supposed.
7. C. Stryienski, *La Galerie du Régent*, 1913, pp. 5ff.
8. Slade's own account of the transaction is given in Buchanan, vol. 1, pp. 158–64; see also Stryienski, op. cit., pp. 135ff.

845 *A Lady seated at a Spinning-wheel*   *Plate 244*

Signed on the spinning-wheel, just above the lady's knee: CNetscher/1665 (CN in monogram).

Oil on oak, with the top corners roughly rounded, 22.5 × 17.7 ($8\frac{7}{8}$ × 7).

At present covered by discoloured varnish.[1]

COPY: A drawn copy: black chalk, 21.3 × 16.5 cm. Signed in ink, top right: P.V.S. 1651 (sic).[2]

PROVENANCE: Perhaps at one time in the collection of Comte de La Motte.[3] In the Blondel de Gagny collection by 1760;[4] Blondel de Gagny sale, Paris, 10 December 1776–22 January 1777 (lot 163), bought by Azincourt (1,499 francs); Anon. [Blondel d'Azincourt] sale, Paris, 17–22 February 1783 (lot 19),[5] bought by Julliot (2,100 francs); Anon. [Prince Galitzin][6] sale, Paris, 28 February sqq. 1835 (lot 25), bought by de Lahante (3,310 francs). In the collection of Sir Robert Peel, Bart., by 1833;[7] purchased with the Peel collection, 1871.

REFERENCES:
General: Smith No. 22; HdG No. 47.
In text:
1. In the National Gallery copy of the catalogue of the 1825 Galitzin sale (see PROVENANCE) a contemporary note on the picture says: 'usée [sic] et écorché'.
2. Present whereabouts unknown. P.V.S. may be meant for Pieter van Slingelandt (Leiden, 1640–91). The date could perhaps be meant for 1681. Photo in RKD – neg. no. L19931.
3. On the back of the panel is a label inscribed in ink: 'Le Cte Delamotte.' It was not in the d[e] L[a]

M[otte] sale, Paris, 29 December 1806–3 January 1807, nor in the de La Motte sale, Paris, 17 March 1823.
4 Descamps, vol. 3, p. 83 ('une jeune fille qui se nettoie les dents').
5. The description in the sale catalogue notes: 'elle paroît tenir un curedent qu'elle porte à sa bouche . . .' making it clear that this is the picture mentioned by Descamps (note 4).
6. A seal with the Galitzin arms is on the back of the panel.
7. Smith, loc. cit.

2953 *Portrait of a Lady and a Girl with Oranges*   *Plate 245*

In the left background is the statue of a woman.

Signed, below right: CNetscher. fec/1679. (CN in monogram).

Oil on canvas, 47.5 × 38.5 ($18\frac{3}{4}$ × $15\frac{13}{16}$).

The oranges held by both the girl and the woman, and pointed to so deliberately by the girl, may well indicate the family's adherence to the cause of the House of Orange. There is an orange tree in the background.

PROVENANCE: In the collection of Mrs Sara Austen (died c.1891) in London, and bequeathed by her to Sir Austen Henry Layard;[1] Layard Bequest, 1913.

REFERENCE:
1. According to Major A. A. M. Layard (affidavit of 1914 in the National Gallery archives).

4790 *Portrait of a Lady*   *Plate 246*

Signed at the bottom of the stonework, right: CNetscher. Fec./1683. (CN in monogram).

Oil on canvas, 78.5 × 62 ($30\frac{7}{8}$ × $24\frac{3}{8}$).

There is a *pentimento* in the lower end of the blue drapery (which was originally longer).

The sitter was formerly supposed to be Mary Stuart (1662–94), daughter of James II, who married William, Prince of Orange (later William III of England), in 1677 and, as Mary II, ascended the English throne with him in 1689.[1] This identification is excluded by comparison with indisputable portraits of the queen such as that by Netscher, also dated 1683, in the Hermitage, Leningrad.[2]

COPY: A copy was with the art dealer H. Jüngeling in The Hague in the early 1960s.[3]

PROVENANCE: In a private collection in London and acquired in 1860 or 1865 by the father of J. J. Humphrey Johnstone;[4] in the latter's collection in the Palazzo Contarini dal Zaffo, Venice. Presented by J. J. Humphrey Johnstone on the occasion of HM King George V's Silver Jubilee, 1935.

EXHIBITION: London 1976, No. 76.

REFERENCES:

1. Presented as a portrait of Mary II. This identification may have been suggested by the orange blossom in her hand or by the pink roses in the left background which at first glance and under the present yellow varnish look somewhat like oranges.
2. Panel (on canvas), 81 × 64 cm. HdG No. 297; Hermitage catalogue, 1981, No. 1082. A replica of the Hermitage portrait, companion to a signed

portrait of William III by Netscher, is in the Rijksmuseum, Amsterdam, 1976 cat. nos. C194, C195. For other portraits of her see Moes, vol. 2, No. 4805, and British Museum, *Catalogue of Engraved British Portraits*, vol. 3, 1912, pp. 183–8.
3. Canvas, 77 × 64 cm. Photo in RKD.
4. According to letters of 1935 from J. J. Humphrey Johnstone (in the National Gallery archives).

Studio of CASPAR NETSCHER

1332 *Portrait of a Young Man* Plate 247

Signed at the bottom of the relief of Cupid overcoming Pan on the left: CN/1679.

Oil on canvas, 47.5 × 38.5 (18¾ × 15³⁄₁₆).

No. 1332 was presented as a portrait of 'Admiral Lord Berkeley'[1] but the only Lords Berkeley who were admirals are excluded on chronological grounds.[2] It was once catalogued as (?) George, 1st Earl of Berkeley (1628–98),[3] but the sitter in this and other versions (see below) is clearly too young for him. If the sitter is any of the Earls of Berkeley, the only suitable one from the point of view of age would be Charles, 2nd Earl (1649–1710). He was envoy to the States of Holland from October 1689 to May 1694 but it is not known whether he was in Holland earlier and Netscher never worked in England.[4] The only portrait with serious claims to represent the 2nd Earl[5] shows a different man from that in No. 1332 and the other versions. The version of No. 1332 in the Rijksmuseum,[6] which is signed and dated 1678, is said to be a portrait of a member of the van Citters family, but the grounds for this identification are not known.

The National Gallery picture has in the past been attributed to Caspar Netscher himself;[7] it is rather weak and is most probably a studio replica of the slightly better version in the Rijksmuseum, with which it agrees exactly. The form and calligraphy of the signature on No. 1332 are unlike Netscher's.

The Rijksmuseum and Stuttgart versions (see VERSIONS) have companion portraits of a young woman seated.[8] These companion pieces are of identical composition except for the hair which is short in the Rijksmuseum version whereas the Stuttgart woman has long ringlets down to her shoulders.[9] The Rijksmuseum woman is dated 1674, that at Stuttgart 1682.

287

VERSIONS AND COPIES: An earlier version in the Rijksmuseum is mentioned above. Another replica, signed and dated 1682, is in the Stuttgart Museum.[10] A copy was sold at Christie's, 23 January 1987, lot 97 (bought in).[11]

PROVENANCE: Presented by Baron Savile, 1891.

REFERENCES:

General: HdG, Netscher No. 176.

In text:

1. Minutes of the National Gallery Board meeting of July 1891.

2. i.e. John, 3rd Baron Berkeley of Stratton (1663–97) and James, 3rd Earl of Berkeley (1680–1736). Also excluded on chronological grounds is Vice-Admiral Sir William Berkeley (1639–66).

3. It is possible that the identification was suggested by the date 1679 on the picture, since in that year George, until then 9th Baron Berkeley, was created 1st Earl of Berkeley.

4. R. de Piles (*Abrégé de la vie des peintres*, 1699, p. 455) and Houbraken (vol. 3, p. 95) say that Netscher declined Charles II's invitations to go to London. George Vertue, writing in 1728, says that Sir William Temple 'recommended Netscher to the Court of King Charles 2d. *about* 1668 at his [Temple's] return from Holland but he stay'd not long here' (*Vertue Note-books*, vol. 2, p. 53, in *Walpole Society*, vol. 20, 1932). His information came from Friedrich Zincke who was not born until 1685 and came to England about 1706, and is clearly of little value in view of the statements by the well-informed Houbraken and de Piles. The legend of Netscher's stay in England doubtless arose from the fact that there exist portraits of English sitters by him, but all those whose identification is certain were painted in Holland: e.g. two of the portraits of Sir William Temple's family – HdG Nos. 202 (*Portrait of Lady Gifford and Diana Temple*: now in the collection of Lady Pamela Hicks) and 274 (*Portrait of Sir William Temple*: National Portrait Gallery; the portrait of his wife, Dorothy Osborne, also in the National Portrait Gallery, is undated but is the companion piece) – are dated 1675, in which year he and his family were in Holland, and so is the portrait of the Earl and Countess of Arlington (Earl of Rosebery sale, London, 5 May 1939, lot 103, bought by Templer) who were also there in that year. Most of the portraits said to be of English sitters by Netscher are either misidentified or misattributed.

In the present context it is perhaps worth remarking that Vertue mentions in 1749 a portrait by Netscher of John, 1st Baron Berkeley of Stratton (*c.*1610(?)–1678), together with his wife and a servant 'in small life . . . half length', dated 1676 (*Vertue Note-books*, vol. 5, p. 76, *Walpole Society*, vol. 26, 1938). This is presumably the portrait, signed and dated 1676, at Berkeley Castle (Canvas, 25 × 28 in.) in which the man is clearly not the same sitter as in No. 1332.

5. Dashwood Heirlooms sale, London, 25 April 1934 (lot 105); three-quarter-length portrait, attributed to a Lely follower; inscribed on the back 'Portrait of Lord Berkeley, brother of Lady Clifford'. According to the Dashwood Heirlooms sale catalogue, p. 15, this portrait entered the collection through the wife of James Vernon (d. 1756), who was the daughter of Lady Clifford, the youngest sister of the 2nd Earl of Berkeley. A photograph of the portrait is in the National Gallery archives.

6. Canvas, 49 × 39 cm. Signed: CNetscher/1678 (CN in monogram). Rijksmuseum, 1976 cat., A1692 as 'Portrait of a Man thought to be a member of the Van Citters family'. HdG No. 190. The sitter cannot be identified with any member of the van Citters family listed by E. W. Moes (*Iconographia Batava*, vol. 1, 1897).

7. By HdG. MacLaren was the first to catalogue the portrait as 'Studio of Caspar Netscher'.

8. The companion portrait in the Rijksmuseum is No. A1693 in the 1976 catalogue. Canvas, 49 × 39 cm. Signed and dated: CNetscher fec. 1674. The Stuttgart companion portrait is Inv. no. 597 (1962 cat.). Canvas, 48.8 × 39.8 cm. Signed and dated: CNetscher 1682.

9. This is due to the ringlets of the woman in the Rijksmuseum painting having been overpainted at a later period. HdG (No. 393) mistakenly states that the faces are different; they are, in fact, identical.

10. Stuttgart catalogue, 1962, inv. no. 608. Canvas, 48.8 × 39.8 cm.; signed: Netscher f. 1682.

11. Canvas, 47.6 × 39.4 cm.

After CASPAR NETSCHER

1879 *A Musical Party*   *Plate 248*

The young man on the left is playing a theorbo. In the centre of the wall behind is a landscape in a carved gilt frame and on the left a wall-sconce. In the left foreground is a lute-case.

Oil on canvas, 55.5 × 45 (21$\frac{13}{16}$ × 17$\frac{11}{16}$).

Considerable wearing in the dark areas and the background.

This is a copy of a composition by Caspar Netscher, the original (or best version) of which is in Munich (Fig. 67), signed and dated 1665.[1] There are a number of other replicas or copies of this design (see below).

VERSIONS AND COPIES: There are versions or copies in Karlsruhe,[2] Rouen,[3] and in the Jean Henri Beissel of Aachen sale, Brussels, 6–8 April 1875 (lot 97).[4] Copies were in the Jhr. C. Ch. Six and others sale, Rotterdam (Venduhuis Notarissen), 18 October 1950 (lot 90);[5] the Gräfin I. Roland Coudenhove-Kalergi and others sale, Lucerne (Fischer), 17 November 1951 (lot 2659);[6] Anon. sale, Stockholm (AB Auktionsverk.), 10–14 November 1981, lot 768;[7] and (with variations) the M. and Th. Klopfer sale, Munich (Helbing), 24 November 1908 (lot 187).[8]

PROVENANCE: In the collection of General Sir John May by 1847;[9] May Bequest, 1854.[10]

REFERENCES:

1. Munich, Alte Pinakothek. Canvas, 50.4 × 45.9 cm. Signed, lower left, on the lute-case: C Netscher f. 1665. 1983 catalogue, No. 618. HdG No. 116.
2. Canvas, 51 × 46 cm. Signed, lower left, CNetscher 1665. 1966 catalogue, No. 265.
3. Canvas, 49 × 39 cm. Rouen, 1911, cat. no. 707. Catalogued as '18th-century Dutch' in O. Popovitch, *Catalogue des Peintures du Musée des Beaux-Arts de Rouen*, 1967, inv. no. 887–2 (not in 1978 catalogue).
4. Canvas, 50 × 45 cm.
5. Panel, 59 × 45 cm. This painting was later in the Mme le L. and others sale, Paris (Charpentier), 30 November 1954, lot 27; and Anon. sale, Paris (Galliera), 12 December 1960, lot 58.
6. Panel, 57.5 × 47 cm. Illustrated in sale catalogue.
7. Canvas, 50 × 44 cm. Photo in RKD.
8. Canvas, 51 × 43½ cm. There is a framed painting in place of the wall-sconce on the left.
9. It was bequeathed (with Nos. 44, 1858 and 1874) in 1847 with a life-interest to Lady May, and ceded by her to the National Gallery in 1854.
10. First catalogued in 1915.

MICHIEL NOUTS, active 1656

The only known certain work by this painter is a woman's portrait in the Rijksmuseum in Amsterdam signed: Michiel.Nouts. Me. fecit. 1656 (Fig. 68). He has been identified with Michiel Servaesz. Nouts (later Nuyts) who was the son of a painter, Servaes Michielsz. Nouts. Michiel was baptised in Delft on 13 April 1628, settled in Amsterdam by September 1656 and was buried there on 15 July 1693. Against this identification is the fact that the documents concerning Michiel Servaesz. Nouts describe him as a musician, never as a painter. But all these documents except the record of baptism relate to his Amsterdam years so it is possible that, if his identification with the author of the Rijksmuseum portrait is correct, he may have given up painting when he moved to Amsterdam; this would account for the small number of pictures by him.

On the other hand there may have been a second Michiel Nouts in Delft; a single mention exists of a painter called Michiel Michielsz. – he remarried in Delft in 1637 – and Bredius has suggested this was a brother of Servaes Michielsz. Nouts (the latter entered the Delft guild in 1627 and is documented there again in the following year). The omission of surnames was still common in the first half of the seventeenth century (e.g. Servaes Nouts himself is also referred to as Servaes Michielsz. in some documents) but the only evidence in support of Bredius' suggestion is that the two men have the same not uncommon patronymic.

In addition to No. 1699 (below), a few paintings have been convincingly attributed to the same hand as the signed Rijksmuseum painting: *A Portrait of a Mother and Two Children* (van Diemen sale, 25 January 1935, lot 42);[1] *A Portrait of a Woman* (Munich, Alte Pinakothek);[2] *A Portrait of a Woman* (Anon. sale, Copenhagen, Rasmussen, 6–7 November 1979, lot 19);[3] and *A Portrait of a Woman* (with the dealer William R. Drown, London, 1961).[4]

REFERENCES:
General: Bredius in OH, vol. 38, 1920, pp. 181–3 and 232.
In text:
1. Panel, 105 × 139 cm. Reproduced in W. Berut, *Die Niederländischen Maler des 17. Jahrhunderts*, Munich, 1962, vol. 4, plate 213.
2. Canvas, 61 × 43 cm. 1957 catalogue, No. 1633.
3. Canvas, 80 × 66 cm.
4. This attribution was made by S. J. Gudlaugsson and H. Gerson on the mount of the photograph in the RKD. The painting bears a false Dou signature and was said to be dated 1653.

Attributed to MICHIEL NOUTS

1699 *A Family Group* — Plate 249

Oil on canvas. The present painted surface measures 178 × 235 (70 × 92½). At some time prior to 1900 the picture was cut in half;[1] the left half measures 178 × 123 (70 × 48½), the right half has been reduced to c.136 × c.107.5 (c.53½ × c.42¼). When the two parts were joined together in 1915, strips of canvas were added to replace the missing portions, as follows: c.14.5 cm. wide along the top, c.28.5 cm. along the bottom and c.5 cm. in the centre between the two sections.

The left half is much worn and retouched. The right half is less so but the girl behind the table is considerably repainted. The best preserved sections of the picture are the woman, the child on her lap, the doll and the pewter inkstand on the table. The whole of the right half below the edge of the table-cloth, the upper third of the curtain and most of the right sleeve and right half of the collar of the girl behind the table are modern restorations.

The picture was at one time ascribed to Vermeer.[2] It was later attributed to Michael Sweerts[3] (1618–64) but this is equally untenable. Valentiner[4] believed the man in No. 1699 to be the same as the man in a drawing by Leendert van der Cooghen in the Berlin

290

printroom,[5] whom he correctly identified as the painter, Vincent Laurensz. van der Vinne[6] (born 1629). Were this so, the woman would be van der Vinne's first wife, Anna de Gaver, who was married to him in December 1656 and died in 1668, and the children would be some of the six he had by her;[7] the boy on the left, Laurens (born 1658), the girl behind the table, Maycken (born c.1661), the child on the right, Jan (born 1663) and the baby Isaack (born 1665). Valentiner thought the colour reminiscent of the Haarlem School and he suggested Leendert van der Cooghen as the author of this portrait as well as of the Berlin drawing, dating the picture 1667 on the basis of the apparent ages of the children. (Van der Cooghen was born in 1632 and died in 1681.) The resemblance of the man in the present picture to the man in the Berlin drawing is slight and identification with van der Vinne and his family is almost certainly excluded by the costume, which is typical of the earlier half of the 1650s; even supposing the sitters to be unfashionable it is difficult to believe they would have dressed in this way as late as 1667. As to the attribution: the only two known certain paintings by van der Cooghen[8] and his few signed drawings are in a completely different style from the National Gallery picture.

Although it has often been suggested that this family group was painted under Vermeer's influence,[9] the connection is not at all close and the exact relation to Vermeer's style is obscure. Nevertheless there is enough to indicate that the picture was painted either in Delft or by someone well acquainted with the Delft painting of the 1650s. If allowance is made for the condition, the style is quite close to that of Nouts' signed portrait of a woman in the Rijksmuseum[10] (see especially the hands). The Rijksmuseum picture is dated 1656; the National Gallery group is perhaps a little earlier.

PROVENANCE: The left half was presented by C. Fairfax Murray in 1900; the right half was purchased from Max Flersheim of Paris in 1910 (with the aid of the Clarke Fund).

REFERENCES:
1. That the two halves are parts of the same picture is proved by the right arm of the girl behind the table, which is continued in the left-hand section.
2. National Gallery catalogue, 1901–15 (No. 1699) and 1911–13 (No. 2764), as Ascribed to Vermeer. (The right half had a separate inventory number, 2764, until 1915, when this number was given to *The Virgin and Child with Two Saints* by B. Fungai.)
3. R. C. Witt in BM, vol. 27, 1915, pp. 91–2, where it is further suggested that it was painted before Sweerts went to Italy, i.e. before 1646. This attribution was first made by E. Plietzsch, *Vermeer van Delft*, 1911, p. 138, and later withdrawn; see Thieme/Becker, vol. 32, 1938, p. 349. In the National Gallery catalogue, 1920–9, pp. 212–16.
4. W. R. Valentiner in *Pantheon*, 1932, pp. 212–16.
5. Reproduced by Valentiner, op. cit., p. 214; signed: LVC.
6. Op. cit., p. 212. The identification is based on the resemblance of the sitter to that in a portrait of 1651 by Judith Leyster traditionally said to be of Vincent Laurensz. van der Vinne and to a self portrait (both in the Frans Halsmuseum, Haarlem), and also on the fact that the Berlin drawing by van der Cooghen appears in a signed *Still Life* by van der Vinne (also in Haarlem).
7. According to van der Willigen (p. 314), van der Vinne had six children by his first wife Anna. See also van der Willigen, Supplement F.
8. i.e. *The Incredulity of St Thomas*, dated 1654, in the Mauritshuis (1977 catalogue, No. 81) and *The Adoration of the Shepherds*, dated 1656, in the Frans Halsmuseum, Haarlem (1969 catalogue, No. 506).
9. Most recently by W. Martin, *De Hollandsche schilderkunst in de zeventiende eeuw*, [1942], vol. 2, p. 208.
10. Canvas, 108 × 85.5 cm. For the signature and date see the biographical notice of Nouts above. Rijksmuseum, 1976 cat. no. A1847.

JACOB OCHTERVELT, 1634–1682

Jacob Lucasz. Ochtervelt.[1] He was born in Rotterdam and baptised in the Reformed Church there in February 1634. Houbraken says Ochtervelt was a pupil of Nicolaes Berchem at the same time as Pieter de Hooch;[2] this would have been in Haarlem in the years around 1650. Ochtervelt was living in Rotterdam in November 1655, when he posted the banns for his marriage (which took place on 14 December): he is recorded in fourteen documents in Rotterdam between 1661 and 1672 (in 1667 he was nominated for the mastership of the St Luke's Guild but lost the election to Cornelis Saftleven). He had moved to Amsterdam by 1674 when he is recorded in the city's tax register for the first time. 1674 is the date on his portrait of the *Regents of the Amsterdam Leper House* in the Rijksmuseum.[3]

By 1679 he had moved to a large house on the Keizersgracht (No. 608). He is mentioned in two documents of 1677 which record attempts to collect money which he had lent. He was buried in the Nieuwezijds Chapel in Amsterdam on 1 May 1682.

Nearly all his paintings are genre subjects and many of them show domestic interiors of the wealthier classes; there are also some portraits and some early landscapes and history paintings. His earliest dated painting is *Granida and Daifilo* of 1654 (Osnabrück, Städtisches Museum).

REFERENCES:
General: S. D. Kuretsky, *The Paintings of Jacob Ochtervelt (1634–1682): with Catalogue Raisonné*, Oxford, 1979.
In text:
1. All the documents relating to Ochtervelt's biography are given in full in Kuretsky, op. cit., pp. 219–30.
2. Houbraken, vol. 2, p. 35.
3. 1976 cat., no. C390.

2143 *A Woman standing at a Harpsichord, a Man seated by her*

Plate 250

In the left background is a painting of a wooded landscape in a black frame. Over the door to the right is a bust.

Oil on canvas, 79.7 × 65.4 (31⅛ × 25¾).

Cleaned in 1977. A curved tear runs from just to the left of the woman's head, through her face and into her shoulder. The background is seriously abraded.

According to MacLaren, the woman's dress, which is identical with that in Ochtervelt No. 3864 below, is of the late 1670s (cf. also the man's wig with that in Netscher No. 1332, which is dated 1679). Kuretsky[1] dated the painting to *c.*1676–80.

PROVENANCE: Collection of Fürstin Carolath-Beuthen, Berlin, 1883; Huldschinsky sale, Berlin (Lepke), 18–20 March 1900, lot 54; presented by Henry J. Pfungst in 1907.

EXHIBITIONS: Berlin, Königlichen Akademie der Künste, 'Ausstellung von Gemälden Alterer Meister im Berliner Privatbesitz', 1883, No. 86;[2] London 1978–9, No. 10.

REFERENCES:
General: Kuretsky, op. cit., cat. no. 95.
In text: **1.** Kuretsky, op. cit., cat. no. 95.
2. The exhibition was reviewed and the painting noted by Bode in JKPK, vol. 4, 1883, p. 209.

2553 *A Young Lady trimming her Finger-nails, attended by a Maidservant*

Plate 251

Cleaning of the painting revealed that a tapestry hangs on the back wall; it appears to show Hagar in the Wilderness.

Oil on canvas, 74.6 × 59 (29⅜ × 23¼).

Cleaned in 1977–8. Seriously abraded in the background.

MacLaren considered that the costume dated from the late 1660s. Kuretsky,[1] however, noted that the painting was related to a series of 'boudoir scenes',[2] datable by costume to the early 1670s, all of which combine the same silver basin and ewer. She considered that the style of the painting 'with its innocent spatial intervals and rather frozen gestures'[3] seems more characteristic of the 1670s, at which time she considers that a decline in the quality of the artist's work took place.

VERSION: An autograph version (with an added chandelier) was said by Plietzsch[4] to be in a German private collection in 1960.

PROVENANCE: This is probably the 'Young Lady just up, and paring her nails Octervelt' [sic] which was in a Dr [Robert] Bragge sale, London(?), 1756 (2nd day, lot 46), bought by Sir John Chapman (£11.13.6).[5] In the collection of George Salting, London; Salting Bequest, 1910.

REFERENCES:
General: Kuretsky, op. cit., cat. no. 76.
In text:
1. Kuretsky, op. cit., cat. no. 76.
2. *Lady with Servant and Dog*: canvas, 93.8 × 76 cm. New York Historical Society, Bryan Collection, inv. no. B–143; *The Letter Reader*: canvas, 91 × 78 cm. Private collection, Cologne; *Lady with Servant and Dog*: canvas, 70 × 57 cm. The Carnegie Institute Museum of Art, Pittsburgh, inv. no. PC134; *The Footwashing*: canvas, 73.5 × 60.5 cm. Present location unknown (with D. Katz, Dieren, 1934–9). These are Nos. 75, 77, 78 and 79 in Kuretsky's catalogue.

3. Kuretsky, op. cit., p. 85.
4. E. Plietzsch, *Holländische und Flämische Maler des 17. Jahrhunderts*, Leipzig, 1960, p. 66.
5. This sale is not recorded in Lugt, vol. 1, and is only known from a MS copy in one of two volumes of extracts from eighteenth-century sale catalogues in the Victoria and Albert Museum (vol. 1, pp. 276ff; pressmark: RC. S. I); the day and month of the sale are not given. (See also the extract given by F. Simpson in BM, vol. 95, 1953, p. 41.)

3864 *A Woman playing a Virginal, Another singing and a Man playing a Violin*

Plate 252

On the wall is a map. On the left half of the inner side of the virginal's lid is an effaced inscription: S?˙D? E?.

Signed over the door: Jac̄ : Ocht(. .)velt : f

Oil on canvas, 84.5 × 75 (33¼ × 29½).

Before 1920 the hair of the two women had been altered and the tail of the dog on the right painted out.[1] These areas of overpainting were removed shortly after the acquisition of the painting.

The map on the wall in the background is based on an atlas-size (47 × 58.5 cm.) map of North and South America (entitled *Americae nova descriptio*) published in Amsterdam in 1661 by Dancker Danckerts.[2]

MacLaren considered that the dress and coiffure of the woman at the virginal (which are identical with those in Ochtervelt No. 2143 above) and those of the man are of the late 1670s. Kuretsky[3] dated the painting *c.*1676–80.

VERSION: A feeble pastiche was in a private collection in Frankfurt in 1974.[4]

PROVENANCE: A. D. S. de Vahl sale, London, 20 February 1920 (lot 142), bought by Peacock (£756). Purchased from Messrs S. T. Smith in 1924.

REFERENCES:
General: Kuretsky, op. cit., cat. no. 94.
In text:
1. A photograph of the picture in this state, taken at the de Vahl sale in 1920, is in the National Gallery archives.
2. This identification was made by Dr J. Welu and published by Kuretsky, op. cit., p. 92.
3. Kuretsky, op. cit.

4. Canvas, 85 × 72 cm. There are a number of changes: in place of the door on the left is a large fireplace; the violinist has become a female lutenist and the seated woman on the right a standing male singer. Its previous provenance was: with van Diemen, Berlin, *c.*1930; with Galerie Stern, Düsseldorf, 1936. Its 1974 whereabouts are noted on the RKD mount. Kuretsky, op. cit., cat. no. 94-A.

JAN OLIS, *c.*1610(?)–1676

He was born in Gorinchem (Gorkum), to the east of Dordrecht; the date of his birth is not known. He may have been in Rome in 1631 (a *Diana and Actaeon* formerly in the Lüdinghausen-Wolff collection in Mitau is said to be signed: J. Olis roma pinsit Ao. 1631). He entered the Dordrecht guild in July 1632. In 1637 he married in Dordrecht and he is mentioned there as having pupils in 1638 and 1641. In 1638 he is referred to as a vintner. He was an alderman of Heusden, near 's Hertogenbosch, several times in the years 1656–61 and was burgomaster in 1657; in 1670 he was a tax-collector. He died in Heusden, 6 June 1676.

Comparatively few works by him are known, mostly genre scenes in the manner of the painters of guardrooms and festive scenes such as Anthonie Palamedesz. of Delft, and a few small portraits somewhat reminiscent of Pieter Codde. He also painted a number of history paintings and still lifes.

REFERENCES: G. H. Veth in OH, vol. 9, 1891, pp. 31–5; Bredius in OH, vol. 57, 1940, pp. 143–4; I. Bergström in OH, vol. 66, 1951, pp. 56–8; L.-J. Bol, *Höllandischen Maler des 17. Jahrhunderts nahe den grossen Meistern*, Munich, 2nd ed., 1982, p. 63.

3548 *A Musical Party* *Plate 253*

The woman is playing a viola da gamba, the man with his back to the spectator a lute, the man on the right a flute and the standing man a violin.

Signed on the central cross-bar of chair-back, right: JOLIS . 1633 (JO in monogram).

Oil on oak, 36.7 × 52.8 ($14\frac{7}{16}$ × $20\frac{13}{16}$).

Cleaned in 1969–70. When the painting was cleaned, the figure of a boy removing a flask from a wine cooler in the left background was considered to be of inferior quality and was painted out.[1]

COPIES: A copy was in the Emil von Mecenseffy and others sale, Vienna (Wawra), 16 April 1918, lot 233 (as Ludolf de Jongh)[2] and a watercolour copy in the Countess of Ancaster and others sale, Christie's, 9 April 1954, lot 6 (as Palamedes) (35 gns to Blum).[3]

PROVENANCE: Presented by A. A. de Pass, 1920.

REFERENCES :

1. The present writer has only seen this figure in photographs. Based on them he considers it to be perfectly consistent with the work of Olis himself.

2. Panel, 47 × 63 cm.

3. Property of the Lady Helen O'Brien. Watercolour on card, 38 × 53 cm.

See also DIRCK VAN DELEN No. 1010

GEORGIUS JACOBUS JOHANNES VAN OS, 1782–1861

Born 20 November 1782 in The Hague; son and pupil of Jan van Os. He first visited Paris in 1812 and after working there and in Amsterdam and The Hague, finally settled in Paris in 1826, and worked for the Sèvres porcelain factory although he frequently returned to the Netherlands, particularly to Haarlem. He died in Paris on 21 July 1861.

His style is based on that of his father. He made paintings and drawings of landscape but specialised in still life and also made lithographs of still-life subjects.

REFERENCES: Van Eijnden and van der Willigen, vol. 3, pp. 247 ff., and Supplement, pp. 235 ff; J. Immerzeel, *De levens en werken der Hollandsche en Vlaamsche kunstschilders* etc., vol. 2, 1843, pp. 284–5; Kramm, vol. 4, p. 1230 f., and Supplement, 1864, p. 115; Scheen, pp. 386–7.

3226 *Fruit, Flowers and Game*   *Plate 254*

On the right is a bas-relief of a bacchante and a satyr; at the bottom, a relief with two putti. Hanging from the barrel of a gun is a partridge; on top of the relief is a snipe. On the marble slab are grapes, peaches, pomegranates etc.

Signed, left, on the edge of the marble slab: G J J Van Os

Oil on mahogany, 80.5 × 61.6 ($31\frac{11}{16}$ × $24\frac{1}{4}$).

PROVENANCE: In the possession of Nieuwenhuys in Brussels;[1] said to have been later in the Scarisbrick collection.[2] It was in the William Benoni White sale, London, 23–24 May 1879 (lot 86), bought by Fraser (46 gns). In the [S. H. Fraser, Northumberland] sale, 21 June 1890 (lot 97),[3] bought by Aston (54 gns). W. W. Aston Bequest, 1919.

REFERENCES :

1. On the back of the panel is a label inscribed: 'Collection / de / Messieurs Nieuwenhuys / à / Bruxelles.'

2. According to the catalogue of the W. Benoni White sale of 1879: 'Painted for M. Nieuwenhuys, from the Scarisbrick Collection.' It was not in the

Charles Scarisbrick sales, London, 10–11 (actually 11–13) May, 17–18 May and 24–25 May, 1861, nor in the [Charles Scarisbrick] sale, London, 25 March 1872.

3. As from the Benoni White, Scarisbrick and Nieuwenhuys collections. The artist's name is printed in the sale catalogue as 'E. Wauters' but this is corrected in Christie's copy of the catalogue to 'G. J. J. van Os'; the markings corresponding to this sale are on the back of the panel.

JAN VAN OS, 1744–1808

He was baptised in Middelharnis, 23 February 1744, and was a pupil of Aert Schouman (1710–92) in The Hague; he was inscribed in The Hague painters' confraternity in 1773. In 1775 he married the painter Suzanne de la Croix. He remained in The Hague and died there 7 February 1808.

He painted fruit and flower pieces. His flower pieces, often in watercolours, are in the tradition of Jan van Huysum. He also painted a number of seascapes in the manner of Willem van de Velde the Younger's followers (e.g. No. 1462 below);[1] these seem to be among his earlier works.

Among his pupils were two of his sons, Georgius Jacobus Johannes van Os, Pieter Gerardus van Os (1776–1839), and his daughter, Maria Margaretha van Os (1780 –1862).

REFERENCES:
General: Van Eijnden and van der Willigen, vol. 2, pp. 334–7; Obreen, vol. 4, 1881–2, p. 221; Scheen, p. 387.
In text:
1. See A. Staring, *De herleving van het stille watergezicht in de 18de eeuw*, Album Amicorum J. G. van Gelder, The Hague, 1973, pp. 306–9.

1380 *Fruit, Flowers and a Fish*   *Plate 255*

Among the fruit are grapes, melons, peaches, plums, a pineapple and a pomegranate; the principal flowers are roses and hollyhocks.

Signed on the marble slab, towards the right: J. Van Os. fecit 1772.

Oil on mahogany, 72.2 × 56.7 ($28\frac{3}{8}$ × $22\frac{15}{16}$).

PROVENANCE: On the back of the panel is an ink inscription: 'Count Mont(. . .a?)'. This inscription has been read[1] as 'Count Montaleau'; the picture was not in the [Montaleau?] sale, Paris, 19 sqq. July 1802. It was in the collection of George Holt, Liverpool, by whom presented in 1892.

REFERENCE: **1.** National Gallery catalogue, 1915–29.

1462 *Dutch Vessels in Calm Water* Plate 256

The passenger vessel on the right, a *tjalk*, has two Dutch vanes. In the right middle distance is a brigantine at anchor.

Signed on the forward vane of the *tjalk*: IVO (very small). On a spar in the foreground, left of centre, are the badly worn remains of some letters, apparently a spurious signature of Willem van de Velde.

Oil on oak, 32.1 × 42.4 ($12\frac{5}{8}$ × $16\frac{11}{16}$).

Worn and retouched in the sky. The man to the right of the barge in the left foreground has been slightly altered.[1]

Van Os painted a number of similar seascapes,[2] all apparently in the early part of his career.

Before 1960 it had been catalogued as by Hendrick Dubbels, the clamps on the lee-board of the vessel laid ashore on the left having been taken for the letters IHD or HD.[3]

PROVENANCE: Presented by Arthur Kay, Glasgow, in 1895.[4]

REFERENCES:
1. Since August 1895 (letter of 1895 from Arthur Kay in the National Gallery archives).
2. Cf. the pair of *Calms* in the Budapest Museum of Fine Arts, both signed: J. van Os f. (1967 cat. nos. 455 and 461) and the *Calm* in the Städelsches Kunstinstitut, Frankfurt (1971 cat., Inv. no. 646: signed: J.van Os fecit).
3. See National Gallery catalogue, 1898–1906 and 1915–29.
4. As by Dubbels.

ADRIAEN VAN OSTADE, 1610–1685

Adriaen Jansz. van Ostade; baptised in Haarlem, 10 December 1610. According to Houbraken[1] he was a pupil of Frans Hals at the same time as Adriaen Brouwer (i.e. about 1627). He is first recorded as a painter in 1632; he must have entered the St Luke's Guild in Haarlem by 1634. He was a *hoofdman* of the Haarlem guild in 1647 and 1661 and *deken* (dean) in 1662. He spent his life in Haarlem, leaving it rarely and for short periods only. He married for the second time in Amsterdam in 1657 but the couple lived in Haarlem: his second wife (who died in 1666) was from a wealthy, devoutly Catholic family and the artist may have become a Catholic at about this time. He was buried in St Bavo's Church in Haarlem on 2 May 1685.

He painted and etched peasant scenes; he also painted a few biblical subjects and small portraits. There is no discernible trace of Hals' influence in the surviving early works which do, on the other hand, show that of Brouwer in both style and subject. Ostade made many watercolour drawings and some fifty etchings.

There are many more or less contemporary imitations and forgeries of his work. Among his pupils were his brother Isack, Cornelis Bega, Michiel van Musscher, Jan Steen and Cornelis Dusart (1660–1704). Dusart often comes very close to van Ostade and in the sale of Dusart's property in 1708 a number of pictures were described as their joint work.[2]

REFERENCES:
General: HdG, vol. 3; L. Godefroy, *L'oeuvre gravée de Adriaen van Ostade,* 1930. B. Schnackenburg, 'Die Anfänge des Bauerninterieurs bei Adriaen van Ostade', OH, vol. 85, 1970, pp. 158–69; Schnackenburg, *Adriaen van Ostade, Isack van Ostade: Zeichnungen und Aquarelle,* 2 vols., Hamburg, 1981. For the documents see van der Willigen, pp. 21–3, 29 and 233–41; OH, 1885, p. 240; Schnackenburg, op. cit., vol. 1, pp. 13–16.

In text:
1. Houbraken, vol. 1, pp. 320 and 347.
2. Bredius. *Künstler-Inventare,* vol. 1., pp. 27ff.

846 *An Alchemist* *Plate 257*

Under the stool in the centre foreground is a paper inscribed: oleum et/ operam/ perdis.

Signed on a shovel hanging beside the fireplace: Av. Ostade./1661 (Av in monogram).

Oil on oak, 34 × 45.2 ($13\frac{3}{8}$ × $17\frac{13}{16}$).

Cleaned in 1951.

The baby in the lap of the woman in the background was painted out, and a bundle substituted, at some time between 1770 and 1892;[1] this overpainting was removed when the picture was cleaned.

With its dark cavern-like interior and figures illuminated by a strong fall of light, this painting shares formal similarities with van Ostade's many scenes from peasant life (see, for example, No. 2540 below). The artist has, however, introduced into his convention of the representation of peasant life the figure of the alchemist which is taken from an existing pictorial tradition. Alchemists, who believed that base metals could be transformed into gold, were the subject of numerous literary and visual satires in the sixteenth and seventeenth centuries: their search for wealth was treated as a paradigm of human folly. A well-known treatment of the subject is the print by Hieronymous Cock after the design by Pieter Bruegel the Elder[2] which shows an alchemist ruining his family in his hunt for gold. In Bruegel's print the moral is reinforced by the presence of a scholar who points to the alchemist with one hand and with the other to a book which has the punning title *Alghe Mist* ('Everything wasted'). In van Ostade's painting the moral of the futility of the alchemist's quest is emphasised by the Latin quotation on the paper by his foot: 'oleum et operam perdis', to lose one's time and trouble. This saying of the Roman comic dramatist Plautus is quoted by the German humanist Agricola in his *De Re Metallica* (1556, p. 2).

Hofstede de Groot[3] states that *Interior with Peasants* of 1663 in the Wallace Collection[4] is a pendant to No. 846, but there seems no convincing evidence for this. He listed a number of the treatments of the subject of an alchemist by Adriaen van Ostade.[5]

PROVENANCE: In the Samuel van Huls sale, The Hague, 3 sqq. September 1737 (lot 32), 600 guilders;[6] Graaf van Wassenaar Obdam sale, The Hague, 19 August 1750 (lot 37),[7] bought by Brouwer for Avet (910 guilders). In the collection of La Live de Jully, Paris, by 1764;[8] La Live de Jully sale, Paris, 5 sqq. March 1770 (lot 13, with pendant) bought by Donjeu (4,105 francs); [Abbé de Gévigney] sale, Paris, 1 sqq. December

1779 (lot 237), bought in (5,000 francs). Smith identified it with a picture in a Lenglier sale, Paris, 10 sqq. March 1788 which was, however, of different composition.[9] An undescribed 'Alchymist' was in an anonymous sale, London, 18 February 1792 (lot 40), bought by Sir F. Bourgeois (135 gns). In the Alexis Delahante sale, London, 14 July 1821 (lot 115),[10] 395 gns; lent by Joseph Barchard to the BI, in 1822, later sold to Emmerson.[11] By 1829 it was in the collection of (Sir) Robert Peel (Bart.);[12] purchased with the Peel collection, 1871.

EXHIBITIONS: BI 1822, No. 33; London 1976, No. 77; London 1978–9, No. 13.

REFERENCES:
General: Smith No. 28; HdG Nos. 397 and (?)398a.
In text:

1. The description in the catalogue of the La Live de Jully sale of 1770 (see PROVENANCE) proves that the picture had not then been altered; the alteration is noted by Smith in 1829 (loc. cit.).

2. R. van Bastelaer, *Les Estampes de Peter Bruegel L'Ancien*, Brussels, 1908, No. 197. Bruegel's drawing for this print, which is in the Kupferstichkabinet in Berlin-Dahlem, is dated 1558. See M. Winner, 'Zu Bruegels Alchemist', *Pieter Bruegel und seine Welt*, Berlin, 1979, pp. 193–202.

3. HdG No. 397.

4. Panel, 34.3 × 40 cm. Wallace Collection cat. 1979, No. P169. HdG No. 464. It was also in the La Live de Jully collection by 1764 but differs in size and date from No. 846 and was not in the Huls or Wassenaar Obdam sales (see under PROVENANCE).

5. HdG Nos. 397a–401. HdG No. 401 is illustrated and discussed in BM, vol. 14, 1908, pp. 84–5.

6. See Hoet, vol. 2, p. 481.

7. 'Een Alchimist, een Vrou, en Jongens, Bijwerk [sic]'; 13 × 17 *duim*. The picture could hardly be recognised by so vague a description but it is identified with that belonging to La Live de Jully in the catalogue of the La Live collection and the latter is certainly the National Gallery picture (see the following note).

8. *Catalogue historique du cabinet de . . . M. de Lalive*, 1764, p. 118. The National Gallery picture is inscribed on the back of the panel in ink: 'L. D. J.' For a supposed pendant, also in the La Live de Jully collection by 1764, see above, note 4.

9. According to the sale catalogue it was '. . . un Chymiste assis près d'un fourneau occupé à retirer un creuset du feu, . . . une femme endormie, le coude appuyé sur un tonneau se voit dans le fond à gauche, & trois enfans; l'un est au haut d'une échelle, & entre dans un grenier'; on panel, 13 *pouces* 7 *lignes* × 19 *pouces*.

10. In the copy of the Delahante 1821 sale catalogue in the RKD there is a contemporary MS annotation against lot 115: 'Now Mr Peel's' (Peel succeeded to the baronetcy in 1830).

11. Smith, loc. cit.

12. Smith, loc. cit.

2540 *The Interior of an Inn with Nine Peasants and a Hurdy-Gurdy Player* Plate 258

Signed at bottom, towards the left: Av. Ostade . 1653 (Av in monogram)

Oil on oak, 39.9 × 55.7 ($15\frac{11}{16}$ × $21\frac{15}{16}$).

PROVENANCE: In the Johan van der Marck (of Leiden) sale, Amsterdam, 25 sqq. August 1773 (lot 236), bought by van Leyden (1,904 guilders); van Leyden (of Amsterdam) sale, Paris, 5 sqq. November 1804 (lot 70), bought by Etienne (5,001 francs). In the van Saceghem collection, Ghent, by 1842;[1] van Saceghem sale, Brussels, 2–3 June 1851 (lot 75), bought by Rothschild (58,500 francs). Théodore Patureau sale, Paris, 20–21 April 1857 (lot 18),[2] bought by Moreau (51,500 francs). Earl of Dudley sale, London, 25 June 1892 (lot 17),[3] bought by M. Colnaghi (£1,470) by whom lent to the RA, 1893. In the collection of George Salting by 1894 when it was exhibited at the Guildhall, London; Salting Bequest, 1910.

EXHIBITIONS: RA 1893, No. 105; London, Guildhall, 1894, No. 69.

REFERENCES:
General: Smith No. 135 and Supplement No. 105; HdG Nos. 535, 537 and 652.
In text:

1. Smith Supplement No. 105.

2. As *Estaminet hollandais*. The Patureau sale catalogue gives as provenance the van Leyden collection and the van Saceghem sale. The identity of the Patureau picture with No. 2540 is confirmed by a painted inscription on the back of No. 2540: 'T.P.Nº 18'; (No. 2540 also has on the back a seal

299

stamped: E. LEROY/COMMISSAIRE EXPERT/DU MUSEE
ROYAL.)
3. According to the National Gallery catalogue,
1915–29, it was also in the [Earl of Dudley] sale,

London, 7 April 1876; the only A. van Ostade in this
sale, lot 99, was an entirely different picture (see
HdG No. 449).

2542 A Peasant courting an Elderly Woman   Plate 259

The man holds a *pas-glas* filled with wine.

Signed, bottom left: Av. Ostade./1653. (Av in monogram).

Oil on oak, 27.3 × 22.1 (10¾ × 8¹¹⁄₁₆).

The picture, or more probably the contemporary print after it by Cornelis Visscher
(see below), was known in the eighteenth century as 'Het schollenmannetje' or 'Het
zoute scholletje'.[1] These names are derived from the fish lying on the table (*zoute scholle*
– in modern Dutch *schol*=salt plaice); although it is not easily distinguished in the
painting, Visscher's and Gole's prints show it to be a flat fish cut in two and scored.

ENGRAVINGS: Etched (in reverse) by Cornelis Visscher (d. June 1662);[2] engraved in mezzotint by Jacob Gole
(*c.*1660–*c.*1737) without the window in the background and other lesser variations;[3] engraved in mezzotint
by Peter Schenk (1660–*c.*1718/19, probably after Visscher's print.[4]

COPY: A copy of this composition in reverse (probably after Visscher's etching) was in the Lucius
O'Callaghan sale, London, 12 October 1956 (lot 75).[5]

PROVENANCE: In the [Hendrick de Wacker van Son (Zon)] sale, Amsterdam, 26 sqq. October 1761 (lot 7),[6]
bought by Eleveld (82 guilders); Michiel Elgersma et al. sale, Amsterdam, 24 sqq. March 1766 (lot 3),[7]
bought by Quinkhard (128 guilders); Jan Maurits Quinkhard sale, Amsterdam, 15 sqq. March 1773 (lot 15),[8]
bought by Pothoven (89 guilders); Pieter Calkoen sale, Amsterdam, 10 sqq. September 1781 (lot 104),[9]
bought by Beekmans (200 guilders). According to Smith[10] it was in a Martin sale, [Paris?], in 1800 where it
was sold for 2,420 francs but this sale is not traceable.[11] In the collection of William Wells, Redleaf, by 1819
when it was exhibited at the BI; William Wells sale, London, 12–13 May 1848 (lot 65), bought by Norton
(111 gns); Marquis of Breadalbane sale, London, 5 June 1886 (lot 43),[12] bought by Lesser (250 gns) and
acquired by George Salting in the same year.[13] Salting Bequest, 1910.

EXHIBITIONS: BI 1819, No. 97;[14] BI 1840, No. 36.[15]

REFERENCES:
General: Smith No. 112; HdG Nos. 291, 292k, 300
and 306a.
In text:
1. According to the catalogue of the Wacker van
Son 1761 sale the picture was known by the print
after it called 'het Schollenmannetje' (see note 6); the
Elgersma sale catalogue of 1766 says that it is known
by Visscher's print called 'het Zoute Scholletje' (see
note 7); the Quinkhard 1773 catalogue says the picture is known as ''t zoute Scholletje' (see note 8) and,
lastly, the Calkoen catalogue, 1781, remarks that it is
engraved by C. Visscher as 'Het zoute Scholletje'
(see note 9). See also J. Wussin, *Cornel Visscher: Verzeichniss* etc., 1865, No. 155, and J. E. Wessely,
Jacob Gole: Verzeichniss etc., 1889, No. 207. Neither
Visscher's print nor Gole's bears either of the above
titles engraved in any of the recorded states. Wussin

(*Jonas Suyderhoef: Verzeichniss* etc., 1861, No. 118)
has confused matters by his statement that
Suyderhoef's engraving after a similar subject by
van Ostade of an entirely different composition was
also called 'Het zoute Scholletie' (this is repeated by
HdG, No. 306); this seems certainly incorrect as
there is nothing in that composition to give rise to
the title, nor is any of the recorded states thus inscribed.
2. Inscribed in the lower margin: A. V. Ostade pinxit (et) excud./C. Visscher fecit aqua forti. W.
Smith, *A Catalogue of the Works of Cornelius Visscher*,
1864, No. 82; J. Wussin, *Cornel Visscher*, 1865,
No. 155. Plate size, 26.4 × 21.9 cm.; subject size,
25.3 × 21.9 cm. See also note 1.
3. Not inscribed in any of the states. Besides the
window in the background, the bowl of charcoal on

the table is omitted and the composition is cut down at the top and the sides. Wessely, op. cit., No. 207; reproduced in Hollstein, vol. 7, p. 232. 27.4 × 19 cm. It is presumably the print listed by HdG under his No. 306a. See also note 1.

4. See Wessely, op. cit., No. 207; with the window in the background once more introduced. The present writer has not seen an impression of this print, which is probably the mezzotint listed by C. Le Blanc, *Manuel de l'amateur d'estampes*, vol. 3, n.d., p. 445, No. 347, as *Rustica simplicitas*.

5. On panel, 24 × 20 cm.

6. (A. van Ostade) 'Een Boertje met een Boerinnetje aan een Tafel zittende te drinken, bekent bij de Prent die daarvan uitgaat, genaamt het Schollenmannetje . . .'; 10¼ × 9 *duim*. HdG (No. 292k) suggests that the Wacker van Son painting might equally well be the original of Suyderhoef's print supposedly called 'Het Zoute Scholletje' (see note 1) but this cannot be since the Wacker van Son sale catalogue states that the man in the picture is seated, while in Suyderhoef's engraving the man is standing (the original of Suyderhoef's print is probably HdG

No. 297). The Wacker van Son collection was probably formed between 1750 and 1760 (see C. P. van Eeghen in OH, vol. 60, 1943, pp. 17–18).

7. 'Een Boere Binnehuis, waar in een Schol . . . *door A. van Ostaden* . . . Bekend door de Prent genaamd het Zoute Scholletje, *door C. Visscher*'; on panel, 11 × 9 *duim*.

8. (A. van Ostade) 'Een fraai Stukje, bekend onder den naam van 't zoute Scholletje . . .'; the catalogue mentions that it has been engraved.

9. The French edition of the Calkoen sale catalogue (but not the Dutch) mentions that the picture was engraved by C. Visscher as 'Het Zoute Scholletje'.

10. Smith, loc. cit.

11. It was not in the Martin sale of 5 sqq. April 1802 in Paris, the only foreign Martin sale in or about 1800 recorded by Lugt.

12. The markings corresponding to this sale are on the back of the panel.

13. The picture is listed in an entry of 1886 in one of Salting's notebooks in the National Gallery library.

14. and **15.** Both times as 'Dutch Courtship'.

2543 *A Peasant holding a Jug and a Pipe* *Plate 260*

Signed, bottom left: AV. ostade. (AV in monogram).

The signature is in a shadow which seems to have been lightly overpainted, and it is therefore difficult to judge, but it may have been reinforced.

Oil on oak, 26.8 × 22 (10⁹⁄₁₆ × 8¹¹⁄₁₆).

Probably painted *c.*1650–5.

COPY: A copy was in the W. Löwenfeld sale, Berlin (?), 17 October 1907, lot 35.[1]

PROVENANCE: Probably in the Comte de Vaudreuil sale, Paris, 24–25 November 1784 (lot 38),[2] bought by Hamont (300 francs). Thomas Capron sale, London, 3 May 1851 (lot 68),[3] bought in (50 gns); Charles Scarisbrick sale, London, 11 sqq. May 1861 (lot 721), bought by Ripp (58 gns); Thomas Howard sale, 10 May 1873 (lot 81)[4] bought by Robinson (66 gns). In the collection of George Salting, London, by 1883;[5] Salting Bequest, 1910.

REFERENCES:
General: Smith No. 86(?); HdG Nos. 142 and 157 (cf. also Nos. 148g, i and j, and 159a, g and j).
In text:
1. Panel, 29 × 22 cm.
2. (A. van Ostade) 'Un homme vu à mi-corps, tenant une cruche de terre & une pipe, il a la tête couverte d'un bonnet noir & d'un gillet [sic] à manches grises.' On wood, 10 × 8 *pouces*.

3. Christie's markings corresponding to this sale are on the back of the picture.
4. As from the Scarisbrick collection. Christie's markings corresponding to the Howard sale are on the back of the picture.
5. According to a note in one of Salting's notebooks (in the National Gallery archives).

After ADRIAEN VAN OSTADE

2541 *A Cobbler at his Stall* *Plate 261*

Falsely signed on the edge of the flap above the cobbler's head: Av.Ostade. 1671. (Av in monogram).

Oil on oak, 22.6 × 18.2 (8⅞ × 7³⁄₁₆).

Prior to 1960 it was catalogued as by Adriaen van Ostade but E. Trautscholdt's suggestion[1] that it is a good copy of a comparatively late impression of van Ostade's etching (Fig. 69), which is in the same direction and with which it agrees exactly[2] (although a little larger), is confirmed by the weakness of the execution. The date had been read as 1657 but is, in fact, the same as that on the etching, i.e. 1671. An original painting of this design is not known; that in the Compiègne Museum (see VERSIONS), which is in the opposite direction to van Ostade's etching, is also a copy.

ETCHINGS: A. van Ostade's etching, mentioned above, is signed and dated 1671.[3] There is also an anonymous engraving in the opposite direction.[4] An etching of this design by David Deuchar, 1784, is probably copied from van Ostade's print.

VERSIONS: A copy of the same design as the etching, but in the opposite direction and with variations of detail, is in the Compiègne Museum.[5] A version or copy of this design, on wood, larger than the National Gallery picture, was in the Dufresne sale, Paris, 26 March 1816 (lot 30),[6] bought by Chariot (1,510 francs). According to HdG[7] there are other copies.

PROVENANCE: In the possession of Agnew, London; in the collection of George Salting, London; Salting Bequest, 1910.

REFERENCES:
1. In BM, vol. 54, 1929, p. 80, note 9.
2. It corresponds to the later states but must be after an impression earlier than the ninth state in which the vine is extended on the right and covers almost completely the trees in front of the gable.
3. 18.7 × 14.9 cm. Bartsch, vol. 1, No. 27; L. Godefroy, *L'oeuvre gravée de Adriaen van Ostade*, 1930, No. 27; The second and eighth states of the print are reproduced.
4. 20.5 × 17 cm. The wall of the house is of brick and the vine is supported, above, by a trellis (see Godefroy, loc. cit.).
5. Panel, 37.5 × 32 cm. Part of the Barthe-Dumez Bequest to the Compiègne Museum, 1923.
6. 14 × 12 *pouces*. According to the sale catalogue: 'gravé et connu . . . sous le nom du Savetier'. HdG (No. 404b) identifies the Dufresne picture with one in an anonymous sale, Amsterdam, 17 September 1766 (lot 61), bought by the painter Louis de Moni, 70 guilders: 'Een Schoenlapper in zyn Winkel, Zynde een Stuk zeer bekend door de Prent die men onder zyn Werk vindt, door hem-zelf geetst. Het is op Doek geschilderd'; 14½ × 12½ *duimen* (Terwesten, p. 573, gives the lot number wrongly as 40).
7. HdG No. 404b.

ISACK VAN OSTADE, 1621–1649

Isack Jansz. van Ostade; painter of peasant life and landscape. He was baptised in Haarlem, 2 June 1621. A pupil of his brother, Adriaen van Ostade, he entered the Haarlem guild in 1643. His earliest known dated picture is of 1639. He apparently lived always in Haarlem, where he was buried on 16 October 1649. His early work is closely dependent on Adriaen's early peasant interiors; in his later years he was more interested in outdoor scenes, often winter pieces.

REFERENCES: Van der Willigen, pp. 29 and 233–41; HdG, vol. 3, 1910; B. Schnackenburg, *Adriaen van Ostade: Isack van Ostade, Zeichnungen und Aquarelle*, 2 vols., Hamburg, 1981 (for the documents concerning Isack's life, see pp. 16, 19).

847 *The Outskirts of a Village, with a Horseman*   Plate 262

Oil on oak, 56.8 × 49.7 (22⅜ × 19⁹⁄₁₆).

ENGRAVING: Engraved (in reverse) by B. A. Dunker, 1770.[1]

PROVENANCE: In the Duc de Choiseul sale, Paris, 6 sqq. April 1772 (lot 45), bought by Aubert (6,699 francs). Bought from Sébastien Erard in Paris by Smith, 1823, and sold by him to (Sir) Robert Peel (Bart.),[2] by whom it was lent to the BI, 1824. Purchased with the Peel collection, 1871.

EXHIBITION: BI 1824, No. 76.

REFERENCES:
General: Smith No. 3; HdG No. 114.
In text:
1. In *Recueil d'estampes* . . . *d'après les tableaux* . . . *de M. le Duc de Choiseul*, 1771, No. 27.
2. Smith, loc. cit.

848 *A Winter Scene, with an Inn by a Frozen Stream*   Plate 263

Signed, bottom left: Isack.van.Ostade.

Oil on oak, 48.8 × 40 (19³⁄₁₆ × 15¾).

Cleaned in 1950.

PROVENANCE: This is possibly the 'frost scene . . . with many figures' in the Baron Nagel sale, London, 21 March 1795 (lot 40),[1] bought by Parke (£105), and the Sir Simon H. Clarke, Bart., and George Hibbert sale, London, 14–15 May 1802 (2nd day, lot 54),[2] bought by Dermer (155 gns). According to Smith[3] it was the 'Winter Scene, with Figures' in Lady Drummond Smith's sale, London, 12 sqq. August 1835 (lot 40), bought by Peacock (165 gns). It was in the collection of Sir Robert Peel, Bart., by 1842;[4] purchased with the Peel collection, 1871.

REFERENCES:
General: Smith Nos. 34(?), 38(?) and Supplement No. 31; HdG Nos. 254 and (?) 292.
In text:
1. Smith (No. 34) describes this picture as a 'View on the canal in winter . . . with a variety of figures skating'.
2. The sale catalogue gives the provenance from Baron Nagel's collection. In the Supplement (No. 20) Smith suggested that this painting – No. 38 in his volume 1 – is the painting then in the collection of the Earl of Dartmouth (HdG No. 277). The description does not fit No. 848.
3. and 4. Smith Supplement No. 31.

1347 *A Farmyard* *Plate 264*

Signed at the bottom, towards the right: Isack Ostade.

Oil on oak, 40 × 41 (15¾ × 16³⁄₁₆).

Cleaned in 1958. Some wearing in the sky and foreground.

Hofstede de Groot[1] says that the picture is dated 1639 or 1641, but no trace can be found of any date. Nevertheless it is probable that this is an early work.

PROVENANCE: In the Heinrich Moll sale, Cologne, 11–12 November 1886 (lot 126), bought by Edward Habich (700 marks). Apparently exhibited with other Habich pictures for some years at the Gemäldegalerie, Cassel; bought from Edward Habich, Cassel (together with Nos. 1336–48) in 1891.[2]

REFERENCES:
General: HdG No. 306.
In text:
1. Loc. cit.
2. It is in the catalogue of the Habich sale, Cassel, 9–10 May 1892 (lot 116) but was bought by the National Gallery before the sale.

2544 *A Landscape with Peasants and a Cart* *Plate 265*

Signed, bottom right: Isack.van.Ostade/1645.

Oil on oak, 52.9 × 45.4 (20¹³⁄₁₆ × 17⅞).

PROVENANCE: In the collection of George Salting, London; Salting Bequest, 1910.

REFERENCE: HdG No. 115.

6404 *The Interior of a Barn with Two Peasants* *Plate 266*

Oil on oak, 30.2 × 40.3 (11⅞ × 15¾).

Cleaned in 1972.

An early work, dependent in style and in subject-matter on Adriaen van Ostade's peasant interiors. The painting apparently had a pendant, showing an interior with an old man seated by a fireside and a woman washing a child, when it was sold in 1777.[1]

PROVENANCE: Prince de Conti sale, Paris, 8 April 1777, lot 314[2] (1,300 francs, with pendant). M. Colnaghi, from whom purchased by W. C. Alexander, 13 May 1886. By descent to the Misses Rachel F. and Jean I. Alexander, who presented it by deed of gift to the National Gallery; entered the collection in 1972.[3]

EXHIBITION: London 1972.

REFERENCES:
General: HdG No. 181.
In text:
1. See under PROVENANCE.
2. In the Conti sale catalogue, lot 314 is described thus: 'Deux tableaux ragoûtantes de colotis, d'un bon effet & très ornés d'accessoires, peints sur bois, chacun de 12 pouces 3 lignes de haut, sur 16 pouces de large. Dans l'un est représentée une femme qui savonne du linge dans un baquet, & un homme qui se chauffe: dans l'autre, un vieillard assis près du feu, & une femme qui nettoie son enfant.'
3. A. Smith, 'Presented by the Misses Rachel F. and Jean I. Alexander: Seventeen Paintings for the National Gallery', BM, vol. 114, 1972, p. 634.

Follower of ISACK VAN OSTADE

963 *An Inn by a Frozen River* *Plate 267*

Oil on oak, 41.6 × 55.7 (16⅜ × 22¹¹⁄₁₆).

Cleaned in 1969.

A false signature – I v Ostad(e) – on the lower plank of the boarding on the right – was removed when the painting was cleaned. Although too coarse in execution for Isack van Ostade, it is a mid-seventeenth century painting and may well be the work of a Haarlem near-contemporary like Claes Molenaer.

PROVENANCE: In the collection of Wynn Ellis, London, by 1850 or 1851;[1] Wynn Ellis Bequest, 1876.

REFERENCES:
General: HdG No. 81.
In text: **1.** Waagen, 1854, vol. 2, p. 296.

ABRAHAM DE PAPE, before 1621(?)–1666

Abraham (or *Abram*) *Isaacksz. de Pape*; probably born before 1621 in Leiden. He was probably a pupil of Dou. He is mentioned in Leiden guild documents from 1644 onwards and was one of the founder members of that guild in 1648; he was a *hoofdman* of it in 1649–50, 1654–5, 1659–60 and 1664–5, and dean in 1651, 1656, 1661 and 1666. He died in Leiden on 15 September 1666.

His few surviving pictures are genre scenes in a style derived from Gerrit Dou (of whose paintings he made many copies), Brekelenkam and Domenicus van Tol. There are also a few portraits. He was a man of some wealth but there are no grounds, other than the rarity of his works, for the suggestion that he painted only as a pastime.

REFERENCES: Obreen, vol. 5, *passim*; Bredius, *Künstler-Inventare*, vol. 5, pp. 1858–67, and vol. 7, pp. 169–72; Leiden 1988, p. 196, cat. nos. 62–4.

1221 *Tobit and Anna* *Plate 268*

Above the fireplace is a map. On the right is a simulated curtain suspended on a rail running across the top of the picture (the rail is at present covered by the frame).

Signed along the right half of the lower edge of the wall-cupboard: A.DE.PAPE.16(58 or 59?); the date is very worn but the third figure is almost certainly 5.

Oil on oak, 40.7 × 56 (16 × 22¹⁄₁₆).

Before 1960 this picture was described as a *Cottage Interior with Figures*, but MacLaren identified its subject as Tobit and Anna on an analogy with the similar picture by Dou (No. 4189 of this catalogue), which might also have passed for a genre painting were it not for the inscription on the contemporary engraving after it. The spinning-wheel is a reference to Tobit 2: 11, and the bare interior of the cupboard on the left an allusion to Tobit's poverty (cf. Tobit 4: 21).

In seventeenth-century Holland paintings were often protected by curtains (for example, those in the background of Eeckhout No. 1459 and Metsu No. 839 of this catalogue). Illusionist representations of such curtains, like that in de Pape's picture, are not infrequent in Dutch painting after the mid-40s.[1]

PROVENANCE: Duke of Marlborough (Blenheim Palace) sale, London, 24 July sqq. 1886 (lot 51*),[2] 240 gns, bought for the National Gallery (out of the Walker Fund).

REFERENCES:

1. The subject of *trompe-l'oeil* curtains is dealt with by P. Reutersward in *Konsthistorisk Tidskrift*, 1956, pp. 97–113.

2. This lot is not in the printed sale catalogue but is added in MS in the auctioneer's copy (as by 'Adriaen de Pape').

EGBERT VAN DER POEL, 1621–1664

Egbert Lievensz. van der Poel; baptised in Delft 9 March 1621. His earliest known dated picture is of 1646; he entered the Delft guild in October 1650. He married in Maassluis, near Rotterdam, on 25 June 1651 but was apparently still living in Delft in October 1654 since a daughter of his was buried there in that month (see page 308, note 3). He had settled in Rotterdam before November 1655, when a son was baptised there. He was buried in Rotterdam on 19 June 1664.

Before 1654 he painted mostly interiors of stables and cottages, canal and winter landscapes and coast scenes; his rustic interiors may derive from those of Cornelis Saftleven of Rotterdam (1607–81). Most of the paintings of his last decade are of nocturnal fires and moonlight scenes, and there are many repetitions of a view of Delft during and after the 1654 explosion (see No. 1061 below). His brother, Adriaen van der Poel (1626–85/6), imitated him.

REFERENCE: A. Goldschmidt in OH, vol. 40, 1922, pp. 57–65.

1061 *A View of Delft after the Explosion of 1654*   *Plate 269*

The town is seen from the north-east. The Nieuwe Kerk is on the extreme left and the Oude Kerk is nearer the centre; between them is the tower of the town hall. The church on the extreme right is the chapel of the hospital of St George (Sint Joris gasthuis) in Noordeinde.

Signed, bottom left: E vander Poel 12 octob / 1654

Oil on oak, 36.2 × 49.5 ($14\frac{1}{4}$ × $19\frac{1}{2}$).

A large part of Delft was destroyed by the explosion of a powder magazine on the morning of Monday 12 October 1654, at 10.30 a.m. This magazine lay in the north-east corner of the town, near to the Geergweg. According to the account given by Dirck van Bleyswijck,[1] at the time of the explosion the magazine contained between 80,000 and 90,000 pounds of powder, and the force of the explosion was so great that it completely destroyed all the houses in the area bounded on the north by the Geergweg, on the west by the Verwersdijk, on the south by the Doelenstraat and on the east by the Singel canal; many houses beyond were destroyed and there was lesser damage throughout Delft. Of the magazine itself, nothing was left and on its site was a deep pool full of water (presumably the one visible towards the right in the picture). The number of those killed was never known; among them was Carel Fabritius, who (according to van Bleyswijck) was taken out of the ruins dying. The explosion was the subject of poems by Joost van Vondel and Pieter de Witt. The area of complete devastation was not rebuilt and served afterwards as a horse market, and much of it is an open space to this day.

The Nieuwe Kerk, the town hall, the Oude Kerk and the Sint Joris chapel still stand (the last-named is now the Lutheran church). As far as can be judged by the surviving buildings and contemporary maps, van der Poel's view seems more or less accurate.

Van der Poel repeated this composition many times; at least a dozen versions have survived (see VERSIONS below). The buildings are in every case the same except for variations of detail (the figures differ in each case). There also exist four or five versions of a related composition by Daniel Vosmaer of Delft[2] (active 1642–66). Both artists could well have been eye-witnesses of the explosion.[3] It will be noted that in three of Vosmaer's versions of this view the figures are apparently by van der Poel.[4]

All the known versions by van der Poel (and some of Vosmaer's) bear the date of the explosion: 12 October 1654. Comparison with van der Poel's *Nocturnal Fire* of 1654 in the Liechtenstein Gallery in Vaduz[5] suggests that at least some of them were painted quite soon after the event, for example, the National Gallery version, but others are probably some years later.

VERSIONS: (This list does not claim to be complete.) The following are of the same design as the National Gallery picture (except for the figures): Marquess of Bath's collection, Longleat;[6] RBK, The Hague;[7] Anon. sale, London, 25 April 1956, lot 102[8] (copy?); M. H. collection, Brussels (1933);[9] Hinrichsen collection, Berlin, post-1932;[10] Curt Bohnewald collection sale, Cologne, Lempertz, 28 March 1969 (lot 14);[11] Jean Dollfus sale, Paris, 20 May 1912, lot 67;[12] Alan Jacobs Gallery, Spring Exhibition, 1972, no. 5;[13] Vienna, Akademie;[14] Prague, Narodni Galerie.[15] The following repeat the same design but show the explosion taking place: Rijksmuseum, Amsterdam;[16] Prinsenhof Museum, Delft;[17] Esher Fine Art Gallery, The Hague (1953);[18] R. Koetser, London, exhibition 1967, cat. no. 11;[19] Emil Brandts sale, Berlin, 12 February 1918, lot 58[20] (copy?). Several other pictures, probably versions of the explosion, are mentioned in sale and exhibition catalogues and elsewhere;[21] some of these may be identifiable with one or other of those listed above.

PROVENANCE: Thomas Farrant sale, London, 2 June 1855 (lot 27),[22] bought by Rutley (8½ gns). John Henderson Bequest, 1879.

REFERENCES:
1. Van Bleyswijck, vol. 2, pp. 622–33.
2. (i). Delft Stadhuis. Panel, 73 × 100 cm.; inscribed: . . . tot Delph, and signed: Daniel Vos-(maer?). (A copy of this version is in the collection of M. G. J. van Lint, The Hague: photo in RKD.) (ii).

Wadsworth Atheneum, Hartford, USA. Panel, 75 × 106 cm.; signed: Den 12 October 1654/Daniel Vosmaer. Sumner Collection, 1943. 96. 1978 cat. no. 166. (iii). In possession of Colnaghi and Co., London, 1923, 49.5 × 66 cm.; signed: Den 12 october

1654/Daniel Vosmaer. (Ex [Augustine Sargent] sale, London, 31 January 1919, lot 145; Anon. sale, London, 11 May 1923, lot 78.) (iv). J. Goudstikker sale, Berlin, 3 December 1940, lot 203. Canvas, 85 × 102 cm.; signed and dated 1654. (Ex Anon. sale, London, 15 May 1914, lot 26; reproduced in the catalogue of the Vermeer exhibition, Rotterdam, 1935, pl. 110.) (v). In the possession of J. Leger, Brussels, 1932; Christie's, 16 July 1971, lot 18 (500 gns to de Wilt). Canvas, 89 × 129 cm.; signed and dated 1654 in full. The costume of some of the figures is apparently of the late 1660s. (vi). Hallwyl collection, Stockholm. Panel, 39 × 54.5 cm.; signed (falsely?): (J?)VM/den 12 october(s?) 1654. This picture follows van der Poel's design and is probably a copy after him. (Reproduced in the Hallwyl collection catalogue, 1928–30, p. 154.) (vii). There is an engraving of Delft after the explosion by S. Fokke (in Wagenaar's *Vaderlandsche Geschiedenis*) inscribed: 'S. Fokke del et fc 1754 Delft van binnen, na de verwoesting, veroorzaackt door't springen van de Krindtooren, in 't jaar 1654/Getekend naar eene Origineele Schildery van *van der Poel*, op de plaats zelve gedaan, en nu berustende by den H^r N. van Bremen/ Is. Tirion excudit.' The original is not known but despite the inscription the print is much nearer the design of Vosmaer's paintings (i–iv above) and is more probably after a lost work by him (it is not after the Delft Stadhuis version, as supposed by Wurzbach, vol. 2, p. 336). (viii). A copy was in the Kaiser-Friedrich Museum, Berlin, Inv. no. 1444 as 'after J. van der Meer van Haarlem' (photo in RKD). (ix). Another view of the explosion, upright in format, which prominently includes a couple on the left who are perhaps portraits, is in the Johnson collection in the Philadelphia Museum of Art (canvas, 68 × 55.6 cm., 1972 cat., no. 500). (x). Other paintings of the subject by Vosmaer are mentioned by Bredius in OH, vol. 12, 1894, p. 164, and *Künstler-Inventare*, vol. 4, 1917, p. 1431; also Wurzbach, op. cit., p. 823.

3. For Vosmaer, see Obreen, vol. 5, p. 168 and S. Donahue in *Vassar Journal*, vol. 9, 1964, p. 1888. As for van der Poel, a daughter of his was buried in the Nieuwe Kerk in Delft on 14 October 1654.

4. i.e. in the pictures in the Delft Stadhuis, the Wadsworth Atheneum and the Goudstikker 1940 sale (see note 2, i, ii, and iv).

5. Panel, 43 × 63 cm. *Führer durch die Fürstlich Liechtensteinische Gemäldegalerie in Wien*, 1931, No. 535.

6. As a view of Breda. Panel, 33.5 × 49.5 cm.; signed: E vander Poel 12 octob/1654. (Ex Winckler collection and Duval sale, 1846.)

7. Panel, 38 × 48 cm.; signed: E vander Poel/14. Oktober 1654. (Ex Burg Saaleck sale, Würzburg,

1935; K. H. sale, Amsterdam, 1940; in possession of Aberls, Cologne, 1941; reproduced in the Burg Saaleck sale catalogue.)

8. Panel, 39.5 × 52 cm.; signed: Eo vander Poel fc/ Ocktober 1654. This painting had previously been in an Anon. sale, Brussels (Palais des Beaux-Arts), 11–12 October 1955, lot 188 (illustrated in catalogue).

9. Panel, 37 × 49 cm.; signed: E vander Poel 1654/ Den 12 ocktober. (Catalogue of the A. Tritsch collection, Vienna, 1907, No. 25; A. Kellner sale, Berlin, 1929.)

10. Panel, 24 × 34 cm.; signed: E vander Poel 1654/den 12 october. (Ex Königswarter sale, Berlin, 1906; A. Wollenburg sale, Berlin, 17 March 1932, lot 195; exhibited at Hoogendijk's, Amsterdam, 1932; reproduced in *Pantheon*, 1932, p. 112.)

11. Panel, 38 × 49 cm.; signed: E vander Poel/den 12 ocktober 1654, illustrated in catalogue. (Ex Berlin sale, 1900; Weber sale, Berlin, 1912; T. Stroefer sale, Munich, 28 October 1937, lot 82; illustrated in catalogue.)

12. Panel, 38 × 49 cm.; signed: E vander Poel fecit/ 12 ocktober 1654. (Ex J. J. Chapuis sale, 1865; reproduced in the Dollfus sale catalogue.)

13. Panel, 36.2 × 48.3 cm. Signed, lower left: E vander Poel/den 12 Oktober 1654. Reproduced in BM, vol. 114, 1972, p. 347.

14. Panel, 33 × 49.5 cm. Signed, lower right: 12 October/E vander Poel 1654. Inv. no. 1387. Reproduced and discussed in Brussels, Musée Royale des Beaux Arts, *Mens en Landschap in de 17de eeuwse Hollandse Schilderkunst uit de Akademie der Bildenden Künste*, Vienna, 1977–8, pp. 68–9.

15. Panel, 36.5 × 48.5 cm. Inv. no. 02354.

16. No. 1889. Panel, 37 × 62 cm.; signed: E vander Poel 1654/12 ockt. 1976 cat. no. A309.

17. Panel, 32 × 39 cm.; signed: E vander Poel (1?)2 Ock 1654.

18. Panel, 41 × 54 cm.; signed: E vander Poel/den 12 october 1654.

19. Panel, 38.5 × 53 cm.; signed: E vander/Poel/12 Ockt./1654. (Ex J. Stumpf sale, Berlin, 1918; reproduced in the Stumpf sale catalogue; B. A. Mayer sale, Berlin, 25 June 1934, lot 36; with Cramer, The Hague, 1965–67 (cat. no. 2, 1965, No. 5; cat. no. 13, 1966–7, No. 12); Paris, Musée des Arts Décoratifs, *La Vie en Hollande en dix-septième siècle*, 1967, No. 23.)

20. Panel, 36 × 48 cm.; signed and dated 1654. Reproduced in the E. Brandts sale catalogue.

21. (a) Exposition au profit du Musée des Arts Décoratifs, Paris, 1878, No. 213; Explosion de la poudrière de Delft; panel, 23 × 34 cm.; signed and dated 1654. (b) Ch. B------ sale, Lyon, 1893 (H. Mireur, *Dictionnaire des ventes d'art*, vol. 6, 1912, p. 10). (c) Kramm mentions a version of the Rijksmuseum picture, with different figures and signed and dated in full, in the Steengracht collection at Moyland Castle (Kramm, Supplement, p. 120). (d) Lippmann-Lissingen collection, Vienna; signed: 12

October. E. van der Poel. 1654. Wurzbach, vol. 2, p. 336).

22. The markings corresponding to this sale are on the back of the panel.

CORNELIS VAN POELENBURGH, c. 1593–1667

Cornelis van Poelenburgh (he also spelled his name *Poelenburch* and *Poelenborch*) was a native of Utrecht according to the title of an engraved portrait of him published in 1649.[1] He was born in 1586 according to Houbraken[2] but this seems too early and c.1593 is preferable.[3] Sandrart[4] says he was a pupil of Abraham Bloemaert of Utrecht and afterwards visited Rome and Florence. He is traceable in Rome by 1617[5] and in 1621 and 1622, and is probably the 'Cornelis van Utrecht', nicknamed 'Satir', who was a member of the Netherlandish artists' society (the *Bent*) in Rome about 1623.[6] He was also in the service of the Grand Duke of Tuscany.[7] He returned to Holland before 1627 and in April of that year the Utrecht provincial assembly bought from him for 575 guilders a painting as a present for the Stadholder's wife.[8] He married in 1629; both he and his wife were Catholics.[9] In 1637 he went to London at the invitation of Charles I and painted some pictures for the king;[10] he was apparently there until 1641 with at least one trip back to Utrecht in 1638.[11] He was an *overman* of the Utrecht painters' college in 1656, and *deken* (dean) in 1657, and 1658[12] and 1664.[13] He was buried in the Magdalenakerk, Utrecht, 12 August 1667.[14]

His style was formed in Rome under the influence of, above all, Adam Elsheimer (died December 1610) and his circle. The greater part of his work consists of Italian landscapes, often with ruins and nudes; he also painted religious and mythological subjects. With Abraham Bloemaert, Herman Saftleven and Dirck van der Lisse he painted scenes from Guarini's *Il Pastor Fido* for Amalia van Solms' *Cleedcamer* in the new Orange palace in Honselaersdijk.[15] He also painted portraits on a small scale, and sometimes put the figures in others' landscapes (e.g. Jan Both No. 209 of this catalogue). He was very successful and had a large workshop and many followers. Among those whose imitations of him are often deceptively close are Dirck van der Lisse, Daniel Vertangen and Johan van Haensbergen, who were among his pupils according to Houbraken,[16] and also Toussaint Gelton. The other pupils listed by Houbraken are François Verwilt and Warnard van Rysen. Arcadian landscapes in his tradition continued to be painted well into the eighteenth century, for example by Gerard Hoet (1648–1733). It appears that Poelenburgh also retouched copies of his own pictures.[17]

REFERENCES:

General: N. C. Sluijter-Seijffert, 'Cornelis van Poelenburch (ca. 1593–1667)', Diss. Leiden, 1984 (with catalogue of works).

In text:

1. Coenrad Waumans' print (after a self-portrait drawing) in *Images de divers hommes d'esprit sublime* etc., published in Antwerp by Jan Meyssens in 1649.

This engraving was reprinted in de Bie, p. 257 (cf. HdG, *Arnold Houbraken und seine 'Groote Schouburgh'*, 1893, pp. 229 ff).

2. *De Groote Schouburgh*, vol. 1, p. 128.

3. See Sluijter-Seijffert, op. cit., pp. 25–6.

4. Sandrart, *Teutsche Academie*, vol. 2, p. 305.

5. Kramm, vol. 5, 1861, p. 1296.

6. There are drawings by him inscribed 'in roomen' and dated 1621 and 1622 (see G. J. Hoogewerff in *Bredius Feest-Bundel*, 1915, p. 112, and idem, *De Bentvueghels*, 1952, pp. 48 and 151).
7. Sandrart, op. cit., vol. 2, p. 370. Duke Cosimo II died in 1621.
8. Kramm, op. cit. pp. 1295–6.
9. Sluijter-Seijffert, op. cit., p. 30.
10. According to the title of the print published in 1649 (see note 1).

11. Sluijter-Seijffert, op. cit., pp. 31–2. Kramm, op. cit. p. 1297.
12. Muller, p. 129.
13. Muller, pp. 33 and 131 (note 1).
14. Kramm, op. cit. p. 1297.
15. J. G. van Gelder, 'Pastor Fido-verstellingen in de Nederlandse Kunst van de zeventiende eeuw', OH, vol. 92, 1978, pp. 227–63, esp. pp. 246–8.
16. Op. cit., vol. 1, p. 129, and vol. 3, p. 169.
17. See Obreen, vol. 2, pp. 72, 79 and 85 (No. 51).

955 *Landscape with Classical Ruins and Women Bathers*   *Plate 270*

Signed, in the centre of the stones in the right foreground: C·P·

Oil on canvas, 35×43.5 ($13\frac{3}{4} \times 17\frac{1}{8}$).

Cleaned in 1981.

Traditionally attributed to Poelenburgh but MacLaren, following Frimmel, re-attributed it to his pupil, Johan van Haensbergen. MacLaren considered the 'drawing of the figures . . . too weak and the foliage too hard' for Poelenburgh and 'as Frimmel has pointed out, some of the women have the hooked noses which are characteristic of Haensbergen'.[1] He related details of the painting to four landscapes[2] which he considered to be by a follower of Poelenburgh, very probably Haensbergen. Finally, however, he noted that the execution of No. 955 is much stronger than any of the signed works by Haensbergen (such as those in Schwerin[3]) and that the attribution remains uncertain.

When the painting was cleaned in 1981 the monogram, which MacLaren believed to be false, was found to be integral to the original paint layer. Cleaning has also revealed the original tonality of the sky and the detailed handling of the ruins. Figures, buildings, landscapes and sky are all, in the view of the present writer, perfectly consistent with the mature work of Poelenburgh (that is, after his return from Italy by 1627). Few of his paintings are dated and he painted many scenes of this type in which there is relatively little compositional or stylistic development but a date of *c*.1630 would be acceptable.

The painting is not included in Sluijter-Seijffert's catalogue of Poelenburgh's work.

PROVENANCE: The picture attributed to Poelenburgh in the Earl of Waldegrave's sale, Strawberry Hill, 25 April–21 May 1842 (11th day, lot 11), bought by H. Goding, with which No. 955 has been tentatively identified, was a different composition.[4] No. 955 was in the Wynn Ellis collection, London; Wynn Ellis Bequest, 1876.

EXHIBITION: London 1982.

REFERENCES:
1. T. von Frimmel in *Studien und skizzen zur Gemäldekunde*, vol. 1, 1913–15, p. 139.
2. In the view of the present writer this group of landscapes – *Landscape with Six Women and a Man* (formerly on loan from the collection of Dr F. H. Fentener van Vlissingen, Vught, to the Centraal Museum, Utrecht, 1952 cat., no. 217), in which the right half of the ruins in No. 955 is repeated: *Diana and Nymphs* (Buccleuch collection: Dalkeith House catalogue, 1911, no. 300) which also repeats this area: and two landscapes with figures in the collection of R. H. Ward in 1932 and which also repeat

elements of No. 955 – do not form a stylistically distinct group. One of the ex-R. H. Ward collection paintings is accepted as autograph by Sluijter-Seijffert, op. cit. (cat. no. 151).
3. Staatliches Museum, Schwerin, *Holländische und flämische Malerei des 17. Jahrhunderts,* 1982, nos. 104

(Inv. no. 2282); 105 (Inv. no. 2398); and 106 (Inv. no. 2397).
4. The Farrer sale catalogue describes it as 'A classical landscape, with three nymphs near Roman ruins, and other figures in the background'.

See JAN BOTH No. 209

WILLEM DE POORTER, 1608 – after 1648

His father, Pieter, came from Flanders; Willem was apparently born in Haarlem. He was active in Haarlem, where he is documented a number of times from 1630 to 1648, and also in Wijk bij Heusden after 1645. He is last mentioned in 1648.

He painted biblical scenes and allegorical and mythological subjects. There are also a few portraits and still lifes. His style, particularly in his earlier works, is based on Rembrandt's paintings of 1631–3 and he may perhaps have been Rembrandt's pupil either shortly after the latter's removal from Leiden to Amsterdam or, less probably, shortly before. His work also owes much to his study of Pieter Lastman and Jan Pynas. His later pictures show some connection with the manner of Leonaert Bramer (1596 –1674), who worked in Delft.

REFERENCE: R. Juynboll in Thieme/Becker, vol. 27, pp. 258–9.

1294 *An Allegorical Subject (? The Just Ruler)*   *Plate 271*

A figure in a cuirass and a richly embroidered cloak, its head encircled by a wreath, lays a sceptre on a globe (or an orb) which stands on a cracked pedestal; beside the globe are two crowns. In the left foreground is a heap of armour and weapons; lances, a drum and a flag are propped in the left background.

Signed, bottom right: W. D. p.

Oil on oak, 50.2 × 37.5 (19¾ × 14¾).

MacLaren suggested that the allegory would seem to be one of 'the vanity of earthly power'. This would perhaps explain the pile of arms at the base of the plinth but not the figure wearing a laurel wreath, a breastplate and holding a sceptre. In Cesare Ripa's *Iconologia,* which was published in a Dutch translation by D. P. Pers in Amsterdam in 1644, the figure of *Merito*[1] is represented sumptuously dressed, wearing a laurel wreath, holding a sceptre and a book in her left hand. With the exception of the book, the figure in No. 1294 corresponds with Ripa's. The allegory may therefore represent Merit assuming temporal power and so, the Just Ruler.[2] There is a closely related allegory by de Poorter in Rotterdam which is dated 1636.[3] It shows a still life of armour, a flag, a sword and a chest of rich vessels and jewellery which are piled up at the base of a broken pedestal very similar to that in No. 1294. It is a *vanitas* painting, an allegory of the futility of worldly power and fortune in the face of mortality. It seems likely that No. 1294 should also be dated *c.*1636.

Despite the signature, the picture apparently passed at one time as the work of Jacob Duck[4] and later of Ferdinand Bol.[5]

PROVENANCE: In the [Henry(?) Chandler] sale, London, 27 March 1857 (lot 74),[6] bought in? (£2.18s). Presented by T. Humphry Ward, 1889.[7]

REFERENCES:

1. C. Ripa, *Iconologia*, Venice, 1645 ed., p. 395. In the Dutch edition (*Iconologia of Uytbeeldinghe des Verstands*) the figure of *Merito* (Verdienst) is illustrated on p. 526/7.
2. The present writer is indebted to Sir Michael Levey for this suggestion.
3. Panel, 55 × 92.5 cm. Museum Boymans-van Beuningen, 1972 cat. no. 1674. The connection between No. 1294 and this painting was mentioned by E. de Jongh, 'Austerity and Extravagance in the Golden Age', *Apollo*, 1967, p. 18.
4. On the back of the panel is a small cutting in eighteenth- or early nineteenth-century print: *Le Duc.* (This is most probably intended for Jacob Duck

(*c.*1600–67) who throughout the eighteenth century and most of the nineteenth was confused with Johan le Ducq (1629/30–76/7).
5. See note 6.
6. On the back of the panel are Christie's markings relating to ten pictures brought to Christie's in February 1857. Earlier in the same sale was a single lot brought to Christie's in January 1857 by Henry Chandler; it seems likely that this was the same person. Of the ten pictures belonging to 'Mr Chandler' in this sale, the only one which could possibly be identified with the present one is lot 74: 'F. Bol Charles V of Spain.'
7. As by de Poorter.

HENDRICK POT, *c.*1585 or earlier (?) – 1657

Hendrick Gerritsz. Pot was probably a native of Haarlem. It has been conjectured that he was born about 1585; Hofstede de Groot believed earlier.[1] He was said to be a pupil of Carel van Mander, who left Haarlem in 1603. He was dean of the Haarlem guild in 1626, 1630 and 1635, and a *hoofdman* in 1634 and 1648. He was in London in 1632 and painted portraits of the king and queen. He was back in Haarlem the following year and may have been the 'Hendrick Gerritsz. of Haarlem' who acquired citizenship of Amsterdam on 6 October 1640.[2] He is recorded again in Haarlem in 1648; later he is recorded on a number of occasions in Amsterdam where he died in 1657, probably not long before 16 October.

He painted a few large allegorical pictures but most of his works are portraits (usually on a small scale) and small guardroom and festive scenes of the type evolved by Willem Buytewech the Elder and Dirk Hals.

REFERENCES:

General: Houbraken, vol. 1, p. 252; van der Willigen, pp. 18–19 and 45; OH, 1887, pp. 161 ff.
In text:
1. *Bulletin Nederl. Oudheidkundig. Bond,* 1914, p. 81.
2. P. Scheltema, *Rembrand*, Amsterdam, 1859, p. 52.

1278 *A Merry Company at Table* *Plate 272*

Signed, top right, on the side of the chimney-piece: HP (in monogram). Scratched into the back of the panel: 1630.

Oil on oak, 32.3 × 49.6 (12¾ × 19⁹⁄₁₆).

The date 1630 scratched on the back may well be that of the painting: it would agree with the style and the costumes.

This is quite explicitly a brothel scene (*bordeeltje*). The amorous proceedings – wine and oysters, both known for their aphrodisiac qualities, are prominent on the table – are supervised by an elderly procuress who makes an obscene gesture with her finger in the bowl of her pipe. (There are numerous examples of this gesture in *bordeeltjes*.) Her age and ugliness are contrasted intentionally with the youth and beauty of the two girls, a comparison with a *vanitas* intention (that is, the inevitability of age, decay and death). In the context of the painting the dog licking the man's fingers in the bottom right-hand corner may be intended to underline the licentiousness of the scene.

COPIES: There was a copy with Alan Jacobs, London, 1984,[1] and a second is in the Museo Correale, Sorrento.[2]

PROVENANCE: Earl of Londesborough sale, London, 7 July 1888 (lot 54),[3] bought by Sir J. C. Robinson (56 gns). Purchased from Messrs Lake, Beaumont and Co. (with the aid of the Lewis Fund), 1889.

EXHIBITIONS: London 1976, No. 82; London 1978–9, No. 6.

REFERENCES:
1. Panel, 47 × 63 cm. (oval format). With S. Nystad, The Hague, 1972. Exhibited at the Stedelijk Museum De Lakenhal, Leiden, 'Een verzameling schilderijen uit de 17de, 18de en 19de eeuwen', 1980, cat. no. 42 (illustrated).
2. Panel, dimensions not known. Photo in RKD.
3. As by Palamedes.

PAULUS POTTER, 1625–1654

Paulus Pietersz. Potter, baptised in Enkhuizen, 20 November 1625,[1] son of Pieter Simonsz. Potter, a painter who had settled in Amsterdam by 1631.[2] He was a pupil of his father, according to Houbraken;[3] the style of some early works has led to the suggestion that he may also have studied with Claes Moeyaert. A 'P. Potter' came in May 1642 to learn painting for a year from Jacob de Wet in Haarlem, according to an entry in the latter's notebook,[4] but it is unlikely that this was Paulus Potter whose earliest certainly dated works are of this year and show no trace of any stylistic connection with de Wet. By August 1646 he was living in Delft and was then received in the guild there.[5] He was in The Hague by 1649, when he entered the guild,[6] and married there in July 1650.[7] Houbraken[8] says he was persuaded to leave The Hague for Amsterdam by Dr Nicolaes Tulp [whose son he later painted] and that he settled there 1 May 1652; he is recorded as living in Amsterdam in January 1653[9] and was buried there, 17 January 1654.[10]

Almost all his paintings are of animals in landscape and, with very few exceptions (the most notable being *The Young Bull* in the Mauritshuis), are on a small scale. Some paintings of similar subjects by Karel Dujardin are very close in style to Potter's (compare Dujardin No. 826 of this catalogue with No. 849 below) and although Dujardin was the elder by three years it seems not unlikely that Potter was the originator. He painted a life-size equestrian portrait of Dirk Tulp in 1653 (in the Six collection, Amsterdam) and made some two dozen etchings of animals.

REFERENCES:

General: T. van Westrheene, *Paulus Potter*, 1867; HdG, vol. 4.

In text:
1. Westrheene, op. cit., p. 40.
2. According to Houbraken, vol. 2, p. 126.
3. Loc. cit.
4. OH, 1919, p. 216.

5. Westrheene, op. cit., p. 50.
6. Westrheene, op. cit., p. 50.
7. Westrheene, op. cit., p. 61.
8. Op. cit., p. 129.
9. Westrheene, op. cit., pp. 68–9, and OH, 1885, p. 308.
10. Westrheene, op. cit., p. 72.

849 *A Landscape with Cows, Sheep and Horses by a Barn*   Plate 273

Signed on the tree trunk in the centre foreground: Paulus. Potter. f. 1651.[1]

Oil on oak, 57.7 × 52.9 ($22\frac{11}{16}$ × $20\frac{13}{16}$).

Cleaned in 1971.

As Hofstede de Groot has noted,[2] Potter is here very close in style to Karel Dujardin (e.g. Dujardin No. 826 of this catalogue).

PROVENANCE: In an Anon. sale in Amsterdam, 11 sqq. May 1756 (lot 10),[3] bought by van der Land for P. Leendert de Neufville (1,700 guilders); [Pieter Leendert de] N[eufville] sale, Amsterdam, 19 June 1765 (lot 75),[4] bought by Locquet (1,505 guilders); Pieter Locquet sale, Amsterdam, 22 sqq. September 1783 (lot 285),[5] bought by Fouquet (7,540 guilders). According to Smith[6] it was later in the collection of Mons. de Noailles. By January 1812 it was in the collection of Baron Gwydyr at Grimsthorpe Castle;[7] Lord Gwydyr sale, London, 8–9 May 1829 (2nd day, lot 76), bought by Collard for Nieuwenhuys (1,205 gns). In the collection of Sir Robert Peel, Bart., by 1834;[8] purchased with the Peel collection, 1871.

REFERENCES:

General: Smith No. 66; HdG Nos. 75 and 76b.

In text:
1. The date is given as 1654 by Smith (loc. cit.) and Nieuwenhuys (p. 189) but is certainly 1651.
2. HdG, vol. 4, p. 585, and Potter No. 75.
3. Cf. Terwesten, p. 137 (incorrectly as lot 11). Although the description of the picture in the Amsterdam 1756 and Leendert de Neufville sales is vague, identity with the National Gallery painting is established by the description in the Locquet sale catalogue.

4. Cf. Terwesten, p. 474 (incorrectly as lot 73). See also note 3.
5. Cf. note 3.
6. Smith, loc. cit.
7. It is presumably the 'Cattle Landscape Paul Potter' in a MS list of Lord Gwydyr's pictures in Grimsthorpe corrected up to 1 January 1812 (copy in the National Gallery library); there was no other Potter in the Gwydyr sale of 1829.
8. Smith, loc. cit., and Nieuwenhuys, p. 188.

2583 *Cattle and Sheep in a Stormy Landscape* Plate 274

Signed, bottom left: Paulus. Potter. f. 1647.

Oil on oak, 46.3 × 37.8 (18¼ × 14⅞).

PENTIMENTI: There are *pentimenti* in the horns of the bull and cow in the foreground, in the outline of the latter and in the legs of the cow in the right background. A third sheep, standing behind the other two, has been painted out by the artist.

A supposed companion, *A Farmyard with Horses and Figures*, of the same date, was also formerly in the Hope collection[1] (see PROVENANCE) but had a different earlier history.

VERSION: According to Smith[2] there is an engraving by Jacques Couché after a painting closely resembling the present one.

COPIES: A copy was in the Hemert tot Dingshof collection, The Hague, in 1955,[3] and a second was with D. Vaarties, Rotterdam, in 1936.[4]

PROVENANCE: In the collection of Jan and Pieter Bisschop of Rotterdam by 1752,[5] and bought with that collection by Adriaen and John Hope of Amsterdam in 1771.[6] John Hope's sons, Thomas Henry and Henry Philip Hope, settled in England *c.*1796; No. 2583 was lent to the BI, 1815, by Henry Philip Hope; after his death in 1839 it passed to his nephew, Henry Thomas Hope of Deepdene, who exhibited it at the BI in 1843 and 1850, and in Manchester in 1857. Exhibited at the RA, 1881, lent by Mrs Henry Thomas Hope, who bequeathed it in 1887 with the rest of the Hope collection to her grandson, Lord Henry Francis Pelham-Clinton-Hope; exhibited at the South Kensington (now Victoria and Albert) Museum, 1891–7,[7] with the Hope collection, a part of which was sold by Lord Francis to Asher Wertheimer, London, in 1898.[8] In the collection of George Salting, London; Salting Bequest, 1910.

EXHIBITIONS: BI 1815, No. 139; BI 1843, No. 89; BI 1850, No. 67; Manchester 1857 (definitive catalogue, No. 1006); RA 1881, No. 82.

REFERENCES:
General: Smith No. 86; HdG No. 50.
In text:
1. Panel, 43.5 × 37.5 cm. HdG No. 156. In the Plettenberg sale, 1738, and the Lormier sale, 1756.
2. Loc. cit.
3. On panel, 49.5 × 38 cm.
4. Panel, 35.5 × 41 cm. Photo in RKD.
5. See Hoet, vol. 2, p. 531. Hoet describes the picture inaccurately as 'vyf Ossen en een Onweers Lugt en Sonne ligt op de Beesten' (1 *voet* 5½ *duim* × 1 *v.* 2½ *d.*) but the description given in the 1771 list of the Bisschop pictures sold to the Hopes (see OH, vol.

28, 1910, p. 175) shows that it was certainly No. 2583.
6. OH, 1910, p. 164. For the Hope collection, see J. W. Niemeijer, 'De Kunstverzameling van John Hope (1737–1784)', *NKJ*, 1982, pp. 127–232. Niemeijer published the MS inventory of John Hope, in which the painting is No. 190 (p. 193).
7. *Catalogue of Pictures . . . lent to the South Kensington Museum by Lord Francis Pelham-Clinton-Hope,* 1891, No. 31.
8. Cf. the introduction to *The Hope Collection,* 1898.

JACOB PYNAS, *c.*1585 – after 1656

Jacob Symonsz. Pynas. He and his elder brother Jan, also a painter, were born in Haarlem. His teacher is unknown. He was in Italy in 1605 and was back in Amsterdam in 1608. He is mentioned in Amsterdam in 1618 and in The Hague in 1622 but seems to have been principally active in Delft where he joined the guild in 1632 and is recorded in 1639; in 1641 and 1643 he was again in Amsterdam. His earliest known work is the

Adoration of the Magi of 1617 (Hartford, Wadsworth Atheneum); his latest a drawing, *Apollo and Daphne*, of 1656 in Paris (Institut Néerlandais).

He belongs to the group of history painters working principally in Amsterdam in the first three decades of the seventeenth century known as the Pre-Rembrandtists, of whom Pieter Lastman is the best known. Like Lastman, by whom he was profoundly influenced, Jacob Pynas had studied the work of Adam Elsheimer in Rome. Pynas' brother-in-law Jan Tengnagel was another Pre-Rembrandtist painter.

According to Houbraken, Jacob Pynas was one of Rembrandt's masters and his fondness for the use of brown tones came from Pynas. This would have been around 1623 but there is no documentary evidence for this statement.

REFERENCE: Ex. cat. (by A. Tümpel), *The Pre-Rembrandtists*, E. B. Crocker Art Gallery, Sacramento, 1974, pp. 67ff.

6460 *Mountain Landscape with Narcissus*   *Plate 275*

Signed, left, on the top edge of the basin: J Pynas 1628.

Oil on panel, 47.6 × 62.8 ($18\frac{7}{8}$ × $25\frac{1}{4}$).

Cleaned in 1979–80, shortly before its acquisition by the National Gallery.

Prior to its being first published by Bauch in 1936,[1] the figure of Narcissus had been painted over and foliage and a rider on a white horse in the middle distance added. The painting was then known as *Landscape with Virgil's Tomb*.[2] When, however, it was cleaned Narcissus was revealed and the real subject of the painting became clear. The basin is decorated with a bas-relief of the Rape of Europa, a theme loosely appropriate both to a basin and to Narcissus in that it combines the subjects of water and love.

PROVENANCE: Collection of Arthur Kay, Edinburgh, by 1936;[3] Arthur Kay of Edinburgh sale, Christie's, 8–9 April 1943, lot 117 (25 gns; bought by Schapiro); Dr E. I. Schapiro collection; E.I. Schapiro sale, Christie's, 30 November 1979, lot 8 (£8,500; bought by S. Nystad); purchased from Nystad by the National Gallery, 1980, with the aid of a fund to commemorate the art historian and critic Keith Roberts (1937–79).

EXHIBITION: London 1986, No. 89.

REFERENCES:
General: C. Brown, 'National Gallery Acquisition in memory of Keith Roberts', BM, vol. 122, 1980, p. 651.
In text:
1. K. Bauch, 'Beiträge zum Werk der Vorläufer Rembrandts', OH, vol. 53, 1936, p. 38, pl. 11.
2. It was praised in 1974 as an example of a landscape in which Pynas 'largely renounced historical staffage figures' (exhibition catalogue, Sacramento, op. cit., p. 30).

3. There is a label on the back of the painting in Kay's hand: 'Primitive semi classical landscape by Jacob Pynas, one of Rembrandt's teachers . . .' and dated 1939. The painting is discussed by Kay in his *Treasure Trove in Art*, 1939, p. 115 ('it immediately became clear that I had at last found a missing link between Jacob Pynas and Rembrandt as landscape painters . . .') and illustrated – with Narcissus overpainted and the rider added – opposite p. 113.

PIETER QUAST, 1606–1647

Pieter Jansz. Quast was born in Amsterdam.[1] In June 1632 his age is given as twenty-six.[2]

He was living in Amsterdam in June 1632 when he married in nearby Sloten;[3] in 1634 he became a member of the guild in The Hague,[4] bought a house there in 1639[5] and was still there in October 1643.[6] By January 1644 he had settled in Amsterdam,[7] and he died there in 1647, probably not long before 6 June.[8]

His work consists mainly of genre and satirical subjects and has a strongly caricatural element. He also painted a number of historical, literary and theatrical subjects such as *Brutus before Tarquinius* of 1643[9] which is an illustration of a poem by P. C. Hooft. His style is based principally on that of Adriaen Brouwer (1605 or 1606–38) with whom he may have come into contact in Amsterdam or Haarlem about 1625–7, and also derives to some extent from Adriaen van de Venne, who had settled in The Hague by 1625. Quast was also a printmaker and book illustrator.

REFERENCES:
General: Bredius in OH, 1902, pp. 65–82.
In text:
1. According to the entry of 1632 in the Amsterdam marriage register (OH, 1885, p. 309).
2. and 3. See note 1.

4. Obreen, vol. 3, p. 263.
5. and 6. Bredius, op. cit., p. 69.
7. Bredius, op. cit., p. 70.
8. Bredius, op. cit., p. 72.
9. The Hague, Mauritshuis, 1977 cat. no. 447.

2856 *A Man and a Woman in a Stableyard*   Plate 276

Signed on a pilgrim bottle standing on a barrel, right: P.[1]

Oil on oak, 45.4 × 57.5 ($17\frac{7}{8}$ × $22\frac{5}{8}$).

At one time attributed to Pieter Codde,[2] but it is entirely characteristic of Quast. It was probably painted in the 1630s.

It is Quast's intention here to ridicule the soldier. He is a swaggering, over-dressed figure who might have stepped from one of the pages of the many contemporary plays by Coster, Rodenburgh and others which mocked the pretentions of soldiers. The vanity of soldiers is also made fun of by Adriaen van de Venne in his *Tafereel van de Belacherende Werelt* (1635); Quast knew van de Venne when he was in The Hague.

PROVENANCE: In the collection of Charles Lock Eastlake,[3] London (Keeper of the National Gallery, 1878–98; died 1906); Mrs Charles Lock Eastlake Bequest, 1911.

EXHIBITION: London 1978–9, No. 27.

REFERENCES:
1. There is a curved horizontal stroke below and to the right of the P. which might well be the tail of a Q, and the signature may have been a P on top of a Q, as for example in Rijksmuseum No. A1756 (1976 cat.).

2. On the back of the panel is a label inscribed: 'Cavalier and Lady in a Court-yard/by Pieter Codde/lent by Charles L. Eastlake . . .'
3. Cf. note 2.

6410 *A Standing Man* *Plate 277*

Signed, lower right: PQVAST (PQ and VA in monogram).

Oil on oak, 35 × 23.5(13¾ × 9¼).

The picture is painted over what appears to be part of another: a figure on horseback (moving from right to left) is accompanied by another on foot. Quast presumably painted over an earlier work of his own and the panel was cut down.

The painting was previously attributed to Pieter Codde[1] and Willem Buytewech the Elder[2] but it is clearly signed by Quast. Formerly described as a portrait, this full-length standing figure is in fact a genre piece rather than a conventional portrait. The man is probably a soldier and the painting is related to the barrack-room interiors painted by Quast in the mid-1630s;[3] they are similar in subject-matter and style to the better-known scenes of military life by Pieter Codde and Willem Duyster. No. 6410 probably dates from the early 1630s.

There was a second painting of a standing figure in the Alexander collection in the same style and with similar dimensions.[4] That painting has been incorrectly attributed to Willem Buytewech the Elder and Jan Martsen the Younger: it is also by Pieter Quast.

PROVENANCE: Lord Haldon sale, Christie's, 28 February 1891, lot 84 (as 'A Different Property') as 'P. Codde: Portrait of a Cavalier'; bought by Colnaghi (£29.8s.), from whom purchased by W. C. Alexander. By descent to the Misses Rachel F. and Jean I. Alexander, who presented it by deed of gift to the National Gallery; entered the collection in 1972.[5]

EXHIBITIONS: RA 1952–3, No. 494 (as Willem Buytewech the Elder); Hull 1961, No. 11; London 1972.

REFERENCES:
1. In 1891 sale, see under PROVENANCE.
2. In exhibition in 1952–3 and in 1961. See under EXHIBITIONS.
3. See, for example, *The Interior of a Guardhouse*, signed and dated 1636 which was in Anon. sale, Sotheby's, 20 October 1971, lot 76 (panel, 18 × 14¾ in.). The central standing soldier is strikingly similar to the figure in No. 6410.
4. Panel, 44 × 31 cm. Exhibited at the RA, 1952–3, No. 532, as Willem Buytewech the Elder. Attributed to Jan Martsen the younger by L. Gowing in BM, vol. 95, 1953, p. 52.
5. A. Smith, 'Presented by the Misses Rachel F. and Jean I. Alexander: Seventeen Paintings for the National Gallery', BM, vol. 114, 1972, p. 634.

ABRAHAM RAGUINEAU, 1623 – after February 1681

He signed his name *Raguineau* and *Ragueneau*. He was baptised in the French church in London, 19 October 1623. By 1640 he was living in The Hague and was still there in April 1646; in January 1647 he was living in 's Hertogenbosch. Later he was in Breda but had moved to The Hague before the end of June 1659; in that year he received payments for teaching the young Prince of Orange. By December 1659 he was apparently living in Leiden, and a daughter of his was baptised there in January 1661. He is mentioned in the records of *Pictura*, the painters' confraternity in The Hague, in

1664–5 and once between 1669 and 1671; he was apparently employed in the prince's household until 1671. He is last heard of at the end of February 1681 when he is said to be living in Zierikzee (Zeeland).

His known works are all portraits; besides that catalogued below, some half-dozen others have survived. There are dated ones of 1654, 1657, 1660, 1662 and 1670. He was paid for official portraits of the prince in 1661[1] and 1667.

REFERENCES:
General: HdG in OH, vol. 17, 1899, pp. 6–8; A. Staring in OH, vol. 65, 1950, pp. 203–4.
In text: **1.** A copy of this portrait is in the Mauritshuis (1977 cat. no. 498).

1848 *Portrait of a Young Man in Grey* Plate 278

Signed, right, in the centre: ARaguineau/pinxit (AR in monogram), and inscribed, top left: A^0 1657/.Ætatis 18.

Oil on oak, in a painted oval, 73.8 × 59.8 (29$\frac{1}{16}$ × 23$\frac{9}{16}$).

Some wearing in the background.

PROVENANCE: Said to have been in the collection of Prince Bariatinsky in Russia and to have been bought at the sale of his collection by F. Meazza.[1] F. Meazza sale, Milan, 15 sqq. April 1884 (lot 164), bought by Aldo Noseda,[2] Milan, from whom it was purchased in 1901.

REFERENCES:
1. This provenance is first mentioned in the National Gallery catalogue of 1906. The foreword to the Meazza 1884 sale catalogue says that some of Meazza's pictures (unspecified) were bought by him in Russia from the collection of the Princes Bariatinsky.
2. HdG in OH, vol. 17, 1899, p. 8.

REMBRANDT VAN RIJN, 1606–1669

Rembrandt Harmensz. van Rijn, son of a miller, Harmen Gerritsz. van Rijn, was born in Leiden; according to Orlers,[1] on 15 July 1606. In May 1620 he was inscribed as a student at Leiden University[2] but was apparently not long there. Orlers says (1641) that he was a pupil first of Jacob Isaacsz. van Swanenburgh of Leiden (c. 1571–1638) with whom he remained for about three years [c. 1621–3?], then of Pieter Lastman in Amsterdam, and that after about six months with Lastman he set up as a painter on his own [in 1624 or 1625?]. The first known dated picture is of 1625.[3] Simon van Leeuwen's statement (1672)[4] that the Leiden portrait-painter Joris van Schooten (1587–1651), the master of Jan Lievens, was also the master of Rembrandt, is almost certainly incorrect. Houbraken says (1718)[5] that after Rembrandt left Lastman's studio he was a pupil for some months of Jacob Pynas; he adds that some say Pynas was Rembrandt's first master. For a time Rembrandt was in close contact with Jan Lievens and they may have collaborated on occasion or shared a studio. Gerrit Dou became Rembrandt's pupil in February 1628 and was with him for about three years.[6] In the winter of 1631–2 Rembrandt moved to Amsterdam, according to Orlers because he was in such

319

demand there.[7] He is recorded as still living in Leiden in June 1631[8] and is first documented in Amsterdam in July 1632.[9] His group portrait of members of the Amsterdam surgeons' guild (the so-called 'Anatomy lesson of Dr Tulp') is dated 1632 and for some years following his move to Amsterdam he was one of the most successful portrait-painters in the city. In June 1634 he married Saskia van Uylenburgh (see No. 4930 below). Although Amsterdam remained his home for the rest of his life, he is recorded in Rotterdam in July 1634.[10] In 1636 he painted *The Blinding of Samson* (Frankfurt) and the Hermitage *Danaë*; between about 1633 and 1639 he painted five pictures of Christ's Passion for the Stadholder, Prince Frederik Hendrik.[11] From about the end of the 1630s onwards he produced fewer portraits, although he continued to paint them until the end of his life. In 1642 he finished the *Nightwatch* (see Gerrit Lundens No. 289); two further scenes from the life of Christ were completed for the Stadholder in 1646;[12] the portrait of Jan Six is of 1654. To 1656 belongs another group portrait of Amsterdam surgeons (the 'Anatomy lesson of Dr Deyman'); in this year he was granted a *cessio bonorum*, a form of bankruptcy, and his property, including a large art collection, was sold in 1658.[13] In 1661–2 he painted a large historical picture, *The Conspiracy of Julius Civilis*, for the new town hall in Amsterdam but it was removed shortly afterwards and one by Jurriaen Ovens substituted. His portrait of the Sampling Officials of the Cloth-makers' Guild in Amsterdam (the 'Staalmeesters') is dated 1662. The last dated painting is of 1669 (see No. 221 below) and he died on 4 October of that year in Amsterdam,[14] and was buried in the Westerkerk, 8 October.[15]

Rembrandt had many pupils during his years in Amsterdam; among them were Ferdinand Bol, Govert Flinck, Carel Fabritius, Samuel van Hoogstraten, Nicolaes Maes, Gerbrandt van den Eeckhout and Aert de Gelder. All except the last are represented in the National Gallery collection.

REFERENCES:
General: HdG, vol. 7; Bredius, *Rembrandt*; Benesch; Bauch; H. Gerson, *Rembrandt Paintings*, London, 1969; Hollstein, vol. 18; Strauss *Doc.* (see the review by C. Brown in BM, vol. 127, 1985, pp. 46–7); *Rembrandt Corpus*, vols 1, 2 and 3.
In text:
1. J. Orlers, *Beschrijvinge der Stadt Leyden*, 2nd ed., 1641, p. 375 (quoted in Strauss *Doc.* 1641/8).
2. Strauss *Doc.* 1620/1.
3. *The Martyrdom of St Stephen*. Lyons, Musée des Beaux Arts (Bredius, *Rembrandt*, No. 531a; *Rembrandt Corpus*, vol. 1, A1).
4. S. van Lee[u]wen, *Korte Beschryving van . . . Leyden*, 1672, p. 189 (see Strauss *Doc.* p. 50 and note 3).

5. Houbraken, vol. 1, pp. 254–5.
6. Orlers, op. cit., p. 380 (see Strauss *Doc.* 1641/9).
7. Orlers, op. cit., p. 375 (Strauss *Doc.* 1641/8).
8. Strauss *Doc.* 1631/4.
9. Strauss *Doc.* 1632/2.
10. Strauss *Doc.* 1634/7.
11. and 12. See Rembrandt No. 47 of this catalogue, note 2.
13. Strauss *Doc.* 1656/12, 1656/11, 1656/14, 1656/16, 1656/18, 1656/19, 1657/1, 1657/6, 1655/7, 1658/3, 1658/5, 1658/19, 1658/29.
14. Strauss *Doc.* 1669/4.
15. Strauss *Doc.* 1669/6.

43 *The Lamentation over the Dead Christ*[1] *Plate 279*

Christ lies at the foot of the Cross, his head in the Virgin's lap and his feet embraced by the Magdalen. In the centre is the Good Thief on his cross, the Bad Thief is on the left. In the distance is an imaginary view of Jerusalem.

Oil on paper and canvas, mounted on an oak panel measuring 31.9 × 26.7 (12$\frac{9}{16}$ × 10$\frac{1}{2}$); the top corners are rounded.

Cleaned in 1987-8.

The part of the painting which is on paper is in grisaille; on the upper added portion there are touches of red and yellow ochre beneath the cross-bar of the central cross and on the drapery of the Bad Thief. Examination of the sky revealed no blue pigment but a mixture of lead white and carbon black.

There is no biblical text describing the Lamentation, although by the time Rembrandt painted the subject there was a well-established iconography. Rembrandt's treatment of the subject has a strong narrative element, conflating a number of scenes from the Passion. The men descending the ladders refer to the Deposition; Mary is usually shown as having fainted either in the Crucifixion or the Deposition; the presence of the other two crosses is more usual in a Deposition; and, in the background at the right, the older man with a feathered headdress may well be Joseph of Arimathea setting out to request permission from Pilate to bury the body of Christ. (This figure is not Longinus, as has been suggested; he is not dressed in Roman armour, nor does he carry a lance. The lance is carried by the accompanying figure on foot.) His presence leads on to the next event in the Passion, the Entombment.

    The Lamentation is the smallest painting by Rembrandt in the National Gallery and, structurally, by far the most complex.

Most of the lower part of the picture is painted on a piece of paper[2] of extremely irregular shape. Within it are Christ and the whole of the group kneeling around him, all the figures standing at the foot of the Cross (except for that on the extreme left) and the view in the right background. It does not include the upper half of the Good Thief, most of the man holding the ladder in front of him and the head of the man standing on the ladder to the left; further, a piece roughly triangular in shape has been cut out of the paper where are now the upper half of the Virgin, Christ's head and the arms of the woman beside the Virgin. These parts are painted on the canvas on which the paper has been mounted. The canvas is slightly larger than the paper, is roughly square and measures approximately 21 × 26 (8$\frac{1}{4}$ × 10$\frac{1}{4}$); its upper edge runs through the waist of the Bad Thief and immediately above the top of the Good Thief's cross, and the bottom edge is just below the group in the foreground. The canvas, with the paper, has then been stuck on the panel, a further piece of canvas measuring 7.5 (on the left)-9 (right) × 26.7 (3-3$\frac{1}{2}$ × 10$\frac{1}{2}$) has been attached to the upper part of the panel and a strip about 2.8-3.3 (1-1$\frac{1}{4}$) added along the bottom. Lastly, the picture surface has been extended by painting up to the edges of the panel. There is no reason to suppose that the oak panel was not attached to the canvas and paper in Rembrandt's lifetime.

The X-radiograph (Fig. 70) shows that the central area of canvas to which the painting on paper was first attached has its threads distorted out of the vertical and horizontal as if at one time it had been crudely stretched and roughly nailed to a stretcher. Also on the left-hand side a strip is missing for part of its length so that there the edge of the canvas does not extend to the edge of the oak panel. It could be that the artist stuck the original painting (which was on paper) on to a discarded scrap of canvas before he decided he would like to develop the composition. A lead white (or red lead?) adhesive seems to have been used and shows up white on the X-radiograph particularly round the edges of the central piece of canvas.

Most of the back of the panel (Fig. 71) is covered by two pieces of paper with an inscription in ink which, except for the last sentence, is in the handwriting of Sir Joshua Reynolds,[3] who once owned the picture (see PROVENANCE). On the upper, and larger piece: '(This?) Picture [was?] graved by [Pi]cart/in what he calls his Impostures/Innocentes whilst in the Cabinet/of M.I. (de?) Barrij of Amsterdam./It passed afterwards into that of/Mr Smith Consul at Venice,/ and from thence to the King, His/Majesty having purchased his ["his" has been crossed out and "Smith's" written above in the same hand] Collection/and library of Books for ten thousand/pounds. At the sale of Mr Dalton/who was keeper of the Kings Pictures/it was bought by Sir Joshua/Reynolds April 21 1791/Sir Joshua has [sic] the Drawing which Rembran [the paper has been trimmed here]/made for this picture behind which/is wrote by Jon^n Richardson Jun. these words.'

The inscription is continued in Reynolds' writing on the lower (and wider) piece of paper, this part being copied from Richardson's inscription on the back of Rembrandt's study in the British Museum (see DRAWINGS): 'Rembrant has labour'd this study for the lower/part of his famous descent from the Cross/graved by Picart & had so often changed/his mind in the disposition of the clair obscur,/which was his Point here, that my Father/& I counted I think seventeen pieces of/paper./Bought by Sir George Beamont at Sir Joshua Reynolds/sale Monday March 16 1795.'[4] The last sentence has been added later in a different hand, apparently Sir George Beaumont's.

Bode and Hofstede de Groot[5] considered No. 43 to be a study for Rembrandt's etched *Descent from the Cross* of 1642[6] and it has, therefore, often been dated *c.*1642 although in fact it is not connected in any way with the etching. Stechow is inclined to date it somewhat later than 1642;[7] Benesch apparently puts it about 1637–8.[8]

MacLaren, however, argued that it was probable that the execution of the picture extended over a period of years and both Bauch[9] and Gerson[10] agreed.

Only the central part of the composition as it now stands is by Rembrandt: the top and bottom sections were added later. The complex evolution of the painting can be clarified by a careful study of the paint surface, the X-radiograph and paint cross-sections taken from key points.

The first stage of the development of *The Lamentation* was a lay-in done directly on to the paper in tones of brown. This thin wash contains black, transparent brown, traces of red and yellow earth and a trace of white. There appears to be no other preparation on the paper. This brown tone is still visible in several areas and was used directly for shadow and half-tone in the first painting stage. It can be seen, for example, in the shadowed side of the man's head immediately above the Virgin and in the middle-ground landscape above that. The dark standing figures in the left foreground are also composed largely of this brown lay-in, with a few lighter scumbles on top. Over this brown tone, Rembrandt applied grey and white lights and highlights. Deeper shadows and linear details were then added in darker browns and blacks. The original size of the paper on which this first stage was painted is not known because Rembrandt used only part of it for the second stage. He cut and tore away parts with which he was dissatisfied, to leave the irregularly shaped piece clearly visible in the X-radiograph as described in detail above. The trimmed and torn paper was then mounted on a slightly larger piece of canvas. This can also be seen in the X-radiograph. Its upper edge slopes down towards the right and passes just below the Good Thief's hands; its lower edge is approximately horizontal and runs just below the main figure group. The canvas can be seen (in the X-radiograph) to have cusping at the top and left, indicating that it was cut from a large, stretched piece. A cross-section reveals that it is prepared with a double ground, on which the paper is directly mounted. The upper layer contains lead white, a little umber and a fine-grained black; the lower layer is reddish-orange earth. The canvas was undoubtedly part of a batch in Rembrandt's studio. Van de Wetering[11] has pointed out that its thread count and weave characteristics match those in other canvas paintings of 1634–5; specifically, he proposes that this piece of canvas was trimmed from the bottom of the *Cupid blowing Bubbles* of 1634 (Ascona, Switzerland, Collection of Baroness Bentinck-Thyssen)[12] before it was painted.

Once the paper was mounted on canvas, Rembrandt reworked certain parts of the composition, notably the area of Christ's head and the upper half of the Virgin's body and her head and that of the man grasping the ladder at the base of the Cross and the figure of the Good Thief. The paint of this second stage is more densely worked than the first. Finally (in this second stage) Rembrandt added a few flourishes, notably the extraordinarily freely painted figure at the right, where he has suggested a head, arms and praying hands with just a few, dragged brushstrokes of pure white.

There is a drawing in the British Museum (Fig. 72; see below under DRAWINGS), undoubtedly by Rembrandt himself, which seems not to be a preparatory drawing in the usual sense but a drawing which Rembrandt worked on at the same time as he was working on this second stage of the grisaille. It is a study for the lower part of the composition, in a horizontal format, in brown, grey and white oil colours and pale brown ink over red chalk. Rembrandt made many drastic alterations to this drawing, which at one stage he cut into two irregular parts and mounted, with several additions, on a large sheet. The group around the dead Christ and the figures at the foot of the Cross are more or less the same as in the painting, while the figures behind and the background are quite different. There are *pentimenti* in the original part of the painting which have a direct connection with the British Museum drawing. For example, a large tower in the centre right background, which can be made out both on the picture surface and in the X-radiograph, can be seen in the drawing. It was clearly tried out in the painting and subsequently painted over. Similarly, there is a woman in a large flat hat standing behind the main group of figures in the drawing: she is visible in the X-radiograph, standing in a similar position. It is clear that experimentation with one version, painting or drawing, led to changes in the other. This very close relationship between the two is confirmed by close examination of the drawing. The parts of the composition which have here been considered as the first stage of the painting – those using the brown lay-in for shadows and half-tones – are executed in pen and ink in the drawing. In the second stage – after the mounting on to canvas – the corresponding areas of the drawing are carried out in much coarser chalk and oil paint.

In the next stage of the evolution of the painting, the canvas was stuck to a larger oak panel, which had rounded top corners, together with two pieces of the same canvas (this has been established by counting the canvas threads), one above and one below. This arrangement can be clearly seen in the X-radiograph. It is unclear when this took place. The upper and lower pieces of canvas have a double ground, identical to each other, though slightly different from that of the central canvas. It could have been done in Rembrandt's studio or in that of a follower or pupil who was familiar with his method of preparing canvases. The painting of these two sections, however, is not by Rembrandt and may not have even been done in his studio. The evidence for this is partly stylistic – the handling of paint is quite unlike that on the central part – and partly technical. Cross-sections from the upper section show a thin varnish layer between the upper ground layer and the paint. Moreover, one cross-section shows a crack in the ground layers which does not continue into the paint. Both these observations suggest that some time had elapsed before the painting was completed. There was, therefore, an intermediate stage in which the upper and lower canvas additions simply contained unpainted grey-brown ground: the entire painting was varnished in this state and only later were the two additions painted, changing the composition from a horizontal to a vertical format. The later paint overlaps the original sky at the upper join, and the horizontal bar of the Good Thief's cross also belongs to this stage. The left edge of the original part is also overpainted – the two figures on the extreme left are not original and are partly painted on the bare wood of the panel beyond the edge of the canvas. The figure of the Bad Thief is entirely composed of later paint, the legs covering a substantial part of Rembrandt's original. The later painter has also added small touches to Rembrandt's own figures: for example, the highlight on the upper arm of the richly dressed woman on the right is identical in composition to the cream sky paint at the top left.

To sum up: there are three distinct stages in the genesis of the painting. The first is a grisaille on paper. Rembrandt was dissatisfied with this and made a copy of the composition on paper in pen and ink – the first stage of the drawing in the British Museum. He then experimented by cutting the drawing diagonally and remounting it, so allowing room for the ladder which he then included, together with other alterations carried out in chalk and paint. He then returned to the painted grisaille, cutting and tearing it and then mounting it on canvas. He then painted the second stage including the ladder which he had developed in the drawing. He then developed the composition of the grisaille further by painting the Good Thief in a lower position rather than incorporating the middle-ground figures or the larger cityscape of the drawing. Finally two further pieces of canvas were added, top and bottom. At first they simply had an unpainted ground which was varnished. Subsequently, however, they were painted and the composition extended to the present vertical format.

In its original, horizontal format, the painting was probably intended as the *modello* for an etching which was never made. A telling detail pointed out by Van de Wetering[13] is that the thief on the left is presumably the Bad Thief, as the other thief hangs in the light and his body is not twisted. For the Bad Thief to hang on Christ's right would be iconographically incorrect, but this would be corrected if the composition were reversed in a print. The only grisaille *modello* which was completed and used for a print is the *Ecce Homo* of 1634 (No. 1400 of this catalogue). There are, however, other grisaille paintings such as *Joseph telling his Dreams*[14] and *St John the Baptist Preaching*[15] which Rembrandt may well have intended to use in this way. All these grisailles date from the mid-1630s and it may be that Rembrandt was planning an ambitious series of prints which was never carried out. *The Lamentation* belongs to this group of works; it should, in its first and second stages, be dated about 1635. In the sequence of Rembrandt's work, it should be placed shortly after *St John the Baptist Preaching* which can be dated 1634–5. There is no reason to think, as MacLaren did, that Rembrandt's work on the painting extended over a period of years; indeed, the numerous changes, and the relationship with the British Museum drawing, suggest a relatively short period of intense activity. An additional reason for dating the grisaille in the mid-1630s is the existence of a painting of this subject by Flinck painted in 1637[16] which seems to presuppose knowledge of No. 43 in its second stage.

Van Gelder[17] thought it possible that Bol was responsible for the painted additions on the top and bottom but, as discussed above, it is more likely that these additions date from significantly later, even from the late seventeenth or early eighteenth century. They were certainly added before 1730, the date of Picart's engraving (see under ENGRAVINGS). Robinson[18] and Harris[19] drew attention to a drawing[20] attributed to Bol which records the painting in its second stage. Sumowski[21] believes the drawing to be by Bol and to date from *c.*1643–5.

It is worth noting that the placing of the three crosses is the same as in Rembrandt's etching of *Christ Crucified between the Two Thieves* which White and Boon date *c.*1641.[22]

The Lamentation was in Venice by 1738 (see PROVENANCE) and it, or a print after it, was apparently known to Giovanni Domenico Tiepolo and probably also to Giovanni Battista.[23]

There are two loosely related paintings which should be mentioned: a large-scale *Lamentation* in the John and Mable Ringling Museum of Art, Sarasota,[24] and an oil sketch of the same subject which in 1961 was in the collection of Dr F.H. Frankhauser in Basle.[25] Neither is by Rembrandt and the latter may be a considerably later pastiche.

DRAWINGS: A study for the lower part in brown, grey and white oil colours and pale brown ink over red chalk is in the British Museum.[26] Rembrandt made many drastic alterations to this study which at some stage he cut into two irregular parts and mounted, with several additions, on a larger sheet. (It appears, however, to be made up of far less than the seventeen pieces of paper which Richardson supposed – see above.) The group around the dead Christ and the figures at the foot of the Cross are more or less as in the painting; the figures behind and the background are different. HdG[27] connected with the National Gallery *Lamentation* a pen and wash sketch of that subject in the Städelsches Kunstinstitut, Frankfurt;[28] it seems to have little or nothing to do with this composition and is probably later.

COPIES: A drawing attributed to Bol is discussed above. An enlarged free copy in the opposite direction, presumably based on Picart's print (see below), was in an Anon. sale, London, 3 July 1953 (lot 159).[29] A smaller copy, also in reverse, was in an Anon. sale, Sotheby's, 7 October 1964, lot 182 (£130 to Winthrop).[30] Another copy with some variations and more space between the Bad Thief and the edge of the picture, in reverse, was in an exhibition of paintings acquired 1954–7 by the National Museum, Warsaw, September–December 1957 (no. 13) as by R. Bonington (?).[31] A copy apparently by John Burnet (1784–1868) made with the intention of making an engraving was in an Anon. sale, Christie's, 6 June 1975, lot 47 (50 gns).[32]

ENGRAVINGS: Etched by Bernard Picart, 1730 (in reverse);[33] a chiaroscuro woodcut was made in Venice by John Baptist Jackson, 1738.[34]

PROVENANCE: In the collection of J. Barij [Jean or Jacob de Bary?], Amsterdam, apparently in 1730.[35] By 1738 it was in the collection of Joseph Smith (Consul Smith) in Venice.[36] It cannot be (as HdG supposed) the grisaille *Deposition* in an Anon. sale in Amsterdam, 25 September 1743 (lot 13),[37] since it was among the pictures bought from Joseph Smith by George III in 1762.[38] Some of these, including the *Deposition* passed into the collection of Richard Dalton, Surveyor of the King's Pictures, who had been concerned in their acquisition;[39] it was in Richard Dalton's sale, London, 9–11 April 1791 (2nd day, lot 19),[40] bought by Grosier (sic) (24 gns), for Sir Joshua Reynolds[41] (d. February 1792). Sir Joshua Reynolds sale, 13 sqq. March 1795 (3rd day, lot 38),[42] bought by Sir George Beaumont, Bart. (41 gns).[43] It was among the pictures presented by Sir George Beaumont to the British Museum for the proposed National Gallery in 1823 and transferred to the National Gallery in 1828.

EXHIBITIONS: BI 1823, No. 95; London 1988–9, No. 6.

REFERENCES:

General: Smith No. 96; Bode and HdG, vol. 4, No. 245; HdG No. 136; Bredius, *Rembrandt*, No. 565; Bauch No. 69.

In text:

1. In the preparation of this entry the present writer has benefited from discussions with Joyce Plesters, Ashok Roy and David Bomford at the National Gallery, London, and Professors Josua Bruyn and Ernst van de Wetering of the Rembrandt Research Project in Amsterdam. The present writer collaborated with Bomford and Roy on an extended technical account of the painting's complex evolution in the catalogue of the exhibition *Art in the Making: Rembrandt*, National Gallery, London, 1988–9, pp. 66–73. The technical sections here are a shortened version of that account. Van de Wetering kindly showed the present writer a draft entry for the painting in volume 3 of the Rembrandt Research Project's *Corpus*.

2. Not on panel transferred to canvas as suggested by W. Stechow in *Jahrbuch der Preussischen Kunstsammlungen*, vol. 50, 1929, p. 227; the two supposed wood cracks are in fact the lines of the canvas joins.

3. The authorship of the inscription is mentioned already in the catalogue of the Reynolds sale in 1795

(see note 42) and is confirmed by comparison with other Reynolds manuscripts.

4. There are some unimportant errors in the transcription of this inscription in *Jahrbuch der Preussischen Kunstsammlungen*, 1929, p. 227, note 1.

5. Bode and HdG, loc. cit., and HdG No. 136.

6. Hollstein No. 82.

7. Stechow, op. cit., p. 226, note 2.

8. O. Benesch, *Rembrandt. Werk und Forschung*, 1935, p. 28; he also dates the British Museum drawing *c.* 1637–8 (see note 26).

9. Bauch No. 69. ('Begonnen wurde das ganze vielleicht schon Ende der 1630er, vollendet offenbar im Anfang der 1640er Jahre.')

10. Gerson in Bredius, op. cit., No. 565 (it 'was being worked on from 1637–8 onwards, for a considerable length of time').

11. In the draft entry referred to above in note 1.

12. Bredius No. 470; *Rembrandt Corpus*, no. A91.

13. In the draft entry referred to above in note 1.

14. Bredius No. 504. Paper on panel, 51 × 39 cm. Amsterdam, Rijksmuseum.

15. Bredius No. 555. Canvas on panel, 62 × 80 cm. Berlin-Dahlem, Gemäldegalerie.

16. Sumowski, *Gemälde*, vol. 2, No. 612. Canvas, 89 × 71.5 cm. Signed, in the middle to the right, G. Flinck. f/1637. Formerly with the art dealer Le Goupy, Paris.

17. J. G. van Gelder, 'Frühe Rembrandt-Sammlungen' in O. v. Simson and J. Kelch, eds., *Neue Beiträge zur Rembrandt-Forschung*, Berlin, 1973, pp. 193–4.

18. F. W. Robinson, 'Rembrandt's Influence in 18th century Venice', NKJ, vol. 18, 1967, p. 188, note 55 (as Bol?).

19. A. Harris. 'Rembrandt's study for "The Lamentation for [sic] Christ" ', *Master Drawings*, vol. 7, 1969, pp. 158–64.

20. Brush and brown ink over black chalk, 16.3 × 24.5 cm. Erhinsbach, Mrs R. Baer-Hohl collection.

21. Sumowski, *Drawings*, vol. 1, Bol No. 146X.

22. Hollstein, B79.

23. See J. Byam Shaw in *Old Master Drawings*, vol. 7, 1932–3, pp. 55–6; M. Levey, *National Gallery Catalogues: The 18th Century Italian Schools*, 1956, p. 101; Robinson, op. cit., pp. 180 ff.

24. Canvas, 180.3 × 198.7 cm. F. W. Robinson and W. H. Wilson, *Catalogue of the Flemish and Dutch Paintings 1400–1900*, John and Mable Ringling Museum of Art, Sarasota, Florida, 1980, No. 116 (attributed to the School of Rembrandt).

25. Panel, 82 × 68 cm. Discussed and illustrated by Robinson in Robinson and Wilson, op. cit. (not paginated).

26. 21.3 × 25.4 cm. Hind, vol. 1, p. 29, No. 60. Benesch, vol. 1, No. 154 (fig. 184) as *c.*1637–8. For an excellent extended discussion of the complex make-up of this sheet, see Harris, op. cit., pp. 158–64.

27. Loc. cit.

28. Benesch, vol. 3, No. 586 (fig. 756), as *c.*1647.

29. Canvas, 99 × 99 cm. A photograph is in the National Gallery's archives.

30. Canvas, 11¼ × 9 in. This is a good copy which may have been made from the original painting with which it closely agrees (although the top corners are not rounded). It could possibly be the copy made for the chiaroscuro woodcut by J. B. Jackson (see under ENGRAVINGS).

31. Canvas, 30.5 × 25 cm. Reproduced in *Rocznik Muzeum Narodowego v. Warszawie*, vol. 5, 1960, p. 317.

32. Canvas, 12½ × 10½ in. An old inscription on the stretcher at the back reads: 'By Burnet From Rembrandt done for the Engraving.' The present writer has been unable to trace an engraving of the painting by Burnet.

33. Inscribed in engraving in the lower margin: 'Gravé par B. Picart en 1730, sur le Camayeux peint par Rembrandt, haut d'un/pied, sur 10. pouces de

large appartenant à J. de Barij à Amsterdam' (in some states '. . . du Cabinet de Mr J. de Barij . . .'). It was published in Picart's *Impostures innocentes ou Recueil d'estampes d'après divers peintres illustres . . .*, Amsterdam, 1734. Subject size, 21.9 = 18.2 cm. 'J. de Barij' may be the Jean de Bary whose pictures were sold in Amsterdam, 26 sqq. November 1759; the *Lamentation* was not in this sale. However, a certain *Jacob* de Bary had a collection of coins and medals which were auctioned in Amsterdam in April 1730 (Lugt 397).

34. Engraved inscription in the lower margin: 'Rembrandt pinxit. alt. p. l. lat. unc. x. Extat Venetiis in domo J: SMITH. J:B:Jackson figuras juxta Archetypum Sculp. & excudit. 1738' (followed by a quotation from John 19: 40, referring to the Entombment) 'Perillustri ac Praeclaro Viro D. Josepho Smith Insigne hoc Opus affabre in Ligno coelavit, & in sui obsequii & grati Animi monumentum humiliter devovet J. B. Jackson.' Subject size, 35 × 28 cm.; the top is rounded instead of flat.

35. When etched by Picart (see note 33).

36. According to the inscription on Jackson's woodcut (see note 34).

37. 'De aflaating van 't Kruys, in 't grauw, door Rembrand van Rijn', 14 guilders 5 (see Hoet, vol. 2, p. 124).

38. The purchase is dealt with in detail by F. Vivian, *Il Console Smith: mercante e collezionista*, Vicenza, 1971. The picture appears in copies of a list of the Dutch and Flemish paintings acquired with the Smith collection by George III in 1762: 'Rembrandt 149 A Deposition from the Cross with numerous figures on board. This is the Piece Engraved by B. Picart in the stile of the Author & again in wood plates in Colour by Jackson of the same size 1 ▸[foot ×] 10 [inches]' (see A. Blunt, *Venetian Drawings . . . in the Collection of HM the Queen*, 1957, p. 23 and Vivian, op. cit., p. 211.).

39. Blunt, op. cit., pp. 15–16.

40. 'Rembrandt The descent from the cross, in chiaro oscura [sic], engraved by Picart.'

41. According to Reynolds' inscription on the back, the picture was bought by him at the Dalton sale; the name of the purchaser is given as Grosier in the auctioneer's copy of the catalogue. This name appears in a variety of forms in the buyer's column of contemporary auction catalogues, and it can usually be shown that he was acting on behalf of Reynolds. He was presumably Joseph Grozer, several of whose prints after Reynolds' portraits are known. (The present writer is grateful to Francis Broun for this identification.)

42. 'Rembrandt THE DESCENT FROM THE CROSS, a capital sketch of this master, engraved by PICART. A particular account is to be seen on the back of it in

Sir JOSHUA's hand writing.' The catalogue of Reynolds' 1795 sale in the Victoria and Albert Museum library has the annotation against this lot: 'a sketch in claro obscuro – once mine'. Since Richard Dalton had been dead since 1791 and the previous owner had been George III, Joseph Grozer is the probable author. In his note on the back Reynolds says that he acquired it on 21 April and since Dalton's sale took place on 10 April, Grozer's brief ownership is possible. (The present writer is grateful to Francis Broun for drawing this note to his attention.)

43. The catalogue of the sale (published in BM, vol. 87, 1945, pp. 263–73) gives the price as £42 (40 gns). However, in the auctioneer's copy of the sale catalogue it is clearly given as £42.1s. (41 gns). The latter price can be confirmed by the entry in Farington's diary for 16 March 1795 (vol. 2, p. 315): 'Sir George Beaumont I breakfasted with, and we went together to the sale. – Sir George bought The Descent from the Cross by Rembrant (sic) for 41 guineas.'

45 *The Woman taken in Adultery*   *Plate 280*

Signed, bottom right: Rembrandt.f.1644.

Oil on oak, top corners rounded, 83.8 × 65.4 (33 × 25¾). The upper corners were probably cut after the picture was painted.[1]

Cleaned in 1941.

PENTIMENTI: There was at first another figure, perhaps two, on the extreme right beside the man with a crutch. There are other *pentimenti* in the face of the turbaned man in red in the right foreground, the top of Christ's head and the head-dress of the man in yellow beyond and above the adulteress.

The story of Christ's forgiveness of the adultress is told in the Gospel of St John, chapter 8.[2] Rembrandt shows the moment when the Scribes and Pharisees bring the adulteress before Jesus and ask whether the sentence of the Mosaic Law, which condemned adulteresses to be stoned, should be carried out. One of them points to the kneeling woman. In the elaborately detailed, decorative treatment of much of the background, the picture recalls Rembrandt's style of the 1630s – for example, the *Simeon and the Infant Christ in the Temple* of 1631[3] – in a way which is otherwise unparalleled in the 1640s. The freely drawn foreground figures are entirely consistent, however, with his style in the mid-1640s.

Benesch[4] identified six preparatory drawings for No. 45 (see under STUDIES AND DRAWINGS) but, with one possible exception, none seems to be by Rembrandt himself and they should be placed among the large group of drawn and painted derivations and copies of this influential composition.[5]

Rembrandt returned to the subject of Christ and the adulteress later in two bold drawings[6] which show him abandoning the spaciousness of the composition of No. 45 in favour of concentrating on the figure group and thoroughly reworking it. The second of these drawings can be at least approximately dated, as it is drawn on the reverse of a death announcement of 14 May 1659. It also carries a quotation from the biblical text in Rembrandt's own hand. Around 1659/60, therefore, Rembrandt was at work on a new version of this composition, but if the drawings were intended to be preparatory to a painting or an etching, the project was apparently never completed.

328

Some elements of *The Woman taken in Adultery* belonging to the Walker Art Center, Minneapolis, by a Rembrandt follower,[7] have been borrowed from Rembrandt's picture. Eeckhout's painting of the subject in the Rijksmuseum, Amsterdam,[8] is probably a reminiscence of the composition.

Sumowski has discussed a number of drawn and painted copies and derivations.[9]

STUDIES AND DRAWINGS: Compositional sketches formerly in the collection of Dr Robert Rudolf, London, in the Louvre and in Dresden apparently show earlier stages in the construction of the main group; in fact they are probably later derivations from the painting.[10]. A sketch in Munich showing the figures to the right of Christ disposed more or less as in the painting is probably a copy.[11] A rough chalk sketch of the whole composition in its final stage is also in Munich; this too is probably a later copy.[12] A chalk study of the weeping woman, the upper half of which agrees fairly closely with the adulteress in the painting, was in a Drouot sale, Paris, 17 December 1924; this drawing may be a preparatory study by Rembrandt.[13] A small half-length study in oils of a weeping woman, closely connected with the figure in the picture but on a larger scale, is in the Detroit Institute of Arts; it has been considered a study for the painting but seems more probably a later derivation from it by another hand.[14] A sketch in the Boymans-van Beuningen Museum, Rotterdam, is probably the work of a pupil of *c.* 1650/5.[15]

COPIES: There was a copy in the B. J. W. H. ten Bruggen Cate (Enschede) sale, Rotterdam (van Marle, Sille en Baan), 22 March 1939, lot 148 (as School of Rembrandt),[16] and another, with variations, in a private collection in Melbourne (1964).[17] A copy of the central part is in the Bruckenthal museum in Sibiu.[18] There is a drawn copy by a follower of Rembrandt in the Kunsthalle, Bremen;[19] a drawn copy of the man kneeling between the pillars in the background in Rotterdam;[20] and a drawn copy by Jacob de Wet of the high priest and part of the altar in his Haarlem sketchbook.[21] The entire background is the subject of a school drawing (probably by Salomon Koninck) in Stockholm.[22]

PROVENANCE: Said to have been painted for Jan Six (1618–1700), Amsterdam,[23] but this is unlikely and there seems to be no evidence that it was even in his collection.[24] It is probably the painting of this subject by Rembrandt which is the highest valued painting in the inventory of the Amsterdam dealer, Johannes de Renialme, 1657,[25] and which is also in the inventory made in 1705 of the collection of Jacob Hinlopen, Amsterdam (deceased).[26] It was in the collection of Willem Six (nephew of Jan Six) in Amsterdam by 1718;[27] at the Willem Six (d. 1733) sale, Amsterdam, 12 May 1734 (lot 5),[28] it was apparently bought in[29] (2,510 guilders); it is said to have remained in the possession of the Six family until 1803 and to have been sold then, with some other pictures, to Coclers of Amsterdam.[30] It was bought from Coclers in the same year by P. J. Lafontaine, Paris,[31] who brought it to England in 1807;[32] at the [Lafontaine] sale, London, 13 June 1807 (lot 44) it was bought in (5,000 gns) and was sold by Lafontaine the following day to John Julius Angerstein.[33] Purchased with the Angerstein collection in 1824.

EXHIBITIONS: London 1947–8, No. 67; London 1976, No. 87; London 1988–9, No. 9.

REFERENCES:

General: Smith No. 112; Bode and HdG, vol. 4, No. 247; HdG No. 104; Bauch No. 72; Bredius, *Rembrandt*, No. 566.

In text:

1. Where the corners have been rounded there are brushstrokes interrupted by the edge of the panel and the paint is also fractured at the edge here. The bevelling on the back of the panel is right-angled and not curved. A black line (perhaps not original) runs more or less continuously round the edge of the panel except at the rounded top corners. For a detailed technical description of the painting, see London 1988–9, pp. 86–91.

2. Held has discussed Rembrandt's interpretation of the text: J. S. Held, 'Das gesprochene Wort bei Rembrandt', in O.v. Simson and J. Kelch, eds.,

Neue Beiträge zur Rembrandt-Forschung. Berlin, 1973, pp. 111–25, esp. p. 119.

3. Mauritshuis, The Hague. Bredius No. 543.

4. Benesch Nos. 531–5 and A42. The possible exception is No. 535.

5. The present writer is very grateful to Dr P. Schatborn of the Rijksprentenkabinet for discussing these drawings with him (see also discussion in Schatborn 1985, pp. 134–5).

6. Benesch, vol. 5, Nos. 1046 and 1047 (figs. 1336 and 1337).

7. Canvas, 115 × 136.5 cm. Falsely signed and dated, Rembrandt 1644. HdG No. 105 (as Rembrandt). Exhibited as by Barent Fabritius in 'Rembrandt and his Pupils', Montreal/Toronto, 1969, No. 55.

8. Rijksmuseum 1976 catalogue, A106; Sumowski, *Paintings*, No. 442. There are two related drawings (Sumowski, *Drawings*, vol. 3, Nos. 642, 643).

9. W. Sumowski, 'Kritische Bemerkungen zur neuesten Gemäldekritik', in Simson and Kelch, op. cit., p. 93. The drawn copies are discussed individually under COPIES. A painted derivation of particular interest in view of its early date is Heinrich Jansen's *Presentation in the Temple* of 1649 in Copenhagen (Canvas. Signed and dated. 63 × 53 cm. Inv. no. 524).

10. Benesch, vol. 3, Nos. 531–4 (figs. 700–3).

11. Benesch, vol. 4, No. C44A (fig. 1072).

12. Benesch, vol. 4, No. A42 (fig. 1106).

13. Benesch, vol. 3, No. 535 (fig. 699).

14. Oak, 20.9 × 16.3 cm. HdG No. 717a. Bredius, *Rembrandt*, No. 366 ('a rather poor painting in the style of Gerbrand van den Eeckhout'). It is certainly not by Rembrandt but is a feeble copy after the National Gallery picture. It has also been incorrectly attributed to Carel Fabritius: see C. Brown, *Carel Fabritius*, Oxford, 1981, cat. R10 ('shares Gerson's low estimate of the painting's quality and considers that the possibility of its being a later Rembrandt-esque pastiche cannot be ruled out').

15. Benesch, vol. 5, No. 964 (fig. 1246); formerly in the Koenigs collection. F. Lugt (op. cit., vol. 3, note to No. 1243) thinks it probably the work of a pupil.

16. Canvas, 83 × 67 cm. Illustrated in catalogue.

17. On panel. No dimensions given. Photograph in RKD.

18. Support and dimensions not known. Photograph in RKD.

19. Pen and wash, 22.2 × 23 cm. Inv. no. 1185 (as Rembrandt School). Discussed and illustrated by Sumowski, 'Kritische . . .', op. cit., p. 93 (note 18).

20. Pen and brown ink, 15.1 × 11 cm. Museum Boymans-van Beuningen, Inv. no. R59. J. Giltaij, *The Drawings by Rembrandt and his School in the Museum Boymans-van Beuningen*, Rotterdam 1988, No. 178 (as Anonymous pupil, *c.* 1640–5). Discussed by Sumowski, 'Kritische . . .', op. cit., p. 93 (note 20).

21. Haarlem, Gemeente Archief Hs No. 230, fol. 45b. Black chalk, 29.4 × 18.1 cm.

22. Nationalmuseum Inv. no. 1676/1875 (as Rem-

brandt School). Discussed by Sumowski, 'Kritische . . .', op. cit., p. 93 (note 19) and in *Drawings*, vol. 6, No. 1541X.

23. J. Young, *A Catalogue of the Celebrated Collection . . . of the late John Julius Angerstein . . .*, 1823, No. 12 (and in the National Gallery catalogue, 1824, No. 11).

24. J. Six (in OH, vol. 27, 1909, p. 81) says the picture was in Jan Six's collection and suggests he must have bought it after 1657 when it was [supposedly] among Johannes de Renialme's possessions. There are apparently no grounds for this statement beyond the fact that the picture was afterwards in Willem Six's collection. Willem Six had many paintings by or attributed to Rembrandt (see HdG Nos. 14, 40, 48, 84, 104, 128, 145, 164e, 233, 234, 522, 607, 627, 832, 925 and 968) yet of all these only one (No. 607) is known to have been previously owned by a member of the Six family and the rest were probably bought by Willem Six himself.

25. '291 Een schildery van 't vrouw in Overspel door Rembrandt van Rhyn'; the valuation, 1,500 guilders, is 600 more than for any other picture in the inventory (Bredius, *Künstler-Inventare*, vol. 1, p. 230).

26. Bredius in BM, vol. 21, 1912, p. 289; according to him it was valued at 2,000 guilders.

27. Houbraken, vol. 1, p. 261.

28. 'Het Vrouwtje in Overspel zig voor Christus vertoonende, door Rembrandt van Ryn, zynde het beste dat ooit van hem gezien is.' (See also Hoet, vol. 1, p. 411.)

29. In the marked copy of the Willem Six sale catalogue in the Six collection, Amsterdam, the purchaser is given as 'Heer Burgemeester Six'.

30. According to J. Six in OH, vol. 11, 1893 p. 155 (note). C. Vosmaer (*Rembrandt*, 1877, p. 536) suggests the National Gallery picture may be the 'Vrouw van Overspel beschuldigt' attributed to Rembrandt in the T. Hellinx (of Alkmaar) sale, Leiden, 6 April 1778 (lot 2, bought by Wubbels, 196 guilders) but this was on canvas and measured 49 × 37 *duim* (with rounded top).

31. According to HdG No. 104.

32. Smith No. 112.

33. See Farington, vol. 8, pp. 3068–9 (14 June 1807).

47 *The Adoration of the Shepherds* *Plate 281*

Signed in the bottom left corner: Rembrandt.f.1646.

Oil on canvas, 65.5 × 55 ($25\frac{3}{4}$ × $21\frac{5}{8}$).

PENTIMENTI: There are numerous *pentimenti*, of which the following are the more important: the Virgin's right elbow was at first lower, also St Joseph's right hand. The clasped hands of the nearer shepherd have been raised and a later outline of his back painted over part of the right arm of the man beside him. The head of the woman beside St Joseph was at first inclined slightly downwards; the woman next to her apparently originally had a red cap or hat (it shows through her forehead). The right hand of the man holding a lantern has been altered.

The ground has been identified as a rough-textured single layer of quartz (silica) combined with a quantity of brown ochre bound in linseed oil. This combination is found in several of the other canvas paintings by Rembrandt in the National Gallery, among them Nos. 221 and 6432 of this catalogue.[1]

The composition is loosely connected (but in the opposite direction) with that of a larger painting of the same subject in Munich (Fig. 73).[2] The Munich picture is also dated 1646 and was one of the last of a series of scenes from the life of Christ painted for the Stadholder, Frederik Hendrik Prince of Orange (died March 1647);[3] judging by the composition and the figures in the background it may have been begun somewhat earlier, like others of the series.[4] In any case comparison of the two compositions suggests that the National Gallery picture is the later.

A drawing formerly in the Henry Oppenheimer collection, London,[5] once thought to be a study for the present picture but certainly by a pupil or follower, may be a copy of a lost Rembrandt drawing showing a slightly earlier stage of the composition, yet seems more likely to be a variant based on the painting.

A similar old man with a lantern appears (inverted) in an *Adoration of the Shepherds* etched by Rembrandt some years later.[6]

There is a red chalk drawing by Nicolaes Maes in Rotterdam,[7] which appears to be a reminiscence of the central group in the National Gallery picture.[8]

DRAWINGS: A drawing formerly supposed to be a study for the picture is mentioned above. A drawing in the Rijksmuseum, Amsterdam, which seems to be loosely connected with the present composition, is probably the work of a follower.[9]

COPIES: A copy was formerly in the Metropolitan Museum, New York.[10] Other copies were in Anon. sale, Christie's, 30 July 1964, lot 51 (25 gns to Dent);[11] and in the André de Hevesy collection, Brussels, in 1954.[12] Another copy, in reverse, was in an Anon. sale, Christie's, 28 February 1964, lot 110 (£20 to Graham).[13]

ENGRAVING: Mezzotint (in reverse) by Samuel Bernard.[14]

PROVENANCE: In the Maréchal de Noailles sale, Paris [1767],[15] lot 53 (2,751 francs); Mme la Présidente de Bandeville sale, Paris, 3 sqq. December 1787 (lot 15),[16] bought by Remy (3,000 francs); Claude Tolozan sale, Paris, 23 sqq. February 1801 (lot 95), bought for an English purchaser (10,000 francs).[17] It was in the collection of John Julius Angerstein by June 1807.[18] Purchased with the Angerstein collection, 1824.

EXHIBITIONS: BI 1815, No. 41; Yokohama, Sogo Museum of Art; Fukuoka, Art Museum; Kyoto, National Museum of Modern Art, 'Bembrandt and the Bible', 1986–7, No. 6; London 1988–9, No. 10.

REFERENCES:
General: Smith No. 58; Bode and HdG, No. 316; HdG No. 77; Bauch No. 78; Bredius, *Rembrandt*, No. 575.
In text:
1. For a full technical description, see London 1988–9, pp. 92–5.

2. HdG No. 78; Bredius, *Rembrandt*, No. 574. Canvas, top corners rounded, 98 × 72 cm. Signed: . . . ndt f. 1646. Munich, Alte Pinakothek, 1983 cat., No. 393.
3. The five earlier pictures, scenes from the Passion, all in the Munich Gallery, were painted between

*c.*1633 and 1639 (Bredius, *Rembrandt*, Nos. 548, 550, 557, 560, 561; Strauss *Doc.* 1636/1, 1636/2 and 1639/2–1639/7). The Munich *Adoration*, together with a lost *Circumcision*, was paid for in November 1646 (Strauss *Doc.* 1646/6).

4. Rembrandt says in a letter of February 1636 that the *Entombment* and the *Resurrection* are 'more than half done' (Strauss *Doc.* 1636/1) but they were not finished until January 1639 (Strauss *Doc.* 1639/2) and the latter is dated in that year. (For a full discussion of the commission and annotated texts of the letters, see H. Gerson, *Seven Letters by Rembrandt*, The Hague, 1961.)

5. W. R. Valentiner, *Klassiker der Kunst: Rembrandt: Handzeichnungen*, vol. 1, [1925], No. 294 (not included in Benesch). From the J. P. Heseltine collection; H. Oppenheimer sale, London, 10 sqq. July 1936 (lot 296). A copy is in the Musée Bonnat, Bayonne (*Dessins de la collection Bonnat*, ii, 1895, No. 26); another similar drawing is known only from a mezzotint by Johann Elias Haid.

6. Hollstein No. 1336 as *c.*1652.

7. J. Giltaij, *The Drawings by Rembrandt and his School in the Museum Boymans-van Beuningen*, Rotterdam, 1988, No. 113; Sumowski, *Drawings*, 1765 (noting Schatborn's observation that it is the initial idea for a signed painting by Maes of 1653 or 1658 in Montreal). Sumowski also records a pen drawing (1957^X) by Maes which presupposes knowledge of No. 47.

8. Egbert Haverkamp-Begemann has informed the present writer of his opinion than No. 47 is a variant copy, by Nicolaes Maes, of the Munich painting. The present writer finds, however, very few stylistic analogies with Maes's work and has preferred to retain the atribution to Rembrandt.

9. Schatborn 1985, No. 62 (as the work of a follower, perhaps Carel Fabritius).

10. Panel, 63 × 53.5 cm. Metropolitan Museum catalogue 1922, No. R28S–1. Presented by Henry G. Marquand, 1888; Metropolitan Museum sale, New York, 7 June 1956 (lot 30).

11. Canvas, 25½ × 21½ in.

12. Canvas, 63 × 50.5 cm. Photo in RKD.

13. Panel, 14½ × 12½ in.

14. Charrington/Alexander, No. 29. Inscribed (within the subject): 'Bernard'. Subject size, *c.*36 × 30.5 cm. The catalogue of the Bandeville sale of 1787 (see PROVENANCE) says there is a mezzotint by Picart; no such print has been traced and it seems probable that the signature 'Bernard' on the mezzotint mentioned above has been taken for that of Bernard Picart.

15. The catalogue of this sale is undated but the year in which it took place is known from other sources, e.g. the Bandeville sale catalogue (see the following note).

16. As from the Maréchal de Noailles collection, 1767. See also note 14.

17. In the copy of the Tolozan sale catalogue in the Institut Doucet, Paris, there is a contemporary MS note to this lot: '10,000^f/pour l'angleterre'.

18. See Farington, vol. 8, p. 3069 (16 June 1807).

54 *A Woman bathing in a Stream (Hendrickje Stoffels?)*   Plate 282

Signed on the bank, bottom left: Rembrandt f 1654.[1]

Oil on oak, 61.8 × 47 (24$\frac{5}{16}$ × 18$\frac{1}{2}$).

Cleaned in 1946.

PENTIMENTI: There are *pentimenti* in the top of the head, the right shoulder and upper arm, and the drapery on the bank behind the woman.

The ground, like those of the other panel paintings by Rembrandt in the National Gallery, is chalk with a thin, warm brown *imprimatura* on the surface.[2]

The model for the bathing woman is probably Hendrickje Stoffels, the artist's mistress. For Hendrickje's biography and a full discussion of this identification, see under No. 6432 of this catalogue.

In July 1654, the year in which this picture was painted, Hendrickje was summoned before the Council of the Reformed Church in Amsterdam and admonished for living with Rembrandt 'like a whore' and was banned from 'celebration of the Lord's Supper'. Rembrandt and Hendrickje's only child, a daughter named Cornelia, was baptised on 30 October 1654. Hendrickje would have been about 28 when this picture was painted. It was the year in which she suffered public humiliation because of her liaison with Rembrandt and bore his child. It is possible that this work, showing the artist's mistress in the guise of an Old Testament heroine or a goddess, such as Susannah, Bathsheba or Diana, had an intensely personal significance.[3] The rich robe lying on the bank would support such an identification.

The picture displays a spontaneity and freedom in the handling of paint which have few parallels in Rembrandt's work (this can be seen on the surface and, even more strikingly, in the X-radiograph). It appears unfinished in some parts, but was clearly finished to Rembrandt's satisfaction as he signed and dated it. Its size and support might suggest that it was a sketch for a larger history painting, but no such painting is known and, unlike Rubens, Rembrandt did not usually make preliminary oil sketches for larger projects.

COPY: A small watercolour pastiche by Hercules Brabazon Brabazon (1821–1906) was in an Anon. sale, London, 15 May 1946 (lot 26).

PROVENANCE: Possibly in the Andrew Hay sale (of 'Pictures . . . collected abroad'), London, 4–5 May 1739 (1st day, lot 20),[4] (£6.19s.) almost certainly in the [Blackwood] sale, 18–19 March 1756 (1st day, lot 60),[5] bought by Raymond (£19.8s.6d.).[6] It was in the collection of Baron Gwydyr (possibly acquired after 1811);[7] Lord Gwydyr sale, London, 8–9 May 1829 (2nd day, lot 72), bought by the Revd William Holwell Carr (165 gns). Holwell Carr Bequest, 1831.

EXHIBITIONS: London 1947–8, No. 68; London 1988–9, No. 11.

REFERENCES:

General: Smith No. 165; Bode and HdG, vol. 5, No. 353; HdG No. 306; Bauch No. 27B; Bredius, *Rembrandt*, No. 437.

In text:

1. MacLaren incorrectly read the date as 1655.
2. For a full technical description, see London 1988–9, pp. 96–101.
3. In this respect it recalls *Het Pelsken* (Vienna, Kunsthistorisches Museum), Rubens's portrait of his young, second wife Helène Fourment in the guise of Titian's Venus. See also J. S. Held, 'Rembrandt and the Classical World' in *Rembrandt after Three Hundred Years: a Symposium*, Chicago, 1974, pp. 55–6.
4. 'Rembrandt. A Woman going into a Bath.'
5. 'Rembrandt A Woman going into the Water holding her Coats pretty high, and laughing at what she sees reflected.' 25 × 19 in. The identification was suggested by F. Simpson in BM, vol. 95, 1953, p. 40; the description quoted there (p. 42) was taken

from an eighteenth-century MS copy of the sale catalogue and is faulty. Mr Simpson has since identified the sale with that held on 18–19 March 1756, of which there exists a printed catalogue; the description given above is taken from this.
6. MacLaren suggested that it might have been lot 76 in the second day of the Pond sale, 1759: 'A woman going into a Bath Rembrandt' (Simpson, op. cit., p. 42) which was bought by Sir Joshua Reynolds. Francis Broun (*Sir Joshua's Rembrandts*, to be published shortly in the proceedings of the Reynolds symposium held at the RA in 1986) has, however, established that this lot was more probably a *Susanna at the Bath*, now in the Louvre (Smith No. 618; HdG Nos. 58 and 61b), which Pond had owned since 1739.
7. The picture is not in a MS list of paintings belonging to Baron Gwydyr at Grimsthorpe Castle, corrected up to 1 January 1812 (a copy of which is in the National Gallery library).

166 A Franciscan Friar

Plate 283

Signed, right, centre: Rembrandt. f. 165(?). Although worn and faint, the signature and first three figures of the date are legible by ultra-violet light.

Oil on canvas, 89 × 66.5 ($35\frac{1}{16}$ × $26\frac{3}{16}$).

Reduced slightly on the right side (where the present edge runs through the illegible last figure of the date).

Cleaned in 1952. Badly worn and cracked in the darks (especially the right background and face shadows) and in the beard.

PENTIMENTI: There are two noteworthy *pentimenti*: the left cuff has been painted over the back of the left hand; and the top of the cowl was at first a little higher, and the paint of the background has been continued over the outline.

This is a damaged and much-treated painting.[1] The canvas is marouflaged to a synthetic board but there is technical evidence that it was transferred to a new canvas. In the process, part of the original ground was removed. The paint surface has the typical appearance of a transferred picture: the fragile paint layers have shrunk and fallen into depressions caused by the transfer process. Cross-sections have revealed a bottom layer of gypsum, which is not a material found in the original grounds of Dutch seventeenth-century pictures. It must represent a layer of additional ground or adhesive applied to the back of the surviving part of the original ground during the transfer to a new canvas. It is likely that the original canvas had a double ground, with orange-red earth for the lower layer and a layer containing a large amount of lead white above it. During the transfer the lower orange ground would have been removed, but survives as vestiges here and there. The *impasto* of the face has been flattened by the radical nature of the transfer.

Rembrandt painted his son, Titus, in a Franciscan habit in 1660 (Amsterdam, Rijksmuseum);[2] a third portrait or study of a Franciscan, dated 1661, is in Helsinki.[3] It has been suggested that the Rijksmuseum picture shows Titus in the guise of St Francis[4] (who was the subject of an etching by Rembrandt in 1657);[5] it is at least no more improbable that the National Gallery painting represents that saint.

Despite the damage it has suffered, there is enough of the picture in good or reliable condition to sustain the traditional attribution to Rembrandt. Before the removal of thick brown varnish in 1952, the date was not visible and the style hard to judge; the picture was generally dated *c*.1661.[6] It is certain that the third figure of the date is 5 and the style seems to be that of *c*.1655 (cf. especially the handling of the habit).[7]

PROVENANCE: Possibly in the Richard Cosway, RA, sale, London, 17–19 May 1821 (2nd day, lot 93),[8] £63. Presented by the Duke of Northumberland, 1838.

EXHIBITION: London 1988–9, No. 12.

REFERENCES:
General: Bode and HdG, vol. 6, 1901, No. 484; HdG No. 191; Bauch No. 205; Bredius, *Rembrandt*, No. 308.

In text:
1. For a full technical description, see London 1988–9, pp. 102–5.

2. Rijksmuseum, 1976 cat.: A3138. Bredius, *Rembrandt*, No. 306.

3. Ateneum, Helsinki, 1962 cat., No. 1527. Bredius, *Rembrandt*, No. 307.

4. Rijksmuseum, 1976 cat., op. cit.

5. White and Boon, no. 107.

6. e.g. HdG (loc. cit.) and in the first edition of Bredius (1937).

7. In the third edition of Bredius, *Rembrandt*, Gerson accepts it as an authentic work of *c.* 1655/6.

8. '*Rembrandt* A Capuchin Friar'; this might, however, equally well be the Helsinki *Capuchin* (ex coll. Comte de Vence, Paris?; in the collection of the Earl of Wemyss by 1835) or, less likely, that in the Rijksmuseum (which was in the Stroganoff collection, St Petersburg, by 1807, when it was engraved in *Collection d'estampes d'après quelques tableaux de la galerie . . . Stroganoff*, 1807).

190 *A Bearded Man in a Cap* *Plate 284*

Signed, left, below the level of the shoulder: Rembrandt. f. 165( ); the last figure is covered by a *pentimento* of the outline of the right arm.

Oil on canvas, 78 × 66.7 (30¾ × 26¼).

Cleaned in 1957.

The canvas is heavily cusped at the left and right, with very little cusping at the top and bottom. This suggests that the canvas was stretched tightly from side to side while being primed, with little tension in the vertical direction. It may well be an example of a canvas cut from a primed length stretched between two long battens and loosely secured at top and bottom. The canvas has a double ground with an orange-red ochreous underlayer containing many coarse silica particles and an upper priming of lead white tinted with umber.[1]

The date has often been read as 1657, but the last figure is not legible. Its resemblance to a 7 is an effect due only to a brush mark in the overlying paint. The minute portion of the figure now visible could only be the extremity of the horizontal top stroke of a 3 or a 7; judging by the placing of the figures in the dates on Rembrandt's paintings of 1653 and 1657 it could be either. 1657 is more acceptable on stylistic grounds.[2]

As with many other studies of this kind by Rembrandt, the sitter has been described as 'A Jewish rabbi'. In the present case this title cannot be traced farther back than 1844[3] and in 1798 the picture was merely described as 'An old man's head'.[4] The man here may possibly be Jewish and is bearded; there is no other reason for supposing him a rabbi. (The old-fashioned type of cap he wears occurs in many of Rembrandt's pictures of gentiles, for example, in some of his self portraits of the 1650s.) The same man may have served as the model for other pictures by Rembrandt and his pupils, e.g. *Aristotle with a Bust of Homer* (dated 1653),[5] the so-called *Portrait of a Rabbi*, dated 1657, in San Francisco[6] and the study of a bearded man, dated 1661, in the Hermitage, Leningrad.[7]

COPIES: A copy by Thomas Gainsborough is at Hampton Court.[8] A copy(?) was in the collection of Alfred O. Kirby, London, in 1903.[9] A copy was in Anon. sale, Christie's, 17 February 1961, lot 50.[10]

ENGRAVING: Mezzotint by Thomas Watson (*c.*1743–81).[11]

PROVENANCE: In the collection of the Duke of Argyll before 1781;[12] Duke of Argyll sale, London, 25–26 May 1798 (lot 104).[13] It was in Jeremiah Harman's collection, Woodford by 1836;[14] Jeremiah Harman sale, London, 17–18 May 1844 (lot 23),[15] bought by Henry Farrer (410 gns) for the National Gallery.

EXHIBITIONS: Arts Council 1945, No. 27; London 1988–9, No. 14.

REFERENCES:
General: Smith Nos. 351 and 459; Bode and HdG, vol. 6, No. 469; HdG No. 392; Bredius, *Rembrandt*, No. 283.
In text:
1. For a full technical description, see London 1988–9, pp. 112–15.
2. O. Benesch, 'Worldly and Religious Portraits in Rembrandt's Late Art', *Art Quarterly*, vol. 19, 1956, p. 340, dates the painting to 1657.
3. In the catalogue of the Harman sale (see PROVENANCE and note 15).
4. In the catalogue of the Argyll sale, 1798; see note 13 below.
5. Metropolitan Museum, New York, 1980 cat., p. 149 (Inv. no. 61.198). HdG No. 413; Bredius, *Rembrandt*, No. 478.
6. California Palace of the Legion of Honor (Mildred Anna Williams collection). Bredius, *Rembrandt*, No. 259A (doubted by Gerson as an original).
7. HdG No. 441; Bredius, *Rembrandt*, No. 309.

8. O. Millar, *The Later Georgian Pictures in the Collection of Her Majesty the Queen*, London, 1969, No. 807 ('Perhaps painted *c*.1770').
9. Letter of 1903 from A. O. Kirby in the National Gallery archives.
10. Canvas, 75 × 62 cm. (bought in).
11. Inscribed: 'Rembrandt pinx^t T. Watson fecit. Done from an Original Picture Painted by Rembrant, in the Collection of the Duke of Argyle. Published as the Act directs for T. Watson Junr in Little Windmill Street Golden Square.' According to Smith (Rembrandt No. 459) there is an engraving by 'J. Watson' which corresponds to Thomas Watson's mezzotint except that the sitter wears a large hat instead of a cap; this print has not been traced (Charrington/Alexander, No. 184; see also No. 183).
12. It was engraved as in the Argyll collection by T. Watson who died in 1781 (cf. note 11).
13. As '*Rembrandt* An old man's head – *engraved*'.
14. Smith No. 351.
15. As from the Duke of Argyll's collection: 'Portrait of a Jewish Rabbi . . .'

221 *Self Portrait at the Age of Sixty-three*   *Plate 285*

Signed and dated, lower left: . . . . . . t: f/1669.

Oil on canvas, 86 × 70.5 ($33\frac{7}{8}$ × $27\frac{3}{4}$).

Cleaned in 1967. Worn in the background and in the sleeve. The fact that only the 't' of the signature remains makes it likely that a strip of about 3 cm. was cut from the left-hand side of the canvas. Cusping of the canvas threads, visible to some degree in the X-radiograph (Fig. 74), confirms this: the cusps at the right are more complete than those at the left.

PENTIMENTI: There are two major *pentimenti* visible in the X-radiograph.[1] First, the turban was originally much higher and fuller and hung down more at the right; it also appears that it was entirely white, like the turban Rembrandt wears in the Kenwood *Self Portrait*.[2] Later Rembrandt reduced it in height and width with broad strokes of background paint, and coloured the upper part brown. Secondly, the hands were originally painted open, and in the painter's right hand was a single brush or mahlstick.

The canvas is prepared with a single layer of brown ground, the main component of which has been identified as quartz (silica) tinted with a little brown-coloured ochre. It is very similar to the ground type in Rembrandt Nos. 6300 and 6432.

The paint layers vary enormously in texture and thickness. The face, turban and collar are painted with very heavy applications of lead white, whereas the remainder of the portrait, including the hands, is painted much more smoothly.

The date, 1669, the last year of Rembrandt's life, and traces of the signature were revealed when the painting was cleaned.[3] The background had been extensively over-painted. The Mauritshuis *Self Portrait*,[4] in which the artist again wears a turban, is also dated 1669.

COPIES: A reduced copy (nineteenth century?) was in the Viscountess Wakefield sale, London, 8 October 1943 (lot 67).[5] Another copy was in the possession of P. Smith, East Bergholt, in November 1960.[6] Another, probably nineteenth-century copy, inscribed: Gerretsz. van Rijn 1660, was in the collection of Mme M. de Rees, Cannes, in 1960.[7] A copy of the head was in the collection of E. M. H. Os in The Hague in 1941.[8]

PROVENANCE: In the collection of William van Huls in London; at his sale, London, 6 sqq. August 1722 (lot 22),[9] it was bought by Thomas Brodrick, MP.[10] At the latter's death in 1730 it passed with other pictures to his brother, Alan, 1st Viscount Midleton. In the Midleton collection at Peper Harow; 5th Viscount Midleton sale, London, 31 July 1851 (lot 78), 10 gns, bought for the National Gallery.

EXHIBITION: London 1988-9, No. 20.

REFERENCES:
General: Bode and HdG, vol. 6, No. 433; HdG No. 551; Bauch No. 339; Bredius, *Rembrandt*, No. 55.
In text:
1. For a full technical description, see London 1988-9, pp. 140-3.
2. Bredius, *Rembrandt*, No. 52.
3. G. Martin, 'A Rembrandt Self Portrait from his last year', BM, vol. 109, 1967, p. 355.
4. 1977 cat., No. 840. Bredius, *Rembrandt*, No. 62.

5. Canvas, 59 × 47 cm. It was in the collection of Sir Charles Wakefield by 1914 (label on back).
6. Photo in RKD.
7. Photo in RKD.
8. Panel. Dimensions not known. Photo in RKD.
9. '*Rembrandt* His own Picture.'
10. According to George Vertue, who saw it in 1722: 'at Mr Brodericks Membr parliament a fine head of Rhinbrants own picture bought at Mr Van huls Sale' (see *Walpole Society's* vol, 22, 1934, p. 9).

243 *An Elderly Man as St Paul*   Plate 286

In a roundel in the top right corner is Abraham's Sacrifice (in monochrome).

Signed, right, on the level of the head: Rembrandt/165(9?); the date is discussed below.

Oil on canvas, 102 × 85.5 (40⅛ × 33⅝). The picture may have been cut down a little on each side; the present left edge touches one of the figures in the roundel and on the other side the last letter of the signature is rather near the edge of the canvas and there is no room for the f which Rembrandt nearly always puts after his name on pictures.[1]

Cleaned in 1945-6. There is wearing in the roundel in the top right-hand corner and in the hands. A small damage above the sitter's left eye was repainted in 1972.

The only *pentimento* of any significance is in the collar, where originally more white material would have been visible. The painting has a double ground with a brown (rather than the usual reddish-orange) underlayer and a fairly thick upper layer of greyish brown. The head – and presumabiy the rest of the figure – was laid in with a brown sketch on this grey upper ground layer.[2]

The book and sword are the usual attributes of St Paul, symbolising the word of God and the saint's martyrdom, and are introduced in Rembrandt's other pictures of St Paul.[3] These attributes alone would be sufficient to identify the saint but there is additional evidence. In each of the top corners there is a framed roundel in monochrome (bas-relief?).[4] That on the right is so rubbed that it is impossible to be certain that it ever contained a design but the left-hand roundel is well preserved and represents the angel preventing Abraham from sacrificing Isaac (Fig. 75). Abraham's sacrifice often appears as a prototype of the Crucifixion; here, it is clearly a reference to the eleventh chapter of St Paul's Epistle to the Hebrews, which is a discourse on Faith as evinced by the Elders of the Old Testament:

> 1 Now faith is the substance of things hoped for, the evidence of things not seen.
>
> 2 For by it the elders obtained a good report.

There follow various examples, among them Abraham:

> 17 By faith Abraham, when he was tried, offered up Isaac, etc.[5]

MacLaren was not clear whether the picture was intended solely as a representation of St Paul or was a portrait of a man in the guise of the saint. The present writer, however, considers it unlikely to be a portrait.

The roundel is very summarily painted but is sufficiently clear to show that the composition is connected with Rembrandt's only etching of the same subject, dated 1655.[6] The poses of Abraham and Isaac are the same (the design is inverted in the print) except that in the roundel Abraham holds the knife at Isaac's throat instead of away from him and his head is turned in the opposite direction. On the other hand the angel, who is barely indicated, differs completely from that in the print; he is above and slightly to the left behind Abraham, and appears to be standing looking down at him. No other painting or drawing of the same design as the roundel is known.

The date is probably to be read as 1659. All that remains of the last figure of the date is 0 but there is a mark at the bottom of it to the right which is almost certainly the beginning of the down stroke of 9.[7] The style shows that the picture must be some years later than 1650 and agrees very well with dated works of the late 50s.

Gerson[8] has pointed to 'some obvious weak parts in the picture (the modelling of the hands, the unbalanced colour scheme), due either to heavy wear or to the fact that the picture is only an old copy'. As is mentioned above, there is wearing in the roundel in the top right-hand corner and in the hands. Haak,[9] by contrast, considers it the best of the group of half-length apostles and saints from the years c.1659/60.

Van Regteren Altena has suggested that the sitter is the poet Joost van den Vondel but his comparison with an engraved portrait by Cornelis Visscher is unconvincing.[10]

COPY: A reduced copy was in Sir John Atkins sale, London, 11 May 1955 (lot 34).[11]

PROVENANCE: In the collection of N. W. Ridley Colborne (later Lord Colborne) by 1815, when it was exhibited at the BI;[12] Lord Colborne Bequest, 1854.

EXHIBITIONS: BI 1815, No. 33;[12] BI 1832, No. 48;[13] BI 1843, No. 101;[14] BI 1851, No. 19;[15] London 1947–8, No. 70; London 1988–9, No. 15.

REFERENCES:

General: Smith No. 348; Bode and HdG, vol. 6, No. 460; HdG No. 291; Bauch No. 224; Bredius, *Rembrandt*, No. 297.

In text:

1. The rectangle with a roundel in the top right corner is about 3 cm. narrower than that on the left; it is conceivable, but not particularly likely, that originally they balanced exactly.

2. For a full technical description, see London 1988–9, pp. 116–19.

3. Other paintings of St Paul by Rembrandt with sword and book are in Stuttgart (Bredius, *Rembrandt*, No. 601), Nuremberg (Bredius, *Rembrandt*, No. 602), Vienna (Bredius, *Rembrandt*, No. 603), National Gallery of Art, Washington (Bredius, *Rembrandt*, No. 612).

4. They are painted in thin washes, with a few touches of black to strengthen the outlines. They are hardly visible in ordinary lighting.

5. Abraham's Sacrifice is mentioned as one of the subjects appropriate to accompany a figure of Faith in the Dutch version of Cesare Ripa's *Iconologia* by Dirck Pietersz. Pers (*Iconologia of Uijtbeeldinghe[n] des Verstants* etc., Amsterdam, 1644, p. 147): 'In 't verschiet wordt Abraham mede gestelt, alwaer hy sijnen Soone wilde offeren.'

6. White and Boon No. 35.

7. Smith (No. 348) read the date as 1658 but the existing o could hardly be the upper part of a seventeenth-century 8.

8. Gerson in Bredius, *Rembrandt*, No. 297. (But also see G. Martin in *Apollo*, vol. 90, 1969, p. 266, and K. Roberts in BM, vol. 114, 1972, p. 353.)

9. B. Haak, *Rembrandt: his Life, his Work, his Times*, London, 1969, p. 298.

10. J. Q. van Regteren Altena, 'Rembrandts Persönlichkeit' in O. v. Simson and J. Kelch, eds., *Neue Beiträge zur Rembrandt-Forschung*, Berlin, 1973, pp. 186–7.

11. Canvas, 71 × 63 cm. A photograph is in the National Gallery archives.

12. As 'Rembrandt Head of an old man'. The picture shown at the BI in 1815 and 1832 is identified by Smith (No. 348) with the present picture. (See the comments in Rembrandt No. 1675, note 8, and Follower of Rembrandt No. 51, note 8.)

13. As 'Rembrandt Man's Head' (cf. note 12).

14. and **15.** As 'Head of an old Man' (cf. note 12).

672 *Self Portrait at the Age of Thirty-four*   Plate 287

Signed, on the sill, bottom right: Rembrandt.f 1640 and inscribed below this: Conterfeycel.[1] The signature and date have almost certainly been repainted and the flourish between the t and f of the signature is a later addition. The word Conterfeycel seems to be by a different hand.

Oil on canvas, arched top, 102 × 80 (40⅛ × 31½). (Marouflaged on to synthetic board, 1974.)

Cleaned in 1965. It seems likely that the painting was originally rectangular. Subsequently the top corners were removed to give an arched shape; later, the painting was attached to a new rectangular canvas.[2] A strip 8–9 cm. deep along the bottom edge is also not original.

There is considerable wearing in the background above the sitter's head and some paint losses along the edges of the original canvas.

PENTIMENTI: Originally more of the shirt was visible at the bottom and the sitter's left hand also rested on the sill; three fingers of it are visible in a radiograph a little to the right of the right hand.

The painting has been transferred to another canvas.[3] Two observations confirm this: first, the paint surface has the sunken, wrinkled texture associated with a transferred painting which has subsequently been relined. Secondly, cross-sections show a highly unusual layer of black paint or adhesive between the lower level of the conventional double ground and the present canvas. The original canvas had a double ground of a lower layer of coarse red earth, with on top a thinner fawnish-grey priming of lead white, brown earth and a little charcoal; these layers survived the transfer. The technique is very smooth and meticulous. There is virtually no *impasto*: the effects are achieved with blended colour. Hairs at the back of the neck are suggested by scratching with a stylus or brush-end in the wet paint.

The painting is closely related to a self-portrait etching (Fig. 76) made by Rembrandt in the previous year, 1639.[4] In both the print and the painting there are reminiscences of Raphael's *Portrait of Baldassare Castiglione* (now in the Louvre) and Titian's *Portrait of a Man* (National Gallery No. 1944; see Fig. 77), who in the seventeenth century was identified as the poet Ariosto . Rembrandt certainly knew the *Castiglione*, of which he made a rough sketch[5] at or after the sale of Lucas van Uffelen's pictures in Amsterdam in April 1639, when it was bought by Alfonso Lopez. He could also have seen the 'Ariosto' in Amsterdam, since it (or a copy) was in Lopez's collection there at some time between 1637 and November 1641.[6]

Of the two, the Titian was the more important model. In both the Titian and No. 672 the body is facing to the right; the angle of the head and body is very similar; and the two painters make great play with the representation of the sleeve's rich material. De Jongh[7] has argued that Rembrandt is here self-consciously emulating Titian's portrait and that by showing himself in the guise of the Italian poet he is contrasting his own art of painting with Ariosto's art of poetry and so taking part in the *paragone* debate.

The pose of the sitter and the half-length composition were adopted by a number of Rembrandt's pupils. Bol made a drawn copy of No. 672[8] and used the composition for a *Portrait of a Man* painted shortly after 1640[9] and for a number of what appear to be self portraits: the earliest, in Dordrecht, is dated 1646.[10] The pose was also used by Govert Flinck in a *Portrait of a Man* of 1643;[11] by Gerbrand van den Eeckhout in a *Portrait of a Man*;[12] and by Aert de Gelder in a *Portrait of a Young Man*.[13]

COPY: A copy in reverse was in Anon. sale, Sotheby's, 23 July 1975, lot 130 (£240) (on the reverse it has a label: 'after L. M. BERWICK', presumably the name of a nineteenth-century English engraver who copied the painting).[14] In the RKD there is a photograph of a mezzotint of a copy of the painting inscribed: F. Bol pinx. [sic] Wrenk Sculps.

PROVENANCE: In the collection of General Dupont, Paris; exhibited at the Exposition de la Société des Amis de l'Enfance, Paris, 1861, lent by General Dupont's heirs, Comte de Richemont, Vicomte de Richemont and Baron de Richemont, from whom purchased in September 1861.

EXHIBITIONS: Paris, Exposition de la Société des Amis de l'Enfance, 1861, No. 119; London, National Gallery, 'Second Sight: Titian and Rembrandt', 1980; London 1988-9, No. 8.

REFERENCES:
General: Bode and HdG, vol. 4, No. 256; HdG No. 550; Bauch No. 316; Bredius, *Rembrandt*, No. 34.
In text:
1. Until the 1690s the word *conterfeycel* (more properly, *conterfeytsel*) was the usual Dutch term for portrait. At the end of the century *pourtrait* (*pourtret* etc.) begins to appear but *conterfeytsel* was still frequently used until about 1720, though rarely seen later (see Bredius, *Künstler-Inventare*, and Hoet, *passim*).
2. The painting seems to have been cut to fit an arched top after painting and approximately 1 cm. of the paint surface has been turned over the arched top stretcher and tacked, the tack holes being visible. From the cracks in the paint along the fold lines of the section of turned-over canvas, it seems most likely that it was put on the arched-top stretcher

after the paint had thoroughly dried out and was of some age. The edges all round are quite roughly and crudely cut. It seems reasonable to assume that it was cut down from an originally rectangular shape.

Subsequently the painting was taken off the arched-top stretcher, the tacking margins flattened out and stuck down on a rectangular canvas which supplied the spandrels in the top corners and was also large enough to leave a narrow margin of exposed lining canvas down the side edges and a much wider band, about 8-9 cm. deep, along the bottom edge. The spandrels and the edges were then painted to match, some of this paint encroaching on the original. Both of these operations must have taken place prior to the acquisition of the painting by the National Gallery in 1861. Since then the entire canvas (including the additions) has been relined and in 1974 marouflaged on to a sundeala support in order to flatten the wrinkled canvas.

3. For a full technical description, see London 1988–9, pp. 80–5.

4. White and Boon No. 21.

5. In the Albertina, Vienna (Benesch, vol. 2, No. 451 and fig. 538). Inscribed in Rembrandt's hand: (left) 'de Conte/batasar de/kastijlyone/van raefael' [sic]; (right) 'verkoft/voor 3500 gulden'; (below) 'het geheel Caergesoen tot Luke van Nuffeelen/heeft gegolden F59456:–:Ano 1639'. Lopez is named as the purchaser by Sandrart, *Teutsche Academie*, p. 417 (note 1358). Judging by the relation of the inscriptions to the sketch, they were made at the same time as the latter; if so, the drawing is more likely to have been made shortly after the sale.

6. There is a drawing after Titian's composition by Joachim von Sandrart (Paris, Institut Néerlandais; signed, and inscribed on the reverse: ' t' Portrait van Ariotti'); the engraving after this, by Reynier van Persijn (c.1615–68), is inscribed: 'Ioachimus Sandrart del: et excud. Amsterd: E Titiani Prototypo in oedibus Alph: Lopez.' Sandrart was in Amsterdam from 1637 until after April 1642; Lopez's 'Ariosto' was in Paris by November 1641 (E. W. Moes in OH, vol. 12, 1894, pp. 238–40). It cannot be established for certain that Lopez's 'Ariosto' was the National Gallery picture but, even if not, Sandrart's drawing shows that it was of exactly the same design. (Sandrart apparently also painted a copy of the 'Ariosto'. Lot 154 of the Willem Six sale, Amsterdam, 12 May 1734, was 'Het Pourtrait van L. Ariosto, door Sandrart, na Titiaan'; see Hoet, vol. 1, p. 418.)

7. E. de Jongh, 'The Spur of Wit: Rembrandt's Response to an Italian Challenge', *Delta*, Summer 1969, pp. 49–67; on this subject see also, A. Blankert, 'Rembrandt, Zeuxis and ideal Beauty', *Album Amicorum J. G. van Gelder*, The Hague, 1973, pp. 32–9; C. Brown, *Second Sight; Titian and Rembrandt*, National Gallery, London, 1980.

8. Sumowski, *Drawings*, I, No. 142[X]. Brush and grey ink; black and red chalk. 178 × 128 mm. Washington, National Gallery of Art (B–3984, Rosenwald collection).

9. Munich, Alte Pinakothek, 1983 cat., No. 609. Canvas, 87.5 × 72.5 cm. (the female pendant is No. 610 in the catalogue). A. Blankert, *Ferdinand Bol*, Doornspijk, 1982, cat. no. 143, p. 144ff.

10. Blankert, op. cit., cat. no. 60 (dated 1646; Dordrechts Museum, Dordrecht); cat. no. 61 (dated 1647; with Knoedler, New York, 1924); cat. no. 62 (Anon. sale, Sotheby/Parke Bernet, New York, 4 June 1980, no. 50); cat. no. 63 (dated 164(8)); Los Angeles County Museum of Art, Inv. no. 55.28. Also influenced by No. 672 but less close in composition is the 'self-portrait' type of which the best example is in the Springfield Art Institute, Springfield, Mass. (Inv. no. 42.02; Blankert, op. cit., cat. no. 14).

11. Panel, top corners rounded, 71 × 52 cm. Signed and dated on the left: G. Flinck f. 1643. Sir Berkeley Sheffield et al. sale, Christie's, 16 July 1943, lot 106. J. W. von Moltke, *Govaert Flinck 1615–1660*, Amsterdam, 1965, cat. no. 434 (with its pendant, no. 435). The late Sir Charles Clore's Charitable Personal Settlement sale, Sotheby's, 11 December 1985, lot 62 (£154,000). With Colnaghi, London, 1986.

12. See *Rembrandt after Three Hundred Years*, Chicago, No. 49.

13. Krantz collection, Aachen. Canvas. Dimensions not known – see Blankert in *Album Amicorum J. G. van Gelder*, op. cit., p. 38, note 18.

14. Canvas, 98 × 80 cm.

775 *Portrait of an Eighty-three-year-old Woman*   Plate 288

Inscribed on the left, centre: Æ·S ⅤϾ ·83; signed, right, centre: Rembrandt·f / 1634.

Oil on oak, oval, 68.7 × 53.8 ($27\frac{1}{16}$ × $21\frac{3}{16}$). The panel has been enlarged by later additions to 71.1 × 55.9 (28 × 22): these additions form a hollow oval about 2 cm. wide all round, attached by glueing edge-to-edge and reinforced by wooden blocks at the top and bottom. The original part of the panel is probably much the same size and shape as when it was painted, but it is possible that it was trimmed and bevelled slightly when the additions were fitted; since the edges are hidden by the additions, it is difficult to be sure. Although one of the old copies of the picture is rectangular, there is no evidence that this panel was made into an oval after it was painted and there are many Rembrandt portraits of this shape at this period.[1]

Cleaned in 1956.

The ground is of the standard type for a panel painting of this period, consisting of a layer of natural chalk bound in animal glue and finished with a lightly applied *imprimatura* containing a little lead white, yellowish-orange and brown earth pigments and a trace of black. The ground and *imprimatura* are very thin and the colour, a warm beige, is clearly influenced by the colour and grain of the wood beneath. This uncovered preparation is visible in several places, notably in a small rectangle between the ruff and the woman's right cheek and at the junction of ruff, head-dress and background. The underlying wood grain can be seen in the shadowed side of the face. As with other early panel paintings by Rembrandt (for example, No. 850 below) it is comparatively thinly painted. The blacks and darks are thinly and translucently painted, whereas the whites and lights are more thickly painted, often with a heavy impasto.[2]

PENTIMENTI: There are *pentimenti* in the upper outline of the cap and in the lower contour of the right cheek.

On a drawing by Jan Stolker (1724–85) in the British Museum (Fig. 78), ultimately derived from the present portrait, the sitter is identified as Françoise van Wassenhove (*not* Wassenhoven, as sometimes stated), the widow of Eduard Poppius (1576/7–1624), a Remonstrant preacher.[3] In this drawing, in place of the age inscription on the National Gallery picture, is: 'Ætatis 72./1647'. According to an inscription by Stolker on the back of the drawing, he made his copy after a drawing by Hendrik van Limborch (1681–1759) said to have been copied from the original. The erroneous date and the identification may, therefore, be due to van Limborch, or may go back to some old painted copy which he took to be original. (It should be noted that in the Stolker drawing mentioned above, as well as in the fanciful drawing mentioned under COPIES, the field of composition does not extend so far below as in the National Gallery painting.) Stolker omitted both inscription and identification from his mezzotint of the same portrait (see ENGRAVINGS) to which he gave only the title 'Avia', literally 'grandmother' but here presumably intended to signify merely 'an old woman'. (It is worth noting, however, that Waagen[4] described the painting as 'Portrait of his grandmother'.) The mezzotint (unlike the drawing) shows the portrait in a rectangular format. One impression of this engraving, in the Berlin printroom, has been inscribed later 'Juffrouw Roos'; this identification was perhaps prompted by the fact that the original belonged at one time to the Amsterdam dealer, C. S. Roos (see PROVENANCE).

ENGRAVINGS: Mezzotint (in reverse; rectangular) by Jan Stolker (1724–85);[5] line-engraving by Johannes Pieter de Frey, 1801(?);[6] mezzotint by Charles Howard Hodges, 1814.[7]

COPIES: A copy (oval) is in the Marquess of Linlithgow's collection at Hopetoun House;[8] another (also oval) was in the possession of Edward T. Noonan, Chicago, in 1890.[9] A copy thought to be by Thomas Gainsborough was in existence in 1905.[10] A rectangular copy, from the collection of Dr Staehelm-Herzog, Basle, was in the M.C. B--- sale, Brussels, 10 December 1928 (lot 57).[11] A sepia drawing by Jan Stolker in the British Museum is discussed above; the portrait also appears, in irregular octagonal form, in the background of a fanciful drawing by Stolker of Rembrandt in his studio (British Museum).[12]

PROVENANCE: Most probably in the Klaas van Winkel et al. sale, Rotterdam, 20–21 October 1791 (lot 6).[13] In the possession of the dealer, C. S. Roos, Amsterdam, in 1814.[14] Chevalier Sébastien Erard sale, Paris, 7 sqq. August 1832 (lot 121), bought in (4,000 francs); S. Erard sale, London, 22 June 1833 (lot 16),[15] bought in (210 gns). It was in the collection of William Wells, Redleaf, by 1835, when it was exhibited at the BI; William Wells sale, London, 12–13 May 1848 (lot 115),[16] bought by (Sir) Charles Eastlake (£252). Purchased from Sir Charles Eastlake's widow, 1867.

EXHIBITIONS: BI 1835, No. 50;[17] London 1988–9, No. 3.

REFERENCES:

General: Smith Nos. 490 and 590; Bode and HdG, vol. 2, No. 106; HdG No. 856; Bauch No. 476; Bredius, *Rembrandt*, No. 343; *Rembrandt Corpus*, vol. 2, A104.

In text:

1. See for example, *Rembrandt Corpus*, vol. 2, Nos. A50, A58, A59, A60, A62, A63, A71, A72, A82, A83, A84, A86, A87.

2. For a full technical description, see London 1988–9, pp. 48–51.

3. Hind, vol. 4, p. 173, No. 3. Oval. Inscribed left of the head: 'Ætatis 72./1647'; below the portrait: 'Francoise van Wassenhoven. [sic]'; underneath the drawing: 'Rembrandt Pinxt: 1647. J: Stolker Del.' The reverse is inscribed by Stolker: 'Franchoise van Wassenhoven, Huysvrouw van Eduardus Poppius. Naar Een tekening die de Heer Hendrik van Limburg naar 't origineel Schildery getekent hadt, gevolt door I: Stolker. dit Zelve portrait is door my in Zwarte Kunst gbragt.' (The drawing was in the Ellinckhuysen sale, Amsterdam, 19–20 November 1878, lot 241.)

4. Waagen, 1854, vol. 3, p. 311.

5. Charrington/Alexander No. 165. Engraved inscription in state II: 'Rembt Pinx. J: Stolker, Fec. & Excud: Avia S:Cruys, Excud:'

6. The writer has not seen an impression of this engraving. It is presumably the print listed as 'Rem-

brandt's mother, 1801' by G. K. Nagler (*Neues allgemeines Künstler-Lexicon*, vol. 4, 1837, p. 489) and C. Le Blanc (*Manuel de l'amateur d'estampes*, 1854–88, vol. 2, p. 254, No. 18).

7. Charrington/Alexander No. 77. Engraved inscription below: 'C. H. Hodges. fecit. Het Origineele Schildery is berustende in de Versameling van de Heer C. S. Roos te Amsterdam . . . 1814.'

8. Reproduced in *Hopetoun House* (Pilgrim Press), (1955?), p. 23. It is dated 1636 according to Waagen (op. cit., note 2).

9. Letter and photograph of 1890 in the National Gallery archives.

10. Mentioned in BM, vol. 11, 1907, p. 99, where it is attributed to Gainsborough.

11. 65 × 49 cm. Reproduced in the sale catalogue, pls. 23 and 24.

12. Hind, p. 173, No. 1.

13. 'Rembrand. Een oude Dames Portrait hebbende een witte Kraag om den hals en een witte Muts op het hoofd, in 't zwaart gekleed op een ligte agtergrond, op paneel ovaal, hoog 29 en breed 24 duim, 1634.'

14. According to the title of Hodges' mezzotint (see note 7).

15. 16. and **17.** As 'Rembrandt's mother'.

850 *Portrait of Philips Lucasz.*

Plate 289

Signed on the right, towards the bottom: Rembrandt/1635.[1]

Oil on oak, 79.5 × 58.9 ($31\frac{5}{16}$ × $23\frac{3}{16}$). The panel was reduced in size after the picture was painted (see below).

Cleaned in 1941–2 and in 1977.

The ground is the usual one for Rembrandt's panels, consisting of a chalk underlayer with a thin, warm brown *imprimatura* containing umber. This can be seen at a number of places in the hair and around the eyes. As in No. 775 of this catalogue, the darks are thinly painted and the wood grain visible in some parts of the background while the lights (especially the highlights on the forehead, nose and cheekbone) have a thick rough impasto.

At first sight No. 850 seems to be one of Rembrandt's oval portraits of the early Amsterdam period, similar to No. 775 of this catalogue. But the oak panel has straight bevelling on the back, widest at the bottom, narrow at the sides and absent altogether at the top. This indicates that it has been cut down from a rectangle and has lost most at the top, some at the sides and least at the bottom, assuming equal original bevelling on all four sides. There are other indications that it has been cut down. For example, the brushstrokes of the background and coat continue fully up to the edge, whereas normally they would diminish as they reached the true edge of the panel. Also, the paint at the edge of the present panel has flaked and crumbled, as if fractured by the act of cutting. It is more difficult to establish when the alteration from rectangle to oval was made. Scraps of paper stuck to the back of the panel appear to be late seventeenth or early eighteenth century in date and follow the oval shape. The X-radiograph (Fig. 79) reveals the presence of the sitter's left hand, touching the gold chain across his chest. The position of the hand does not fit well with the present oval format and the present edge cuts through the light-coloured cuff at the wrist. We may assume, therefore, that it was in place when the portrait was rectangular. It is likely that it was planned at an early stage in the composition since a cross-section shows a thin sketching layer in bone black beneath the brownish-yellow paint of the flesh. When the portrait was cleaned in 1941 and again in 1977, it was noted that the paint covering the hand was not original and it was totally removed in 1977 to reveal the hand. The hand was clumsy and shapeless and much yellower in tone than the paint of the face. The highlights on the fingernails were present and there is a ring on the little finger which suggests that the hand was more or less finished. The formlessness can be explained either by a lack of final modelling or by the loss of the upper layers as a result of scraping. It seems probable that the painting-out of the hand coincided with the reduction of the panel to an oval. The paint must have been hard and brittle when the panel was cut and so this was probably not done in the 1630s and therefore it is unlikely to have been done by Rembrandt himself. After the 1977 cleaning the appearance of the hand was considered unsatisfactory and it was painted over again.[2]

Recently it has been claimed that the lace collar, chain, bust and hand are the work of an assistant, who also painted the companion portrait of Lucasz.'s wife, Petronella Buys.[3] The present writer (with David Bomford and Ashok Roy) has argued against this view elsewhere.[4] In the view of the present writer both No. 850 and its companion portrait are by Rembrandt and any routine passages can be adequately explained by the hectic pace of Rembrandt's portrait painting activity at this period of his career.

Philip or Philips Lucasz. (Lucasse) of Middelburg was born at the end of the sixteenth century. In 1625 he became *Opperkoopman* and *Secunde* on the island of Amboina and from 1628 to 1631 he was governor. In 1631 he was appointed Councillor Extraordinary of the Dutch East Indies. He was in charge of the trading fleet of the Dutch East India Company which sailed for Holland in December 1633; he left Holland again on 2 May 1635 and by 20 September of that year was back in Batavia as director-general of trade. He was given command of a naval expedition to Ceylon in September 1640 and died at sea on board the fluteship *Santvoort* on 5 March 1641. He married Petronella Buys of The Hague (born *c.*1605) in the Netherlands on 4 August 1634; she returned with him to Batavia and their daughter Françoise was baptised there on 30 September

1635.[5] She returned in 1641 to Holland when she lived on the Keizersgracht in Amsterdam;[6] she remarried in Vlissingen in 1646 and died in that town in 1670.[7]

The portrait of Petronella Buys, dated 1635 (Fig. 80),[8] was identified by Hofstede de Groot by means of an inscription on its back; the form of the inscription implies that there was a companion portrait of her first husband, Philips Lucasz.[9] He pointed out that the present portrait has the same shape, size, support and date, and suggested that it is the companion portrait in question;[10] the pictures certainly correspond in composition and style and no other surviving man's portrait by Rembrandt fills the requirements so well.[11] De Groot believed that the heavy gold chain of four (or five?) strands in the National Gallery picture provides further evidence in favour of identification with Philips Lucasz.; gold chains, not a common item of men's dress, were often given as a reward for service, among others by the directors of the East India Company to commanders who brought their merchant fleets home successfully, as Lucasz. had done in 1634.[12]

The fact that portraits of Lucasz. and his wife are recorded in the collection of Jacques Specx (see below under PROVENANCE), the husband of Maria Odilia Buys, Petronella's sister, makes it most likely (as Miss van Eeghen suggested[13]) that they were intended as a present to Specx and his wife before Lucasz. and his wife set sail. The portrait must have been painted before Lucasz.'s departure for the Indies.

PROVENANCE: (Pasted round the edges of the back of the panel are fragments of a printed list of French naval appointments, the earliest of which is 1641, the latest 1673.)[14] Rembrandt portraits of P. Lucasz. and his wife, of 1635, apparently belonged to the latter's brother-in-law, Jacques Specx, and were inherited by his daughter, Maria Specx, in 1655.[15] It was in the collection of Sir Robert Peel, Bart., by 1836;[16] purchased with the Peel collection, 1871.

EXHIBITIONS: London 1947–8, No. 65; London 1988–9, No. 4.

REFERENCES:
General: Smith No. 488; Bode and HdG, vol. 2, No. 116; HdG No. 660; Bauch No. 376; Bredius, *Rembrandt*, No. 202. *Rembrandt Corpus*, vol. 3, No. A115.

In text:
1. The signature is on a somewhat worn shadow of the curtain but is not itself worn; it is clearly genuine and not retouched. The name may originally have been followed by an f (as in the signature of the presumed companion portrait of Petronella Buys – see note 8) which may have been cut off when the panel was reduced in size, but there is a quarter of an inch between the final letter of Rembrandt and the edge of the panel. Gerson (in Bredius, *Rembrandt*, op. cit.) prefers to read the date as 1633. The companion portrait of Petronella Buys is clearly dated 1635 and Gerson suggests that the painting out of the hand in No. 850 and the reduction to an oval format could have been done in order to make a pair with the *Petronella Buys*, which may have been commissioned a little later. In fact the last digit of the date on No. 850 is certainly a 5. The portrait of Petronella Buys was presumably made into an oval at the same

time as No. 850 (although this is speculative – the present writer has been unable to examine the back of the *Petronella Buys*).
2. For a full technical description of No. 850, see London 1988–9, pp. 52–7.
3. This claim was made by J. Bruyn in a lecture delivered in a symposium on Rembrandt held at the National Gallery, London, in January 1988. Subsequently this view was adopted in the *Rembrandt Corpus*, op. cit. The third volume of the *Corpus* appeared when this catalogue was in its final proof stage and so it was impossible to consider the detailed arguments at length here. They are not, however, significantly different from those expressed by Bruyn in his 1988 lecture.
4. London 1988–9, pp. 56–7.
5. The correct date of the marriage and of the baptism were discovered by Dr M. E. van Opstall of the Algemeen Rijksarchief in The Hague. The present writer is grateful to Mr J. V. Earle of the Victoria and Albert Museum for this information (see his article, 'Genji meets Yang Guifei: a Group of Japanese Export Laquers', *Transactions of the Oriental*

Ceramic Society, 1982–3, pp. 45–75, esp. p. 67 and notes 50, 51).

6. See W. P. Coolhaas, *Het Huis 'De Dubele Arend'*, Amsterdam, 1973, pp. 29–62 (Jacques Specx), pp. 62–3 (Petronella Buys).

7. The biographical details are taken from François Valentijn, *Oud en nieuw Oost-Indiën*, 1724–6 (see S. Keijser's edition, especially vol. 1, 1855, pp. 127, 128, 131, 425, and vol. 2, 1856, pp. 446, 450, 467, 470); see also HdG in OH, vol. 31, 1913, pp. 238, 239, Miss I. H. van Eeghen in *Amstelodamum*, vol. 43, 1956, p. 116; and Earle, op. cit. (note 5).

8. Oval panel, 76 × 58 cm. Signed: Rembrandt f./ 1635. Bredius, *Rembrandt*, No. 349. *Rembrandt Corpus*, vol. 3, No. CIII. André Meyer sale, Sotheby Parke Bernet, New York, 22 October 1980, lot 12 ($900,000). Wildenstein and Co., New York (1985).

9. The inscription which is now covered was read by HdG as: 'Jonckvr. petronella Buijs: sijne Huijvsvr(n?)aer dato getrout aen de H^r Borgerm^r Cardon' (facsimile in OH, vol. 31, 1913, p. 236). Petronella Buys married Jean Cardon (Jan Cardauw) in 1646 (OH, 1913, p. 238).

10. OH, 1913, pp. 237 ff.

11. Although HdG (OH, 1913, p. 237) says there are no traces of an inscription on the back of the National Gallery portrait, there are in fact the remains of letters written in ink(?) on the panel; they are, however, not legible even by means of infra-red photography.

12. OH, 1913, pp. 239–40. In Pieter van Dam's *Beschrijvinge van de Oostindische Compagnie* (book 1, vol. 2, p. 314: ed. F.W. Stapel) it is said that Philips Lucasz. received on 31 January 1635 '1000 rijcxdaelders voor zijn goede diensten'. It is not expressly stated that this was for a gold chain or in the form of a gold chain. The present writer is grateful for this reference to Professor W. P. Coolhaas.

13. In *Amstelodamum*, op. cit.

14. Some of these fragments were removed in 1945 and are now preserved in the National Gallery archives.

15. See van Eeghen, loc. cit. Specx was an important early patron of Rembrandt. Also in his inventory of 1655, in which the portraits of Lucasz. and his wife are listed, was *St Peter in Prison* of 1631 (Bredius, *Rembrandt*, No. 607); *The Abduction of Europa* (Bredius, *Rembrandt*, No. 464) and a 'St Peter's Boat' which may be *Christ on the Sea of Galilee* of 1633 (Bredius, *Rembrandt*, No. 547). It is, therefore, quite possible that the portraits of Lucasz. and his wife were commissioned by Specx rather than by Lucasz. himself.

16. Smith No. 488.

1400 *Ecce Homo* *Plate 290*

Grisaille in tones of brown, grey, yellow and white.

Christ stands in the centre of a group of soldiers; below him is Pilate, expostulating with the Jews. The prominent rod of justice has not been torn from his hand but is being pressed upon him by the high priests, who are urging him to sentence Christ to death. In the right background is a herm with the head of a Roman emperor. The hours on the clock in the right background are Roman numerals with VI at the top and I at the bottom; the single hand is approaching six o'clock.[1] The edge of the head-dress of the high priest at the front (who firmly clutches the rod) bears in Hebrew letters the name of God = י ה ו ה (JHWH) followed by א ל = (AL or EL, possibly the beginning of the word Elohim, or 'God').[2]

Signed beneath the clock in the right background: Rembrandt. f./1634 (see below).

Oil on paper (stuck on canvas), 54.5 × 44.5 ($21\frac{7}{16}$ × $17\frac{1}{2}$). There is a thin black line painted along each of the edges except the right.

Cleaned in 1983–4.

There is some wrinkling and a little tearing of the paper, which presumably occurred when it was laid down on to canvas. There is also extensive foxing of the paper – black spots of mould growth on the adhesive used for mounting it – but these were reduced by retouching during the recent cleaning. Cross-sections suggest that a very thin layer of some preparation of the paper is present (perhaps, like No. 43 of this catalogue, made of chalk and glue).

The first stage of working was an ink drawing of the principal elements of the composition. This was followed by a much broader lay-in with a brush using dark earth colours with a little black. Some parts of the picture were not developed beyond this 'dead-colour' stage, as can be seen clearly in the figures to the right of Christ, in the curtains and the architecture at the upper left, and in the steps at the lower left. It is not clear whether Rembrandt ever intended to work up these areas or whether they were intended as a rough guide for the related etching (see below): they are worked up in the etching but correspond almost exactly in position. The main figure group and the architecture at the right were then worked up in tones of grey and brown, lead white and lead-tin yellow, into a highly finished state over the lay-in. Finally, as Royalton-Kisch first noted,[3] the painting was traced or incised directly for the transfer of the design on to the etching plate. The incised lines follow figure outlines, architecture, draperies and minute details such as Christ's hair and hands and hatched shadows on his body. In the detailed areas almost every feature is incised – individual locks of hair, fingers and folds of drapery – but in the sketched areas only broad outlines are incised.[4]

The subject is known as *Ecce Homo* from Pilate's words in John 19: 5. The events are described later in the chapter (verses 13–16): Pilate shows Christ to the people, who, urged on by their priests, demand his condemnation.

This is the preparatory study for an etching by Rembrandt, the first (unfinished) state of which is dated 1635, and the second and subsequent states 1636 (Fig. 81).[5] The print, which is inverted, is of the same size and varies slightly from the grisaille; the principal differences are that the crowd on the right here and the figures above on Christ's left have been elaborated in the etching, as have many of the accessories, and the clock is only summarily indicated. It is one of the Rembrandt prints that had most popular success; in the eighteenth century it was apparently known as 'The Thirty Guilder Print'.[6]

This is the only known case in which Rembrandt produced such an elaborate full-scale study for an etching. That it was used for this purpose can be seen when the painting is studied in a raking light as many of its outlines have been indented with a stylus to transfer the design to the plate. (There are places, such as the base of the column where the outlines of the stone blocks are disregarded and the stylus hatches over the design.) It has been argued, most recently by Royalton-Kisch,[7] that the etching is a collaboration between Rembrandt and another artist; Royalton-Kisch identifies Rembrandt's collaborator as Jan van Vliet, who etched eleven plates after designs by Rembrandt in the 1630s. This might well explain the need for such a detailed grisaille: it would have been given by Rembrandt to Van Vliet as a guide for his reproductive print. The print of *The Descent from the Cross*,[8] which is dated 1633 and for which the original painting (now in the Alte Pinakothek, Munich)[9] was available, is of the same size as the *Ecce Homo*. It too contains substantial passages by another hand, perhaps that of Jan van Vliet. The production of these two prints, among the largest and most ambitious ever undertaken by Rembrandt, was a deliberate emulation of the reproductive engravings made after Rubens' work by engravers who were closely supervised by the painter. Although the two prints were eagerly collected during Rembrandt's lifetime and later – they were considered a pair in the eighteenth century – Rembrandt abandoned this procedure, presumably unhappy with the quality of Van Vliet's work. This would explain why the *Ecce Homo* is the only grisaille which is an elaborate full-scale study for a print.

Münz[10] has suggested that the composition may be based in part on an engraving of 1581 after Maerten de Vos by J. Sadeler. In fact, the composition is of a traditional northern type which can be found in manuscript illumination as early as the last quarter of the fifteenth century. A late example of this tradition, which Rembrandt may have used as his starting-point, is an engraving by Callot after Stradanus.[11]

COPIES: There are a large number of copies of this composition, all of them after the etching (this list is not intended to be exhaustive): (i) in the church in Hela, West Prussia, dated 1647;[12] (ii) in the town hall in Reval, Estonia; by J. van Aken, dated 1667;[13] (iii) in the Kunsthalle, Karlsruhe;[14] (iv) in the Kunsthalle, Kiel;[15] (v) in the collection van der Feltz, Brummen;[16] (vi) in the collection Armand von Ernst-von Stürler, Berne, 1932;[17] (vii) in the collection Prince U. van Schönburg, Guteborn bei Ruhland (Lausitz), 1934;[18] (viii) with the dealer L. Dimon, Montpellier, 1934;[19] (ix) in the collection P. H. Zonneveld, Amsterdam, 1947;[20] (x) Anon. sale, Christie's, 2 July 1954 (lot 41) (20 gns to Engel);[21] (xi) Anon. sale, Christie's, 24 October 1958 (lot 24) (35 gns to van der Kar);[22] (xii) Anon. sale, Christie's, 10 June 1960 (lot 124), as Dietricy (30 gns to Hawthorne);[23] (xiii) Anon. sale, London, 21 July 1965 (lot 143), as de Poorter (£150 to Dent).[24] A pastiche also based on the etching was in an Anon. sale, London, 4 November 1949 (lot 106), as G. van den Eeckhout.[25]

DRAWINGS: Münz[26] suggests a drawing in the Louvre[27] and one (formerly?) in the possession of Paul Cassirer, Amsterdam,[28] were used for the heads of some of the Jews in this composition. Benesch apparently believes they are later than the etching.[29] In any case the resemblance is slight.

ETCHING AND ENGRAVING: For Rembrandt's etching see above. Smith[30] notes an anonymous engraving after this composition.

PROVENANCE: Perhaps identical with the 'Ecce Homo' in grisaille in the inventory of Rembrandt's goods made in July 1656 in connection with his bankruptcy;[31] possibly in the inventory of Jan van de Cappelle's possessions made between January and August 1680.[32] According to Smith it was sold with another grisaille in the Willem Six sale, Amsterdam, 12 May 1734;[33] the only possible lot in that sale is 175 which consisted of *three* undescribed grisailles by Rembrandt, bought by de Barij (30 guilders).[34] In the 1738 inventory of Valerius Röver,[35] however, no. 8, valued at the high price of 125 guilders and marked 'bijgeleijt 1738', is: 'de capitaalste tekening die van Rembrandt bekent is, verbeeld de groote Ecce Homo, waar na hij de print heeft gesneden – met olieverwe op papier int graauw geschildert'. This is almost certainly No. 1400 which makes it unlikely (but not impossible) that it was in the Six sale. It was later purchased by Johan Goll van Franckenstein of Amsterdam, who sold it in 1827 to the Amsterdam dealer, A. Brondgeest, from whom it passed into the possession of Thomas Emmerson, London.[36] By 1836 it was in the collection of Jeremiah Harman;[37] J. Harman sale, London, 17–18 May 1844 (lot 92), bought by John Smith (112 gns) who sold it to G. Blamire.[38] George Blamire sale, London, 7–9 November 1863 (lot 57),[39] bought by Mulvaney (16 gns). In the collection of Sir Charles Lock Eastlake (d. 1865); bought from the executors of Lady Eastlake for a nominal sum (in accordance with the terms of Sir Charles' will) in 1894.

EXHIBITIONS: London, Whitechapel Art Gallery, 1948, No. 41; British Museum, Department of Prints and Drawings, 'Rembrandt and the Passion', 1984; London 1988–9, No. 2.

REFERENCES:
General: Smith No. 88; Bode and HdG No. 214; *Klassiker der Kunst: Rembrandt: Gemälde*, 1909, p. 157; HdG No. 128; Bredius, *Rembrandt*, No. 546; *Rembrandt Corpus*, vol. 2, A89.

In text:

1. In *Rembrandt Corpus*, op. cit., it is suggested that Rembrandt was trying to combine the information given in John 19:14 – 'And it was the preparation of the passover, and about the sixth hour' – with the Western way of indicating time, in which that hour corresponds to 12 noon. In the etching the clockface is only summarily indicated and has no numbers.

2. *Rembrandt Corpus*, op. cit.

3. M. Royalton-Kisch, 'Rembrandt: Two Passion Prints Reconsidered', *Apollo*, vol. 119, 1984, pp. 130–2 (and, in expanded form, in *De Kroniek van het Rembrandthuis*, 1984, vol. 1/2, pp. 2–23).

4. For a full technical description, see London 1988–9, pp. 42–7.

5. 54.9 × 44.7 cm. White and Boon No. 77.

6. See Z.C. von Uffenbach, *Merkwürdige Reisen durch Niedersachsen, Holland und Engelland*, 1753, vol. 3, p. 581 (quoted by HdG, *Die Urkunden über Rembrandt*, The Hague, p. 447, No. 390).

7. See note 3, above.

8. White and Boon No. 81.

9. Bredius, *Rembrandt*, No. 550.

10. L. Münz, *Rembrandt's Etchings*, 1952, No. 204.

11. *Rembrandt Corpus*, op. cit. (Callot's engraving is illustrated on p. 466).

12. See Strauss *Doc.* 1647/1.

13. See Strauss *Doc*, 1647/1.

14. Panel, 122 × 92 cm; grisaille. Acquired with the Lucchesi collection in 1803 for the Mannheim Gallery and transferred to Karlsruhe with the rest of the Mannheim pictures in 1937.

15. Panel, 117 × 116 cm. Inv. no. 163. 1958 cat., p. 119 (as Ascribed to Jurriaen Ovens). It is attributed by Sumowski (*Gemälde*, vol. 2, no. 935) to Heinrich Jansen (1625–1667).

16. Medium and size not known. Photo in RKD.

17. Canvas, 96 × 82 cm.

18. Canvas, 192 × 160 cm. Photo in RKD.

19. Canvas, 91.5 × 71.5 cm.

20. Canvas, 152 × 132 cm.

21. Panel, 58 × 43 cm.

22. Canvas, 89 × 71 cm.

23. Panel, 21 × 16 in.

24. Panel, 53 × 46 cm.

25. Canvas, 193 × 126 cm.

26. Loc. cit.

27. Benesch, No. 273 and fig. 322.

28. Benesch, No. 339 and fig. 410.

29. Loc. cit. Although Benesch says these drawings are 'several years' later than the etching in style, he nevertheless dates them *c.*1635 and *c.*1636 respectively.

30. Smith, loc. cit.

31. See Strauss *Doc.* 1656/12, no. 121: 'Een exce-homo in 't graeuw, van Rembrant.'

32. 'Een Ecce homo, grauw, van Rembrant van Rijn' (OH, vol. 10, 1892, p. 32; also HdG, *Urkunden*, op. cit., p. 411, No. 350).

33. Smith No. 88.

34. 'Drie Graauwtjes' (Hoet, vol. 1, p. 419, wrongly as lot 174). Smith does not give the lot number in the Six sale. He states that the present picture was sold with the grisaille of *Joseph telling his Dreams* (Smith No. 18; Rijksmuseum, Amsterdam, No. 2024 A7) for 14 florins; according to the marked sale catalogue in the Six collection this was the price paid for lot 174 (i.e. lot 173 in Hoet, loc. cit.) which was a 'Christus Beeld', presumably a head or bust of Christ (bought by Daelens, 14 florins, 10 st.). Smith adds to the confusion by stating elsewhere (Smith No. 18) that *Joseph telling his Dreams* was sold in the Willem Six sale with an unspecified 'companion' for 84 florins; this does not correspond with the price paid for any of the Rembrandt lots in the marked sale catalogue.

35. The inventory is in the University Library, Amsterdam (Hs. IC24). The identification is made by J. G. van Gelder, 'Frühe Rembrandt-Sammlungen', in O. v. Simson and J. Kelch, eds., *Neue Beiträge zur Rembrandt-Forschung*, Berlin, 1973, p. 193.

36. Smith No. 88.

37. Smith No. 88.

38. HdG (No. 128) says that, according to a MS note in Smith's own copy of his *Catalogue Raisonné*, Smith sold the picture to 'G. Blainie'; this is obviously a misreading of G. Blamire, in whose collection it certainly was.

39. The markings for this sale are on the back of the picture.

1674 *Portrait of Jacob Trip* *Plate 291*

Signed on the right, a little above the level of the sitter's left hand: Rembr (interrupted by the present edge of the canvas). The signature is fully visible only in ultra-violet light but is apparently genuine.

Oil on canvas, 130.5 × 97 (51⅜ × 38¼).

Cleaned in 1956.

The truncated signature at the right edge and the lack of cusping indicate that the canvas has certainly been cut down on the right, possibly by about 5 cm. The partial cusping at the top and bottom, visible in the X-radiograph, suggests that these edges have also been trimmed, but not by so much. Allowing for turnovers, the original width of the canvas could well have corresponded with the standard 1½ ell (1.05 m.) measurement.

PENTIMENTI: There are two principal *pentimenti*. His right hand has been moved to a lower position: the earlier, slightly higher hand can be seen clearly on the picture surface and the X-radiograph suggests that it may have been holding his stick at this stage. Secondly, the deep, high-backed winged chair in which Trip now sits was not part of the original design. The X-radiograph shows a quite different arrangement: Trip originally sat forward on a much simpler round-backed chair and was silhouetted against a light background.

The canvas is prepared with a double ground comprising a coarse-textured lower layer of orange-red earth pigment, covered by an upper layer of dull khaki. Both layers are heterogeneous, with silica particles and small quantities of red lake pigment in addition to the main ochreous component in the lower, and a mixture of coarse lead white, chalk, yellow ochre, umber and charcoal in the upper ground. It seems likely that the grounds of this portrait and its companion (No. 1675) were applied in Rembrandt's studio rather than that the canvases were obtained ready grounded.[1]

Jacob Jacobsz. Trip, merchant of Dordrecht, was born in 1575 in Zaltbommel (Gelderland). He settled when young in Dordrecht; in 1603 he married Margaretha de Geer (see No. 1675 below). His brother, Elias, was associated in business with their brother-in-law, Louis de Geer, one of the greatest iron-masters and armament manufacturers of the time, and after 1626 Jacob also took a part in their transactions. He was buried in Dordrecht, 8 May 1661. Two of his sons, Louis and Hendrick, also dealt in armaments; the palatial Trippenhuis in Amsterdam was built for them in 1660–2.[2]

The sitters in this and the companion picture (No. 1675) were identified by Hofstede de Groot.[3] The same man and woman are depicted at various ages in a series of likenesses by different painters; their identity is established by a pair of portraits by Jacob Gerritsz. Cuyp which came from the de Geer family.

Besides the present picture at least seven portraits of Jacob Trip are known: two by Jacob Gerritsz. Cuyp (dated 1649 [Fig. 82] and 1651),[4] one by Aelbert Cuyp (dated

1652)[5] and four by or after Nicolaes Maes (one datable 1659 or 1660).[6] Of Margaretha de Geer there are three portraits by J. G. Cuyp, two by Maes and two by (or attributed to) Rembrandt (see Nos. 1675 and 5282 below). De Groot has suggested in explanation of the unusual number of portraits that they were destined for the sitters' children; Jacob and Margaretha had twelve or more, of whom at least five were still alive in 1660–1.[7] Judging by the style, a date of c.1661 seems most likely for Rembrandt's portrait of Jacob Trip. It is unclear whether or not it was begun before Trip's death in May 1661 (see below).

Trip and his wife spent their lives in Dordrecht but it seems more likely that Rembrandt painted them when they were visiting Amsterdam, where their sons Louis and Hendrick were then living, than that he went to Dordrecht. Rembrandt had had an earlier contact with the Trip family, having painted in 1639 Alotte Adriaensdr., the widow of Jacob's brother Elias,[8] and her daughter, Maria Trip.[9]

Dudok van Heel[10] has argued that it is likely that Nos. 1674 and 1675 were commissioned by the sitters' son, Hendrick Trip, in order to hang in the Trippenhuis. Miss van Eeghen[11] has concurred and added the supposition that the portrait of Jacob Trip may have been painted from a prototype rather than from the life. The likely prototype would have been the portrait of 1649 by J. G. Cuyp.

COPY: A half-length copy (omitting the stick) was in the J. H. A. Duynstee collection, Delft, 1909.[12]

PROVENANCE: This picture and the companion portrait of Margaretha de Geer (No. 1675 below) are said to have belonged to the Lee family in the eighteenth century.[13] In any case, by 1837 they were in the collection of Sir William Fowle Middleton-Fowle, 2nd Bart., who inherited Lee family property,[14] and were lent by him in that year to the BI and again in 1858. They passed by inheritance to his nephew, Sir George Nathaniel Broke-Middleton, Bart., and thence in 1887 to his great-niece, Lady de Saumarez, from whom they were purchased in 1899 (with the aid of gifts from J. P. Heseltine and Alfred C. de Rothschild).

EXHIBITIONS: BI 1837, No. 73;[15] BI 1858, No. 100;[16] London 1976, No. 94; London 1988–9, No. 16.

REFERENCES:

General: Smith Supplement No. 6; Moes No. 8068; Bode and HdG, vol. 7, No. 512; HdG No. 393; Bauch No. 429; Bredius, *Rembrandt*, No. 314.

In text:

1. For a full technical description (including detailed arguments concerning the grounding of the canvases in Rembrandt's studio), see London 1988–9. pp. 120–5.

2. See HdG in OH, vol. 45, 1928, pp. 255–64. In the NNBW (vol. 10, col. 1050) Jacob Trip is erroneously said to have died probably in 1663. He died in May 1661; the entry in the register of deaths in the Dordrecht archives shows that the date given by HdG, 8 May 1661, is in fact that of his burial. For a detailed modern account of the Trip family, see P. W. Klein, *De Trippen in de 17de eeuw: een studie over het ondernemersgedrag op de Hollandse stapelmarkt*, Assen, 1965. For the Trippenhuis, see R. Meischke and H. E. Reeser, eds., *Het Trippenhuis te Amsterdam*, Amsterdam, 1983.

3. In OH, loc. cit.

4. (a) Panel, 72×58.3 cm. Dated 1649 and inscribed Aetatis 74. Collection of Professor Egbert Haverkamp-Begemann, New York, 1985 (formerly Chicago, Art Institute). (b) Panel, 73.5×59.5 cm. Dated 1651 and inscribed Aetatis 75. Denver, Colorado, Denver Art Museum.

5. W. J. Russell collection, Amsterdam; Bust; signed and dated 1652; inscribed Ætatis 74.

6. (a) Budapest Museum (1967 catalogue, No. 233). Three-quarter length. Pair to a portrait of Margaretha de Geer (1967 catalogue, No. 231). (b) Mauritshuis, The Hague (1977 catalogue, No. 90). Repetition of the Budapest picture; signed (and illegibly dated) and inscribed: AE^T 84. (c) Formerly in the collection of Baron van Wassenaer van Katwijk, Nederhemert Castle (Gelderland). Version or copy of the Budapest/Mauritshuis design. (Destroyed with the rest of the collection in 1944; reproduced in *De monumenten van geschiedenis en kunst in de Provincie Gelderland*, vol. 1, i, 1932, p. 119.) (d) In the possession of Barbizon House, London, 1921. Half length,

72.5 × 59 cm; signed. (Reproduced in *Barbizon House, 1921; An illustrated record*, 1921, No. 37.) This may be the painting hanging in the dining hall at Jesus College, Cambridge (or that may be a fifth version).

7. OH, 1928, p. 264.

8. Boymans-van Beuningen Museum, Rotterdam (van der Vorm collection), 1972 cat., vdV64 (Bredius, *Rembrandt*, No. 355).

9. The portrait of Maria Trip (1619–83), daughter of Alotte Adriaensdr. (1589–1656), Elias Trip's second wife, is on loan to the Rijksmuseum (1976 cat., C597) from the van Weede Family Foundation. It is signed and dated 1639 (Bredius, *Rembrandt*, No. 356; there is a preliminary drawing in the British Museum). Miss van Eeghen (in Meischke and Reeser, op. cit., pp. 72–3 and note 105, p. 122) has argued that a pair of portraits in Washington (Bredius, *Rembrandt*, Nos. 327 and 402) may show Jacob Trip Louysz. (1636–64) and his wife, Margarita Trip Hendricksdr.(1636–1711), who were the son of Louys Trip and the daughter of Hendrick Trip: they were both grandchildren of Jacob Trip and Margaretha de Geer.

10. S. A. C. Dudok van Heel, 'Het maecenaat Trip, opdrachten aan Ferdinand Bol en Rembrandt van Rijn', *De Kroniek van het Rembrandthuis*, vol. 31, 1979, pp. 14–26.

11. Miss I. H. van Eeghen in Meischke and Reeser, op. cit., p. 72.

12. Photo in RKD. Support and dimensions unknown.

13. Letters of 1898 from Lord de Saumarez (in the National Gallery archives).

14. A niece of Baptist Lee (1690–1768) married Nathaniel Acton; their daughter became the wife of Sir William Fowle Middleton (who assumed the additional surname of Fowle in 1822), 1st Baronet and father of Sir William Fowle Middleton-Fowle, 2nd Bart.

15. As 'A Portrait, supposed to be John Lutma, the Goldsmith'; its identity with No. 1674 is proved by the description in Smith Supplement No. 6.

16. As 'A Goldsmith of Antwerp'.

1675 *Portrait of Margaretha de Geer, Wife of Jacob Trip*

Plate 292

Oil on canvas, 130.5 × 97.5 (51⅛ × 38⅖); lower edge irregular.

Cleaned in 1955. There is an area of damage between the right arm of the chair and the edge of the picture.

PENTIMENTI: There are a number of important *pentimenti*. The most notable change is in the position of the sitter's left hand. It was first painted side-on, thumb and forefinger showing, resting in her lap; then resting on the arm of the chair to the right of the present position; and finally, as we see it now. These earlier positions can be seen clearly in the X-radiograph, the evidence of which is confirmed by cross-sections.[1] The ruff was also altered more than once: at first it was tilted more towards the viewer. The X-radiograph reveals that the sitter's white cuffs were originally trimmed with lace and that the handkerchief had a slightly different shape.

Study of the cusping in the X-radiograph shows that this portrait, like its companion (No. 1674), has been trimmed at all four edges, the largest loss being at the right edge. Both paintings were trimmed to the same size and it is most likely that both were reduced at the same time.

The canvas has a double ground identical to that of No. 1674 and, as in that painting, it is likely that the canvases were grounded in Rembrandt's studio.[2]

Margaretha de Geer, daughter of Louis de Geer, was born in Liège, 10 November 1583; the de Geer family left Liège in 1595, settling first in Aachen and then in Dordrecht. Margaretha married Jacob Trip in 1603 and died in Dordrecht in 1672. She was the sister of Louis de Geer the Younger, the great armaments dealer.[3]

For the identification of the sitter see No. 1674 above.

Six other portraits of Margaretha de Geer are known; three by Jacob Gerritsz. Cuyp (one dated 1649 and the others [see Fig. 83] dated 1651),[4] two by Nicolaes Maes[5] and one attributed to Rembrandt (No. 5282 below).

The picture is in the same style as the companion portrait (No. 1674 above) and was presumably also painted about 1661. The sitter's gown and ruff are in a style which came into fashion more than forty years earlier.

A drawing by Rembrandt in the Boymans-van Beuningen Museum, Rotterdam,[6] has been supposed to represent the same woman; the resemblance is slight and the identification excluded by the style of the drawing which is of *c.*1640 or earlier whereas the woman in it appears to be almost as old as the sitter in the present portrait.

COPY: According to HdG a copy was in an Anon. sale, London, 15 February 1904.[7]

PROVENANCE: See No. 1674 above.

EXHIBITIONS: BI 1837, No. 121;[8] BI 1858, No. 102;[9] London 1976, No. 95; London 1988–9, No. 17.

REFERENCES:

General: Smith Supplement No. 14; Moes No. 2659; Bode and HdG, vol. 7, No. 493; HdG No. 857; Bauch No. 523; Bredius, *Rembrandt*, No. 394. In text:

1. For a full technical description see London 1988–9, pp. 126–9.

2. For a detailed discussion of the ground, see London 1988–9, pp. 126, 128.

3. HdG in OH, vol. 45, 1928, p. 255; NNBW, vol. 10.

4. (a) Aix Museum (1900 catalogue, No. 248). Signed and dated 1649 and inscribed: Ætatis 65. Companion of the portrait of Jacob Trip now in the Haverkamp-Begemann collection, New York (see No. 1674 above, note 4). (b) Rijksmuseum, Amsterdam, 1976 cat., A611. Signed and dated 1651 and inscribed: Ætatis. 66. (c) Formerly in the collection of HdG. Replica of the Rijksmuseum portrait. Signed and dated 1651 and inscribed: Ætatis 66. Reproduced in OH, 1928, p. 257.

5. Budapest Museum (1967 catalogue, No. 231). A version or copy was formerly in the collection of Baron van Wassenaer van Katwijk, Nederhemert

Castle; companion to the portrait mentioned in No. 1674 above, note 6(c); destroyed in 1944 (reproduced in *De monumenten van geschiedenis en kunst in de Provincie Gelderland*, vol. 1, i, 1932, p. 119).

6. Benesch, vol. 4, No. 757 and fig. 958. H. R. Hoetink has identified the sitter as Margaretha de Geer while accepting Benesch's dating of 1635–40. He also identifies a further head on a sheet of studies in the Fogg Museum as the same sitter (H. R. Hoetink, 'Nog een portret van Margaretha de Geer', *Miscellana I. Q. van Regteren Altena*, Amsterdam, 1969, p. 150–1). Benesch (No. A10) dates the sheet to the first half of the 1630s.

7. According to HdG (No. 857) it was lot 80 but this was a genre scene attributed to Piazzetta; he was presumably referring to lot 79: 'Rembrandt Portrait of a lady, in dark dress, with ruff'; 43 × 7 in.; bought by Cohen.

8. It is described in the BI catalogue as 'Head of an elderly Female' but its identity with No. 1675 is established by the description in Smith Supplement (1842) No. 14.

9. As 'Rembrandt's Mother'.

4930 *Saskia van Uylenburgh in Arcadian Costume*   Plate 293

Below, on the left, between Saskia's skirt and her staff, are the worn remains of a false signature and date:[1] Rem(..)a(.)/1635.

Oil on canvas, 123.5 × 97.5 (48⅝ × 38⅜). It is conceivable that the picture has been reduced in size; the evidence suggests that the reduction was slight. The date on the picture, although false, accords well with the style and may, therefore, have been copied from a genuine signature on a part of the original canvas, which has been cut off. The most important evidence is presented by a seventeenth-century drawn copy in the British Museum;[2] Haverkamp-Begemann has attributed it to Lambert Doomer[3] and Sumowski to Ferdinand Bol.[4] Sumowski's arguments are more compelling. It shows the composition extended (the background foliage) a little at the top and to the right and fractionally on the left. This drawing presumably is an accurate copy of the painting made shortly after it was painted. Several old painted copies of this design, none apparently older than the eighteenth century, and an engraving of 1763 have different proportions. In two of the copies (those of the Bonde and Cevat collections – see COPIES) the field of the composition is extended a little on the right but otherwise corresponds with that of the National Gallery picture. Pether's mezzotint of 1763 (see ENGRAVING) shows the composition extended substantially on all sides and the figure continued to about half-way between knee and foot; this print, however, is obviously rather carelessly executed and these differences may not have been in the picture he was copying. Lastly, in the copy from the Lechmere collection (and now in the Kisters collection Fig. 84); there is about twice as much space between the figure and the edges on both sides and at the top, and the figure is continued to the ground. It is true that almost all the known full-length life-size portraits by Rembrandt were painted about this time, yet the additional part is somewhat empty and the lower part of the figure has been partially hidden by plants in a clumsy way that suggests it was not taken from an original by Rembrandt but is the invention of a copyist. It seems most likely that the British Museum drawing is an accurate copy of the painting's original appearance and that the present canvas has been cut down along the top and right edges and minimally along the left edge.[5] It is worth noting that the National Gallery picture is approximately the same size as the Hermitage painting of Saskia in a similar guise made the year before. Unfortunately, there is no clear technical evidence that confirms whether and by how much the composition has been reduced, but a repair to the canvas may have been carried out using a piece trimmed from the edge.

Cleaned in 1938. A patch, roughly wedge-shaped and about 16 cm. high, has been inserted on the right side of the neck; the top is near the right corner of the mouth and the bottom on the upper part of the right breast. It was formerly covered in part by a false curl[6] which was removed when the picture was cleaned; the missing part was then restored to agree with the corresponding area in the old copies.

Examination of the X-radiograph (Fig. 85) shows that the canvas has too fine and detailed a weave to be Rembrandt's original. No. 4930 seems, therefore, to have been transferred to a new canvas.[7] However, unlike No. 672 which has also probably been transferred, the imprint of the original canvas in the back of the ground layers (and therefore its image in the X-radiograph) has been almost entirely lost. Presumably the back of the ground was sanded or scraped down during the transfer. The new canvas was then applied with a ground or adhesive which is opaque to X-radiography and consequently it is the image of the replacement canvas that we see. It is just possible to make out the faint remains of the original canvas weave in a few areas where it was not entirely scraped away. Study of the area of the repair at the left of Saskia's neck shows that the regular weave of the transfer canvas underlies the more irregular weave of the inserted piece, which is inclined at a slight angle to it. The intriguing possibility that the insert may have been cut from a trimmed-off piece of the original canvas suggests itself. A cross-section from this area confirms that this is highly likely: below layers of later paint is one layer of old paint on top of a double ground apparently the same as is found elsewhere on the painting. In this small area, therefore, we are probably seeing the only well-preserved image of the original weave. The repair must be an early one, since it clearly pre-dates the transfer.

The canvas is prepared with a double ground similar to that of No. 6350. The lower ground is of a coarse, impure orange-red earth, while the second layer is a rather cool grey consisting of granular lead white combined with some umber and black earth pigment.[8]

PENTIMENTI: X-radiographs reveal extensive changes: on the right-hand side a second figure, wearing a flat hat and with eyes cast down, can clearly be seen. Saskia's right hand was originally lower and did not hold a staff. There are further changes in the confused area of her left arm and hand, which make it possible that she was not originally holding flowers. There are other, smaller changes in her bodice and skirt. The circlet holding Saskia's veil was at first lower.

Saskia van Uylenburgh or Ulenborch was the daughter of a burgomaster of Leeuwarden in Friesland and was born there on 2 August 1612.[9] (The surname is spelled in a dozen different ways in contemporary documents but these are the forms generally used by the family.[10]) Rembrandt had dealings with Saskia's cousin, Hendrick van Uylenburgh, an art-dealer in Amsterdam, even before he left Leiden; he lent him a thousand guilders in 1631 and lodged in his house in Amsterdam from 1632 until, probably, his marriage in 1634. Saskia went to stay with a married sister in Amsterdam and was betrothed to Rembrandt in June 1633; they were married in Sint-Annaparochie, not far from Leeuwarden, on 22 June 1634. Saskia brought Rembrandt a large dowry; after her death her estate was valued at more than forty thousand guilders. Of their four children only Titus, born in September 1641, was alive at the time of her death, which occurred in Amsterdam, 14 June 1641.

The identity of the model is established by Rembrandt's drawing of Saskia in the Berlin Printroom made three days after their betrothal in 1633.[11]

The date on the picture has often been read as 1633; it is certainly 1635. Like the signature it is obviously false but may have been copied from a genuine inscription later removed (see above) since it is not incompatible with the style, though the picture could conceivably be a year or so later.

Rembrandt had already painted Saskia in 1634 in similar guise in a picture now in the Hermitage, Leningrad (Fig. 86).[12] Each picture was at one time fancifully called *A Jewish Bride*; more recently they have been thought to represent Flora, the Roman goddess of Spring and flowers. Held has supported the identification as Flora,[13] but Kieser[14] and more recently Louttit[15] and Kettering[16] have placed the costume within the contemporary pastoral tradition. Louttit concluded that it is 'a portrait of the artist's wife in the guise of a shepherdess whose floral garland and long curling locks of hair are well in accordance with literary notions and visual examples of ideal dress for Dutch arcadians'.[17] Detailed references to illustrations of pastoral plays and poems are cited in the article. Kettering stressed that the identifications as Flora and as a shepherd-ess in the contemporary pastoral mode are not mutually exclusive and that Rembrandt might well have had both traditions in mind. The low bustline adds an element of eroticism appropriate both to Flora and shepherdesses: 'the shepherdess has been transformed into noble Flora, the queen of the shepherdesses.'[18]

Comparison with the numerous pictures of shepherdesses painted at this period, especially in Utrecht, strongly supports the idea that Rembrandt was indeed working in the current Arcadian fashion. The first pastoral play in Dutch, Hooft's *Granida en Daifilo*, was written about 1605 and became so popular that eight editions had appeared by 1679.[19] Arcadian subjects began to appear in the early 1620s in pictures by Utrecht artists; particularly popular were half-length figures of shepherds and shepherdesses and portraits of sitters in idealised pastoral dress, but pictures of girls with a shepherd's staff and holding a bouquet or a wreath are not infrequent.[20] By the 1630s, perhaps earlier, the same subjects were being painted in Amsterdam; typical examples are Dirck Santvoort's *Shepherd* and *Shepherdess* of 1632 in Rotterdam.[21] This kind of picture certainly appears in the Rembrandt circle at this time and a *Saskia as Shepherdess* of 1636 by Flinck in Braunschweig[22] has a companion *Shepherd* (in the Rijksmuseum)[23] with the features of Rembrandt himself.

The present writer has suggested, on the basis of a study of the X-radiograph, that Rembrandt originally had a quite different subject in mind, that of Judith, freely based on Rubens' interpretation of the subject now in Braunschweig (Fig. 87).[24] The figure standing on the right would be Judith's servant and Judith's hand would originally have carried a curved sword. The unresolved area on the right between Saskia's left hand and her servant's hand, which includes several downward strokes, may have indicated the bag in which Holofernes' head was contained or the head itself. It is related to a drawing of the subject by Rembrandt in the Louvre.[25] If this hypothesis is correct, Rembrandt became dissatisfied with the *Judith*, based on Rubens' composition, at a quite advanced stage and in her place painted Saskia in Arcadian costume.

ENGRAVING: There is a mezzotint of this design (inverted) by William Pether, 1763,[26] almost certainly engraved from a copy.

COPIES: William Henry Fortescue (later Lord Clermont) apparently owned a copy in 1763.[27] A copy is in the collection of Baron Carl J. Bonde, Ericsberg, Sweden;[28] another was in the collection of D. H. Cevat, London, 1951.[29] A copy in which the figure is seen full length, said to be from the collections of Sir Joshua Reynolds and Sir Edmund Lechmere, is in the possession of Mrs Heinz Kisters, Kreuzlingen, Switzerland.[30] A copy of the figure from the waist upwards was in the J. Goudstikker sale, Lange, Berlin, 3 December 1940 (lot 156).[31] All these show the figure without the false curl formerly on No. 4930. There is a drawn copy by Ferdinand Bol in the British Museum, discussed above.

PROVENANCE: In the Duc de Tallard sale, Paris, 22 March sqq. 1756 (lot 156),[32] 602 francs, bought by Remy, almost certainly for the Duke of Montagu;[33] it was in the latter's collection at Montagu House, London, c.1780.[34] In 1790 it was inherited with his collection by the duke's daughter, who was married to the 3rd Duke of Buccleuch. On loan to the National Gallery, 1917. Bought from the 8th Duke of Buccleuch in 1938 (with the aid of the Champney, Florence, Hornby-Lewis, Lewis, Lindley and Temple-West Funds, and a contribution from the NACF).

EXHIBITIONS: Manchester 1857 (provisional catalogue, No. 668; definitive catalogue, No. 666); Edinburgh 1883, No. 421; RA 1899, No. 77; RA 1929, No. 154; Amsterdam, Rijksmuseum, 'Rembrandt', 1932, No. 6; RA 1938, No. 129; London, NACF, 1945–6, No. 4; London 1947–8, No. 66; London 1988–9, No. 5.

REFERENCES:

General: Smith No. 493; Bode and HdG, vol. 3, No. 186; HdG No. 205; Bauch No. 261; Bredius, *Rembrandt*, No. 103; *Rembrandt Corpus*, vol. 3, No. A112.

In text:

1. The statement that the signature was removed when the picture was cleaned in 1938 (BM, vol. 74, 1939, p.144) is incorrect.

2. Brush and brown and grey ink, 219 × 173 mm. Inv. no. Oo.10-133. Hind, vol. 1, no. 139 (as anonymous copy after Rembrandt).

3. E. Haverkamp-Begemann, in *Rembrandt after Three Hundred Years*, Chicago, Art Institute, 1969, p.23.

4. Sumowski, *Drawings*, I, no. 127[X]. Sumowski points out that according to a note on the verso of a drawn copy after Lastman in Berlin (Benesch No. 448) Bol painted a copy of Rembrandt's Flora though it is impossible to say whether it was a copy of No. 4930 or of the version in Leningrad. This evidence does, however, tend to support Sumowski's attribution of the British Museum drawing to Bol. He also asserts – less convincingly – that the drawing (and the painted copy) was probably used by Bol for his painting known as *Saskia and Rembrandt in a Landscape* formerly in the collection of Lord Somerleyton (although Blankert [*Ferdinand Bol*, Doornspijk, 1982] does not accept that painting as by Bol).

5. In any case the measurements given by Smith, loc. cit. (55 × 45 in.) and in the catalogue of the Manchester 1857 exhibition (58¼ × 51¼ in.) are erroneous as the picture has not been reduced since Smith's time.

6. There are many reproductions of the picture before the removal of the false curl, e.g. *Klassiker der Kunst: Rembrandt*, 1909, p. 135; Bredius, loc. cit.

7. This was first suggested by Ernst van de Wetering, for whose assistance the present writer is most grateful.

8. For a full technical description – including an account of the remarkable variety of pigments present in the painting – see London 1988–9, pp. 58–65.

9. This and the following biographical details are taken mostly from P. Scheltema, *Rembrand*, 1859; W. Eekhoff, *De Vrouw van Rembrandt*, 1862; and Strauss *Doc*.

10. See Strauss *Doc. passim*. Saskia herself signs 'Saskia Ulenborg' in 1635 (OH, 1908, p. 221) and 'Saskia van Ulenborch' in 1642 (Strauss *Doc.* 1642/2).

11. Reproduced in Benesch, vol. 2, fig. 514 (No. 427). It is inscribed by Rembrandt: 'dit is naer mijn huysvrou geconterfeyt/do sy 21 jaer oud was den derden/dach als wij getroudt waeren/den 8 Junijus/ 1633.'

12. HdG No. 206; Bredius, op. cit., fig. 102. 125 × 101 cm. Signed: Rembrandt./f 1634.

13. J. S. Held, 'Flora, Goddess and Courtesan', in *De Artibus Opuscula XL: Essays in honour of Erwin Panofsky*, New York, 1961, p. 207.

14. E. Kieser, 'Uber Rembrandts Verhältnis zur Antike', *Zeitschrift für Kunstgeschichte*, vol. 10, 1941/ 2, p. 155.

15. M. Louttit, 'The Romantic Dress of Saskia van Ulenburch: Its Pastoral and Theatrical Associations', BM, vol. 115, 1973, pp. 317–26.

16. A. M. Kettering, *The Dutch Arcadia: Pastoral Art and its Audience in the Golden Age*, Montclair, N. J., 1983, esp. pp. 61–2.

17. Louttit, op. cit., p. 322.

18. Kettering, op. cit., p. 61.

19. See S. J. Gudlaugsson, 'Representations of Granida in Dutch Seventeenth-century Painting' in BM, vol. 90, 1948, pp. 226 ff. and 348 ff., and vol. 91, 1949, pp. 39 ff.

20. For example the two pictures by Paulus Moreelse, dated 1632 and 1633, reproduced in C. H. de Jonge, *Paulus Moreelse*, 1938, figs. 184 and 185 (Nos. 281 and 283).

21. Boymans-van Beuningen Museum, 1972 cat., Nos. 1772 and 1773. The *Shepherd* is signed and dated 1632.

22. Herzog Anton Ulrich-Museum, Braunschweig, R. Klessmann, *Die Holländischen Gemälde*, 1983, No. 252.

23. Rijksmuseum 1976 cat. no. A3451.

24. C. Brown, 'Rembrandt's Saskia as Flora X-rayed', in *Essays in Northern European Art presented to Egbert Haverkamp-Begemann*, Doornspijk, 1983, pp. 49–51. One important piece of corroborative evidence has come to light since the article was published. Rüdiger Klessmann, Director of the Herzog Anton-Ulrich Museum, Braunschweig, has kindly informed the present writer that the Rubens *Judith* is probably the painting mentioned in a Leiden inventory of the 1620s – and so would have been accessible to Rembrandt.

25. Benesch, No. 176.

26. Charrington/Alexander, No. 126. State 3 has the engraved title: 'REMBRANDTS WIFE in the Character of a JEW BRIDE. From the Original picture Painted by Rembrandt, in the collection of the Right Hon[ble] William Henry Fortescue. Published . . . 1763.' In this engraving the field of the composition is extended on all sides and the figure is continued to well below the knees.

27. See the engraved inscription on W. Pether's mezzotint of 1763 quoted in note 25. (Fortescue was created Baron Clermont in 1773, and in 1777 Earl.) It has been supposed that the original of Pether's print was the National Gallery picture but there can be little doubt that the latter was bought for the Duke of Buccleuch in 1756 (see PROVENANCE) and therefore could not have belonged to Fortescue in 1763.

28. Canvas, 121.5 × 96.5 cm. Reproduced in *Svenska Hem*, Stockholm, 1913, p. 244; see also O. Granberg, *Catalogue raisonné de tableaux . . . dans les collections privées de la Suède*, vol. 1, 1886, No. 348.

29. Canvas, 130 × 104 cm.; the 1951 sale catalogue gives the wrong width. Reproduced in Bode and HdG No. 187, and *Klassiker der Kunst*, 1909, p. 535.

30. Canvas, 194 × 131 cm. Exh. *Meisterwerke aus Baden-Württembergischen Privatbesitz*, Staatsgalerie, Stuttgart, 1958–59, No. 157 (ill. in catalogue).

31. 70 × 54 cm.

32. As 'Une Mariée Juive'. The description agrees with the National Gallery picture but the size is given as '45 pouces de haut, sur 54 pouces de large'. There can be little doubt that it is the picture later in the collection of the Duke of Montagu (see the following note); 54 is presumably a misprint for 34. In any case it cannot be the Reynolds/ Lechmere copy, as sometimes supposed (e.g. HdG No. 205, note).

33. In some of the marked copies of the sale catalogue the purchaser is given as 'Remy pour l'Angleterre' (Remy is the name of one of the two auctioneers of this sale); the same annotation is made against lot 141, Rubens' *Watering Place*, which also was in the Duke of Montagu's collection later.

34. It is No. 114 of a MS list of pictures at Montagu House made about 1780: 'Rembrandt a Jew Bride, ½ Length'; the size is not given.

6300 *Portrait of Frederick Rihel on Horseback* *Plate 294*

There are faint remains (but visible with infra-red photography) of a signature and a date, lower left: R....brandt 1663(?).

Oil on canvas, 294.5 × 241 (116 × 95).

Cleaned in 1960. The condition is good: the background is deliberately sketchy. There is a damage immediately to the left of the upper part of the horse's right hind leg.

This large canvas consists of three pieces seamed together with a simple running stitch. The upper seam runs horizontally through the horse's bit and the pommel of the sword; the lower seam runs horizontally just below the horse's right front hoof and the top of the front left hoof. The top strip of canvas is approximately 106 cm. wide, the centre strip 114 cm. and the lower strip 74.5 cm. The top one corresponds to the standard 1½ ell canvas measurement; the centre one is wide for this measurement but could just fall within a generous interpretation of it; the lower strip was cut from a larger piece of canvas.

The ground is composed of silica with a little brown ochre. It is the same as the ground of, for example, Rembrandt No. 221 in this catalogue. The design of the painting has been sketched in with broad strokes of blackish paint applied with a brush. This bold underdrawing is visible everywhere in the infra-red photograph and seems to have been used to define both the horse and the rider, as well as foreground and background elements. The horse's legs are clearly outlined in this way, including a *pentimento* of a right hind leg to the right of the present one; and there are bold black strokes in the area of Rihel's hat. Other *pentimenti* can be seen in the infra-red photograph: Rihel's hat was initially taller in the crown and wider at the brim, and there are several changes of outline in the horse's head and legs. Cross-sections reveal one other significant modification of the design: in the area of the lower section of the sky, Rembrandt originally laid in thickly painted foliage greens, and later painted them out, again thickly, with the present sky. The infra-red photograph is also valuable in clarifying the details of the composition as there can be no doubt that the painting has darkened – partly through varnish discoloration and partly because a dark ground always becomes more prominent as the paint ages and becomes more transparent – and certain background areas have become difficult to read.[1]

The horse performs a *levade*. The rider is leading – or taking part in – a procession which winds around a stretch of water in the lower left where the prow of a boat can be seen. On the left the façade of a building is roughly sketched. In front of it is a coach in which three occupants and a groom on the running board can be made out: the heads of the driver and two coachmen at the rear can also be seen. The coach is part of the procession, as are the two (or three) riders on horseback (who all wear hats) on the right behind the principal rider.

The identification of the rider as the Amsterdam merchant Frederick Rihel (1621–81) was first proposed by Bredius on the basis of a portrait of him listed in the inventory of his property drawn up after his death in 1681: *Het conterfijtsel van de overleden te paert door Rembrandt.*[2] There is nothing in the known provenance of the painting (see below, under PROVENANCE) to link it with Rihel; there is, however, only one other known equestrian portrait by Rembrandt, the so-called *Polish Rider* in the Frick Collection, which dates from the mid-1650s.[3] There is, unfortunately, no known portrait of Rihel to confirm Bredius' identification (although there is much supporting evidence, see below). Luttervelt[4] argued against the identification of the rider as Rihel. He identified the procession in which the horseman is taking part as the entry of Prince William of Orange into Amsterdam in 1660 and the building sketched at the left as the Heiligewegspoort, the gate by which the prince entered the city.[5] Although Rihel, who was a member of the Amsterdam civic guard, did take part in the procession, he was not at that time an officer which Luttervelt believed to be the status of the rider because of the sash he wears. Luttervelt proposed a different candidate: Jacob de Graeff (1642–90), who was a *vendrig* (cornet) of the guard of honour which accompanied the prince into Amsterdam. This identification fails, however, on the youth of the sitter (who would have been only eighteen in 1660) and on comparison with extant portraits of de Graeff such as that by Gerard ter Borch in the Rijksmuseum.[6] Miss van Eeghen[7] subsequently revived Bredius' original identification making use of an engraving of the 1660 procession. She also examined Rihel's 1681 inventory in some detail and found there a number of items of dress and accoutrements similar to those worn by the rider. She also pointed out that the bachelor Rihel's great love of horses would explain the unusual (at least for Rembrandt) commission. Further investigation of the inventory by the present writer (with the generous assistance of Sebastian Dudok van Heel) has confirmed that many of the rider's items of clothing, etc., can be matched with items listed there. There are, for example, pistols ('Twee sach pistolen'), swords ('Een groote stocade' and others), gloves with silver fringes ('Een paer sware handtschoenen met silver franje'), a variety of sashes some with silver and gold fringes ('Een orange sluyer met goude en silver franje') and with matching gloves, and a leather jerkin embroidered with gold thread ('Een leere kolder en een wambair met goudte geboort'). The inventory also lists the luxurious trappings of Rihel's horses.[8] It is also important to note that the guard of honour which accompanied Prince William into Amsterdam in 1660 was not exclusively recruited from the civic guard,[9] nor did the normal ranks apply on this occasion: Jacob de Graeff, for example, who served as *vendrig* in this procession, was not, in 1660, either *vendrig* or sergeant in the civic guard. The fact that the dress of the rider in No. 6300 does not accord with formal civic guard uniform (which was in any case not strictly regulated in the seventeenth century) is not an objection to the identification as Rihel.

To sum up: it seems extremely likely that the rider in No. 6300 is Frederick Rihel and that he commissioned this portrait to commemorate his part in the procession which accompanied Prince William of Orange into Amsterdam in 1660.

Frederick (Frédéric) Rihel was baptised on 17 October 1621 in the church of St Thomas in Strasbourg.[10] His father, also Frédéric, was a manufacturer of paper. His mother, Rosine Storck, was the daughter of Peter Storck, who had served as *ammeistre* (lord mayor) of Strasbourg. The Rihel family were well-known printers in the city in the sixteenth and early seventeenth centuries. Frederick Rihel is first recorded in Amsterdam in 1642: he lodged with the Bartolotti family. Rihel settled in Amsterdam and enjoyed a successful career as a merchant. He lived (at least after 1674) on the Herengracht and did not marry. He became a *vendrig* in the civic guard on 29 September 1677. He died on 6 January 1681 and was buried in the Nieuwe Lutherse Kerk.[11]

A drawing of a coach in the British Museum has been associated with No. 6300. It has been dated by Hind[12] and Benesch[13] to c.1649, which was once thought to be the date of the portrait.[14] The drawing does not appear to have a close connection with No. 6300.

It has recently been suggested by Professor Josua Bruyn[15] that the horse is by another hand, an assistant in Rembrandt's studio. He has grouped together a number of paintings which show Rembrandt's influence in the 1660s and attributed them to the same assistant, whom he has tentatively identified as Titus van Rijn, Rembrandt's son. He has written that 'the horse is an anomaly due to the heavy shadows in dense, leaden greys and browns, and the peculiar, almost ornamental stylisation of the mane. The same characteristics appear in various other Rembrandtesque paintings, notably a *Sacrifice of Abraham* in a private collection in England.'[16] While the religious paintings of this group do show some stylistic similarities – all reflecting an awareness of Rembrandt's style in the 1660s and also perhaps that of the early Aert de Gelder – the present writer cannot see the stylistic analogies with No. 6300. Nor is there any evidence to connect Titus with authorship of this group. The stiffness and lack of animation in the horse are better explained by Rembrandt's unfamiliarity with the format of the large-scale Baroque equestrian portrait. In the course of a detailed technical examination of the painting,[17] it was found to be entirely consistent with other paintings by Rembrandt from the 1660s and no discontinuity in technique between horse and rider was discovered.

ETCHING: By P. J. Arendzen.

PROVENANCE: Count Ferdinand of Plettenberg and Witten sale, Amsterdam, 2 April 1738, lot 130 (88 guilders);[18] G. Bicker van Zwieten sale, The Hague, 12 April 1741, lot 129 (90 guilders).[19] It is said to have been purchased about 1750 by the 2nd Earl Cowper.[20] It is recorded at Panshanger, the residence of the Earls Cowper, by Passavant[21] in 1833. It remained at Panshanger until 1953, after it had passed by inheritance from Lady Desborough to her daughter Lady Salmon, who placed it on loan to the Leeds City Art Gallery. It was purchased by the National Gallery in 1959, by private treaty sale, with contributions from the NACF and the Pilgrim Trust.

EXHIBITIONS: BI 1815, No. 123; RA 1881, No. 165; RA 1952–3, No. 270; Amsterdam, Rijksmuseum, and Rotterdam, Boymans-van Beuningen Museum, 'Rembrandt', 1956, No. 53; London 1976, No. 96; London 1988–9, No. 19.

REFERENCES:

General: HdG, No. 772; Bauch No. 440; Bredius, *Rembrandt*, No. 255.

In text:

1. For a full technical description, see London 1988–9, pp. 134–9.

2. 'Rembrandtiana', OH, 1910, pp. 193–5. There was a traditional identification of the rider as Marshal Turenne (see, for example, Waagen, 1854, vol. 3, p. 16) but he bears no resemblance to the well-documented features of the Marshal of France.

3. Bredius, *Rembrandt*, No. 279. For the identification of the rider as the portrait of a young Polish nobleman, possibly Szymon Karol Oginski, see B. J. P. Broos, 'Rembrandt's Portrait of a Pole and his horse', *Simiolus*, vol. 7, 1974, pp. 193–218.

4. R. van Luttervelt, 'De Grote Ruiter van Rembrandt', NKJ, vol. 8, 1957, pp. 185–210.

5. The identification of this structure as the Heiligewegspoort by Luttervelt depends entirely on the procession being that of Prince William into Amsterdam in 1660. There is no significant architectural resemblance.

6. 1976 cat. no. A3963.

7. Miss I. H. van Eeghen, 'Frederick Rihel een 17de Eeuwse Zakenman en Paardenliefhebber', *Amstelodamum*, vol. 45, 1958, pp. 73–81. This article was in response to Luttervelt's (see note 3) and the latter replied to it: R. van Luttervelt, 'Frederick Rihel or Jacob de Graeff?', *Amstelodamum*, vol. 45, 1958, pp. 147–50.

8. Rihel's inventory, drawn up by the notary N. Brouwer, and dated 6 January 1681 runs to twenty-one pages (Notarial Archives, Gemeente Archief van Amsterdam, No. 3942, Folios 17–27). Among the relevant items are: among the paintings, 'Den prins van Oranje te paert met een compagnie soldaten (F. 18); Het conterfijtsel van de overleden te paert door Rembrandt' (F. 18) and the next item 'Een d°[ditto] conterfijtsel daer hij te voet gaet', then: 'twee ouden moffen met breedt lindt, een porde piedl en een draaghbandt met franje' (F. 18 v); 'Twee sach pistolen' (F. 18 v); 'Een degentje met een silver gevert' (F. 19) and the two following items:

'Noch twee degens; Een groote stocade'. 'Een paer sware handtschoenen met silver franje' (F. 19); 'Een orange sluyer met goude en silver franje' (F. 19); and the three following items: 'Een witte armosyen sluyer met gout en silvere Kant; Een blaauwe en een oranje sijde sluyer sonder Kant off franje; Een blaeuwe en groene gebraayde bontrock met gout door werkt; Een silver geborduurde draegbandt met een paer dito handtschoenen' (F. 19); 'Een hoedt bandt met een gout slot (soo gevordeelt werdt) met rteentjens beset' (F. 20); and in the bedroom, another portrait of Rihel: 'Een conterfijtsel van de overleden in een gesneden vergulde lijst' (F. 20 v); 'Een twee grote silvere nestels' (F. 22) (contained 'in een geslote kasje'); 'Een leere kolder en een wambair met goudte geboort' (F. 22 v); 'Een leere draegh-bandt, en een geborduurde draeghbandt met een dito pordepeed' (F. 22 v); on folio 27 are listed his 'twee appel grauwe paerden' and their luxurious trappings.

9. The names of the members of this procession – listed by Miss van Eeghen, op. cit., p. 75, note 2 – can be compared with the relevant lists in J. A. Jochems, *Amsterdams Oude Burgervendels (Schutterij) 1580–1795*, Amsterdam, 1888.

10. The date of Rihel's birth and the information about his family are here published for the first time. It was kindly supplied to the present writer by the Strasbourg city archivist, F. J. Fuchs, in 1975 (letter in National Gallery archives).

11. Rihel's life in Amsterdam is discussed in detail by Miss van Eeghen (op. cit.).

12. Hind, vol. 1, No. 71.

13. Benesch, vol. 4, No. 756 (Fig. 954). Benesch also associates the drawing of a *Skeleton Rider* in the Hessisches Landesmuseum, Darmstadt (Benesch, vol. 4, No. 728, Fig. 921) with No. 6300 and also dates it *c*.1649. It is not, however, to be closely associated with the portrait.

14. See, for example, in the first edition (1937) of Bredius, *Rembrandt*, No. 255.

15. In a lecture at a Rembrandt symposium held in the National Gallery, London, in January 1988, and

subsequently in the exhibition catalogue *Een gloeiend palet: Schilderijen van Rembrandt en zijn school*, Museum Boymans-van Beuningen, Rotterdam, 1988, pp. 78–8.
16. *Een gloeiend palet*, op. cit., p. 78.
17. Published in full in London 1988–9, pp. 134–9.
18. Hoet, vol. 1, p. 505. At the time of the von Plettenberg sale, Anthony Rutgers told William VIII of Hesse-Kassel that the painting was in poor condition and advised him against its purchase (information supplied by Sebastian Dudok van Heel).
19. Hoet, No. 2, p. 21.
20. Information supplied by Lady Monica Salmond (see H. Honour, 'An Equestrian Portrait by Rembrandt', *Leeds Art Calendar*, vol. 7, No. 22, Summer 1953, p. 7 and note 2). M. L. Boyle, *Biographical Catalogue of the Portraits at Panshanger*, 1885, p. 38, stated that the painting was sold from a private collection in Amsterdam in 1740 (see also Smith, vol. 7, 1836, No. 323) and bought by the Earl of Grantham. This may have been a mistaken reference to the Bicker van Zwieten sale (see above); there is no indication that the Earl of Grantham ever owned the picture.
21. J. D. Passavant, *Kunstreise durch England und Belgien*, 1833, p. 100. See also Waagen, 1854, vol. 3, p. 16.

6350 *Belshazzar's Feast*   Plate 295

Signed and dated above the shoulder of the falling woman on the right: Rembrand/F 163(?). The signature and date can be best seen in ultra-violet light. There is a damage after the 'd'. Much of the penultimate digit of the date is damaged so that only the top of the 3 remains; the last digit is lost.

Inscribed, top right-hand corner, in Hebrew, to be read vertically from right to left: Mene mene tekel upharsin.[1]

Oil on canvas, 167.6 × 209.2 (66 × 82⅜).

Cleaned in 1964. There is a tear in the top left-hand corner. There is wearing to the right of the inscription and to the right of Belshazzar's left hand where there is also a marked craquelure.

The canvas consists of two equal widths of the standard 1½ ell measurement, joined by a central vertical seam. A number of important observations about this canvas have been made by Ernst van de Wetering.[2] First, there is the same distinct vertical weave fault about 20 cm. in from each vertical edge, made visible by the X-radiograph (Fig. 88). This means that the two pieces were cut from the length, placed one on top of the other in the same direction, seamed along one edge and then opened up flat. Secondly, the same weave fault, thread count and general weave characteristics are found in other paintings by Rembrandt – for example, *Abraham's Sacrifice* in Munich.[3] Without doubt the Munich canvas came from the same bolt as the London one and they were probably seamed and prepared at the same time. Thirdly, narrow wedge-shaped pieces of canvas were at some time cut from all four sides, perhaps during an early lining. This was detected by a study of the cusping which becomes progressively shallower along each side, and by measuring the widths of each canvas piece, which differ at the top and bottom. The result is that the whole picture is tilted slightly anti-clockwise. The seam slopes to the left, the table runs uphill and the wine spilt by the woman on the right falls towards the right instead of vertically.

The canvas is prepared with a double ground similar to that in Nos. 672 and 4930. The lower layer is of a fairly pure orange-red earth with on top a light fawnish-grey consisting of granular lead white combined with some umber and black pigment.

PENTIMENTI: Belshazzar's turban was at first higher at the back, before the crown was added. To Belshazzar's right is the shadowy face of a man, which was subsequently painted out. Belshazzar's right hand was apparently open, the fingers straighter and not clenched; and the dish beside it was taller. There is some highlighted drapery at his waist which has been subsequently glazed over. There are small changes in the lettering of the inscription, but these are in the size of the letters and not their forms. The shadowy musician at the back on the left cannot be seen at all in the X-radiograph and must be painted exlusively in earth colours.[4]

The subject is taken from Daniel 5: 1–5. Daniel's interpretation of the inscription is given in verses 26–8.

Hausherr[5] has shown that the same formula for the inscription was used by Mennaseh ben Israel in his *De termino vitae* of 1639 (Fig. 89). He argued that Rembrandt, who etched a portrait of ben Israel in 1636[6] and moved to a house opposite his in 1639, obtained the formula directly from ben Israel. He has been unable to trace another example of the use of this formula, and that Rembrandt obtained it from ben Israel seems likely. Hausherr argued that the date of publication of *De termino vitae* supports a date for No. 6350 of *c.*1639, a dating which was proposed by Sumowski.[7] However, the date of publication cannot be used as a *terminus post quem* for the execution of No. 6350. Rembrandt could have obtained the formula from ben Israel before the publication of the book; indeed, the two *pentimenti* in the inscription may suggest that Rembrandt did not have the formula as published in front of him when he began work. It should also be noted that the lettering in the two inscriptions does not exactly correspond. Van Gelder[8] preferred the traditional dating of the painting, that is, around the middle of the 1630s.[9] (Gerson[10] also favoured this dating.) Van Gelder pointed out that in No. 6350 motives of early paintings such as the *Judas returning the Thirty Pieces of Silver*[11] are repeated for the last time. However, very similar poses also recur in *The Wedding Feast of Samson*[12] of 1638 in Dresden. In violence of expression and gesture and in the dramatic effects of light, the painting recalls *The Blinding of Samson*[13] of 1636 in Frankfurt and there are also analogies of pose in *The Angel taking Leave of Tobias*[14] of 1637 in the Louvre. A date of *c.*1636–8 would seem most likely for No. 6350.

There is a similarity in the pose of the woman on the right with the man centre left, seen from the back, in Rembrandt's etching of *Christ driving the Money Changers from the Temple*[15] of 1635. Hofstede de Groot has suggested that *A Man in Oriental Costume*[16] of 1633 in Munich is a study for the figure of Belshazzar in No. 6350 but this is unlikely.

ENGRAVING: A derivation from the right half of the painting, without the falling woman, was engraved by Pollard.[17] The mezzotint by Henry Hudson records a different composition.[18]

COPIES: A copy attributed to Samuel van Hoogstraten is in Sanssouci.[19] Another copy is in the Rushbrook parish church, near Bury St Edmunds.[20] HdG[21] mentions a copy by Peter Tillemans which is recorded as being in the collection of Charles Jennens, London, in 1761.

PROVENANCE: First recorded at Knowsley Hall in 1736;[22] it was purchased by Hamlet Winstanley for James Stanley, 19th Earl of Derby (d. 1 February 1735/6) for £125.[23] Bought by the National Gallery from the Earl of Derby with the assistance of the NACF, 1964.

EXHIBITIONS: BI 1822, No. 21; BI 1852, No. 24; Manchester 1857, No. 695; RA 1899, No. 58; RA 1952–3, No. 160; Stockholm, Nationalmuseum, 'Rembrandt', 1956, No. 18; Manchester 1957, No. 131; London 1988–9, No. 7.

REFERENCES:

General: Bode and HdG, vol. 3, No. 168; HdG No. 52; Bauch No. 21; Bredius, *Rembrandt*, No. 497 *Rembrandt Corpus*, vol. 3, No. A110.

In text:

1. The inscription is given here in Roman letters. The last word according to the Chaldean text is 'Upharsin' and according to the Vulgate 'phares', see E. Pannier, in F. Vigouroux, *Dictionnaire de la Bible*, vol. 1, 1895, col. 1422.

2. Professor van de Wetering kindly conveyed these observations to the present writer before the publication of volume 3 of the *Rembrandt Corpus*.

3. Bredius No. 438. The Munich painting bears the inscription 'Rembrandt verandert en overgeschildert', 1636 (Rembrandt changed and overpainted). The painting is a studio version, reworked by Rembrandt himself, of the painting of 1635 (Bredius No. 498) in Leningrad.

4. For a full technical description, see London 1988–9, pp. 74–9.

5. R. Hausherr, 'Zur Menetekel-Inschrift auf Rembrandts Belsazarbild', OH, vol. 78, 1963, pp. 142–9.

6. Hollstein No. B269.

7. W. Sumowski, 'Eine Anmerkung zu Rembrandts Gastmal des Belsazar', OH, vol. 71, 1956, p. 233.

8. J. G. van Gelder, 'Rembrandt and his Circle', BM, 1953, p. 38.

9. This dating is favoured by Bode and HdG and Bredius (*Rembrandt*, in the first edition, 1937): see under REFERENCES: General.

10. Bredius, *Rembrandt*, No. 497.

11. Bredius, *Rembrandt*, No. 539A.

12. Bredius, *Rembrandt*, No. 507.

13. Bredius, *Rembrandt*, No. 501.

14. Bredius, *Rembrandt*, No. 503.

15. Hollstein No. B69.

16. HdG No. 348. Bredius, *Rembrandt*, No. 178.

Gerson considers that it is more likely to be a study for a biblical scene than a 'portrait' but does not relate it to No. 6350.

17. There is a copy of this engraving in the National Gallery dossier.

18. Charrington/Alexander No. 92. Hudson's mezzotint carries the inscription (in the first state): 'Painted by Rembrandt Engraved by H. Hudson KING BELSHAZZAR beholding the HAND WRITING on the WALL. From the original Picture in the Collection of Thomas Fullwood Esquire To whom this Print is most respectfully inscribed By his obliged & obed^t serv^t HENRY HUDSON. Published as the Act directs, 14 Feb 1785, by H. Hudson No. 28 Newman Street, Oxford Street, London.' The painting was in Fullwood's sale, London, 12 April 1791, lot 86 (bought by Fortescue). It may be identical with the *Belshazzar's Feast* ascribed to Rembrandt in Dr Robert Bragge's sale, 1 May, 1753, lot 39 or perhaps with the copy ascribed to Tillemans (see under COPIES).

19. E. Henschel-Simon, *Die Gemälde und Skulpturen in der Bildergalerie von Sans souci*, 1930, No. 76. This picture was engraved by A. L. Krüger *c.*1770 as by F. Bol.

20. This information was supplied by Anthony Blunt.

21. HdG No. 52. His source is R. and J. D. Dodsley, *London and its Environs Described*, 1761, vol. 5, p. 90.

22. See G. Scharf, *Catalogue of the Collection of Pictures at Knowsley Hall*, 1875, No. 70.

23. Scharf, op. cit. T. Pennant, *A Tour from Downing to Alston-Moor*, 1801, p. 46, stated that Hamlet Winstanley (1698–1756) bought many of the pictures then at Knowsley for James, 19th Earl of Derby, who succeeded to the earldom in 1702.

6432 *Portrait of Hendrickje Stoffels*   *Plate 296*

Signed (falsely?), lower left: Rembrandt f./16(?5 or 6)9.

Oil on canvas, 101.9 × 83.7 (40$\frac{1}{4}$ × 33$\frac{3}{4}$).

Cleaned in 1976. There is a heavy craquelure on the face. There are small paint losses, notably on the left eyelid and on either side of the mouth. There is wearing in the wrap.

PENTIMENTI: The X-radiograph reveals substantial changes in the position of the hands. Rembrandt seems originally to have painted Hendrickje with folded arms or with her hands clasped in her lap, as in the British Museum drawing (see Fig. 90). The left arm was across the body, as in the final version, but not tucked into the wrap. The right arm dropped vertically from the shoulder and folded across to link with the left. He then moved the right hand upwards and introduced the arm of the chair to support it. The left hand was then concealed within the folds of the wrap. In making these alterations, Rembrandt seems to have obliterated the original image with vigorous scrubbed brushstrokes of lead white and then painted the present design on top.

The ground consists of a mixture of quartz (silica) and small amounts of brown-coloured ochre and lead white. It is very similar in its make-up to the ground layer in Nos. 221 and 6300 by Rembrandt of this catalogue.[1]

Hendrickje Stoffelsdr. Jeger or Jagher(s), generally called Hendrickje Stoffels in contemporary documents,[2] was born in 1625/6 or a little earlier.[3] She is first mentioned as a member of Rembrandt's household in a document of 1 October 1649. She gave evidence on the artist's behalf in a breach of promise suit brought against him by Geertge Dircx, a woman he had employed as a nurse for Titus, his son by his marriage to Saskia van Uylenburgh.[4] (Saskia had died in 1642.) Hendrickje replaced Geertge both as Titus' nurse and as Rembrandt's mistress. In July 1654 she was summoned before the council of the Reformed Church and admonished for living in sin with Rembrandt;[5] Rembrandt and Hendrickje's only child, a daughter, Cornelia, was baptised on 30 October 1654.[6] Hendrickje remained in Rembrandt's household for the rest of of her life. She made a will in 1661;[7] she was buried in the Westerkerk, Amsterdam, on 24 July 1663.[8]

There is no documented portrait of Hendrickje Stoffels but there are a number of paintings representing the same model and dating from the time when she was living with Rembrandt. The recurrence of this model and the affection and informality with which she is painted point to her being Hendrickje. In the view of the present writer there are (at least) four portraits and one painted study, as well as No. 6432, which show the same model, who can reasonably be identified as Hendrickje. They are the portrait in the Louvre,[9] painted in the early 1650s and possibly a pair to the *Self Portrait* in Cassel which is dated 1654; the portrait of a woman leaning at an open door in the Gemäldegalerie, Berlin-Dahlem,[10] painted in the late 1650s; the portrait as Venus with Cupid in the Louvre,[11] which is a copy by a pupil after a Rembrandt composition of the late 1650s; the portrait in the Metropolitan Museum, New York,[12] which is dated 1660 and is the companion to a *Self Portrait* in the same collection (in style and technique this is the closest to No. 6432); and the study of *A Woman Bathing* of 1654, which is No. 54 of this catalogue.

The painting bears a signature and a date in the lower left-hand corner. After cleaning in 1976 three digits became clearly legible: 16( ) 9. The third is either a 5 or a 6: there is damage at the point where the two are differentiated. The second date, 1669, the year of the artist's death and six years after Hendrickje's death, is impossible on stylistic grounds. The former, 1659, is possible. The signature, however, is too large and uncharacteristically formed if it is compared with signatures of the 1650s. The most likely explanation is that the signature is not authentic, but was added to the painting later. Technical analysis of the paint suggests that this was done in the seventeenth or early eighteenth century.[13]

Stylistically the painting belongs to a group of three-quarter length painted and etched portraits of the 1650s: in the 1651 etching of Clement de Jonghe[14] and in the 1652 painting of Nicolas Bruyningh in Cassel,[15] Rembrandt can be seen experimenting with the three-quarter-length pose and the spatial relationship between sitter, chair and picture space. Other near-contemporary examples of this portrait format are the etchings of Jan Lutma[16] and Arnold Tholinx.[17] It seems likely that it was about this time that Rembrandt painted Hendrickje in this informal portrait.

The drawing in the British Museum[18] has been dated 1655–6. A comparison of the drawing with the X-radiograph of No. 6432 suggests that the drawing could be an early stage of the composition of the painting – or was made in connection with it. It would seem, therefore, that a reasonable date for No. 6432 would be *c.* 1654–6, when the sitter was aged about thirty-two. It should be stressed, however, that this is hypothetical and it is possible that the date 1659, even if it was added by a hand other than Rembrandt's, has some basis in fact. No. 6432 cannot date from after 1660: the Metropolitan portrait[19] shows that by 1660 Hendrickje had aged markedly.

Certain formal aspects of the painting remain difficult to clarify: the precise nature of the material of Hendrickje's wrap (probably woollen); the table (or bed) sketched in the right foreground; and the background. Although these are all unfinished in the sense of a formal portrait, they did not perhaps need to be finished in an informal portrait of this kind.

DRAWING: A related drawing in the British Museum is discussed above.

COPY: An early nineteenth-century English copy, presumably made after 1817 (see PROVENANCE), has been in the collection of the Royal Society of Arts since 1862. (It was exhibited in 1867 as a portrait of the artist James Barry's mother.[20])

PROVENANCE: Purchased by William Buchanan in Amsterdam in 1817 for 'Mr Gray';[21] collection of Edward Gray, Haringey House, Hornsey;[22] Gray's entire collection was purchased from his heirs in December 1838 or January 1839 by William Buchanan for £15,000. The collection was bought from Buchanan by James Morrison for the same sum on 30 January 1839;[23] collection of James Morrison, Basildon Park, Berkshire; Morrison family collection.[24] Purchased from the Walter Morrison Pictures Settlement by private treaty sale, 1976.

EXHIBITIONS: Leeds 1868, No. 731; RA 1882, No. 63; RA 1899, No. 93; London, Grosvenor Galleries, Third National Loan Exhibition, 1914, No. 84; BFAC, Winter Exhibition, 1936–7, No. 64; London 1976, No. 91; London 1988–9, No. 13.

REFERENCES:
General: Bode and HdG, No. 140; HdG No. 715; Bauch No. 521; Bredius, *Rembrandt*, No. 113; C. Brown and J. Plesters, 'Rembrandt's Portrait of Hendrickje Stoffels', *Apollo*, vol. 106, 1977, pp. 286–91.
In text:
1. For a full technical description, see London 1988–9, pp. 106–11.
2. She is called Hendrickje Stoffels in most of the contemporary documents concerning her (but see note 5 below). Stoffels was, however, her patronymic (i.e. Stoffelsdochter), her father being Sergeant Stoffel Jeger (see J. Goudwaard in *Amstelodamum*, vol. 43, 1956, pp. 114–15 and 163–4).
3. In a document of 1 October 1649 she is said to be twenty-three; in one of October 1661 she is said to be thirty-eight (Strauss *Doc.* 1649/9).
4. Strauss *Doc.* 1649/9.
5. 'Hendrickie Jaghers ... bekent dat se met Rembrandt de schilder Hocrerije heeft ghepleecht' (Strauss *Doc.* 1654/11, 12, 14, 15).
6. Strauss *Doc.* 1654/18.

7. Strauss *Doc.* 1661/6.

8. See I. H. van Eeghen in *Amstelodamum*, vol. 43, 1956, pp. 115–16.

9. Bredius, *Rembrandt*, No. 111.

10. Bredius, op. cit., No. 116.

11. Bredius, op. cit., No. 117.

12. Bredius, op. cit., No. 118.

13. For an extended discussion see Brown and Plesters, op. cit., esp. pp. 288–9.

14. Hollstein No. B272.

15. Bredius, op. cit., No. 268.

16. Hollstein No. B276.

17. Hollstein No. B284.

18. Benesch, vol. 5, No. 1174 (Fig. 1471).

19. Bredius, op. cit., No. 118.

20. The present writer is indebted to Mr J. S. Skidmore for this information.

21. Buchanan, vol. 2, p. 349.

22. See Brown and Plesters, op. cit., pp. 286–7.

23. This complicated transaction is discussed in detail by the present writer in Brown and Plesters, op. cit., p. 287.

24. Waagen 1854: there is a short account of Morrison's collection in vol. 2, pp. 260–3 and an extensive account in the Supplement volume, published in 1857, pp. 105–13 (Harley Street) and pp. 300–12 (Basildon Park). On p. 304 is this description of No. 6432, which hung at Basildon Park:

'Rembrandt. A female portrait which passes for that of his daughter. She is seated in an armchair, and is dressed in white with a furred robe. The background is dark. To the knees. On canvas. 3 ft. 9 in. high, 2 ft. 9 in. wide. Very transparent in colouring, and of broad and masterly treatment.'

There is also an interesting discussion of the paint-ing, in particular its date and condition, in Wilhelm Bode's *Studien zur Geschichte der Holländischen Malerei*, Braunschweig, 1883, pp. 551–2:

'About the same time, apparently from the year 1665 (the last digit of the date is not clear) is a third portrait of a young, about eighteen-year-old girl which takes its place somewhere in the middle between the two portraits mentioned above. The owner of this precious painting which unfortunately through cleaning has lost something of its original magic is Mrs Morrison of Basildon Park. The description "Rembrandt's daughter" which the picture bears is inadmissible, for Cornelia was born in 1654; but the presentation of the subject indicates that she must have stood in some close relationship to Rembrandt. She sits in an armchair resting her right arm on its arm. The manner in which the precious white fur is thrown about her form suggests that . . . it veils a very incomplete toilette: where, because of the right arm which is within the fur, it has fallen open, the chemise and the bare bosom is seen, on which falls a golden chain, hanging round the neck at the throat. In the foreground on the table is a purple cover; in the background a brick-red hanging; both in a darker tone. In opulence and luminosity close to the Berlin picture [Bredius, *Rembrandt*, No. 116] this portrait can be ranked with the Louvre picture [Bredius No. 111] as regards the magic of the chiaroscuro, the mastery of execution and through the indescribable expression of feminine charm.'

HdG (op. cit.) commented on the difficulty in reading the signature and date: 'Painted about 1660. Signed on the left at the foot, "Rembrandt F. 166" – the name and date have been partly repainted and are thus hard to read . . .'

ATTRIBUTED TO REMBRANDT

5282 *Portrait of Margaretha de Geer,*   Plate 297
Wife of Jacob Trip

Signed on the left, below the level of the shoulder: Rembrandt.f/1661.

Oil on canvas, 75.3 × 63.8 (29$\frac{5}{8}$ × 25$\frac{1}{8}$).

Cleaned in 1983. The sitter's black dress is considerably worn at the lower right.

X-radiographs reveal light-coloured cuffs and the sitter's wrists at the lower edge.

A number of technical features of this painting, which has always been previously accepted as by Rembrandt, raise doubts about its precise status. None is, however, conclusive and it has been thought best to maintain the attribution to Rembrandt.[1]

The canvas has a double ground with a lower layer of chalk and an upper layer comprising a mixture of granular lead white, chalk and charcoal black, with red and yellow earth pigments in small quantities. Two features of the ground are unusual when compared with other Rembrandt paintings which have a double ground. Usually the lower layer is not chalk but an orange or reddish-brown ochre, as in the larger portrait of the same sitter in the National Gallery (No. 1675). Secondly, the particle form of the yellow earth pigment in the upper ground is unlike that of most specimens of yellow ochre in paint and ground samples taken from the Gallery's other Rembrandts. The pigment is present as yellow rod-like crystals, rather than rounded particles, which are the common form. However, extensive technical analysis has not revealed any materials in No. 5282 which are anachronistic for a seventeenth-century painting.

The ground is partly radioabsorbent and therefore the canvas structure is clearly visible in the X-radiograph. It can be seen that on all edges of the painting the outermost part of the canvas has been used as a tacking edge which has subsequently been flattened into a plane with the picture surface. The survival of what must be the original tacking edge in a painting of this age is very unusual. In addition, the canvas does not appear to be cusped: this indicates that it was cut from a larger prepared piece of canvas and attached lightly to a conventional strainer before painting. It was neither prepared with ground in its present size nor painted in a stretching frame: in both these regards it does not accord with Rembrandt's usual procedure. Neither of these factors is impossible to reconcile with an authentic Rembrandt, but taken together with the unusual ground type, it does raise doubts about the attribution of the painting to Rembrandt.

The handling of the paint is also different from No. 1675. In the larger portrait of Margaretha Trip, the technique is careful, painstaking and worked over and over again to achieve the final likeness. By contrast, No. 5282 is fluid, rapid and almost careless in execution. The brushstrokes in a number of passages – note, for example, the curious curved brushstroke of the upper part of the nose which gives it a strange dented shape unlike the nose in No. 1675 – lack the precision in defining form evident in the larger portrait.

If it is by Rembrandt, No. 5282 is a variant of the larger portrait (No. 1675). Both pictures would presumably have been begun in the same sitting or series of sittings, as Margaretha would have travelled from Dordrecht to Amsterdam for this purpose. If the larger portrait was intended for the Trippenhuis (as is argued above, under No. 1674), it is perfectly possible that the smaller painting would have been intended for the Trips' own house in Dordrecht or to be given to another member of the family. However, taking the technical and stylistic evidence into account, there are two possibilities: No. 5282 is either an extremely skilful imitation of the work of Rembrandt painted between 1660 and 1818 (when it is first recorded, see under PROVENANCE) or an authentic painting whose function and execution have led to considerable physical differences from No. 1675.

The sitter and other portraits of her are discussed in the entry for Rembrandt No. 1675 above. As in that painting, she wears the costume of forty or more years earlier.

COPIES: A copy was in the Christopher Lorimer and others sale, Sotheby's, 4 May 1966, lot 14 (£20 to Mrs H. Ward).[2] A reduced copy is in the Glasgow Art Gallery.[3] According to HdG[4] an unfinished copy was in the Neeld collection, Grittleton; it was apparently not there in 1942.[5] Another copy, said to be signed and dated 1638, was in the collection of O. van de Veegaete, Ghent, in 1961.[6] Another was in the collection of Jonkheer Herman Trip in The Hague in 1968.[7] There is a picture of a woman painting a copy of No. 5282, attributed to Richard Parkes Bonington (1802–28), in the Gabriel Renand collection.[8]

PROVENANCE: In the collection of Lord Charles Townshend by 1818, when it was exhibited at the BI;[9] [Lord Charles Townshend] sale, London, 4 June 1819 (lot 26),[10] bought in (235 gns); Lord Charles Townshend sale, London, 11 April 1835 (lot 49),[11] bought by John Smith[12] (£231). By 1836 in the collection of Baron J. G. Verstolk van Soelen,[13] The Hague, which was bought en bloc in 1846 by Thomas Baring, Humphrey Mildmay, S. Jones Loyd (later Baron Overstone) and Chaplin,[14] the present picture falling to Jones Loyd who exhibited it at the BI in 1848. Inherited by his daughter, Lady Wantage,[15] in 1883. Given by Lady Wantage to the Earl of Crawford and Balcarres in 1920;[16] on loan to the Mauritshuis, The Hague, in 1921. Purchased from the Earl of Crawford and Balcarres by the NACF in 1941 and presented to the National Gallery.

EXHIBITIONS: BI 1818, No. 6; BI 1848, No. 49; Manchester 1857 (provisional catalogue, No. 665; definitive catalogue, No. 677); RA 1870, No. 39; RA 1888, No. 109; Amsterdam 1898, No. 113; London, RA, 1899, No. 15; London, Grafton Galleries, 1904, No. 8; Amsterdam, Rijksmuseum, 'Rembrandt', 1906, No. 113; London, Grafton Galleries, 1909–10, No. 51; Paris, 'Exposition hollandaise' 1921, No. 29; RA 1929, No. 111; Amsterdam, Rijksmuseum, 'Rembrandt tentoonstelling', 1932, No. 34; London, NACF, 1945–6, No. 16 London 1988–9, No. 18.

REFERENCES:

General: Smith No. 516; Bode and HdG, vol. 7, No. 492; HdG No. 863; Bauch No. 524; Bredius, *Rembrandt*, No. 395.

In text:

1. A detailed technical description, which presents all these arguments in full, is given in London 1988–9, pp. 130–3.

2. Canvas, 75 × 62 cm. It was formerly in the Mrs L. Carrington Wertheim sale, London, 27 November 1957, lot 187.

3. Glasgow Art Gallery and Museum, *Dutch and Flemish Paintings*, 1961, No. 557. Canvas, 42 × 36.8 cm.

4. Loc. cit.

5. It is not in an inventory of the Grittleton pictures made in 1942, nor was it in the Neeld collection sales, London, 9 June 1944 and 8 February 1946.

6. Support and dimensions not known. Photo in RKD.

7. Panel, 27 × 21 cm. Previously in the Dettlinger collection, Dordrecht.

8. Reproduced in A. Shirley, *Bonington*, 1940, pl. 63 (there dated 1825).

9. 'Rembrandt Portrait of an elderly female.'

10. 'Rembrandt A Portrait, an Old Lady.'

11. 'Rembrandt Portrait of an Old Lady of quality in a ruff and a black dress trimmed with fur, seated in a chair . . . 25 in. by 30, with arched top' (prior to 1921 the picture was in a frame with an arched top which covered the top corners; cf. HdG No. 863).

12. See Smith No. 516 (where the date of the picture is wrongly given as 1660).

13. Smith No. 516.

14. See Northbrook catalogue, pp. ix–x and 199.

15. *A Catalogue of Pictures forming the Collection of Lord and Lady Wantage*, 1905, No. 185.

16. Letter of 1945 from Lord Crawford (in the National Gallery archives).

FOLLOWER OF REMBRANDT

51 *A Seated Man with a Stick* *Plate 298*

Signed, falsely, in the left bottom corner: R( )mbrandt/( )6( ). The signature and date are almost effaced; they were discovered when the picture was cleaned in 1936.

Oil on canvas, 137.5 × 104.8 (54 × 41¼). About 2 cm. more of the painted surface (apparently original) has been turned over the edge of the stretcher at the top and on the right; *c.* 1.2 cm. more on the left.

Cleaned in 1936 and 1967.

The background had been extensively overpainted. This was not removed when the picture was cleaned in 1936. It was taken off in 1967.

There is a *pentimento* in the top of the stick.

The painting was formerly known as 'A Jew Merchant', a title apparently first given to it in 1832.[1]

MacLaren was the first to doubt the picture as the work of Rembrandt. He pointed out a number of weaknesses (especially the meaningless brushstrokes on the nose, the drawing of the right shoulder and the rather niggling treatment of the right sleeve) and suggested that it may be 'at least in part, possibly wholly, the work of a pupil in Rembrandt's studio'. The present writer believes that it is in its entirety the work of a pupil or later imitator of Rembrandt.

Sumowski[2] has attributed the painting to Samuel van Hoogstraten and dated it to the late 1640s. Gerson[3] did not consider it to be by Hoogstraten.

MacLaren stated that it was probably painted about 1648–50. The present writer considers that it could well be a late seventeenth-century or even early eighteenth-century imitation.

COPY: A copy is in the Gemäldegalerie, Cassel.[4] Another was in Anon. sale, Sotheby's, 20 October 1971, lot 159 (as German School, *c.*1800; with pendant [see below] to J. Coburn £120).[5]

ENGRAVING: Mezzotint by Samuel William Reynolds, 1816.[6]

PROVENANCE: Most probably the undescribed picture by Rembrandt which, according to Joseph Farington, was sold by Sir Thomas Lawrence to Sir George Beaumont, Bart., in July 1797;[7] probably lent to the BI, 1815 (No. 34),[8] by Beaumont. It was among the pictures presented by Sir George Beamont in 1823 to the British Museum for the future National Gallery and transferred to the National Gallery in 1828.

EXHIBITIONS: BI 1815, No. 34(?);[9] London 1947–8, No. 69.

REFERENCES:

General: Smith No. 415; Bode and HdG No. 384; HdG No. 391; Bredius, *Rembrandt*, No. 257.

In text:

1. In W. Young Ottley's *Descriptive Catalogue of the Pictures in the National Gallery*, 1832, p. 36.
2. Sumowski, *Gemälde*, vol. 2. Hoogstraten No. 854. He comments on its Venetian manner and relates it to a painting of a young man (whom he

identifies as Willem Drost) formerly on the London art market (his No. 853) and the signed and dated (1653) painting of an *Old Man at a Window* in Vienna (his No. 880).
3. Bredius, *Rembrandt*, No. 257.
4. Cassel catalogue, 1929, p. 64 (No. 253). Canvas, 122 × 96 cm. It is in the 1749 Cassel inventory (No. 301) and is to be identified with HdG No. 469.

5. On metal, 37.5 × 29 cm. Photo in National Gallery archives. It had a pendant on the same support and of the same size showing *A Young Man lighting a Candle*.

6. Charrington/Alexander, No. 151. States 1 and 2 are inscribed: 'Lady Beaumont'; state 3 is inscribed 'Rembrandt Pinx^t London ... 1816 S. W. Reynolds, Sr Sculp^t.'

7. Farington, vol. 3 (9 and 16 July 1797); Farington simply described it as 'his [Lawrence's] picture by Rembrandt' in the first entry. On 16 July he records: 'Sir Geo. Beaumont called – Lawrence has wrote to him offering his Rembrant [sic] for 150 gs. on condition that He may have it back in 4 yrs if he chooses for 200 gs, says He gave 400 for it – Sir George declined the conditions, but offered 200 gs. for it,

which Lawrence has accepted'. It is almost certainly the 'half length portrait by Rembrant [sic], to be sent to the BI to form part of an Exhibition of pictures by deceased Artists, for Students to study' (Farington, vol. 8, 8 August 1806, p. 2834). Beaumont is not known to have possessed any other portrait attributed to Rembrandt.

8. The description in the BI catalogue, 'Head of a Rabbi', is not very apt but there does not seem to have been any other Rembrandt portrait or study in Beaumont's collection. Half- and three-quarter lengths were not infrequently described as 'heads' in eighteenth- and early nineteenth-century catalogues (cf. Rembrandt No. 243, note 12 and No. 1675, note 8).

9. See note 8 above.

FOLLOWER OF REMBRANDT

1247 *A Young Man and a Girl playing Cards* *Plate 299*

Oil on canvas, 123.5 × 104 (48⅝ × 41).

Cleaned in 1952–3. The girl's hair and flesh are worn (especially the lower part of the face); there is a retouched horizontal seam 26.8 cm. from the bottom edge. There is a prominent craquelure throughout.

PENTIMENTI: There are various *pentimenti*. The girl's right hand and the cards she is holding have been altered; the white undersleeve at her right wrist has been painted over the red sleeve; there were at first two fillets round her hair, the coil on top was different and the tress on her left cheek was apparently originally slightly different.

Catalogued as by Nicolaes Maes until 1960. The resemblance to Maes' style seems to have been noted first by Waagen[1] and subsequently it was generally accepted as an early work by him;[2] although Hofstede de Groot was not quite sure of Maes' authorship he could offer no alternative.[3] There is some likeness to Maes' early style, especially in the treatment of the man's head, yet there is no early work by him in which the handling is as coarse (especially the hands) and the draughtsmanship so little assured, and it is difficult to accept as his. Certainly the present picture and No. 757 of this catalogue, an early large-scale work by Maes, cannot be by the same hand.

The style seems to derive from that of Rembrandt's subject pieces of about 1645–50 and suggests the painter was either a pupil of Rembrandt or in direct contact with him, even though this kind of genre scene is rather unusual in Rembrandt's immediate circle. Münz[4] put forward the name of Barent Fabritius; there are, however, considerable differences of style between the present picture and any certain work by Barent.[5]

Mme Brière-Misme[6] published a picture of a man and a woman playing cards, with a gipsy woman watching them, by Cornelis Bisschop of Dordrecht (1630–74);[7] in her view this composition, which is signed and dated 1657, is based on the present picture and confirms the attribution of the latter to Maes, on the grounds that Bisschop sometimes imitated Maes' style [of 1655 onwards]. She considered that the National Gallery picture may therefore be dated between 1653, when Maes returned to Dordrecht, and 1657. More recently Sumowski[8] has attributed No. 1247 to Bisschop himself. Though an interesting attribution, this must remain speculative as no signed Bisschop, in the view of the present writer, shows the broad handling which is so characteristic of No. 1247.

COPY: There is a pen and wash sketch inscribed 'Rembrand' in the Rijksprentenkabinet said to be by J. Andriessen apparently after this painting, although the positions of the man's arms are different and there is no sign of the fireplace on the right.[9]

PROVENANCE: Possibly identical with 'A man and woman at cards' attributed to Rembrandt in the Thomas Bladen sale, London, 10–11 March 1775 (2nd day, lot 61),[10] 95 gns, bought by the Bishop of Bristol (Dr Thomas Newton).[11] It was in the collection of the 5th Baron Monson (1809–41) at Gatton Park, Surrey;[12] when exhibited at the RA in 1886, it was lent by the 7th Baron Monson (later Viscount Oxenbridge);[13] Viscount Oxenbridge (Gatton Park) sale, London, 12 May 1888 (lot 9),[14] 1,310 gns, bought for the National Gallery (with the aid of the Lewis Fund).

EXHIBITION: RA 1886, No. 85.[13]

REFERENCES:
General: HdG, Maes No. 109.
In text:
1. Waagen, 1857, p. 344.
2. e.g. W. R. Valentiner, *Nicolaes Maes*, 1924, pp. 43–4.
3. HdG, loc. cit.
4. L. Münz in *Die graphischen Künste*, N.F., vol. 2, 1937, p. 159.
5. For Barent Fabritius, see D. Pont, *Barent Fabritius*, Utrecht, 1958.
6. C. Brière-Misme in OH, vol. 68, 1953, pp. 184–6.
7. 110 × 137 cm. The picture was in the Paris art market in 1953.
8. Sumowski, *Gemälde*, vol. 3, pp. 1962, 1966 and 1993.
9. Photo in RKD. Neg. no. 16998.
10. 'REMBRANDT A man and woman at cards, the force of colouring and the attention in the characters, pronounce it in the best time of the master.'

11. It was not among the pictures belonging to Dr Newton exhibited for private sale in London, 8 April sqq. 1788, nor in his picture sales at Christie's, 30 April 1790 and 22 March 1794, nor in the Revd N. D. H. Newton's sale of paintings from Dr [Thomas] Newton's collection, London, 3 June 1808.
12. According to the catalogue of the Gatton Park sale, 1888, the pictures then sold came from the collection of Frederick John, 5th Baron Monson, at Gatton Park, 'formed early in the present century'. The present picture was seen in 1854–7 at Gatton Park (then occupied by the Countess of Warwick) by Waagen (loc. cit.). In a letter of 15 April 1851 Lord Monson says it was bought from Woodburn (kindly communicated by Sir Ellis Waterhouse).
13. and 14. As by Maes.

FOLLOWER OF REMBRANDT

2538 *Diana bathing surprised by a Satyr(?)*   *Plate 300*

The head, right shoulder and arm of a figure peering round the tree behind Diana are visible only in strong light.

In the bottom left corner are the remains of a false signature: Rembran( ) (difficult to see; the last four letters are almost effaced).[1]

Oil on oak, 46.3 × 35.4 ($18\frac{1}{4}$ × $13\frac{15}{16}$). Originally painted with rounded top corners; the blank spandrels have been overpainted later.

Cleaned in 1953. Extensive damage in the upper right half of the picture and scattered losses in the darks; the dark foliage is also very heavily cracked and has darkened.

The presence of the hounds makes it likely that Diana is represented here. The scarcely visible figure behind the tree may be intended for a satyr or, less probably, Actaeon. The subject of Diana surprised by satyrs is not common in Dutch painting but occurs frequently in Flemish pictures of this period.

Until 1960 this painting was generally accepted as a Rembrandt of *c.* 1635.[2] However, both composition and execution are far too feeble for him and it is clearly by a pupil or follower. It does not seem to be based on Rembrandt's style of *c.* 1635 (e.g. the *Diana, Actaeon and Callisto* of 1635 in Anholt[3]) but rather on that of the late 1630s (e.g. the Czartoryski *Landscape with the Good Samaritan*[4] and the Buckingham Palace *Christ appearing to the Magdalen,*[5] both dated 1638), and the picture may be a little later, about 1640. There is a slight resemblance to van den Eeckhout's earliest work[6] but, more convincingly, Bauch has suggested that the painting is in the style of Flinck,[7] and Sumowski[8] has supported this attribution.

PROVENANCE: In the possession of R. Langton Douglas, London, and sold by him to George Salting, London, probably in 1909.[8] Salting Bequest, 1910.

REFERENCES:
General: HdG No. 198; Bredius, *Rembrandt*, No. 473.
In text:
1. Although certainly false it is probably old since it resisted tests made with undiluted acetone in 1953.
2. e.g. by HdG and Bredius (see REFERENCES: General).
3. Bredius, *Rembrandt*, No. 472; *Rembrandt Corpus*, vol. 2, No. A92.
4. Bredius, op. cit., No. 442.
5. Bredius, op. cit., No. 559.
6. MacLaren's suggestion that the painting showed some resemblance to van den Eeckhout's early work was supported by Gerson (in Bredius, op. cit.) but Sumowski (*Gemälde*) did not include the painting in his van den Eeckhout catalogue. A valid comparison would be with van den Eeckhout's *Landscape with Bathing Men* (Amsterdam, Rijksmuseum: 1976 cat., A1612) which is Sumowski's catalogue No. 544. The landscape technique is quite different from (and far superior to) that in No. 2538.
7. Bauch, p. 49 (note to Bredius, op. cit., No. 473).
8. Sumowski, *Gemälde*, vol. 5, No. 2073.
9. HdG in *L'art flamand et hollandais*, vol. 12, 1909, p. 166, and letter of 1934 from R. Langton Douglas (in the National Gallery archives). Messrs Agnew have no record of ever having possessed the picture as HdG states (letter of 1929 from Agnew's in the National Gallery archives).

FOLLOWER OF REMBRANDT

3214 *A Man seated reading at a Table in a Lofty Room*   Plate 301

Above the shelves of books on the right are a pair of globes.

Along the handrail of the stairs, right, are rather faint traces of an obviously false signature: Rem(.)randt. This was not removed during cleaning.

Oil on oak, 55.1 × 46.5 ($21\frac{11}{16}$ × $18\frac{5}{16}$).

Cleaned in 1985. The arched recess in the background wall was found during cleaning to have been slightly retouched but otherwise it is contemporary with the rest of the picture.

Astrologers, alchemists and philosophers engaged in study were popular subjects in Dutch seventeenth-century painting.[1] Rembrandt painted several pictures with such subjects at the end of the 1620s and in the early 1630s.[2]

Until relatively recently the painting has been considered an authentic Rembrandt of about 1628–9.[3]

The attribution of this painting to Rembrandt was first doubted in print by J. Bruyn in the proceedings of the Rembrandt symposium in Chicago in 1969:[4] he considered it to be an eighteenth-century 'proto-romantic interpretation' of the style of Rembrandt's Leiden period by a British or German painter. In the subsequent discussion,[5] the painting was defended by Gerson ('a beautiful early Rembrandt'), Bauch and Slive. Subsequently the Rembrandt Research Project, of which Bruyn is a member, have included the painting in the Rejected Attributions section of the first volume of their *Corpus*.[6] They consider it to be 'a well-preserved and fairly old Rembrandt imitation, probably dating from the late 17th or early 18th century and painted in the southern Netherlands'. They believe it to be by the same hand as the *Travellers Resting* (*Rest on the Flight to Egypt*) in the Mauritshuis.[7] Their criticisms are technical and stylistic. They consider that 'the construction of the panel made up of three horizontal scarf-joined planks is unthinkable for a seventeenth-century Dutch panel of upright format'. As far as the stylistic arguments are concerned, they note the resemblance of the illuminated back wall to those in the Hamburg *Simeon in the Temple*[8] and the Stuttgart *St Paul*[9] and of the silhouetted shapes on the right to the still life of books in the Nuremburg *St Paul*;[10] however, in No. 3214 they discern a lack of refinement in the execution and 'an exaggeration aimed at effect'. There is, they believe, basing themselves on the X-radiographs, 'a weak connection between brushwork and indication of form'. The scratch marks used to emphasise contours and lines of script are entirely untypical in their view, as is the use of colour.

In the oak panel on which No. 3214 is painted the grain runs horizontally, an unusual feature for a painting of this shape. There is a horizontal join not quite half way up. The edges of this join have been chamfered and, as can be seen in X-radiographs (Fig. 91), overlap by about 6 mm. when stuck together. Joins of this type can be found in panel paintings by Rubens but have not been found in any by Rembrandt, where joins are usually butt joints. However, while unusual, this scarcely constitutes incontrovertible proof that the painting is not by Rembrandt. The dendrochronological analysis carried out by Bauch and Eckstein[11] gives the felling area as the South Netherlands and the earliest possible felling date as 1614. Cross-sections reveal a very thin chalk and glue ground such as has been noted in Rembrandt Nos. 775 (of 1634) and 850 (of 1635), above. The technique of painting the whites and lights thickly with heavy lead white impasto and the darks and particularly the blacks thinly and translucently is also very similar to the technique seen in Nos. 775 and 850. An analysis of the pigments has not revealed anything inconsistent with a dating of *c.* 1630.

There is therefore no compelling technical reason that the painting could not be by Rembrandt. There are, however, a number of stylistic features which seem to the present writer to be inconsistent with an attribution to Rembrandt. A striking feature is that the outlines of some details in the painting – for example, the hinges of the window, cracks on the wall, the pattern of the table carpet, etc. – were incised in the paint when it was quite firm as the incised outlines are sharp. This would have been done with the wooden end of a brush or a metal stylus. While Rembrandt does occasionally use this technique in his early work it is never done in this fussy, literal-minded manner, nor is it employed on a mass of relatively unimportant details as it is here. Secondly, the arch on the back wall, which MacLaren believed to be false, is in fact integral to the original paint layer: it is clumsily drawn and its volume ill-defined. Thirdly, the contrast between the detailed, even pedantic, draughtsmanship of the globes, etc. on the shelves at the right and the loose, almost careless, treatment of the figure is inconsistent with Rembrandt's manner of *c.* 1630.

To sum up: the scientific evidence suggests that the artist of No. 3214 knew a good deal about Rembrandt's technical procedures, in particular the way in which he prepared his grounds. The panel *may* have originated in the southern Netherlands but could have been available to an artist in the United Provinces. There is nothing in the pigments inconsistent with the painting having been executed during the seventeenth century. There are, however, a number of powerful stylistic arguments against an attribution to Rembrandt himself. The likelihood is that No. 3214 is the work of an early, perhaps contemporary, follower or imitator of Rembrandt. It may well be by the same artist as the *Travellers Resting* in the Mauritshuis.[12]

PROVENANCE: No. 3214 may conceivably be identical with one (or more) of these early sales: David Ietswaard sale, Amsterdam, 22 April 1749, lot 35 ('Een Schrijvend Man in zijn Kamer door denzelven [Rembrandt], h. lv. 10d., br. lv. 7d.' [56.5 × 48.4 cm.]; [Hamilton] sale, London, 24–25 January 1765, 1st day, lot 12 ('Rembrandt. A Philosopher in his Study'); Earl of Harrington sale, London, 30–31 March 1781, 2nd day, lot 60 ('Rembrandt: Philosopher in his Study: 9 gns to Beauvoir'). It was almost certainly in the collection of Richard Cosway, RA, London, in 1791.[13] A 'Philosopher in his study' by Rembrandt was in the Bryan sale, London, 17–19 May 1798 (3rd day, lot 32), 84 gns.[14] No. 3214 was bought by Warburton Davies, probably between 1820 and 1830;[15] it was inherited by his great-nephew, Lieut.-Gen. Sir Francis John Davies of Elmley Castle, from whom it was purchased (out of the Temple-West Fund) in August 1917.

REFERENCES:
General: Bauch No. 119; Bredius, *Rembrandt*, No. 427; *Rembrandt Corpus*, vol. 1 cat. C12. In text:
1. Other examples in the National Gallery are Bol No. 679 and van Deuren No. 2589; A. van Ostade No. 846 is a satirical treatment of the subject. The subject is discussed (in the context of Rembrandt and his pupils) and many further examples given by H. van der Waal in *Steps towards Rembrandt: Collected Articles, 1937–72*, Amsterdam, 1974, p. 143 ff.
2. For example: *Two Scholars Disputing*, 1628, panel 71 × 58.5 cm. Melbourne, National Gallery of Victoria (Bredius, *Rembrandt*, No. 423); *A Scholar in a Lofty Room*, 1631, panel, 60 × 48 cm. Stockholm, Nationalmuseum (Bredius, *Rembrandt*, No. 430); *A*

Scholar in a Room with a Winding Stair, 163(?3), panel 29 × 33 cm. Paris, Louvre (Bredius, *Rembrandt*, No. 431).
3. The picture was first published by Sir C. J. Holmes in BM, 31, 1917, pp. 171–2. It was accepted by Bredius (*Rembrandt*, 1st ed., 1937, No. 427), Bauch (op. cit.), MacLaren, and by Gerson in Bredius, *Rembrandt* (op. cit.). Gerson noted: 'an oil sketch in greyish colours of excellent quality, painted around 1628.'
4. The Art Institute of Chicago, *Rembrandt after Three Hundred Years: A Symposium – Rembrandt and his Followers (1969)*, Chicago, 1973, p. 37.
5. *Rembrandt after Three Hundred Years: A Symposium . . .*, op. cit., pp. 43–4.

6. *Rembrandt Corpus*, vol. 1, cat. C14.

7. Bredius, *Rembrandt*, No. 556; *Rembrandt Corpus*, cat. C12.

8. Bredius, *Rembrandt*, No. 535.

9. Bredius, *Rembrandt*, No. 601.

10. Bredius, *Rembrandt*, No. 602.

11. *Rembrandt Corpus*, cat. No. C14 (p. 529).

12. See note 7 above.

13. *A catalogue of the entire collection of Richard Cosway . . . in . . . his house in Pall Mall*, 1791, p. 21, No. 16: 'REMBRANDT. An old man reading at a win-
dow, into which the sun shines through a watery atmosphere. – The shadow of the divisions of the window are on the white wall, which constitutes the eye of the picture . . .' This picture was not in Richard Cosway's sale, London, 2–3 March 1792; it is conceivably lot 88 (1st day) of the Richard Cosway sale, London, 17–19 May 1821: 'REMBRANDT An Interior, with a powerful effect of light.'

14. See Buchanan, vol. 1, p. 290.

15. According to Sir Francis Davies (letters of August 1917 in the National Gallery archives).

FOLLOWER OF REMBRANDT

6274 *An Old Man in an Armchair* *Plate 302*

Signed in the top right corner: Rembrandt. f./1652.

Oil on canvas, 111 × 88 (43$\frac{5}{8}$ × 34$\frac{5}{8}$).

Cleaned in 1963.

The Venetian, and in particular the Tintorettesque, influence apparent in this portrait was stressed by MacLaren and subsequently by Clark.[1] Gerson,[2] however, doubted the attribution of the painting to Rembrandt: he felt that the overall structure, and in particular the loose and 'painterly' treatment of the beard, fur coat and right hand, was weak. He noted that the man's left hand and sleeve were painted in different styles. In his view such divergences are not to be found in Rembrandt's autograph portraits of the early 1650s, an outstanding period for his portraiture. He suggested that comparison should be made with the *Old Man* of 1651 at Chatsworth;[3] the *Portrait of Nicolaes Bruyningh* of 1652 in Cassel;[4] and the *Portrait of Jan Six* painted in 1654 in the Six Foundation, Amsterdam.[5]

Sumowski defended the painting in 1970[6] ('die Ausdrucksstärke des Londoner Bildes überhaupt für schulermöglich zu halten') but in a more recent letter to the present writer has described it as a school piece.

Martin[7] has defended the painting but the present writer agrees with Gerson that a greater degree of stylistic coherence must be expected in a portrait of this date – or indeed of any other possible date – if the painting were autograph. It has been suggested that No. 6274 may possibly be by the same hand as the *Apostle Thomas* in Cassel.[8] That painting, however, has recently been cleaned and the authentic signature of Nicolaes Maes revealed. No. 6274 is not by Maes and so must, in the present state of knowledge, be attributed to an unknown pupil or early follower of Rembrandt.

ENGRAVING: Engraved in mezzotint by Charles Phillips, 1766.[9]

PROVENANCE: Almost certainly among the pictures at Chiswick House collected by the 3rd Earl of Burlington (d. 1753) which passed by inheritance to the 4th Duke of Devonshire;[10] in any case in the Duke's collection at Chiswick House, apparently by 1761[11] and certainly by 1766.[12] Acquired (under the Finance Act, 1956) from the 11th Duke of Devonshire, August 1957.

EXHIBITIONS: BI 1837, No. 55; RA 1876, No. 243; Amsterdam, 1898, No. 85; RA, Rembrandt Exhibition, 1899, No. 54; RA 1929, No. 126; RA 1938, No. 125; London, Agnew's, Devonshire Collection Exhibition, 1948, No. 22; RA 1952–3, No. 172.

REFERENCES:
General: Smith No. 326; Bode and HdG, vol. 5, No. 381; HdG No. 292; Bauch No. 206; Bredius, *Rembrandt*, No. 267.
In text:
1. K. Clark, *Rembrandt and the Italian Renaissance*, London, 1966, p. 130.
2. Bredius No. 267.
3. Bredius No. 266.
4. Bredius No. 268.
5. Bredius No. 276.
6. W. Sumowski, 'Kritische Bemerkungen zur neuesten Gemälde Kritik', in O. v. Simson and J. Kelch, eds, *Neue Beiträge zur Rembrandt-Forschung*, Berlin, 1973, p. 107.
7. In his review of Gerson's revised edition of Bredius in *Apollo*, vol. 90, 1969, p. 266.
8. HdG No. 182. See discussion in *Rembrandt after Three Hundred Years*, Chicago, 1969, No. 27.
9. Charrington/Alexander, No. 132.

10. The 4th Duke of Devonshire married in 1748 a daughter and co-heir of the 3rd Earl of Burlington.
11. It is presumably one of the two Rembrandts in the list of pictures at Chiswick in *London and its Environs Described*, published by R. and J. Dodsley in 1761: 'A portrait, Rembrandt' (vol. 2, p. 118) and 'A man half length, Rembrandt' (vol. 2, p. 121); these descriptions are repeated in *English Connoisseur*, 1766, vol. 1, pp. 33 and 37. (The other Rembrandt mentioned would be Bredius No. 266.)
12. One state of Phillips' mezzotint after the picture (see ENGRAVING, above) is inscribed: '. . . The Studious Philosopher. From the Original Picture Painted by Rembrandt in the Collection of . . . the Duke of Devonshire at Chiswick. John Boydell excudit 1766' (J. Chaloner Smith, *British Mezzotinto Portraits*, 1883, C. Phillips No. 6).

IMITATOR OF REMBRANDT

2539 *A Study of an Elderly Man in a Cap*   Plate 303

Falsely signed on the right, centre: Rembrandt. f./164(8?).[1]

Oil on canvas (irregular edges), 67 × 53 (26$\frac{3}{8}$ × 20$\frac{7}{8}$).

Cleaned in 1952. Much worn, especially in the cap and the face shadows. A jagged tear runs from the right background through the cap to the left eye.

Published as Rembrandt by Bode[2] and accepted by Hofstede de Groot[3] and Valentiner[4] (who date it *c.*1650) but already doubted in the National Gallery's 1929 catalogue.

A small section from the 'n' of the signature has been examined and there is no evidence that it is a later addition to the painting but appears to be integral to it, although it is not by Rembrandt. The ground is dark brown and single-layered. Its principal component is silica and it is very similar to the grounds of Rembrandt Nos. 221 and 6300 in this catalogue.

Several paint cross-sections have been analysed. They suggest that the painting is a seventeenth-century work painted by an artist familiar with Rembrandt's techniques and not an eighteenth- or nineteenth-century imitation.

PROVENANCE: According to HdG[5] it was in the collection of the Duke of Sutherland but it cannot be traced in any of the Stafford House catalogues or in any Sutherland sale. However, in a copy of Smith's *Catalogue Raisonné* thought to have been annotated by the author it is noted that the painting was 'Sold by Duchess [of Sutherland] with other pictures to Mr Morant in 1846 who parted with them to Mr Emery, Rutley and Co. . . .'. It was at one time in the possession of Sulley & Co., London,[6] and was bought by George Salting, London, by 1906.[7] Salting Bequest, 1910.

REFERENCES:
General: HdG, Rembrandt Nos. 394 and 742.
In text:
1. The date, which is worn and faint, is given in the 1913 catalogue as 165(?). Since the cleaning of the picture the third figure can be seen to be 4; the last figure, of which only the upper half remains, is almost certainly 8 (W. Bode in *Zeitschrift für bildende Kunst*, 1906, p. 10, describes the picture as 'of the year 1648').

2. Bode, loc. cit.
3. HdG, loc. cit., and in *L'art flamand et hollandais*, vol. 12, 1909, p. 164.
4. W. Valentiner, *Rembrandt: Wiedergefundene Gemälde (Klassiker der Kunst)*, 1921, N.62 and p. 60.
5. HdG No. 742.
6. HdG No. 742.
7. Bode, loc. cit.

ROELANT ROGHMAN, 1627–1692

Roelant (he also signs, less frequently, *Roeland*) Roghman, landscape painter and topographical artist, was baptised on 14 March 1627 in the Nieuwe Kerk, Amsterdam. His father Hendrick Lambertsz. Roghman was an engraver and his mother Maria Savery was the sister of the painter Roelandt Savery. He was named Roelant after his uncle. Little is known of his life, though he was apparently active in Amsterdam. Houbraken mentions that he was a 'great friend' of Rembrandt, and he is recorded in Amsterdam in 1661 and 1664. In 1646 and 1647 he made more than 200 topographical drawings in black chalk, with a grey wash, showing castles and manor houses in the north Netherlands. He also made topographical etchings. Houbraken says that Roghman lived in the Amsterdam almshouse and that he died unmarried. Roghman was buried on 3 January 1692 in the cemetery of S. Anthonie in Amsterdam. Jan Griffier (born *c.* 1646 or 1652) is said to have been his pupil.

REFERENCES: Houbraken, vol. 1, pp. 173–4; [Sumowski, *Gemälde*, vol. 4, pp. 2479–2500.]

1340 *A Mountainous Landscape*[1]   *Plate 304*

Oil on canvas, 63.5 × 74.3 (25 × 29¼).

For the attribution, compare the signed painting, *Mountainous Landscape with Fisherman*, in the Rijksmuseum, Amsterdam (Fig. 92).[2]

PROVENANCE: In the collection of Edward Habich, Cassel; exhibited for some years in the Gemäldegalerie, Cassel. It appears in the catalogue of the Edward Habich sale, Cassel, 9–10 May 1892 (lot 123), but was purchased privately, together with Nos. 1336–48, by the National Gallery in 1891.

REFERENCES:
General: [Sumowski, *Gemälde*, No. 1673.]
In text:
1. W. Bernt (*Die Niederländischen Maler des 17. Jahrhunderts*, vol. 2, Munich, 1960, p. 677, No. 678) illus-

trates an exact replica of No. 1340 which he describes as monogrammed, measuring 107 × 159 cm. and being in Cassel (Gemäldegalerie, No. 228). In fact, inventory No. 228 is a quite different painting. There is no mention of the Roghman in any recent Cassel catalogues and it seems likely that the painting illustrated by Bernt is in fact No. 1340 which (see PROVENANCE) was on loan to Cassel prior to the Habich sale in 1892.
2. 1976 cat., A4218.

JACOB VAN RUISDAEL, 1628 or 1629(?)–1682

Jacob Isaacksz. van Ruisdael; although his name is very often spelled *Ruysdael* in contemporary documents, and in later times *Ruysdael* or *Ruijsdael*, he himself always used the spelling *Ruisdael*.[1] He was born in Haarlem;[2] the date is not known but in a document of June 1661 he is said to be thirty-two[3] (the ages of some other painters mentioned in the same document are, however, incorrect). His father, Isaack Jacobsz. van Ruisdael (1599–1677) (originally de Goyer), was a frame-maker who dealt in works of art and also painted landscapes[4] and he may have been Jacob's first teacher. Jacob may also have studied with his uncle, Salomon van Ruysdael, whose influence is apparent in the earlier pictures. The earliest dated works are of 1646 although he did not apparently become a member of the Haarlem guild until 1648.[5] About 1650 he visited Bentheim (over the German border) probably with Nicolaes Berchem[6] of whom, according to Houbraken,[7] he was a 'great friend' and who on occasion painted the figures in Ruisdael's landscapes. By June 1657 he had settled in Amsterdam.[8] He appears to have continued living in Amsterdam, but the identified views in some of his pictures show that he also travelled in Holland. A 'Jacobus Rijsdael' apparently took a degree as a doctor of medicine in Caen in France in October 1676 and was inscribed in the list of Amsterdam doctors;[9] further, Houbraken says Ruisdael performed surgical operations with success in Amsterdam.[10] It is unclear whether this refers to the painter or whether – as seems more likely – there has been a confusion between two men with the same name. There are very few dated works after 1653. He was still living in Amsterdam in January 1682[11] and probably died there, but he was buried in St Bavo in Haarlem, 14 March 1682.[12]

Ruisdael's early works show, besides the influence of Salomon van Ruysdael, that of Cornelis Vroom. The many *Waterfalls* he painted from the end of the 1650s onwards (the earliest known dated one is of 1659) were inspired by those painted by Allart van Everdingen after his visit to Scandinavia. The figures in his landscapes are occasionally by other artists, for example Nos. 909 and 1390 below, although not so often as has been supposed. In his earlier years he made a number of etchings. Besides pupils such as Hobbema he had many followers and imitators, among them his cousin, Jacob Salomonsz. van Ruysdael (in his later works), Cornelis Decker, Roelof van Vries – all of whom are represented by pictures in the National Gallery – Johan van Kessel and Jan Griffier the Elder (*c*.1646 or 1652–1718).

REFERENCES:

General: HdG, vol. 4; K. E. Simon, *Jacob van Ruisdael*, 1927 (additions 1930); J. Rosenberg, *Jacob van Ruisdael*, 1928; H. F. Wijnman in OH, vol. 49, 1932, pp. 49 ff, 173 ff and 258 ff; S. Slive and H. R. Hoetink, exhibition catalogue, *Jacob van Ruisdael*, The Hague, Mauritshuis; Cambridge, Mass., Fogg Art Museum, 1981–2.

In text:

1. For Jacob van Ruisdael's signature, see No. 627 below.

2. According to a document of 1667 (OH, 1915, p. 24); see also Houbraken, vol. 3, 1721, p. 65.

3. OH, 1888, p. 21; see also Wijnman, op. cit., p. 59, note 1.

4. See C. Brown in BM, vol. 124, 1982, p. 193.

5. Van der Willigen, p. 256; Wijnman, op. cit., p. 174.

6. See Rosenberg, op. cit., p. 20 (note).

7. Loc. cit.

8. Wijnman, op. cit., p. 176.

9. Wijnman, op. cit., pp. 261–2.

10. Loc. cit.

11. Wijnman, op. cit., p. 263.

12. Wijnman, op. cit., p. 266.

44 *A Bleaching Ground in a Hollow by a Cottage* *Plate 305*

Signed at the bottom, towards the right: JvRui∫dael; JvR in monogram.[1]

On the back is stuck a piece of paper with three lines of inscription in ink, apparently in a seventeenth-century hand; the only certainly decipherable words are the last two: op harlem.

Oil on oak, 52.5 × 67.8 ($20\frac{11}{16}$ × $26\frac{11}{16}$).

Cleaned in 1958.

The bleaching of linen was one of the main industries of Haarlem in the seventeenth century, her bleaching grounds being considered the best in Europe. Probably painted in the late 1640s, i.e. before Ruisdael left Haarlem for Amsterdam.

PROVENANCE: In the collection of General Sir John May by 1847;[2] Sir John May Bequest, 1854.[3]

REFERENCES:

General: HdG No. 95; Rosenberg, op. cit., No. 63.

In text:

1. Rosenberg (loc. cit.) read a date (16)47. There is in fact no trace of a date after Ruisdael.

2. It was bequeathed by Sir John May (with Nos. 1858, 1874 and 1879) in 1847 with a life interest to Lady May, and ceded by her to the National Gallery in 1854.

3. It does not appear in the National Gallery catalogue until 1892.

627 *A Waterfall in a Rocky Landscape* *Plate 306*

Falsely signed on the rock on the left, just above the tree-trunk: J Ruysdael f (JR in monogram).

Oil on canvas, 98.5 × 85 ($38\frac{3}{4}$ × $33\frac{1}{2}$).

Cleaned in 1959–60.

Although this picture is certainly the work of Jacob Isaacksz. van Ruisdael, the signature is false. On documents Ruisdael himself always spelled his name with an i, never with y or ij, and usually with a long s (∫).[1] Further, the calligraphy of his signatures on documents closely resembles that of the signatures on the majority of his pictures. There is, therefore, good reason to suppose that where the signatures on his paintings differ from those on the documents in handwriting or spelling they are spurious.[2] The signature on the present picture differs in both respects.

The *Waterfall by a Cottage in a Hilly Landscape* (No. 628 of this catalogue), which was with the present picture in the Brabeck and Stolberg collections, was formerly supposed to be the companion piece but it is not by Jacob Isaacksz. van Ruisdael and the two pictures originally differed in size, No. 627 having been later enlarged to match the other.[3] (No. 628 is here catalogued as by Jacob Salomonsz. van Ruysdael.)

The present picture is most probably a work of the 1660s.

ENGRAVING: Aquatinted (in reverse) in black and brown by Johann Theophilus Prestel (1739–1808) in or shortly before 1802.[4]

PROVENANCE: In the collection of Graf Friedrich Moritz von Brabek in Söder, near Hildesheim (Hanover), by 1792;[5] after his death in 1814 it passed with the rest of his collection to Graf Andreas von Stolberg,[6] at whose sale in Hanover, 31 October sqq. 1859 (lot 235; 7,800 thalers), it was bought for the National Gallery.

REFERENCES:
General: HdG No. 239; Rosenberg, op. cit., No. 182.
In text:
1. See, for example, the facsimiles of his signature reproduced in OH, vol. 6, 1888, pp. 22–3, and vol. 33, 1915, p. 194.
2. Jacob Isaacksz. van Ruisdael's name is frequently written with a y by others even in contemporary documents, and this spelling (Ruysdael) is also common in books of the eighteenth century and the first half of the nineteenth; another misspelling, less common, is Ruijsdael.
3. The enlargement must have been made before 1792, since the size of both pictures is given as 3 *Fuss* 3 *Zoll* × 2 F. 10 Z. in F. W. B. Ramdohr's *Beschreibung der Gemälde-Galerie des Freiherrn von Brabek zu Hildesheim*, 1792 (pp. 24–5, Nos. 30 and 31).

4. Inscribed: 'Peint par J. Ruijsdael. Gravé par J. T. Prestel./Chute D'eau./D'après le Tableau original de la Galerie de Söder appartenant à Mᵣ le Bⁿ de Brabeck./H 3.P. 2½p. L.2.P. 9½p. No. 59.' In an article on the Söder Gallery in the *Westphälischer Anzeiger*, 1802, No. 99, Prestel's engraving is said to have been made recently (see J. G. Meusel's *Archiv für Künstler und Kunstfreunde*, vol. 1, part i, 1805, p. 141). This engraving is sometimes wrongly described as a mezzotint.
5. Ramdohr, op. cit., No. 31. The collection was formed by Graf Friedrich Moritz von Brabek in the second half of the eighteenth century, according to the catalogue of the Stolberg sale, 1859, p. 3.
6. Stolberg sale catalogue, p. 3.

737 *A Landscape with a Waterfall and a Castle on a Hill*   *Plate 307*

Signed, bottom left: vRuiſdael (vR in monogram).

Oil on canvas, 101 × 86 (39¾ × 33⅞).

Probably a work of the 1660s.

PROVENANCE: In the Joannes Meynders sale, Amsterdam, 23 April 1838 (lot 37), bought either by Brondgeest (4,001 guilders) or by Smith and Chaplin (4,400 guilders).[1] In the collection of Johann Moritz Oppenheim by 1842;[2] Johann Moritz Oppenheim Bequest, 1864.

EXHIBITION: BI 1853, No. 12.

REFERENCES:
General: Smith Supplement No. 72; HdG No. 241; Rosenberg, op. cit., No. 183.
In text:
1. According to Smith (loc. cit.) it was bought at this sale by his firm and Chaplin; the marked copy of

the sale catalogue in the RKD gives Brondgeest as the purchaser. Smith gives the height of the picture wrongly as 27½ in. but the correct height is stated in the sale catalogue.
2. Smith, loc. cit.

746 *Ruins in a Dune Landscape* *Plate 308*

Signed, probably falsely, bottom right: JvRuiſdael (JvR in monogram). About 2.5 cm. to the right of the signature and just above it a false date: 1673.[1]

Oil on oak, 41.5 × 57 ($16\frac{5}{16}$ × $22\frac{7}{16}$); made up by false additions on all sides to 43.2 × 58.5 (17 × 23).

Cleaned in 1959.

The ruins have not been identified. The high dunes in the background recall the landscape in the vicinity of Haarlem where Ruisdael was probably still living at the time this picture must have been painted (see below).

The date is certainly false and comparison with authentically dated works by Ruisdael shows that this landscape must be of the early 50s.

PROVENANCE: Apparently the 'Landscape with Ruins' by J. Ruisdael in an anonymous sale of pictures 'the property of a Baronet' [Sir John Pringle, Bart?] at Phillips, London, 14 March 1835 (lot 80), bought by Bryant (bought in?), 170 gns.[2] It was in the Duc de Morny sale, Paris, 31 May sqq. 1865 (lot 76), bought by Mündler (6,800 francs). Purchased from Emanuel Sano, Paris, in June 1865.

REFERENCES:
General: Smith Supplement, No. 105; HdG No. 757; Rosenberg, op. cit., No. 472.
In text:
1. The signature is very clumsy; the date does not even seem to be in a seventeenth-century hand. Rosenberg, loc. cit., read the date as 1653; the cleaning in 1959 showed that it is, beyond doubt, 1673.
2. Smith (loc. cit.) mentions a picture of the same description and size as the National Gallery landscape in a Sir John Pringle and others sale at Phillips in 1835, which was bought in for 170 gns; HdG (loc. cit.) gives the date of the sale as 1838. No Pringle sale of 1835 or 1838 is recorded in Lugt. There were, however, two anonymous sales of pictures at Phillips in 1835; the National Gallery picture was not in that of 18–20 July and the only Ruisdael in the 14 March sale is lot 80, which did in fact fetch 170 gns.

854 *A Pool surrounded by Trees, and Two Sportsmen coursing a Hare* *Plate 309*

Signed near the bottom and towards the left: JvRuiſdael (JvR in monogram).

Oil on canvas, 107.5 × 143 ($42\frac{1}{4}$ × $56\frac{1}{4}$).; original edges on all sides.[1]

Cleaned in 1958. The sky is badly worn.

Dated by Rosenberg[2] in the early 1660s. There are a number of forest landscapes of this type – one of the most outstanding is the *Marsh in a Forest* in Leningrad.[3] The only dated example is the painting in the Clowes collection *Wooded Landscape with a Pool*:[4] only the first three digits of the date – 166 – can be read. Slive dates the Leningrad painting *c*.1665[5] and this would also seem to be an acceptable date for No. 854.

PROVENANCE: In the [Miss Fanshaw] sale, London, 21 March 1835 (lot 92),[6] bought in (230 gns). Bought privately by John Smith in 1842[7] and sold by him to Sir Robert Peel, Bart., in 1843.[8] Purchased with the Peel collection, 1871.

REFERENCES :

General: Smith Supplement No. 64; HdG No. 481; Rosenberg, op. cit., No. 320.

In text:

1. The original primed edges of the canvas are turned over the stretcher.

2. Rosenberg, op. cit., p. 50.

3. Rosenberg, op. cit., No. 313; Slive and Hoetink, op. cit., No. 36.

4. HdG No. 548. H. A. Clowes collection, Ashbourne, Derbyshire.

5. Slive and Hoetink, op. cit., No. 36.

6. The markings relating to this sale are on the back of the lining.

7. Smith, loc. cit.

8. MS note in a copy of Smith's *Catalogue Raisonné* thought to be his own.

855 *A Waterfall at the Foot of a Hill, near a Village*   Plate 310

Signed in the bottom right corner: JvRuiſdael (JvR in monogram).

Oil on canvas, 84.8 × 100 (33⅜ × 39⅜); the bottom edge is original.

Probably a work of the second half of the 1660s.

PROVENANCE: In the Josephus Augustinus Brentano sale, Amsterdam, 13 sqq. May 1822 (lot 300), bought by (van der Yver for?) Nieuwenhuys[1] (6,300 guilders). In the collection of Lord Charles Townshend by 1824, when it was exhibited at the BI; Lord Charles Townshend sale, London, 11 April 1835 (lot 46), bought by Nieuwenhuys (690 gns) for Sir Robert Peel, Bart.[2] Purchased with the Peel collection, 1871.

EXHIBITION: BI 1824, No. 59.

REFERENCES:

General: Smith No. 178 and Supplement No. 55; HdG No. 242; Rosenberg, op. cit., No. 184.

In text:

1. Smith (No. 178) as bought by Nieuwenhuys, so also in the marked copies of the Brentano sale catalogue in the Institut Doucet and the Cabinet des Estampes, Paris. That in the RKD has van den Yver.

2. Smith Supplement No. 55.

986 *Two Watermills and an Open Sluice at Singraven*   Plate 311

Signed in the bottom left corner: Ruiſdael.

Oil on canvas, 87.3 × 111.5 (34⅜ × 43⅞).

Cleaned in 1967.

In about 1650 Ruisdael travelled to Bentheim and it was presumably on that trip that he visited the watermills that belonged to the manor house of Singraven near Denekamp, a village in the eastern part of the Province of Overijssel. (Denekamp is thirteen kilometres from Bentheim.) He used them as the prototypes for many paintings of watermills[1] and they were later painted by his pupil Hobbema (see No. 832 of this catalogue). The setting is invented: there are no mountains or even hills in the immediate vicinity of Denekamp.

A variant of the present composition is in the Strasbourg Museum[2] and another, formerly in the Neeld collection, is in a private collection in England;[3] in these the right-hand mill is half-demolished. In a third variant in the Morrison collection[4] the right-hand mill is still further destroyed. The landscape backgrounds in all these and the National Gallery picture are different and in the Strasbourg, ex-Neeld and Morrison compositions the right edge runs through the mill; there are many other lesser variations. A further version of the same view is known only from an engraving of 1782 made when it was in the Tronchin collection;[5] it is close to the ex-Neeld version but the composition extends farther to the right, showing two men sketching on the river bank. A picture in the Weimar Museum[6] may well be a copy[7] after another variant of this view.

The same two mills are seen from a point on the opposite bank of the stream in a picture in the Getty Museum, Malibu,[8] and another in the collection of Mrs G. E. Naylor.[9] In the former, which is dated 1653, both mills are intact; in the latter the right-hand mill is in ruins and there are many other differences. A picture in Rotterdam[10] seems to be a reminiscence of the view seen in the Getty and Naylor compositions, but with considerable variations.

Finally, the same two mills are seen from the other side, i.e. from upstream, in a painting formerly in the Habich collection[11] and a variant in the Mensing sale, 1938.[12] Another variant of this view, in the Poullain collection in 1780, is known only from an engraving.[13] In all these both mills are whole.

A drawing (in the Amsterdam printroom)[14] of the mills from about the same viewpoint as the No. 986, Strasbourg, etc. group and differing from all of them was formerly attributed to Ruisdael but is not now accepted as his.

The variations in the structure of the mills and the landscape background to be seen in the above-mentioned paintings and drawings make it obvious that they were not intended as strictly accurate views and the state of the right-hand mill would not by itself be a reliable guide to their chronology. Nevertheless stylistic considerations support a dating related to the progressive deterioration of the buildings. On the grounds of style it seems most probable that, as K. E. Simon has suggested,[15] the Habich picture is the earliest representation of the two watermills; the Mensing variant must be of much the same date. The National Gallery painting appears to be a little later, but perhaps earlier than the Strasbourg and ex-Neeld collection variants, although the exact relationship between these three is difficult to determine. The Morrison composition may well be a somewhat later elaboration, but the other pictures just mentioned all seem to be earlier than the Getty view of 1653 (the Naylor variant is obviously the later version of this design). The Habich landscape was probably painted in or shortly after 1650 and No. 986 is probably to be placed within the years 1650–2.

VERSIONS: Variants of this composition with the right-hand mill in ruins are in Strasbourg Museum, the S. A. Morrison collection and, a private English collection (see above). A weak variant by another hand (or a copy after a lost Ruisdael) related to the Strasbourg and ex-Neeld paintings is in the collection of William Berkman, New York.[16]

PROVENANCE: Almost certainly in the Thomas Emmerson sale, London, 15–16 June 1832 (lot 151),[17] £504. In the collection of Wynn Ellis, London, by 1845.[18] Wynn Ellis Bequest, 1876.

EXHIBITIONS: BI 1860, No. 94; RA 1871, No. 56; The Hague, Mauritshuis, and Cambridge, Mass., Fogg Art Museum, 'Jacob van Ruisdael', 1981–2, No. 22.

REFERENCES:

General: Smith No. 17; HdG No. 148; Rosenberg, op. cit., No. 100 and fig. 63.

In text:

1. The identification was originally made – on the basis of paintings by Hobbema – by K. Döhmann and W. H. Dingeldein, *Singraven, De Geschiedenis van een Twentsche Havezate*, vol. 3, 1934, pp. 144–5. See discussion in Slive and Hoetink, op. cit., p. 79.

2. Strasbourg 1938 catalogue, No. 169. Panel, 35 × 44 cm.; (?)signed in monogram. (HdG No. 157; Rosenberg, op. cit., No. 108.)

3. L. W. Neeld sale, Christie's, 9 June 1944 (lot 27), 2,700 gns, bought Vokins. Panel, 51 × 66.5 cm.; signed in monogram. (HdG No. 147; Rosenberg, op. cit., No. 99.)

4. Canvas, 86 × 91 cm. HdG Nos. 150 (with wrong size) and 661; Rosenberg, op. cit., No. 103.

5. François Tronchin of Geneva sale, Paris, 23–24 March 1801 (lot 163); panel, 19½ × 25 *pouces*. HdG No. 196. The engraving, by J.-J. de Boisseu, is inscribed: 'Peint par Jacque Ruisdaal, Tiré du Cabinet de Monsieur Tronchin . . . Gravé à L'Eau forte par . . . De Boisseu 1782.' See the exhibition catalogue, *De Genève à l'Ermitage: les collections de François Tronchin*, Musée Rath, Geneva, 1974, No. 218.

6. Canvas, 54.6 × 66 cm. Signed. HdG No. 158

7. According to Simon, op. cit., p. 74, and Rosenberg, op. cit., p. 116, note 7.

8. Signed in monogram and dated 1653. HdG No. 169d; Rosenberg, op. cit., No. 102. Slive and Hoetink, op. cit., No. 23.

9. Swaythling sale, London, 12 July 1946 (lot 34), 2,600 gns: bought Duits. J. E. Fattorini collection. Inherited by Mrs Naylor. HdG Nos. 152 and 171 (the latter with the description etc. of HdG No. 169d); Rosenberg No. 107 (but not No. 102). Discussed under Slive and Hoetink, op. cit., No. 23.

10. Signed in monogram. HdG No. 165; Rosenberg, op. cit., No. 94. Boymans-van Beuningen Museum: 1972 cat. no. 2520.

11. Signed with monogram. Edward Habich sale, Cassel, 9–10 May 1892 (lot 125); reproduced in the sale catalogue. HdG No. 170; Rosenberg, op. cit., No. 97.

12. Signed with monogram. A. W. M. Mensing sale, Amsterdam, 15 November 1938 (lot 88); reproduced in the sale catalogue.

13. Engraved by Le Veau in *Collection de Cent-vingt Estampes gravées d'après les Tableaux qui composoient le Cabinet de M. Poullain . . . décédé en 1780*, 1781, No. 88. This print is in the opposite direction to the Habich and Mensing compositions.

14. Rijksprentenkabinet No. A1390. J. Giltay, 'De tekeningen van Jacob van Ruisdael', OH, vol. 94, 1980, cat. no. 4. Although Giltay accepts the drawing as an autograph Ruisdael, Slive and Hoetink (op. cit., p. 79) reject it as a late seventeenth-century imitation, perhaps by Dirk Dalens.

15. Simon, op. cit., p. 28.

16. This painting – panel, 52 × 68 cm. – was in an Anon. sale, Lucerne, (Fischer), 16 June 1959 (lot 2434). It was exhibited (from the Berkman collection) in *Cinco siglos de obras maestras de la pintura en colecciones norte-americanas cedidas en préstamo a Costa Rica*, Museo de Jade, San José, 1978, No. 21 (wrong dimensions).

17. 'Ruysdael The Water Mill . . . rivalling the finest works of Hobbima.' The description of the Emmerson picture given by Smith (No. 17) agrees very well with No. 986 except that he says the path on the hill in the right background goes through 'corn and other fields'; in the National Gallery painting there is only grass here.

18. According to a MS note in a copy of Smith's *Catalogue Raisonné* thought to be his own: 'Now in the possession of Wynn Ellis Esqre 1845.'

987 *A Torrent in a Mountainous Landscape*

Plate 312

Signed at the bottom, towards the left: JvR (in monogram); the signature is worn.

Oil on canvas, 122 × 130 (48⅛ × 51¼).

Cleaned in 1958. A large damage in the sky near the left edge; smaller damages elsewhere.

This painting was traditionally ascribed to Ruisdael.[1] Rosenberg[2] included it in his catalogue raisonné of Ruisdael's works. MacLaren, however, considered it 'too formless for him [Jacob van Ruisdael] and the execution too woolly'. He attributed it to Johan van Kessel, who was probably a pupil of Ruisdael, comparing it with the signed

Waterfall in the Rijksmuseum, Amsterdam.[3] The present writer does not see significant discrepancies between No. 987 and other waterfalls by Ruisdael from the late 1660s. Van Kessel is altogether more precise in handling, particularly in his laboured, descriptive treatment of both water and trees. The composition of the Rijksmuseum painting also represents a simplification of Ruisdael's waterfalls.

PROVENANCE: In the possession of de Lelie, Amsterdam, by 1842;[4] J. A. A. de Lelie sale, Amsterdam, 29 July 1845 (lot 186), bought by Haelen (3,700 guilders).[5] In the collection of Wynn Ellis, London, by 1859,[6] when it was exhibited at the BI. Wynn Ellis Bequest, 1876.

EXHIBITION: BI 1859, No. 106.

REFERENCES:

General: Smith Supplement, Ruisdael No. 46; HdG, Ruisdael Nos. 243 (the description is confused with his No. 242) and 368; Rosenberg, op. cit., No. 185.
In text:
1. Smith and HdG, op. cit.
2. Rosenberg, op. cit.
3. Rijksmuseum 1976 cat. no. A696. Canvas, 94 × 74.5 cm. Signed: J.v.Kessel.

4. Smith, loc. cit. (wrongly as 'de Lille').
5. According to HdG No. 368.
6. It cannot be the only *Waterfall* by Ruisdael seen in the Wynn Ellis collection in 1850 or 1851 by Waagen (1854, vol. 2, p. 297, No. 5), as HdG (No. 243) suggests, since it is described as small.

988 A Road winding between Trees towards a Distant Cottage

Plate 313

Signed, bottom left: JvR (in monogram).

Oil on oak, 32.6 × 30.4 ($12\frac{13}{16}$ × 12).

Probably painted at the end of the 1640s.

LITHOGRAPH: This is apparently the painting reproduced in a lithograph (31.9 × 30.1 cm.) by L. Ekeman-Allesson (1791–1828) inscribed: Das Original Gemälde befindet sich in den Cabinet Sr Excellenz des Herrn Grafen/Carl von Rechberg Königl. baier. Oberst Ceremonienmeister etc. etc.

COPY: A copy is in the collection of S. Buchenan, Niendorf.[1]

PROVENANCE: Apparently (see LITHOGRAPH above) in the collection of Graf Carl von Rechberg, Stuttgart, *c.*1820; almost certainly the 'Landscape – a Sandy Road' by Ruisdael lent by Lt.-Gen. Sir Herbert Taylor, to the BI, 1837, No. 72.[2] Wynn Ellis Bequest, 1876.

EXHIBITION: BI 1837, No. 72.[3]

REFERENCES:

General: Smith No. 296 and Supplement No. 37(?); HdG Nos. 602, 618 and (?)911; Rosenberg, op. cit., No. 321.
In text:
1. Canvas, 35 × 32 cm. Photo in RKD.

2. Smith's description of this picture, which he calls an 'early production' (loc. cit.) agrees very closely with the National Gallery composition but he gives the size as 14 × 11 in.
3. See note 2, above.

989 *Three Watermills with Washerwomen* Plate 314

Signed, probably falsely, at the bottom, towards the right: J R.

Oil on canvas, 60 × 74 (23⅝ × 29⅛).

Considerable wearing, especially in the darker parts in the centre of the painting.

Rosenberg[1] believed it to have been painted in Ruisdael's last years and notes that the same watermills are seen in a flat landscape by Ruisdael (formerly?) in the S. Borchard collection, New York.[2] It was doubted by Simon[3] and by MacLaren who ascribed it to a 'follower of Jacob van Ruisdael'. He considered that the treatment of the distance was derived from Ruisdael's style of the early 50s rather than later. In the view of the present writer, it is an autograph – rather worn – painting and should be dated *c.* 1670.

PROVENANCE: In the Coclers (of Liège) sale, Paris, 9 sqq. February 1789 (lot 93),[4] bought by Marin (880 francs); imported into Great Britain by Chaplin in 1836.[5] Wynn Ellis Bequest, 1876.

REFERENCES:
General: Smith, Ruisdael No. 59 and Supplement No. 29; HdG, Ruisdael Nos. 149, 158f and 162; Rosenberg, op. cit., No. 101.
In text:
1. Loc. cit.
2. Present whereabouts unknown. Rosenberg, op. cit., No. 104. HdG (No. 153) states incorrectly that this picture was in the Maurice Kann sale, Paris, 9

June 1911; there was no Ruisdael painting with a watermill in this sale.
3. Simon, op. cit., p. 73.
4. The description in the sale catalogue mentions bathers in the foreground; there are apparently two(?) on the right in the National Gallery picture.
5. Smith Supplement, Ruisdael No. 29.

990 *An Extensive Landscape with a Ruined Castle and a Village Church* Plate 315

Signed in the water, bottom right: JvRuiſdael (JvR in monogram).

Oil on canvas, 109 × 146 (43 × 57½).

Cleaned in 1939, 1947 and 1971; there are scattered small damages in the sky. Some damages also along the bottom edge.

There are at least four other landscapes by Ruisdael that show the same view or part of it. Most of these, as well as No. 990, are said in nineteenth-century catalogues to be views near Haarlem, and one of them was so described as early as 1761. Hofstede de Groot[1] has suggested the church in the centre is that of Beverwijk (St Agatha), about seven miles north of Haarlem.

In the various versions of this view the only part of the church sufficiently visible to be identifiable is the tower. The fifteenth-century tower of Beverwijk church (St Agatha) was completely restored in 1913 after a fire but its appearance in Ruisdael's time is shown in a painting by Jan Abrahamsz. Beerstraaten (1622–66).[2] This shows that it had entirely different fenestration from that of the tower in Ruisdael's paintings and did not have the balustrade that appears in them, and it seems unlikely that Ruisdael intended to represent Beverwijk. Furthermore, judging by the orientation of the church the view must be towards the south, and if this were Beverwijk the characteristic silhouette of the Grote Kerk of Haarlem (St Bavo) should be visible on the horizon (as in many of Ruisdael's views in the vicinity of the town); it appears, however, in only one of the versions.[3]

If No. 990 is the picture in the Gildemeester sale of 1800, as seems most probable (see PROVENANCE), it was then said to be a view in Gooiland (a district to the east of Amsterdam extending from the Zuider Zee to below Hilversum). The same suggestion has been made (apropos the partial version of this view in the Smith College Museum mentioned below) by Vorenkamp,[4] who thinks it might be a view in the vicinity of Blaricum in Gooiland; according to him the two towers are in the style of the local architecture.

In any case the differences between the versions show that Ruisdael was not attempting strict topographical accuracy here.

Several versions of this composition are listed below. That nearest to No. 990 is the picture formerly in the Hope and Kempner collections (Fig. 93); it has some variations of detail in the buildings and the landscape, and the lighting is different. Ruisdael No. 2561 of this catalogue varies considerably from both No. 990 and the ex-Kempner picture. Yet another variation of this view is in the Petit Palais, Paris; if not original it is presumably an old copy of a lost Ruisdael, and is nearest in design to No. 2561. The ruins and moat reappear, with variations, in the foreground of a version in a private collection in England.[5] In a view in the Smith College Museum, Northampton, USA,[6] the two churches and the windmill occur in approximately the same positions but the surrounding country is quite different.

All the variants are much smaller than No. 990. No. 2561 below has often been described as a study for it but the nature of the differences makes this improbable. The ex-Kempner picture is very much nearer to No. 990 but it, too, seems to be a version rather than a study.

The small figure of a man standing among the ruins in the right foreground and the swans in the moat are by Ruisdael; the two peasants and their animals in the left foreground are clearly by Adriaen van de Velde.

Rosenberg acceptably dates No. 990, on stylistic grounds, in the second half of the 60s.[7] Adriaen van de Velde's death in January 1672[8] gives a *terminus ante quem*. To judge by the style, No. 2561 and the ex-Kempner version were also painted about this time.

VERSIONS: A small version is in a private collection, New York (ex-Kempner).[9] Smith describes a picture in the E. W. Lake collection (afterwards in the Artis sale, 1851) as a small 'repetition' of Ruisdael No. 990.[10] Ruisdael No. 2561 of this catalogue is a small variant of the composition. Another variant is in the Dutuit collection at the Petit Palais, Paris.[11]

PROVENANCE: Identified by Smith[12] with a picture by Ruisdael in the Jan Gildemeester Jansz. sale, Amsterdam, 11 sqq. June 1800 (lot 190),[13] bought by Thys (315 guilders).[14] In the collection of the Marquis de Marialva, Paris, who died in 1823; bought privately by John Smith apparently in 1825[15] and in the John Smith sale, London, 2–3 May 1828 (lot 78★), bought by Richard Abraham[16] (450 gns); exhibited with the rest of Abraham's collection at the American Academy of Fine Arts, New York, in 1830;[17] Richard Abraham sale, London, 28 June 1831 (lot 69), 275 gns. In the collection of Richard Sanderson, London, by 1835;[18] Richard Sanderson sale, London, 17 June 1848 (lot 23),[19] bought by Brown (480 gns). It was in the Wynn Ellis collection, apparently by 1850 or 1851, certainly before 1854;[20] Wynn Ellis Bequest, 1876.

EXHIBITIONS: New York, American Academy of Fine Arts, 1830; London 1947–8, No. 75; London 1976, No. 98; The Hague and Cambridge, Mass., 1981–2, No. 43.

REFERENCES:

General: Smith No. 214; HdG Nos. 136, 758 and 844d; Rosenberg, op. cit., No. 24.

In text:

1. See HdG Nos. 35b, 36, 750 and 758.

2. Formerly in the possession of Douwes, Amsterdam. Signed: JB; a photograph is in the National Gallery archives. A watercolour drawing by Carel Frederik Bendorp (1736–1814) in the Leiden University Library shows the church unaltered since Beerstraaten's time. For the topography of Beverwijk, see H. J. J. Scholten, 'Salomon van Ruysdael in de contreien van Holland's landengte', OH, vol. 77, 1962, pp. 1 ff.

3. HdG No. 775, identical with HdG No. 812; Rosenberg, op. cit., No. 63a, identical with Rosenberg, No. 512; Private collection, England. (See below, note 5.) The minute spire on the horizon in the centre of No. 990, just to the left of the windmill, is too small to be identifiable but could hardly be intended for St Bavo. The Sanderson 1848 sale catalogue says that Haarlem 'great church' forms 'a prominent object in the distance'; this can only refer to the church in the centre mid-distance or that towards the left, and the identification is wrong. HdG (No. 66a) is mistaken in saying that the tower of 'Haarlem church' can be seen in the smaller of the two National Gallery views (No. 2561).

4. A. P. A. Vorenkamp in *Smith College Museum of Art Bulletin*, June 1947, pp. 9–10.

5. Smith No. 215; HdG Nos. 775 and 812; Rosenberg, op. cit., No. 512. 53.5 × 61 cm.; signed. The size is often given wrongly as 29 × 32 in., e.g. in the Toronto exhibition catalogues of 1926, 1940, 1950 and 1954. The picture was in the collection of Bouchier Cleve, Foots Cray Place (R. and J. Dodsley, *London & its Environs Described*, vol. 2, 1761, p. 315: 'A view near Haarlem Ruysdale') and passed to Sir George Yonge; Yonge sale, London, 24–5 March 1806 (lot 65), bought by Mortimer; William Wells sale, London, 12–13 May 1848 (lot 58), bought in; exhibited at the RA, 1876, No. 6, lent by W. Wells; William Wells sale, London 10–12 May 1890 (lot 95), bought by M. Colnaghi. It was in the collection of Samuel S. Joseph, London, by 1891 when it was lent to the RA (No. 77). Later in the collection of J. H. Dunn, London; sold by Knoedler, London, in October 1923 to Frank P. Wood of Toronto, where it was often exhibited, 1926–54. Also exhibited Knoedler, New York, Loan Exhibition of Dutch Masters, November 1925, No. 20. Inherited in 1955 by Mrs R. M. Nesbitt, Haslemere. Except for the foreground this picture repeats, with variations, a view of Overveen in Berlin (HdG No. 57; Rosenberg, op. cit., No. 40).

6. Canvas, 31.5 × 41 cm. From the Lespinasse de Langeac(?) collection, Paris; J. L. Laneuville sale, Paris, 6 November 1811, bought by Pérignon; James Simon (Berlin) sale, Amsterdam, 25–6 October 1927 (lot 41); J. Goudstikker, Amsterdam; bought by Smith College in 1943. HdG Nos. 35b and 128; reproduced by Vorenkamp, loc. cit., and in the Simon sale catalogue.

7. Op. cit., p. 54. This dating is supported by Slive and Hoetink, op. cit., No. 43.

8. He was buried in Amsterdam on 21 January 1672 (OH, vol. 4, 1886, p. 144).

9. Canvas, 39.5 × 44.5 cm. In the Kalkbrenner collection, Paris, 1835; [G. T. Braine] sale, London, 6 April 1857 (lot 31), bought by Nieuwenhuys; Adrian Hope sale, London, 30 June 1894 (lot 61), bought by M. Colnaghi; Lt.-Col. E. Molyneux sale, London, 10 December 1898 (lot 120), bought by Agnew; Kempner collection, Berlin, 1911. According to Slive and Hoetink (op. cit., p. 125) the painting is now in a private collection, New York. (HdG No. 750; Rosenberg, op. cit., No. 463; reproduced in the Hope 1894 sale catalogue.) Smith (Supplement No. 10) calls it a view 'in the vicinity of Haarlem'.

10. 40.5 × 44.5 cm. C. J. West (of Norwich) sale, London, 21 March 1835 (lot 60), bought by Lake; E. W. Lake sale, London, 11–12 July 1845 (lot 106), bought by Artis; R. Artis sale, London, 17 May 1851 (lot 38), bought by Gibson. (HdG No. 776.) The identification of this picture with National Gallery No. 2561 (National Gallery catalogue, 1915–29) is disproved by the descriptions in the catalogues of the Lake and Artis sales (which are almost word for word the same): 'A landscape exhibiting a picturesque view over a flat country [the Artis catalogue adds 'in the Environs of Haarleim' (sic)]. In the centre is a church, with its spire partially concealed by trees; and beyond, to the left, a windmill. [It is not possible to say whether, in these two catalogues, right and left refers to the spectator or the picture.] In the foreground are the ruins of a fortification with its stagnant moat. The brilliant sky is partially screened by masses of clouds, from which bursts a transient gleam of sunshine, which glances . . . on the windmill and the adjacent fields, whilst the rest of the landscape is partially obscured by shadow . . . carefully finished . . .' According to Smith (Supplement No. 85) it is a 'carefully finished repetition in small' of his No. 214 (National Gallery No. 990).

11. Canvas, 42 × 46 cm.; signed. Dutuit collection catalogue, 1925, No. 927; HdG No. 74. K. E.

Simon considered it an old 'repetition', not by Ruisdael (see pp. 79–80 of the 1930 addenda to his *Jacob van Ruisdael* of 1927). It is accepted, however, as autograph by Rosenberg (op. cit., No. 61) and Slive and Hoetink (op. cit., p. 125).

12. Smith No. 214.

13. 'VUE EN GOILAND . Sur une colline au devant du tableau se voyent des débris de murailles, derrière lesquels un berger fait pâtre ses brebis. Le paysage offre des moissons en herbe, et des pays incultes sont vers le fond. Un ciel ornageux [sic] réfléchissant sur la terre, y produit un effet . . . de clair obscur . . .'; canvas, 43 × 57 *pouces*.

14. Not Tays, as in HdG (No. 136).

15. Smith No. 214.

16. There is a nearly contemporary MS annotation in the copy of the Abraham 1831 sale catalogue in the RKD; the catalogue says the picture belonged formerly to the Marquis de Marialva, the MS note adds: '& Mr Smith in whose Coll^n it was bo^t by Mr Abrahams for 420^{Gs} now in the Possession of Richd Sanderson Esqr sold by Mr Smith for 330£.' Abraham's exhibition and his subsequent arrest in New York is discussed by Slive and Hoetink (op. cit., p. 126).

17. See p. 4 of the Abraham 1831 sale catalogue.

18. Smith No. 214.

19. As 'A grand extensive View . . . towards Haerlem' etc.; see also note 3.

20. Waagen (1854, vol. 2, pp. 296–7) describes the picture when in the Wynn Ellis collection. Earlier in the same volume (pp. 288–9) he describes it as in the Richard Sanderson collection. Although the two descriptions vary, there can be no doubt that both refer to the National Gallery picture. It is improbable that Waagen saw the picture in the Sanderson collection when he visited England in 1850 and 1851 (see Waagen, op. cit., vol. 1, pp. iii and iv); the picture was in the Sanderson sale of 1848 and the form of the entry in the auctioneer's copy of the sale catalogue

shows it was not bought in. Waagen had seen the Sanderson pictures in 1835 (*Works of Art and Artists in England*, 1838, vol. 2, pp. 399–400); as the descriptions of them in the 1854 *Treasures of Art* repeat almost word for word those in the 1838 volume it seems highly likely that he did not see them again on his later visits but included them in the 1854 publication in the belief that they were still in the same collection. The matter has been further confused because the provisional catalogue of the Manchester Art Treasures exhibition of 1857 makes it appear that the National Gallery picture was lent by Sanderson to that exhibition; the reference to it is, however, omitted in the definitive edition of the catalogue and its inclusion in the earlier edition is clearly an error. The provisional catalogue lists two Ruisdaels as Sanderson's: No. 843, 'Landscape, with Figures by A. Van de Velde. W[aagen], vol. 2, p. 288' and No. 846, 'Extensive Landscape with figures by Adrian Van de Velde. W[aagen] vol. 2, p. 289'. Besides the National Gallery picture, Sanderson owned one other Ruisdael, a rocky landscape with a waterfall (see Waagen, 1854, vol. 2, p. 289, and HdG Nos. 384 and 721; the page references to Waagen have been mixed up in both the provisional catalogue and the definitive edition). In the definitive catalogue there is only *one* Sanderson Ruisdael, No. 699 'Landscape, with Figures by A. Van de Velde. W[aagen] vol. 2, p. 288'; this is certainly the waterfall landscape, as is proved by a sketch made at the time by George Scharf (p. 69 of sketch-book No. 50 in the archives of the National Portrait Gallery). This picture had been bought in at Sanderson's sale, London, 17 June 1848, lot 14, and remained in his collection until the R. Sanderson (deceased) sale, London, 20 March 1858 (it was lot 12). W. Bürger in *Trésors d'art exposés à Manchester* . . . (1857, p. 296) mentions *two* Sanderson Ruisdaels without describing them; he was doubtless misled by the entries in the provisional catalogue.

991 A Landscape with a Ruined Building at the Foot of a Hill by a River

Plate 316

Signed towards the bottom on the right: JR (in monogram).

Oil on oak, 22.8 × 29.3 (9 × 11$\frac{9}{16}$).

Cleaned in 1957.

There is a larger version of this composition in Berlin (Fig. 94)[1] and a still larger one in the Dresden Gallery (Fig. 95).[2] The Berlin and Dresden landscapes vary slightly from each other; their most important variation from No. 991 is in the right foreground, where they have an upright birch tree in place of the fallen one.

MacLaren considered this painting to be of poor quality and probably an old pastiche of either the Dresden or Berlin paintings. The present writer believes that it is an autograph work and agrees with Rosenberg that all three versions should be dated to *c.* 1655.

VERSIONS: Versions of this design in Berlin and Dresden are discussed above. Another, in an Anon. sale, Munich, 5–6 December 1911 (lot 177),[3] is probably an eighteenth-century(?) pastiche of the Dresden picture.

PROVENANCE: Perhaps in the collection of Wynn Ellis by 1850 or 1851.[4] Wynn Ellis Bequest, 1876.

REFERENCES:
General: HdG No. 619; Rosenberg, op. cit., No. 411 and fig. 48.
In text:
1. Oak, 46 × 62 cm.; signed with a monogram. 1978 cat. no. 884B. HdG No. 748; Rosenberg, op. cit., No. 462.
2. Canvas, 75 × 96 cm.; signed with a monogram. 1979 cat. no. 1494. HdG No. 753; Rosenberg, op. cit., No. 467.

3. Canvas, 93.5 × 115 cm. Reproduced in the sale catalogue.
4. It is probably the 'Ruins near water . . . somewhat dark in the trees' see by Waagen (1854, vol. 2, p. 297). A piece of English newspaper of 1854 or 1855 is pasted on the back of the panel.

1390 *The Shore at Egmond-aan-Zee*   Plate 317

In the distance on the right is the tower of Egmond church.

Signed on the right, towards the bottom: JvRuiſdael (JvR in monogram).

Oil on canvas, 53.7 × 66.2 (21⅛ × 26 1/16); the bottom edge is apparently original.

Egmond-aan-Zee is on the North Sea to the west of Alkmaar.

The church of Egmond no longer exists, having been engulfed by the sea (the last remains of the tower fell in 1743[1]) but it can be identified from old engravings.[2] No. 1390 was once described as a view of the shore at Scheveningen but the church tower is quite different from that of Scheveningen (which still stands; cf. W. van de Velde No. 873 of this catalogue).

The figures are not by Ruisdael and seem to be by the same hand as those in the coast scene in the von Pannwitz collection[3] which Rosenberg attributes, probably correctly, to Gerrit van Battem (1636–84).[4] (The figures in the supposed companion piece at Polesden Lacey – see below – are apparently not by the same painter.)

Probably painted in the mid-1670s. The *Coast near Muiden* at Polesden Lacey (Fig. 96)[5] was perhaps painted as the companion piece; the two pictures have the same history between 1772 and 1893 (see PROVENANCE).

ENGRAVINGS: Engraved (in reverse) by Jacques Philippe Le Bas between 1743 and 1771;[6] anonymous engraving *c.* 1771.[7]

COPIES: A copy was in the Earl Sondes et al. sale, Christie's, 5 February 1971, lot 89 (110 gns, bought by Weston).[8] Another copy – or perhaps the same painting – was in an Anon. sale, Heidelberg (Tenner), 5–7 May 1977, No. 5625 (as Dutch School, 18th century).[9]

PROVENANCE: Duc de Choiseul sale, Paris, 6 sqq. April 1772 (lot 67), bought by Boileau (together with the companion, lot 68, 1,701 francs); Prince de Conti sale, Paris, 8 sqq. April 1777 (lot 400, together with the companion), bought by Langlier (2,401 francs); [Dulac and Lachaise] sale, Paris, 30 November sqq. 1778 (lot

355, with the companion), 2,299 francs; in the collection of the Marquis de Marigny (later Marquis de Ménars; died 1781);[10] Marquis de Ménars sale, Paris, 18 March–6 April 1782 (lot 102, with the companion), bought by Hamon (1,851 francs); Mons. B---- [of Caen] sale, Paris, 3 December 1827 (lot 9), bought by Delahante (5,400 francs). In the collection of Baron J. G. Verstolk van Soelen, The Hague, by 1835;[11] the collection was sold in 1846 to Thomas Baring, S. Jones Loyd, Humphrey St John Mildmay and Chaplin, No. 1390 being among the pictures which fell to Mildmay.[12] Henry Bingham Mildmay sale, London, 24 June 1893 (lot 64), bought for the National Gallery (2,900 gns).

EXHIBITION: Arts Council 1945, No. 31.

REFERENCES:
General: Smith No. 19; HdG No. 927; Rosenberg, op. cit., No. 570.
In text:
1. See van der Aa, vol. 4, p. 85.
2. e.g. Rademaker, vol. 4, Nos. 41–3 (said to be views of the church in 1620). The church appears in a number of other paintings by Ruisdael, e.g. in Glasgow, Stockholm and in the Philips collection, Eindhoven (Rosenberg, op. cit., Nos. 31, 33 and 58).
3. HdG Nos. 926 and 931; Rosenberg, op. cit., No. 568 and fig. 125. Wrongly described by both as the shore at Scheveningen.
4. Rosenberg, op. cit., p. 60 and note; he points out that there are very similar figures in two signed gouaches by van Battem in the Berlin Printroom (reproduced in the 1931 catalogue of the drawings, vol. 2, pl. 62).
5. Canvas, 55.5 × 69.5 cm.; signed. HdG No. 102; Rosenberg No. 572a. Slive and Hoetink, op. cit., No. 49.
6. As 'Vue de Skervin', 'Skervin' = Scheveningen. In the title of the print Le Bas styles himself 'Graveur du Cabinet du Roy' which he did not become until 1744. Le Bas's engraving is mentioned in the *Recueil d'estampes gravées d'après les tableaux du Cabinet de Monseigneur le Duc de Choiseul*, 1771. Said by Walford (J. Walford, 'Jacob van Ruisdael and the Perception of Landscape', Diss. Cambridge, 1981, p. 8) to have been engraved by Le Bas 'before 1754'. A print was owned by Constable. His print of 'Scheveling' (its description in the collection of the Duke de Choiseul) is mentioned in a letter to his wife, 25 October 1812 (R. B. Beckett, ed., *John Constable's Correspondence*, 6 vols., Ipswich, 1962–8, vol. 2, pp. 89–90). It is possible that Constable was influenced by the print when he painted his *Weymouth Bay* (National Gallery, No. 2652) of 1816(?).
7. In *Recueil d'estampes . . . du Cabinet . . . Choiseul*, 1771, No. 117. Size given there as '25 pouces sur 20'.
8. Canvas, 50.8 × 68.5 cm.
9. Canvas, 52 × 69 cm. Illustrated in the catalogue (plate X).
10. According to Smith No. 20.
11. Smith No. 19.
12. MS note in a copy of Smith's *Catalogue Raisonné* thought to be his own, 'Sold at the Baron's death in 1847 with the rest of the Coll^n to Messrs Jones Loyd and Co.'

2561   *An Extensive Landscape with Ruins*   *Plate 318*

Signed in the foreground, left of centre: JvR (in monogram). Before the picture was cleaned in 1950 the signature read: JvRuiſdael, but most of it was false, being on top of a retouched loss, and was therefore removed with the retouching. Only part of the JvR monogram and the tops of other letters remain; the monogram alone seems original.

Oil on canvas, 34 × *c*. 40 (13⅜ × *c*.15¾); the painted surface has been increased in width by false additions on both sides (concealed by the frame) to 41.2 cm.

Cleaned in 1950. There is a prominent craquelure in the sky.

This and other versions of this view are discussed in the entry for Ruisdael No. 990 above. Probably painted in the second half of the 1660s or the early 70s.

COPY: A copy was in an Anon. sale, London, 21 October 1949 (lot 153).[1]

VERSIONS: See above.

PROVENANCE: The picture has been misidentified[2] with a variant which was in the C. J. West (1835), E. W. Lake (1845) and R. Artis (1851) sales.[3] No. 2561 was probably in the Edward Wright Anderson sale, London, 7 May 1864 (lot 47),[4] bought by Rutley (110 gns). It was exhibited in Leeds in 1868, and in London in 1895 by Edward Aldam Leatham (d. 1900). It was in the collection of George Salting, London, by 1904;[5] Salting Bequest, 1910.

EXHIBITIONS: Leeds 1868, No. 583;[6] London, Guildhall, 1895, No. 112;[7] The Hague, Mauritshuis, and London, Tate Gallery, 'Shock of Recognition: The Landscape of English Romanticism and the Dutch Seventeenth-Century School', 1970–1, No. 85.

REFERENCES:
General: HdG Nos. 36, 66a, 90 and (?)779d; Rosenberg, op. cit., Nos. 25 and 26.
In text:
1. Canvas, 42 × 42 cm. From the Charles Meigh sale, London, 9 June 1855 (lot 58), bought in; [Meigh] sale, London, 18 June 1859 (lot 210), bought by Miss Meigh; [Miss Meigh] sale, London, 1 June 1861 (lot 44), bought by Graves; William Dickinson sale, London, 5 December 1919 (lot 146), bought by Smith.
2. In the National Gallery catalogue, 1915–29.
3. This picture is of different composition and size; see Ruisdael No. 990, note 10.
4. 'J. Ruysdael. An Extensive Landscape, with a church in the distance, the ruins of a fort and a moat in the foreground. Effect of storm, beautiful effect of light illumines the middle distance.' E.A. Leatham was buying pictures in the 1860s; lot 54 of the same sale (HdG, Berchem No. 193) was also bought by Rutley and later in Leatham's collection.
5. This can be deduced from an entry in one of Salting's notebooks in the National Gallery archives.
6. As 'View of Haarlem'; the exhibition label is on the back of the picture. HdG (No. 36) gives the exhibition number as 572; this was a different picture lent by E. A. Leatham (in the exhibition catalogue it is merely described as 'A Landscape' by J. van Ruisdael). He lists No. 2561 a second time with the correct exhibition number (HdG No. 90).
7. As 'View of Haarlem . . . The spire of Haarlem Cathedral . . . in mid-distance . . .'; the exhibition label is on the back of the picture.

2562 *A Ruined Castle Gateway* *Plate 319*

Signed below, towards the left: vRuiſdael (vR in monogram).

Oil on oak stuck on to millboard and subsequently remounted on an oak panel,[1] 46.7 × 64.5 (18⅜ × 25⅜).

Cleaned in 1986. The oak panel shows through in many places in the sky.

The ruins were once incorrectly identified as those of the castle of Burgvliet near Bergen-op-Zoom (Province of North Brabant).[2] The castle was burnt down in 1581 by the French soldiers besieging Breda;[3] the identification is based on a drawing of ruins in the British Museum ascribed to J. A. Beerstraten inscribed: Burgvliet bij Bergen op Zoom.[4] The resemblance is superficial and in any case the drawing can hardly represent Burgvliet since it shows typically Italian houses beside ruins that appear to be Roman.

The present writer considers this to be a work of the early 1650s; Simon[5] apparently considered the smaller variant mentioned below to be rather later.

ENGRAVING: There is said to be an engraving after the picture.[6]

VERSION: A variant, formerly in the Cook collection, Richmond, was on the Dutch art market in 1952.[7]

PROVENANCE: In the [Morel et al.] sale, Paris, 3 sqq. May 1786 (lot 55), bought by Le Brun (2,300 francs); [Calonne] sale, Paris, 21 sqq. April 1788 (lot 72),[8] bought by Le Rouge (3,500 francs); Coclers sale, Paris, 9 sqq. February 1789 (lot 90),[9] bought by Marin (2,750 francs). Probably in the collection of Comte de

Vaudreuil and in an Anon. sale, London, 4–5 March 1791 (2nd day, lot 24),[10] bought by Slade (67 gns). In the collection of William Smith, MP,[11] and sold thence privately;[12] in the collection of Admiral Lord Radstock by 1822, when it was exhibited at the BI;[13] in Lord Radstock's sales, London, 19 April 1823 (lot 51),[14] bought in, and 12–13 May 1826 (2nd day, lot 30), bought by Norton (175 gns). In the collection of Charles Bredel by 1832, when it was exhibited at the BI;[15] when exhibited in Manchester in 1857 it was lent by the Misses Bredel; lent to the RA in 1872 by Miss Bredel; Miss Bredel sale, London, 1 May 1875 (lot 124), bought by Rose (2,200 gns). Earl of Dudley sale, London, 25 June 1892 (lot 22), bought by Lesser (£1,470). It was probably purchased in 1893 by George Salting;[16] Salting Bequest, 1910.

EXHIBITIONS: BI 1822, No. 123; BI 1832, No. 62; Manchester 1857 (provisional catalogue, No. 851; definitive catalogue, No. 973); RA 1872, No. 89.

REFERENCES:

General: Smith No. 44; HdG Nos. 786 and 768a; Rosenberg, op. cit., No. 473.

In text:

1. The original oak panel was at some time during the nineteenth century planed down very thin and attached to millboard. This in turn was attached to an oak panel. With the exception of the Calonne sale (see PROVENANCE and note 8) the painting is said to be painted on wood in eighteenth- and nineteenth-century sale and exhibition catalogues.

2. In the National Gallery catalogue, 1925 and 1929 (where the name is erroneously given as 'Bergoliet').

3. See van der Aa, vol. 2, p. 840.

4. Hind, vol. 3, p. 22 and pl. 11. Inscribed: 'J. Berestraten ad viv. fec[it] 1666' and in another hand: 'Burgvliet bij Bergen op Zoom'.

5. Simon, op. cit., p. 36 (see also p. 30).

6. According to the catalogue of the 1826 Radstock sale (see PROVENANCE).

7. HdG No. 767; Rosenberg, op. cit., No. 480. On panel, 26.5 × 37 cm.; signed with monogram. Reproduced in the *Catalogue of the Paintings at Doughty House*, vol. 2, 1914, No. 353, and in the catalogue of a P. de Boer exhibition, Amsterdam, 1952 (No. 47).

8. Although the picture in the Calonne sale cata-logue is said to be on canvas, the description and size agree with the National Gallery landscape; provenance from the Morel sale is noted.

9. As from the Morel and Calonne sales.

10. 'Ruysdael A landscape with ruins of a gate known in France by the title of Ruysdael's gate . . . from the cabinet of Le Comte Van Dreuil' [sic]; the name is given correctly as 'Comte Vaudreuil' on the title-page of the sale catalogue. The National Gallery picture was certainly described as 'Ruisdael's Gate' when in the Radstock collection (see notes 13 and 14); that the Radstock picture is No. 2562 and not the Cook variant is proved by the measurements in the sale catalogue).

11. According to the catalogue of the 1826 Radstock sale.

12. Smith No. 44.

13. and 14. As 'Ruisdael's Gate'.

15. As 'Ruysdael's Arch'. According to the catalogue of the Bredel sale, 1875 (see PROVENANCE) the picture was also exhibited at the BI 1845; this is incorrect.

16. In one of Salting's notebooks in the National Gallery's archives is the following note concerning this picture: 'price asked £1600 in '93.'

2563 *A Road leading into a Wood*   Plate 320

Signed, bottom left: vR (in monogram).

Oil on canvas, 54.5 × 71 ($21\frac{7}{16}$ × $27\frac{15}{16}$).

Damaged, lower right, in 1943 during wartime storage.

MacLaren considered the group of two men and a woman with a dog on the right of the road to be by a different hand from the man and dog in the centre. He noted that they are painted on top of the background and thought that they might be a later addition. In fact they were simply added on top of the landscape by Ruisdael himself.

Accepted by Hofstede de Groot, Simon[1] and Rosenberg and dated in the first half of the 60s by the last-named,[2] but doubted by MacLaren who described it as 'apparently the work of a contemporary imitator'[3] and by Slive (orally, to the present writer) who considers it to be the work of a follower. In the view of the present writer it is an autograph work by Jacob van Ruisdael. Rosenberg's dating may be slightly too late: a date in the second half of the 1650s is preferable. There is a variant of this composition in the Sutherland collection. That picture is not dated 1671 as has been thought.[4]

ENGRAVING: Engraved in reverse by R. A. Wieilh, 1770.[5]

PROVENANCE: In the collection of the Duc de Choiseul by 1770;[6] Choiseul sale, Paris, 6 sqq. April 1772 (lot 65), bought by Boileau (910 francs); said to have been in an Anon. sale, Paris(?), 1774, 400 francs.[7] The picture in the Coclers (1789), Tolozan (1801) and L[apeyrière] (1825) sales with which the National Gallery picture has been identified[8] was of entirely different composition.[9] The present picture was brought to England in 1840 by 'Fradel' [Henri-Joseph Fradelle?] and sold to Pennell, from whom it was bought by John Smith.[10] It was in the collection of William Theobald by 1842;[11] W. Theobald sale, London, 10 May 1851 (lot 72),[12] bought by Gritten (251 gns) by whom it was sold to Gibbons.[13] Lent by Albert Levy to the RA in 1875; Albert Levy sale, London, 31 March–6 April 1876 (lot 361), bought by George Salting (£714). Salting Bequest, 1910.

EXHIBITIONS: RA 1875, No. 64; RA 1891, No. 80.

REFERENCES:
General: Smith No. 26 and Supplement No. 66; HdG No. 566; Rosenberg, op. cit., No. 322.
In text:
1. Simon, op. cit., pp. 39 and 42.
2. Rosenberg, op. cit., p. 41.
3. According to a note in the National Gallery dossier, MacLaren thought an attribution to Jacob Salomonsz. van Ruysdael possible.
4. Cf. Simon, op. cit., p. 39, and in addenda (1930), p. 79. HdG No. 484. The date is very difficult to read but is *not* 1671.
5. In *Recueil d'estampes gravées d'après les tableaux du Cabinet . . . Choiseul*, 1771, No. 23. The etching is dated 1770. Although the size of the picture is given as '20 *Pouces* sur 15' on the print, the sale catalogue gives it correctly as 20 × 26 *pouces*.
6. See the preceding note.
7. According to Smith No. 26.
8. See HdG No. 566.
9. There is only one Ruisdael in these three sales that could be confused with the National Gallery picture; the descriptions given in the three sale catalogues agree well enough, the most detailed being that in the catalogue of the L[apeyrière] sale, Paris, 19 sqq.

1825 (not 1815 as HdG, loc. cit. states): (lot 145) 'Forêt marécageuse . . . Des bouquets d'arbres plantés à gauche et au milieu du point de vue y forment, par le rapprochement de leur épais rameaux, une espèce de voûte obscure, sous laquelle on voit des canards barbotans dans les eaux stagnantes d'un marais. A droite est un chemin sablonneux près duquel un berger fait pâtre trois brebis. De ce même côté une échappée de vue met à découvert la campagne lointaine. Un vieil arbre presque sans branches, en partie dépouillé de son écorce et désséché par le soleil, se fait principalement remarquer au centre de la composition où il produit un grand effet. Le Ciel couvert de nuages indique un jour de pluie.' From the collection of M. Aynard; canvas, 22 × 28 *pouces*. (A picture very close to this description was in the A. Schloss sale, Paris, 5 December 1951, lot 48, reproduced; HdG No. 506.)
10. Smith Supplement No. 66.
11. Smith Supplement No. 66.
12. The markings corresponding to this sale and a cutting from the relevant part of the sale catalogue are on the back of the picture.
13. HdG No. 566.

2564 *A Rocky Hill with Three Cottages, a Stream at its Foot*   Plate 321

Signed at the bottom, towards the right: vR (in monogram).

Oil on canvas, 55 × 66 (21⅝ × 26).

There is an area of damage in the centre of the painting and considerable wearing in the sky.

Although accepted as autograph by Rosenberg, MacLaren considered this painting too formless to be by Ruisdael himself and suggested that more probably it is the work of a follower or imitator. The present writer believes it to be entirely acceptable as an autograph Jacob van Ruisdael of the 1650s. The monogram, though possibly strengthened, is characteristic.

PROVENANCE: Apparently in the collection of Frederick Perkins by 1835;[1] George Perkins sale, London, 14 June 1890 (lot 20), bought by M. Colnaghi (£735); perhaps acquired in the same year by George Salting.[2] Salting Bequest, 1910.

EXHIBITION: Sheffield 1956, No. 43.

REFERENCES:
General: Probably Smith No. 264; HdG Nos. 718 and 809a; Rosenberg, op. cit., No. 323.
In text:
1. The composition, size and support agree with those of a picture in the Frederick Perkins collection described by Smith (No. 264) except that he mentions only two cottages and adds that there is, besides the two figures on the hill, a woman with a bundle on her back talking to a man seated at the base of the hill. (The description in the catalogue of the Perkins sale of 1890 repeats word for word that in Smith.) The third cottage is, in fact, only partly visible at the right edge of the picture and might well have been omitted in a description; there is, however, no trace of the additional figures. Either Smith was mistaken or some figures, presumably false, have been removed since.
2. In a notebook (of 1900 onwards) in the National Gallery archives Salting has noted against this picture: '1890/cost 771. 15.'

2565 A Cottage and a Hayrick by a River   Plate 322

Signed, bottom right, in the water: JvR (in monogram).

Oil on oak, 26 × 33.4 ($10\frac{1}{4}$ × $13\frac{3}{16}$).

Cleaned in 1974.[1]

Rosenberg[2] apparently dates this picture to the earlier years of Ruisdael's Amsterdam period, i.e. shortly after 1656. It seems rather to belong to a group of works painted in the years 1646–50 and, like others in this group, it shows the lingering influence of Salomon van Ruysdael in the composition.[3]

In the Lambert, Clos and Woodburn sales (see PROVENANCE) there was a companion piece, A Cornfield.[4]

VERSION: A variant is in the Detroit Institute of Arts.[5]

DRAWING: A related black chalk drawing was in the Nicholas Argenti sale, Christie's, 16 March 1956 (lot 40, 35 gns: to Scharf).[6]

ENGRAVINGS: Engraved (in reverse) by Carl Wilhelm Weisbrod;[7] etched anonymously (before 1835);[8] engraved in reverse by T. Hodgkins (when in Woodburn's possession).

PROVENANCE: In the Chevalier Lambert and [du Porail] sale, Paris, 27 sqq. March 1787 (lot 76), bought by Hamon (1,000 francs); later in the possession of J. B. P. Le Brun.[9] By 1792 in the collection of Claude Joseph Clos, Paris;[10] C. J. Clos sale, Paris, 18–19 November 1812 (lot 34), bought by Constantin (with the companion, lot 33, 1,884 francs). Samuel Woodburn sale, London, 15 sqq. May 1854 (lot 842), bought by Nieuwenhuys (156 gns). In the collection of George Salting, London; Salting Bequest, 1910.

REFERENCES:
General: Smith No. 51; HdG No. 704; Rosenberg, op. cit., No. 434.
In text:
1. The monogram, which MacLaren believed to be false, was found during cleaning to be original.

2. Op. cit., p. 36.
3. Ruisdael's river landscapes are discussed by Stechow, p. 59.
4. On panel, 25.5 × 33 cm.; HdG No. 137.
5. On panel, 40 × 51 cm.; signed in monogram. Not in HdG or Rosenberg. Illustrated and discussed by Stechow, p. 59.
6. 6 × 8 in. Although not listed in Giltay's cata-

logue of Ruisdael drawings (OH, vol. 94, 1980, pp. 187–202) there seems no reason to doubt that this is an autograph drawing of the late 1640s.
7. In Le Brun, vol. 1, between pp. 56 and 57.
8. Smith, loc. cit.
9. Weisbrod's engraving (cf. note 7) is inscribed: 'Tiré du Cabinet de M^r le Brun.'
10. Le Brun, op. cit., p. 57.

2567 *Vessels in a Fresh Breeze*   *Plate 323*

Signed on the right, towards the bottom: JvRuiʃdael (JvR in monogram).

Oil on canvas, 44.5 × 54.6 ($17\frac{3}{4}$ × $21\frac{1}{2}$).

Cleaned in 1959. Some wearing in the sky.

None of Ruisdael's seascapes is dated and there has been little agreement about their chronology. Rosenberg dated some in the 1640s[1] while Stechow believed that none was painted before 1660.[2] Slive[3] has discussed this question: he stressed the influence of Porcellis on the painting in Stockholm[4] and dated this picture and a number of related seascapes in the late 1640s or early 1650s. In the view of the present writer No. 2567 does not belong with this early group but rather with the *View of the IJ on a Stormy Day* in Worcester[5] which Slive dates to the early 1660s. MacLaren suggested a dating in the late 1650s, but the early 1660s is preferable.

PROVENANCE: Sold by Gritten in 1841 and in the collection of William Theobald by 1842;[6] William Theobald sale, London, 10 May 1851 (lot 62), bought by Gritten (71 gns). In the collection of Revd Frederic Leicester by 1853, when it was exhibited at the BI; Revd Frederic Leicester sale, London, 18–19 May 1860 (lot 153), bought in[7] (155 gns). Albert Levy sale, London, 31 March–6 April 1876 (lot 363), bought by George Salting (290 gns); Salting Bequest, 1910.

EXHIBITIONS: BI 1853, No. 88; RA 1891, No. 66; Brighton 1979, No. 7.

REFERENCES:
General: Smith Supplement No. 56; HdG No. 956; Rosenberg, op. cit., No. 590.
In text:
1. Rosenberg, op. cit., pp. 15, 40.
2. Stechow, p. 122.
3. Slive and Hoetink, op. cit., pp. 49, 89, 99, 139. In conversation with the present writer Slive has reasserted his dating of No. 2567 to the 1650s, that is, significantly earlier than the Worcester painting (see note 5 below).
4. Slive and Hoetink, op. cit., No. 11 (the painting

has been said to be dated 1649 but is in fact undated). Rosenberg, op. cit., No. 600; Stockholm catalogue, 1958, No. 4033.
5. Slive and Hoetink, op. cit., No. 32. Rosenberg, op. cit., No. 594. Worcester catalogue, 1974, No. 1940.52.
6. Smith, loc. cit.
7. According to the National Gallery 1929 catalogue it was bought by White, but the auctioneer's copy of the sale catalogue shows that it was bought in.

Follower of JACOB VAN RUISDAEL

2566 *The Skirts of a Forest*   *Plate 324*

Falsely signed, bottom right: JRuysdael f. (JR in monogram).[1]

Oil on canvas, 57.5 × 70.5 (22⅝ × 27¾).

There is considerable wearing in the sky.

Accepted by Hofstede de Groot and Rosenberg but rejected by Simon[2] and MacLaren. It appears to be the work of a contemporary (or slightly later) follower or imitator.

VERSION: A replica is in the collection of R. E. O. Cavendish.[3]

PROVENANCE: Possibly in the collection of the 3rd Duke of Dorset (d. 1799) in (?)1770;[4] said to have been in Lord de La Warr's collection.[5] In the collection of George Salting, London; Salting Bequest, 1910.

REFERENCES:
General: HdG No. 619a; Rosenberg, op. cit., No. 324.
In text:
1. The signature runs partly over old damage and is in abnormal spelling.
2. Simon, op. cit., p. 75.
3. Canvas, 63.5 × 79 cm.; signed with a monogram: JvR. Smith Supplement No. 26; HdG No. 555. In the collection of the 5th Earl of Burlington (later 7th Duke of Devonshire) by 1842; Lord Richard Cavendish sale, London, 12 December 1930 (lot 41), bought in; exhibited at the RA, 1952–3, No. 306. Reproduced in the Cavendish 1930 sale catalogue. It is misidentified with the present picture in the National Gallery catalogue, 1915–29.
4. A small slip of paper inscribed in ink: J:F Duke (of?) Dorset/(1?)770, and apparently cut from a larger document, was formerly attached to the back of the picture's nineteenth-century stretcher (now in the National Gallery archives). This inscription presumably refers to John Frederick, the 3rd Duke,

who succeeded in 1769. The present picture is not among those described in the duke's collection at Knole in *The Ambulator*, 1774, p. 113 ff., nor in the list of his paintings at Knole given in *The Tunbridge Wells Guide*, 1786, pp. 186–97. (It is worth noting that a *Lucretia* attributed to Guido Reni sold at Sotheby's, 25 November 1970 (lot 65), was said to have been sold by John Frederick, 3rd Duke of Dorset, to the 5th Earl of Plymouth in 1771.)
5. In one of George Salting's notebooks in the National Gallery archives is the following annotation against this picture: 'from collⁿ of Duke of Dorset/& Lᵈ Delawarr' (the second line added later but in Salting's hand). This note may refer to the 5th Earl de La Warr (died 1869) who married in 1813 the 3rd Duke of Dorset's younger daughter and co-heir, Lady Elizabeth Sackville [-West] (created Baroness Buckhurst, 1864; died 1870). This picture was not in the [Earl de La Warr] sales, London, 1 July 1852 and 5 June 1854.

Imitator of JACOB VAN RUISDAEL

996 *A Castle on a Hill by a River*   *Plate 325*

Falsely signed at the bottom, to the right: MHobbem( ) 16( ) (MH linked). The third figure of the date is possibly 5.

Oil on canvas (left and right edges irregular), 140 × *c.*176 (55 × *c.*69¼).

Considerable wearing throughout; many discoloured retouchings in the sky.

Catalogued until 1960 as by Hobbema and accepted as such by Hofstede de Groot.[1]

The signature and date are, however, false and the picture is in fact by an imitator of Ruisdael. It shows Bentheim Castle from a different point of view from that in any of Ruisdael's known views of it[2] and is possibly based on a lost work by him. It is probably by a seventeenth-century Dutch imitator. Slive (orally, to the present writer) considers it to be by Johan van Kessel and Alice Davies is to include it as an early work in her forthcoming catalogue of van Kessel (No. 11).

PROVENANCE: Edmund Higginson, Saltmarsh Castle, by 1842; sale, E. Higginson, Christie's 4–6 June 1846, No. 120, as van Kessel (Norton, £78 15s.); Wynn Ellis, London;[3] Wynn Ellis Bequest, 1876.

REFERENCES:
1. HdG, Hobbema No. 16; G. Broulhiet, *M. Hobbema*, 1938, No. 207.
2. Rosenberg, op. cit., Nos. 9–22.
3. HdG (loc. cit.) thought the present picture must be identical with a Hobbema seen in the Wynn Ellis collection by Waagen in 1850 or 1851 (1954, vol. 2, p. 297) but this is excluded by Waagen's description:

'A watermill, with a truly luminous horizon.' The only other Hobbema in the Wynn Ellis collection mentioned by Waagen (loc. cit.), 'A landscape, of peculiarly clear chiaroscuro; gleams of sunshine in the foreground and middle distance', is most probably No. 995 of this catalogue.

RACHEL RUYSCH, 1664–1750

She was born in Amsterdam, the daughter of Frederick Ruysch, Praelector of the Surgeons' Guild, a distinguished anatomist and botanist, and his wife Maria, the daughter of the classicist architect, Pieter Post. She was a pupil in Delft of the still-life painter, Willem van Aelst. According to her earliest biographer, Johan van Gool,[1] she married the portrait painter Juriaan Pool in 1693: the couple had ten children. They both joined the guild in The Hague in 1701. Her flower pieces achieved great contemporary renown. From 1708 until 1716 she was court painter to the Elector Palatine Johan Wilhelm, visiting Düsseldorf in 1710 and 1713.

She painted only flower still lifes, developing the style of her master Willem van Aelst towards a more decorative treatment and a marked lightening of palette.

REFERENCES: General: M. H. Grant, *Rachel Ruysch 1664–1750*, Leigh-on-Sea, 1956; J. Sip, 'Notities bij het stilleven van Rachel Ruysch', *NKJ*, 19, 1968, pp. 157–70.
In text: 1. Van Gool, vol. 1, pp. 210 ff.

6425 *Flowers in a Vase*   *Plate 326*

Signed, lower right, on the ledge: Rachel Ruysch.

Oil on canvas, 57 × 43.5 (22½ × 17⅛).

Cleaned in 1975.

PROVENANCE: Bequeathed by Alan Evans, 1974.

JACOB SALOMONSZ. VAN RUYSDAEL, 1629/30(?)–1681

Born in Haarlem,[1] son of Salomon van Ruysdael and cousin of Jacob Isaacsz. van Ruisdael, the most famous member of the family. The date of his birth is not known; in September 1681 he was said to be fifty-one.[2] He apparently always spelled his surname *Ruysdael*, like his father; never *Ruisdael* or *Ruijsdael*. He is said to have entered the Haarlem guild in 1664;[3] he married in Haarlem in February 1664 and was still there in December 1665;[4] by July 1666 he had moved to Amsterdam.[5] In 1667 he was named as an executor in the will of Jacob Isaacsz. van Ruisdael;[6] he remarried in Amsterdam in 1673 (Ruisdael was a witness at his betrothal) and at that time had a hosiery shop there.[7] He is documented again in Amsterdam in April 1675[8] and was living there in 1681, in November of which year, having become insane, he was sent to the workhouse in Haarlem; he died there on 13 November 1681.[9]

Bredius[10] was the first to propose the attribution to Jacob Salomonsz. van Ruysdael of a group of woody landscapes signed with a distinctive JvR monogram that are stylistically dependent, to a considerable degree, on the later work of Salomon van Ruysdael; this has been generally accepted. The earliest dated picture in this group is of 1650, the latest of 1668. Some of these landscapes also show the influence of Jacob Isaacsz. van Ruisdael. There are also a number of waterfalls painted in direct imitation of Ruisdael's but also related in style, though to a lesser extent, to the woody landscapes already mentioned; one of these, No. 628 below, bears Jacob Salomonsz.'s signature. None of these waterfalls is dated but they are presumably later than the woody landscapes.

REFERENCES:

1. He is described as a native of Haarlem in the Haarlem marriage register, 1664, and in a document of 1681 (H. F. Wijnman in OH, vol. 49, 1932, pp. 273, 265).
2. Wijnman, op. cit., p. 265.
3. According to a list of Haarlem painters compiled by Vincent Laurensz. van der Vinne (1629–1702) and amplified by his grandson, Vincent Laurensz. van der Vinne the Younger; see van der Willigen, pp. 258–9 (cf. p.x).
4. Van der Willigen, p. 259; see also Wijnman, op. cit., p. 273.
5. Van der Willigen, p. 259.
6. OH, vol. 33, 1915, p. 25.
7. OH, vol. 6, 1888, pp. 23–4.
8. Wijnman, op. cit., p. 274.
9. Wijnman, op. cit., pp. 264–5.
10. A. Bredius in *Kunstchronik*, 1885, cols. 506–7, and *Die Meisterwerke des Rijksmuseums zu Amsterdam*, 1886–8 (pp. 52–3 of the [1891] French edition).

628 *A Waterfall by a Cottage in a Hilly Landscape*   Plate 327

Signed just above the right end of the lower of two crossed tree-trunks below the cottage on the left: Ruy∫dael (the signature is very faint; the first letter is possibly intended for vR in monogram).[1]

Oil on canvas, 103.5 × 86.9 ($40\frac{3}{4}$ × $34\frac{1}{4}$).

Cleaned in 1967.

Formerly attributed to Jacob Salomonsz. van Ruysdael's cousin, Jacob Isaacksz. van Ruisdael, and thought to be the companion piece to the *Waterfall in a Rocky Landscape*,

No. 627 of this catalogue. The two pictures, however, originally differed in size[2] and the present one, although accepted by Hofstede de Groot[3] as the work of Ruisdael, is too poor to be by him. While the composition and execution are for the most part fairly closely imitated from Jacob Isaacksz., the centre background and the figures and animals on the bridge can be paralleled in the group of landscapes signed JvR that are generally accepted as the work of Jacob Salomonsz. (see the biographical notice above). The attribution of this picture to him, first put forward by K. E. Simon[4] and followed by J. Rosenberg,[5] is supported by the signature. This is certainly a seventeenth-century hand and differs from Jacob Isaacksz.'s habitual signature in spelling and calligraphy[6] but resembles closely that with which Jacob Salomonsz. signed documents.[7]

ENGRAVING: Aquatinted (in reverse) in black and brown by Johann Theophilus Prestel (1739–1808) in or shortly before 1802.[8]

PROVENANCE: In the collection of Graf Friedrich Moritz von Brabek in Söder, near Hildesheim (Hanover), by 1792;[9] after his death in 1814 it passed with the rest of his collection to Graf Andreas von Stolberg,[10] at whose sale in Hanover, 31 October sqq. 1859 (lot 229; 7,025 thalers), it was bought for the National Gallery.

REFERENCES:

1. The signature on No. 628 is erroneously stated in the National Gallery catalogue, 33rd edition (1861) and subsequently, to be signed in the same form as No. 627 (here catalogued as by Jacob Isaacksz. van Ruisdael). The two signatures differ, in fact, in form and spelling and are in completely different handwriting.
2. See Jacob van Ruisdael No. 627 of this catalogue.
3. HdG, Ruisdael No. 240.
4. Simon, op. cit., p. 74 (also in Thieme/Becker, vol. 29, p. 193).
5. Rosenberg, op. cit., note to No. 182.
6. For notes on Jacob Isaacksz.'s signature see J. van Ruisdael No. 627 of this catalogue.
7. See, for example, the facsimile of Jacob Salomonsz.'s signature on the contract of his second marriage in 1673 (reproduced in OH, vol. 6, 1888, p. 23) where it appears immediately above that of Jacob Isaacksz., his witness on that occasion.

8. Inscribed: 'Peint par J. Ruysdael. Gravé par J. T. Prestel./Chute D'eau./D'après le Tableau original de la Galerie de Söder appartenant à M[r] le B[n] de Brabeck/H. 3 P.2½ p. L. 2 P.9½ p./No. 60.' In an article on the Söder Gallery in the *Westphälischer Anzeiger*, 1802, No. 99, Prestel's engraving is said to have been made recently (see J. G. Meusel's *Archiv für Künstler und Kunstfreunde*, vol. 1, part i, 1805, p. 141). This print is sometimes wrongly described as a mezzotint.
9. F. W. B. von Ramdohr, *Beschreibung der Gemälde-Galerie des Freiherrn von Brabek zu Hildesheim*, 1792, p. 24, No. 30. The collection was formed by Graf Friedrich Moritz von Brabek in the second half of the eighteenth century, according to the catalogue of the Stolberg sale, 1859, p. 3.
10. Stolberg sale catalogue, p. 3.

SALOMON VAN RUYSDAEL, 1600/3(?)–1670

Salomon Jacobsz. van Ruysdael, originally *Salomon de Go(o)yer* (i.e. from Gooiland; his father was Jacob de Gooyer);[1] he spelled his name *Ruysdael* or, very occasionally, *Ruijsdael* and, during 1628–31, *Ruyesdael*, but never *Ruisdael*. He was born in Naarden in Gooiland; the dates usually given, 1600 or 1602, are hypothetical. His brother, Isaack van Ruisdael, who was apparently older, was probably born in 1599; Salomon can hardly have been born after 1603 since he was inscribed in the painters' guild in Haarlem in 1623 (as 'Salomon de Gooyer'). He lived in Haarlem throughout his life. His earliest-known dated painting is of 1626[2] and he is praised as a landscape painter in

Samuel Ampzing's *Beschryvinge ende lof der stad Haerlem*, 1628. He was buried in Haarlem, 3 November 1670.

The identity of his master is not known. His earliest pictures are painted under the influence of Esaias van de Velde who was working in Haarlem 1610–18, and there are many parallels between his earlier style and that of Jan van Goyen. Besides landscapes and seascapes he also painted, in his old age, a few still-life pictures. He was the uncle of Jacob van Ruisdael and the father of Jacob Salomonsz. van Ruysdael.

REFERENCES:
General: H. F. Wijnman in OH, vol. 49, 1932, pp. 49 ff; W. Stechow, *Salomon van Ruysdael*, 2nd edition, 1975.
In text:
1. For this and the following biographical data see Stechow, op. cit., pp. 11–12.

2. Stechow, op. cit., cat. no. 136A. This painting, a *View of the Horse Market at Valkenburg* was in the van der Burgh sale, Christie's, 29 June 1979, lot 88 (£12,000).

1344 *A Landscape with a Carriage and Horsemen at a Pool* Plate 328

Signed at the bottom, right of centre: SVRvySDAEL/1659 (SVR in monogram).

Oil on oak, 49.9 × 63.3 (19$\frac{5}{8}$ × 24$\frac{7}{8}$).

PROVENANCE: Possibly bought in Paris by Edward Habich;[1] in his collection in Cassel and exhibited at the Gemäldegalerie, Cassel, 1881–91.[2] It appears in the catalogue of the Habich sale, Cassel, 9–10 May 1892 (lot 129) but was purchased by the National Gallery, together with Nos. 1336–48, in 1891.

EXHIBITION: Arts Council 1945, No. 32.

REFERENCES:
General: Stechow, op. cit., No. 245.
In text:
1. Habich bought many of his pictures in Paris and No. 1344 has a nineteenth-century French newspaper stuck on the back.

2. See JKPK, 1881, *Amtliche Berichte*, col. 97, No. 68, and O. Eisenmann, *Führer durch die Kgl. Gemäldegalerie zu Cassel*, 5th edition [1883], p. 44.

1439 *A River Landscape with Fishermen* Plate 329

Signed bottom, left, below the boat: S.vR 1631 (vR in monogram).

Oil on oak, 36.6 × 65.5 (14$\frac{3}{8}$ × 25$\frac{13}{16}$).

Infra-red reflectography (Fig. 97) has revealed extensive underdrawing in charcoal or black chalk beneath the trees, cottage and footbridge.[1] The figures and boat were not drawn in at this stage.

PROVENANCE: Apparently in the Revd Chauncey Hare Townshend collection by 1857.[2] Revd C. H. Townshend Bequest to the South Kensington (now Victoria and Albert) Museum, 1869.[3] On loan to the National Gallery from the Victoria and Albert Museum since 1895.

EXHIBITION: London 1986, No. 55.

REFERENCES:
General: Stechow, op. cit., No. 435.
In text:
1. The reflectograms are illustrated and discussed in an essay by David Bomford in the catalogue of the exhibition, London, 1986, pp. 52–5.

2. Waagen, 1857, p. 179.
3. *Catalogue of the National Gallery of British Art at South Kensington*, 1893, part I, p. 179, No. 1356–69 (as by Jan van Goyen).

5846 *A River with Fishermen drawing a Net*   *Plate 330*

Oil on oak, 46.3 × 62.8 ($18\frac{1}{4}$ × $24\frac{3}{4}$).

Cleaned in 1948 and 1976–7. Some wearing in the sky and damage along the horizontal join immediately above the top of the mast of the boat in the centre.

At one time attributed to Jan van Goyen[1] but certainly a work of Salomon van Ruysdael of the early 1630s (cf. No. 1439 above, dated 1631). It is dated by Stechow *c*.1632–3.[2]

PROVENANCE: Apparently in the collection of Arthur James by 1908;[3] part of the Arthur James collection bequeathed by his wife, Mrs Mary Venetia James, 1948.

REFERENCES:
General: Stechow, op. cit., No. 489B.
In text:
1. There is a cutting, probably from a Christie catalogue of the third quarter of the nineteenth century, stuck on the back of the panel: 'J. VAN GOYEN./A river scene, with boats and figures.'

2. Stechow, op. cit., No. 489B.
3. Information supplied by Victor Cavendish-Bentinck (letter of 1949 in the National Gallery archives).

6338 *A View of Deventer seen from the North-west*   *Plate 331*

In the foreground, the river Ijssel, with five men in two boats drawing up a net and Dutch sailing vessels close-hauled. In the distance, Deventer, with, from the left, the Noordenbergtoren, the double-spired Bergh Kerk (St Nicholas) and on the right the Grote Kerk (St Lebuinus), with the Maria Kerk (Onze Lieve Vrouwekerk) before it, and the Vispoort to its right.

Signed with initials and dated, on the nearer boat in the foreground: SVR. 1657 (VR linked).

Oil on oak, 51.8 × 76.5 ($20\frac{3}{8}$ × $30\frac{1}{8}$).

Cleaned in 1972.

A *pentimento* is visible in the spire of the Grote Kerk.

Deventer is on the right bank of the Ijssel in the Province of Overijssel. The Grote Kerk dates from the eleventh century with additions and alterations of the thirteenth and fifteenth centuries; the tower dates from 1463, and the belfry was designed by Hendrick de Keyser and erected 1612–13.[1] The Maria Kerk, adjacent to it, is of the fifteenth to sixteenth[2] centuries and the Berg Kerk is of the thirteenth century. The Noordenbergtoren was built in 1487,[3] its spire was destroyed in 1587[4] and the whole was demolished in 1778.[5] The Vispoort is first mentioned in 1337[6] and was demolished about 1860.[7] An engraved view of Deventer of 1615[8] shows the spires of eight religious foundations to the north of the Grote Kerk. It is likely that there was a bridge in Deventer across the Ijssel in 1657.[9]

First identified as a view of Deventer by Stechow.[10] The view is not topographically strictly accurate. The tower[11] of the Grote Kerk has been simplified and the belfry should have a more pronounced dome and be supported by an octagonal grouping of columns, joined by semicircular arches.[12] In view of the number of spires omitted it is not possible safely to identify any of those depicted between the Noordenbergtoren and the Berg Kerk, but presumably the one on the extreme left is that of the St Elizabethsgasthuis.[13]

Stechow records two other views of Deventer by Ruysdael.[14]

PROVENANCE: Coll. F. Kleinberger, Paris, from whom bought by Augustus de Ridder (died 1911) by 1910;[15] August de Ridder sale, G. Petit (Paris), 2 June 1924 (lot 66), bought Agnew for 130,000 francs;[16] from whom bought by Sir Algernon Freeman Firth (died 1936);[17] inherited by Mrs Dorothy Gertrude Dewar (died 1943);[18] sold by Mrs Michael Dewar to Agnew's;[19] from whom bought by Rudolph Ernst Brandt in 1945.[20] Presented to the National Gallery by William Edward Brandt, Henry Augustus Brandt, Walter Augustus Brandt and Alice Mary Bleecker in memory of Rudolph Ernst Brandt in 1962.

REFERENCES:

General: Stechow, op. cit., No. 291.

In text:

1. See E. H. ter Kuile and M. D. Osinga, *Kunstreisboek voor Nederland*, vol. 3, *Samengesteld in opdrecht van de Rijkscommissie voor de Monumentensorg* etc., 1949, pp. 236–8.

2. E. H. ter Kuile etc., op. cit., p. 238.

3. B. van 't Hoff, 'De oude afbeeldingen van Deventer, gezien van de overzijde de Ijsel', *Verslagen en Mededelingen van de Vereniging tot boefening van Overijsselsch regt en geschiedenis*, vol. 72, 1957, p. 68.

4. Loc. cit., p. 69.

5. Letter from the director of the Museum 'de Waag', Deventer, in the National Gallery archives.

6. Loc. cit.

7. Loc. cit.

8. B. van 't Hoff, op. cit., pp. 75–6 and fig. 8. The engraving is by C. J. Visscher.

9. See note 3.

10. In the first edition (1938) of his monograph: *Salomon van Ruysdael* (op. cit.).

11. See *La Hollande illustrée*, Paris, 1909, p. 125, a photo of the tower is reproduced on p. 131.

12. Loc. cit.

13. See C. J. Visscher's engraving referred to in note 8.

14. See Stechow, op. cit., p. 501.

15. See W. Bode, *Die Gemäldegalerie des Herrn A. de Ridder in seiner Villa zu Schonberg bei Cronberg im Taunus*, 1910, p. 36.

16. Marked extract from the sale catalogue in the National Gallery archives.

17. 18. 19. and **20.** Information kindly provided by R. Kingzett of Agnew's.

6348 *A View of Rhenen seen from the West* — Plate 332

In the foreground, the left bank of the Rhine with cows standing nearby and a sailing vessel, close-hauled. In the distance, Rhenen with the tower of the Cunerakerk and the Koningshuis before it.

Signed with initials and dated in the left foreground: S.VR. 1648 (VR linked).

Oil on oak, 30.5 × 41.3 (12 × 16¼).

Cleaned in 1964.

Rhenen, in the Province of Utrecht, lies on the left bank of the Rhine. The tower of the Cunerakerk was built between 1492–1531 and still stands, though much restored.[1] The Koningshuis was built in 1630–1 for Frederick V of the Palatinate, the 'Winter King', on the site of the nunnery of St Agnieten, and designed by Bartholomeus van Bassen.[2] It was used after Frederick's death by his widow, Elizabeth, but soon fell into disrepair.[3] It was pulled down in 1812.[4]

Already identified as a view of Rhenen in 1945 (see below) and there seems no reason to doubt the identification. A comparison with Saenredam's drawing of 1644 in the Teylers Museum[5] shows that Ruysdael's rendering of the tower of the Cunerakerk and the façade of the Koningshuis is cursory and inexact. In particular the tower should be surmounted by a spire on a cupola and the east wall of the palace ought to be gabled. A view of Rhenen of 1660 by Ruysdael is in the Getty Museum, Malibu,[6] and another of the town seen from the east is in the Barnes Foundation Museum of Art, Merion, Pennsylvania.[7] The tower in those views is also imprecisely rendered.

PROVENANCE: Coll. David Hart, Leytonstone, c.1850; David Hart sale, Christie's, 11 March 1870 (lot 71), bought by Colnaghi for £81; by whom sold to a Mr Noble, Leeds, by 1871; inherited by his niece, Miss Steele, 1990; bought from her executors by H. Buttery, 1935; coll. Asscher and Welcker, London, 1936; from whom bought by Nicholas A. Argenti, 1938;[8] bequeathed by Nicholas A. Argenti with a life interest to Mrs Argenti to the National Gallery, 1963.

EXHIBITIONS: Arts Council 1945, No. 33; London 1986, No. 57.

REFERENCES:
General: Stechow, op. cit., No. 521A.
In text:
1. See the *Catalogue Raisonné of the Works by Pieter Jansz. Saenredam published on the Occasion of the Exhibition Pieter Jansz. Saenredam*, 1961, Centraal Museum, Utrecht, pp. 155–6. For a view of the interior see van Bassen, No. 3164 of this catalogue.
2. See the biography of van Bassen in this catalogue.
3. 'The Princess of Orange, who stopped at Rhenen for a night in November 1655 . . . told her aunt (Elizabeth of Bohemia) that she had a mind to crie, to see the house so spoiled.' Carola Oman, *Elizabeth of Bohemia*, 1938, p. 418, where *passim* an account is

also given of Elizabeth's connections with Rhenen.
4. See van Bassen, No. 3164 of this catalogue.
5. *Catalogue Raisonné of the works by Pieter Jansz. Saenredam*, op. cit., No. 105 and pl. 105.
6. 1972 cat., no. 116. Stechow, op. cit., cat. no. 205.
7. Stechow, op. cit., cat. no. 309 (dated in the 1660s).
8. This and the previous information concerning provenance was provided by the late Nicholas Argenti. The entry for the Hart sale reads: 'Solomon Ruysdael. A River Scene, with boats and figures, a village church in the distance . . .'

6419 *River Scene*   Plate 333

Signed and dated, on a barrel bottom left: SvR/1632 (vR in monogram).

Oil on oak, 51.5 × 96.5 (20¼ × 38).

Cleaned in 1972. Some damage along the horizontal join in the centre of the panel.

PROVENANCE: Purchased at a sale, probably in Derbyshire, before 1929, for Miss I. E. H. Cuming Butler (Erwood Hall, Buxton).[1] Bequeathed by her to the National Gallery, 1972.

REFERENCES:
General: Stechow, op. cit., No. 438A.
In text: 1. Stechow, op. cit., No. 438A.

PIETER SAENREDAM, 1597–1665

Pieter Jansz. Saenredam; painter of church interiors and topographical views. Born in Assendelft, 9 June 1597, son of the engraver, Jan Saenredam. He went as a child to Haarlem and became a pupil in May 1612 of Frans Pietersz. de Grebber, in whose studio he remained until 1622. In 1623 he entered the painters' guild in Haarlem, and spent most of his life there. His earliest dated painting, *The Expulsion from the Temple* in Copenhagen (Statens Museum), is from 1626. He also made topographical drawings in 's Hertogenbosch (1632), Assendelft (1633), Alkmaar (1634 or 1635?, 1638 or 1639? and 1661), Utrecht (1636), Amsterdam (1641) and Rhenen (1644). He was buried in Haarlem, 31 May 1665.

He was in contact with the architects Jacob van Campen and Salomon de Bray, and perhaps also Bartholomeus van Bassen. He was one of the first architectural painters to reproduce buildings with fidelity (that is to say, in his drawings; in his pictures accuracy is often modified for compositional reasons).

REFERENCES: P. T. A. Swillens, *Pieter Janszoon Saenredam*, 1935; Utrecht, Centraal Museum, *Catalogue Raisonné of the Works by Pieter Jansz. Saenredam published on the Occasion of the Exhibition Pieter Jansz. Saenredam*, 1961 (referred to below as Utrecht, *Cat. Rais.*); for the biographical data see de Bie, p. 246, and van der Willigen, pp. 20, 261–2. (G. Schwartz and M. J. Bok, *Pieter Saenredam: De schilder in zijn tijd*, 1989, was published when this catalogue was in proof. It has only been possible to incorporate their catalogue numbers into the entries.)

1896 *The Interior of the Buurkerk at Utrecht*   Plate 334

Hanging on a column in the centre background is a guild board of sixteenth-century type, in the window beside it is a painted glass roundel with a man's head. In the recess of the pier on the right are the Tables of the Commandments, above which appear the head and shoulders of Moses. Higher on the same pier are a sword and shield (sable, a lion rampant argent); at the bottom of it is a crude drawing in red of the sons of Aymon on the horse Bayard and, to the right of this, one in white of a woman.

Signed beneath the first-mentioned drawing: de buer kerck binnen utrecht/aldūs geſchildert int iaer 1644/van/Pieter Saenredam. (This inscription is in white except for the painter's name, which is in black.)

Oil on oak, 60.1 × 50.1 (23⅝ × 19¾).

Cleaned in 1960–1. Slight wearing throughout.

The hatchment on the extreme right was apparently an afterthought of the artist added when the picture was already framed since there is a gap of about 5 cm. between its right edge and that of the picture.

The Buurkerk was originally the only parish church in Utrecht. The surviving structure is mostly of the fourteenth and fifteenth centuries; the multiple columns seen in the present picture are remains of a thirteenth-century building. Saenredam's view is from the door in the north side, looking more or less towards the south-west. The interior remains much the same; Saenredam has made it appear rather taller than it is.

The rough drawing above the signature represents the four sons of Aymon of Dordogne: Renaud de Montauban and his brothers, Alard, Guichard and Richard. After a quarrel in which Renaud killed Charlemagne's nephew (his son in the German and Dutch versions), he and his brothers escaped on his magic horse, Bayard. The story of their adventures is derived from the thirteenth-century *chanson de geste* of Renaud de Montauban, later known under the title of *Les quatre fils Aymon*. It was very popular throughout most of Europe up to the eighteenth century; the most famous later version of the legend is Tasso's *Rinaldo* (1562). Netherlandish versions of the story were published in 1602 and 1619[1] and in Holland, as elsewhere, the four brothers frequently appear on pottery, metalwork, textiles and so forth, and as shop signs.[2]

It was Saenredam's practice to make first a drawing of his subject on the spot; from this he made a cartoon, sometimes years later, and the main lines of the composition were transferred from the cartoon to the panel (compare No. 2531 below). In the present case there is a drawing by Sacnredam of the interior of the Buurkerk from the same viewpoint, dated 16 August 1636, in the municipal archives in Utrecht (Fig. 98).[3] The National Gallery picture corresponds to the right half of the drawing. A painting corresponding to the left half of the drawing, and of the same size as No. 1896, is in the Kimbell Art Museum, Fort Worth (Fig. 99); it is signed and dated 1645.[4] The drawing is on a much smaller scale than the pictures and is presumably Saenredam's first study of the subject; the intermediate cartoon has not survived.

The figures in Saenredam's paintings are in various styles and some are by other artists. The old ascription of those in No. 1896 to Cuyp[5] is obviously wrong. Stechow has attributed them to Jan Both.[6] The two boys and the dog in the foreground are in his style but not so mannered as his usually are and there is no evidence that Saenredam was in Utrecht in 1644 nor that Both left it then.[7] The little figures in the background – two with a boy, and the man further to the left – do not seem to be by the same hand as those in the foreground. They are perhaps by Saenredam himself; figures in the same style appear, for example, in the Kimbell picture (mentioned above) and in the Munich *St Jacobskerk* of 1642,[8] as well as in some of Saenredam's drawings.[9]

Schwartz[10] has suggested that Saenredam intends a deliberate contrast between the imposing architecture and the children's art of the drawing of the *vier heemskinderen*, 'between the sanctimonious and the simple'.

DRAWINGS: See above.

PROVENANCE: Said to have been in the 'van der Pott' (Pot?) collection, Rotterdam;[11] all or part of this collection was bought in 1824 or 1825 by Charles Galli and taken to Edinburgh.[12] The present picture was exhibited with others for sale by Galli at the Royal Institution Rooms, Edinburgh, 1826, No. 35.[13] It was in the collection of Alexander Allan, Edinburgh, by 1866, when it was exhibited in York;[14] Alexander Allan sale, Edinburgh, 11 January 1896 (lot 39),[15] bought by William B. Paterson of Glasgow who sold it, probably in the same year, to Arthur Kay, Glasgow.[16] Presented by Arthur Kay, 1902.

EXHIBITIONS: York, Yorkshire Fine Art and Industrial Exhibition, 1866, No. 502;[17] RA 1902, No. 225; Birmingham Museum and Art Gallery, 1950, No. 54; Utrecht, Centraal Museum, 'Pieter Jansz. Saenredam', 1961, No. 127.

REFERENCES:
General: P. T. A. Swillens, op. cit., No. 160; Utrecht, *Cat. Rais*, op. cit., No. 127. Schwartz and Bok, op. cit. 127.

In text:

1. *Een schoone historie van de vier Heemskinden*, Amsterdam, 1602; *Historie van de vier vroome Ridders genaemd de vier Hemskinderen Reynout en syne Broeders*, Antwerp, 1619.

2. A brief account of the Dutch version of the story and its popularity is given in J. ten Brink, *Geschiedenis der Nederlandsche Letterkunde*, 1897, pp. 57–62.

3. Signed: 'den 16ᵉ augustij / int Jaer 1636. / P: Saenredam' and inscribed: 'BUIER / KERCK, / binnen / vtrecht.' Chalk and ink, 26.6 × 41.7 cm. Utrecht, *Cat. Rais.*, op. cit., No. 129.

4. Oak, 58.5 × 49.5 cm. Inscribed on the left-hand pillar: pieter Saenredam 1645 dit geschildert na de buer kerck van Utrecht. Utrecht, *Cat. Rais.*, op. cit., No. 128. Acquired by the Kimbell Art Museum, 1986.

5. See notes 13, 14 and 15.

6. W. Stechow in Thieme/Becker, vol. 29, p. 306, and in *Magazine of Art*, March 1953, p. 134.

7. Saenredam was, however, apparently in Rhenen (Province of Utrecht) at the end of June and the early part of July 1644 (see Swillens, op. cit., Nos. 161–6). The National Gallery picture was presumably not painted in Utrecht, but from the drawing made in 1636.

8. Utrecht, *Cat. Rais.*, op. cit., No. 134.

9. For example in a drawing of St Bavo, Haarlem, dated 1636 (Utrecht, *Cat. Rais.*, op. cit., No. 45).

10. G. Schwartz, 'Saenredam, Huygens and the Utrecht Bull', *Simiolus*, vol. 1, 1966–7, pp. 69–93, esp. p. 91, note 43.

11. According to the catalogue of the Allan sale, 1896. This provenance is also mentioned in a review of the York exhibition in *York Herald*, 1866 or 1867 (Eighth Notice, note on No. 490).

12. Cf. PROVENANCE of Hobbema No. 830 of this catalogue.

13. As 'Interior of a Church and Figures. – Saenredam, Figures by Albert Cuyp'.

14. As by Saenredam and Cuyp.

15. As by Saenredam and Cuyp. A cutting from the relevant part of the Allan sale catalogue, formerly on the back of the picture, is in the National Gallery archives. According to the Allan catalogue the picture is 'signed and dated 1630' and 'engraved by Van Amstel, 1714' [sic]. The engraving referred to must be No. 21 of Cornelis Ploos van Amstel's prints after old master drawings and was made in 1774 (reproduced in *Print Collector's Quarterly*, vol. 13, 1926, p. 311). This is the only Ploos van Amstel engraving supposedly after Saenredam; the drawing from which it was taken was an entirely different composition, showed a different church and in any case was almost certainly not by Saenredam. The date mentioned, 1630, is on the print; the costume of the figures in the print must be some twenty years later.

16. Letters of 1896 from W. B. Paterson and 1901 from Arthur Kay (in the National Gallery archives). The picture was certainly in Kay's collection by 1899 (see HdG, *Utrechtsche Kerken. Teekeningen en schilderijen van Pieter Saenredam*, 1899, note to pl. 22).

17. As by Saenredam and Cuyp.

2531 *The Interior of the Grote Kerk at Haarlem*   Plate 335

The church is seen from the north side of the choir, a little to the east of the north transept. In the distance are, on the left, parts of the south side of the choir and the south transept; on the right, part of the south aisle on the wall of which, between the pew and a column, there can be seen part of a painting of the exterior of the church (see below).

Oil on oak, 59.5 × 81.7 (23$\frac{7}{16}$ × 32$\frac{1}{8}$).

Cleaned in 1975–6. Slight wearing throughout, especially in the darks.

For the Grote Kerk (St Bavo) see Berckheyde No. 1451 of this catalogue. Saenredam's view shows the interior more or less in the state in which it remains today; he has, however, taken some liberties with the architecture for reasons of composition (see below). The picture of the exterior hanging in the south aisle is still in the church (see Berckheyde No. 1451).

The picture bears no date[1] but the preliminary drawing of this view (Fig. 100) is inscribed by the artist: '29 May 1636, this drawing finished by me . . . in the Grote

Kerk at Haarlem, from the life',[2] and the cartoon from which the design was transferred to the panel is inscribed: 'This composition was drawn in the Grote Kerk at Haarlem and finished on 21 November 1636 and finished painting, the same size, at the beginning of May, 1637.'[3]

The right half of the cartoon is missing but the surviving part agrees closely (except for the figures) with the corresponding portion of the National Gallery picture; its height is within 1.25 cm. of the latter and the reverse has been blackened for transfer. Since Saenredam did not make replicas of his paintings there can be no doubt the picture referred to in the second inscription quoted is the National Gallery panel, and that it was begun after 21 November 1636 and finished early in May 1637.

The drawing and the cartoon agree in detail with the drawing of 29 May 1636 mentioned above but the proportions of parts of the architecture have been altered; in particular the columns in the foreground have been made to appear much wider and taller, and the arches borne by them have been suppressed.

DRAWINGS: See above.

PROVENANCE: At one time in the collection of Arthur Kay, Glasgow.[4] In the sale of pictures belonging to Revon (Château de Dampierre), F. E. Lintz (The Hague) and others, Amsterdam, 27 April 1909 (lot 143).[5] In the collection of George Salting, London (died December 1909); Salting Bequest, 1910.

EXHIBITIONS: Utrecht, Centraal Museum, 'Pieter Jansz. Saenredam', 1961, No. 43; London 1976, No. 100.

REFERENCES:
General: Swillens, op. cit., No. 143; Utrecht, *Cat. Rais.*, op. cit., No. 43. Schwartz and Bok, op. cit., cat. no. 43.
In text:
1. Swillens, loc. cit., erroneously states that the picture is signed.
2. Drawing in the Haarlem municipal archives; inscribed: 'A° 1636 den 29 Maij / dese voleijndt met teijckenenn / van mij P. Saenredam / inde groote kerck / binnen haerlem naer / het leven.' 46.1 × 38.3 cm. Swillens, op. cit., No. 98 and fig. 82; Utrecht, *Cat. Rais.*, op. cit., No. 44.

3. Drawing in the Haarlem municipal archives; inscribed: 'deese ordonnanty Is / geteijckent inde groote / kerck binnen haerlem / ende / geijndicht met teijckenen / Int Iaer 1636 den 21en novem. / & geijndicht met schilderen / int begin vande maent / maij 1637. dus groot.' (Transcription made by Dr G. H. Kurtz, former municipal archivist of Haarlem; it differs very slightly from that in Swillens, op. cit., and in Utrecht, *Cat. Rais.*, op. cit., No. 45.)
4. A. Kay, *Treasure Trove in Art*, 1939, p. 65.
5. Reproduced in the sale catalogue.

HERMAN SAFTLEVEN, 1609–1685

Herman Hermansz. Saftleven, son of a painter, Herman Hermansz. Saftleven the Elder (died 1627). According to the title of an engraved portrait of him published in 1649,[1] he was born in Rotterdam in 1609; this date is confirmed by a document of 1627 in which he is said to be seventeen.[2] He had settled in Utrecht by May 1633, when he married, and lived there for the rest of his life (except for a stay in the Rhineland). In 1635 he painted one of four scenes from Guarini's *Pastor Fido* commissioned by the Stadholder[3] (the others are by Abraham Bloemaert, Cornelis van Poelenburgh and Dirk van der Lisse). He served on numerous occasions as *overman* and dean of the Utrecht painters' college. He travelled in the Rhineland and along the Moselle and in December 1667 was living in Elberfeld in the Rhineland. He died in Utrecht, 5 January 1685.

There are peasant interiors in the 1630s in the style of his elder brother, Cornelis (1607/8–81), and the literary subject mentioned above, but he began to devote himself to landscape already in the 1630s.[4] His earliest landscapes are close to those painted at the same period by Jan van Goyen and Pieter de Molijn. From the beginning of the 40s onwards he shows increasingly the influence of the Italianising Utrecht painters, particularly Cornelis van Poelenburgh and Jan Both. Finally, in the 50s he developed a manner based on the miniature-like landscapes of the later Flemish followers of Jan Brueghel the Elder. Most of these later landscapes, of which a considerable number exists, are reminiscences of Rhineland scenery; the figures sometimes show a religious or mythological subject. He also made topographical and botanical drawings and was active as an etcher.

REFERENCES:

General: J. Nieuwstraten, 'De Ontwikkeling van Herman Saftlevens Kunst tot 1650', NKJ, vol. 16, 1965, pp. 81–117; W. Schulz, *Herman Saftleven 1609–1685 Leben und Werke*, Berlin, 1982.

In text:

1. The inscription is engraved below Coenrad Waumans' print after a self portrait in a collection of portraits published in Antwerp by Jan Meyssens in 1649 (*Image de divers hommes d'esprit sublime*). This engraving was reprinted in de Bie, p. 275.

2. For Saftleven's biography see Schulz, op. cit., pp. 1–11.

3. Schulz, op. cit., cat. no. 22.

4. Cf. also the inscription on the print published in 1649 (see note 1): 'au commencement il faisoit paijsans, paijsanes, et granges: mais à présent il a sa seule delectation en paijsages.'

2062 Christ teaching out of St Peter's Boat on the Lake of Gennesaret

Plate 336

Signed, bottom left, on a rock, above and to the left of a child's head: HS/1667 (HS in monogram).

Oil on oak, 46.7 × 62.8 ($18\frac{3}{8}$ × $24\frac{3}{4}$).

Cleaned in 1976. Cleaning revealed that the grain of the panel had become prominent in some areas and was subsequently retouched.

The subject is taken from Luke 5: 1–3.

The subject, which provides an opportunity to paint a fantastic lake landscape, is also treated by Saftleven in a painting of 1626 in Edinburgh[1] and another of 1648 in a private collection.[2] There are compositionally related paintings of 1666[3] and 1667.[4]

PROVENANCE: Lt.-Col. Walter R. Tyrell sale, 12 March 1892 (lot 151),[5] bought by Eastlake. Presented by Charles Lock Eastlake (former Keeper of the National Gallery), 1906.

EXHIBITION: London 1976, No. 101.

REFERENCES:

General: Schulz, op. cit., No. 149.

In text:

1. Schulz, op. cit., No. 26.

2. Schulz, op. cit., No. 55.

3. Schulz, op. cit., No. 146. Present location unknown.

4. Schulz, op. cit., No. 150. Munich, Bayerische Staatsgemäldesammlungen, No. 5133.

5. As by Brueghel.

DIRCK SANTVOORT, 1610 or 1611–1680

Dirck Dircksz. Santvoort (he occasionally adds the prefix *van*), son of a painter, Dirck Pietersz. Bontepaert; he and his brothers adopted the surname Santvoort. He was born in Amsterdam; in March 1651 he is stated to be forty. He was probably a pupil of his father and was a member of the Amsterdam guild in 1636. He apparently always lived in Amsterdam (he is recorded there in 1641, 1648, 1650, 1652, 1657–8, 1665(?) and 1673) and was buried there on 9 March 1680.

His works are, with very few exceptions, portraits.[1] Although he sometimes shows signs of Rembrandt's influence, throughout his life he continued to paint in a *retardataire* style based on that of Cornelis van der Voort and Nicolaes Eliasz.

REFERENCES:
General: Obreen, vol. 3, p. 118; OH, 1885, p. 312; 1886, p. 73; 1889, pp. 35ff.; Wurzbach, vol. 2; Bredius, *Künstler-Inventare*, 1915–22, vol. 1, p. 217, and vol. 6, p. 1884; W. Stechow in Thieme/Becker, vol. 29.
In text: **1.** There is a *Supper at Emmaus* of 1633 in the Louvre (inv. no. 1828).

3154 *Portrait of a Girl with a Finch*   *Plate 337*

Signed, top right: D. D. Santvoort fe / 163(1?).[1]

Oil on oak, 62.7 × 50 ($24\frac{11}{16}$ × $19\frac{11}{16}$); all edges other than the left have been irregularly cut.

Most of the background, originally grey, has been covered with brown overpaint; the hair is thin.

PROVENANCE: It has been suggested that the picture might possibly be from the collection of William II of Holland[2] but it was not in the 1843 catalogue nor in the sales of 1850 and 1851. Said to have been for some seventy years prior to 1916 in the possession of the family of Tilson Lee,[3] who presented it in 1916.

REFERENCES:
1. The date was previously read as 1630. Although the signature and date are partially obscured by the brown overpaint that covers the background, an infra-red photograph shows that the last figure is almost certainly 1.

2. Tilson Lee in a letter of 1916.
3. See preceding note.

ROELANDT SAVERY, 1576–1639

Roelandt Jacobsz. Savery; he also signs his name *Roelant* (occasionally *Roeland*, *Roelaent* or *Roelaendt*) and sometimes *Saverij* (rarely *Saverey*).[1] According to the title of an engraved portrait of him (after Paulus Moreelse) made eight years after his death, he was born in 1576 in Kortrijk (Courtrai) in Flanders[2] (where his elder brother Jacob was also born); in a document of June 1629 he is said to be about fifty-one. He moved with his family (via Antwerp) to the north Netherlands. They apparently went first to Haarlem where Jacob was paid for a picture in St Bavo's in 1585 and is recorded as a member of the guild in 1587. By 1591, however, the family was in Amsterdam. Jacob was granted citizenship in October of that year; he was to die there in 1603. According to van Mander,[3] Roelandt was a pupil of Jacob. Hans Bol became a citizen of Amsterdam in the same year, 1591, and was undoubtedly in close contact with the Savery brothers. Roelandt's early work shows the influence of Bol and also of Gillis van Coninxloo (who had settled in Amsterdam by 1595). Roelandt was still in Amsterdam in August 1603; shortly afterwards he left for Prague, where he settled in 1604 in the service of the Emperor Rudolf II. He remained in the service of the Emperor until Rudolf's death in 1612; in 1606–7 he travelled through the Tyrol making studies of both the landscape and the flora and fauna.[4] He stayed on in Prague to work for Rudolf's successor, the Emperor Matthias, but in February 1613 the artist received money for a three-month trip to Amsterdam and there is no firm evidence that he ever returned to central Europe.

In January 1616 he was in Amsterdam and he remained there until 1619, when he moved to Utrecht; he entered the guild there in the same year. In 1626 the Utrecht provincial assembly paid 700 guilders for a painting by Savery to be presented to the Princess of Orange. He died in Utrecht and was buried in the Buurkerk on 25 February 1639.

Savery's rocky landscapes, which feature animals prominently and often include dramatic waterfalls and ruined buildings, frequently represent such appropriate biblical or mythological subjects as the Garden of Eden or Orpheus charming the animals. Many contain reminiscences of the landscape of the Tyrol. He also painted flower still lifes and animals, among them 'portraits' of horses. He also made at least one etching.[5]

Although Savery's landscapes may seem at first to be simply Alpine variations on a traditional Antwerp landscape theme, he was not thought *retardataire* by contemporaries and was widely influential. Gillis d'Hondecoeter, Willem van Nieulandt and the Willaerts family owe a great debt to his landscape style; Herman Saftleven, Anthonie Waterloo and Jacob van Ruisdael also reveal familiarity with his work.

His nephew Hans Savery was his pupil and assistant.

REFERENCES:

General: K. Erasmus, *Roelant Savery*, 1908; J. Spicer, 'The Drawings of Roelant Savery', Diss., Yale University, 1979 (unpublished); catalogue of the exhibition, *Roelandt Savery in seiner Zeit (1576–1639)*, Cologne, Wallraf-Richartz Museum; Utrecht, Centraal Museum, 1985–6 (catalogue by K. Müllenmeister et al.) (See review by J. Spicer in BM, vol. 128, 1986, pp. 167–8.)

In text:

1. This biography is based on that given in the first chapter of Spicer's thesis (op. cit.) and in the biographical essay by K. Müllenmeister in the exhibition catalogue Cologne/Utrecht, 1985–6, op. cit., pp. 30–38. The detailed documentary references are given there; in the latter the portrait print after Moreelse is reproduced as is a family tree of the Saverys (taken from the 1976 Utrecht thesis, *De Zuidnederlandse immigratie in Amsterdam en Haarlem omstreeks 1572–1630*, by J. G. C. A. Briels).

2. Houbraken, I, p. 57.

3. Van Mander, fol. 260v.

4. Sandrart, vol. 2, p. 305.

5. According to Spicer, op. cit., *The Uprooted Tree* (Wurzbach 1) is Savery's only etching.

920 *Orpheus*   *Plate 338*

Among the birds and beasts are, on the left, a lion and lioness, a pelican, an ostrich and a buffalo; on the right an elephant, a camel and parrots.

Signed, on a rock at the bottom, towards the left: ROELANDT·/SAVERY·Ft /1628.

Oil on oak, 53 × 81.5 (20⅞ × 32⅛).

Cleaned in 1980. Some damage along the horizontal join at the right-hand side.

The legend of Orpheus and the power of his music to enchant not only all living creatures but also trees and rocks is widespread in classical literature (cf. Ovid, *Metamorphoses*, Book 10, especially verses 180–2, and Book 11, especially verses 1–3); its popularity in later times is probably due to its occurrence in Boethius and Ovid. The frequency with which this subject and the Garden of Eden are depicted in Savery's pictures[1] is obviously largely due to the opportunity they provide for painting landscape and animals. Orpheus should properly be playing a lyre not, as anachronistically here, a violin.

PROVENANCE: S. J. Ainsley Bequest, 1874.

REFERENCES:
General: Erasmus, op. cit., No. 58.
In text: **1.** Some of Savery's paintings of Orpheus are listed by Erasmus, op. cit., opposite p. 206.

CORNELIS VAN DER SCHALCKE, 1611–1671

Cornelis Symonsz. van der Schalcke; baptised on 15 February 1611 in Haarlem, where he apparently spent his whole life. He succeeded his father as verger of St Bavo in 1636; he was buried in Haarlem, 5 March 1671.

His surviving works are few, and almost all landscapes; dated ones range from 1640 to 1665.[1] He was formerly considered a follower of Jan van Goyen and he certainly painted some landscapes in that style, but other pictures show the influence of such Haarlem painters as Pieter de Molijn, Salomon van Ruysdael and Isack van Ostade, and the rediscovered *View of Haarlem from the North* (formerly in the Singer collection, Vienna; see No. 974 below) suggests that in his later years he was also acquainted with Philips Koninck's work.

REFERENCES:
General: J. Q. van Regteren Altena, 'Cornelis Symonsz. van der Schalcke', in OH, vol. 43, 1926, pp. 49–60; A. Heppner, 'Neuerwerbungen niederländischer Meister im Kaiser–Friedrich–Museum, Berlin', *OH*, 49, 1932, pp. 47–8; L. J. Bol, *Holländische Maler des 17. Jahrhunderts,* 1982, pp. 176–8.

974 *An Extensive River Landscape, with Two Sportsmen and their Greyhounds*

Plate 339

Oil on canvas, 100.5 × 149.5 (39½ × 58⅞).

Cleaned in 1951.

The horizon was apparently 2.5–4 cm. higher at first.

Once described as a view of the river Scheldt with Antwerp Cathedral in the distance;[1] it is possible that the tall tower in the left distance is intended for that in Antwerp, but the identification is far from certain.

Formerly attributed to Philips Koninck[2] and later to his brother and teacher, Jacob Koninck.[3] The attribution to Philips Koninck is obviously untenable and the few signed works by Jacob are all very different.[4] H. Gerson[5] pointed out that the picture is closely related in style to a landscape with a view of Haarlem from the dunes of Overveen north of the town formerly in the A. Singer collection, Vienna, which bore a Philips Koninck signature (Fig. 101).[6] This signature was later found to be false and that of van der Schalcke was discovered beneath.[7] There can be no doubt that the National Gallery picture is, in fact, by the same hand as the Singer landscape and its attribution to van der Schalcke is confirmed by comparison with the landscape in Berlin signed and dated 1652[8] (cf. especially the figures and the foreground). It appears to be later than the Berlin picture and is presumably of about the same date as the ex-Singer one, which is probably of 1659;[9] this dating would be consistent with the hypothesis that it displays a knowledge of the work of Philips Koninck, whose earliest dated comparable landscape is of the early 50s.

PROVENANCE: Apparently in the [Dr Reichel, of Dresden] sale, London, 27 November 1847 (lot 102),[10] bought by Rutley (£5). In the Wynn Ellis collection, London; Wynn Ellis Bequest, 1876.

REFERENCES:

1. This identification is mentioned already in the National Gallery catalogue, 1877.
2. National Gallery catalogue, 1877–1915.
3. National Gallery catalogue, 1920–9; the attribution to Jacob Koninck was made by P. M. Turner (in BM, vol. 14, 1908–9, pp. 360–5).
4. e.g.: *River Landscape*, signed (in the possession of van Diemen, Amsterdam, before 1935; subsequently sold by the Gallerie S. Lucas, Vienna); *Landscape with an Inn*, signed (Anon. sale, London, 22 February 1937, lot 71; photograph in the National Gallery archives); *River by a Fortified Town*, signed and dated 1663 or 1665 (reproduced in BM, vol. 14, 1908–9, p. 361); *Landscape*, signed and dated 1667 (with P. de Boer, Amsterdam, 1959); *Landscape*, signed (Christie's, 6 and 7 June 1974, lot 208); *River Landscape*, signed (Basle Museum: inv. No. 1384).
5. H. Gerson, *Philips Koninck*, 1936, No. 33.
6. Canvas, 72 × 106 cm.; Gerson, op. cit., No. 59; reproduced in *De Kunst*, 25 November 1922. It then bore a signature: P koninck 1670 (or 1678). According-

ing to a note on the RKD mount, the painting was with E. Ganz, Neuchâtel, in 1949.
7. When the picture was cleaned in 1936 van der Schalcke's signature was uncovered beneath the false Koninck one (letter of 1954 from H. Gerson in the National Gallery archives). The Singer picture is a distant view of Haarlem seen from the north; it is presumably identical with the view of Bloemendael (which lies just north of Haarlem), painted by van der Schalcke in 1659, which formerly hung in St Bavo in Haarlem and which was sold in 1862 to a dealer who is known to have changed the signature to that of Philips Koninck (see van der Willigen, p. 263).
8. Panel, 40 × 61 cm. Berlin catalogue, 1975, No. 2080.
9. See note 7.
10. On the back of the stretcher are the markings connected with this sale. The only picture in the Reichel sale which might be identified with the pre-

sent one is lot 102: 'Dutch Large Landscape'; this lot and two others belonging to Dr Reichel are not in the printed catalogue of the sale but have been added in manuscript at the end of the auctioneer's copy.

GODFRIED SCHALCKEN, 1643–1706

Godefried Cornelisz. Schalcken; born in 1643[1] in Made[2] (North Brabant) not far from Dordrecht, to which his parents moved in 1654.[3] Houbraken[4] says he was first a pupil of Samuel van Hoogstraten [presumably in Dordrecht] and afterwards of Dou; his pupillage with the latter is confirmed by the inscription on his etched portrait of Dou.[5] He was living in Dordrecht again by 1665[6] and is recorded there also in 1679, 1682(?), 1685, 1686 and 1691.[7] He became a member of *Pictura*, The Hague painters' confraternity, in February 1691[8] but was living in Dordrecht in November 1691.[9] He came to England in (May?) 1692[10] and there are portraits by him dated 1693 (and 1694?) with the inscription 'Londini'.[11] He may have stayed here until 1697 since his name does not reappear in *Pictura*'s records until 1698; on the other hand Vertue,[12] in a note of 1713–21, says he came here on two separate occasions. He painted several portraits of King William III. By June 1698 he was back in The Hague,[13] of which he had become a citizen by August 1699;[14] he is recorded there also in 1700[15] and 1702.[16] About 1703 he may have been working in Düsseldorf for the Elector Palatine, Johann Wilhelm.[17] In 1704 and 1705 he was in The Hague,[18] where he died on 13 or 16 November 1706.[19]

Schalcken had great success, particularly with his genre scenes by artificial light and his portraits (some of these also by candlelight). His style was based in the first place on Dou's and his earlier works are small cabinet scenes in imitation of Dou; later he worked on a larger scale. Although best known as a painter of night pieces, more than half his paintings are daylight scenes. Besides genre and portraits he painted a number of religious and mythological subjects, and a few literary and allegorical ones. His candlelight paintings were closely imitated by Arnold Boonen (1669–1729) and continued to be imitated until less than a hundred years ago; one of the last to do so was Pieter van Schendel (1806–70).

REFERENCES:
General: G. H. Veth in OH, 1892, pp. 1–11; HdG, vol. 5. For an interesting discussion of J. C. Weyernan's Life of Schalcken (1729), see P. Hecht in *Simiolus*, 11, 1980, pp. 23–38. (T. Beherman, *Godfried Schalcken*, 1988, appeared while this catalogue was in proof. It has only been possible to include catalogue numbers in the entries.)
In text:
1. Houbraken, vol. 3, p. 175.
2. Obreen, vol. 6, pp. 1–2.
3. OH, 1892, p. 2.
4. Loc. cit.
5. See Dou No. 192 of this catalogue, note 2.
6. Obreen, vol. 6, p. 2.
7. Veth, op. cit., pp. 2–3

8. Obreen, vol. 6, p. 2.
9. OH, 1892, p. 3.
10. OH, 1892, p. 4.
11. E. Trautscholdt in Thieme/Becker, vol. 29, 1935, p. 569.
12. *Walpole Society*, vol. 18, 1930, p. 29 (see also op. cit., vol. 20, 1932, p. 139).
13. and **14.** OH, 1892, p. 4.
15. Obreen, vol. 5, p. 170.
16. and **17.** OH, 1892, p. 5.
18. OH, 1892, pp. 5–6.
19. According to Houbraken (op. cit., p. 176) he died on 16 November 1706; G. H. Veth as 13 November (OH, 1892, p. 6).

199 *Allegory of Virtue and Riches* *Plate 340*

Above, left, is a sculpture of a weeping putto; below, left, a bas-relief of two embracing children.

Oil on copper, 17.1 × 13.1 (6¾ × 5³⁄₁₆).

MacLaren identified the scene as 'Lesbia weighing her sparrow against jewels'. The pet sparrow of his mistress, Lesbia, is the subject of two poems by Catullus: ii, *ad passerem Lesbiae*, and iii, *Luctus in morte passeris*. As the woman here is shown with a tear on either cheek, and a weeping putto is also introduced into the picture, MacLaren thought it possible that the artist had in mind poem iii:

> Passer Mortuus est meae puellae
> Passer deliciae meae puellae
> Quem plus illa·oculis suis amabat.

The sparrow is not dead, however, in the painting, which makes the woman's obvious grief hard to account for in this interpretation, and, moreover, there is no reference in the poem to Lesbia weighing the sparrow against jewels. The present writer prefers the interpretation suggested by Knüttel[1] that the painting is an allegory of virtue and riches. For her the bird stands for virtue and true love (as does the visually related bas-relief of embracing putti) which the woman is trying to outweigh with the piled-up jewels. She weeps because she has sacrificed virtue and true love for riches; the sculpted Cupid in the background also grieves. Knüttel relates the painting to an emblem by J. H. Krul in his *Minne-Beelden toe-ghepast de lievende ionckheydt* (1634, p. 28: *Minst gheacht, meeste Kracht*). The image shows a pair of scales in which a virtuous and a rich suitor are being weighed, to the disadvantage of the rich man.

In the Fagel collection (and in the Fagel, Panné and Smith sales: cf. PROVENANCE) there was a companion painting of a woman releasing a sparrow from a box by Frans van Mieris the Elder (now in the Rijksmuseum [Fig. 102]);[2] this has been interpreted as an allegory on the loss of virginity.[3] The van Mieris is dated 1676 and Schalcken's picture could well be of the same date.

PROVENANCE: In the collection of the Greffiers Fagel, 1752;[4] the Greffiers Fagel (of The Hague) sale, London, 22–23 May 1801 (2nd day, lot 40), 51 gns. Philippe Panné sale, London, 26–28 March 1819 (3rd day, lot 80), bought by Bonnemaison (75 gns). Bought later by John Smith;[5] John Smith sale, London, 2–3 May 1828 (lot 29), 56 gns. By 1833 it was in the collection of Richard Simmons;[6] Simmons Bequest, 1847.

REFERENCES:
General: Smith No. 47; HdG No. 91. C. Brown, 'Godfried Schalcken's Allegory of Virtue and Riches' in Ed. M. Wintle, *Modern Dutch Studies: Essays in honour of Professor Peter King*, 1988, pp. 249–258; Beherman, op. cit., No. 50.
In text:
1. B. Knüttel, 'Spielende Kinder bei einer Herkulesgruppe', OH, 1966, pp. 247–8.
2. Panel, 17.5 × 14 cm. Rijksmuseum 1976 cat., C182; O. Naumann, *Frans van Mieris the Elder*, Doornspijk, 1981, vol. 2, cat. no. 108.

3. E. de Jongh, *Zinne- en minne-beelden in de Nederlandse schilderkunst van de 17de eeuw*, Amsterdam, 1967, pp. 40–2.
4. Hoet, vol. 2, p. 412.
5. Smith, loc. cit. Smith apparently confused the painting with the Rijksmuseum Schalcken. A MS note against No. 59 of his F. van Mieris catalogue in a copy of his *Catalogue Raisonné* thought to be his own reads: 'Sold to Richᵈ Simmons Esqʳ who bequeathed it to the Nation in 1847.'
6. Smith, loc. cit.

997 An Old Woman at a Window scouring a Pot

Plate 341

Signed, bottom right: G Schalcken.

Oil on oak, 28.5 × 22.8 (11⅛ × 9).

The old woman, the broken pot, the butterfly and the empty candle-holder are all elements which taken together identify the painting as a *vanitas*, an allegory of the transience of life.[1]

An early work in the style of Dou, probably of the 1660s.

PROVENANCE: In the collection of Wynn Ellis by 1861 when it was exhibited at the BI. Wynn Ellis Bequest, 1876.

EXHIBITION: BI 1861, No. 20.

REFERENCES:
General: HdG No. 117; Beherman, op. cit., No. 141.
In text: **1.** Schalcken painted several *vanitas* pictures (e.g. HdG Nos. 94, 96, 97 and 98).

998 A Woman singing and a Man with a Cittern

Plate 342

In the background is a painting, the only visible part of which is two naked legs.

Signed, bottom left: G Schalcken

Oil on oak, 26.6 × 20.4 (10½ × 8). Cleaning revealed that the painting, which is on a rectangular panel, has an arched top. The top corners had been overpainted to make the painting appear rectangular.

Cleaned in 1982–3. Severe wearing in the dark areas.

Both style and costume suggest that the picture was painted *c.*1665–70.

A supposed companion picture was in the Conti and Destouches sales[1] (see PROVENANCE). It shows a candlelit scene of a child playing with a doll, the figures to the right. Both the subject and the composition make it an unlikely pendant to No. 998.

PROVENANCE: In the collection of the Comte de Vence by 1759;[2] Comte de Vence sale, Paris (24 sqq. November 1760), 9 sqq. February 1761 (lot 116), bought by Président Le Rebourg (620 francs), who apparently sold it in 1768 to Mons. de La Borde.[3] Said to have been in La Live de Jully sale, Paris, 2–14 May 1770;[4] Duc de Choiseul sale, Paris, 6 April sqq. 1772 (lot 104), bought by Boileau (1,560 francs). Said to have been in the Randon de Boisset sale, Paris, 27 February sqq. 1777.[5] Prince de Conti sale, Paris, 8 April sqq. 1777 (lot 409, with companion), bought by Destouches (1,200 francs); Destouches sale, Paris, 21 March sqq. 1794 (lot 60), bought by Serot (Séroet?), 1,003 francs. Possibly exhibited at the BI, 1822, No. 31[6] by C. Hanbury Tracy. Wynn Ellis Bequest, 1876.

EXHIBITION: BI 1822, No. 31(?).[7]

REFERENCES:
General: Smith No. 5; HdG No. 159; Beherman, op. cit., No. 161.
In text:
1. HdG No. 230. It was not in the Vence or La Live de Jully sales (see PROVENANCE).
2. *Catalogue des tableaux . . . de M. le Comte de Vence*, 1759, p. 19.

3. According to a contemporary MS note in a copy of the Vence sale catalogue at the RKD.
4. According to the Conti 1777 sale catalogue, but it is not in the La Live de Jully 1770 sale catalogue nor in the *Catalogue historique de Cabinet de . . . M. de Lalive*, 1764.
5. According to Smith, together with a companion

(see note 1) but neither is in the Randon de Boisset
1777 sale catalogue.

6. 'A Musical Party' by Schalcken.

7. See above under PROVENANCE and note 6.

999 *A Candlelight Scene: A Man offering a Gold Chain and Coins to a Girl seated on a Bed*   *Plate 343*

On the lower part of the bedpost is a carved cupid.

Signed, top left: G. Schalcken.

Oil on copper, 15.5 × 18.9 ($6\frac{1}{8}$ × $7\frac{7}{16}$).

Cleaned in 1971.

There are *pentimenti* in the outline of the man's face and the top of the girl's bodice.

Probably painted in the later 1660s.

PROVENANCE: Wynn Ellis Bequest, 1876

REFERENCE: HdG No. 253; Beherman, op. cit., No. 200.

HERCULES SEGERS, 1589 or 1590–after January 1633

Hercules Pietersz. Segers; although the spelling *Seghers* sometimes occurs in contemporary documents, the painter himself used the form *Segers* (and occasionally spelled his Christian name *Herkeles*). In the earlier documents he is called, and signed himself, *Hercules Pietersz.* without the surname. He was born in Haarlem,[1] the son of Pieter Segers, a cloth merchant who had fled from the southern Netherlands, and Cathalina Herculesdr.;[2] his age is given as twenty-four in December 1614 and in March 1623, about thirty-four.[3] By 1596 the family had moved to Amsterdam and he is presumably the unnamed son of Pieter Segers who was a pupil of Gillis van Coninxloo in Amsterdam probably up to the time of the latter's death[4] (Coninxloo was buried 4 January 1607),[5] and is probably also the Hercules Pietersz. who bought at Coninxloo's sale in Amsterdam, March 1607, drawings, prints and a painting of a rocky landscape by him.[6] A 'Hercules Pieters' is said to have entered the Haarlem guild in 1612.[7] By December 1614 Hercules Segers was back in Amsterdam and in January 1615 married Anna van der Brugg(h)en, a native of Antwerp, in Sloterdijk outside Amsterdam.[8] He is traceable in Amsterdam in 1616,[9] 1618,[10] 1619 (when he bought a house there),[11] 1621 (when he is referred to for the first time as 'Hercules Segers'),[12] 1623,[13] 1626[14] and finally in July 1629.[15] Segers painted and etched two views of Rhenen (in the Province of Utrecht) probably shortly before 1630.[16] His house in Amsterdam had been sold upon foreclosure in January 1631[17] and in May of that year he was staying in Utrecht and sold some seventy pictures to an Amsterdam merchant;[18] he seems to have made other deals involving paintings there.[19] In January 1633 he was living in The Hague, active as an art dealer (and may be the 'Hercules de Haerlem' who came to live in a house there in 1632).[20] There is no later record of him. In 1638 a certain Cornelia de

Witte is described in The Hague as the widow of 'Hercules Pietersz.';[21] the latter is not necessarily Segers since the dead man's profession is not stated and Segers' only known marriage was to Anna van der Bruggen. Samuel van Hoogstraten[22] cites Segers as an example of an artist who was treated badly by fortune and whose true worth was discovered only after his death; according to Hoogstraten, Segers despaired of ever achieving success, took to drink and died after falling downstairs when drunk.

He may have been at some time in Flanders since a landscape with a view of Brussels by Hercules Segers was in the inventory of the painter Jan van de Cappelle in 1680.[23]

There are four (possibly five) signed paintings and others which can be assigned to him with confidence on the basis of comparison with these and the etchings, of which many more have been preserved. There are no dated works and attempts at dating have led to much confusion; an acceptable chronology has been established by E. Haverkamp Begemann (see below). Some of Segers' pictures betray their Flemish sources; these are probably his earlier works. He played an important part in the development of certain aspects of Dutch landscape painting, both fantastic and realistic, notably panoramic views, above all through Philips Koninck and Rembrandt (who owned eight pictures by him[24]).

Segers is best known today for his remarkably original etchings, of which the modern catalogue[25] lists fifty-four, with only 183 impressions in all. This unusually small number of impressions was a consequence of Segers' unconventional working procedure: he regarded each impression as a unique work of art. Hoogstraten says of Segers that he 'printed . . . paintings'.[26]

REFERENCES:

General: Bredius in OH, 1898, pp. 1–11; E. Haverkamp-Begemann, Catalogue of the Segers exhibition at Rotterdam, 1954; E. Haverkamp-Begemann, K. G. Boon and E. Trautscholdt, *Hercules Segers: The Complete Etchings*, Amsterdam, 1973.

In text:

1. He is described as a native of Haarlem in the Amsterdam marriage register, 1614 (Bredius, op. cit., pp. 3–4).
2. See the documents of 1615 published by Bredius, op. cit., p. 5.
3. Bredius, op. cit., pp. 3–4.
4. N. de Roever in OH, 1885, p. 44.
5. De Roever, op. cit., p. 40.
6. De Roever, op. cit., pp. 42 and 52.
7. According to a list of Haarlem painters compiled by Vincent Laurensz. van der Vinne (1629–1702) and apparently amplified by his grandson, Vincent Laurensz. van der Vinne the Younger; see van der Willigen, p. 352 (cf. p. x).
8. Bredius, op. cit., p. 4.
9. and 10. Bredius, op. cit., p. 5.

11. De Roever, op. cit., p. 52 (note); see also OH, 1942, p. 150.
12. Bredius, op. cit., pp. 5–6; see also OH, 1942, p. 154.
13. Bredius, op. cit., p. 4.
14. Bredius, op. cit., p. 6.
15. Bredius, op. cit., p. 4.
16. Cf. Haverkamp-Begemann in the Segers exhibition catalogue, Rotterdam, 1954, No. 9.
17. OH, 1942, p. 155.
18. Bredius, op. cit., p. 6.
19. and 20. Obreen, vol. 4, pp. 314–15.
21. Cf. E. Trautscholdt in Thieme/Becker.
22. Hoogstraten, p. 312.
23. Among the five Segers paintings owned by Jan van de Cappelle was 'Een lantschap van Hercules Segers, sijnde de stadt Brussel' (OH, 1892, p. 35, No. 108).
24. Strauss *Doc.* 1656/12.
25. Haverkamp-Begemann et al., op. cit.
26. Hoogstraten, op. cit.

Imitator of HERCULES SEGERS

4383 *A Mountainous Landscape*   *Plate 344*

On the back of the panel is a small brand: C.v.Rÿn; the first letter may possibly have been G or O but a P has later been cut on top of it.[1]

Oil on oak, 57.8 × 82.2 (22¾ × 32⅜); this includes the strip along the top which is certainly part of the original picture.[2]

The grain of the panel shows through in the sky, which is thin. The picture is not unfinished, as has been supposed.[3]

Traditionally ascribed to Rembrandt.[4] Holmes published it as a Hercules Segers[5] and this attribution was acceped generally until 1960.[6] Although it has some affinities with certain of Segers' prints, there is no signed painting by him in quite this style. It appears to be by the same hand as the *Mountainous Landscape* in the Bredius Museum in The Hague; this picture has recently been discussed at length by Blankert,[7] who argues for an attribution to Segers. He believes that a damaged signature revealed by cleaning: (I?).V (   ) may be a false van Goyen signature (the painting was attributed to van Goyen by Bredius). Haverkamp-Begemann,[8] however, considers that both the Bredius painting and No. 4383 are the work of an imitator of Segers' etchings rather than his paintings. The present writer concurs. A third picture apparently by the same painter is the landscape with a view of Rhenen in the collection of the late Isaac de Bruijn in Muri, near Berne;[9] another, less certainly by the same hand, is the small *Mountainous Landscape* in the possession of Goudstikker, Amsterdam, in 1930.[10] In these paintings, as well as the Bredius picture and No. 4383, the style is based on Segers' etchings rather than his paintings.

PROVENANCE: Possibly at one time in the possession of a C(?) or P. van Rijn.[11] It was probably acquired by Charles Peers (who succeeded his father in 1818 and died in 1853);[12] it was purchased from his descendant, (Sir) Charles Peers, in 1928.

REFERENCES:

1. In any case it is *not* 'R. van Ryn' as stated in BM, vol. 52, 1928, p. 216. It is perhaps the name of a previous owner.
2. The paint of the top strip (7.5–8.2 cm. wide) is homogeneous with that of the main panel and the secondary craquelure is of identical form. The slight difference in appearance between the two parts is due to the difference of the grain of the woods. Furthermore, when at some time the top member was reattached, the two abutting edges have been planed down a little, so that the brushstrokes do not quite register.
3. See note 6 below.
4. When in the Peers collection (see PROVENANCE). It is possible that the name branded on the back was taken for Rembrandt's.
5. C. J. Holmes in BM, vol. 52, 1928, pp. 210–21.

6. Bredius thought it one of Segers' latest works; W. Bode, who believed it to be unfinished, considered it a Segers earlier than the Uffizi landscape, which he dated in the last period (letters of 1928 in the National Gallery archives). M. J. Friedländer supported Bode's view (letter in National Gallery archives). H. C. Collins (*Hercules Seghers*, Chicago, 1953) also accepted the attribution of No. 4383 to Segers and considered it a late work (in the period 1633–8).
7. A. Blankert, *Museum Bredius: Catalogus van de Schilderijen en Tekeningen*, The Hague, 1978, cat. no. 149 (as 'Hercules Segers of een navolger').
8. Quoted by Blankert, op. cit., pp. 119–20.
9. Reproduced in OH, vol. 51, 1934, p. 90, where it is tentatively ascribed to Jan Ruisscher by A. Welcker (pp. 92–3).

10. Reproduced in the J. Goudstikker 1930 catalogue, No. 67; exhibited in Rotterdam, 1930–1 (No.
15).

11. See note 1.
12. Letters of 1928 and 1952 from Sir Charles Peers
(in the National Gallery archives).

HENDRICK SORGH, 1610 or 1611–1670

Hendrick Maertensz. Sorgh (he occasionally also signs *Sorg, Sorch* and *de Sorch*); his
father's surname was originally Rochusse or Rokes[1] but, contrary to what is sometimes
said, Hendrick Sorgh does not appear to have used it. He was a native of Rotterdam;[2] a
self portrait dated 1645, already mentioned by Houbraken, is inscribed 'Aet.34'.[3]
Houbraken[4] says Sorgh was a pupil of David Teniers [he almost certainly means the
younger Teniers, born in 1610] and Willem Buytewech [the Elder]. Sorgh's earlier
work, however, is much more reminiscent of Adriaen Brouwer than of Teniers, and
shows no stylistic connection with Buytewech, who in any case died in 1624. Sorgh is
recorded in Rotterdam in 1630, married there in 1633 and lived there for the rest of his
life.[5] His appointment to the honorary municipal posts of *broodweger* in 1657 and
brandmeester in 1659 as well as his participation with the *schepen* of Rotterdam in a rabbit
hunt at Vlaardingen, suggests that he achieved some local eminence. In 1659 he was a
hoofdman of the Rotterdam guild.[6] He was buried in Rotterdam, 28 June 1670.[7]

Most of his pictures are of peasant interiors and, in later years, market scenes; there
are also some portraits on a small scale and river views, and a few religious, mythological and allegorical subjects. He painted chiefly in the Brouwer tradition until at least
1648; in the 50s he developed, with his Rotterdam contemporaries Cornelis and Herman Saftleven, a distinctive style of peasant painting. Pieter Nijs, Pieter Crijnse Volmarijn and Cornelis Dorsman were pupils of Sorgh.[8]

REFERENCES:
General: P. Haverkorn van Rijsewijk in OH, vol.
10, 1892, pp. 238–50; L. T. Schneeman, 'Hendrick
Maertensz. Sorgh: A Painter of Rotterdam', unpublished PhD thesis, Pennsylvania State University,
1982.
In text:
1. See Haverkorn van Rijsewijk, op. cit., p. 238.
2. According to the entry in the Rotterdam marriage register, 1633 (Haverkorn van Rijsewijk, op.
cit., p. 243).

3. Haverkorn van Rijsewijk, op. cit., p. 240, and
catalogue of Boymans Museum, Rotterdam, 1916,
No. 427; cf. Houbraken, vol. 2, p. 90.
4. Houbraken, loc. cit.
5. Haverkorn van Rijsewijk, op. cit., pp. 241–5.
6. and 7. Haverkorn van Rijsewijk, op. cit., p. 245.
8. See the biographical notice of Sorgh in Phi-
ladelphia/Berlin/London, 1984, pp. 302–3.

1055 *A Woman playing Cards with Two Peasants*   Plate 345

Signed and dated, on the lintel of the door: Sorgh 1644.

Oil on oak, oval, 26.3 × 36.1 (10⅜ × 14¼). The picture has probably been cut down to
an oval since it was painted.

Cleaned in 1977. Worn in the darks, especially at the left side. Cleaning revealed the
signature and date.

At one time attributed to Heemskerck[1] (presumably Egbert van Heemskerck, 1634–1704).

Companion piece to No. 1056 below.

This pair of paintings has as its subject the fools that women can make of men. In each case a third person is present to point the moral. In No. 1055 the woman has cheated the peasant of his hard-earned money: his basket of eggs and the duck suggest that he is on his way to market. His foolishness is mocked by the older man holding a clay pipe. In No. 1056 the man holding a wineglass and embracing the girl is also going to lose his money as the procuress at the door will make him pay dearly for the young woman's favours.

PROVENANCE: John Henderson Bequest, 1879.

EXHIBITION: London 1978–9, No. 21A.

REFERENCES:
General: Schneeman, op. cit., No. 59.
In text: **1.** There is an ink inscription on the back of the panel: 'Painted by Heemscerk.'

1056 *Two Lovers at Table, observed by an Old Woman* *Plate 346*

Signed and dated, upper right: H. Sorgh 1644.

Oil on oak, oval, 26.4 × 36.4 ($10\frac{3}{8}$ × $14\frac{5}{16}$). Probably cut down to an oval since the picture was painted.

Cleaned in 1977. Slight wearing in the background. Cleaning revealed the signature and date.

There is a *pentimento* in the table-cloth.

Companion piece to No. 1055 above. For a discussion of the subject, see No. 1055.

COPY: A copy, in a rectangular format, was in an Anon. sale, Christie's, 4 March 1966, lot 127 (280 gns: bought Singer).[1]

PROVENANCE: John Henderson Bequest, 1879.

EXHIBITION: London 1978–9, No. 21B.

REFERENCES:
General: Schneeman, op. cit., No. 58.
In text: **1.** Panel, 24.7 × 34.9 cm. (no trace of a signature).

JOHANNES SPRUYT, 1627/8–1671

He was born in Amsterdam. His teacher is unknown, although Jan Baptist Weenix has been suggested.[1] He is described as a painter when he married in Amsterdam in 1659, and is recorded again in the city in 1660 and in 1665. He was buried in the Noorderkerk on 8 September 1671.

He painted scenes with prominent birds and fowls similar to those of Melchior d'

Hondecoeter. There is a self portrait of Spruyt and a pendant portrait of his wife, both signed by the artist and dated 1661, in a Dutch private collection.[2]

REFERENCES:
General: A. Bredius, 'Het schildersregister van Jan Sysmus', OH, vol. 8, 1890, p. 16; idem, 'Johannes Spruyt', OH, vol. 27, 1909, pp. 125–32.
In text:
1. By Bredius in op. cit., OH, vol. 27, 1909, p. 126.

2. Mr A. J. Baron van Styrum, Wassenaar. See the exhibition catalogue, *Pryst de Lijst*, Amsterdam, Rijksmuseum, 1984, pp. 198–9.

1013 *Geese and Ducks* *Plate 347*

Oil on canvas, 119.5 × 155.5 (47 × 61¼).

Cleaned in 1958. Worn in the darks.

Formerly attributed to Melchior d'Hondecoeter. It is, however, certainly by Spruyt.[1] There are closely related paintings in the Bredius Museum in The Hague,[2] in Culzean Castle, Ayrshire (Fig. 103)[3] and in the collection of Lord Forester, Willey Park, Shropshire.[4]

Probably painted *c.* 1660.

PROVENANCE: Wynn Ellis Bequest, 1876.

REFERENCES:
In text:
1. The present writer is grateful to Fred Meijer (RKD) for this attribution and for the references to related paintings.
2. 1978 cat., no. 153.

3. National Trust of Scotland. Signed and dated 1657.
4. Exhibited Birmingham 1953, No. 87.

JAN STEEN, 1625 or 1626–1679

Jan Havicksz. Steen was born in Leiden; when he was inscribed as a student at Leiden University in November 1646 he was said to be twenty. Houbraken says he was a pupil of Jan van Goyen; Weyerman says his masters were, first, Nicolaus Knüpfer in Utrecht, then Adriaen van Ostade in Haarlem and finally Jan van Goyen in The Hague. In March 1648 he became a member of the newly founded guild in Leiden. By September 1649 he was living in The Hague and in the following month married there Jan van Goyen's daughter, Margaretha. He was still living in The Hague in July 1654, though in April 1653 he had paid dues to the Leiden guild. His father, a brewer, leased a brewery for him in Delft, 1654–7, and Jan Steen painted a Delft scene in 1655; from 1656 to 1660 he was living in Warmond, a few miles from Leiden, and there is no evidence that he ever stayed long in Delft. He had settled in Haarlem by 1661, in which year he entered the guild, and is recorded there infrequently until 1670, when he inherited a house in Leiden. He is recorded in Leiden until the end of his life; he obtained permission to keep an inn there in 1672 and was a *hoofdman* of the Leiden guild in 1671, 1672 and 1673 and *deken* in 1674. He was buried in Leiden, 3 February 1679.

Steen was prolific in his production and varied in his subject-matter. In addition to his numerous genre scenes, he painted portraits, many biblical and mythological subjects and a few landscapes. He is not known to have had any pupils but had a close imitator in Richard Brakenburgh (1650–1702).

REFERENCES: T. van Westrheene, *Jan Steen*, 1856; HdG, vol. 1; Bredius, *Jan Steen*, [1927]; C. W. de Groot, *Jan Steen, Beeld en Woord*, 1952; W. Martin, *Jan Steen*, 1954; exhibition catalogue: The Hague, Mauritshuis, *Jan Steen*, 1958–9; Lyckle de Vries, 'Jan Steen: "de Kluchtschilder"', unpublished doctoral thesis, Groningen, 1977; B. D. Kirschenbaum, *The Religious and Historical Paintings of Jan Steen*, Oxford, 1977; K. Braun, *Alle tot nu toe bekend schilderijen van Jan Steen*, 2 vols., Rotterdam, 1980. For the documentary sources see Westrheene, op. cit., pp. 69, 74, 78, 92; van der Willigen, pp. 38, 267–70; Obreen, vol. 5, pp. 207, 250; Bredius, op. cit., esp. pp. 90–5.

856 *A Young Woman playing a Harpsichord* *to a Young Man* Plate 348

The boy in page's dress in the background carries a theorbo. Above the door is a coat-of-arms (now effaced). In the central compartment of the upper border of the tapestry is a female(?) figure seated on the ground.

Inscribed on the inner side of the top of the harpsichord: ACTA· VIRVM/PROBANT and on the inner side of the keyboard cover: Soli·Deo·Gloria. There seems to have been an inscription at the top of the left-hand page of the music book on the harpsichord; none of it is now legible.

Signed just above the keyboard: IOHANIS STeeN FECIT 16(·) (9?).

Oil on oak, 42.3 × 33 (16⅝ × 13).

The faces of the two principal figures, the tapestry, the bed in the background and the coat-of-arms are badly worn and retouched.

The design of seahorses and arabesques above the keyboard occurs also on the instrument in Vermeer's *Lady at a Virginal* in the collection of HM the Queen and there is a very similar decoration printed on paper on an Antwerp virginal of 1620 preserved in the Musée Instrumental du Conservatoire in Brussels.[1] Biblical quotations and proverbs similar to those in the present picture are often found on virginals and harpsichords (compare Metsu No. 839 of this catalogue).

The date is much damaged and the third figure is now completely illegible. Smith[2] gave it as 1671 but comparison with dated works by Steen shows that this date is quite impossible. The year 1656 had been suggested[3] but under magnification the last figure appears to be 9. The costume is that of the later 50s and early 60s and there are dated works of 1660 and 1661 in a comparable style. If the last figure is in fact 9 the only date which would fit is 1659; in any case the picture is unlikely to have been painted before 1659 or later than 1665. Braun[4] reads the date as 1659.

PROVENANCE: In an Anon. ('collector from Friesland') sale, Amsterdam, 29 September 1802 (lot 50), bought by J. Smit (676 guilders); in the collection of Anna Maria Ebeling (wife of Paul Iwan Hogguer) who died in 1812; A. M. Ebeling (Hogguer) sale, Amsterdam, 18 sqq. August 1817 (lot 79), bought by Nieuwenhuys (1,170 guilders); Le Rouge sale, Paris, 27 sqq. April 1818 (lot 55), bought by Delahante (7,740 francs). In the collection of (Sir) Robert Peel (Bart.) by 1823, when it was exhibited at the BI. Purchased with the Peel collection, 1871.

EXHIBITIONS: BI 1823, No. 77; The Hague, Mauritshuis, 'In the Light of Vermeer', 1966, No. 27; London 1976, No. 104.

REFERENCES:
General: Smith No. 113; HdG No. 409; Braun, op. cit., No. 106.
In text:
1. B. Nicolson, *Vermeer's Lady at the Virginals*,
London, 1946, fig. 15.
2. Smith No. 113.
3. National Gallery catalogue, 1913–29.
4. Braun, op. cit.

1421 *Two Men and a Young Woman making Music on a Terrace*

Plate 349

The man on the right is playing a lute. In the distance, below the terrace, is a formal garden, beyond which is the tower of a church.

Signed on the parapet, right: JSteen (JS in monogram).

Oil on canvas, 43.8 × 60.7 ($17\frac{1}{4}$ × $23\frac{7}{8}$).

Tears in the centre of the canvas, above and to the left of the head of the man holding a glass, have been repaired.

The picture can be assigned on stylistic grounds to the early 1670s. Braun[1] dates the painting to 1673–6. The costume of the two men is archaic and it has been suggested that they are based on those of the contemporary theatre, e.g. the old man seated in the centre may be intended for the Pantalone of the *commedia dell'arte*[2] (cf. No. 1378, After Steen, below).

PROVENANCE: In the collection of the Hon. William Pole-Tylney-Long-Wellesley (later 4th Earl of Mornington) in Brussels by 1842;[3] Earl of Mornington sale, Ixelles, 15–18 June 1846 (lot 14), bought by Nieuwenhuys (3,800 francs), who sold it to Adrian Hope.[4] In the Adrian Hope collection, Paris, in 1856;[5] Adrian Hope sale, London, 30 June 1894 (lot 62), £819, bought for the National Gallery.

EXHIBITION: London 1976, No. 109.

REFERENCES:
General: Smith Supplement No. 26; HdG No. 410; Braun, op. cit., No. 360.
In text:
1. Braun, op. cit.
2. S. J. Gudlaugsson, *De Komedianten bij Jan Steen en zijn tijdgenooten*, 1945, pp. 27 and 50.
3. Smith, loc. cit. Although the catalogue of the Mornington sale of 1846 (cf. PROVENANCE) describes the collection of which the present picture formed a part as the property of 'Lord Wellesley, Comte de Mornington', it is clear that this refers not to the 3rd Earl, William Wellesley-Pole, but to the 4th (who succeeded his father in 1845), since Smith (loc. cit.) calls him 'Hon. Long Pole Wellesley' [sic] and it was the 4th Earl who took the additional surnames Tilney-Long (in 1812).
4. Westrheene, op. cit., p. 134, No. 156.
5. Westrheene, loc. cit.

2555 *A Man blowing Smoke at a Drunken Woman, and Another Man with a Wine-pot*

Plate 350

Signed in the top left corner: JSteen. (JS in monogram).

Oil on oak, 30.2 × 24.8 ($11\frac{7}{8}$ × $9\frac{3}{4}$).

MacLaren suggested – on the basis of the costume of the man at the left – that the painting should be dated in the later 1660s. In fact the costume is not distinctive enough to allow such a precise dating. A rather earlier dating – in the first half of the 1660s – is preferred by the present writer. Braun[1] rejects the attribution of the painting to Steen, believing it to be in imitation of his work. The subject of female drunkenness was often painted by Steen. This scene may be intended to illustrate the saying: 'De Wijn is een spotter' ('Wine is a mocker') (see also No. 6442 below).

PROVENANCE: In the collection of George Salting, London; Salting Bequest, 1910.

REFERENCES:
General: Braun, op. cit., No. B–219.
In text: **1.** Braun, op. cit.

2556 *A Pedlar selling Spectacles outside a Cottage*

Plate 351

Signed on the lintel of the cottage door: JSteen (JS in monogram).

Oil on oak, 24.6 × 20.3 ($9\frac{11}{16}$ × 8).

Probably painted in the early 1650s, shortly before the *Village Wedding* of 1653 in Rotterdam.[1] Braun[2] dates it to 1649–53.

In the Krauht, Amsterdam 1778 and Blanken sales there was a companion piece, *A Fortune Teller* (not No. 2557 below).

VERSION: A larger version(?) was in the Jan Twisk sale, Amsterdam, 3–4 October 1837 (lot 45),[3] bought by Chaplin (331 guilders).

PROVENANCE: Johan Balthasar Krauht et al. sale, The Hague, 7–8 October 1771 (lot 8), bought by Schuller (200 guilders with the pendant); Anon. sale, Amsterdam, 1 October 1778 (lot 144)[4] bought by Yver (160 guilders with the pendant); G. C. Blanken sale, The Hague, 4–5 June 1800 (lot 17), bought by Valette (43 guilders). In the possession of Agnew, London, and later in the collection of George Salting, London. Salting Bequest, 1910.

REFERENCES:
General: HdG No. 274; Braun, op. cit., No. 16.
In text:
1. HdG No. 455; Boymans-van Beuningen Museum: 1972 cat., No. 2314.
2. Braun, op. cit.
3. HdG (loc. cit.) identifies the Twisk picture with that in the Blanken sale but although the description in the Twisk sale catalogue agrees with No. 2556 the size is given as *2p. 4d.* × *2p.*
4. The identity of No. 2556 with the picture in the Krauht, Amsterdam 1778 and Blanken sales is proved by the description in the catalogue of the Amsterdam 1778 sale: 'Voor een Huis vertoond zich een Kramer met een Marsje, vertoonende een Bril, om die te verkoopen aan een oude Vrouw, die in de Deur staat, en dezelve met het leezen van een Papier, scheint te probeeren; over welke houding, een Man, die op een Bank zit, scheint te grim-lachen'; on panel, $9\frac{1}{2}$ × 8 *duim*.

2557 *Peasants merry-making outside an Inn, and a Seated Woman taking the Hand of an Old Man*

Plate 352

Signed near the bottom on the right: JSteen (JS in monogram).

Oil on oak, 24.3 × 20.3 ($9\frac{9}{16}$ × 8).

The influence of Joost Droochsloot (1586–1666), who worked in Utrecht, is very evident in this picture, especially in the multiplicity of small figures. It is probably a work of the late 1640s, or at least earlier than the *Winter Landscape* in the collection of Baron Rutger von Essen, Skokloster (Sweden), which was painted before July 1651.[1] Braun[2] dates No. 2557 to 1647–50.

Although it could be supposed that the woman in the foreground is telling the fortune of the old man, this picture is not the *Fortune Teller* which was the companion piece to No. 2556 above in the Krauht, Amsterdam 1778 and Blanken sales[3] (see PROVENANCE of No. 2556).

PROVENANCE: In the possession of Agnew, London, and afterwards in the collection of George Salting, London; Salting Bequest, 1910.

REFERENCES:
General: Braun, op. cit., No. 7.
In text:
1. It was sold to Field-Marshal Wrangel in July 1651 (see HdG No. 881a and W. Stechow in *Zeitschrift für bildende Kunst*, vol. 62, 1928–9, p. 173; reproduced).
2. Braun, op. cit.
3. The description in the catalogue of the Anon. Amsterdam sale of 1 October 1778 (lot 145) shows that this was an entirely different composition: 'De

wederg[a]de . . . Dit verbeeld een Waarzegster, staande met een Kind op haar Rug, en een Mand aan de Arm, voor een Huis, over welkers Onderdeur een oud Man legt, die zy goed Geluk scheint te voorspellen; een Meisje, met een Kan in de hand, staat daar na te luisteren; terwyl zich op den tweede grond vertoond, een Boerin staande met Melk-Emmers, die mede deel, in de Voorzegging scheint te nemen . . .'

2558 *A Peasant Family at Meal-time ('Grace before Meat')*

Plate 353

A little girl on the right of the table is saying grace.

Signed, bottom left: JSteen. (JS in monogram).

Oil on canvas, 44.8 × 37.5 ($17\frac{5}{8}$ × $14\frac{3}{4}$).

There are numerous paintings by Steen of peasants saying grace before meals;[1] one of them is inscribed 'ons dagelyckx Broot' (our daily bread).[2] The earliest picture of this subject by Steen is that in the Morrison collection, dated 1660.[3]

Probably painted in the middle 60s. It is dated by Braun[4] to 1664–8.

ENGRAVINGS: When in the Leuchtenberg collection it was lithographed by L. S. Troendlin[5] and etched by J. N. Muxel, 1851.[6]

PROVENANCE: [Van Tol] sale, Soeterwoude (near Leiden), 15 June 1779 (lot 19), bought by Roos (146 guilders). In the collection of Prince Eugène [de Beauharnais], Duke of Leuchtenberg (d. 1824), in Munich;[7] removed with the rest of the collection to St Petersburg by his second son, Maximilian, 3rd Duke of Leuchtenberg (d. 1852), between 1851[8] and 1852; inherited by his son, Nikolai Maximilianovich, Prince Romarowski, 4th Duke of Leuchtenberg (d. 1891), and lent (with other works) to the Gallery of the Imperial Academy of Fine Art, St Petersburg, from 1886; inherited by his younger natural son, Duke Georgi Nicolaievich of Leuchtenberg, and in his collection in St Petersburg in 1904.[9] Later in the possession of Sulley

& Co., London.[10] It was in the collection of George Salting, London, by 1906, when it was lent to the Rembrandt Tercentenary Exhibition in Leiden. Salting Bequest, 1910.

EXHIBITIONS: Leiden, Rembrandt Tercentenary Exhibition, 1906, No. 63; London, Dowdeswell Galleries, 1909, No. 28.

REFERENCES:

General: Smith No. 167; HdG Nos. 378 and 867; Braun, op. cit., No. 231.

In text:

1. Cf. HdG Nos. 374–83. The scene is known in Dutch as *Gebed voor de Maaltijd*. For a discussion see ex. cat. Philadelphia/Berlin/London, 1984, No. 102.
2. HdG No. 374. In the collection of the Duke of Rutland.
3. HdG No. 375. Inscribed on a placard hanging on the back wall is a quotation from Proverbs 30: 7–9. See ex. cat. Philadelphia/Berlin/London, 1984, No. 102.
4. Braun, op. cit.
5. In *Auswahl der vorzüglichsten Gemälde der Herzog-*

lich *Leuchtenbergischen Gallerie*, published by Cotta, n.d.

6. *Gemälde-Sammlung . . . des Herzogs von Leuchtenberg in München. In Umrissen gestochen von . . . J. N. Muxel*, 2nd ed., 1851, No. 152.
7. [J. N.] Muxel, *Catalogue des tableaux de la galerie de feu S.A.R. le Prince Eugène Duc de Leuchtenberg à Munich*, 1825, No. 142.
8. Cf. note 6. It was seen in St Petersburg in 1862 by Waagen, *Die Gemäldesammlung in der Kaiserlichen Eremitage zu Petersburg . . . andere dortige Kunstsammlungen*, 1864, p. 384 (and cf. p.v.).
9. See *Trésors d'art en Russie*, vol. 4, 1904, p. 17 and pl. 4.
10. According to HdG No. 378.

2559 *An Interior with a Man offering an Oyster to a Woman* Plate 354

In the right background is an engraved view, probably of Antwerp.

Signed in the top left corner: JSteen (JS in monogram).

Oil on oak, 38.1 × 31.5 (15 × 12⅜).

Cleaned in 1977.

MacLaren considered the costume to be of the first half of the 1660s. Braun[1] dated the painting to 1662–6.

VERSIONS: A signed variant is in the Oslo Museum (C. Langaard collection);[2] a repetition, according to HdG, was in the R. Visscher-Burckhard collection, Basle.[3]

PROVENANCE: No. 2559 or one of the other versions was perhaps in the Robert de Neufville sale, Leiden, 15 sqq. March 1736 (lot 11),[4] 64 guilders, and the following sales: Johan van der Marck sale, Amsterdam, 25 sqq. August 1773 (lot 306), bought by J. Wubbels (186 guilders); Johannes Lodewijk Strantwijk sale, Amsterdam, 10 May 1780 (lot 241), bought by Wubbels (190 guilders); Anon. sale, Amsterdam, 7 May 1804 (lot 149, with companion[5]), bought by Pruissenaar (39 guilders); J. Kleinenbergh sale, Leiden, 19 sqq. July 1841 (lot 213),[6] bought by Lamme (1,071 guilders), apparently for Nieuwenhuys.[7] No. 2559 was in the collection of Sir Hugh Hume Campbell, Bart., at Marchmont House, Berwickshire, by 1856;[8] Sir H. H. Campbell sale, London, 16 June 1894 (lot 49), bought by Horace Buttery (£210), by whom sold to George Salting in July 1894.[9] Salting Bequest, 1910.

EXHIBITIONS: London, Dowdeswell Galleries, Steen Exhibition, 1909, No. 38; London 1978–9, No. 22.

REFERENCES:

General: Smith Supplement No. 62(?); HdG No. 855.

In text:

1. Braun, op. cit.
2. Panel, 38 × 31.7 cm. From the Tardieu collection and the L[eboeuf] de M[ontgermont] sale,

Paris, 16–19 June 1919 (lot 207), reproduced in the sale catalogue. In this version, among other variations, the engraved view in the background is of London (so inscribed).

3. MS note in HdG's own copy of his *Catalogue Raisonné* in the RKD.

4. 'Een heerlyk en Uytvoerig stuckjen door Jan Steen Verbeeldende een Oester huys'; 1 *voet* 2½ *duim* × 1 *voet.*

5. The companion piece was the *Man blowing Smoke in the Face of a Sleeping Woman* in the Dr Martin Schubart sale, Munich, 23 October 1899 (lot 67); HdG No. 762.

6. The woman in the Kleinenbergh picture is said by Smith to have a yellow gown (cf. Smith Supplement No. 62, but the colour is not given in the sale catalogue); if this is correct it cannot be either the National Gallery or the Oslo picture since in the

former the woman wears a bright red jacket and a grey skirt and in the latter a red skirt and a darker red jacket.

7. The copies of the Kleinenbergh sale catalogue in the Amsterdam Printroom and the Victoria and Albert Museum Library give Lamme as the purchaser; according to Smith, loc. cit., it was bought by Nieuwenhuys.

8. Westrheene, op. cit., No. 146 (also Waagen, 1854, p. 442).

9. Letter of 1953 from Horace A. Buttery (in the National Gallery archives).

2560 *Skittle Players outside an Inn*   *Plate 355*

On the left is the inn sign-board (a white swan).

Oil on oak, 33.5 × 27 ($13\frac{3}{16}$ × $10\frac{5}{8}$).

The grass and foliage are considerably blanched.

There are *pentimenti* in almost all the foreground figures; the fence shows through some of them.

The date 1672 on the copy in the Rijksmuseum (see below) is an invention of the copyist; there is no trace of a date on the present picture which is quite different from the dated works of the 70s and clearly in an earlier style. It has been dated c.1650(?) by W. Martin[1] and c.1652 in the 1929 National Gallery catalogue. The works of 1651 and earlier that have since come to light[2] show that it cannot be among Steen's first productions, nor can it be placed anywhere among those of the years 1652–9.[3] Stechow[4] has suggested that it is of c.1660; MacLaren was inclined to place it even a little later, about 1662–3 (cf. *Peasants drinking and dancing in an Arbour* of 1663 in the National Gallery of Art, Washington[5]). There would be some slight support for the later dating if the picture is the *Landscape with Skittle-players in the Haarlemmer Hout* of the 1713 sale (see PROVENANCE), since Steen was apparently living in Haarlem in the early 60s. Braun[6] dated the painting to 1660–2.

COPY: A copy is in the Rijksmuseum, Amsterdam (falsely signed and dated 1672.)[7]

ENGRAVING: Engraved (in reverse) by Emanuel de Ghendt.[8]

PROVENANCE: Possibly in the Jacob Cromhout and Jasper Loskart sale, Amsterdam, 7–8 May 1709 (lot 78),[9] 53 guilders, and/or the Cornelis van Dyck sale, The Hague, 9–10 May 1713 (lot 40),[10] 51 guilders. It was in the Pieter Testas the Younger sale, Amsterdam, 29 March sqq. 1757 (lot 41), bought by J. ten Compe (172 guilders) and (probably) the Coenraad van Heemskerck sale, The Hague, 7 October 1765 (lot 30),[11] bought by Foucquet (140 guilders); Randon de Boisset sale, Paris, 27 February sqq. 1777 (lot 128), bought by Poullain (1,600 francs); Poullain sale, Paris, 15 sqq. March 1780 (lot 77), bought by Boileau (2,600 francs); Comte de Vaudreuil sale, Paris, 24–25 November 1784 (lot 63), bought by Paillet (3,401 francs). In the possession of J. B. P. Le Brun by 1792;[12] Destouches sale, Paris, 21 March sqq. 1794 (lot 104), bought by Drouillet or Boileau[13] (4,500 francs); said to have been in a Gérard(?) Saint-Maurice sale in Paris in 1796 or 1797,[14] 3,430 francs; in an Anon. [Montaleau?] sale, Paris, 19 sqq. July 1802 (lot 144), bought by Henri (2,900 francs); d[e] P[reuil] sale, Paris, 25–29 November 1811 (lot 95), bought by Lebrun (4,950 francs). In the collection of the Prince de Talleyrand, Paris, apparently by 1814;[15] it is in the catalogue of the [Talleyrand] sale announced for 9 July 1817 (lot 29) but this sale did not take place and the whole collection was bought by William Buchanan.[16] Buchanan sold No. 2560 to Edward Gray, Harringay House, London,[17] apparently in 1817;[18] it had passed to Alexander Baring (later 1st Baron Ashburton) by 1829, when it was exhibited at the BI; exhibited at the RA in 1871 and 1890, lent by Lord Ashburton. The Ashburton collection was sold *en bloc* in 1907 to Messrs Agnew and others. In the collection of George Salting, London, by 1909, when it was lent to the Steen Exhibition, Dowdeswell Galleries, London. Salting Bequest, 1910.

EXHIBITIONS: BI 1829, No. 58; RA 1871, No. 202; RA 1890, No. 118; London, Dowdeswell Galleries, Jan Steen Exhibition, No. 29; London 1976, No. 106.

REFERENCES:

General: Smith No. 33; Westrheene, op. cit., Nos. 63 and 438; HdG Nos. 737 and (?)738a; Braun, op. cit., No. 135.

In text:

1. In *Monatschefte für Kunstwissenschaft*, vol. 3, 1910, pp. 187–8.

2. Cf. W. Stechow in *Zeitschrift für bildende Kunst*, vol. 62, 1928–9, p. 173 ff., and H. Gerson in *Kunsthistorische Mededeelingen*, vol. 3, 1948, pp. 50–6.

3. The dated works after 1651 and before 1660 include: *A Village Wedding*, 1653 (Boymans-van Beuningen Museum, Rotterdam, 1972 cat., No. 2314, HdG No. 455); *Portrait of a Man and a Girl outside a House in Delft* (the so-called 'Burgher of Delft and his Daughter'), 1655 (Lady Janet Douglas-Pennant, Penrhyn Castle, HdG No. 878); *A Girl at her Toilet*, 1657 (Adolphe Schloss sale, Paris, 5 December 1951, lot 53; HdG No. 341); *Two Women outside a House listening to Musicians*, 1659 (National Trust, Ascott; HdG No. 438).

4. Op. cit., p. 175.

5. HdG No. 655.

6. Braun, op. cit.

7. Rijksmuseum 1976 catalogue, A1763. On oak, 35 × 28 cm. Falsely signed on the centre bar of the

fence, left: J Steen/1672 (JS in monogram).

8. In Le Brun, vol. 1, oppos. p. 78.

9. 'Kegel-Speelders van Jan Steen.'

10. 'Landtschap en Kegelspel van den selve [Jan Steen], met kleyne Beelden, verbeeldende den Haerlemmer Hout . . .'; size not given.

11. 'Jan Steen. Vrolyke en met Kegelen spelende Boertjes, voor een Herberg.' Panel, 1 *voet* 1 *duim* × 10¾ *duim*.

12. See note 8.

13. The marked copy of the Destouches sale catalogue in the British Library gives Drouillet as the purchaser; that in the RKD has Boileau.

14. Smith (No. 33) says it was in a Saint-Maurice sale, 1797, sold for 3,430 francs. The only recorded Saint-Maurice sale of about this time is the Gérard Saint-Maurice sale, 1796 (see G. Duplessis, *Les ventes de tableaux . . . aux 17 et 18 siècles*, 1874, No. 2009). No copy of the catalogue of this sale is recorded in Lugt.

15. See p. i of the catalogue of the Talleyrand sale announced for 9 July 1817.

16. Buchanan, vol. 2, p. 308.

17. Buchanan, vol. 2, p. 335.

18. Buchanan, vol. 2, p. 348.

5637 *The Interior of an Inn ('The Broken Eggs')* Plate 356

Signed, bottom right, on the side of the bench: JSteen (JS in monogram).

Oil on canvas, 43.3 × 38.1 ($17\frac{1}{16}$ × 15).

The man holding the woman's skirt appears frequently in Steen's paintings and has the features of the artist himself.[1]

Probably a work of 1665–70. Braun[2] dated the painting to 1664–8.

COPY: A copy was in the N. Katz et al. sale, Brussels, 9 March 1953 (lot 89).

PROVENANCE: It has been identified[3] with a picture in the Ewout van Dishoek sale, The Hague, 9 sqq. June 1745 (lot 77) but this was probably a different composition.[4] According to Smith it was in a sale in Paris in 1825, bought for 1,410 francs.[5] It was in the collection of E. de Boursault, Paris, by 1833;[6] it is in the catalogue of the Boursault sale, Paris, 7 sqq. May 1832 (lot 51), but according to Smith it was purchased with the Boursault collection by Henry Artaria for Edmund Higginson,[7] in whose collection at Saltmarsh Castle it was certainly by 1841.[8] Edmund Higginson sale, London, 4–6 June 1846 (lot 198), bought in (170 gns); Edmund Higginson sale, London, 16 June 1860 (lot 29), bought by W. S. King (137 gns).[9] In the collection of

Joseph Bond by 1864, when it was exhibited at the BI; [Joseph Bond] sale, London, 2 May 1874 (lot 102), bought by Lord Powerscourt (£105); [Viscount Powerscourt] sale, London, 29 June 1878 (lot 72), bought in (98 gns). It was later in the possession of R. Langton Douglas;[10] said to have been in the collection of Alfred Beit (died 1906)[11] and certainly in the collection of his brother (Sir) Otto Beit (Bart.) by 1909 when it was lent to the Steen Exhibition at Dowdeswell Galleries; Sir Otto Beit Bequest, 1941.

EXHIBITIONS: BI 1864, No. 45; London, Dowdeswell Galleries, Jan Steen Exhibition, 1909, No. 16;[12] Leiden, Steen Exhibition, 1926, No. 22.

REFERENCES:
General: Smith No. 127 and Supplement No. 69; T. van Westrheene, op. cit., No. 96; HdG Nos. 664 and 848; Braun, op. cit., No. 226.
In text:
1. Compare, for example, the *Self Portrait* in the Rijksmuseum (1976 cat. no. A383).
2. Braun, op. cit.
3. HdG No. 848; elsewhere (No. 814) he identifies the Dishoek picture with that mentioned in the following note.
4. 'Un homme qui prend la Servante par la Juppe [sic], par J. Steen' (see also Hoet, vol. 2, p. 173). The sale catalogue gives the size of this picture as 1 *pied* 9 *pouces* × 1 *pied* 4 *pouces*; it is, therefore, more probably the painting of very similar subject in the possession of Messrs Smith in 1842 (Smith Supplement No. 97) and exhibited at Agnew's, London, May–June 1939 (No. 2), which is on panel and measures $21\frac{1}{2}$ × 18 in. (see also note 3).

5. Smith No. 127.
6. Smith No. 127.
7. Supplement No. 69.
8. H. Artaria, *Catalogue of the Gallery of Edmund Higginson . . .*, 1841, p. 130 (as *Les Œufs Cassés*).
9. According to MS notes in a copy of Smith's *Catalogue Raisonné* thought to be his own it was bought at the Higginson sale (1860) for Edm^d Forster of Clewer [MS notes to Smith No. 127, and also to Supplement No. 69].
10. According to a MS note in HdG's own copy of his *Catalogue Raisonné* in the RKD.
11. HdG No. 664a. It is not in Bode's *Art Collection of Mr Alfred Beit . . . London*, 1904.
12. It appears only in the first edition of the exhibition catalogue; it had been withdrawn from the exhibition by the second edition, in which it is replaced by *The Drinkers*.

6442 *The Effects of Intemperance* — Plate 357

Signed, on the step, lower centre: JSteen (JS in monogram).

Oil on panel, 76 × 106.5 (30 × 42).

There is an inscription HOSPITAL above the round window of the building in the right background: it was not removed during cleaning.

Cleaned in 1977.

The woman slumped on the left, whose purse is being picked by a child, on the extreme left, is sleeping off the effects of alcohol. She illustrates the proverb 'De Wijn is een spotter' (Wine is a mocker'). As in many other paintings by Steen, it is the foolishness of their elders which encourages the children to misbehave.[1] Here the child throwing roses in front of the pig illustrates a popular saying about foolish behaviour.[2] In the background an old man is seducing a young girl, another of the pitfalls of alcohol. Above the head of the drunken woman hangs a basket in which can be seen reminders of the fate of those who lack self-discipline – the crutch and clapper of the beggar (*Lazarusklep*) and the birch of judicial punishment.

Steen's moralistic message is that it is only by actively resisting the temptations of excessive indulgence in sensual pleasures that poverty and degradation can be avoided.

De Vries dates the painting to 1663–5[3] which seems acceptable to the present writer.

COPIES: An old copy was in the collection of D. A. J. Kessler, London, in 1929.[4] Another – or possibly the same – copy was in the collection of Percy B. Meyer in 1953.[5]

PROVENANCE: Bought by the English art dealer Chaplin in Amsterdam, 1829; Emmerson sale, London, 2 May 1829 (lot 116); Delafield collection; Norton collection; H. A. J. Munro sale, London, 6 April 1878, lot 105: purchased by Graves for W. B. Beaumont, later created Lord Allendale. Purchased by the National Gallery from the Trustees of the Allendale Settlement under the terms of a private treaty sale, 1977.

EXHIBITIONS: RA 1929, No. 192; RA 1938, No. 244; RA 1952–3, No. 569; Aberystwyth/Cardiff/Swansea, 'Dutch Genre Paintings', 1958, No. 48; The Hague, Mauritshuis, 'Jan Steen', 1958–9, No. 30.[6]

REFERENCES:

General: HdG, No. 111 (the description and part of the provenance refer to the copy which was with Meyer in 1953, see above); ex. cat., The Hague, Mauritshuis, op. cit., No. 30.
In text:
1. This is in effect the sense of all the *In weelde Siet Toe* (Beware of luxury) and the *Bedurven huishouwen* (Dissolute households) paintings. For recent discussions of these themes (with previous literature) see Philadelphia/Berlin/London, 1984, cat. nos. 104 and 109.

2. 'Strooit geen rozen voor de varkens.'
3. In the Mauritshuis, ex. cat., op. cit.
4. Dimensions and support not known. This copy is mentioned in Mauritshuis, ex. cat., op. cit.
5. The provenance of HdG No. 111 under 'Sales' refers to this copy which is on canvas (43 × 54 in.).
6. The misleading provenance given by HdG was clarified by De Vries in the Mauritshuis ex. cat., op. cit.

After JAN STEEN

1378 *An Itinerant Musician saluting Two Women in a Kitchen*

Plate 358

The old man has a flute in his breeches pocket.

Inscribed on the side of the fireplace, right: JSt 1670 (JS in monogram); later the t has been repainted and the letters een painted on top of the date.[1]

A long inscription in ink on the back of the supporting canvas is now illegible.

Grisaille. Oil on thick paper, stuck on canvas, 46 × 36.8 (18⅛ × 14½).

Many darkened retouchings throughout.

W. Martin[2] was the first to declare it a copy of a picture (in colours) in the collection of Mrs G. E. Naylor (see VERSIONS); he suggested it was made by or for Jan Stolker (1724–85) in connection with his mezzotint of 1762 after this design. It does, in fact, follow the Naylor picture (Fig. 104), except in minutiae, with slight extensions of the composition at top and bottom. Hofstede de Groot[3] rejected this suggestion and re-affirmed the attribution to Steen. Nevertheless it seems distinctly too weak for Steen (comparison with the Naylor picture is particularly enlightening) and no other grisaille is attributable to him. Stolker's mezzotint, however, is much inferior to the grisaille and, more important, differs from it in a number of details (and also from the Naylor composition); it is also a good deal smaller than the grisaille. It is not unreasonable to suppose Stolker engraved his print from the copy in colours which he made after Steen and which is described in the catalogue of Stolker's sale (see VERSIONS). On the other hand there is a mezzotint of 1771 by 'S. Paul' (pseudonym of Samuel de Wilde, 1748–1832) of almost exactly the same size as the grisaille and which agrees with it in all but the most minute particulars (and also with the Naylor picture).[4] It is, therefore, more than probable that the grisaille was made by (or for) de Wilde in preparation for his print.

There is no date on the Naylor picture. That on the National Gallery picture (which does not appear in either of the two mezzotints) was perhaps copied from one formerly on the original, which could well have been painted in 1670. De Vries[5] preferred a date of c.1665; Braun[6] too dates the original c.1665.

S. J. Gudlaugsson,[7] referring to the original, suggested that the musician with his old-fashioned dress is derived from the Pantalone of the *commedia dell'arte*.

De Groot[8] related the subject to a saying of Jacob Cats: 'Geen perle dient bij nacht gekocht; geen vrijster bij een Keers gezocht' ('Pearls should not be bought by night; nor a lover sought by candlelight').

VERSIONS: The original of this composition (ex-Swaythling collection) is in Mrs G. E. Naylor's collection.[9] A copy by Jan Stolker was in Stolker's sale, Rotterdam, 27 sqq. March 1786 (lot 26);[10] another copy was in the Hindrichs collection, Arnhem, in 1894.[11]

ENGRAVINGS: There is a mezzotint of this design (in reverse) by Jan Stolker, 1762,[12] and another (also in reverse) by 'S. Paul' (= Samuel de Wilde), 1771.[13]

PROVENANCE: This or a similar picture was in the van Loon collection, Amsterdam, in 1833;[14] it is presumably the grisaille in the Samuel Woodburn sale, London, 15 sqq. May 1854 (lot 127),[15] bought by Norton (7 gns). It was in the collection of Sir William H. Gregory by 1879, when it was exhibited at the RA; Sir W. H. Gregory Bequest, 1892.

EXHIBITION: RA 1879, No. 86.

REFERENCES:

General: Smith No. 153; HdG No. 420.

In text:

1. The overpainting of the 'signature' and date is in the same dark grey as the many small retouchings on the picture; it was presumably done after 1879 since the catalogue of the RA exhibition of that year (No. 86) gives the 'signature' and date in their original form. The last two figures of the date can still just be seen underlying the later part of the inscription and are more clearly visible in a macrophotograph (4½×).

2. W. Martin in *Onze Kunst*, 1909, pp. 161–2, and in *Monatshefte für Kunstwissenschaft*, vol. 3, 1910, p. 186 (also in *Zeitschrift für bildende Kunst*, 1927–8, p. 341).

3. HdG in *Art in America*, vol. 16, 1927–28, p. 250 (footnote), and in *Repertorium für Kunstwissenschaft*, vol. 50, 1929, p. 134.

4. For example: in the Naylor picture, the National Gallery grisaille and Paul's mezzotint the birdcage(?) hanging from the ceiling has twenty-six vertical bars visible, whereas in Stolker's print there are only seventeen; the mussel and egg-shells scattered in the foreground correspond exactly in the three first-mentioned but are different in the last.

5. In the Mauritshuis, The Hague, ex. cat., op. cit.

6. Braun, op. cit., No. 253.

7. S. J. Gudlaugsson, *De Komedianten bij Jan Steen* etc., 1945, p. 27.

8. C. W. de Groot, *Jan Steen, Beeld en woord*, Utrecht/Nijmegen, 1952, p. 120.

9. Smith Supplement No. 109; HdG Nos. 421 and 814 f. On panel, 39.5 × 35.5 cm. Signed in the same position as on the National Gallery copy: JSteen (JS in monogram). Its provenance is as follows: apparently in the collection of John Blackwood in 1771 (see note 13); Marquess Camden sale, London, 12 June 1841 (lot 51), bought by Bredel (£231); Miss Bredel sale, London, 1 May 1875 (lot 126), bought by Annoot, 630 gns (the muddled description in the Bredel sale catalogue makes it appear that the picture in that sale was grisaille but this is certainly not the case since it is beyond any doubt the painting later in the Field and Swaythling collections); George Field sale, London, 10 June 1893 (lot 34; as from the Bredel collection), bought by Tooth (690 gns); in the collection of Samuel Montagu (later 1st Baron Swaythling) by 1894, when it was exhibited at the

RA, No. 94; Swaythling sale, 12 July 1946 (lot 37); Duits, London; J. E. Fattorini collection, Bradford; inherited by his daughter, Mrs G. E. Naylor; Steen Exhib., The Hague, 1958–9 (No. 37; lent by Mrs Naylor).

10. 'Jan Stolker na Jan Steen. In een Binnen-Huis, ziet men eenige Boeren en Boerinnen aan den haard zitten, tegens welken een potzig gekleede Speelman een grappig Compliment schijnt te maken; nevens ander huisraad, zo in vertrek als in het verschiet door een openstaande deur ziende, geplaatst, staat op de voorgrond een Koperen Ketel, terwijl eenige Mosselschelpen en Eyerdoppen over den vloer verspreid liggen: zeer fraay in de Couleur en manier van dien Meester, op Paneel hoog 15½ breed 13½ duim' [= c.39 × 34 cm.].

11. Reproduced in *Eigen Haard*, 1894, p. 157.

12. The size of the engraved subject (not plate size) is 34 × 27.9 cm. Inscribed: 'JSteen Pinx^t JStolker Fec. / Opgedragen aan . . . den Heere Arnout Gevers / Oud Schepen der Stad Rotterdam . . . / door . . . Jan Stolker, 1762.'

13. Subject size, 45.7 × 35.4 cm. Inscribed: '. . . Done from the Original Picture Painted by John Steen, in the Possession of John Blackwood, Esqr by S. Paul./London . . . 1st Jany 1771.'

14. See Smith No. 153. It is not among the Steens in the collection of Mme van Loon listed by Westrheene, op. cit., pp. 104–5.

15. 'J. Steen Interior with an old man addressing two females, who are seated near a fireplace, two smokers behind. *Admirably painted en grisaille.*'

HARMEN STEENWYCK, 1612 – after 1656

Harmen Evertsz. Steenwyck (occasionally also *Steenwijck*); still-life painter. He was born in Delft; in 1628 he went to Leiden to study painting under his uncle, David Bailly (1584–1657), and remained with him for some five years; he was joined there by his brother Pieter. Harmen was living in Delft in 1644; in 1654 he was in the East Indies but had returned by 1655 and the last mention of him is in Delft in January 1656.

The comparatively few known works by Harmen Steenwyck and his brother are almost all still-life paintings, several of the *vanitas* type (see No. 1256 below). They are related in style to Pieter Claesz.'s and Willem Heda's works of the 1620s and 30s, and to the still lifes of Pieter Potter.

REFERENCE: Bredius in OH, vol. 8, 1890, pp. 143 ff.

1256 *Still Life: An Allegory of the Vanities of Human Life*   Plate 359

In the centre is a recorder, inscribed with the letter A; on the right is visible part of a shawm and in the background a lute (or a theorbo). Behind the skull is a Japanese sword in a black scabbard inlaid with mother-of-pearl. The writing on the open page of the book in front is not intended to be legible.

Signed on the box beneath the stoneware bottle: H. Steenwyck

Oil on oak, 39.2 × 50.7 ($15\frac{7}{16}$ × $19\frac{15}{16}$).

The bust of a man with a wreath, in profile towards the left, shows faintly through the bottle.[1]

Cleaned in 1976.

Still-life pictures of this type, symbolising the vanity and transience of human life, began to be popular in Holland by the 1620s. The biblical source is Ecclesiastes, chapters 1–7, and a painting of this kind came to be known as a *vanitas* (cf. Ecclesiastes 1: 2: 'Vanitas vanitatum . . . et omnia vanitas'); the term is used already in the seventeenth century.[2]

The books symbolise human knowledge and the musical instruments the pleasures of the senses. The sea-shell is a collector's rarity and represents wealth;[3] the Japanese sword[4] is an emblem either of wealth or of military power. In an earlier stage of the composition there was in place of the bottle a sculptured bust of a man wearing a wreath, almost certainly intended for a Roman emperor, a frequent symbol of earthly power. All these objects are dominated by the death's head, while the chronometer and the expiring lamp allude to the transience and frailty of human life.

PROVENANCE: In the collection of Sir John Savile Lumley (later Baron Savile) by 1882 when lent to an exhibition in Brussels (see EXHIBITIONS); presented by him in 1888.

EXHIBITIONS: Brussels, Société Néerlandaise de Bienfaisance Exhibition, 1882, No. 237; London 1976, No. 110.

REFERENCES:

1. It can be seen clearly in the infra-red photographs and in the X-radiograph.
2. See Bredius, *Künstler-Inventare*, 1915–22, *passim*. For *vanitas* still lifes see ex. cat. *IJdelheid der IJdelheden*, Leiden, the Stedelijk Museum De Lakenhal, 1970; and ex. cat. *Still-life in the Age of Rembrandt*, Auckland, 1982, esp. pp. 187 ff.
3. Sea-shells appear in a woodcut in Roemer-

Visscher's *Sinne-poppen* of 1614 (1949 reprint, edited by L. Brummel, p. 4) with the legend 'Tis misselijck waer een geck zijn gelt aen leijt' (it is sickening what a fool spends his money on); the accompanying text censures the extravagance of shell-collecting.
4. The same sword appears in a *vanitas* by Harmen Steenwyck in the Stedelijk Museum De Lakenhal in Leiden (1983 cat., No. 408).

ABRAHAM STORCK, 1644–1708

Abraham Jansz. Sturckenburg; he later called himself *Sturck* or, usually, *Storck*. The son of an Amsterdam painter, Jan Jansz. Sturck, later Sturckenburch (*c.*1603–64/70), he was baptised in Amsterdam, 17 April 1644. He appears to have lived always in Amsterdam and was a member of the guild there. He recorded the visit of Czar Peter the Great to Amsterdam in 1697 and the reception of the Duke of Marlborough on the Amstel in 1704. He was buried in the Sint Anthoniskerkhof on 8 April 1708.

He painted seascapes and Dutch harbour scenes in the manner of Ludolf Bakhuizen, fanciful views of Italian harbours in the style of J. B. Weenix, and some topographical views, mainly of Amsterdam; he also made some etchings. His brother Jacobus (1641–after 1693) painted in the same style.

REFERENCES: I. H. van Eeghen in OH, vol. 68, 1953, pp. 216–22; S. A. C. Dudok van Heel in *Jaarboek Amstelodamum*, vol. 69, 1982, pp. 76–7.

146 *A River View*   *Plate 360*

In the centre is a *boeier* yacht and farther to the right a *tjalk*, both with Dutch vanes; beyond them a States yacht (*statenjacht*) with the arms of the Province of Holland on her stern and a Dutch ensign; in the left middle distance is a man-of-war.

Signed, bottom left: A:Storck Fecit.

Oil on canvas, 58.4 × 73.7 (23 × 29).

Cleaned in 1975. Prominent craquelure in the sky.

MacLaren suggested that the church in the centre might be the Sint Laurens Kerk in Rotterdam. The resemblance, however, is only of a general nature and if the view is compared with the *View of Rotterdam* in Dulwich,[1] it is clear that this is not the same town. No. 146 may well not be intended as a topographically accurate view.

Probably to be dated in the decade 1690–1700.

PROVENANCE: Lt.-Col. John Harvey Ollney Bequest, 1837.

REFERENCE: **1.** Dulwich Picture Gallery, 1980 catalogue, No. 608.

GERARD TERBORCH *See* BORCH

HENDRICK TERBRUGGHEN *See* BRUGGHEN

JAN JANSZ. TRECK, 1605/6–1652

Still-life painter. Born in Amsterdam; in 1633 he is said to be about twenty-seven years old. He is first mentioned as a painter in 1623, and is documented in Amsterdam fairly often from 1631 to 1650. The inventory of his estate drawn up after his death is dated September 1652.

His paintings are closely related to the work of Jan Jansz. den Uyl the Elder (1595 or 1596–1639 or 1640), who was his brother-in-law and his teacher, and like den Uyl's still-life pictures they are a continuation of the style of the Haarlem still-life painters (e.g. W. C. Heda and Pieter Claesz.).

REFERENCES: Bredius, *Künstler-Inventare*, vol. 6, 1919, pp. 2085–96; Vroom, 1980, vol. 1, pp. 210–13, vol. 2, Nos. 642–56.

4562 *Still Life with a Pewter Flagon and Two Ming Bowls* Plate 361

Signed in red below, at the edge of the white cloth: JJ Treck/1651 (JJ in monogram; the whole signature enclosed in a red scutiform border).[1]

Oil on canvas, 76.5 × 63.8 (30⅛ × 25⅛).

Cleaned in 1988.

There is substantial flaking of the paint, probably caused by rolling of the canvas. The blue decoration of the two bowls has turned brownish green and the vine-leaves are probably a little browner than originally.

The two bowls are late Ming blue and white of a type first imported into Holland not long before the picture was painted.

Precisely the same elements can be found slightly rearranged in a still life by Treck in Budapest which is dated 1645.[2] There is a still life of very similar composition by Jan Jansz. den Uyl, signed and dated 1637, in a private collection, Laren.[3]

PROVENANCE: In the possession of Robson and Sons, Newcastle-upon-Tyne, in 1930; Anon. sale, London, 21 November 1930 (lot 87),[4] bought by Asscher and Welcker (75 gns). In a Still Life and Flower Paintings exhibition at A. Tooth and Sons, London, 1931, No. 15; purchased from Tooth's (out of the Mackerell and Cockerill Funds) in February 1931.

EXHIBITIONS: Arts Council 1945, No. 38; London 1976, No. 111; Delft, Stedelijk Museum Het Prinsenhoef, Cambridge, Mass., Fogg Art Museum, and Fort Worth, Kimbell Art Museum, 'A Prosperous Past: The Sumptuous Still Life in the Netherlands 1600–1700', 1988–9, cat. no. 36.

REFERENCES:
1. The correct date was revealed during cleaning. It had previously been incorrectly restored to read 1649.
2. Budapest Museum of Fine Arts, 1967 cat., No. 1064. Panel, 66.5 × 50 cm.; as dated 1645.
3. Vroom, op. cit., vol. 2, No. 651: incorrectly as dated 1651.)
3. Vroom, op. cit., vol. 2, den Uyl No. 658.
4. As by 'Heda'.

MOSES VAN UYTTENBROECK, *c.*1600–1646/7

Little is known of his life. In 1620 he joined the guild of St Luke in The Hague and he is recorded as a member until 1638. There is no evidence that he ever visited Italy. He was praised by Constantijn Huygens in his manuscript autobiography which was written in about 1630. He painted a number of pictures for Prince Frederik Hendrik of Orange and was extensively employed by him on the decoration of the palace in Honselaersdijk in the late 1630s and the 1640s. A series of pictures painted for the House of Orange are today in Schloss Grunewald in Berlin. He must have died between 1646 when there is a document which refers to him and 1647 when his wife is described as a widow.

Uyttenbroeck was a history painter, specialising in scenes of mythological figures in landscape. His principal literary source was Ovid's *Metamorphoses*. He was a member of a generation of Dutch painters – which included Pieter Lastman, Cornelis van Poelenburgh and Bartholomeus Breenbergh – who were profoundly influenced by the style of Adam Elsheimer.

REFERENCE: U. Weisner, 'Die Gemälde des Moses van Uyttenbroeck', OH, vol. 79, 1964, pp. 189–228.

6476 *A Mythological Subject*   *Plate 362*

Signed and dated, lower right: M.v.WB (WB in monogram)/1628.

Oil on oak, 56 × 86.4 (22 × 34).

Some underdrawing in black chalk can be seen on the left. *Pentimenti* in the outlines of the haunches of the two uppermost cows have become visible.

The subject has not been satisfactorily identified. It has been described as *The Nurture of Bacchus*[1] but the figure with a crown of leaves is not a child. It could equally well be a pastoral love scene such as that of Daphnis and Chloë.

Uyttenbroeck is not known to have visited Italy and the building on the right, in front of which two large Corinthian columns stand, is loosely based on the many engraved views of Roman monuments which would have been available to him.

PROVENANCE: Anon. sale, Christie's, 23 April 1982 (lot 50). Purchased by the National Gallery for £64,800.

REFERENCE: **1.** 1982 sale catalogue (see under PROVENANCE).

WALLERANT VAILLANT, 1623–1677

He occasionally signs also *Wallerand* and *Vaillandt*. He was baptised on 30 May 1623 in Lille, then a Flemish possession, and was the son of a merchant who settled in Amsterdam *c*.1642. He is said to have studied painting under Erasmus Quellinus in Antwerp. In 1647 he entered the guild in Middelburg. He was presumably in Amsterdam by 1649, when he painted a portrait of Jan Six, and is recorded there in 1652. In 1658 he was in Frankfurt. About this time he turned from etching to mezzotint; he was one of the first to practise this technique and may have been Prince Rupert's instructor. Vertue, writing in 1713–21, says that Vaillant visited England,[1] and one of his prints has a title in English[2] but there seems to be no other evidence of such a visit. He was in Paris from 1659 until 1665 when he was once more in Amsterdam; he is recorded there in 1668 and 1672 but in 1675 he paid dues to the Middelburg guild; he died in Amsterdam, 28 August 1677.[3]

He was chiefly active as a portraitist, mostly in chalks, and as a mezzotinter; there are, however, some genre subjects by him and a few still-life pictures (including *trompe l'oeil* still lifes). His brother, Jacques, and his half-brothers, Bernard and Andries, also made pastel portraits, in the same style.

REFERENCES:
General: J. E. Wessely, *Wallerant Vaillant: Verzeichniss seiner Kupferstiche* etc., 2nd ed., 1881; M. Vandalle, 'Les frères Vaillant', in *Revue belge d'archéologie et d'histoire de l'art*, vol. 7, 1937, pp. 341–60. For the biographical data see also Sandrart, *Teutsche Academie*, vol. 2, p. 374; Houbraken, vol. 2, pp. 102–4; Kramm, vol. 6, p. 1667; Obreen, vol. 6, pp. 175, 213; OH, vol. 4, 1886, pp. 143, 269;

vol. 11, p. 156; vol. 12, p. 166; *Walpole Society*, vol. 18, 1930, p. 33.

In text:

1. *Walpole Society*, op. cit.

2. Wessely, op. cit., No. 175.

3. Vaillant's birth and death dates are recorded on a commemorative medal struck in 1677; see A. O. van Kerkwijk in *Feest-bundel Dr Abraham Bredius*, 1915, pp. 133–4.

After WALLERANT VAILLANT

3591 *A Boy seated drawing*

Plate 363

Oil on canvas, 127 × 99.5 (50 × 39¼).

The boy's head is worn and retouched and the eye is new; elsewhere some of the darks are rubbed. The fig-leaf on the cast of the child may be a later addition.[1]

The cast of the child is from Michelangelo's *Virgin and Child* in Notre Dame in Bruges.[2]

There is no foundation for the suggestion,[3] made apropos of W. Vaillant's mezzotint of this composition, that the boy is his brother and pupil, Andries (1655–93).

The picture was erroneously ascribed in the Carbery sale (see PROVENANCE) to Joseph Frans Nollekens (1702–48). It was attributed to Wallerant Vaillant by Hofstede de Groot,[4] who pointed out that the composition was mezzotinted by him (see ENGRAVING). Some years later there appeared a picture of exactly the same design (now in the Louvre; Fig. 105) which was attributed by Schneider to Jan Lievens, as a typical early work of his Leiden period; he called the National Gallery version a 'replica' of this.[5] The attribution of No. 3591 to Vaillant is also rejected by Mlle Bergmans,[6] on the grounds of the difference of technique from the signed picture of the same subject in Lille (see below) and other works. It is true that the boy in the Louvre version is not dissimilar from those in some of Lievens's early works (e.g. *A Man drinking* in East Berlin and the *Bust of a Young Man* in Salzburg[7]) but the execution is both different and inferior, and the composition and accessories are not in his manner. It is perhaps worth mentioning also that Lievens is not named on Vaillant's mezzotint of this composition, although most (but not all) of his prints after other masters are inscribed with their names. The attribution of this composition to Vaillant is supported not only by the evidence of the print but also by the existence of a variant signed by him and dated 1658 (see VERSIONS). Besides this, Vaillant made at least two other paintings[8] and two other mezzotints[9] of boys drawing from casts. It can be argued against Vaillant's authorship that the Louvre and National Gallery pictures are in a style rather different from that of his few signed genre paintings, for example, the picture of 1658 and that in Lille. On the other hand, these two also differ quite as much from each other and it appears that Vaillant did not develop a consistent style except in portraiture. The present writer considers that the Louvre version is a fairly youthful production by Vaillant. The National Gallery version is feebler and it is probably a copy of the Louvre picture (it will be noted that both come from Irish collections, as do also two of the copies mentioned below[10]).

ENGRAVING: A mezzotint by W. Vaillant[11] agrees almost exactly (in reverse) with the Louvre and National Gallery pictures except for the omission of the cast of a foot in the top left corner.

VERSIONS AND COPIES: A version of identical design in the Louvre, Paris,[12] is discussed above. A copy, inferior to No. 3591, is in Antwerp Museum.[13] Reduced copies, on panel, are in the Walter L. Kopp collection, Fredericksborg, Denmark,[14] and (with minor variations) in the collection of Baron Kilmaine, Combe Wood (1947).[15] A pastiche (or copy of a variant) with only a woman's bust on the left was formerly in the collection of the Earls of Ranfurly in Ireland.[16] A painting of the same subject by W. Vaillant, signed and dated 1658, with a boy in almost identical pose but with different accessories, is in the Bonnefanten-museum, Maastricht (Fig. 106).[17]

PROVENANCE: In the collection of Lady Carbery, Castle Freke, Co. Cork; in her sale, London 4 March 1921 (lot 33),[18] bought by J. G. Lousada and presented by him and his wife (through the NACF) to the Tate Gallery, 1921;[19] transferred to the National Gallery in 1922.

REFERENCES:

1. It does not appear in either the Louvre version or Vaillant's mezzotint (see ENGRAVING).
2. See L. Dimier in OH, vol. 44, 1927, p. 128.
3. First in R. Weigel's *Kunstcatalog*, 1838, vol. 5, No. 5832.
4. HdG in BM, vol. 43, 1923, p. 139.
5. H. Schneider, *Jan Lievens*, 2nd edition, revised by R. Ekkart, Amsterdam, 1973, No. 129 and p. 26, note 1. (The first edition was published in 1932 and the 1973 edition is a reprint with additional text material.) Schneider identifies the Louvre picture with one by Lievens in the possession of Margaretha Gallié de Brais, The Hague, in 1677 (see Bredius, *Künstler-Inventare*, vol. 1, p. 217); the inventory merely calls it 'a little draughtsman' (*een tyckenaertje*) and there are no other grounds for connecting it. Slive (in *Bulletin of the Allen Memorial Art Museum*, vol. 20, 1963, p. 123) supported Schneider's attribution of the Louvre painting to Lievens but Ekkart in his revised edition of Schneider's monograph (op. cit., see esp. p. 327, No. 129) rejects it.
6. Mlle S. Bergmans in *Biographie Nationale Belge*, vol. 26, 1936–8, col. 36.
7. Schneider/Ekkart, op. cit., Nos. 124 and 171 (on loan to the Residenzgalerie, Salzburg, from Graf Czernin).
8. (a) Lille Museum No. 777. Signed W ....ant. (b) A picture signed and dated 1658 in the Bonnefantenmuseum, Maastricht; see VERSIONS. (c) A picture of a boy drawing from a cast, probably by Wallerant Vaillant, is in the collection of Brodie of Brodie, Brodie Castle (photograph in the National Gallery archives). It is signed: 1656/(·) Vaillant; the initial, which may be in monogram with the V, is not clear. The picture differs in style from (a) and (b) above, and from the Louvre and National Gallery pictures. (d) The Antwerp Museum catalogue, 1970 (No. 617), mentions a painting of a boy drawing in the Emmaburg collection, Hergenrath; the writer has seen neither the picture nor a reproduction.

9. Wessely, op. cit., Nos. 1 and 23 (the subject of the latter is *not* a girl, as Wessely supposes).
10. i.e. the Kilmaine and Ranfurly pictures.
11. Wessely, op. cit., No. 21. 27.5 × 21.3 cm. Inscribed: W. Vaillandt fecit et Excudit.
12. Louvre cat., *Ecoles Flamande et Hollandaise,* 1979, RF2562. Canvas, 129 × 100 cm. Schneider/Ekkart, op. cit., pl. 14. In the collection of the Duke of Leinster, Carton, Ireland, and exhibited by him at the RA 1878, No. 245, as by Wallerant Vaillant; Duke of Leinster sale, London, 14 May 1926 (lot 100), as by W. Vaillant; presented by Georges Wildenstein to the Louvre, 1926.
13. Antwerp Museum catalogue, 1970, No. 617, as attributed to W. Vaillant. Canvas, 130 × 100 cm. It came from the former Episcopal Palace in Antwerp before 1826.
14. Panel, 75 × 59 cm. Reproduced in Winkel and Magnussen, *Kunst i privat Eje*, vol. 3, 1945, p. 244. It came from an Anon. sale, London, 6 May 1927 (lot 85), bought by Groen, and is presumably the copy of the Louvre picture on panel, 73.5 × 58 cm. which is mentioned by Schneider (op. cit., No. 129) as on the English and German art markets in 1923–7.
15. Attributed to Michiel Sweerts. Panel, 70 × 52 cm. The picture was in the Kilmaine collection in Ireland. There are different casts behind that of the infant Christ, and other slight variations.
16. Canvas, 130 × 99 cm. Earl of Ranfurly sale, London, 31 July 1939 (lot 10); Anon. sale, London, 25 February 1949 (lot 132). According to the Ranfurly sale catalogue, this copy is by the Hon. Diana Jane Pery, 1784; she was the daughter of Viscount Pery and married in 1785 the 2nd Viscount Northland, later 1st Earl of Ranfurly.
17. 1958 cat., inv. no. 673. Canvas, 119 × 90 cm. Signed, lower left, W? vaillant f. 1658.
18. and 19. As by J. F. Nollekens.

ADRIAEN VAN DE VELDE, 1636–1672

Adriaen van de Velde, son of Willem van de Velde the Elder and brother of the younger Willem van de Velde, was baptised in Amsterdam, 30 November 1636. He was probably a pupil of his father and, according to Houbraken, of Jan Wijnants (in Haarlem); he was also influenced by Philips Wouwermans. The subjects of many of his paintings and etchings have led to the suggestion that he visited Italy; nothing is recorded of such a journey. By 1657 he was living in Amsterdam and seems to have spent the rest of his life there. He was buried in Amsterdam on 21 January 1672.

Most of his pictures are landscapes, in which figures and animals are often prominent (dated ones from 1654 onwards); they include a few coast and winter scenes. There are also a number of religious, mythological and allegorical subjects, portraits and genre pieces, and he made a number of etchings (the earliest dated etching being 1653). His earlier paintings of animals in landscape are related to Paulus Potter's; in the 60s he also painted Italianate landscape in the manner of Nicolaes Berchem. He often painted the figures and animals in landscapes by other artists, for example Jacob van Ruisdael (see No. 990 of this catalogue), Philips Koninck (see No. 4251) and Frederick de Moucheron (see No. 842), and his figure style was very frequently imitated by his contemporaries. He made both compositional drawings (for paintings and etchings) and studies for individual figures and animals. As Robinson (see REFERENCES) has pointed out, he often combines animals from more than one drawing in a single painting and he uses the same preparatory drawing for a number of paintings (see No. 2572 below). Dirck van Bergen, his pupil, often comes very close to his manner, and Pieter and Gabriel van der Leeuw also painted in his style.

REFERENCES: HdG, vol. 4; W. W. Robinson, 'Preparatory drawings by Adriaen van de Velde', *Master Drawings*, vol. 17, 1979, pp. 3–23. For the documents see OH, vol. 4, 1886, pp. 143–4, and vol. 16, 1898, p. 69.

867 *A Farm with a Dead Tree*   Plate 364

Signed, bottom left: A.V. Velde.f / 1658.

Oil on canvas, 54.2 × 62.5 ($21\frac{5}{16}$ × $24\frac{5}{8}$).

The influence of Potter is apparent in this picture.

PROVENANCE: In the Johan Christoph Werther sale, Amsterdam, 25–26 April 1792 (lot 162), bought by Brentano (20 guilders); Claude-Joseph Clos sale, Paris, 18–19 November 1812 (lot 41), bought by Laneuville (4,735 francs); in the collection of the Duc de Dalberg, Paris, and in the Duc de Dalberg sale, London, 13–14 June 1817 (2nd day, lot 45),[1] bought in (285 gns). In the Varroc and Lafontaine sale, Paris, 28 May sqq. 1821 (lot 95),[2] bought in (9,010 francs); Var[r]oc sale, London, 22–23 March 1822 (lot 89),[3] bought by (Sir) Robert Peel (Bart.), 360 gns. Purchased with the Peel collection, 1871.

REFERENCES:
General: Smith No. 90; HdG No. 95.
In text:
1. As from the Clos collection. The Duc de Dalberg was erroneously styled 'The Duke de d'Alberg' in the 1817 sale catalogue.
2. and **3.** As *La ferme de Harlem*.

441

868 Peasants with a Bullock and Sheep fording a Stream

Plate 365

Oil on canvas, 32.4 × 37.8 (12¾ × 14⅞).

MacLaren believed it to be probably a very late work.[1] A copy (see below under COPY) is said to be dated 1662 and that may be the approximate date of No. 868.

A supposed companion piece, *Landscape with a Woman milking a Cow*,[2] was in the Carignan and Selle collections (see PROVENANCE).

VERSION: A replica is in the Budapest Museum.[3]

COPY: A copy said to be signed and dated 1662 was in the second Russian sale, Berlin, 4 June 1929 (lot 42).[4]

PROVENANCE: In the collection of the Prince de Carignan;[5] Selle sale, Paris, 19–28 February 1761 (lot 25, with pendant), bought by Thibault (2,362 francs); Randon de Boisset sale, Paris, 27 February sqq. 1777 (lot 137), bought by the Duc de Praslin (7,000 francs); Choiseul-Praslin sale, Paris, 18 sqq. February 1793 (lot 86), bought by Paillet (6,700 francs); Helsleuter [van Eyl Sleuter?] of Amsterdam sale, Paris, 25 sqq. January 1802 (lot 180), bought by Lafontaine (9,901 francs). In the collection of Sir Simon H. Clarke, Bart., by 1818, when it was exhibited at the BI; Sir Simon H. Clarke sale, London, 8–9 May 1840 (lot 98),[6] bought by Seguier (£798) probably for Sir Robert Peel, Bart., in whose collection it was certainly by 1842.[7] Purchased with the Peel collection in 1871.

EXHIBITION: BI 1818, No. 26.

REFERENCES:
General: Smith No. 8 and Supplement No. 28; HdG No. 69.
In text:
1. Cf. *Peasants with Cattle at a Fountain*, dated 1670, and *Peasants with Cattle crossing a Ford*, dated 1671 (HdG Nos. 36 and 71; both in Munich).
2. HdG No. 100; in the collection of August de Ridder in 1912.
3. HdG No. 68; Budapest 1967 catalogue, No. 196. On canvas, 34 × 41.3 cm.; in the Esterhazy collection, Vienna, in 1812.
4. Canvas, *c.*33 × 41 cm.
5. According to the catalogue of the Selle 1761 sale.
6. According to the Clarke 1840 sale catalogue, the picture was in the Robit collection, but it is not in the catalogue of the Robit sale, Paris, 11 sqq. May 1801, and it cannot be one of the four undescribed A. van de Velde landscapes with cattle from the Robit and other collections exhibited for sale by Bryan in London, November 1801–May 1802 (see *Catalogue of . . . pictures brought from Paris, principally from Mr Robit's . . . collection; and other distinguished cabinets*, 1801, Nos. 10, 11, 141 and 154) since it was certainly in the Helsleuter sale of January 1802.
7. Smith Supplement No. 28. According to the MS notes in a copy of Smith's *Catalogue Raisonné* thought to be his own it was bought by Sir Robert Peel at the Clarke sale in 1840.

869 Golfers on the Ice near Haarlem

Plate 366

In the distance is Haarlem with the Grote Kerk in the centre.

Signed at the bottom, towards the left: A.V.Velde. f/1668.

Oil on oak, 30.3 × 36.4 (11¹⁵⁄₁₆ × 14⁵⁄₁₆).

There are *pentimenti* in the arm and club (*Kolf*) of the man about to strike the ball, in the man leaning on his club and in the outlines of the boy and girl to the right of the sledge.

ENGRAVING: Engraved in reverse by J. Aliamet;[1] anonymous English engraving.

COPY: A copy (in reverse and so probably after the engraving) was in an Anon. sale, Braunschweig (Hünerberg), 4 May 1961 (lot 57).[2]

PROVENANCE: In the Pierre-Jean Mariette sale, Paris, 15 November sqq. 1775 (lot 10), bought by Boileau for the Prince de Conti (4,000 francs); Prince de Conti sale, Paris, 8 sqq. April 1777 (lot 414), bought by Remy (4,000 francs). In the collection of the Comte de Pourtalès, Paris, and among the Dutch and Flemish pictures bought from this collection in 1826 by John Smith and Thomas Emmerson.[3] By 1834 in the collection of Sir Robert Peel, Bart.;[4] purchased with the Peel collection, 1871.

REFERENCES:

General: Smith No. 31; HdG No. 370.

In text:

1. When in the Mariette collection as *Les amusemens de l'hiver.*

2. Panel, 31 × 43 cm.

3. Smith, loc. cit.

4. Smith, loc. cit.

982 *The Edge of a Wood, with a Sleeping Shepherd, Sheep and Goats*   Plate 367

Signed on a log, bottom right: A.V. Velde.f/1658.

Oil on oak, 27.7 × 38.1 ($10\frac{7}{8}$ × 15).

There is a picture of exactly the same type by van de Velde in Frankfurt, also dated 1658.[1]

PROVENANCE: In the [Wynn Ellis] sale, London, 6 June 1864 (lot 57), bought in (105 gns); Wynn Ellis Bequest, 1876.

REFERENCES:

General: HdG No. 207.

In text: **1.** *Deer at the Edge of a Wood.* Panel. 27 × 38 cm. Signed, lower right: A v Velde. F. 1658. Frankfurt 1971 catalogue, inv. no. 1048; HdG No. 337.

983 *A Bay Horse, a Cow, a Goat and Three Sheep near a Building*   Plate 368

Signed, bottom left: A. V. Velde/1663.

Oil on canvas, 31 × 37 ($12\frac{3}{16}$ × $14\frac{9}{16}$).

The goat appears also, with only slight variations, in No. 1348 below. The cow is repeated in a landscape with cattle, sheep and goats near a stream, of the same date as the present picture, in the Thyssen-Bornemisza collection,[1] and in a landscape with cattle and sheep at a pool, signed and dated 1670, formerly(?) in the collection of Anthony de Rothschild.[2] It is also in three versions of *Mercury and Argus*: one, dated 1663, in the Liechtenstein collection;[3] another, dated 1664, formerly in the collection of J. Paul Getty at Sutton Place;[4] and a third, dated 1665, at the Petit Palais in Paris.[5]

DRAWINGS: The cow appears in drawings in the Amsterdams Historisch Museum (Fig. 107),[6] the Louvre,[7] and the Pierpont Morgan Library, New York.[8] The sheep appears in another drawing in the Amsterdams Historisch Museum (Fig. 108).[9]

PROVENANCE: Almost certainly in the possession of Mennechet, Paris, in 1840;[10] probably in the [Comte de] M[orny] sale, Paris, 24 May 1852 (lot 27), bought Mündler. It is possibly the 'Woody Landscape, with horses, cattle, sheep and goats', signed and dated 1663, lent by Samuel Wheeler to the BI in 1854 and 1867, which was in the Samuel Wheeler sale, London, 29 July 1871 (lot 102), bought by M. Colnaghi (215 gns). Wynn Ellis Bequest, 1876.

EXHIBITIONS: BI 1854, No. 64(?); BI 1867, No. 39(?).

REFERENCES:
General: Smith Supplement No. 10(?); HdG Nos. 208, 292(?), 298(?) and 343a(?).
In text:
1. HdG No. 216. *Thyssen-Bornemisza Collection: Catalogue Raisonné of the Exhibited Works of Art*, 1986, No. 315a; I. Gaskell, *The Seventeenth Century Dutch and Flemish Paintings in the Thyssen-Bornemisza Collection* (in the press), No. 108.
2. HdG No. 286.
3. Canvas, 71 × 91 cm. Cat. 1927, No. 689.
4. Canvas, 69 × 89 cm.
5. Canvas, 70 × 92 cm. Cat. 1982, vol. 2, No. 808.
6. Fodor collection, Inv. no. A10346. Robinson, op. cit., No. D-24.
7. *Musée du Louvre, Inventaire Général des Dessins des Ecoles du Nord, Ecole Hollandaise* (by Frits Lugt), 1931, vol. 2, No. 783.
8. Robinson, op. cit., No. C-2. This drawing is preparatory to the Thyssen painting.
9. Fodor collection, Inv. no. A10345. Robinson, op. cit., No. D-18.
10. Smith Supplement No. 10. Smith's description of the Mennechet picture agrees closely with the National Gallery painting but he mentions only one sheep by the cow and he gives the measurements as $14\frac{1}{4} \times 14\frac{1}{2}$ in.

1348 *A Goat and a Kid* *Plate 369*

Oil on canvas, 42.5 × 50.5 ($16\frac{3}{4} \times 19\frac{7}{8}$).

The goat is repeated alone in No. 983 above, which is dated 1663. The same goat, but with head slightly lowered, is in the *Jacob departing from Laban* in the Wallace Collection, also dated 1663.[1] Both goat and kid are repeated almost exactly, but without a space between them, in the *Mercury and Battus* of 1671 in Prague.[2]

The goat appears alone, being milked by a woman, in a signed painting by Dirck van Bergen in the Rijksmuseum,[3] and once more with the kid in a landscape with women and animals at a pool, by Bergen, in the collection of Lord Tollemache, Helmingham Hall.[4]

The animals are typical of Adriaen van de Velde though on a scale unusually large for him; this and their frequent appearance in other pictures by him suggests that No. 1348 was primarily intended as a careful study for use in other compositions. The landscape in the background was added afterwards; in places a gap has been left between it and the outlines of the animals, especially along the front of the goat's head where a narrow margin of buff ground shows. The background is unlike that in any certain work by van de Velde. The cold bluish colour of the foliage and the glittering highlights suggest a later phase of Dutch painting than his and it is unlikely that he is the author of this part of the picture. Hofstede de Groot[5] thought it might be by Frederick de Moucheron, to whom it is ascribed in the Habich sale catalogue. The foreground, however, seems to be by van de Velde.

PROVENANCE: In the collection of Edward Habich, Cassel, and exhibited with other Habich pictures at the Gemäldegalerie, Cassel, 1881–91.[6] It appears in the catalogue of the Edward Habich sale, Cassel, 9–10 May 1892 (lot 150)[7] but was purchased from Habich before the sale, together with Nos. 1336–47, in 1891.

REFERENCES:
General: HdG No. 326.
In text:
1. HdG No. 2. Wallace Collection 1979 cat., P80.
2. HdG No. 22. Narodni Galerie, Prague, Inv. no. D05680, no. 97. See discussion in Robinson, op. cit., cat. no. B–16.

3. Rijksmuseum 1976 catalogue, C105.
4. 51 × 118 cm.
5. Loc. cit.

6. JKPK, 1881, *Amtliche Berichte*, col. 97, No. 65.
7. As by A. van de Velde and F. Moucheron.

2572 *A Landscape with a Farm by a Stream*   *Plate 370*

Signed, bottom centre: A.V.Velde f / 1661.

Oil on canvas, 32.3 × 35.4 ($12\frac{11}{16}$ × $13\frac{15}{16}$).

A number of small retouchings in the sky.

As Hofstede de Groot has indicated,[1] this is one of the latest of a group of early works
(*c.*1658) of similar style and subject.[2]

DRAWING: There is a preparatory drawing for the cow in the Amsterdams Historisch Museum (Fodor
collection).[3]

PROVENANCE: Perhaps the *Landscape, with Cattle and Figures*, lent by Frederick Perkins to the BI in 1836; in the
collection of George Perkins, Chipstead (died 1879); George Perkins sale, London, 14 June 1890 (lot 25),
bought by M. Colnaghi (£861). Bought by George Salting in 1890;[4] Salting Bequest, 1910.

EXHIBITIONS: (?) BI 1836, No. 51; RA 1891, No. 91; BFAC 1900, No. 57.

REFERENCES:
General: HdG No. 81.
In text:
1. Loc. cit. HdG gives the date wrongly as 1663.
2. e.g. two landscapes in Berlin (HdG Nos. 180 and
348, the former dated 1658); in the Fritz Gans collection, Frankfurt (HdG No. 332, dated 1658); in the
Earl of Wemyss collection, Gosford (HdG No. 333,
dated 1658) and in the Thieme collection, Leipzig

(HdG No. 350, dated 1658).
3. Red and black chalk, 19.4 × 30.8 cm. Inv.
no. A10346. See Robinson, op. cit., cat. no. D-24
(where he lists other paintings for which van de
Velde used this drawing).
4. Note in one of Salting's notebooks in the National Gallery archives.

See also

JAN VAN DER HEYDEN   No. 992;

PHILIPS KONINCK   No. 4251;

FREDERICK DE MOUCHERON   No. 842;

JACOB VAN RUISDAEL   No. 990;

WILLEM VAN DE VELDE   No. 873;

JAN WIJNANTS   Nos. 884 and 2532

ESAIAS VAN DE VELDE, 1587–1630

He was baptised in Amsterdam on 17 May 1587. He was the son of Hans van de Velde, a painter, who had been born in Antwerp. He was probably a pupil of Gillis van Coninxloo in Amsterdam: Arnout van Buchell mentions a landscape by Coninxloo with figures by Esaias. Esaias' father bought drawings at the auction of Coninxloo's work after his death in 1607. Hans van de Velde died in 1609 and the family (including Esaias) moved to Haarlem in the same year. Esaias married in 1611 and was inscribed in the Haarlem guild in 1612. His earliest dated works are from 1614. In 1618 he moved to The Hague and joined the guild in the same year.

During his years in Haarlem Jan van Goyen and possibly Pieter de Neyn were his pupils. He remained for the rest of his life in The Hague. He was buried in The Hague, 18 November 1630.

He painted genre scenes (notably 'merry companies'), cavalry skirmishes and scenes of plunder but his principal activity was as a landscape painter; he played an important part in the development of realism in Dutch landscape painting. He sometimes painted the figures in others' landscapes, and he also made a number of etchings.

REFERENCE: G. Keyes, *Esaias van den Velde 1587–1630*, Doornspijk, 1984 (with all previous literature).

6269 *A Winter Landscape*   Plate 371

Signed, lower centre: E.V.VELDE. 1623.

Oil on oak, 25.9 × 30.4 ($10\frac{3}{16}$ × $11\frac{15}{16}$).

Infra-red photographs (Fig. 109) reveal a very free black chalk underdrawing. There are drawing lines beneath all the main landscape features, the house and the trees on either side. The figures, however, are not drawn but painted directly at a late stage in the composition: the initial drawing lines of the road and foreground can be seen to pass straight through them.[1]

PROVENANCE: In an Anon. sale, London, 4 July 1956 (lot 91), bought by Slatter (£950); exhibited at E. Slatter's gallery, London, April 1957, No. 9, and purchased from him (out of the Colnaghi Fund) in 1957.

EXHIBITIONS: London 1976, No. 113; London 1986, No. 66.

REFERENCES: General: Keyes, op. cit., cat. no. 84.
In text: **1.** The infrared photograph is illustrated and the underdrawing discussed by David Bomford in his essay in the ex. cat. London, 1986, pp. 52–3.

JAN VAN DE VELDE, 1620–1662

Jan Jansz. van de Velde, son of Jan van de Velde the engraver (1593–1641). Born in Haarlem; in June 1642 his age is given as twenty-two, and in April 1643, twenty-three.[1] The earliest dated painting is apparently of 1639.[2] He is recorded in Amsterdam in 1642 and 1643. He is said to have died in 1662, in Enkhuizen.[3]

All his known paintings are of still life in the tradition of Pieter Claesz. and Willem Heda of Haarlem.

REFERENCES:
General: Vroom, vol. 1, pp. 222–30; vol. 2, Nos. 675–710.
In text:
1. OH, 1886, p. 217.
2. H. Seifertová-Korecká, *Jan Jansz. van de Velde's Stilleben in der Kreisgalerie in Liberec*, OH, vol. 81, 1966, pp. 51–4.

3. Vroom (No. 705) lists a painting of 1663. This painting, now in a Swedish private collection is, however, actually dated 1661 (Stockholm, Nationalmuseum, *Holländska Mästare; Svensk ägo*, 1967, cat. no. 168).

1255 *Still Life: A Goblet of Wine, Oysters and Lemons*   *Plate 372*

Signed along the edge of the table or ledge: Jan·vande· Velde· fecit· An° 1656.

Oil on oak, 40.3 × 32.2 ($15\frac{7}{8}$ × $12\frac{11}{16}$).

Worn; the grain of the panel shows through badly in the background.

The green glass goblet is a Rhenish *roemer*.

PROVENANCE: In the collection of John Savile Lumley (later Sir John Savile Lumley and Baron Savile) by 1873, when it was lent to an exhibition in Brussels. Presented by Lord Savile, 1888.

EXHIBITION: Brussels, Société Néerlandaise de Bienfaisance Exhibition, 1873, No. 284.

REFERENCE: Vroom No. 695.

WILLEM VAN DE VELDE the Younger, 1633–1707

Willem Willemsz. van de Velde, son of Willem van de Velde the Elder (born 1611) and elder brother of Adriaen van de Velde, was baptised in Leiden, 18 December 1633.[1] The family had settled in Amsterdam by 1636 (when Adriaen was born). Willem the Younger presumably studied first with his father (most of whose work consists of *penschilderijen*, pen drawings of ships on panel or canvas in an engraver-like style).[2] Houbraken[3] says he was a pupil of Simon de Vlieger; this was probably partly or wholly in Weesp where de Vlieger appears to have settled by March 1650.[4] By March 1652 (when he married a woman from Weesp) van de Velde was living in Amsterdam.[5] His earliest known dated picture is of 1651. He continued to live in Amsterdam and was probably still there in August 1671.[6] The French invasion of 1672 having made it difficult to earn a living in Holland, the elder van de Velde decided to try to find employment in England (he had already paid an extended visit to England *c.*1660–2) or, if that failed, in Italy (according to Peter Blaeu in a letter of 1674 to Cardinal Leopoldo de' Medici) and he came here late in 1672 or early in 1673.[7] The younger van de Velde was certainly here by 1672 since at least one picture of that year is inscribed by him 'In Londen'.[8] He painted several *sopraporte* for Ham House in 1673.[9] At the beginning of 1674 father and son were taken into the service of Charles II: the warrant of appointment specifies that each is to be paid a hundred pounds a year, the father for 'taking and making of Draughts of seafights' and the son for 'putting the said Draughts into Colours';[10] this salary was in addition to what they received for the pictures.[11] An important early royal commission was for designs for tapestries commemorating the Battle of Solebay. (In his later years the father occasionally did paint in oils, as Houbraken[12] says.) They continued to live in England for the rest of their lives, but made several brief visits to Holland, and remained in the service of Charles II and James II. Much of their work seems to have been done in Greenwich (they had a studio in the Queen's House)[13] and they apparently lived there until 1691, when they moved to Westminster,[14] where the father died in 1693.[15] Van de Velde the Younger also died in Westminster, 6 April 1707,[16] and was buried at St James's in Piccadilly.

The earlier works of the younger van de Velde support Houbraken's statement that he was a pupil of de Vlieger. Already in his Dutch period shipping played an ever more important part in his seascapes; after the first few years in England his pictures are no longer seascapes so much as representations of specific vessels and naval events, and many of the later ones are somewhat mannered. He appears to have employed a number of assistants during his years in Amsterdam and, to an even greater extent, during his years in London. He often painted several replicas of particular compositions which vary in quality according to the degree of studio participation. According to Vertue (writing 1721/5)[17] he had a son who copied his works; it has been supposed that this was Willem the Younger's son, Willem, who was born in 1667.[18] Weyerman (1729) mentions a son named Cornelis, who lived in London and painted in his manner.[19] Willem van de Velde the Younger had many English imitators and followers, who continued to paint in an adaptation of his manner throughout the eighteenth century.

REFERENCES:

General: HdG, vol. 7; H.P. Baard, *Willem van de Velde de oude. Willem van de Velde de jonge* (Palet Serie), [1942]; M. S. Robinson, *Van de Velde Drawings*, 2 vols., Cambridge, 1958, 2nd rev. ed., 1973 (henceforth referred to as Robinson, *Drawings*); M. S. Robinson, *The Willem van de Velde Drawings in the Boymans-van Beuningen Museum, Rotterdam*, 3 vols., Rotterdam, 1979; ex. cat., NMM, *The Art of the Van de Veldes*, 1982; M. S. Robinson, *The Paintings of the Willem van de Veldes*, forthcoming (henceforth referred to as Robinson, *Paintings*).

In text:

1. OH, 1898, p. 69.
2. For a discussion of this technique, see D. Freedberg, A. Burnstock and A. Phenix in *Print Quarterly*, vol. 1, 1984, pp. 149–68.
3. *De Groote Schouburgh*, vol. 2, p. 325.
4. See the biographical note on de Vlieger, p. 472.
5. OH, 1886, p. 217.
6. His daughter Sara was baptised in Amsterdam in August 1671 (OH, 1901, p. 62).
7. Van de Velde *père* was still in Amsterdam in

September 1672; Peter Blaeu, writing in June 1674, says he left for England 'più di un anno e mez(z)o fa' (JKPK, vol. 32, 1911, Beiheft, pp. 46 and 47).
8. and 9. See No. 981, notes 3 and 5.
10. *Walpole Society*, vol. 26, 1938, p. 75; see also Robinson, *Drawings*, vol. 1, p. 12. Blaeu (see note 7), whose information came indirectly from the elder van de Velde, says '. . . il Re d'Inghilterra . . . ha . . . commesso da fare una Opera grande di diverse battaglie . . . lui [the elder van de Velde] farà li dissegni, il figlio le pitture . . . '.
11. JKPK, op. cit. (see note 7), p. 48.
12. *De Groote Schouburgh*, vol. 1, p. 355. See as an example of the elder van de Velde's canvases, the *Calm: the English Yacht Portsmouth at Anchor* inscribed and dated 1675 in the NMM (inv. no. GH.264).
13. See ex. cat., NMM, op. cit., pp. 15–16.
14. Robinson, *Drawings*, vol. 1, pp. 12 and 15.
15. Houbraken, vol. 1, pp. 355–6.
16. According to the title of J. Smith's engraving of 1707 (J. E. Wessely, *John Smith. Verzeichniss* etc., 1887, No. 259).

17. *Walpole Society*, vol. 18, 1930, p. 159.

18. P. Haverkorn van Rijsewijk in OH, 1901, pp. 62 and 63.

19. Weyerman, vol. 3, p. 386. Vertue, on the other hand, says Cornelis was the brother of Willem the elder and depicted sea-fights in black and white (*Walpole Society*, vol. 18, 1930, p. 159). About ten paintings signed C. V. Velde have been identified by Robinson as the work of Cornelis and will be discussed in his forthcoming Catalogue of Paintings.

150 *A Dutch Vessel in a Strong Breeze* *Plate 373*

The small vessel reducing sail in the centre is a *kaag* close-hauled or a point free on the port tack with her mainsail half lowered and her sprit horizontal in the slings. A vane striped blue and yellow is at the masthead and a flag striped with the same colours at the peak. On the left a *weyschuit* with her mast lowered pulls towards the *kaag* in rough sea. Crossing close ahead of the *kaag* is a *smalschip* or similar vessel close-hauled on the starboard tack.

Signed on the rudder of the kaag: W.V.V. (very small).

Oil on canvas, 23.2 × 33.2 ($9\frac{1}{8}$ × $13\frac{1}{16}$).

A number of discoloured retouchings in the dark clouds on the left.

Robinson[1] considers that it was painted for the most part by van de Velde the Younger *c*.1670. A picture of a similar subject is in the Nationalmuseum, Stockholm.[2]

COPY: A copy (English, nineteenth century?) was in the collection of Mr W. H. Zimpel, Perth, Australia, in 1959.[3] This, or another copy, on millboard, was in the possession of F. C. Hirst, Chalfont St Giles, Buckinghamshire, in 1982.[4]

PROVENANCE: Lord Farnborough Bequest, 1838.

REFERENCES:
General: HdG No. 481; Robinson, *Paintings*, No. 202.
In text:
1. Robinson, *Paintings*, op. cit.
2. Stockholm, 1958 catalogue, No. 672; panel, 15 × 16 cm.; signed: W.V.V.
3. Dimensions not known. Photograph in National Gallery dossier.
4. Seen by Robinson, who considers that it might be by George Chambers.

870 *Calm: A Dutch Ship coming to Anchor and Another under Sail* *Plate 374*

In the left foreground a *kaag* is just moving ahead in a light breeze with her sprit-sail half lowered and her sprit nearly horizontal. Her foresail is lowered; there is a striped vane at the masthead and a tricolour flag at the peak. Close ahead is a small ship, probably an Indiaman, coming to anchor. She has a flag at the fore. There are two vessels under sail close on her starboard bow. In the right background is an armed flute; sailing with her close to starboard is a *hoeker* with her square mainsail set. Other ships and vessels becalmed beyond.

Signed, bottom left (in the sea): w v velde 1657.[1]

Oil on canvas, 55 × 62 ($21\frac{5}{8}$ × $24\frac{3}{8}$).

Despite his doubts about the signature,[2] Robinson considers this an autograph painting of 1657 made by Willem the Younger for the van de Velde studio.

PROVENANCE: It is presumably the 'Sea Calm' lent to the BI, 1821, by George Watson Taylor.[3] It was certainly in the George Watson Taylor sale, London, 13–14 June 1823 (1st day, lot 61), bought by (Sir) Robert Peel (Bart.) 390 gns. Purchased with the Peel collection, 1871.

EXHIBITION: BI 1821, No. 28.

REFERENCES:
General: Smith No. 112; HdG No. 195; Robinson, *Paintings*, No. 203.
In text:
1. Robinson, op. cit., observes that the signature is in an unusual place and may not be genuine.
2. See above, note 1.

3. There was apparently no other W. van de Velde in the Watson Taylor collection. Smith, loc. cit., says that it was exhibited at the BI in 1826, but this exhibition was of paintings from the Royal Collection only.

871 *Dutch Vessels close Inshore at Low Tide, and Men Bathing*

Plate 375

On the left, a *kaag* with her sprit-sail set and foresail lowered; she has a skiff hauled up on deck across her stern. She is lying head-on to a large *wijdschip* which has her mainsail and square topsail set. The *wijdschip* has an orange and white striped flag at the peak and a multi-striped vane including the same colours at her masthead (these may originally have been intended for red and white, the colours of Hoorn). Close on her starboard quarter is a *weyschuit* or similar type rigged with a jib-headed mainsail. In the right middleground is a sprit-rigged fishing pink with a spoon bow. Several ships in the right background at anchor, one with a flag and pendant at the main.

Oil on canvas, 63.2 × 72.2 (24⅞ × 28⅜).

Cleaned in 1971.

Robinson[1] notes that the flag and vane of the *wijdschip* may identify it as a vessel from Vlieland and Terschelling; if so, the coast is likely to be near Den Helder and the ships would be lying in the Marsdiep.

Robinson[2] considers it to be painted in large part by Willem the Younger himself in 1661. Of the four known versions of the composition (see VERSIONS) Robinson considers this the best.

A very similar composition with the same date, was in the M. C. D. Borden sale, New York, 13 February 1913 (lot 57);[3] another, undated (but according to Robinson painted a few years later) is in the Gemäldegalerie, Cassel.[4] In the Cassel painting the figures may well be by Adriaen van de Velde. In No. 871 the figures seem to be by Willem the Younger himself.

VERSIONS: There is what Robinson considers to be a studio version (probably also of 1661) in the Akademie der Bildenden Künste, Vienna.[5] A second studio version (perhaps painted some time later) is in the National Gallery of South Australia in Adelaide.[6] A third studio version (perhaps painted after 1661) was in Anon. sale, Lucerne (Galerie Fischer), 2 September 1933, No. 469.[7]

PROVENANCE: According to Smith a picture of this composition was in the Richard Creed sale, 1813, bought by Norton (140 gns).[8] In the collection of the Duc de Berry, Paris (died 1820);[9] exhibited with the Berry collection for sale by private contract at Christie's, April–June 1834 (No. 64), and bought by C. J. Nieuwenhuys, who sold it to Sir Robert Peel, Bart.[10] Purchased with the Peel collection, 1871.

EXHIBITION: London, NMM, 'The Art of the Van de Veldes', 1982, No. 23.

REFERENCES:
General: Smith Nos. 89(?) and 229; HdG No. 196; Robinson, *Paintings*, No. 204(1).
In text:
1. Robinson, op. cit.
2. Robinson, op. cit.
3. HdG No. 312; reproduced in the catalogue of the Hudson-Fulton Celebration Exhibition, New York, 1909 (No. 134).
4. HdG No. 187. Robinson, op. cit., No. 374.
5. Panel, 61 × 82 cm. Signed: W.V.V. HdG (No. 228) mistakenly calls it a replica or copy of the Borden collection picture (see above). Robinson, op. cit., No. 204(2).

6. Canvas, 59.1 × 71.8 cm. Adelaide 1960 cat. Inv. no. O.1862. Robinson, op. cit., No. 204(3).
7. Canvas, 60 × 75 cm. Said in the sale catalogue to be signed and dated 1661. This was apparently the painting with Antony Reyre, London, in the early 1930s (then recorded as on canvas, 59.5 × 71 cm.). Robinson, op. cit., No. 204(4).
8. See Smith Nos. 229 and 89. No Creed sale is recorded in Lugt.
9. Nieuwenhuys, p. 264.
10. Nieuwenhuys, p. 265.

872 *Dutch Ships and Small Vessels Offshore in a Breeze* Plate 376

In the left foreground is a *kaag*. Her white sprit-sail is lowered on deck and is partly falling over the side. To the right is a *smalschip* at anchor with both foresail and mainsail lowered on deck: she has a skiff lying astern of her. In the right background, a ship at anchor. She has a flag at mizzen, being the rear-admiral perhaps of a squadron of Indiamen. She is firing a gun to port. Sailing away from her is a *kaag* or similar vessel close-hauled on the starboard tack under a half-lowered mainsail. In the centre background, a small ship running out from the land under her fore course and mizzen. There are sand dunes in the distance on the left.

Signed on a floating spar, below, in the centre: WVV.

Oil on oak, 41.5 × 58.6 ($16\frac{5}{16}$ × $23\frac{1}{16}$).

Although there are no obvious landmarks to confirm the identification, the coast in the distance has been described as the island of Texel.[1] If this were so, the land indicated by the sandbank in the left foreground would be near Den Helder.

Robinson[2] considers that it was probably painted mainly by Willem the Younger for the van de Velde studio, *c.*1660. He believes it possible that the foreground water was painted by Hendrick Dubbels, who is thought to have been working in the van de Velde studio shortly before he was made bankrupt in 1665.

PROVENANCE: In the Nicolaas Nieuhoff sale, Amsterdam, 14–17 April 1777 (lot 211),[3] bought by Fouquet (1,050 guilders). [Richard(?) Hart Davis] sale, London, 1 June 1814 (lot 16), bought by Smith (155 gns). According to John Smith[4] it was in a Lord Charles Townshend sale at Christie's in 1818 and fetched 83 gns, but there is no Townshend sale recorded in 1818 and the picture was not in the [Lord Charles Townshend] sale (at Stanley's), London, 4 June 1819.[5] It was in the collection of (Sir) Robert Peel (Bart.) by 1823, when it was exhibited at the BI; purchased with the Peel collection, 1871.

EXHIBITION: BI 1823, No. 76.

REFERENCES:

General: Smith No. 92; HdG Nos. 233 and 482; Robinson, *Paintings*, No. 205.

In text:

1. According to the catalogue of the Nieuhoff sale (see PROVENANCE).

2. Robinson, op. cit.

3. Smith identifies No. 872 with lot 211: 'Haut de 16½ large de 22 pouces B. Ce Morceau, qui fait le Pendant du Précédent, represente une Mer agitée, qui est ornée de Différents Vaisseaux & de Diverses Chaloupes. On voit, dans le Lointain, l'isle du Tex-el.' Lot 210 (bought by P. Yver) was an alleged companion picture of fishing boats and a frigate in a calm; of the same size, on canvas stuck on panel. It was in the L. Boreel sale, Amsterdam, 23 September 1814 (lot 20), bought by Nieuwenhuys (cf. HdG No. 245).

4. Loc. cit.

5. The only W. van de Velde in this sale was lot 31, *A Calm* (bought by Byng), which is now in the collection of the Earl of Strafford (HdG No. 230).

873 *The Shore at Scheveningen* — Plate 377

On the dunes, right, are the village and church of Scheveningen. The coach in the right foreground has the arms of Amsterdam on the rear. A number of fishing pinks are coming in to land.

Oil on canvas, 42.6 × 56.5 (16¾ × 22¼); false additions have been made later at the bottom (1.9 cm. wide) and on the right (.3 cm.).

Cleaned in 1956.

Scheveningen lies on the coast of the North Sea, about three miles from The Hague. The late fifteenth-century church seen in this picture still stands. This is a view looking north-east along the shore.

Robinson[1] considers that this is a collaboration between Willem the Younger and Adriaen van de Velde c.1660. The foreground figures, the wagon and horses are probably by Adriaen and the church and houses of Scheveningen may be also by him.[2]

Both this and the related picture of 1659 in the collection of Dr G. Henle, Duisburg (Fig. 110),[3] are probably reminiscences of a painting of the same subject by Simon de Vlieger,[4] who died in 1653. Style and costume indicate that the present work was painted within a year or two of the Henle collection picture.

PROVENANCE: A 'View of Scheveningen, storm coming on' was in the Blackwood sale, 1757 (2nd day, lot 60), bought by Jenens (£17.6.6).[5] No. 873 was in the [Juriaans] sale, Amsterdam, 28 August 1817 (lot 68*), bought by de Vries (1,975 guilders); Gerrit Schimmelpenninck sale, Amsterdam, 12 July 1819 (lot 124), bought by Brondgeest (1,794 guilders).[6] In the collection of Comte de Pourtalès, Paris, and among the pictures bought from that collection in 1826 by John Smith and Thomas Emmerson.[7] By 1835 it was in the collection of Sir Robert Peel, Bart.[8] Purchased with the Peel collection, 1871.

REFERENCES:

General: Smith No. 119; HdG Nos. 13 and 15; Robinson, *Paintings*, No. 206.

In text:

1. Robinson, op. cit.

2. Cf. the figures in Adriaen van de Velde's *View of the Coast of Scheveningen* of 1658 in the Gemälde-galerie, Cassel (HdG, Adriaen van de Velde No. 355) and his *Coast Scene* of 1660 at Buckingham Palace (HdG, Adriaen van de Velde No. 357; White No. 203).

3. HdG No. 12. Exhibited in Brussels, 1935 (No. 784). Robinson, op. cit., No. 270.

4. Buchenau sale, Amsterdam, 9 April 1940 (lot 526); reproduced in Baard, op. cit., p. 42.

5. See the extract from a MS sale catalogue published by F. Simpson in BM, vol. 95, 1953, p. 42.

6. HdG catalogues this painting as Adriaen van de Velde No. 363.

7. Smith, loc. cit.

8. Smith, loc. cit. Peel paid £800 for the painting.

874 An English Vessel and Dutch Ships Becalmed   *Plate 378*

In the right foreground is a small English two-masted armed ketch; she has a white flag with St George's cross. A small *weyschuit* or similar vessel is approaching her. In the left middle distance, broadside on, is a small Dutch ship, probably an Indiaman, at anchor; a *smalschip* is close alongside to port. Further away a flute at anchor can be partially seen. Several ships at anchor in the right distance.

Signed, probably falsely, in the right bottom corner: VV (very small).

Oil on oak, 22.7 × 27.6 ($8\frac{15}{16}$ × $10\frac{7}{8}$). Some wearing in the sky and rigging; the rigging has been retouched.

Robinson[1] considers that it was substantially painted by Willem the Younger for the van de Velde studio, *c.* 1660. He notes that the ketch seems to be a Dutch-built vessel – a *wadconvooier*, a type used in the area at the Waddenzee between the Zuiderzee and the Elbe as a 'protection vessel' – in English ownership, presumably one sailing regularly to Holland.

VERSIONS: An exact replica or copy was in the Charles Sedelmeyer sale, Paris, 25–28 May 1907 (lot 193; sold for 5,600 francs).[2] A (nineteenth-century?) copy was in an Anon. sale, Brussels (Galerie Giroux), 29 November 1956 (lot 106).[3]

ENGRAVING: Engraved in reverse by Remi-Henri-Joseph Delvaux, *c.*1771.[4]

PROVENANCE: In the Duc de Choiseul sale, 6 sqq. April 1772 (lot 85), bought by Boileau (979 francs);[5] Prince de Conti sale, Paris, 8 April sqq. 1777 (lot 317 with pendant), bought by Langlier (1,260 francs). It may be the 'Calm, Men-of-War' lent by Joseph Burchard (sic) to the BI in 1823 since, according to Smith,[6] it was in a Joseph Barchard sale, 1828,[7] sold for £300. It was in the collection of Sir Robert Peel, Bart., by 1835;[8] purchased with the Peel collection, 1871.

EXHIBITION: BI 1823, No. 70(?).

REFERENCES:
General: Smith No. 11; HdG No. 87; Robinson, *Paintings*, No. 207(1).
In text:
1. Robinson, op. cit.
2. On panel, 24 × 31.5 cm.; from the Harrison collection. Reproduced in the Sedelmeyer sale catalogue. Robinson, *Paintings*, No. 207(2).
3. Panel, 72.4 × 81.3 cm. It is presumably based on the engraving, having the ketch to the left and the ship at anchor to the right. Robinson, *Paintings*, No. 207(3).
4. In *Recueil d'estampes . . . d'après les tableaux du . . . Duc de Choiseul*, 1771, No. 29.
5. According to Smith, loc. cit., it was sold at the Choiseul sale for 760 francs (so also HdG, loc. cit.),

but this was lot 86 (bought by Aubert, 759 francs), the description of which in the sale catalogue shows that it was the picture now in the Hermitage, Leningrad (HdG No. 222; Robinson, *Paintings*, No. 10). The correct lot number in the Choiseul sale, i.e. 85, is given in the Conti sale catalogue. (The sizes of the two pictures have been confused in the Choiseul sale catalogue, but are given correctly on the engravings after them in the *Recueil . . . Choiseul*, 1771, Nos. 29 and 30.)
6. Loc. cit.
7. There is no Barchard sale of 1828 recorded in Lugt. The only Barchard sale listed by Lugt is of 6 May 1826; there was no W. van de Velde in it.
8. Smith, loc. cit.

875 *Two Small Vessels and a Dutch Man-of-War in a Breeze*   *Plate 379*

In the left foreground a *kaag*; she has a red, white and blue striped flag at the peak and a vane of the same colours at the masthead. On the right and a little further away is another *kaag*. In the left middle distance is a ship with a red lion rampant, the arms of the Province of Holland, on her tafferel and a Dutch ensign and jack. She is towing a boat with three men in it. In the right distance, two ships at anchor and small vessels under sail.

Signed on a floating spar, bottom left: W V V.

Oil on oak, 24.2 × 29.8 ($9\frac{1}{2}$ × $11\frac{3}{4}$).

The ships on the horizon and the rigging are slightly worn and the latter has probably been retouched.

Robinson[1] considers that it was painted by Willem the Younger for the van de Velde studio, *c.*1660.

PROVENANCE: Possibly in the [Richard(?) Hart Davis] sale, London, 1 June 1814 (lot 8), 71 guineas. Smith identifies it with a picture in the L[apeyrière] sale, Paris, 19–26 April 1825 (lot 167),[2] bought by Lafontaine (3,410 francs). Bought by Delahante(?) and sold to M. M. Zachary.[3] It was probably in the collection of Sir Robert Peel, Bart., before 1830;[4] purchased with the Peel collection, 1871.

REFERENCES:
General: Smith No. 87; HdG No. 483; Robinson, *Paintings*, No. 208.
In text:
1. Robinson, op. cit.
2. Smith, loc. cit. The description in the Lapeyrière sale catalogue is vague but agrees fairly well with the National Gallery picture; the size, however, is given as 12 *pouces* high by 11 *pouces* wide (on panel).
3. There is a contemporary MS note in Smith's

own copy of the Lapeyrière sale catalogue (in the RKD): 'Lafontaine / sold to / Mr Zachary / now / Mr Peel's.' (Since Peel succeeded his father as 2nd Baronet in May 1830, the note was presumably made before then.) From this note it appears possible that Smith later confused Delahante with Lafontaine.
4. See the preceding note. In any case it was in the Peel collection by 1835 (see Smith No. 87).

876 *A Small Dutch Vessel close-hauled in a Strong Breeze* Plate 380

In the foreground is a small gaff-rigged vessel, known as a *galjoot*,[1] close-hauled, with a blue and white vane. In the left middle distance is a ship with a Dutch pennant at the main; another ship, with a Dutch ensign, is at anchor in the right middle distance and further ships are on the horizon.

Signed, bottom left, on a floating spar: W.V.V.

Oil on canvas, 32.7 × 40.3 ($12\frac{7}{8}$ × $15\frac{7}{8}$).

Robinson[2] considers that No. 876 was painted by Willem the Younger for the van de Velde studio, probably in 1672 (cf. No. 981, dated 1673). The blue and white striped vane at the *galjoot*'s masthead may indicate a vessel from the area of the Texel. It is possible that she is being used as a pilot vessel to go out to an incoming ship.

PROVENANCE: In the Daniel de Jongh sale, Rotterdam, 26 sqq. March 1810 (lot 32),[3] bought by Le Brun (300 guilders); later apparently in an unidentified French(?) sale.[4] In the collection of Comte de Pourtalès, Paris, and among the pictures bought from that collection in 1826 by John Smith and Thomas Emmerson.[5] By 1835 in the collection of Sir Robert Peel, Bart.;[6] purchased with the Peel collection, 1871.

REFERENCES:
General: Smith Nos. 81 and 159; HdG No. 484; Robinson, *Paintings*, No. 209.
In text:
1. The vessel is short for a *galjoot* but is identified as

one by the shape of her stern and her standing gaff rig; she is without the usual small mizzenmast of a *galjoot*.

2. Robinson, op. cit.

3. The de Jongh provenance is mentioned in a cutting on the back (see the following note).

4. Stuck on the back of the panel is a cutting, probably from a sale catalogue: 'GUILLAUME VANDEN VELDE. / 125. Une Mer agitée par un coup de vent. On re- / marque sur le devant un léger bâtiment, et dans le / fond deux vaisseaux de guerre. Ce fin et précieux / Tableau, de l'effet le plus piquant, est

aussi de sa plus belle manière. Il vient de la collection de / M. *Daniel de Jongh*, de Rotterdam, n° 32 du / catalogue de sa vente. – Hauteur 0,325ᵐ, lar- / . . . . 0,406ᵐ .T.' There is a copy of this catalogue in the British Library bound in a volume of catalogues (press mark 562 e 24(4)). It lacks the title-page but there is an old annotation on p. 3: *Le Brun*. Against no. 125 is 700/Coquille. Coquille bought a number of Dutch and Italian pictures at the sale.

5. Smith No. 159.

6. Smith No. 159.

978 *A Dutch Yacht, surrounded by Many Small Vessels, saluting as Two Barges pull alongside* — Plate 381

In the centre is a States yacht (*statenjacht*) with a Dutch ensign and, at the peak, a Dutch pennant; on her stern are the arms of the Province of Holland and, above, those of Amsterdam. The elaborate row-barge alongside her has the Amsterdam arms on her stern. The second row-barge, in the foreground towards the left, has a Dutch ensign; on the stern are the arms of an admiralty (two crossed anchors). In the right foreground is a *boeier* yacht with a plain white flag at the masthead and, on a staff at the stern, a pennant with a red and white fly and a golden wreath on a blue ground in the head.

Signed inside the wreath in the head of the *boeier* yacht's pennant (right foreground): W/VV, and dated on the stern of the row-barge in the foreground towards the left: ANN(O?) 1[6]61 (the second figure of the date is covered by the end of the flag).

Oil on canvas, 90 × 126 (35⅜ × 49⅝).

Cleaned in 1958. Rather worn, especially the shadows, rigging and the boats on the horizon at the right.

The date 1[6]61 on the stern of the barge fits the style of the picture.

The *boeier* yacht prominently shown on the right is presumably one being used by the van de Veldes. The pendant at the ensign staff is a private one, having in chief the monogram W/VV within a wreath, and instead of the usual red, white and blue striped fly, the fly is white with narrow red stripes top and bottom.

An occasion such as the one represented here must have been fairly common around 1660. It may represent the departure of admiralty officials from Amsterdam on their way across the Zuiderzee, perhaps to visit the fleet lying in the Texel to the north. The barges are unlikely to have crossed the Zuiderzee and the land in the distance with a church tower might be near Scheteldouckshaven, now called Uitdam.[1] The closer land on the left of the picture would then be near Muiden and the Pampus island outside Amsterdam. On an important occasion such as the visit of the young William of Orange (afterwards William III) to Amsterdam in June 1660 at a river fête held in his honour, he sailed at the head of a fleet of a hundred yachts according to the account in *Hollantse Mercurius*.

PROVENANCE: Probably the picture of vaguely similar description and same size in the Robit sale, Paris, 11 sqq. May 1801 (lot 163),[2] bought by Gambot (3,010 francs). In the collection of the Comte de Pourtalès, Paris; among the pictures bought from that collection by John Smith and Thomas Emmerson[3] and in the Pourtalès collection sale, London, 19–20 May 1826 (lot 116), bought by Phillips (presumably bought in), 500 gns; Thomas Emmerson sale, London, 15–16 June 1832 (lot 150), 580 gns. Foster's, London, 25 June 1836, lot 89. In the collection of Wynn Ellis, London;[4] exhibited as from the Wynn Ellis collection at the RA in 1871.[5] Wynn Ellis Bequest, 1876.

EXHIBITIONS: RA 1871, No. 76; Brighton 1979, No. 8.

REFERENCES:
General: Smith No. 123 and (probably) No. 48; HdG Nos. 18c(?) and 111; Robinson, *Paintings*, No. 211.
In text:
1. Robinson, *Drawings*, No. 765.
2. 'Il représente une grande étendue de mer du côté du Texel, et paraîtrait retracer une fête des Etats de Hollande. Parmi les différentes navires qui figurent . . . dans cette grande composition, on en distingue plusieurs où sont portés des personnages de la première magistrature . . . La quantité des bâtimens et barques se détache sur un ciel pur et frais qui caractérise parfaitement l'effet d'une calme.' On canvas,

36 × 48 *pouces* (92 × 130 cm.).
3. Smith No. 123.
4. It is conceivable but not probable that it is 'A quiet sea. Clear and genuine, but not happy in composition' (by van de Velde) which Waagen saw in the Wynn Ellis collection in 1850 or 1851 (Waagen, 1854, p. 297, No. 2) but the description would apply equally well to any of lots 136 and 142–5 of the Wynn Ellis sale, London, 27 May 1876, all of which were calms with shipping.
5. The description in the RA 1871 catalogue ('Vessels Becalmed') would hardly suffice to identify the picture but the exhibition label is on the back of it.

979 *A Dutch Ship, a Yacht and Smaller Vessels in a Breeze* Plate 382

In the right foreground is a *kaag* with a multi-striped red and white flag at her peak. In the centre and a little further away is a States yacht (*Statenjacht*) with a tricolour flag at the peak and a small pennant at the ensign staff. On her tafferel is a yellow shield bearing a red lion, the arms of the Province of Holland, between arms and trophies. To the left, further away, is a Dutch ship with a Dutch flag at the main, a yellow jack with a red lion on it (again representing the Province of Holland) and a plain red ensign. On her tafferel is a dolphin. In front of her is a large *weyschuit* or fishing pink. Just behind the ship, only partially seen, is a large flute with a full-length figure on her stern.

Signed on a floating spar, bottom right: W V V.

Oil on canvas, 33 × 36.5 (13 × 14⅜).

Cleaned in 1972. Severely worn in the sky.

Robinson[1] considers that it was painted in part by Willem the Younger for the van de Velde studio, *c*.1660.

A drawing in the Amsterdams Historisch Museum (Fodor collection) is probably an eighteenth-century copy of what may be another version of No. 979: it lacks the States yacht and the *weyschuit* and in place of the flute is a small transom-sterned ship. The *kaag* has a topsail yard but no bowsprit.

PROVENANCE: In the collection of Dr Fletcher, Gloucester, by 1835;[2] Ralph Fletcher sale, London, 9 June 1838 (lot 63), bought in (84 gns). In the collection of Wynn Ellis by 1858, when it was exhibited at the BI.[3] Wynn Ellis Bequest, 1876.

EXHIBITION: BI 1858, No. 117.[4]

REFERENCES:
General: Smith No. 168; HdG Nos. 438 and 510; Robinson, *Paintings*, No. 212.
In text:
1. Robinson, op. cit. He is doubtful that the drawing of the ships and vessels is of the standard of Willem the Younger and considers it a strong possibility that a better version may be found.

2. Smith, loc. cit.

3. and 4. Although merely called 'A Fresh Breeze' in the BI 1858 catalogue, its identity with the present picture is established in G. Scharf, *Artistic and descriptive notes on . . . pictures in the British Institution exhibition . . . 1858*, 1858, p. 75.

980 *Boats pulling out to a Yacht in a Calm*   *Plate 383*

On the right, a *weyschuit* is pushing off from the shore; the sail is lowered into the boat. There are two other boats pulling away from the *groyne* (jetty) on the right. In the left background a sprit-rigged States yacht (*statenjacht*) is becalmed with mainsail and foresail set; she has yellow flags and pennants at the peak and masthead. A ship's boat is pulling towards her in the centre background; and beyond the yacht three ships are at anchor, one firing a salute. Other ships are at anchor in the right distance.

Signed on a spar in the bottom right corner: W V V.

Oil on canvas, 43×50.5 ($16\frac{15}{16} \times 19\frac{7}{8}$).

Cleaned in 1956.

Robinson[1] suggests that this is probably a scene on the Dutch coast near Den Helder with shipping lying in the Marsdiep on the occasion of a visit to the fleet by States deputies. He considers that it was painted largely by Willem the Younger for the van de Velde studio, *c*.1665 and notes that it is related to a group of pencil and wash drawings dated 1665 and 1666.

PROVENANCE: Said to have been purchased privately in Rotterdam by a Mr Netscher.[2] In the collection of Edward Solly by 1835;[3] Edward Solly sale, London, 31 May 1837 (lot 80), bought by Norton (210 gns). In the collection of Wynn Ellis, London, by 1850 or 1851.[4] Wynn Ellis Bequest, 1876.

EXHIBITION: RA 1871, No. 201.

REFERENCES:
General: Smith No. 247 and Supplement No. 42; HdG No. 112; Robinson, *Paintings*, No. 213.
In text:
1. Robinson, op. cit.
2. Smith No. 247.

3. Smith No. 247.

4. Waagen, 1854, vol. 2, p. 297, No. 1 (cf. Studio of W. van de Velde No. 977, note 2). HdG (loc. cit.) wrongly identifies it with Waagen, loc. cit., No. 2, which may possibly be National Gallery No. 978.

981 *Three Ships in a Gale*   *Plate 384*

In the left foreground a ship with sails furled and yards lowered in a very heavy sea; she is presumably lying to a sea anchor, though no warp can be seen. Red vanes at all three mastheads, a white device on two of them. Behind her is a ship with only her foremast standing: her fore yard is aportlast. The bowsprit has broken off just outside the forestay. She has a tattered Dutch flag at the fore top masthead. In the right distance is a ship largely hidden by the heavy seas lying-to on the starboard tack under her mizzen with the fore and main courses set and the sheets let fly.

Signed on a floating spar, below, towards the centre: W. Vande. Velde. Londe 1673.[1]

Oil on canvas, 74.5 × 94.5 (29⅜ × 37¼).

Cleaned in 1973.

Robinson[2] notes that the white device on two of the red flags may be a jug which would signify a ship from Flushing. He considers the painting to be entirely the work of Willem the Younger in 1673.

Besides the present picture, several others painted by the younger van de Velde in the first year or so of his settling in England are inscribed as painted in London (e.g. paintings in Greenwich[3] and Rotterdam[4] and three of the four *sopraporte* in the Duchess's Bedchamber at Ham House).[5]

DRAWINGS: Three drawings at the NMM are associated by Robinson[6] with this composition (Figs. 111, 112, 113). They are nos. 692, 719 and 1372 in his catalogue.[7] He dates all three c.1700 and suggests that they are partial copies – or reminiscences – of the painting.

VERSION: A studio version, slightly smaller, with the ship in the far right omitted, was in Anon. sale, Sotheby's, 8 July 1964 (lot 80) (as Willem van de Velde III (sic)), £80 to Byrne.[8]

PROVENANCE: In the collection of Jean-Henri Eberts, Paris; bought from him in September 1766 by the Markgräfin Karoline Luise of Baden, Karlsruhe (720 livres);[9] in the inventories of the Baden collection in Karlsruhe (1784, No. 85,[10] and 1823, No. 29[11]). Given in exchange by Grossherzog Leopold of Baden in December 1831 to the dealer Noë,[12] by whom it was brought to England in 1833 and sold to Emmerson.[13] In 1835 it was in the collection of Richard Artis, London;[14] it was in the collection of William Hornby, The Hook, near Southampton, by 1842.[15] In the collection of Wynn Ellis, London,[16] by whom it was lent to the RA, 1871; Wynn Ellis Bequest, 1876.

EXHIBITION: RA 1871, No. 246.

REFERENCES:
General: Smith No. 182 and Supplement No. 22; HdG No. 401; Robinson, *Paintings*, No. 214(1).
In text:
1. The last letter of Londe is an e of exactly the same form as the final e of vande (the two 'e's in Velde are of the modern type; van de Velde used both kinds indifferently) and the word is identical in form and spelling with those in the signatures of two of the Ham House pictures (cf. note 5). The spelling Londe instead of Londen is explained by the fact that a final n is often not sounded in Dutch.
2. Robinson, op. cit.
3. *English Ships in Distress*, signed: In Londen 1672 / W.V. Velde. Acquired by the NMM, Greenwich, in 1955.
4. *The Roadstead at Texel* [?] (HdG No. 18); signed: W. V. Velde in Londe 1673. Museum Boymans-van Beuningen, 1972, cat. no. 1892.
5. i.e. *Fishing Vessels in a Calm Sea*, signed: W V Velde Londe / 1673; *Fishing Vessels in a Choppy Sea*, signed: Vande, Velde, Londe / 1673 and *A Man-of-War firing a Salute*, signed: W V Velde in Londe(·)

A°1673.
6. Robinson, op. cit.
7. Robinson, *Drawings*, op. cit.
8. Canvas, 23½ × 31 in. This was apparently the painting which had been sold at Christie's, on 8 November 1963 (lot 183) as Bakhuizen and purchased there by R. Preston for 35 gns. He sold the painting in 1964 to M. Leslie, Westerham, Kent. Robinson, *Paintings*, No. 214 (2).
9. G. Kircher, *Karoline Luise von Baden als Kunstsammlerin*, 1933, pp. 137–8. see also J. Lauts, *Karoline Luise von Baden*, Karlsruhe, 1980; J. Lauts, 'Studien zum Kunstbesitz der Markgräfin Caroline Luise von Baden', *Jahrbuch der Staatlichen Kunstsammlungen in Baden-Württemberg*, vol. 21, 1984.
10. Kircher, op. cit., p. 184.
11. Kircher, op. cit., p. 208.
12. Dr Jan Lauts verified the date of the transaction in the Karlsruhe archives (letter of 1953 in the National Gallery archives).
13. Smith No. 182.
14. Smith No. 182; Waagen, *Kunstwerke und Künst-*

ler in England, 1838, vol. 2, p. 210 (p. 403 of the English edition).

15. Smith Supplement No. 22.

16. It is impossible that the picture was in the Wynn Ellis collection in 1834 as stated in the National Gal-lery catalogue, 1915–29; both Smith and Waagen (see note 14) say that it was in the Artis collection in 1835 and by 1842 it was (according to Smith, Supplement No. 22) in the Hornby collection.

2573 A Dutch Ship and Other Small Vessels in a Strong Breeze

In the left foreground is a *kaag* with her sprit-sail half brailed; she has a blue and white vane at her masthead and an orange and white flag at the peak. Further away and to the right, there is another *kaag*; she has lowered her mainsail and sprit on deck and is running before the wind under bare poles. Further away still to the right is a ship close-hauled on the port tack under fore cruise and mizzen, fore topsail mastheaded and main topsail settled half-way. She has a Dutch flag at the main. She has on her tafferel a shield on which there is a lion rampant, the coat-of-arms of the Province of Holland; the coat-of-arms on the rail above is probably the Amsterdam arms with lion supporters. In the centre middle distance there are two fishing pinks close-hauled on the starboard tack. In the centre distance, a ship at anchor with only her main staysail set. Dunes in the left distance; a States yacht and other vessels at anchor well off the shore.

Signed on the orange and white vane of the vessel in the left foreground: W V Velde 1658 (very small).

Oil on canvas, 55 × 70 ($21\frac{5}{8}$ × $27\frac{9}{16}$).

Robinson[1] considers it to have been substantially painted by Willem the Younger for the van de Velde studio, and showing the influence of Simon de Vlieger.

PROVENANCE: In the Corneille-Louis Reynders sale, Brussels, 6 sqq. August 1821 (lot 102), bought by Verbelen for Nieuwenhuys[2] (900 florins). In the collection of Sir Robert Peel, 2nd Bart., by 1835;[3] sold by Sir Robert Peel, 4th Bart., in 1897,[4] to Agnew.[5] In the collection of George Salting, London; Salting Bequest, 1910.

REFERENCES:
General: Smith No. 107; HdG No. 485; Robinson, *Paintings*, No. 215.
In text:
1. Robinson, op. cit.
2. According to a contemporary MS note in the copy of the sale catalogue in the RKD, Verbelen was acting for Nieuwenhuys at this sale.

3. Smith, loc. cit. (as 'View on the Texel').
4. According to a label formerly on the back of the picture (now in the National Gallery archives).
5. According to HdG, loc. cit. There is an Agnew label on the back of the picture.

2574 Small Dutch Vessels Aground at Low Water in a Calm

On the right is a group of four vessels close together, just aground in an inlet on a sandy shore. In the foreground a bezan-rigged *weyschuit* or fishing pink with her sail lowered and a man stowing the sail. Just beyond a *kaag* with her brown sprit-sail half lowered and the sprit horizontal in the slings. On the *kaag*'s starboard quarter is another *kaag* with sail lowered and beyond these vessels can be seen the white standing-gaff mainsail of a *wijdschip* or *galjoot*. On the sand in the left foreground a *weyschuit* is lying with her sail lowered into the boat. In the left background there are two sailing vessels, probably *kaags*, and a boat. Several ships at anchor in the left distance.

Signed on a spar in the centre foreground: W. V. V.

Oil on canvas, 32.9 × 36.9 (12$\frac{15}{16}$ × 14$\frac{1}{2}$). There is a prominent craquelure throughout.

Robinson[1] considers this to be a production of the van de Velde studio, perhaps only partly by Willem the Younger, *c.*1660. He believes that a better version of this picture may be found.

VERSION: A version, apparently in poor condition, is in a private collection in Hamburg, 1987. (Photo in RKD.) Probably an eighteenth-century copy.[2]

PROVENANCE: In the collection of Lord Bateman, Kelmarsh Hall, Northamptonshire; Lord Bateman sale, London, 11 April 1896 (lot 147), bought by Agnew (£378). George Salting Bequest, 1910.

REFERENCES:
General: HdG No. 324; Robinson, *Paintings*, No. 216.
In text: **1.** Robinson, op. cit.
2. Dimensions and support not known. Photo in RKD. The distinctive features of this version are that there is no man standing at the bow of the *weyschuit* on the left and there are no peak halyards to the white-sailed vessel on the right. Robinson, *Paintings*, No. 216(2).

6407 *Dutch Vessels lying Inshore in a Calm, One saluting*   Plate 387

To the right is a *kaag* viewed from a little before the port beam at anchor just afloat off a sandy shore. Her white sprit-sail is brailed up and the foresail lowered on the foredeck; she has a yard for spreading the square topsail, which may be the sail lying furled on the after deck. She has a blue-white-blue flag at the peak and a vane at the masthead of the same colours. Marking the end of the spit of sand in the centre foreground is a post or withy with an oval basket on top. Further to the left is a man standing at the water's edge with a pole and a basket. On the extreme left is a *weyschuit* with her mast lowered; there are two men in the boat. A little further out on the left is a States yacht starboard bow view with a standing-gaff mainsail, square topsail and foresail set. She is firing a salute to port where there are four other vessels. A ship at anchor is in the right distance; small vessels are under sail.

Signed and dated on a piece of wood on the shore, lower left: W. V. Velde 1660.

Oil on canvas, 54.6 × 69.5 (21$\frac{1}{2}$ × 27$\frac{3}{8}$).

Cleaned in 1972. Some wearing in the sky.

According to Robinson,[1] painted partly by Willem the Younger in the van de Velde studio in 1660. He considers that the figures may be by Hendrick Dubbels.

PROVENANCE: Presumably the *Calm* by van de Velde lent to the BI in 1864 by the 4th Earl of Mexborough; Collection of the Earl of Mexborough; by descent to the Hon. H. J. Savile (Viscount Pollington). Hon. H. J. Savile sale, London, 16 February 1904; bought by W. C. Alexander. Passed by descent to the Misses Rachel F. and Jean I. Alexander, who presented it by deed of gift to the National Gallery; entered the collection in 1972.

EXHIBITIONS: BI 1864, No. 84; London 1938, No. 194; London 1972.

REFERENCES: General: HdG No. 197; A. Smith, 'Presented by the Misses Rachel F. and Jean I. Alexander: Seventeen Paintings for the National Gallery', BM, vol. 114, 1972, p. 634. Robinson, *Paintings*, No. 217. In text: **1.** Robinson, op. cit.

6465 *Dutch Ships in a Calm* *Plate 388*

To the left is a fishing buss starboard quarter-view under sail close alongside a *hoeker* port bow view at anchor on the buss's port beam. The buss has her square foresail filling, the mainsail furled and the yard lowered to within a few feet of the rail and her mizzen hoisted but not yet filling. She has a horn on her tafferel. A boat with three men in it is close on her starboard bow. The *hoeker* has her square mainsail half hoisted. In the right is a *kaag* port quarter-view close-hauled on the port tack under a brown sprit-sail and a white foresail. In the right background is a ship at anchor viewed from a little abaft the port beam, a flag at the main.

Signed, on the stern of the fishing buss: WVV.

Oil on panel, 35.7 × 43.2 (14$\frac{1}{8}$ × 17).

Robinson considers it to have been substantially painted by Willem the Younger for the van de Velde studio, *c.* 1660. He has discovered no fewer than eight versions of this composition, of which he believes No. 6465 to be the best.

VERSIONS AND COPIES: (i) Canvas, 43 × 50.5 cm. Hamburger Kunsthalle, Hamburg. Inv. no. 226. HdG 194. According to Robinson, probably by the van de Velde studio.[1] (ii) Canvas. Dimensions unknown. Private collection, Switzerland. Seen by M. Robinson at Agnew's, 1984.[2] (iii) Canvas, 33.7 × 40.8 cm. With D. Katz, Dieren, *c.*1940. Photo in RKD. Collection of G. Brand, Heemstede (Holland), 1987.[3] (iv) Canvas, 42 × 50 cm. Sale at R. Heiniger and Co., Wichtrach (Switzerland), 8 June 1974, no. 292. With Waterman, Amsterdam, 1974.[4] (v) Canvas, 42 × 50 cm. Amsterdam, collection of G. W. Lundens van Schalcken; G. W. Lundens van Schalcken sale, Amsterdam, 18 November 1913, lot 104. HdG 314.[5] (vi) Canvas, 40 × 47 cm. Collection of J. H. Borghouts, Utrecht, *c.*1973.[6] (vii) Canvas, 30.5 × 40 cm. Sotheby's, 16 December 1970 (lot 45).[7]

PROVENANCE: Possibly with J. P. B. Lebrun, Paris; possibly in the collection of Baron Delessert, Paris; Baron Delessert sale, 18 March 1869, no. 96 (as from the Cabinet Le Brun, no. 44. an IX); possibly on the art market in Basle in 1942 and in the collection of Professor Ruzicka, Zürich, in 1947 (but these references may be to the painting recorded as (v) under VERSIONS AND COPIES); probably in the collection of J. McKay of Hythe; E. Speelman, London; Agnew's; sold by Agnew's to R. E. Brandt, 1948; by descent to Mrs Alice Bleecker, by whom presented in 1981.

REFERENCES:

General: Possibly Smith Supplement No. 35; possibly HdG No. 278; Robinson, *Paintings*, No. 107(1). In text:
1. Robinson, *Paintings*, No. 107(2).
2. Robinson, *Paintings*, No. 107(3).
3. Robinson, *Paintings*, No. 107(4). Painted possibly by one of the Elder's studio, *c.*1690. According to a paper on the back from the collection of Sir Richard Waldie-Griffiths, Bart. (1784–1878).
4. HdG No. 314; Robinson, *Paintings*, No. 107(5);

collection of H. A. J. Munro of Novar; Christie's, 18 May 1867, (lot 109) (sold for £25 4s.); Christie's, 12 July 1912, (lot 21), bought by Kleinberger, Paris, for 130 gns.
5. Robinson, *Paintings*, No. 107(6). Photo in RKD.
6. Robinson, *Paintings*, No. 107(7). A poor copy, perhaps early eighteenth century. Photo in De Boer archive, Amsterdam.
7. Robinson, *Paintings*, No. 107(8). A poor copy.

VELDE

Studio of WILLEM VAN DE VELDE the Younger

149 *Calm: Two Dutch Vessels*   Plate 389

In the centre is a *smalschip* and, behind her, a *kaag* or similar vessel. Both have Dutch flags and the *smalschip* has also a small white and blue flag. On the right on a spit of sand is a *weyschuit*, her mast and sail lowered into the boat. In the right background, a small ship becalmed. Other ships at anchor in the distance.

Signed, right, on the sand bank: W.V.V.[1]

Oil on oak, 20.9 × 27.9 (8¼ × 11).

According to Robinson[2] this is 'probably a version entirely by the Studio from an original by Willem the Younger *c*.1660'. He considers the execution to be far below the artist's best work in the 1660s and suggests that No. 149 may be a studio copy from the end of the seventeenth century or even an early eighteenth-century copy, not by the studio. He notes four other versions of this composition (see VERSIONS), one of which he considers may be the original. The present writer considers that 'Studio of van de Velde' is the most satisfactory attribution.

A painting of a calm with an English snow and a Dutch man-of-war in the Marquess of Lansdowne's collection at Bowood has the same provenance as the National Gallery picture from 1827 onwards and has been supposed to be the companion piece.[3] It is in exactly the same style but differs slightly in size.

VERSIONS: Robinson considers the best version of this composition to be the painting which was in the Mame collection sale, Paris, 26–29 April 1904, No. 44.[4] There is what Robinson considers to be a late eighteenth-century copy in the National Gallery, Oslo.[5] A version of about the same quality as No. 149 was in a private collection (T. Aelbi, Lausanne?) in 1978[6] and another was recently with Douwes, Amsterdam.[7]

PROVENANCE: In an unidentified Dutch sale, probably of the eighteenth century;[8] in the Gerrit Muller sale, Amsterdam, 2 April 1827 (lot 74), bought with lot 75, the companion (see above), by A. Brondgeest for John Smith[9] (3,500 guilders); [Hon. G. J. Vernon] sale, London, 15–16 April 1831 (2nd day, lot 37), bought by Emmerson (£105); Thomas Emmerson sale, London, 15–16 June 1832 (lot 121),[10] 109 gns; in the collection of Brook Greville by 1835;[11] Brook Greville sale, London, 30 April 1836 (lot 76), bought by Seguier for Lord Farnborough (135 gns). Lord Farnborough Bequest, 1838.

EXHIBITION: BI 1835, No. 149(?).[12]

REFERENCES:
General: Smith No. 129 and Supplement No. 17; HdG Nos. 194a and 259; Robinson, *Paintings*, No. 201(1).
In text:
1. The signature has been much strengthened and may be entirely false.
2. Robinson, op. cit.
3. HdG Nos. 258 and 357. It was with the National Gallery picture in an unidentified eighteenth(?)-century sale and the Muller, Vernon, Emmerson and Greville sales; at the last-named sale (lot 75) it was bought by the 3rd Marquess of Lansdowne (*not*, as stated in Smith Supplement No. 16, by William

Wells). See also *Catalogue of the Collection of . . . the Marquess of Lansdowne* 1897, p. 121, No. 128 On oak, 22.9 × 27 cm.; the measurements were checked by MacLaren at the Lansdowne collection exhibition at Agnew's, London. 1954–5 (No. 24). On the back (as on the back of the National Gallery picture; see note 8) is stuck a cutting from an 'eighteenth(?)-century sale catalogue: 'Een stil Water met een Tweemast Engelsche Vis-/schuit, in 't verschiet een Fregat, en meer an-/dere Vaartuigen, helder en aangenaam geschild-/derd door *W. van de Velde*, op paneel, hoog / 8¾, breet 10¼ duim.'
4. Illustrated in sale catalogue. Panel, 24 × 32 cm.

462

Smith Supplement No. 34. HdG No. 290. Robinson, *Paintings*, No. 201(2). Present whereabouts unknown. It was in the Sabatier collection; Raymond Sabatier sale, Paris, 30 May 1883, lot 92. It was presumably acquired by Sabatier at or shortly after the Delessert sale in 1869.

5. Panel, 27 × 32 cm. Inv. no. 691. Robinson, *Paintings*, No. 201(3).

6. Dimensions not known. Robinson, op. cit. (under No. 201(1)).

7. Canvas, 30.5 × 36.5 cm. Robinson, op. cit. (under No. 201(1)).

8. On the back of the panel is stuck a cutting, probably from an eighteenth-century sale catalogue: 'Een dito tot een weerga, waar in men ziet twee / Damlopers, benevens een Fregat en andere / Vaartuigen in 't verschiet, niet minders als de / voorgaande, door *denzelven*, hoogte en breedte / als [voren?].' The name of the painter: 'W:v:de Velden' and the

size (8½ × 10¼ *duim*) have been added in an early hand. Cf. the cutting on the back of the supposed companion piece in the Lansdowne collection (see note 3).

9. The printed price list gives A. Brondgeest as the purchaser, but see Smith No. 129. Smith records in his Day Book (vol. 2; Victoria and Albert Museum Library) on 20 November 1829 selling to the Hon. George John Vernon for £400 'A Pair of exquisite Pictures of Sea Views during a Calm. Painted by W. Vander Velde in handsome frames very richly orna[d] & gilt in oil Gold – from the Colln of M. Muller'.

10. As from the Muller collection.

11. Smith No. 129. In 1835 Brook Greville lent two van de Velde sea pieces to the BI. No. 24 is probably the Lansdowne painting and No. 28 probably No. 149.

12. See above, note 11.

977 *Small Dutch Vessels in a Breeze*   Plate 390

To the left a *kaag* or similar vessel; it has a Dutch vane. To the right a small sprit-rigged vessel, probably a *weyschuit*, close-hauled on a port tack. In the background a ship at anchor, probably an Indiaman, with a flag at the fore as vice-admiral of a fleet and a plain red flag as an ensign.

Signed (perhaps falsely) on the buoy in the bottom right corner: VV.

Oil on oak, 21 × 29.6 (8¼ × 11⅝).

Cleaned in 1972. Severe wearing in the sky.

Robinson[1] considers that No. 977 is a studio work with little participation by Willem the Younger, perhaps copied from an original version painted in the late 1650s.

PROVENANCE: Wynn Ellis[2] Bequest, 1876.

REFERENCES:
General: HdG No. 361; Robinson, *Paintings*, No. 210.

In text:
1. Robinson, op. cit.
2. The 1929 National Gallery catalogue states that the picture was in the Wynn Ellis collection *c*.1855; this is based on HdG's mistaken identification of it with the 'quiet sea, of a tender warm colour . . .

small' from the Edward Solly collection mentioned by Waagen (1854, vol. 2, p. 297, No. 1) which is in fact National Gallery No. 980. Wynn Ellis lent three pictures by van de Velde to exhibitions at the BI: 1858, No. 117; 1860, No. 77; 1867, No. 124. Either of the last two could also refer to National Gallery Nos. 978 or 980.

JACOB VAN VELSEN, active 1625; died 1656

Jacob Jansz. van Velsen was probably born in Delft, where his parents married in 1594. He is probably not the painter 'Jacob Jansz.' mentioned in Delft in 1617 as twenty years old, since he was not accepted as a master in the Delft guild until 1625. He seems to have spent his life in Delft but died in Amsterdam, 16 September 1656.

Very few works by him are known (some of them bear dates in the years 1631–3); with one exception, a *Self Portrait* of 1631,[1] they are all genre paintings in the style of the earlier work of Anthonie Palamedesz. (1601–73) who became a master in the Delft guild four years earlier than van Velsen.

REFERENCES:
General: Bredius, *Künstler-Inventare*, vol. 3, pp. 875–7 and 885–6, and vol. 7, pp. 239–40.
In text: **1.** Panel, 26 × 20.6 cm. Collection A. E. Popham, London. Exhibited at the RA, 1952–3, No. 487.

2575 *A Musical Party* *Plate 391*

Signed, top right: J v Velsen. 1631 . . .

Oil on oak, 40 × 55.8 (15¾ × 21¹⁵⁄₁₆).; there is about another 3 mm. of the panel left unpainted on all sides except the right.

A little wearing in the shadows.

The picture at one time bore a false Anthonie Palamedesz. signature; this was removed before 1895.[1]

PROVENANCE: In the collection of Henry Doetsch, London, which was formed c.1875–95;[2] Henry Doetsch sale, London, 22–25 June 1895 (lot 380),[3] bought by C. Fairfax Murray (170 gns). In the collection of George Salting, London; Salting Bequest, 1910.

EXHIBITIONS: London, Whitechapel Gallery, 1904, No. 324; London 1978-9, No. 7.

REFERENCES:
1. See *Zeitschrift für bildende Kunst*, 1895, p. 248. It also appears in the National Gallery catalogue, 1911–21, as by Anthonie Palamedesz.
2. According to J. P. Richter (in the preface to the Doetsch sale catalogue).
3. As by J. van Velsen. The Doetsch sale catalogue wrongly identifies the picture with one of the same date engraved by François-Antoine Aveline (1727– 80) as *Le musicien espagnol* (inscribed: 'J E Velsen pinxit 1631 Aveline sculpsit London sold by P. C. Canot') but this shows a woman with a lute accompanying a singing man seated by her (cf. Kramm, vol. 6, p. 1694). The original of that composition is apparently the painting (panel, 27.5 × 91.5 cm.; signed and dated 1631) which was in the James A. Murnaghan collection, Dublin, in 1967.

PIETER VERBEECK, c.1610/15? – between 1652 and April 1654

Pieter Cornelisz. Verbeeck (he also signed himself *Verbeecq*). Born in Haarlem, son of the marine painter, Cornelis Verbeecq. Inscribed as a master in the painters' guild in Alkmaar in 1635, and still living there in 1638. In 1642 he was apparently living in Utrecht; from 1643 onwards in Haarlem, where he probably died.

There are a number of signed paintings and signed etchings. A few battle pieces, one dated 1638, and several etchings dated 1639 are in the style of the early Rembrandt. Later he seems to have painted exclusively landscapes with horses alone or with riders. In Utrecht he appears to have come under the influence of the Italianate landscape painters and his later works show also that of Paulus Potter (see No. 1009 below) and

Isack van Ostade; they are also connected stylistically with the early work of Philips Wouwermans.

REFERENCE: H. Gerson, 'Leven en werken van . . . Pieter Verbeeck', in E. A. van Beresteyn's *De genealogie van het geslacht van Beresteyn*, 1940.

1009 *A White Horse standing by a Sleeping Man* Plate 392

Signed on the lower plank of the fence, right: P. Verbeecq.

Oil on oak, 31.8×27 ($12\frac{9}{16} \times 10\frac{5}{8}$).

Cleaned in 1953. Some damage along a vertical split which runs just to the right of the centre of the painting.

Until 1953 the signature was hidden by a false signature of Paulus Potter (Paulus. Potter f)[1] to whom the picture was for a long time attributed.[2] The attribution to Verbeeck, first made by Bredius,[3] has been proved correct by the discovery of the original signature.

The influence of Potter is apparent, especially in the horse. There is an etching (in the opposite direction), probably by Verbeeck himself,[4] of the horse, man and dog (Fig. 114), which agrees in detail with the relevant parts of the picture and is on exactly the same scale. The horse in No. 1009 and the related etching is very close to one in a print of two horses by Potter, signed and dated 1652,[5] and may have been taken from it.

ETCHING: An etching of this composition is discussed above.

VERSION: The composition is repeated on the left-hand side of a panel (46.5 × 63 cm.), signed, from the collections of the Comte de Rohan-Chabot, Paris, and F. C. Butôt, Amsterdam, which was with H. H. Cevat, Lausanne, in 1965. The group is placed in an extensive landscape with a right foreground group of a man seen from behind holding a dog by a leash, talking to a boy who points to the right.

PROVENANCE: Lent to the BI, 1842,[6] by Colonel [Richard Hobart] Fitzgibbon (later 3rd Earl of Clare); Earl of Clare sale, London, 17 June 1864 (lot 20),[7] bought by Haines[8] (90 gns). William Delafield sale, London, 30 April 1870 (lot 77),[9] bought by Pearce[10] (71 gns). In the Wynn Ellis collection, London; Wynn Ellis Bequest, 1876.

EXHIBITION: BI 1842, No. 137.[11]

REFERENCES:
General: Gerson, op. cit., No. A18.
In text:
1. HdG (Potter No. 151) says that Waagen mentions a date, 1656, on the picture. He is presumably referring to Waagen, 1854, vol. 2, p. 296, but this relates to the *Stag Hunt*, formerly ascribed to Pieter Potter, then also in the Wynn Ellis collection (Lagoor No. 1008 of this catalogue), which was, in fact, dated (falsely) 1651.
2. The attribution to Potter was defended by HdG (vol. 4, Potter No. 151 and p. 585).
3. In *Onze Kunst*, vol. 20, 1911, p. 53, and BM, vol. 23, 1913, p. 185.
4. The etching is C8 in Gerson's catalogue of Verbeeck's work, op. cit. The impression in the British Museum (Sheepshanks collection) is mistakenly

ascribed to Johan le Ducq (1629/30–76/7); reproduced in Gerson, op. cit., pl. 14, No. 1.
5. Bartsch No. 12.
6. As by Paul Potter.
7. As by Paul Potter and Wijnants.
8. HdG (Potter No. 151) gives the buyer's name as Johnson but the correct name in Messrs Christie's marked copy of the sale catalogue, in which there is also a marginal annotation in another hand against lot 20: 'Delafield'.
9. As by Paul Potter. Christie's markings relating to the Delafield sale are on the back of the picture.
10. Probably bought for Wynn Ellis, for whom Pearce apparently often bought (cf. Berchem No. 1004, note 3).
11. As by Paul Potter.

JOHANNES VERMEER, 1632–1675

Johannes Reyniersz. Vermeer, son of Reynier Jansz. Vos or Vermeer, was baptised in Delft on 31 October 1632. His father, a silk-weaver, may at one time have dealt in works of art. Vermeer married in Delft in April 1653 and entered the guild there in December 1653. In the same year Vermeer witnessed a document in Delft with Gerard ter Borch. His earliest known dated work is of 1656 (see below). He spent the rest of his life in Delft, and was a *hoofdman* of the guild in 1662–3 and 1670–1. In 1672 he was called to The Hague to advise on the authenticity of paintings attributed to Holbein, Raphael, Giorgione and Titian. He was buried in the Oude Kerk in Delft on 15 December 1675. Vermeer apparently experienced financial difficulties in his last years and in 1676 his widow petitioned for bankruptcy.

Nothing is known for certain about his training. The artist most likely to have been his master is Leonaert Bramer who testified to his character at the time of his betrothal but Vermeer's early work shows no trace of Bramer's influence. There is no evidence whatsoever to support the idea that Carel Fabritius was Vermeer's master.

Vermeer's earliest dated picture, *The Procuress* of 1656 in the Dresden Gallery, shows clearly that he had studied the work of the Utrecht followers of Caravaggio, and a painting by Dirck van Baburen appears in the background of two of his pictures (see No. 2568 below).

REFERENCES: A. Blankert, J. M. Montias and G. Aillaud, *Vermeer*, New York, 1988 (with all the documents and a full bibliography). For further biographical information about Vermeer and his family, see J. M. Montias, *Vermeer and his Milieu*, Princeton, 1989.

1383 *A Young Woman standing at a Virginal*   Plate 393

On the wall behind is a landscape painting and a picture of Cupid with his bow, holding up a (?)card. A landscape is painted on the inside of the virginal's lid. There is a skirting of blue and white Delft tiles with single figures.

Signed in the top left corner of the side of the virginal: IVMeer (or IMeer; the capitals are in monogram).

Oil on canvas, 51.7 × 45.2 (20$\frac{3}{8}$ × 17$\frac{13}{16}$).

Cleaned in 1967. The blue chair in the right foreground is blanched: this may be caused by 'ultramarine disease'.

The painting of Cupid appears also in the background of another picture by Vermeer: *Girl interrupted at her Music* in the Frick Collection, New York.[1] It has been reasonably attributed to Cesar van Everdingen[2] and it may be the *Cupido* mentioned in the inventory of Vermeer's widow's possessions drawn up in 1676. De Jongh[3] has related its presence in the painting to an emblem in Otto Vaenius' *Amorum Emblemata* (Antwerp, 1608) which shows a Cupid lifting up a small tablet while treading another under foot. The raised tablet bears the number one while the numbers two to ten are inscribed on the latter. The accompanying verses praise fidelity to one rather than the love of many. He suggests that Vermeer intended to introduce the idea of fidelity in his painting by the inclusion of this picture within the painting. It should be noted, however, that there is no trace of a digit on the card (or tablet) held up by the Cupid.

More recently this idea has been expanded upon. The idea that Nos. 1383 and 2568 form a pair has been revived:[4] they are almost exactly the same size and belong stylistically to the same period in Vermeer's career. (They have, however, differing provenances in the eighteenth century.) It has been argued that the two paintings have as their deliberately contrasted subjects two kinds of love, faithful and mercenary (the mercenary theme of No. 2568 deriving from the presence of Baburen's *The Procuress* on the back wall, see below) and as such participate in the ever-popular theme of the choice between two paths in life, known in its most familiar form in the subject of *Hercules at the Crossroads*. The present writer is sceptical of this interpretation which depends on a series of quite unverifiable hypotheses. It seems more likely that the paintings simply allude in a non-specific way to the traditional association of music and love.[5]

The landscape on the left is in the manner of Jan Wijnants. No. 1383 is painted in the meticulous technique of Vermeer's late years. It has been dated by both MacLaren and Blankert[6] to *c*.1670.

PROVENANCE: No. 1383 may be identifiable with the 'Young lady playing on the virginal' by Vermeer in the collection of Diego Duarte, Antwerp, 1682,[7] or that in an Anon. sale [possibly the collection of Jacobus Abrahamsz. Dissius of Delft (d. October 1695)[8]], Amsterdam, 16 May 1696 (lot 37), 42 guilders,[9] or the 'Woman virginal player in a room' in an Anon. sale, Amsterdam, 11 July 1714 (lot 12), 55 guilders,[10] but any of these might equally well be the *Young Woman seated at a Virginal* (No. 2568 below). No. 1383 is presumably the 'Young lady standing before a virginal to play, with pictures on the wall' in the Jan Danser Nijman sale, Amsterdam, 16–17 August 1797 (lot 169),[11] bought by Berg (19 or 49 guilders). It is said to have been in the collection of Edward Solly,[12] London; it was not traceable in any of the many Solly sales.[13] It was certainly in the Edward William Lake sale, London, 11–12 July 1845 (lot 5),[14] bought by Farrer (15 gns) and the [J. P. Thom] sale, London, 2 May 1855 (lot 22),[15] bought by Grey (14½ gns). By 1866 it was in the collection of Etienne-Joseph-Théophile Thoré (pseudonym: 'W. Bürger'), Paris,[16] by whom it was lent to exhibitions in Paris (1866) and in Amsterdam (1867). Thoré died in 1869 and the picture passed with a large part of his collection to the Lacroix family, Paris;[17] it was in the 'Thoré-Bürger' collection sale, Paris, 5 December 1892 (lot 30),[18] 29,000 francs, bought by Lawrie & Co. of London, from whom it was purchased in the same month.

EXHIBITIONS: Paris, Palais des Champs-Elysées, Exposition Retrospective, May 1866, No. 108; Amsterdam, Arti et Amicitiae Society, 1867, No. 274; London 1976, No. 116.

REFERENCES:
General: HdG No. 23; Blankert et al., op. cit., cat. no. 25.
In text:
1. Blankert et al., op. cit., B2. Although Blankert is correct to point out the poor state of preservation of the painting, there can be no doubt about its attribution to Vermeer.
2. A. Delbanco, *Abraham Bloemaert*, 1928, p. 64, note. Jan van Bronchorst (*c*.1603–61) is mentioned as an alternative by A. B. de Vries, *Jan Vermeer van Delft*, 1948 (English ed.), p. 95.

3. E. de Jongh, *Zinne- en Minnebeelden in de Schilderkunst van de 17de eeuw*, 1976, pp. 49–50.
4. By Christine Armstrong in a paper delivered at the Frick Collection, New York, in 1976.
5. For this traditional association see, for example, de Jongh, op. cit.
6. Blankert et al., op. cit.
7. Item 176 of the inventory of Diego Duarte's pictures made in 1682 was: 'Een stukxken met een jouffrou op de clavesingel spelende met bywerck van Vermeer, Kost . . . guld. 150' (see Blankert et al., op. cit., pp. 211–12).

8. See Elisabeth Neurdenberg in OH, vol. 59, 1942, pp. 72–3, and vol. 66, 1951, pp. 37–9.

9. 'Een Spelende Juffrouw op de Clavecimbael van dito [Vermeer]' (see Hoet, vol. 1, p. 36).

10. 'Een Klavecimbaelspeelster in een Kamer, van Vermeer van Delft' (see Hoet, vol. 1, p. 176).

11. 'Een Juffrouw, staande voor een Clavecimbael te speelen; aan de Wand hangen Schilderijen . . .'; canvas, 20 × 17 *duim* (not lot 159 as HdG states).

12. According to the catalogue of the Lake sale 1845. The picture is sometimes said to have been in the Solly sale of 8 May 1847 (e.g. by HdG, No. 23) but this is due to a misreading of the provenance given by W. Bürger (in GB–A 1866, part ii, pp. 556–7, No. 29; Bürger mentions the Lake sale but gives its date wrongly as 1847).

13. It is not in the catalogues of any of the Solly sales listed in Lugt, vols. 1 and 2.

14. A cutting of the relevant part of the Lake sale catalogue is pasted on the back; see also note 12.

15. The markings connected with this sale are on the back of the picture.

16. See W. Bürger in GB–A 1866, ii, pl. 556, No. 29; etching by Valentin (opposite p. 326).

17. See A. Heppner in OH, vol. 65, 1938, p. 140 (cf. H. Havard, *Van der Meer de Delft*, [1888], p. 37, No. 32).

18. Reproduced in error in the sale catalogue as lot 32, which was National Gallery No. 2568.

2568 *A Young Woman seated at a Virginal*   Plate 394

In the background hangs a painting by Dirck van Baburen of a man offering money to a young woman playing a lute, while an old woman stands by them pointing to the palm of her hand. On the inner side of the cover of the virginal is painted a landscape. In the left foreground stands a viola da gamba; part of a tapestry can be seen above it. There is a skirting of single-figure blue and white Delft tiles.

Signed on the wall, behind the woman's head: IVMeer (or IMeer; the capitals are in monogram).

Oil on canvas, 51.5 × 45.5 ($20\frac{1}{4}$ × $17\frac{15}{16}$).

Cleaned in 1965. There is some wearing in the wall to the right and some shadows are slightly worn.

The painting was severely damaged during an attack in 1968; an approximately circular cut runs the length of the face through the nose and to the right of the head. It was repaired and restored.

Baburen's painting appears also in the background of Vermeer's *Concert* in the Gardner Museum, Boston.[1] The original is in the Boston Museum of Fine Arts (Fig. 115), signed and dated 1622,[2] and there is an old copy in the Rijksmuseum, Amsterdam.[3]

Baburen's composition depicts a procuress and her clients.[4] Whether by the inclusion of the Baburen within his painting Vermeer intended to suggest that the young girl in the foreground was a prostitute or represented mercenary love or infidelity is impossible to determine. It is, however, difficult to believe that such a relationship between background and foreground was intended in the Gardner Museum *Concert* where Baburen's *The Procuress* reappears. The present writer believes that, as in No. 1383, Vermeer is simply alluding in a non-specific manner to the traditional association of music with love.[5]

MacLaren believed No. 2568 to be a little later in date than No. 1383 which he dated *c.*1670. Blankert[6] dates it to 1674–5 on stylistic grounds. The present writer considers that such close dating of Vermeer's work cannot be justified and that Nos. 2568 and 1383 are both of his late style and can therefore both be dated *c*.1670.

It has been suggested[7] that the composition was inspired by Gerrit Dou's painting of the same subject in the Dulwich Gallery, which was perhaps painted by 1665.[8] Though the components are the same the design is very different and it is hardly necessary to presume any connection or even common origin.

PROVENANCE: No. 2568 was perhaps in the collection of Diego Duarte, Antwerp, 1682, or in an Anon. sale [Jacobus Abrahamsz. Dissius of Delft?], Amsterdam, 16 May 1696 (lot 37), or in an Anon. sale, Amsterdam, 11 July 1714 (lot 12), but the descriptions of these pictures would also fit No. 1383 above. It was in the collection of Graf von Schönborn in Pommersfelden, near Bamberg, allegedly by 1746;[9] Pommersfelden Gallery sale, Paris, 17 sqq. May 1867 (lot 78), bought by W. Bürger (pseudonym for Etienne-Joseph-Théophile Thoré) 2,000 francs. Thoré died in 1869 and the picture passed with the greater part of his collection to the Lacroix family, Paris;[10] 'Thoré-Bürger' sale, Paris, 5 December 1892 (lot 32[11]), bought by Charles Sedelmeyer (25,000 francs) and sold by him to Lawrie & Co., London, in February 1893.[12] Lent by T. Humphry Ward to the RA in 1894. In the collection of George Salting, London, by 1900, when it was exhibited at the BFAC; Salting Bequest, 1910.

EXHIBITIONS: RA 1894, No. 93; BFAC 1900, No. 15; London 1976, No. 117.

REFERENCES:
General: HdG No. 25; Blankert No. 31.
In text:
1. Blankert No. 17.
2. Canvas, 101 × 108.5 cm. Inv. no. 50.2721. See ex. cat. Philadelphia/Berlin/London, 1984, No. 1.
3. Rijksmuseum 1976 catalogue, No. C612.
4. Similar scenes were apparently sometimes intended to represent the Prodigal Son, e.g. Baburen's picture of 1623 in Mainz, but see ex. cat. Philadelphia/Berlin/London, 1984, No. 1.
5. See above, under No. 1383, for more detailed arguments and references.
6. Blankert, op. cit.
7. See K. Boström in *Kunsthistorische Mededeelingen*, 1949, p. 24.
8. HdG No. 132. A picture of this description by Dou was mentioned in September 1665 (W. Martin, *G. Dou*, 1901, pp. 74 and 172).
9. According to the Pommersfelden sale catalogue (1867) it is in the Pommersfelden catalogue of 1746. The present writer has not been able to consult this. The picture is not in the *Verzeichniss der Schildereyen in der Gallerie des hochgräflichen Schönbornischen Schlosses zu Pommersfelden*, Ansbach [1774], nor among the paintings mentioned in J. G. Meusel's *Museum für Künstler und für Kunstliefhaber*, vol. 2, 1788, pp. 3–39, nor in J. Heller, *Die gräflich Gemäldesammlung zu Schloss Weissenstein in Pommersfelden*, 1845. It is No. 60 of the 1857 Pommersfelden catalogue; see also G. Parthey, *Deutscher Bildersaal*, vol. 2, 1864, p. 98.
10. See OH, vol. 55, 1938, p. 140.
11. Reproduced in error as lot 30.
12. According to a MS note in the copy of *Illustrated Catalogue of 300 Paintings . . . which have at various times formed part of the Sedelmeyer Gallery*, 1898 (No. 85) belonging to the RKD; the annotations in this were transcribed from Sedelmeyer's own copy.

ANDRIES VERMEULEN, 1763–1814

Born in Dordrecht, 21 March 1763; pupil of his father, Cornelis Vermeulen, a landscape painter. He lived for some time in Amsterdam and died there, 6 July 1814. He chiefly painted landscapes based on seventeenth-century models: in the first part of his career he painted landscapes in the manner of Hobbema[1] and later he concentrated on ice scenes in a style derived from Isack van Ostade.

REFERENCE: **1.** For example, a signed and dated (1782) *Landscape*, panel, 29.5 × 38.5 cm., which was with the dealer Abels in Cologne, 1959 (photograph in RKD).

1850 *A Scene on the Ice* *Plate 395*

Signed on the bank, left, just above the rushes: A. Vermeulen.

Oil on oak, 39.8 × 49 ($15\frac{11}{16}$ × $19\frac{5}{16}$).

There is a horizontal split which has been repaired running the entire width of the panel just above the centre.

There is a similar winter landscape in Frankfurt which is signed and dated 1800.[1] No. 1850 should be dated to about the same time.

PROVENANCE: Miss Susannah Caught Bequest, 1901.

REFERENCE: **1.** Städelsches Kunstinstitut. Panel, 62 × 85 cm. Inv. no. 672.

HENDRICK VERSCHURING, 1627–1690

Born in Gorinchem (Gorkum) in 1627, according to Houbraken,[1] who says Verschuring learned drawing as a child from Dirck Govaertsz., a Gorinchem portrait painter, until his thirteenth year when he became a pupil of Jan Both in Utrecht, with whom he remained for six years (see also the biographical notice of Both). He then went to Italy where he apparently stayed, with one break, for eight years[2] and by 1657 he was again in Gorinchem.[3] His earliest dated painting is apparently from 1656.[4] He continued to live there and became a member of the magistrature. He was drowned while on a short journey, 26 April 1690.[5]

Besides the pictures of cavalry battles for which he is best known, he painted Italian scenes, usually with horses; there are also some etchings.

REFERENCES:

1. Houbraken, vol. 2, p. 193, where the date is misprinted as 1672; that Houbraken intended 1627 is proved by his statement that Verschuring was sixty-three when he died in 1690. The date is corrected to 1627 in the second edition (1753).
2. Houbraken, op. cit., p. 194, and especially, Kramm, vol. 6, p. 1732.

3. Harmen de Mayer's engraving after Verschuring's portrait of a Gorinchem preacher (who died in 1658) is inscribed: 'H. Verschuren Pinxit 1657' (see Kramm, loc. cit., and Hollstein, vol. 14, p. 24).
4. Christie's, 9 July 1982 (lot 91).
5. Houbraken, op. cit., p. 195.

3134 *Cavalry attacking a Fortified Place* *Plate 396*

Signed at the bottom, left of centre: H. Verschuring. f(e?).

Oil on canvas, 91 × 113.5 ($35\frac{3}{4}$ × $44\frac{3}{4}$).

The architecture and cypress trees show that the scene is a southern one, presumably Italian, and the picture no doubt reflects Verschuring's experience of Italy. The painting, however, is unlikely to date – as MacLaren suggested – from Verschuring's Italian years. A very similar battle scene, signed and dated 1677, was in the Czernin collection in Vienna in 1936[1] and No. 3134 probably also dates from around 1677.

470

PROVENANCE: In the [Hart] sale, London, 24 January 1852 (lot 64),[2] bought by Barnes (£11.5s.). Presented by Augustine Sargent, 1917.

REFERENCES:
1. Canvas, 103 × 138 cm. 1936 Czernin collection catalogue, No. 210.
2. As by Hughtenburgh. The markings corresponding to this sale are on the back of the panel. In the catalogue of the sale lot 64 is a *View of Lake Albano* by Moore but in the auctioneer's copy this is crossed out and 'Hugtenburg A battle' substituted in MS.

JAN VICTORS, 1619–1676 or later

He signs his name *Jan* or *Johannes* (rarely *Johan*) *Victors* or, less frequently, *Victoors, Victoor* and *Victor*. (Jacobus or Jacomo Victor (1640–1705), the bird painter, was his half-brother.) He was baptised *Hans* at the Oude Kerk in Amsterdam on 13 June 1619: he may have studied with Rembrandt before 1640 and is documented in Amsterdam from 1642 onwards. He is last mentioned in Amsterdam in January 1676; later in that year he went to the Dutch East Indies as a *siecketrooster* (literally, comforter of the sick) and apparently died there.

Until nearly the mid-1650s his paintings are mostly religious subjects and portraits in a strongly Rembrandtesque style; from *c.*1650 onwards he painted numerous peasant genre scenes in a more individual style. They are related in style to the genre scenes of Nicolas Maes.

REFERENCES: Bredius in *Künstler-Inventare*. vol. 2, 1916, pp. 596–600, and vol. 7, 1921, pp. 255–6; see also OH, 1886, p. 219. [Sumowski, *Gemälde*, vol. 4.]

1312 *A Village Scene with a Cobbler*   Plate 397

On the left an old woman is buying vegetables; in the right background a quack has set up his stall beneath his distinctive Chinese umbrella. A goose is painted on the end of the barrel on the right, and the signature: Jan Victors.

Oil on canvas, 63 × 78.5 (24$\frac{13}{16}$ × 30$\frac{7}{8}$).

The costume of the old woman buying vegetables, with its prominent gold braiding on the bodice, was worn in the Province of North Holland, and can also be seen, for example, in the *Self Portrait of Gabriel Metsu with his Wife* in Dresden (Fig. 116).[1] Isabella de Wolff, Metsu's wife, came from Enkhuizen.[2]

The model for the cobbler reappears in Victors' *The Swine Butcher* in the Rijksmuseum, signed and dated 1648,[3] and in another painting of the same subject by Victors in the York City Art Gallery, signed and dated 1651.[4] To judge by the style the present picture is of about the same date as these.

COPY: An old copy was with the dealer J. Gans, Voorburg, 1953.[5]

PROVENANCE: In the Boursault sale, Paris, 7 sqq. May 1832 (lot 60); by 1841 it was in the collection of Edmund Higginson, Saltmarsh Castle;[6] Edmund Higginson sales, London, 4–6 June 1846 (lot 138), bought in (74 gns), and London, 16 June 1860 (lot 4), bought by Enson (£42). In the T. A. Stewart sale, London, 13 April 1876 (lot 52),[7] bought in (19 gns). Purchased from Messrs Colnaghi, London, in 1890.

EXHIBITION: London 1978–9, No. 3.

REFERENCES:
General: [Sumowski, op. cit., No. 1793.]
In text:
1. 1979 cat., Inv. No. 1732. Dated 1661.
2. For a discussion of Isabella de Wolff's costume and other examples of this costume see B. J. A. Renckens and J. Duyvette, 'De Vrouw van Gabriel Metsu, Isabella de Wolff, geboortig van Enkhuizen', OH, vol. 74, 1959, pp. 179–82.
3. Rijksmuseum 1976 catalogue, No. C259. [Sumowski, op. cit., No. 1791.]

4. Canvas, 92.8 × 86.5 cm. [See under Sumowski, op. cit., No. 1791.]
5. Support and dimensions not known. Photograph in RKD.
6. H. Artaria, *Descriptive Catalogue of the Gallery of Edmund Higginson*, 1841, p. 159.
7. The date of this sale is written on the back of the frame.

SIMON DE VLIEGER, *c.*1601–1653

Simon Jacobsz. de Vlieger was born about 1601, most probably in Rotterdam.[1] The date of his birth may be established from a document of 16 May 1648, stating that he was then 'out omtrent 47 jaren' ('about forty-seven years old').[2] On 10 January 1627 he married Anna Gerrits van Willige. This marriage took place in Rotterdam, where he is also recorded in 1628, 1630 and on 27 April 1634.[3] From 1 May 1634 he rented a house called 'Kranenburch' in Delft for a period of three years and on 18 October of that year became a member of the guild.[4] On 14 December 1637, he was still living in Delft, but bought a house in Rotterdam from the painter and art dealer Crijn Hendrickse Volmarijn. Instead of instalment payments on the purchase of the house he committed himself to deliver paintings regularly to the merchant: 'als hij voor andere luyden dagelicx maeckt' ('of the kind he produces daily for other people').[5] On 12 March 1638 he was living in a house known as 'Houttuyn' in Delft, where he was until 1 May 1638.[6] On 19 July 1638, he is recorded as 'schilder woonende tot Amsterdam', where he executed designs for decorations for the festivities honouring Queen Maria de' Medici's entry into the city on 13 August 1638.[7] In December 1640 and in March 1642 he was paid for tapestry cartoons by the town of Delft[8] and in 1642 he was commissioned to paint the wings of the organ of the Grote Kerk in Rotterdam, for which he was paid in 1645.[9] The wings, depicting King David and other figures, were destroyed in 1788. During these years he lived in Amsterdam: he acquired citizenship on 5 January 1643.[10] On 17 September 1644, he sold his house in Rotterdam[11] and on 4 January 1648 he signed the contract for the design of the large window in the south transept of the Nieuwe Kerk in Amsterdam. The window, showing Maximilian I's legendary bestowal of the imperial crown on the arms of the city of Amsterdam, was removed before 1740.[12] De Vlieger was still living in Amsterdam in November 1648.[13] He had settled in Weesp (then a fashionable resort some ten miles from Amsterdam) in January 1649 when he bought a house there.[14] His daughter, Cornelia, was married to the Amsterdam painter Paulus van Hillegaert the Younger in that city in 1651.[15] On 2 February 1652 he was mentioned in Rotterdam as a widower,[16] but he died in Weesp in March 1653.[17] His death was lamented in verses by the poet Frederik Verloo.[18]

Although de Vlieger painted and drew landscape, animals and figures subjects, the largest part of his work is his seascape paintings. His developed style, formed in the 1630s under the influence of Jan Porcellis's marines, was the point of departure for van de Cappelle and Hendrick Dubbels as well as Willem van de Velde the Younger. He made about twenty etchings, all either landscapes or animal studies; the latter are early examples of the animal prints which later became so popular in Holland.

REFERENCES:
General: J. Kelch, 'Simon de Vlieger als Marinemaler (diss.), Berlin 1971, pp. 1–10, notes pp. 124–30 (with all previous bibliography).
In text:
1.and **2.** Kelch, pp. 1, 124, notes 1, 2.
3. Kelch, pp. 2, 124, notes 3, 8, 9.
4. Kelch, pp. 2, 125, notes 11, 12.
5. Kelch, pp. 2–3, 125, note 13.
6. Kelch, pp. 2–3, 125, note 13.
7. Kelch, pp. 3, 125, notes 15, 16.
8. Kelch, pp. 5–6, 128, notes 33, 34.

9. Kelch, pp. 6, 128, notes 35, 36.
10. Kelch, pp. 3, 125, note 18.
11. Kelch, pp. 3, 116, note 19.
12. Kelch, pp. 6–8, 128–129, notes 37–48.
13. Kelch, pp. 3, 126, note 20.
14. Kelch, pp. 4, 126, note 21.
15. Kelch, pp. 4, 126, note 22.
16. Kelch, pp. 4, 126, note 23.
17. Kelch, pp. 4, 126, note 24.
18. Kelch, pp. 10, 129, note 55.

3025 *A Dutch Man-of-War and Various Vessels in a Breeze*   Plate 398

In the middle distance, on the right, is a frigate with a Dutch flag at the main; in the left foreground a gaff-rigged *wijdschip*.

Signed, on a spar, bottom left: VLIEGE(R?).

Oil on oak, 41.2 × 54.8 ($16\frac{1}{4}$ × $21\frac{1}{2}$).

MacLaren considered that it was probably painted in *c.*1640–5 and Bol[1] concurred in this dating. Kelch,[2] however, prefers to date the picture about 1638–40.

VERSIONS:[3] There are two (or possibly only one) versions of this composition, both unsigned, and with very slight differences: Anon. sale, Sotheby, 30 June 1971 (lot 91);[4] Anon. sale, Christie's, 29 May 1981 (lot 438).[5]

PROVENANCE: In the collection of Baron Huntingfield, Heveningham Hall, Suffolk; Lord Huntingfield sale, London, 25 June 1915 (lot 128), bought by Agnew (£42), from whom purchased by the National Gallery (out of the Mackerell Fund) in the same year.

REFERENCES:
General: Kelch, op. cit., cat. no. 35.
In text:
1. L. J. Bol, *Die Holländische Marinemalerei*, Braunschweig, 1973, p. 182.
2. Kelch, op. cit., pp. 45–6, 155, and cat. no. 35.

3. The present author is indebted to Jan Kelch for drawing these versions (or version) to his attention.
4. Panel, 41 × 54.5 cm. ($16\frac{1}{4}$ × $21\frac{1}{2}$ in.).
5. Panel, 40.6 × 53.7 cm. (16 × $21\frac{1}{8}$ in.).

4455 *A View of an Estuary, with Dutch Vessels at a Jetty and a Dutch Man-of-War at Anchor*   Plate 399

Some of the vessels at the jetty on the left have Dutch vanes; the largest, a gaff-rigged *wijdschip*(?), also has a small blue flag, that behind it has blue and white vanes and the small vessel (a *kaag*) nearest the spectator has a red and white one. The man-of-war, a frigate at anchor in the right middle distance, has the arms of the Province of Holland on her stern; she has a Dutch flag at the main, a white and blue jack and a plain red ensign. In the distance is another man-of-war at anchor, with a Dutch ensign.

Signed on a floating spar in the right foreground: S DE VLIEGER.

Oil on oak, 88.5 × 122 (34$\frac{7}{8}$ × 48).

Cleaned in 1969.

There are very many small retouchings to cover the grain of the panel.

Possibly a view of the toll-house on the Maas (see PROVENANCE).

MacLaren considered that it was probably painted *c*.1645–50 on the basis of costume, especially that of the man standing by the corner of the building on the jetty. Bol[1] and Kelch[2] concur in this dating.

There are several paintings in which de Vlieger painted the River Maas with a jetty on the left from a similar point of view, for example, the picture in Rotterdam.[3]

PROVENANCE: It is perhaps the picture (of the same size) by de Vlieger of the Maas and the toll-house in the Josué van Belle sale, Rotterdam, 6 September 1730 (lot 101),[4] 34 guilders. It was in t1e collection of Earl Sydney (died 1890) and was bought (probably from the executors of his heir, the Hon. Robert Marsham-Townshend) through Messrs Sulley and Co. by Lord Revelstoke in April 1915.[5] Lord Revelstoke Bequest, 1929.

EXHIBITION: London 1976, No. 119.

REFERENCES:
General: Kelch, op. cit., cat. no. 57.
In text:
1. L. J. Bol, *Die Holländische Marinemalerei*, Braunschweig, 1973, p. 184.
2. Kelch, op. cit.
3. Museum Boymans-van Beuningen, 1972 cat., No. 1923. For other examples, see Kelch, op. cit.,

cat. nos. 15, 54, 77.
4. 'Een Stuk zynde het Gezigt van 't Tolhuys en de Maes met Schepen, door de Vlieger', 2 *voet* 11 *duim* high × 4 *voet* 1$\frac{1}{2}$ *duim* wide (= *c*.35 × 49$\frac{1}{2}$ in.); see Hoet, vol. 1, p. 360.
5. Letter of 1929 from Lord Revelstoke's executors (in the National Gallery archives).

WILLEM VAN DER VLIET, 1583 or 1584(?)–1642

Willem Willemsz. van der Vliet. He was born in Delft, according to Houbraken,[1] who says that he was fifty-eight at the time of his death in December 1642. He was a member of the Delft guild by 1615 and in 1634 *hoofdman*, and seems to have passed his life in Delft, where he was buried on 6 December 1642.[2] He was praised by Dirck van Bleyswijck in his *Beschrijvinge der Stad Delft* (1667) as a good portrait painter and 'not unskilful' (*niet ongelukkig*) at *Inventien en historien* (literally 'inventions and histories' i.e. history paintings).

His few known works, almost all portraits, are dated in the years 1624–40. A genre painting of 1624 shows two men, one lighting a pipe from a candle and the other drinking soup; an allegory of 1627[3] shows a seated man with four figures holding or wearing masks; and a painting of 1629[4] shows an old man in a brown habit displaying a bag of bones. His nephew, Hendrik Cornelisz. van der Vliet, the painter of church interiors, was his pupil and painted some portraits in his style.

REFERENCES:
1. Vol. I, p. 121.
2. See Obreen, vol. 1, pp. 5, 30, and vol. 6, 1884–7, p. 9.
3. Canvas, 112 × 149 cm. Sotheby's, 3 March 1983, lot 69.
4. Panel, 64 × 50 cm. Private collection, London.

1168 *Portrait of Suitbertus Purmerent*   *Plate 400*

He holds a *biretta* in his right hand. The crucifix has the legend: INRI. The lettering on the spine of the lower of the two books on the table is apparently not intended to be legible.

Signed, bottom right: Æta: 45. aᵒ 1631 (Æ in monogram) / w.vander vliet / fecit.

Oil on oak, 113.5 × 85.4 (44⅝ × 33⅝).

The background is extensively retouched.

Suitbertus Hendriksz. Purmerent (1587–1650) was born in The Hague. Both he and his twin brother, Petrus, became Roman Catholic priests. He was sent to Delft in 1613 and became the priest at the Catholic church in the Begijnhof there in 1615; he was appointed archpriest of Delfland, 10 February 1631. He left Delft in 1643 to avoid persecution but returned later.[1]

The sitter has been identified by the Revd C. J. van der Knaap;[2] this identification is confirmed by the portrait of him at a later age by Hendrik Cornelisz. van der Vliet (1611/12–75) in the Old Catholic church in the Begijnhof in Delft.[3]

Suitbertus Purmerent was born on 4 December 1587 and was, therefore, only in his forty-fourth year in 1631, despite the inscription on the picture. This portrait was possibly painted in connection with his appointment as archpriest of Delfland in 1631.

PROVENANCE: In the collection of William Russell by 1878, when it was exhibited at the RA; William Russell sale, London, 5–6 December 1884 (lot 147), bought for the National Gallery (with the aid of the Clarke Fund).

EXHIBITION: RA 1878, No. 163.

REFERENCES:
1. NNBW, vol. 10, 1937, col. 762; further information from the Revd C. J. van der Knaap.
2. Letter of 1954 (in the National Gallery archives).
3. Panel, 76 × 58 cm. (photograph in the National Gallery archives). It is one of a series of thirteen portraits of former parish priests in the presbytery of the Old Catholic church in the Begijnhof. There is an engraving of the bust (in reverse) by Reinier van Persijn (before 1614 – before 1669) in *Batavia Sacra*, vol. 2, p. 226, inscribed: 'H. van Vliet pinx.'

ROELOF VAN VRIES, 1630 or 1631 – after 1681

Born in Haarlem; said to be twenty-eight in 1659, in which year he was in Amsterdam, where he is last mentioned in 1681. He entered the Leiden guild in 1653 and the Haarlem guild in 1657.

His style is based on Jacob van Ruisdael's and is very similar to that of Salomon Rombouts (active in Haarlem 1652–60; died before 1702) and Cornelis Decker (active 1640; died 1678) of Haarlem, with whose paintings his are often confused.

REFERENCES: Van der Willigen, p. 38; Obreen, vol. 5, p. 215; OH, 1886, p. 298.

134 *A View of a Village*   *Plate 401*

Oil on oak, 64.8 × 49 (25½ × 19⅝).

Worn; the sky retouched. A vertical split which has been repaired runs the entire length of the panel just to the left of centre.

The picture has previously been attributed erroneously to Frans Decker of Haarlem (1684–1751),[1] and, with better reason, to C. G. Decker.[2] It is a characteristic work of van Vries (cf., for example, the signed landscapes in Munich[3] and Stockholm[4]).

PROVENANCE: Lt.-Col. John Harvey Ollney Bequest, 1837.[5]

REFERENCES:

1. National Gallery catalogue, 1847–62, 1891 and 1915–29.
2. National Gallery catalogue, 1892–1901.
3. Alte Pinakothek Inv. No. 562. Signed: R. vries f.

4. Stockholm, Nationalmuseum, 1928 catalogue, Nos. 690 and 692; each signed: R. Vries f. (listed but not described in 1958 catalogue).
5. As by Decker.

CORNELIS VROOM, 1591/2–1661

Cornelis Hendricksz. Vroom, son of the marine painter, Hendrick Cornelisz. Vroom (1566–1640). It is not known exactly when he was born; in February 1649 he declared he was about fifty-eight years old. He is first mentioned as a painter in Samuel Ampzing's *Het Lof der Stad Haerlem in Holland* (2nd ed., 1621). In 1635 he was a member of the Haarlem painters' guild (he had presumably joined long before), but had left it by 1642 after a quarrel. He may have been in England in 1627 and in the following year 'Young Vroom' (who could be Cornelis or his younger brother Frederick) received £80 from Charles I. His association with the Stuart court continued for a number of years. He also worked for the Stadholder, Frederik Hendrik. He was wealthy (his father was very successful) and his paintings are comparatively rare.

His early work consists of marine paintings in a manner derived from that of his father but showing a knowledge of the work of Jan Porcellis. He then turned to landscapes (the earliest example is dated 1622). He seems to have always lived in Haarlem, where he was buried on 16 September 1661.

His early landscapes derive from Elsheimer and Esaias van de Velde, but his conception of landscape, above all after 1630, is largely original and foreshadows much of Jacob van Ruisdael's, whose early woodland scenes were strongly influenced by his.

REFERENCE: G. Keyes, *Cornelis Vroom: Marine and Landscape Artist*, 2 vols., Alphen aan de Rijn, 1975 (with all previous literature). (See also the review by P. Biesboer in *Simiolus*, vol. 10, 1978–9, pp. 207–10.)

3475 *A Landscape with a River by a Wood* Plate 402

Signed on the river bank, in the centre: CVROOM/ 1626 (CVR in monogram).

Oil on oak, 31.2 × 44.2 ($12\frac{1}{4}$ × $17\frac{3}{8}$).

The landscape is indebted to Elsheimer compositions like *The Small Tobias*[1] and *The Flight into Egypt*,[2] both available to Vroom in the form of prints by Hendrick Goudt. Despite its small size, No. 3475 is a complex and innovatory composition and foreshadows certain features of the early work of Jacob van Ruisdael.

PROVENANCE: Lent by (Sir) Robert Clermont Witt to the BFAC, 1919, and presented by him (through the NACF) in 1919.

EXHIBITIONS: BFAC 1919, No. 34; London 1976, No. 120; London 1986, No. 76.

REFERENCES:
General: Keyes, op. cit., cat. no. P27.
In text:
1. Frankfurt, Historisches Museum; K. Andrews, *Adam Elsheimer*, Oxford, 1977, cat. no. 20.
2. Munich, Alte Pinakothek. Andrews, op. cit., cat. no. 26.

JACOB VAN WALSCAPPELLE, 1644–1727

Flower, fruit and still-life painter. His name was originally Jacobus Cruydenier; by 1667 he had adopted the surname of a great-grandfather, van Walscapel. He signed himself variously *Jacob Walscapel*, *Walscappel*, *Walscapele*, and *Walscappelle*, occasionally with the addition of the prefix *van*.

He was born in May 1644 in Dordrecht but probably went early to Amsterdam where his brother-in-law Ottmar Elliger the Elder, who painted many flower pieces, lived before 1666. According to Houbraken[1] he was a pupil of the flower painter Cornelis Kick until Kick left Amsterdam in 1667, and this is borne out by the style of some of his pictures.[2] From 1673 until his death he held municipal posts in Amsterdam and Houbraken's statement[3] that he eventually gave up painting is supported by the dates on his pictures, of which comparatively few are known. He died in Amsterdam, 16 August 1727.

REFERENCES:
General:
J. Knoef in OH, vol. 56, 1939, pp. 261–5.
In text:
1. Houbraken, vol. 2, p. 334.
2. For example *Flowers in a Glass Vase*, 1667, can-
vas, 66.5 × 52.7 cm. Victoria and Albert Museum (Ionides Bequest). Inv. no. CAI. 87. 1973 cat. No. 372.
3. Houbraken, op. cit.

1002 *Flowers in a Glass Vase*   *Plate 403*

Signed, bottom right: Jacob: Walscappe (The rest of the signature has been cut off).

Oil on canvas, stuck on oak, 59.8 × 47.5 (23$\frac{9}{16}$ × 18$\frac{11}{16}$).

Certainly cut down on the right (see the signature) and probably also on the other sides.

PROVENANCE: Wynn Ellis Bequest, 1876.

REFERENCE: Vroom, vol. 2, No. 747.

JAN WEENIX, 1642–1719

Born in Amsterdam,[1] in 1642;[2] son and pupil of Jan Baptist Weenix. He was a member of the Utrecht painters' college in 1664 and is still recorded in it in October 1668;[3] afterwards he lived in Amsterdam, where he married in 1679.[4] He was court painter (*c.*1702 to 1714 or later) to the Elector Palatine Johann Wilhelm and made a series of paintings of live and dead game for Schloss Bensberg.[5] He was buried in Amsterdam, 19 September 1719.[6]

Besides numerous paintings of dead game, he painted during his early years a number of Italianate scenes in the style of his father and some portraits and genre subjects.

REFERENCES:

General: S. A. Sullivan, *The Dutch Gamepiece*, Montclair, N.J., 1984, pp. 62–6, 106.
In text:
1. He is described as a native of Amsterdam in a document of 1679 (OH, 1886, p. 300).
2. Houbraken (vol. 2, pp. 78, 81) states that four years after the marriage of Jan Baptist Weenix and Josina d'Hondecoeter, their son was fourteen months old. The marriage took place in 1639. When

Houbraken's *De Groote Schouburgh* began to appear in 1718, he stated that Weenix was 76 (misprinted as 16). Cf. W. Stechow in *Art Quarterly*, vol. 11, 1948, pp. 181 and 197, note 2.
3. Kramm, vol. 6, p. 1835.
4. OH, 1886, p. 300.
5. Cf. van Gool, vol. 1, p. 80.
6. OH, 1886, p. 300.

238 *A Deerhound with Dead Game and Implements of the Chase*   *Plate 404*

On the ground lie a stag and a heron. A stag hunt is in progress in the right background.

Signed, bottom right: J Weenix f 1708

Oil on canvas, 173.5 × 157 (68$\frac{1}{4}$ × 61$\frac{3}{4}$).

Cleaned in 1985; some wearing throughout.

PROVENANCE: Marquess of Lansdowne sale, London, 19–20 March 1806 (1st day, lot 36), 56 gns; [Harris and Panni] sale, London, 9 February 1811 (lot 35), bought by N. W. Ridley Colborne (later Lord Colborne), 80 gns. Lord Colborne Bequest, 1854.

6462 *An Italian Courtyard*   *Plate 405*

Signed, lower right: J Weenix 16(6?)

Oil on canvas, 84.5 × 68.5 (33½ × 27).

Cleaned in 1981.

A pair of lovers attended by a negro servant sit on steps in front of an open-air tavern and the portico of a *palazzo* with a Michelangelesque *Slave* in the small square before it.

There is damage in the area of both the signature and the date, but the reading given above seems to be correct. (It appears that Jan Baptist Weenix always signed himself Gio[vanni] Batt[ist]a Weenix after his return from Italy in 1646 or 1647.) This type of Italianate genre scene was devised by Jan Baptist Weenix, Jan Weenix's father, and in the years around 1660 father and son worked closely together. Jan Baptist is known to have died before November 1663 (his last-known dated work is of 1658).[1] No. 6462, although dependent on Jan Baptist in composition, resembles in palette and technique other similar scenes by Jan Weenix. A close comparison is *The Prodigal Son* of 1668 in the Residenz in Salzburg (Fig. 117).[2]

The foreground lovers have been identified as Anthony and Cleopatra[3] shown at the moment in Pliny's account when Cleopatra dissolved her pearl earring in a glass of vinegar. In fact the woman, who is elegantly dressed but not regal, is dipping a biscuit, given to her by the servant, into a wineglass held by her lover.

PROVENANCE: Collection of Mrs Gifford-Scott; Anon. sale, Sotheby's, 16 July 1980 (lot 11) (as 'Anthony and Cleopatra by J. B. Weenix'), bought in; purchased by private treaty from Mrs Gifford-Scott who bequeathed the equivalent sum to the National Gallery in 1983.

REFERENCES:

1. For Jan Baptist Weenix's biography, see below. His last dated work is in the Mauritshuis: *Italian Landscape with Inn and Ruins*. It is signed: Gio Batta Weenix f. A° 1658 $\frac{\text{IOM}}{\text{20D}}$ op het huys ter My. 1977 cat., No. 901.

2. 1962 catalogue, No. 205. Signed: J. Weenix 1668.
3. In the Sotheby's sale, 1980. See above under PROVENANCE.

JAN BAPTIST WEENIX, 1621–1660/1(?)

Before 1643 he signed himself *Johannes Weenincks* or *Weenincx*; after his return from Italy he invariably signed *Gio*[vanni] *Batt*[ist]*a Weenix*.

According to Houbraken[1] he was born in Amsterdam in 1621 and taught first by Jan Micker [in Amsterdam], afterwards by Abraham Bloemaert in Utrecht and finally, for about two years, by Nicolaes Moeyaert [in Amsterdam], and at the age of eighteen married a daughter of the landscape painter, Gillis de Hondecoeter, grandfather of Melchior de Hondecoeter. He was living in Amsterdam in October 1642, when he made a will before setting out to study in Italy ('hebbende te trecken na Italien, om syn konst te exprementeren').[2] He must have gone to Italy late in 1642 or early in 1643 and stayed there, according to Houbraken, for four years. He was mostly in Rome, and worked for Cardinal Giovanni Battista Pamphili[3] (who became Pope Innocent X in 1644). In the Netherlandish artists' society in Rome (the *Bent*) he was given the cognomen 'Ratel' (i.e. rattle).[4] He was still in Rome in June 1646[5] but by June 1647 he was once more in Amsterdam.[6] He had settled in Utrecht by 1649, in which year he was an officer of the painters' college there.[7] He went to live at the Huis ter Mey(e), not far from Utrecht; this was three years before his death, according to Houbraken, who says he died there at the age of thirty-nine.[8] If the birth date given by Houbraken is correct, he must have died in 1660 or 1661; in any case before November 1663 when he is mentioned in his sister's will as deceased.[9]

There are dated works of most of the years from 1641 to 1658; the latest known is dated 20 October 1658 and inscribed 'op het huys ter My'.[10] After his return from Italy he painted fanciful Italian landscapes and seaports, and still life with dead game; his still-life pictures show affinities with contemporary Flemish painters such as Frans Snyders (1597–1657). There are also some portraits.

He was productive and worked very rapidly; Jan Weenix told Houbraken that his father could paint three life-size half-length portraits in a single day and that he had several times seen the elder Weenix paint a picture 6 or 7 feet (2.2–2.5 m.) wide in the same time.[11]

REFERENCES:

General: W. Stechow in *Art Quarterly*, vol. 11, 1948, pp. 181–98; Utrecht 1965, pp. 174 ff.

In text:

1. Houbraken, vol. 2, pp. 77–8.
2. Published by Bredius in OH, 1928, p. 177.
3. Cf. Houbraken, op. cit., p. 79.
4. Houbraken, op. cit., p. 77.
5. Stechow, op. cit., p. 182.
6. Kramm, vol. 6, p. 1836.
7. Muller, p. 129.
8. Houbraken, op. cit., p. 81.
9. Bredius, loc. cit.
10. Mauritshuis, The Hague; 1977 cat., No. 901.
11. Houbraken, op. cit., p. 82.

1096 *A Huntsman cutting up a Dead Deer, with Two Deerhounds*

Plate 406

In the left background is a stag hunt.

Signed, bottom right: Gio Ba(tt?) Ween(.) The letters of the signature are loosely formed and the fact that the final 'ix' is not legible does not necessarily mean that the painting has been cut down on the right.

Oil on canvas, 196 × 265 ($77\frac{1}{4}$ × $104\frac{1}{4}$).

Cleaned in 1986–7. General wearing throughout; the technique is very broad and the paint thinly applied in many areas.

PROVENANCE: Presented by Henry Reene to the British Museum in 1756; transferred by the Trustees of the British Museum to the National Gallery in 1880.

ADRIAEN VAN DER WERFF, 1659–1722

Born in Kralingen, just outside Rotterdam, 21 January 1659.[1] According to Houbraken he was, when a child, a pupil for a short time of Cornelis Picolet in Rotterdam and later, for four years [c.1671–5] of Eglon Hendrik van der Neer[2] [in Rotterdam], and set up as an independent master at the age of seventeen [i.e. in 1676].[3] There are dated works from 1678 onwards (and of almost every year to 1722). He spent almost the whole of his life in Rotterdam. In 1696 he began to work for the Elector Palatine who in 1697 appointed him court painter at 4,000 guilders a year on condition that he painted for the Elector during six months of the year (in 1703 this was increased to nine months a year);[4] from this time onward the Elector commissioned many pictures from him either for his gallery or as presents to others (e.g. No. 3909 below). Van der Werff visited Düsseldorf in 1697, 1698, 1703 and 1712 to deliver pictures and paint the Elector, who made him a knight in 1703 (after this date he often adds the word Chev[alie]r to his signature on paintings) and in 1712 gave him 6,000 ducats for a Diana and Callisto painted in 1704.[5] He also worked for the King of Poland and the Duke of Brunswick;[6] in 1718 the French regent bought a picture from him for 5,000 guilders.[7] He died in Rotterdam, 12 November 1722.[8]

His earlier works, under the influence of Eglon van der Neer, are in the tradition of the Leiden 'fine painters'; at the beginning of his career a large part of his production consisted of small portraits such as No. 1660 below. After his success in figure painting (chiefly religious and mythological subjects) he painted only a few portraits (some of them life-size). The work of his maturity, which was greatly influenced by contemporary French classical taste, is smooth and highly finished and was greatly admired in his own time, and he achieved greater fame and wealth than almost any other Dutch painter of the seventeenth and eighteenth centuries; Houbraken[9] calls him the greatest Dutch artist. Besides painting, he designed the façades of various merchants' houses in Rotterdam and drew the plans for the new Bourse there. His principal pupil and assistant was his brother, Pieter van der Werff (1661–1722), who imitated him closely and made many copies of his works.

REFERENCES:

General: Houbraken, vol. 3, pp. 387–408; van Gool, vol. 2, pp. 376–410; HdG, vol. 10; E. Wiersum in Rotterdamsch Jaarboekje, 1927, pp. 1–15; ex. cat., Rotterdam, Historisch Museum, Adriaen van der Werff, 1973 (with extensive bibliography); B. Gaehtgens, Adriaen van der Werff: 1659–1722, Berlin 1987. [Gaehtgens' book appeared when this catalogue was already in proof and so it has been possibly only to note the numbers in her catalogue, but not to give an account of her discussions of the artist's biography and the National Gallery paintings.]

In text:

1. Houbraken, op. cit., p. 388.
2. Houbraken, op. cit., p. 389.
3. Houbraken, op. cit., p. 392.
4. Houbraken, op. cit., pp. 396–7.
5. Houbraken, op. cit., pp. 396–9.
6. Houbraken, op. cit., pp. 398–400.
7. Houbraken, op. cit., p. 403.
8. According to van Gool, op. cit., p. 391, he died on 12 November 1722 and was buried on 17 November; HdG says 22 November.
9. Houbraken, op. cit., p. 388.

1660 *Portrait of a Man in a Quilted Gown*   *Plate 407*

In the background is a statue of a draped female figure holding a wreath in her right hand (see below).

Signed on the stone parapet, bottom left: Adriaen vander Werff. fec./an° 1685.

Oil on canvas, 47.3 × 38.3 ($18\frac{5}{8}$ × $15\frac{1}{16}$).

Described by Hofstede de Groot as a self portrait,[1] but the features are entirely different from those of authentic self portraits of van der Werff[2] and in any case the sitter is obviously older than twenty-six (van der Werff was born in January 1659).

    The statue in the background appears to be based on the so-called 'Farnese Flora' (now in the Museo Nazionale, Naples),[3] but the pose is reversed (the bunch of flowers which the Naples 'Flora' holds is a restorer's addition). This statue had considerable fame in the sixteenth and seventeenth centuries. Van der Werff, who never visited Italy, no doubt saw a drawing or engraving of it;[4] the inversion of the pose suggests the latter.

COPY: Anon. sale, Sotheby's, 16 July 1980 (lot 153).[5]

PROVENANCE: HdG[6] suggested that No. 1660 might be the 'self portrait' of van der Werff, of the same size as No. 1660, in the W. B. van der Kooi sale, Leeuwarden, 1 sqq. May 1837 (lot 79). No. 1660 was bought from a dealer by Sir Edward Malet, London;[7] presented by him in 1898.

EXHIBITION: Amsterdam 1989–90, No. 56.

REFERENCES:
General: HdG No. 202; Gaehtgens, op. cit., No. 115.
In text:
1. At first glance the sitter appears to be indicating himself with his left hand (as is often the case in self portraits) but he is, in fact, only holding the front of his robe. HdG, op. cit.
2. e.g. the self portrait, signed and dated 1699, in the Rijksmuseum, Amsterdam (1976 catalogue, No. A465). For van der Werff's self portraits, see Gaehtgens, op. cit., cat. nos. 105–10.
3. F. Haskell and N. Penny, *Taste and the Antique*, 1981, pp. 217–19.
4. It was engraved (in a restored condition) in Cavalleriis, *Antiquae Statuae Urbis Romae*, Liber Primus, n.d. [before 1561], pl. 11, and by Jan de Bisschop in his *Icones*, vol. 1, The Hague, 1668, pl. 41. See Haskell and Penny, op. cit.
5. Panel, 21 × 14 in. Rounded at top, falsely signed. A copy with slight variations.
6. Loc. cit.
7. As a self portrait. Letter of 1898 from Sir E. Malet (in the National Gallery archives).

3049 *A Boy with a Mousetrap*   *Plate 408*

Signed along the bottom: A. Vander. Werff. fe.

Oil on oak, 19.2 × 13.3 ($7\frac{9}{16}$ × $5\frac{1}{4}$).

Cleaned in 1971. The grain of the wood has become visible in some areas, most noticeably in the boy's face and hat.

The companion piece, *A Boy putting a Bird into a Cage* (see Fig. 118),[1] was also in the Choiseul, Conti, Merens and Lake collections (see PROVENANCE).

    De Jongh[2] has argued that this painting and its companion are an iconographically related pair on the subject of moderation in love. He points out that the subjects of a mouse and a mousetrap occur in classical literature as the image of punished intemperance and that it is also in this sense that they are employed by Alciati in his emblem *Capitus ob gulam* (Trapped by greed). In Holland in the seventeenth century the image is used in this way by Vondel in his *Vorstelijcke Warande der dieren*. In Jacob Cats' emblem *Fit spolians spolium* (The hunter hunted) a man who pays for a stolen kiss with his heart is compared to a mouse who pays for his hunger with his life. Daniel Heinsius in his *Emblemata Amatoria* (in *Nederduytsche Poemata*, Leiden, 1621) compares the man who cannot live without love to a mouse poised between a trap and a cat. De Jongh considers that it is in this sense that No. 3049 should be understood. The pendant showing boys with a birdcage and a cat he relates to the idea of love's pleasurable captivity – the cage as an emblem of the 'sweet slavery of love' – while the bird which escapes from the cage is traditionally associated with the loss of virtue.

Considered by MacLaren to be 'perhaps a work of the early 1680s', but according to Gaehtgens (op. cit.) one of the earliest group of genre paintings by van de Werff from *c*.1678–9.

ENGRAVING: Line-engraving (reversed) by P. Maleuvre, *c*.1771.[3]

PROVENANCE: Duc de Choiseul sale, Paris, 6 sqq. April 1772 (lot 84), bought by Boileau (1,402 francs with companion); Prince de Conti sale, Paris, 8 sqq. April 1777 (lot 470, with companion), bought by Fouquet of Amsterdam (915 francs); Lucas Merens sale, Amsterdam, 15 April 1778 (lot 127, with companion) bought by Fouquet (450 florins with companion). In the collection of Edward William Lake, London; E. W. Lake sale, London, 11–12 July 1845 (lot 20), bought by Farrer (£84); also in an unidentified French sale of the nineteenth century.[4] Later in the possession of E. Hirschler & Co., Vienna.[5] Henry L. Florence Bequest, 1916.

EXHIBITIONS: Amsterdam 1976, No. 75; London 1978–9, No. 24.

REFERENCES:

General: Smith No. 76; HdG No. 171; Gaehtgens, op. cit., No. 6.
In text:
1. HdG No. 170. Present whereabouts unknown. A copy, ex. coll. W. Gaskell Harvey, in the Marshall Brooks sale, London, 13 February 1946 (lot 76), bought by Tooth (later with Koetser, London, 1946) was wrongly described as the Choiseul picture.
2. Amsterdam 1976, ex. cat., *Tot Lering en Vermaak*, No. 75. All the literary references discussed above are given there in full.

3. In *Recueil d'estampes . . . d'après les tableaux du . . . Duc de Choiseul*, 1771, No. 52, pl. 53.
4. On the back is a cutting from a sale catalogue: 'Werff (P. [sic] van der). L'Enfant à la souricière. Tableau / [de] belle qualité provenant du duc de / [Ch]oiseul. Il a été gravé.'
5. Their label and seal are, on the back of the panel (Fig. 119).

3909 *The Rest on the Flight into Egypt* *Plate 409*

The Virgin is supporting the sleeping Christ; in the background St Joseph lies asleep.

Signed in the right bottom corner (small): Chev^r v^r werff. / An^o 1706.[1]

On the back of the panel are two seals, one with van der Werff's coat-of-arms,[2] the other with his personal device.[3]

Oil on oak, 54.5 × 43 ($21\frac{7}{16}$ × $16\frac{15}{16}$).

This picture was apparently commissioned by van der Werff's patron, the Elector Palatine, Johann Wilhem (see PROVENANCE). It can probably he identified with a painting of this subject listed under the date 1706 in a manuscript of autobiographical notes in the artists own hand: 'een Slapend Christusje met Maria en Joseph, te Romen aen seker cardinael vereet door den Ceurvost.'[4]

ENGRAVING: Mezzotinted by Pieter van Bleeck, 1748 (reversed).[5]

VERSION: A version or copy, with rounded top, was in the collection of Chevalier Sébastien Erard, Passy, 1831,[6] and in the Erard sale, Paris, 23 sqq. April 1832 (lot 168), 1,110 francs. A (late?) copy with rounded top and minor variations was in the J. C. F. Gundrey sale, London, 14 May 1958 (lot 149).[7]

PROVENANCE: Presented by the Elector Palatine Johann Wilhelm to Cardinal Pietro Ottoboni, apparently in 1707.[8] Cardinal Ottoboni died in February 1740; No. 3909 was probably bought at the sale of his collection in Rome by Dr Robert Bragge,[9] by whom it was brought to England;[10] in a Dr [Robert] Bragge sale in London in 1742 (1741 O.S.), lot 46, sold for £156.[11] By 1748 it was in the collection of the Revd Dr Newton[12] (presumably Dr Thomas Newton who became Bishop of Bristol in 1761 and died in 1782).[13] It was later in the collection of Welbore Ellis Agar and is in the catalogue of the Agar sale announced for 2–3 May 1806 in London (2nd day, lot 50), but the whole collection was bought before that date by the 2nd Earl Grosvenor[14] (later 1st Marquess of Westminster). In the collection at Grosvenor House, London.[15] Duke of Westminster sale, London, 4 July 1924 (lot 60), bought by A. de Casseres (210 gns), from whom purchased (with the aid of the Florence Fund) in 1924.

EXHIBITIONS: BI 1834, No. 118; London 1976, No. 123.

REFERENCES:

General: Smith No. 70; HdG No. 54; Gaehtgens No. 69.

In text:

1. Not 1705 as HdG states (loc. cit.).

2. The arms vary slightly from those given in J. B. Rietstap, *Armorial général*, 1950 ed., vol. 4, p. 1073, but are identical with those in Jacob Houbraken's engraving after a self portrait of van der Werff in Houbraken, vol. 3, pl. O (opposite p. 388).

3. A laurel wreath over a palette and brushes; above is the motto: QUEM PROBANT NOBILITANT, below: A. V. WERFF/EQUES. It seem to have been van der Werff's practice to affix his seals to his pictures; e.g. both are on the back of the Mauritshuis *Flight into Egypt* of 1710 (see Mauritshuis 1977 catalogue, No. 209) and the *Self Portrait* of 1699 in the Rijksmuseum, Amsterdam (1976 catalogue, No. A465).

4. The document is in the Historisch Museum, Rotterdam. It is transcribed in full in Gaehtgens, op. cit., Document No. 5, pp. 440–1.

5. Inscribed '1748 PVB [in monogram] / Done from one of the most capital Pictures of the Chevalier Vander Werf which was painted in / the Year 1706 for the Elector Palatin, who presented it to the Cardinal Ottoboni at Rome, after whose death it / was brought into England by Robert Bragge MD., and is now in the Collection of Rev[d] D[r] Newton.' (Published in *Recueil Baran*, vol. 2, 1762, p. 149.) Smith (No. 68) mentions an 'anonymous' mezzotint after the same design; according to him it was engraved from a painting then in the collection of '- - Bragge Esq.' and he seems to imply that this picture was on panel, 25½ × 17 in., and had an arched top. The wri-

ter has been unable to trace any such anonymous mezzotint and it appears quite likely that Smith is referring to van Bleeck's print which, as its inscription shows, is certainly after the National Gallery picture. HdG (No. 52), who did not know that No. 3909 had been in Bragge's possession, supposed the anonymous mezzotint to be after the arch-topped version or copy which was in the Erard collection (see VERSION).

6. *Catalogue des tableaux . . . de M. le Chevalier Erard*, 1831, No. 168: panel, 24 × 16 *pouces*.

7. Panel, 65 × 43 cm.; photographs in the National Gallery archives. According to the sale catalogue it is Smith No. 68; it also claims to be from the collection of W. Bragge, but see note 4.

8. On the back of the panel is an old inscription in ink: 'Wander Werff / Dusseldorf anno 1707 / Donato al Card[le] Ottoboni / dal(...) Sig(e?) Elettore / Palatino / Per mano di / Mons[r] Stefano Vescovo (......)a.' Since the painting is dated distinctly 1706, the date 1707 presumably refers to the time of the gift. Pietro Ottoboni was made a cardinal in 1689; his property was sold after his death (see G. Moroni, *Dizionario di erudizione storico-ecclesiastica*, vol. 50, 1851, p. 73).

9. According to the title-page of the catalogue of the sale by private contract of paintings belonging to Dr Newton (Bishop of Bristol), Richard Cumberland and others, London, 8 April sqq. 1788, some of the pictures possessed by Dr Newton (who owned No. 3909; see PROVENANCE) were bought by Dr Bragge 'at the sale of the late Cardinal Ottoboni's collection in Rome'.

10. See note 5.

11. 'A Reposo, a present from yᵉ Elec. Pal. to C. Ottoboni Van der Werff' (see also F. Simpson in BM, vol. 95, 1953, p. 42). This sale is not recorded in Lugt, and is only known from a partial copy in a MS volume of extracts from eighteenth-century sale catalogues in the Victoria and Albert Museum Library (press mark: R. C. S. I.; pp. 162–3); the day and month of the sale are not given.

12. According to the inscription of van Bleeck's engraving (see note 5).

13. It was not among those of Dr Thomas New-ton's pictures exhibited for sale by private contract in London, 8 April sqq. 1788, nor in his picture sales at Christie's, 30 April 1790 and 22 March 1794.

14. See the foreword to the catalogue of the sale of pictures from the Grosvenor and Welbore Ellis Agar collections, London, 27 June 1807.

15. J. Young, *Catalogue of the Pictures at Grosvenor House*, n.d. [1821], No. 121 (with a small engraving opposite p. 39); *Catalogue of the Collection . . . at Grosvenor House*, 1913, No. 64.

JACOB DE WET the Elder,
active 1632; died after 5 September 1675

Jacob Willemsz. de Wet (he occasionally spells his name *de Wett*) known as Jacob de Wet the Elder to distinguish him from his son, Jacob(us) Jacobsz. de Wet. He was apparently a native of Haarlem;[1] the birth date usually given, *c.*1610, is apparently conjectured from the date of his first marriage (1635). He was active as a painter by 1632[2] and married in Haarlem in May 1635.[3] He was in Amsterdam March/April 1636[4] but was also living in Haarlem in that year.[5] He is presumably *not* the 'Jacobus de Wit' who was inscribed in the guild in Alkmaar in 1637,[6] nor is there any reason to identify him with the Jan de Wet, said to have been born in Hamburg in or about 1617, who was a pupil of Rembrandt.[7] He is mentioned in Haarlem records fairly often from 1638 to 1668[8] (and was a *hoofdman* of the guild there in 1645 and 1660, and dean in 1661).[9] He is documented in Haarlem in 1673 and 5 September 1675;[10] there is no later record of him.

His pictures are almost all religious and mythological subjects, often in a landscape setting; their style suggests he may have been a pupil of Rembrandt in the 1630s. Very occasionally he painted pure landscape, such as No. 1342 below, and in his sketchbook there are drawings of views around Haarlem. His son, Jacobus de Wet the Younger (*c.*1641–97), at first imitated him closely.[11]

REFERENCES:

General: P. van Meurs in OH, vol. 18, 1900, pp. 227 ff; Bredius in OH, vol. 37, 1919, pp. 215–22. [Sumowski, *Gemälde*, vol. 4.]

In text:

1. See van der Willigen, p. 329, and van Meurs, op. cit., p. 227.

2. A painting of *Paul and the Magician Bar-Jesus before the Proconsul Sergius Paulus* (Acts 13: 6–12), panel 79 × 63 cm., signed and dated 1632, was in the Raedt van Oldenbarnevelt sale, Amsterdam (F. Muller), 6 November 1900 (lot 144). There is a signed painting of 1633 in the Landesmuseum, Darmstadt.

3. Van Meurs, loc. cit.

4. OH, 1886, p. 300.

5. According to van der Willigen, loc. cit.

6. Obreen, vol. 2, p. 30.

7. Kramm, vol. 6, pp. 1845–6, and Thieme/Becker, vol. 35, p. 458.

8. OH, 1919, pp. 219–21.

9. Van der Willigen, pp. 21–2 and 324.

10. OH, 1919, pp. 221–2.

11. There are pictures by the son signed De Wet Jong and Jong de Wet which are otherwise indistinguishable from his father's work.

1342 *A Landscape with a River at the Foot of a Hill* Plate 410

Signed, bottom right: J.d. Wet (partly painted out).

Oil on oak, 53 × 72.5 (20$\frac{7}{8}$ × 28$\frac{9}{16}$).

Many retouchings in the sky, and along the horizontal join.

The right half of the picture is repeated with variations in the right background of Jacob de Wet's *Abraham giving the Shewbread to Melchizedek* in the National Gallery of Ireland, Dublin.[1] In composition and palette No. 1342 is similar to the signed and dated *Eliezer and Rebecca* of 1646 in Leningrad[2] and so a date of *c.*1646 is acceptable. This is the only known landscape by de Wet without biblical figures. He made landscape drawings in his Haarlem Sketchbook (Gemeente Archief, Haarlem, Hs 230).

PROVENANCE: In the collection of Edward Habich, Cassel, and exhibited with other pictures from that collection in the Gemäldegalerie, Cassel, for some years before 1891. It appears in the catalogue of the Edward Habich sale, Cassel, 9–10 May 1892 (lot 160), but was purchased, together with Nos. 1336–48, by the National Gallery in 1891.

REFERENCES:
General: [Sumowski, op. cit., No. 1871.]
In text:
1. Dublin, Dutch Paintings, No. 1315. [Sumowski, op. cit., No. 1866.]
2. 1958 cat. no. 3011. [Sumowski, op. cit., No. 1841.]

For JAN WIJNANTS *See* pp. 503–6

EMANUEL DE WITTE, 1615/17–1691 or 1692

On pictures he invariably spells his name *De Witte*; in documents he signs *De Wit* as often as *De Witte*. He was born in Alkmaar;[1] the date given by Houbraken,[2] 1607, is certainly wrong since in July 1639 de Witte is said to be about twenty-three, in August 1656 'about forty', in September 1659 'about forty-two' and in October 1673 'about fifty-five'. He entered the Alkmaar guild in 1636; by July 1639 he was in Rotterdam and is mentioned there again in June 1640. By October 1641 he was presumably living in Delft since a daughter of his was then baptised there, and he became a member of the Delft guild in June 1642; he is recorded there in 1644, 1646, 1647 and 1649. In March 1650 he rented a house in Delft for a year and may, therefore, have continued to live there until at least spring 1651. A note in the Delft guild records, apparently made not long after, says he has left Delft and he was apparently in Amsterdam in January 1652; he was betrothed there in September 1655. He probably spent the rest of his life in Amsterdam (he is documented there fairly often from 1656 to 1673 and again in 1683 and 1687). In 1658 he was painting a picture for the King of Denmark.[3] He died in Amsterdam. Houbraken[4] says he apparently committed suicide, and was found in an Amsterdam canal that had been frozen ever since his disappearance eleven weeks before; since Houbraken says de Witte was buried in 1692 he must have died late in 1691 or early in 1692.

According to Houbraken, de Witte was a pupil of the still-life painter Evert van Aelst (1602–57) in Delft.[5] De Witte began as a figure painter;[6] his earliest known pictures, a *Danae* of 1641 (London, private collection)[7] and a *Vertumnus and Pomona* of 1644 (Rotterdam, Boymans-van Beuningen Museum)[8] seem to show the influence of the Utrecht School. Two small portraits of 1648 (also in Rotterdam)[9] are more in the style of ter Borch's miniature portraits of that period. A *Holy Family* of 1650[10] is in the manner of Dou. Only after 1650 does he seem to have devoted himself to painting the church interiors which form the greater part of his work. His earliest picture of this kind with a certain date is of 1651; it is close to the new kind of church interior that Gerrit Houckgeest had begun to paint by that year and Hendrick van Vliet by 1652.[11] After 1650 de Witte painted besides church interiors (most of which are partly or wholly imaginary) a few domestic interiors and fanciful views of harbours; after 1660 he also painted some market scenes, in which portraits are sometimes introduced (e.g. No. 3682 below). Houbraken[12] says he was 'famed for his knowledge of perspective'. After 1660 de Witte put himself at various times under contract to paint in return for his keep; this may explain the markedly varied quality of his later work. The last-known dated picture is of 1689.

REFERENCES:

General: I. Manke, *Emanuel de Witte 1617–1692*, Amsterdam, 1963 (for the artist's biography see pp. 1–6: the documents are given in full on pp. 63–71. With all previous literature); ibid., in *Pantheon*, 1972, pp. 389 ff.

In text:

1. According to the entry of his betrothal in the Amsterdam marriage register, 1655: so also Houbraken, vol. 1, p. 282.

2. Loc. cit.

3. Houbraken (p. 284) says two pictures were ordered from de Witte for the King of Denmark.

4. Op. cit., p. 287.

5. Op. cit., p. 283.

6. See also Houbraken, p. 283.

7. Manke, op. cit., cat. no. 5.

8. Manke, op. cit., cat. no. 3.

9. Manke, op. cit., cat. nos. 8, 9.

10. Manke, op. cit., cat. no. 1.

11. For an extended discussion of the relationship between these three church painters, see W. Liedtke, *Architectural Painting in Delft*, Doornspijk, 1982.

12. Op. cit., vol. 2, p. 81.

1053 *The Interior of the Oude Kerk, Amsterdam, during a Sermon*   *Plate 411*

In the upper part of the left and centre windows are coats-of-arms; that of the city of Amsterdam is in the centre.

Oil on canvas, 51.1 × 56.2 (20$\frac{1}{8}$ × 22$\frac{1}{8}$).

Cleaned in 1970. Some wearing in the darks in the lower half of the picture.

The gilding round the panels of the organ gallery and of the corbel on the extreme left, above, is in gold leaf or gold paint.

This is a fairly accurate view of the nave and north aisle of the Oude Kerk (St Nicholas) in Amsterdam, taken from a point slightly to the west of the south entrance. The painter has taken certain liberties with the architecture; he has suppressed the triforium gallery and a pew round the column in the right foreground similar to that on the left; he has made the columns much taller and more slender than they actually are, and the windows of the north aisle broader. The window tracery in the church has since been altered by restoration but the pulpit and the small organ in the north aisle remain as seen here.

The church is seen from the opposite side of the nave in No. 6402 (below).

The picture cannot have been painted before 1658 since it shows the small organ after the renovation of 1658 or 1659.[1] Manke[2] dates the painting to c.1660.

PROVENANCE: Said to have been in the collection of Edward Solly[3] (d. before June 1837). In the William Beckford (d. May 1844) sale, Lansdown Tower, Bath, 20 sqq. November 1845 (lot 337),[4] 47 gns. In the collection of Misses Lavinia and Sarah Solly by 1873;[5] Miss Sarah Solly Bequest, 1879.

REFERENCES:
General: Manke, op. cit., No. 49.
In text:
1. Various inaccurate dates have been given for the renovation of the small organ (e.g. in *Voorlopige Lijst der Nederlandsche Monumenten van Geschiedenis en Kunst*, vol. 5, part ii, 1928, p. 42) but M. Fokkens (*Beschrijvinge der Wijdt-Vermaarde Koop-stadt Amstelredam*, 1662, pp. 186–7) says that the large organ was reconstructed in the years 1660 and 1661 and the small one two years earlier, the outer sides of the latter's doors being painted with musical instruments by Cornelis Brisé ('In deze Kerk zijn twee Orgelen, een groot en een kleynder, 't groote is nu in 't Jaar 1660. en 1661. op nieuws weer heerlijkker opgemaakt . . . Het kleyne is ook twee Jaar te vooren heel kunstigh van nieuws opgemaakt, en nu veel heerlijkker dan oyt te vooren, 't is met cierlijk houtwerk kunstight gewrocht, met Engelen en Stadts Wapens alom vergult, met groote Galderyen . . . de Deuren zijn van buyten door C. Brisée geschildert, zoo kunstigh met Luyten, Bassen, Violen, Fluyten', etc.). Approximately the same dates are given in Filips von Zesen's *Beschreibung der Stadt Amsterdam*, 1664, p. 339: 'Auch hat man alhier zwo schöne Orgeln: eine grosse, und eine kleine; welche man allee beide, jene um das 1660 jahr, diese aber ohngefähr zwei jahr zuvor, erneuert und herlich ausgezieret . . .' (This passage has been misread and von Zesen's accuracy unnecessarily questioned by A. Noach, *De Oude Kerk te Amsterdam*, 1939, pp. 118, 193, etc.) The small organ appears again in several de Witte interiors of the Oude Kerk: e.g. *before* reconstruction in a painting dated 1654 (or more probably, 9): Manke, op. cit., No. 44; *after* reconstruc-

tion in pictures dated 1659 (Hamburg Kunsthalle: Manke, op. cit., No. 70) and 1660 (Manke, op. cit., No. 75).
2. Manke, op. cit.
3. According to Miss Sarah Solly (in her will dated 1873) the picture was from the Beckford collection and had belonged to her father, Edward Solly. Her executor, William Shaen, Edward Solly's nephew, did not believe it had ever been in the Solly collection (letter of 1879 in the National Gallery archives). It was not in any of the Solly sales, 1825–47, listed in Lugt, vols. 1 and 2, nor was it in the Solly sale, London, 30 May 1863, the S. R. Solly sale, London, 11–12 April 1867, or the S. and J. Solly sale, London, 11 November 1871.
4. 'De Wit. Interior of a Cathedral, with Figures habited in the dresses of the times. The period chosen is when the clergyman is delivering his sermon.' The name of the purchaser is not given in the only two recorded marked copies of the sale catalogue (see Lugt, op. cit.) but in that which belonged to E. K. Waterhouse this lot is noted as 'sold' whereas several others are marked 'bought in' (letter of 1955 from F. Simpson). On canvas, 20 × 22 in. This picture is not to be confused with lot 48 of the William Beckford sale, Bath, 24 sqq. July 1848; though the descriptions in the sale catalogues are word for word the same, the picture in the 1848 sale measured $17\frac{1}{4} \times 13\frac{1}{4}$ in. In a list of Beckford's paintings, of 1844, there are two pictures described as 'Interior of a Church with Figures' by de Witte, one of them a 'Small Upright' (inventory in the possession of the Duke of Hamilton).
5. Miss Solly's will, naming this picture, is dated January 1873.

3682 *Adriana van Huesden and her Daughter at the New Fishmarket in Amsterdam(?)*

Plate 412

The large vessel in the left background has a Dutch flag and pennant; the smaller vessel at the quay has a red and white vane.

Oil on canvas, 57.1×64.1 ($22\frac{1}{2} \times 25\frac{1}{4}$).

Cleaned in 1971.

The picture has been identified,[1] almost certainly correctly, with one painted by de Witte *c.*1661–3 which, with three others, was the subject of litigation between the painter and Adriana van Heusden in 1669–71. (The arguments in support of this identification are given below.) Some time after 1658 de Witte went to live in the house of Joris de Wijs, an Amsterdam notary, who contracted to feed and lodge him and pay him 800 guilders a year in return for all the pictures he might paint while in his house.[2] Among those painted there for de Wijs was one described as a small picture of the New Fishmarket near the Haarlem Lock in Amsterdam, in which was a portrait of de Wijs's wife, Adriana van Heusden, with her little daughter;[3] it was seen at de Wijs's house by Pieter de Hooch and another painter, Hieronymus Pickaart.[4] By September 1663 de Witte had gone to live elsewhere[5] and had taken with him four pictures, including the one with Adriana van Heusden's portrait;[6] he afterwards lodged with Laurens Mauritsz. Doucy in whose house the picture was seen by various people about 1664–5.[7] According to de Hooch, Doucy's son sold it about 1667 to a painter, Johannes Collaert,[8] who paid de Witte's debts with Doucy in 1667.[9] About 1668 an ebony frame was made for the picture.[10] In 1669 Adriana van Heusden and her second husband, Johan or Johannes van Heden, claimed the four pictures de Witte had taken away because they had been painted in her first husband's house and therefore belonged to her by the terms of the painter's agreement with de Wijs.[11] De Witte was ordered by a court in November 1669 to hand over the four pictures to van Heden or pay him 450 guilders compensation,[12] but did not do so. In May 1670 Collaert sent the picture of Adriana and two others to the Heerenlogement in Amsterdam for sale, but the sale was stopped and the pictures attached by van Heden.[13] On 6 April 1671 de Witte promised to return the pictures or indemnify van Heden[14] and a few days later (10 April) Collaert signed a document stating that he had sold the picture of Adriana to de Witte;[15] this may have been untrue, to judge by their subsequent actions. On 14 April de Witte agreed that before he gave back the four pictures he would complete the two unfinished ones, alter another to suit Adriana's taste and freshen up and restore the picture of Adriana in the fishmarket[16] which had become mildewy.[17] De Witte, however, was evidently determined not to give up the last-mentioned picture since he asked Collaert to substitute for the original, which was still at the Heerenlogement, a copy then in the latter's house. Collaert at first refused to do this, whereupon de Witte threatened that he would receive nothing for the picture. Collaert therefore bought from someone in Amsterdam a *second* copy which he took to the Heerenlogement; he removed the original from its frame on the pretext of cleaning it, replaced it by the copy and took it away to his house where it still was in June 1671.[18] The subsequent history of this affair is not known but since it was at the request of Johannes van Heden that Collaert made a deposition confessing his trick it seems possible that Adriana and her husband may eventually have succeeded in recovering the disputed painting.

There are many reasons for supposing that the National Gallery fishmarket scene is that painted for Joris de Wijs. The housewife buying fish is obviously a portrait. This and the replica discussed below are the only de Witte fishmarket scenes that also contain a portrait of a little girl. The picture of Adriana cannot have been painted before the early part of 1661, when the New Fishmarket opened,[19] or later than the summer of 1663, since de Witte had left her house by the beginning of September in that year and she could have laid no claim to the picture if it had been painted afterwards. The present composition is the only known one by de Witte with a woman's portrait in which the costume is of the early 60s; the replica is, in fact, dated 1662. Lastly, although no identifiable building is visible, the view in the background is over open water, as would be the case if this were the New Fishmarket in Amsterdam which lay between the Haarlem Lock and the open harbour in the IJ (see Hobbema No. 6138).

The picture, which at one time bore a false de Hooch signature,[20] was acquired as a work of de Witte and so catalogued in 1925. In 1923 there came to light a replica (Fig. 120) signed (or inscribed): E. De. Witte (A?) 1662 (see COPIES AND VERSIONS); this was taken to be the original of the design and the National Gallery version was consequently catalogued in 1929 as a copy. Despite the signature, however, this replica (which is damaged[21]) is distinctly inferior to No. 3682 in quality and is either a weaker repetition by de Witte, or, as E. Trautscholdt has suggested, a contemporary copy;[22] in this connection the two copies mentioned in the lawsuit in 1671 come to mind. Manke, on the other hand, believes the National Gallery painting to be a contemporary copy and the other version the original.[23] The National Gallery picture is, without doubt, not only an original by de Witte but of exceptional quality among his genre pieces. Hofstede de Groot accepted it as the work of de Witte except for the three principal figures which he thought more probably by Bartholomeus van der Helst.[24] They are, however, completely acceptable as de Witte's, although the portraits of the housewife and the child may imply acquaintance with van der Helst's portraiture.

Both style and costume support a date in the first half of the 60s. If it is the picture of Adriana van Heusden the date can be narrowed down to 1661–3 and whether or not the date 1662 on the replica is genuine this may well be the year in which No. 3682 was painted.

COPIES AND VERSIONS: Two contemporary copies of the picture painted for Joris de Wijs were in the hands of Johannes Collaert in Amsterdam in 1671 (see above). A replica (or copy?; see above) of No. 3682, signed and dated 1662, was in the collection of E. Hockliffe, London, by 1923;[25] it was bought in London by A. S. Drey of Munich c.1928 and sold by 1929, to Henry Blank, Newark, USA;[26] and was in the Henry Blank sale, New York, 16 November 1949 (lot 26).

PROVENANCE: As suggested above, this is probably the picture of the New Fishmarket, painted c.1661–3 for Joris de Wijs of Amsterdam, which was in the house of Laurens Mauritsz. Doucy there by c.1664–5, sold by his son in 1667 to Johannes Collaert, also of Amsterdam, and still in the latter's possession in 1671 although claimed since 1669 by Adriana van Heusden and her husband, Johannes van Heden. A painting of 'the fishmarket by the Haarlem Lock at Amsterdam' by de Witte was in the David Jetswaart sale, Amsterdam, 22 April 1749 (lot 270), 15 guilders.[27] No. 3682 or a picture of almost identical composition was in the Prince de Conti sale, Paris, 8 April–6 June 1777 (lot 334), and again in the [Prince de Conti] sale, Paris, 15 sqq. March 1779 (lot 139), bought by Duquesnoy (122 francs); each time as by Metsu.[28] The National Gallery picture was apparently in the Thomas Henry sale, Paris, 23–25 May 1836 (lot 52), attributed to P. de Hooch[29] (900 francs), and was probably also in the [Louis Thielens of Brussels] sale, Paris, 27 March 1841 (lot 26),[30] 800 francs. No. 3682 appeared as a P. de Hooch in the Charles Scarisbrick sale, London, 11 sqq. May 1861 (lot 211),[31] bought by Seguier (52 gns). It is said to have been in the Watson Taylor collection at Erlestoke Park, near Devizes, from about 1863 as a Jan Steen; it was sold as such in the Simon Watson Taylor sale at Erlestoke Park in November 1919 (£1,600), being acquired apparently about 1922 by Messrs Agnew,[32] from whom it was bought in October 1922.

REFERENCES:

General: Manke, op. cit., No. 222a.

In text:

1. C. Misme in GB-A, 1923, i, pp. 148–50.

2. Bredius, *Künstler-Inventare*, vol. 5, pp. 1837–8.

3. The description varies in the documents relating to the lawsuit: viz. 'een stukje schilderij . . . uytbeeldende de nieuwe Vismarkt, aan de Haarlemmer Sluys, van Heusden' (see OH, vol. 7, 1889, p. 166); 'de Nieuwe Vismarct van dese stadt Amsterdam, daerin geschildert staet de Wed[uwe] van Joris de Wijs' (loc. cit.); 'een stuckien daerinne deselve Wedue van de Wijs met haer dochtertie in geconterfeijt staet' (*Künstler-Inventare*, vol. 5, p. 1839); 'seecker stuckien schilderije sijnde het conterfaytsel van J^e Adriana van Heusden' (*Künstler-Inventare*, vol. 5, p. 1840). Despite the variations, it is clear from the documents that all refer to the same picture.

4. According to a declaration made by them in November 1670 (OH, vol. 7, 1889, p. 166).

5. According to a declaration made in that month by Adriana at the request of de Witte (*Künstler-Inventare*, vol. 5, p. 1834).

6. The other three paintings were a fishmarket with the Jan Rodenpoort tower, a small interior of a church during a sermon and a small winter piece (see *Künstler-Inventare*, vol. 5, pp. 1837–9 and 1841); the last two were unfinished (op. cit., p. 1839, but see also note 16).

7. OH, vol. 7, 1889, p. 166.

8. According to de Hooch's testimony of November 1670 (OH, 1889, pp. 166–7).

9. *Künstler-Inventare*, vol. 5, p. 1835.

10. OH, 1889, p. 166.

11. *Künstler-Inventare*, vol. 5, p. 1837.

12. Ibid., p. 1839.

13. OH, 1889, p. 166, and *Künstler-Inventare*, vol. 5, p. 1840.

14. *Künstler-Inventare*, vol. 5, p. 1839.

15. Ibid., p. 1840.

16. Ibid., p. 1841–2. In this document the two unfinished pictures are said to be the market with the Jan Rodenpoort tower and the winter scene (but see note 6 above).

17. Ibid., p. 1844.

18. Ibid., p. 1844.

19. See Hobbema No. 6138, note 6.

20. See note 31.

21. See the 1925 National Gallery catalogue and C. J. Holmes in *Commemorative Catalogue of the Exhibition of Dutch Art . . . Royal Academy (1929)*, 1930, p. xxiv.

22. In Thieme/Becker, vol. 36, p. 123. HdG (*Repertorium für Kunstwissenschaft*, vol. 50, 1929, p. 144) considers it a replica of equal quality.

23. Manke, op. cit.

24. HdG, loc. cit.

25. Canvas, 57 × 64 cm. Letters of 1923 and 1925 from E. Hockliffe are in the National Gallery archives. A photograph taken when the picture was in E. Hockliffe's collection shows that it was an almost exact replica of No. 3682. Some minor details have since been altered by restoration; the head of the old man behind the old woman in shadow in the centre, originally the same as in No. 3682, is now quite different.

26. Letter of 10 March 1953 from Mrs M. H. Drey (in the National Gallery archives). Exhibited in Detroit, October–November 1929 (No. 78), lent by Henry Blank. Reproduced in the Detroit exhibition catalogue and the Blank 1949 sale catalogue.

27. Hoet, vol. 2, p. 255.

28. Canvas, 21 × 23 *pouces*. There is a thumbnail sketch of the picture, by Saint-Aubin, in a copy of the 1779 sale catalogue (reproduced in *Catalogues de ventes . . . illustrés par Gabriel de Saint-Aubin*, edited by E. Dacier, vol. 10, 1919).

29. HdG, P. de Hooch No. 284, has the wrong measurements; the Henry sale catalogue gives the size as 21 *pouces* × 23 *pouces* 6 *lignes*.

30. 'DEHOOG (P). Le marché aux poissons; c'est un portrait exact des marchands et des acheteurs de la Hollande où . . . les deux classes ont encore conservé leur costume. Une belle bourgeoise hollandaise se présente à la boutique d'une vendeuse de poisson; elle est richement assortie et semble dire à la dame: vous perdrez vos pas et vous ne trouverez mieux que chez moi. En effet, le saumon, la raie, le cabilleau et tous les poissons de mer sont d'une beauté qui doit décider en sa faveur. Nous avons eu déja occasion de voir ce tableau en vente, et toujours il a été regardé comme un bon tableau de Dehoog.' Mme C. Misme (op. cit., p. 147) has supposed this to be the de Witte now in the Museum Boymans-van Beuningen, Rotterdam, but this is impossible since the Rotterdam picture was still in the Montcalm collection at the time of the Thielens sale (*Description des Tableaux . . . de l'Hotel de Montcalm*, 1836, No. 52; Montcalm Gallery sale, London, 4–5 May 1849, lot 96, bought by Anthony; each time as by P. de Hooch). The Rotterdam picture was earlier in the C---- (of Switzerland) sale, Paris, 27 May 1835 (lot 5), as by P. de Hooch; it was bought for the Boymans Museum in London, 7 April 1864.

31. 'P. DE HOOGHE. [In the auctioneer's copy of the sale catalogue the name is crossed out and 'De Witte' substituted in manuscript.] A fisherman's hut; a lady with a child conversing with a fisherman [sic] at a stall, shaded by an awning, other figures seen behind, and a seashore in the background. Signed by the Master.' Despite the discrepancies in this description there can be no doubt that this is the National Gallery picture which has the markings for the Scarisbrick sale on the back.

32. See *The Times*, 5 February 1923. The writer has not been able to consult a copy of the 1919 sale catalogue.

6402 The Interior of the Oude Kerk, Amsterdam, during a Sermon

Plate 413

Signed, lower right: E de Witte.

Oil on canvas, 79.1 × 63.1 ($31\frac{3}{16}$ × $24\frac{13}{16}$).

Some wearing in the darks.

The uppermost glass in the right-hand window bears the arms of the city of Amsterdam; the glass in the central window depicts the four Evangelists with their emblems.

The view is of the nave and south aisle of the Old Church (St Nicholas) in Amsterdam from a point in the north aisle, almost exactly opposite the point from which No. 1053 is taken. As in that picture, the scene has been slightly altered by de Witte: for example, the small organ – shown correctly, in the north aisle, in No. 1053 – has here been transposed to the south aisle. As with No. 1053 the appearance of the organ[1] suggests a date soon after 1658–9. Manke[2] dates the picture *c*.1660.

PROVENANCE: James Whatman sale, Christie's, 2 July 1887 (lot 14), as 'E de Witt and Terburg: Interior of the Cortz Kirch [sic], Amsterdam'. Bought by Colnaghi from whom purchased by W. C. Alexander. Passed by descent to the Misses Rachel F. and Jean I. Alexander, who presented it by deed of gift to the National Gallery; entered the collection in 1972.

EXHIBITIONS: RA 1938, No. 207; RA 1952–3, No. 625; Utrecht, Centraal Museum, 'Nederlandse architectuurschilders 1600–1900', 1953, No. 114; London 1972; London 1976, No. 126; Edinburgh, National Gallery of Scotland, 'Dutch Church Painters', 1984, No. 36.

REFERENCES:
General: Manke, op. cit., No. 53; A. Smith, 'Presented by the Misses Rachel F. and Jean I. Alexander: Seventeen Paintings for the National Gallery', B.M., vol. 114, 1972, p. 634.

In text:
1. See under No. 1053, above.
2. Manke, op. cit.

JAN WOUWERMANS, 1629–1666

Jan Pauwelsz. Wouwerman or *Wouwermans*, the youngest brother of Philips Wouwermans (see his biographical notice for the spelling of the name), was baptised in Haarlem, 30 October 1629.[1] He entered the Haarlem painters' guild in May 1655 and is recorded in Haarlem in 1656, 1659, 1660.[2] He died there, (27?) November 1666 (buried 1 December).[3]

Not many works by him are known; most of them are landscapes in the style of Jan Wijnants (like No. 1345 below) and show the typical dune scenery near Haarlem; others are reminiscent of his brother, Philips Wouwermans, and Jacob van Ruisdael. He also painted some winter landscapes and there is a view of the Grote Kerk of Haarlem in the Frans Halsmuseum in Haarlem.

REFERENCES:
1. Van der Willigen, p. 337.
2. Van der Willigen, p. 341.
3. Kramm, Supplement, 1864, p. 166, and van der Willigen, loc. cit.

1345 *A Landscape with a Farm on the Bank of a River*   *Plate 414*

Signed at the bottom, right of centre: Jwouwerman (Jw linked).

Oil on oak, 40 × 55.7 ($15\frac{3}{4}$ × $21\frac{15}{16}$).

PROVENANCE: Count Potocki sale, Paris, 8 May 1884 (lot 58). No. 1345 or a copy was in Moll sale, Cologne (Lempertz), 11 November 1886 (lot 193).[1] In the collection of Edward Habich, Cassel, and exhibited for some years in the Gemäldegalerie, Cassel. It appears in the catalogue of the Edward Habich sale, Cassel, 9–10 May 1892 (lot 164), but was bought from Habich in 1891 by the National Gallery, together with Nos. 1336–48.

REFERENCE: 1. The photograph in the sale catalogue shows the painting in reverse.

PHILIPS WOUWERMANS, 1619–1668

Philips Wouwermans or *Wouwerman*, eldest son of a painter, Paulus (Pauwels) Joosten Wouwerman(s), was baptised in Haarlem, 24 May 1619.[1] Various spellings of the surname occur in the seventeenth century and later but the only ones used by Philips and his brothers are *Wouwerman* and *Wouwermans*.[2] He may have been a pupil of his father[3] (who died in September 1642[4]); according to Cornelis de Bie[5] he studied with Frans Hals. He is said to have run away to Hamburg to marry at the age of nineteen (i.e. in 1638 or 1639) and to have worked there for some weeks with Evert Decker[6] (active 1630; died 1647; painter of religious and historical subjects). He became a member of the guild in Haarlem in September 1640;[7] he was one of the officers of the Haarlem guild in 1645.[8] The earliest known dated picture (of which there are very few) is of 1644.[9] He appears to have spent the rest of his life in Haarlem and died there on 19 May 1668[10] (buried 23 May[11]).

His early works seem to show some stylistic connections with Jan Wijnants and Pieter Verbeeck but it is not clear who was the originator in either case. He appears to have been influenced by Pieter van Laer ('Bamboccio'; 1592/5–1642) and indeed Houbraken accused him of plagiarism from the latter.[12] He was very productive; besides the many landscapes, usually with horses (and especially battles, camps and hunts), there are a few religious and mythological subjects. He had great contemporary success and is said to have been able to leave his daughter a dowry of 20,000 guilders.[13] He had many followers; his paintings were much sought after in France in the eighteenth century and many were engraved there by Jean Moyreau (1690–1762).

REFERENCES:

General: HdG, vol. 2.
In text:
1. Van der Willigen, p. 337.
2. Cf. Bredius, vol. 16, pp. 37–8.
3. Cf. Houbraken, vol. 2, p. 70.
4. Van der Willigen, loc. cit.
5. *Het Gulden Cabinet*, 1661, p. 281.
6. According to a note written in 1679 by Mathias Scheits in his copy of Carel van Mander; Scheits, a Hamburg painter, had been a pupil of Wouwermans in Haarlem (*v.* Houbraken). See C. Vosmaer in *Kunstkronijk*, vol. 13, 1871, p. 12.
7. Van der Willigen, p. 336.
8. Van der Willigen, p. 339.

9. *Soldiers attacking a Carriage*, canvas, 107 × 144 cm. Signed and dated 1644. Vaduz, collection of the Prince of Liechtenstein.
10. Houbraken, p. 76.
11. Van der Willigen, p. 339.
12. Houbraken, pp. 73–5. See Utrecht 1965, note 23, p. 258; A. Blankert, 'Over Pieter van Laer als dier- en landschapschilder', OH, vol. 83, 1968, pp. 117–34: J. Michalkowa, 'Quelques remarques sur Pieter van Laer', OH, vol. 86, 1971, pp. 188–95.
13. Houbraken, p. 71.

878 *Cavalrymen halted at a Sutler's Booth* Plate 415

Signed near the bottom edge, towards the left: PHILS.W (PHILS in monogram).

Oil on oak, 51.5 × 41.7 (20¼ × 16⁷⁄₁₆).

Cleaned in 1959. Some wearing in the sky. There is a vertical damage near the top left-hand corner.

Probably a work of the 1650s.

ENGRAVING: Line-engraving (in reverse) by Jacques-Philippe Le Bas, 1740.[1]

PROVENANCE: In the collection of Duplex de Bacquencourt by 1740;[2] Comte de Dubarry sale, Paris, 21 sqq. November 1774 (lot 36), bought by Langlier (4,000 francs);[3] Poullain sale, Paris, 15 sqq. March 1780 (lot 55), bought by the Duc de Chabot[4] (3,641 francs). In the John Webb sale, London, 30–31 May 1821 (lot 161),[5] bought by (Sir) Robert Peel (Bart.), 210 gns. Purchased with the Peel collection, 1871.

EXHIBITIONS: BI 1821, No. 137(?);[6] BI 1822, No. 41(?).[7]

REFERENCES:

General: Smith No. 112; HdG No. 856.
In text:
1. In *Oeuvres de Ph. Wouvermens* [sic] . . . *gravées* . . . *J. Moyreau*, 1737 etc., No. 100 (as *Halte d'officiers*).
2. According to Le Bas's engraving (see note 1), 'Tiré du Cabinet de M' Duplex de Bacquencourt'.

3. See *Catalogues de ventes . . . illustrés par Gabriel de Saint-Aubin*, vol. 3, 1910.
4. C. Blanc, *Le trésor de la curiosité*, vol. 2, 1858, p. 10, gives Pailliet as the purchaser, but the marked copies of the sale catalogue in the Institut Doucet, Paris, and the RKD have 'Chabot' and 'Duc de Rohan Chabot' respectively. The picture was not in

any of the following sales: [Duc de Chabot], Paris, 23 sqq. May 1780; Duc de Ch[abot], Paris, 10 sqq. December 1787; [Duc de Chabot?], Paris, 17–22 December 1787; L.-A.-A. Rohan-Chabot, Paris, 8–9 December 1807.

5. As 'La Belle Laitière'. According to the Webb 1821 sale catalogue, the collection was formed in the previous fifteen years.

6. As 'A Landscape, with Travellers'. There was apparently no other Wouwermans of this description in Peel's collection before 1823.

7. As 'A Camp Scene, with Horses and Figures'; see also note 6.

879 The Interior of a Stable

Plate 416

Signed, bottom right: PHILS.W (PHILS in monogram).

Oil on canvas, 47 × 67 ($18\frac{1}{2}$ × $26\frac{3}{8}$). On all sides there is a further centimetre (approximately) of grey priming (formerly turned over the stretcher).

Wouwermans painted many stable interiors; very similar ones are in the Fitzwilliam Museum, Cambridge (HdG No. 478), Dresden (HdG No. 482) and Munich (HdG No. 493). The present picture is probably a work of the later 1650s.

COPY: A copy, apparently after No. 879, was in Anon. sale, London, 14 March 1829 (lot 52), bought by Pritchett (£17 6s 6d): 'Wouwermans: Interior of the Stable of an Inn, and Cavaliers settling their reckoning: repetition of the celebrated picture formerly in the collection of W. Smith, Esq.'

PROVENANCE: In the Servad sale, Amsterdam, 25 June 1778 (lot 121), bought by Fouquet (3,300 francs); Comte de Merle sale, Paris, 1 sqq. March 1784 (lot 62),[1] bought by Le Rouge (7,900 francs). It was apparently exhibited at the BI in 1818, lent by William Smith, MP.[2] In the George Watson Taylor sale, London, 13–14 June 1823 (2nd day, lot 59), bought by Emmerson (530 gns); in the collection of (Sir) Robert Peel (Bart.) by 1829.[3] Purchased with the Peel collection, 1871.

EXHIBITION: BI 1818, No. 66(?).[4]

REFERENCES:
General: Smith No. 171, HdG No. 491.
In text:
1. Blanc (op. cit., p. 93) referring to the Merle sale, says that the picture was engraved by Jean Moyreau and also in his own *Histoire des peintres de toutes les écoles*; it is, however, not in Moyreau's *Oeuvres de Ph. Wouvermens*, 1737–62, nor engraved separately by him, and the only engraving of a Wouwermans stable in Blanc's *Histoire* etc. (*Ecole Hollandaise*, part ii, p. 9) is after a similar picture now in the Dresden Gallery (HdG No. 482) which was, in fact, engraved by Moyreau in 1734 when in the Comtesse de Verrue's collection (op. cit., No. 15, as *L'Ecurie*). Furthermore, this engraving by Moyreau disposes of the suggestion made in the 1929 National Gallery catalogue that the present picture is the (only) Wouwermans *Stable* in the Comtesse de Verrue's sale, 27 March sqq. 1737 (lot 102; cf. Blanc, op. cit., vol. 1, p. 9) since the

print agrees exactly (in reverse) with the Dresden painting; nor can the National Gallery picture be, as suggested, the *Interior View of a Stable* in the [Delahante et al.] sale, London, 3 March 1810 (lot 108) since that is said in the sale catalogue to be from the Verrue collection.
2. Smith, loc. cit., says that the present picture was exhibited at the BI in 1818. He does not mention the owner at that time but the only Wouwermans stable interiors in the 1818 exhibition were No. 66, 'Stable, with horses and figures', lent by W. Smith, MP, and No. 119, 'Inside of a Stable, with horses and figures', lent by G. J. Cholmondeley; the description of the latter in the catalogue of the G. J. Cholmondeley sale (London, 23 April 1831) shows that it was not the National Gallery picture.
3. Smith, loc. cit.
4. See above, note 2.

880 *A View on a Seashore, with Fishwives offering Fish to a Horseman* *Plate 417*

Signed in the bottom right corner: PHILS. W (PHILS in monogram).

Oil on oak, 35.3 × 41.2 ($13\frac{7}{8}$ × $16\frac{3}{16}$).

Reputed to be the last picture painted by Wouwermans;[1] there seems to be no stylistic reason for this tradition.

COPY: A copy (in reverse) was in Anon. sale, Sotheby Parke Bernet, New York, 11 March 1977 (lot 10), as School of Philips Wouwermans.[2]

PROVENANCE: In the collection of Queen Isabella Farnese[3] (who married Philip V of Spain in 1714 and died in 1766); perhaps among the pictures removed from the Spanish royal palaces by the French, 1809–13.[4] It was apparently bought in Spain by George A. Wallis and consigned for sale to W. Buchanan, London, in 1813.[5] In the collection of Lord Charles Townshend by 1818, when it was exhibited at the BI; [Lord Charles Townshend] sale, London, 4 June 1819 (lot 29), bought by Rutley (305 gns). In the collection of Joseph Barchard and bought privately in 1823 by Thomas Emmerson;[6] sold by John Smith to (Sir) Robert Peel (Bart.),[7] by 1824.[8] Purchased with the Peel collection, 1871.

EXHIBITIONS: BI 1818, No. 20; London 1976, No. 127.

REFERENCES:
General: Smith No. 295; HdG No. 977.
In text:
1. This is first mentioned in the BI 1818 catalogue (No. 20); see also Buchanan, vol. 2, pp. 245 and 248, and Smith, loc. cit.
2. Panel, 32 × 43 cm.
3. The back of the panel is stamped with the royal arms surrounded by the legend: ELISABETH DEI GRATIA HISPANIARVM REGINA. Isabella acquired altogether eighteen paintings by Wouwermans (see P. de Madrazo, *Viaje artístico de tres siglos por las col-* *ecciones de cuadros de los reyes de España*, 1884, p. 191). Buchanan (loc. cit.) says that it was painted for Queen Isabella, but Wouwermans died twenty-four years before she was born!
4. Cf. P. de Madrazo, op. cit., chapter 19.
5. Buchanan, vol. 2, pp. 236–7 and 245. It was one of a number of pictures, some of which were bought for Buchanan and others entrusted to him for sale.
6. Smith, loc. cit.
7. Smith, loc. cit.
8. Buchanan, vol. 2, p. 248.

881 *A White Horse, and an Old Man binding Faggots* *Plate 418*

Signed, bottom left: W (there may be the remains of a PHILS monogram in front of the W).

Oil on oak, 31.8 × 26.3 ($12\frac{9}{16}$ × $10\frac{3}{8}$).

Apparently a work of Wouwermans' middle period.

PROVENANCE: In the Randon de Boisset sale, Paris, 27 February sqq. 1777 (lot 94), bought by Quesnet (2,740 francs). Mme Le Rouge sale, Paris, 27 sqq. April 1818 (lot 74), bought by Delahante (4,101 francs) who brought it to England and sold it to John Webb.[1] John Webb sale, London, 30–31 May 1821 (lot 165), bought in ?[2] (105 gns). In the second Fonthill Abbey sale, 10 sqq. October 1823 (lot 283),[3] bought by Emmerson[4] (63 gns). Sold by Peacock to (Sir) Robert Peel (Bart.),[5] by whom exhibited at the BI in 1824. Purchased with the Peel collection, 1871.

EXHIBITIONS: BI 1824, No. 105; Sheffield 1956, No. 60.

REFERENCES:
General: Smith No. 134; HdG No. 1006.

In text:
1. Smith, loc. cit.
2. Smith loc. cit., says it was bought by Foster; HdG, loc. cit., says Peile [sic]. According to a contemporary note in the copy of the sale catalogue at the RKD it was bought in.
3. It is unlikely that it was in the collection of William Beckford. It is not in the catalogue of the Beckford sale, Fonthill Abbey, announced for 15 (16)

October 1822; this sale did not take place, Fonthill and its contents having been bought by Farquhar, and in the 1823 Fonthill sale were included many pictures which did not come from Beckford's collection (cf. [C. Redding], *Memoirs of W. Beckford*, 1859, vol. 2, pp. 239–40).
4. According to HdG, loc. cit.
5. Smith, loc. cit.

882 *A Dune Landscape with a River and Many Figures*   *Plate 419*

Signed in the bottom right corner: PHLS W (PHLS in monogram).

Oil on oak, 23.5 × 30.5 (9¼ × 12).

Cleaned in 1950.

PROVENANCE: Sold by John Smith in 1823;[1] in the collection of (Sir) Robert Peel (Bart.) by 1829.[2] Purchased with the Peel collection, 1871.

EXHIBITION: Arts Council 1945, No. 41.

REFERENCES:
General: Smith No. 435; HdG No. 1071.
In text:
1. Smith, loc. cit.
2. Smith, loc. cit.

973 *A Stream in the Dunes, with Two Bathers*   *Plate 420*

Oil on oak, 27 × 35.5 (10⅝ × 14).

Cleaned in 1953. Wearing throughout, especially in the sky. When the picture was cleaned a fisherman seated in the left foreground with a creel beside him was found to be a later addition and removed.

PROVENANCE: In the [Wynn Ellis] sale, London, 427 March 1858 (lot 33), bought in (25 gns); Wynn Ellis Bequest, 1876.

REFERENCE: HdG No. 1072.

975 *A Stag Hunt*   *Plate 421*

On the hill on the right is a hermit outside his hut.

Signed, bottom right: PHLS W (PHLS in monogram).

Oil on canvas, 75 × 104.2 (29½ × 41).

The style is that of Wouwermans' last years. Perhaps painted *c*.1665.

PROVENANCE: Bought from the (Corneille-Louis?) Reynders collection, Brussels, by Buchanan[1] and in the collection of Edward Gray, Haringay House, by 1824;[2] bought from Gray's collection by Buchanan.[3] In the collection of Sir Thomas Baring, Bart., by 1840, when it was exhibited at the BI; Sir T. Baring sale, London,

497

2–3 June 1848 (lot 111), bought by Earle[4] (£105). It has been identified[5] with a *Stag Hunt*, said to have been in Lord Northwick's collection, which was in the Robert White sale, London, 11 June 1853 (lot 66), bought in (150 gns) and the [R. White] sale, London, 16 February 1861 (lot 115), bought by Wilson (130 gns), but judging by the description in both the sale catalogues this was a different composition. In the Wynn Ellis collection, London; Wynn Ellis Bequest, 1876.

EXHIBITION: BI 1840, No. 30.

REFERENCES:
General: Smith No. 477 and Supplement No. 226; HdG No. 623.
In text:
1. Buchanan, vol. 2, p. 303. The 'Reyndaers' mentioned by Buchanan is presumably the Corneille-Louis Reynders whose pictures were in a sale in Brussels, 6 sqq. August 1821; the present picture was not in this sale.

2. Buchanan, loc. cit.
3. Smith Supplement No. 226.
4. HdG (No. 623) says it was bought by Brown, but the auctioneer's marked copy of the sale catalogue gives Earle as the purchaser.
5. In the National Gallery catalogue, 1915–29.

1060 *Two Vedettes on the Watch by a Stream* Plate 422

Signed, bottom right: PHL W (PHL in monogram).

Oil on oak, 31.6 × 35.7 ($12\frac{7}{16}$ × $14\frac{1}{16}$); the width increased by false additions to 38.4 cm.

There is some wearing throughout.

There are *pentimenti* in the outline of the man behind the woman and the baby.

An early work.

PROVENANCE: Aubrey Paul sale, London, 5 July 1855 (lot 15), bought by Rutley (46 gns).[1] John Henderson Bequest, 1879.

REFERENCES:
General: HdG No. 901.
In text: 1. The markings corresponding to this sale are on the back of the panel.

2282 *Two Horsemen at a Gipsy Encampment* Plate 423

Signed at the bottom, towards the left: PHILS W (PHILS in monogram).

Oil on oak, 32 × 35.9 ($12\frac{5}{8}$ × $14\frac{1}{8}$).

Some wearing in the darks.

Traditionally this painting was considered to be an autograph work but MacLaren believed the execution to be weak and thought that it could be a contemporary imitation. He catalogued it as 'Ascribed to Wouwermans'. The present writer considers it to be entirely acceptable as the work of Wouwermans himself.

PROVENANCE: In the Marin sale, Paris, 22 sqq. March 1790 (lot 73), bought by Jaubert (800 francs); Claude Tolozan sale, Paris, 23 sqq. February 1801 (lot 150), bought by Henry (2,000 francs). In the collection of Comte de Pourtalès, Paris; Comte de Pourtalès sale, London, 19–20 May 1826 (lot 52), bought by Norton

(105 gns). Lent by Martin H. Colnaghi to two exhibitions in London in 1902 and 1904. Martin H. Colnaghi Bequest, 1908.

EXHIBITIONS: RA 1902, No. 202; London, Whitechapel Art Gallery, Dutch Exhibition, 1904, No. 302.

REFERENCES: Smith No. 203; HdG No. 933.

2554 *A Horse being shod outside a Village Smithy*   Plate 424

Signed, bottom right, on the frame of the grindstone: PHILS. W (PHILS in mono-gram).

Oil on oak, 46.1 × 62.2 (18$\frac{1}{8}$ × 24$\frac{1}{2}$).

A comparatively early work.

PROVENANCE: Possibly in the collection of Dutch paintings bought from Johann Christian Berens of Riga before 1778 by Herzog Peter von Kurland,[1] who acquired the estate of Sagan, Silesia, in 1795 and died there in 1800.[2] It was in the ducal collection at Sagan[3] and by 1858 had passed by inheritance into that of Fürst Hohenzollern-Hechingen (who married Duke Peter's second daughter) in Löwenberg (Silesia).[4] It was sold from Löwenberg, probably *c*.1881,[5] and was in the collection of Dr Martin Schubart, Munich, before 1889, when it was exhibited in Leipzig; exhibited in Munich 1895; Dr M. Schubart sale, Munich, 23 October 1899 (lot 85), 19,000 marks. Said to have been later in the Heshuysen collection, Haarlem;[6] by 1902 it belonged to George Salting, London, when it was exhibited at the RA; George Salting Bequest, 1910.

EXHIBITIONS: Leipzig 1889, No. 272; Munich 1895, No. 77; RA 1902, No. 196.

REFERENCES:
General: HdG No. 134.
In text:
1. See J. Bernoulli, *Reisen durch Brandenburg, Pommern, Preussen, Curland . . . in den Jahren 1777 und 1778*, 1779, vol. 3, p. 247. N. von Holst (in *Baltische Monatschefte*, vol. 10, 1938, pp. 570–1) has attempted to show that the Dutch pictures in Sagan in 1849 must have been bought before *c*.1780 by Duke Peter of Kurland. At least one, however, was bought after 1792 (HdG, Rembrandt No. 81) and no fewer than three others after the death of Duke Peter, *viz*. a Steen (HdG No. 762) acquired after 1804, an Adriaen van de Velde after 1833 (HdG No. 345) and a Willem van de Velde the Younger after 1835 (HdG No. 311).
2. See Holst, op. cit., p. 570.

3. HdG No. 134. The only known copy of a printed catalogue of Sagan pictures, 1849, is in the library of Schloss Sagan and has not been consulted.
4. See G. Parthey, *Deutscher Bildersaal*, vol. 2, 1864, p. 804, No. 86. According to the catalogue of the Schubart 1899 sale (see PROVENANCE) it was No. 12 of the Hohenzollern-Hechingen catalogue, 1858; the present writer has not been able to consult a copy of the latter.
5. A number of pictures were sold privately from Löwenberg in or about 1881; at least four of those afterwards in the Weber collection, Hamburg, were bought in 1881. There were several in the Schubart collection before 1889.
6. HdG No. 134.

6263 *Cavalry making a Sortie from a Fort on a Hill*   Plate 425

Among the burning buildings in the left background is a Gothic church.

Signed, bottom left: PHILWouwermans/Ao 1646 (PHIL in monogram).

Oil on canvas, 139 × 190.5 (54$\frac{3}{4}$ × 75). A further 2.5 cm. of the painted surface is turned over the edge of the stretcher at the top, and about 2 cm. right and left.

This is one of the largest battle paintings by Wouwermans. It is unlikely that it is intended to represent any specific action. The colours borne by various of the combatants do not identify them with any particular country or force, and both buildings and landscape appear to be imaginary.

PROVENANCE: An 'encounter or skirmish of cavalry' by Wouwermans with the same date as the present picture was in the Guerin sale in The Hague, 13 September 1740 (lot 7), but this is described as a 'small piece'.[1] The National Gallery picture comes from the collection of the Dukes of Marlborough at Blenheim Palace; a Wouwermans 'Battle Piece' was there by c.1783[2] but this might equally well be the *Cavalry Encounter on a Hill* which was in that collection.[3] Two Wouwermans battle pieces were there in 1816.[4] No. 6263 can first be identified with certainty in the Blenheim Palace collection in 1842.[5] 8th Duke of Marlborough sale, London, 24 July sqq. 1886 (lot 57), bought by Baron Ardilaun (450 gns); in the collection of Lord Ardilaun in Clontarf, near Dublin; on his death in 1915 it passed to his nephew, the Hon. Benjamin John Plunket, Bishop of Tuam and Meath. In an Anon. sale, London, 3 May 1940 (lot 104), bought in. Later purchased by W. R. Drown, London; sold by him to the National Gallery in May 1956.

REFERENCES:
General: Smith Supplement No. 86; HdG No. 778 (and 770b?).
In text:
1. 'Een zeer fraay stukje, vertoonende een Rencon-ter of Schermutzeling van Ruitery &c., . . . door Philips Wouwerman, Anno 1646' (Terwesten, p. 26). This is HdG No. 770b.
2. *The New Oxford Guide*, 6th ed. [1783?], p. 99.

3. HdG No. 750; G. Scharf, *Catalogue raisonné . . . of the Pictures in the Blenheim Palace*, 1862, p. 103. It was lot 56 of the Marlborough sale, 1886.
4. S. H. Spiker, *Travels through England, Wales and Scotland in . . . 1816*, vol. I, 1820, p. 40: 'two very fine Battle-pieces by Wouwermanns.'
5. Smith Supplement No. 86. (Scharf, op. cit., p. 104).

Ascribed to PHILIPS WOUWERMANS

976   *Cavalry attacking Infantry*   Plate 426

Signed, bottom left: PHILS.W (PHILS in monogram).

Oil on oak, 33.4 × 63.1 ($13\frac{3}{16}$ × $24\frac{13}{16}$).

Some wearing throughout.

Wouwermans' battle scenes were almost certainly never intended as representations of specific engagements and even the nationality of the combatants is rarely indicated (compare No. 6263 above). The present picture was once described merely as a battle of cavalry and infantry; the replica in Leningrad, however, has been designated a combat between Poles and Swedes (see VERSION). The horsemen advancing from the left have fur-trimmed caps and curved swords, and one in the centre wields a battle-hammer; these features suggest that Poles are intended and this interpretation is sup-ported by their red banners.[1] The body of soldiers meeting their attack wear mid-seventeenth-century Western European dress and are only distinguished by their blue flags, which are quite possibly intended for the Swedish colours.[2] The Swedes were at war with Poland from 1655 to 1660; despite the early successes of their invasion of Poland the Swedes were eventually overwhelmed. The proposed identification of the subject is not excluded by the probable date of the picture (see below) and it may be noted that at this period Sweden was also the enemy of the Dutch, who made a naval expedition against her in support of the Danes in 1658–9.

Both the National Gallery version and the Leningrad one are related in style to the *Battle between Polish and Turkish Cavalry* in Leningrad, which is dated 1656;[3] if anything they may be a little later. The present picture is rather poorly executed and is quite probably by a studio assistant; the Leningrad replica, which is larger, is apparently in poor condition and Hofstede de Groot rightly made reservations about its originality.[4]

VERSION: A much larger replica of this composition is in the Hermitage Museum, Leningrad.[5]

PROVENANCE: In the Rutland House (Edward Manners) sale, London, 19–23 November 1827 (lot 53), 215 gns; by 1829 in the collection of Col. Ainslie.[6] In the collection of Wynn Ellis, London, by 1845;[7] Wynn Ellis Bequest, 1876.

EXHIBITION: BI 1860, No. 46.

REFERENCES:

General: Smith No. 491; HdG No. 747.

In text:

1. In the seventeenth century the Polish flag was red with a white eagle or an arm holding a sword.

2. The Swedish flag then, as now, was blue with a gold cross.

3. HdG No. 788; A. Somof, *Ermitage Impérial. Catalogue de la Galerie des Tableaux*, vol. 2 (*Écoles néerlandaises*, etc.), 1901, No. 1021.

4. See HdG No. 760. The surface of the picture is obscured by dark varnish and substantial repainting.

5. A. Somof, op. cit., No. 1022 (as *Combat of Poles with Swedes*); HdG No. 760. On canvas, 60.7 × 103.8 cm.; signed with the monogram. Ac-quired by Empress Catherine II in 1770. The only variation, apart from minor details, is that the rearing horse and its rider seen in the right distance of the National Gallery version do not appear in the Leningrad picture, but there appears to be a patch of darker repaint covering this area. (The horse and rider are also omitted in E. Huot's lithograph after the picture in *Galerie Impériale de l'Ermitage*, vol. 1, 1845 1st series.)

6. Smith, loc. cit.

7. MS note in a copy of Smith's *Catalogue Raisonné* thought to be his own; Waagen (1854, vol. 2, p. 296) saw it in Wynn Ellis's collection in 1850 or 1851.

JOACHIM WTEWAEL, 1566–1638

Joachim Anthonisz. Wtewael. He was born in Utrecht. According to van Mander he studied with his father, a glass-engraver, until he was eighteen and subsequently trained as a painter in Utrecht with Joos de Beer. After two years with de Beer he spent two years in Italy and two more years in France in the entourage of Charles de Bourgneuf de Cucé, Bishop of St Malo. Wtewael had returned to Utrecht by 1592 when he entered the saddlers' guild to which painters then belonged. He spent the rest of his life in Utrecht and was successful as a flax merchant as well as a painter. He served on the town council in 1610 and again in 1632 and was one of the founder members of the St Luke's Guild in Utrecht in 1611. He designed stained-glass windows for the St Janskerk in Gouda and is said to have worked as a sculptor. His latest dated paintings are from 1628 and he seems not to have been active as a painter during the last decade of his life.

Wtewael's distinctive style is based on 'Haarlem Mannerism', developed in Haarlem by Hendrick Goltzius, Cornelis van Haarlem and Carel van Mander. It was the last of these who introduced designs by Bartholomeus Spranger (a native of Antwerp who,

501

after a prolonged stay in Italy, had become one of Rudolf II's court artists in Prague) into Haarlem in 1583. Spranger's elegant, sophisticated and erotic court art dominated painting in Haarlem for a decade. However, while the three Haarlem artists subsequently abandoned Spranger's manner for more naturalistic styles, Wtewael (and his Utrecht contemporary Abraham Bloemaert) practised an individual interpretation of 'Sprangerism' long after it had been given up in Haarlem. Wtewael responded to later developments, such as the art of Caravaggio brought back to Utrecht in the early 1620s, but never wholly abandoned Spranger's style.

His eldest son, Peter (1596–1660),[1] was a painter, trained by his father, and the guild records list three other pupils, Hendrick de Keyser, Peter van Winsen, and Andries van Bochoven.

REFERENCES: General: A. W. Lowenthal, *Joachim Wtewael and Dutch Mannerism*, Doornspijk, 1986 (for the artist's biography, see pp. 25–37; with all previous literature).
In text: **1.** A. W. Lowenthal, 'Some Paintings by Peter Wtewael (1596–1660)', BM, vol. 116, 1974, pp. 458–67.

6334 *The Judgement of Paris* *Plate 427*

Signed and dated, bottom left: Jo wte.wael (Jo in monogram) / fecit / An° 1615.

Oil on oak, 59.8 × 79.2 (23½ × 31⅛).

Jupiter permitted Eris, the personification of strife, to attend the marriage of Peleus and Thetis. This is the scene in the right background. While there, she provoked a quarrel between the goddesses as to who was the fairest. Mercury brought Venus, Juno and Minerva to the shepherd Paris on Mount Ida to judge between them. His choice of Venus led indirectly to the outbreak of the Trojan War.[1]

Although Wtewael painted a number of other versions of *The Judgement of Paris*[2] and of *The Marriage of Peleus and Thetis*[3] this is the only painting by him which conflates the two scenes into a single composition. In the foreground group there are reminiscences of *The Judgement of Paris* engraved after Raphael by Marcantonio Raimondi.[4] The figure of Minerva, seen from behind, is based on that of Ceres in Goltzius' *Wedding of Cupid and Psyche* engraving of 1587.[5] The river god in No. 6334 is derived from the figure of Neptune in the engraving. The figures display Wtewael's study of Goltzius' classicising figure style.[6]

There is a painting by Wtewael formerly in a German private collection (Fig. 121) in which the central group is virtually a repetition in reverse of that in No. 6334 (see VERSION).

VERSION: Panel, 81 × 104.5 cm. Present location unknown.[7]

DRAWING: A drawing[8] of three heads in the collection of Sir Brinsley Ford, London, may include a study for the head of Juno.

PROVENANCE: Collection of Lord Donegal; collection of Henry Doetsch, London. Doetsch sale, Christie's, 22–25 June 1895 (lot 344); with the art dealer Ronald A. Lee, Hampton Court; collection of Claude Dickason Rotch, by whom bequeathed to the National Gallery in 1962.

EXHIBITIONS: London, Victoria and Albert Museum, Third International Art Treasures Exhibition, 1962, No. 42; London 1976, No. 129.

REFERENCES:

General: Lowenthal, op. cit., cat. no. A-63.
In text:
1. Homer, *The Iliad*, Book 24, 25–30.
2. Lowenthal, op. cit., cat. nos. A-21, A-22, A-22, A-25, A-26, A-64.
3. Lowenthal, op. cit., cat. nos. A-4, A-20, A-49, A-50, A-53, A-81.
4. Ill. Bartsch No. 245.
5. The print was designed by Spranger and en-graved by Goltzius. Ill. Bartsch No. 277. Hollstein, vol. 8, No. 322.
6. Lowenthal, op. cit., draws attention to similar-ities in figure style to Goltzius' *Vertumnus and Pomona* of 1613 (Amsterdam, Rijksmuseum; 1976 cat., No. A2217).
7. Lowenthal, op. cit., cat. no. A-64.
8. Lowenthal, op. cit., discussed under cat. no. A-64. Black chalk on blue paper: 208 × 248 mm.

JAN WIJNANTS, active 1643; died 1684

Jan (occasionally also *Johannes*) Wijnants; the spelling *Wynants* occurs on some of his pictures. He was a native of Haarlem;[1] there has been considerable difference of opin-ion about the probable date of his birth. Bredius[2] suggested *c.*1630–5 which is certainly too late as there are dated pictures of 1643. Bode[3] identified the artist with a Jan Wijnants who was a member of a Haarlem rhetoricians' society in 1626[4] and thought he must therefore have been born not later than 1605. It is, however, not stated that this man was a painter and he may well be the art dealer of the same name, mentioned in the records of the Haarlem guild in 1642,[5] who was possibly the painter's father (the painter is called Jan Wijnants *the younger* in a document of 1660)[6] and whose eldest son, Jan, was in Rotterdam in August 1653.[7] The earliest known dated picture by Jan Wijnants is apparently of 1643 (from 1645 onwards there are many with dates); for this and other reasons Hofstede de Groot[8] supposed he was born not later than 1620–5. He must have lived in Haarlem in his earlier years; throughout his life the subject of almost all his pictures is the characteristic dune scenery near Haarlem (the dunes in his pictures have sometimes been mistaken for distant mountains and this has led some writers to postulate travels for which there is no evidence whatsoever). In 1659 he was still living in Haarlem[9] but had moved to Amsterdam by December 1660 (when betrothed)[10] and he is recorded there several times until his death.[11] In 1672 he is described as 'painter and innkeeper'.[12] He was buried in Amsterdam, 23 January 1684.[13]

Wijnants' known pictures, of which there is a considerable number, are, with one apparent exception,[14] landscapes and usually scenes in the dunes. The figures in them are very often (Hofstede de Groot supposed always) the work of another artist, often Adriaen van de Velde who was, according to Houbraken, Wijnants' pupil. Other collaborators include Dirk Wijntrack and Jan Lingelbach.

REFERENCES:

General: Bredius in OH, vol. 29, 1911, pp. 179–84; HdG, vol. 8.
In text:
1. According to the entry of his betrothal in the Amsterdam marriage register, 1660 (OH, 1886, p. 302).
2. Op. cit., p. 180.
3. W. Bode, *Great Masters of Dutch and Flemish Paint-ing*, 1909, p. 211.
4. OH, 1884, p. 165, note 3.
5. Van der Willigen, p. 343.
6. Bredius, op. cit., p. 181.

7. Bredius, op. cit., p. 180.
8. HdG, op. cit., pp. 427–8.
9. Bredius, op. cit., p. 180.
10. OH, 1886, p. 302.
11. Bredius, op. cit., pp. 181 ff.

12. and 13. Bredius, op. cit., p. 182.
14. A *Vertumnus and Pomona* signed and dated 1679, canvas, 165 × 134 cm., was with S. Nystad, The Hague, in 1979.

883 *A Landscape with a Dead Tree, and a Peasant driving Oxen and Sheep along a Road*

Plate 428

Signed on the end of the felled tree in the left foreground: J. Wynants/1659.

Oil on canvas, 80 × 99.4 (31½ × 39⅛).

Cleaned in 1966.

The figures and animals are apparently by Jan Lingelbach.

PROVENANCE: Smith[1] identifies this picture with one in the Blondel de Gagny sale, Paris, 10 December 1776–22 January 1777 (lot 75),[2] bought by Le Brun (3,750 francs), but the description in the sale catalogue does not fit very well. No. 883 was in the [Trouard] sale, Paris, 22 sqq. February 1779 (lot 127), 2,400 francs, and the comte de Vaudreuil sale, Paris, 24–25 November 1784 (lot 45),[3] bought by Le Rouge (2,800 francs); later in the collection of William Smith, MP,[4] and afterwards in the John Webb sale, London, 30–31 May 1821 (lot 160), bought by (Sir) Robert Peel (Bart.), 250 gns; purchased with the Peel collection, 1871.

EXHIBITION: BI 1822, No. 178.

REFERENCES:
General: Smith No. 93; HdG No. 269.
In text:
1. Loc. cit.
2. 'Un tableau . . . sur toile de 2 pieds 7 pouces de haut, sur 3 pieds 3 pouces de large; il représente un terrain sablonneux; une haie, des broussailles & des arbres dans l'éloignement. Sur le premier plan à gauche, un arbre dégarni de beaucoup de ses feuilles; une pièce d'eau, proche de laquelle sont des vaches, des moutons & des figures sur des plans différents. Toutes ces figures & animaux sont de la main d'*Adrien Vanden Veld*.' HdG (No. 281) identifies the Blondel de Gagny painting with a picture in the Lucas Merens sale, Amsterdam, 15 April 1778 (lot 140), bought by Yver for van Leyden, and van Leyden of Amsterdam sale, Paris, 5–7 November 1804 (lot 109), bought by Le Brun (4,502 francs). According to Smith (loc. cit.) No. 883 was the landscape in the van Leyden sale, but the description in the sale catalogue shows that it was a different composition.
3. The description in the Vaudreuil sale catalogue agrees closely with the National Gallery picture, and gives the provenance from the Trouard sale.
4. According to the catalogue of the John Webb sale of 1821.

884 *Peasants driving Cattle and Sheep by a Sandhill, and Two Sportsmen with Dogs*

Plate 429

Signed, bottom left: J W (possibly false).

Oil on oak, 28.6 × 38.1 (11¼ × 15).

Probably painted towards the end of the 1660s.

The grain of the wood is prominent in the sky.

The figures are in the style of Adriaen van de Velde but are not certainly by him.

PROVENANCE: Anon. sale, Antwerp, 5 July 1784 (lot 13), bought by Peeters (605 florins); [van Bortel?] sale, Antwerp, 12 May 1806 (lot 1), bought by Sluis (1,290 florins); H. J. Stier d'Aertselaer sale, Antwerp, 29 July

1822 (lot 23), bought by Nieuwenhuys (2,005 florins); [Joseph Barchard] sale, London, 6 May 1826 (No. 17), bought by Nieuwenhuys (255 gns). In the collection of Sir Robert Peel, Bart., by 1835;[1] purchased with the Peel collection, 1871.

REFERENCES:
General: Smith No. 94; HdG Nos. 138 and 380.
In text: 1. Smith, loc. cit.

971 *A Landscape with a High Dune and Peasants on a Road*   *Plate 430*

Signed below towards the right, by the side of the track: J.W.

Oil on canvas, 40.9 × 53.7 (16⅛ × 21⅛).

Extensive retouchings in the sky.

The figures and animals are in the style of Jan Lingelbach.

PROVENANCE: In the possession of Fossard, Paris, in 1834;[1] in the [Fossard] sale, Paris, 22 April 1835 (lot 24), bought in (2,810 francs); [Fossard] sale, Paris, 8–9 March 1843 (lot 2), bought in (2,700 francs). In the collection of Wynn Ellis, London, by 1850 or 1851;[2] it is probably the 'Landscape and Figures' exhibited by Wynn Ellis at the BI, in 1859. Wynn Ellis Bequest, 1876.

EXHIBITION: BI 1859, No. 6(?).

REFERENCES:
General: Smith No. 69; HdG No. 539.
In text:
1. Smith, loc. cit.
2. Waagen, 1854, vol. 2, p. 297.

972 *A Landscape with Two Dead Trees, and Two Sportsmen*   *Plate 431*
with Dogs on a Sandy Road

Signed, bottom right: J Wijnants (worn; probably false).

Oil on oak, 29 × 36.8 (11⁷⁄₁₆ × 14½).

Probably a work of the later 1660s or early 70s.
   The figures are in the style of Adriaen van de Velde.

PROVENANCE: Perhaps in an Amsterdam sale, 16 June 1800 (lot 3), bought by Andriesse (205 guilders). Probably to be identified with lot 71 of the [Wynn Ellis] sale, London, 27 March 1858, which was bought in (61 gns). Wynn Ellis Bequest, 1876.

REFERENCES: HdG Nos. 222 and 555.

2532 *A Landscape with a Woman driving Sheep through a*   *Plate 432*
Ruined Archway

Signed, bottom left: J Wijnants 1667.

Oil on canvas, 35.8 × 43.5 (14¹⁄₁₆ × 17⅛).

The figures are probably by Adriaen van de Velde.

VERSION: A version or copy on wood, signed and dated 1667, was in the [Hon. W. F. B. Massey-Mainwaring] sale, London, 23 May 1903 (lot 71),[1] bought in (30 gns). A copy is in the Fitzwilliam Museum, Cambridge.[2] A further copy was in the Krupp sale, Cologne (Heberk), on 29 October 1894 (lot 200, as A. van de Velde and J. Wynants) and then in Anon. sale, Cologne (Lempertz), 1 June 1978 (lot 128), as Netherlandish seventeenth century.[3]

PROVENANCE: In the van Saceghem collection, Ghent, by 1835;[4] van Saceghem sale, Brussels, 2–3 June 1851 (lot 86), bought by Le Roy (5,100 francs); Théodore Patureau sale, Paris, 20–21 April 1857 (lot 48),[5] bought by Meunier or E. le Roy[6] (7,600 francs), and acquired in the same year by Sir Hugh Hume Campbell, Bart; Sir H. H. Campbell sale, London, 16 June 1894 (lot 52), bought by Horace Buttery (£252), by whom it was sold to George Salting in July 1894.[7] Salting Bequest, 1910.

EXHIBITION: BI 1857, No. 74.

REFERENCES:

General: Smith No. 107; HdG No. 358.
In text:
1. On wood, 36.5 × 45 cm. From the Carl Triepel sale, Munich, 28 September 1874 (lot 60); Gräfin Reigersberg sale, Cologne, 15–16 October 1890 (lot 181); Krupp et al. sale, Cologne, 29 October 1894 (lot 200). HdG (No. 410) identifies this version with the picture in the van Saceghem and Patureau sales (see PROVENANCE) but the catalogues of these sales show that the latter was on canvas, as is No. 2532, whereas the other version is on panel.

2. Panel, 36.5 × 44.8 cm.; Daniel Mesman Bequest, 1834. 1960 cat. (by H. Gerson) No. 292 (as copy after Jan Wynants).
3. Panel, 35.5 × 45 cm.
4. Smith, loc. cit.
5. As from the van Saceghem sale, 1851.
6. According to the marked copy in the Cabinet des Estampes, Paris, it was bought by Meunier; HdG (No. 410) gives E. Le Roy as the purchaser.
7. Letter of 1953 from Horace A. Buttery (in the National Gallery archives).

2533 *A Track by a Dune, with Peasants and a Horseman* Plate 433

Signed, bottom right: J Wijnants / 1665.

Oil on oak, 29.7 × 36.8 ($11\frac{11}{16}$ × $14\frac{1}{2}$).

Cleaned in 1974.

The figures in the foreground are in the style of Jan Lingelbach.

VERSION: A copy was in the August de Ridder sale, Paris, 2 June 1924 (lot 87).[1]

PROVENANCE: In the collection of William Wells, Redleaf, by 1835;[2] William Wells sale, London, 12–13 May 1848 (lot 36), bought by Farrer (£210); lent by Mrs Charles Cope to the RA in 1872; Charles Cope sale, London, 8 June 1872 (lot 51), bought by J. Heugh (390 gns); John Heugh sale, London, 10–11 May 1878 (lot 263),[3] bought by Agnew (250 gns), perhaps for the 7th Viscount Powerscourt (died 1904).[4] In the George Salting collection, London; Salting Bequest, 1910.

EXHIBITIONS: BI 1845, No. 30; RA 1872, No. 175; London 1976, No. 128.

REFERENCES:
General: Smith No. 19; HdG No. 138a.
In text:
1. (HdG No. 634.) On canvas, 30 × 38 cm.; falsely signed. Reproduced in W. Bode, *The Collection of Pictures of the late Herr A. de Ridder*, 1913, pl. 68 (not in the 1910 edition).
2. Smith, loc. cit.
3. The markings corresponding to this sale are on the back of the picture.

4. On the back of the panel is a cutting from the relevant part of the Heugh sale catalogue, inscribed: 'Bought by Mervyn, Viscount Powerscourt.' The auctioneer's copy of the sale catalogue gives Agnew as the buyer, and there is a printed Agnew label on the back on top of the Heugh sale markings (see note 3).

Glossary

bambocciata	Scene of everyday life; this Italian word was used to describe such scenes painted by Dutch artists in Rome. It was derived from the name Bamboccio given by his colleagues in the association of Northern artists in Rome, the *Schildersbent*, to Pieter van Laer, who was the first to paint such scenes. *Il Bamboccio* (in Dutch, *Bamboots*) literally means a rag doll or puppet.
boeier	A round type of Dutch vessel with a deep rail similar to a *kaag*, but with a curved spoon bow; usually sprit-rigged.
bordeeltje	A small painting showing a brothel scene.
chitarrone	A large, long-necked bass lute used primarily to accompany solo singing.
deken	Dean of the guild of St Luke (the guild to which painters belonged). In some guilds this post was known as a *hoofdman*.
dienaar	Servant or studio assistant
duim	(= *pouce*) lit. thumb, a unit of measurement, 2.57 cm, or 1/11th of a *voet*
Fijnschilders	The name given to a group of painters based principally in Leiden whose work is characterised by its high finish. The style was originated by Gerrit Dou and developed by the van Mieris family.
fluitschip	A full-sterned vessel with narrow works built up aft, usually a merchant ship (English: flute)
galjoot	A small Dutch coasting vessel rigged with a standing gaff on the mainmast and with a small lateen missen (English: galliot)
hoeker	A Dutch fishing vessel similar in build to a *galjoot* but with a square foresail and mainsail (English: hooker)
hoofdman	The senior official in the guild of St Luke, elected from among the members to serve for a limited term, usually one or two years. Guild regulations varied from town to town but in Delft, for example, there were four *hoofdmannen* who served for two years (see *deken*).
kaag	A Dutch vessel like a *boeier* but with a straight raking stem and clinker-built.

modello	An oil sketch (or a drawing) which is preparatory to the full-scale, finished work.
pas-glas	Tall, thick glass
ontbijtje	A breakfast still life
roemer	A bulbous beer glass
smalschip	A small Dutch transport vessel, sprit-rigged
snaauwschip	A square-rigged two-masted vessel usually employed as a Despatch vessel (English: snow).
Statenjacht	A 'States yacht' used for transporting members or guests of the States General. They had large cabins aft.
tafferel	The upper part of a vessel's stern on which was placed a device or an escutcheon.
theerak	A wooden rack used to support teapots and teacups.
timmerman	Carpenter (or house-builder)
tjalk	A Dutch sprit-sail barge
trekjacht	A yacht which travelled along the canals between the principal towns of the United Provinces drawn by a horse. They provided regular commercial services.
vanitas	A scene, usually a still life, which conveyed the futility of human endeavour in the face of mortality. The term is taken from the prophet of *Ecclesiastes*: 'Vanity of Vanities, all is vanity . . . '
veerpont	Ferry-boat
vendrig	Ensign or standard-bearer (in a militia company)
voet	Lit. a foot. A unit of measurement: an Amsterdam foot was equivalent to 28.31 cm (11 inches)
weyschuit	A small Dutch open boat with a straight raking stern usually rigged with a sprit.
wijdschip	A small Dutch transport vessel of the same build as a *smalschip* but slightly larger.
zoll	A German unit of measurement. There were 12 *zoll* to a *schuh*. (A Nuremberg *schuh* was 30.4 cm – a *zoll* was 2.53 cm; A Vienna *schuh* was 31.61 cm – a *zoll* was 2.63 cm.)

List of Paintings acquired since the 1960 Edition of the Catalogue

List of Attributions changed from the 1960 edition of the Catalogue

Old attribution	Inventory number	New attribution
Abraham BEGEIJN (or BEGA)	1007	Lodewijck van LUDICK
Ascribed to Nicolaes BERCHEM	240	Nicolaes BERCHEM
Ascribed to Pieter van den BOSCH	2551	Attributed to Pieter van den BOSCH
After CORNELIS van Haarlem	1893	CORNELIS van Haarlem
Ascribed to Aelbert CUYP	2548	Attributed to Aelbert CUYP
DELFT School, *c.*1650–1655	2552	DELFT School, *c.*1660–1665
DUTCH School, *c.*1650–1655	960	Attributed to Willem van DRIELENBURGH
Ascribed to Jan van GOYEN	137	Attributed to Jan van GOYEN
Ascribed to Johan van HAENSBERGEN	955	Cornelis van POELENBURGH
Gerrit HEDA	1469	Willem Claesz. HEDA
Gerrit HEDA	5787	Willem Claesz. HEDA
Ascribed to Bartholomeus van der HELST	4691	Bartholomeus van der HELST
Melchior d' HONDECOETER	1013	Johannes SPRUYT
Johan van KESSEL(?)	987	Jacob van RUISDAEL
LEYDEN School	2589	Olivier van DEUREN
Jan LOOTEN	901	Joris van der HAAGEN
Ascribed to Isack van OSTADE	963	Imitator of Isack van OSTADE
Cornelis van POELENBURGH	2909	Hendrik Frans van LINT (Flemish School, excluded from the present catalogue)
REMBRANDT	3214	Attributed to REMBRANDT
REMBRANDT	5282	Follower of REMBRANDT
REMBRANDT	6274	Follower of REMBRANDT
Ascribed to REMBRANDT	51	Follower of REMBRANDT
After REMBRANDT	289	Gerrit LUNDENS

Old attribution	Inventory number	New attribution
REMBRANDT and Gerrit DOU	4189	Gerrit DOU
Ascribed to Jacob van RUISDAEL	991	Jacob van RUISDAEL
Ascribed to Jacob van RUISDAEL	2564	Jacob van RUISDAEL
Follower of Jacob van RUISDAEL	989	Jacob van RUISDAEL
Follower of Jacob van RUISDAEL	2563	Jacob van RUISDAEL
Style of Hercules SEG(H)ERS	4383	Imitator of Hercules SEGERS
Wallerant VAILLANT(?)	3591	After Wallerant VAILLANT
Ascribed to Adriaen van de VELDE	984	Dirck van der BERGEN
Willem van de VELDE the Younger	149	Studio of Willem van de VELDE the Younger
Willem van de VELDE the Younger	977	Studio of Willem van de VELDE the Younger
Ascribed to Philips WOUWERMANS	2282	Philips WOUWERMANS

INDEXES

Index to Religious Subjects

Index to Profane Subjects

Index to Portraits

Doubtful identifications are indicated by a question mark. The names of the sitters in Eeckhout 1459 and Lundens 289 are given here although some of them cannot be identified individually in the pictures. An asterisk (*) indicates that the subject or person is only a minor part of the picture.

Topographical Index

An asterisk (*) indicates that the subject is only a minor part of the picture.

AMSTERDAM:
Haarlemmersluis (Haarlem lock): Meindert Hobbema 6138
Haaringpakkerstoren (Herring-Packers tower): Meindert Hobbema 6138
*Heiligewegspoort: Rembrandt 6300
New Fishmarket: Emanuel de Witte 3682
Oude Kerk (interior): Emanuel de Witte 1053; Emanuel de Witte 6402;
Singel: Meindert Hobbema 6138
Westerkerk: Jan van der Heyden 6526

ANTWERP(?):
Cornelis van der Schalcke 974

BENTHEIM CASTLE:
Imitator of Jacob van Ruisdael 996

BREDERODE CASTLE:
Meindert Hobbema 831

COLOGNE:
Cathedral: Jan van der Heyden 866

DELFT:
Nieuwe Kerk: Carel Fabritius 3714; Egbert van der Poel 1061
Oude Kerk: Egbert van der Poel 1061
Oude Langendijk: Carel Fabritius 3714
Sint Joris Gasthuis (Chapel): Egbert van der Poel 1061
Stadhuis (Town Hall): Carel Fabritius 3714; Egbert van der Poel 1061
Town wall: Pieter de Hooch 794
Vrouwenrecht: Carel Fabritius 3714

DEVENTER:
General view: Salomon van Ruysdael 6338

DORDRECHT:
General view: Ludolf Bakhuizen 1000
Groothoofdspoort: Abraham van Calraet 3024; Attributed to Willem van Drielenburgh 960
Grote Kerk: Abraham van Calraet 3024; Aelbert Cuyp 961; Aelbert Cuyp 962; Attributed to Willem van Drielenburgh 960; Jan van Goyen 2580
Huis te Merwede (Merwede Castle): Aelbert Cuyp 1289; Jan van Goyen 1327
The Maas: Aelbert Cuyp 6405
Rietdijksepoort: Jan van Goyen 1327
Vuilpoort: Aelbert Cuyp 961; Aelbert Cuyp 962; Attributed to Willem van Drielenburgh 960

EGMOND-AAN-ZEE: Jacob van Ruisdael 1390

ENKHUIZEN: Ludolf Bakhuizen 204

HAARLEM:
Bakenesserkerk (interior): Johannes Bosboom 2712
Grote Kerk (exterior): Gerrit Berckheyde 1420; Adriaen van de Velde 869
Grote Kerk (interior): Gerrit Berckheyde 1451; Pieter Saenredam 2531
Grote Markt (Market Place): Gerrit Berckheyde 1420; Gerrit Berckheyde 1863
Stadhuis (Town Hall): Gerrit Berckheyde 1863
Vleeshal: Gerrit Berckheyde 1420

THE HAGUE:
Groot Boterhuis: Paulus Constantijn La Fargue 1918
Grote Kerk: Paulus Constantijn La Fargue 1918
Huis ten Bosch: Jan van der Heyden 1914
Waaggebouw: see *Groot Boterhuis*

MERWEDE, HUIS TE: *see* DORDRECHT

MIDDELHARNIS: Meindert Hobbema 830

MONTIGNY-SUR-LOING: Jacob Maris 5568

MONTMARTRE:
Quarries: Matthijs Maris 2874

MUIDEN CASTLE: Arent Arentsz. 3533; Jan Beerstraaten 1311

MUIDERBERG CHURCH(?): Arent Arentsz. 3533

MÜNSTER:
Rathaus (Town Hall – interior): Gerard ter Borch 896

NIJENRODE CASTLE: Jan van der Heyden 994

OUDEWATER: Willem Koekkoek 6472

RHENEN:
General view: Salomon van Ruysdael 6348
St Cunerakerk(?): Hendrick Avercamp 1479
St Cunerakerk (*interior*): Bartholomeus van Bassen 3164

ROME:
Castel Sant'Angelo(?): Attributed to Cesar van Everdingen 3315
Ripa Grande(?): Jan Both 958

ROTTERDAM(?): Jan van der Cappelle 964

SCHEVENINGEN: Willem van de Velde 873

SINGRAVEN: Meindert Hobbema 832; Jacob van Ruisdael 986

UBBERGEN CASTLE: Aelbert Cuyp 824

UTRECHT:
Buurkerk (*interior*): Pieter Saenredam 1896
Cathedral (*exterior of sacristy*): Jan van der Heyden 994

Index of Previous Owners

The dates of *anonymous* sales only are given here; such sales are listed in chronological order under the towns in which they took place.

ABRAHAM, Richard: Jacob van Ruisdael 990

ACHTIENHOVE: Philips Koninck 6398

ACRAMAN, Daniel Wade: Gabriel Metsu 970

ADRIAANSE: Aert van der Neer 732

AERTSELAER: *see* Stier d'Aertselaer

AGAR, Welborne Ellis: Adriaen van der Werff 3909

AGNEW, Messrs T.: Quiringh van Brekelenkam 2550; Attributed to Abraham van Calraet 2548; Jan van de Cappelle 2586; Pieter Codde 2584; Aelbert Cuyp 2545; Olivier van Deuren 2589; Hendrick Dubbels 2587; Jan van Goyen 6423; Frans Hals 2528, 2529; Willem Claesz. Heda 5787; Bartholomeus van der Helst 4691; Meindert Hobbema 2571; Gabriel Metsu 2590, 5225; Jan Molenaer 5416; After Adriaen van Ostade 2541; Salomon van Ruysdael 6338; Jan Steen 2556, 2557, 2560; Willem van de Velde 2573, 2574, 6465; Simon de Vlieger 3025; Emanuel de Witte 3682; Jan Wijnants 2533

AINSLIE, Colonel: Ascribed to Philips Wouwermans 976

AINSLEY, S. J.: Roelandt Savery 920

ALBERG, Duc d': Adriaen van de Velde 867

ALEXANDER, Misses Rachel F. and Jean I.: Jan van de Cappelle 6406; Aelbert Cuyp 6405; Dutch School 6414; Frans Hals 6411, 6413; Philips Koninck 6408; Isack van Ostade 6404; Pieter Quast 6410; Willem van de Velde 6407; Emanuel de Witte 6402

ALEXANDER, W. C.: Jan van de Cappelle 6406; Aelbert Cuyp 6405; Dutch School 6414; Frans Hals 6411, 6413; Philips Koninck 6408; Isack van Ostade 6404; Pieter Quast 6410; Willem van de Velde 6407; Emanuel de Witte 6402

ALLAN, Alexander: Pieter Saenredam 1896

ALLENDALE, Lord: Jan Steen 6442

ALPHEN: *see* Smeth van Alphen

AMORY, Sir J. Heathcoat: Jan van Goyen 6423

AMSTEL: *see* Ploos van Amstel

ANDERSON, Edward Wright: Jacob van Ruisdael 2561

ANDRIESSE: Jan Wijnants 972

ANGERSTEIN, John Julius: Aelbert Cuyp 53; Rembrandt 45, 47

ANONYMOUS DONOR: Attributed to Cesar van Everdingen 3315

ANONYMOUS SALES:
(Note – Where the vendor has since been identified the sale is not listed under this heading.)

Amsterdam
16 May 1696: Johannes Vermeer 1383, 2568
15 May 1708: Karel Dujardin 6296
11 July 1714: Johannes Vermeer 1383, 2568
16 September 1739: Jan Beerstraaten 1311
11 sqq. May 1756: Paulus Potter 849
20 March 1764: Jan van der Heyden 1914
18 March 1767: Nicolaes Berchem 820
26 April 1769: Jan van der Heyden 1914
 1 October 1778: Jan Steen 2556
 9 April 1783: Nicolaes Berchem 1006
16 June 1802: Frans van Mieris 1415
29 September 1802: Jan Steen 856
 7 May 1804: Jan Steen 2559
22 June 1814: Dutch School 2546
 1 April 1883: Frans Hals 6411

Antwerp
12 May 1806: Jan Wijnants 884

London
20 sqq. March 1772: Attributed to Abraham van Calraet 2548
4–5 March 1791: Jacob van Ruisdael 2562
18 February 1792: Adriaen van Ostade 846
.... 1822: Aelbert Cuyp 824
26 June 1824: Gabriel Metsu 2591
27 sqq. July 1832: Gerrit van Honthorst 4503
.... 1834: Karel Dujardin 6296
26 May 1836: Nicolaes Berchem 1006
27 January 1838: Eglon Hendrik van der Neer 2535
15 May 1858: Gerard ter Borch 4596
30 May 1863: Jan Both 958
 7 May 1864: Jan Both 1917
13 July 1895: Pieter Codde 2576

VELDE, Frans van de: Gabriel Metsu 5225

VENCE, Comte de: Godfried Schalcken 998

VERBEEK: Meindert Hobbema 6138

VERBELEN: Willem van de Velde 2573

VERNON, Hon. G. J.: Studio of Willem van de Velde 149

VERSTOLK VAN SOELEN, Baron J. G.: Meindert Hobbema 6138; Philips Koninck 4251; Attributed to Rembrandt 5282; Jacob van Ruisdael 1390

VICARS, Messrs: Judith Leyster 5417

VICTORIA & ALBERT MUSEUM: Gerrit Berckheyde 1863; Abraham van Calraet 1683; Salomon van Ruysdael 1439

VILLERS: Philips Koninck 836

VOET: Caspar Netscher 843

VOYER D'ARGENSON, Marquis: Gerrit Dou 825; Gabriel Metsu 5225

VRIES, de: Nicolaes Maes 159; Willem van de Velde 873

VRIES, J. de: Meindert Hobbema 6138

VUGT, Hendrik van der: Gerrit Berckheyde 1451

WACKER VAN SON (ZON), Hendrick de: Adriaen van Ostade 2542

WALDEGRAVE, Admiral William: see Radstock, Baron

WALES, Prince of (later George IV): Aelbert Cuyp 6405; Jan Hackaert and Nicolaes Berchem 829

WALLACE, Sir Richard: Gerard ter Borch 896

WALLIS, Mrs: Frans van Mieris 1415

WALLIS, George Augustus: Philips Wouwermans 880

WANDELAAR: Gerrit Berckheyde 1451

WANTAGE, Lady: Attributed to Rembrandt 5282

WARD, T. Humphry: Willem de Poorter 1294; Johannes Vermeer 2568

WASSENAAR OBDAM, Graaf van: Willem van Mieris 841; Adriaen van Ostade 846

WASSENAER VAN RUYVEN, Susanna Louisa Huygens, widow of Baron van: see Huygens, S. L.

WATSON, Denis Elliot: Gerrit Dou 4189

WATSON, Sir Renny: Gerrit Dou 4189

WEBB, John: Johan van Huchtenburgh 211; Thomas de Keyser 212; Gabriel Metsu 838;

Philips Wouwermans 878, 881; Jan Wijnants 883

WEITZNER, Julius: Pieter Lastman 6272

WELLESLEY, Hon. William Pole-Tynley-Long-: see Mornington, Earl of

WELLS, William: Ludolf Bakhuizen 1000; Jan van Huysum 796; Adriaen van Ostade 2542; Rembrandt 775; Jan Wijnants 2533

WERTHEIMER, Asher: Meindert Hobbema 2570; Jan Molenaer 5416; Paulus Potter 2583

WERTHEIMER, C.: Frans Hals 6411

WERTHER, Johan Christoph: Adriaen van de Velde 867

WEST: Willem van Mieris 841

WESTMINSTER, Duke of: Adriaen van der Werff 3909

WESTMINSTER, Marquess of: Adriaen van der Werff 3909

WHATMAN, James: Jan van de Cappelle 2586; Emanuel de Witte 6402

WHEELER, Samuel: Adriaen van de Velde 983

WHITE, Frederick Anthony: Bartholomeus van Bassen 3164

WHITE, John Forbes: Johannes Bosboom 2712

WHITE, Robert: Philips Wouwermans 975

WHITE, William Benoni: Paulus Theodorus van Brussel 3225; Georgius Jacobus Johannes van Os 3226

WICKHAM, Mrs Gordon: Paulus Theodorus van Brussel 5800

WIGZELL: Quiringh van Brekelenkam 2549

WILKES, Dr W. D.: Style of Jan van Huysum 3165

WILLEMSEN, Jacobus: Karel Dujardin 828

WILLETT, John W.: Gabriel Metsu 970

WILLIAM II, King of the Netherlands: Paulus Theodorus van Brussel 5174, 5800; Dirck Santvoort 3154

WILLIAMS, Sir Frederick Martin, Bart.: Eglon Hendrik van der Neer 2535

WILLIAMS, Romer: Willem Duyster 1386, 1387

WILMER, Lt.-Col. Worthington: Quiringh van Brekelenkam 1329

WILSON: Philips Wouwermans 975

WINKEL, Klaas van: Rembrandt 775

WINKLER, Gottfried: Frans van Mieris 1415

WINSTANLEY, Hamlet: Rembrandt 6350

Index by Year of Acquisition

961   Aelbert CUYP. Bequeathed.

962   Aelbert CUYP. Bequeathed.

963   Imitator of Isack van OSTADE. Bequeathed.

964   Jan van de CAPPELLE. Bequeathed.

965   Jan van de CAPPELLE. Bequeathed.

966   Jan van de CAPPELLE. Bequeathed.

967   Jan van de CAPPELLE. Bequeathed.

968   Gerrit DOU. Bequeathed.

969   Aert van der NEER. Bequeathed.

970   Gabriel METSU. Bequeathed.

971   Jan WIJNANTS. Bequeathed.

972   Jan WIJNANTS. Bequeathed.

973   Philips WOUWERMANS. Bequeathed.

974   Cornelis van der SCHALCKE. Bequeathed.

975   Philips WOUWERMANS. Bequeathed.

976   Ascribed to Philips WOUWERMANS. Bequeathed.

977   Studio of Willem van de VELDE the Younger. Bequeathed.

978   Willem van de VELDE the Younger. Bequeathed.

979   Willem van de VELDE the Younger. Bequeathed.

980   Willem van de VELDE the Younger. Bequeathed.

981   Willem van de VELDE the Younger. Bequeathed.

982   Adriaen van de VELDE. Bequeathed.

983   Adriaen van de VELDE. Bequeathed.

984   Dirck van den BERGEN. Bequeathed.

985   Karel DUJARDIN. Bequeathed.

986   Jacob van RUISDAEL. Bequeathed.

987   Jacob van RUISDAEL. Bequeathed.

988   Jacob van RUISDAEL. Bequeathed.

989   Jacob van RUISDAEL. Bequeathed.

990   Jacob van RUISDAEL. Bequeathed.

991   Jacob van RUISDAEL. Bequeathed.

992   Jan van der HEYDEN. Bequeathed.

993   Jan van der HEYDEN. Bequeathed.

994   Jan van der HEYDEN. Bequeathed.

995   Meindert HOBBEMA. Bequeathed.

996   Imitator of Jacob van RUISDAEL. Bequeathed.

997   Godfried SCHALCKEN. Bequeathed.

998   Godfried SCHALCKEN. Bequeathed.

999   Godfried SCHALCKEN. Bequeathed.

1000   Ludolf BAKHUIZEN. Bequeathed.

1001   Jan van HUYSUM. Bequeathed.

1002   Jacob van WALSCAPPELLE. Bequeathed.

1004   Nicolaes BERCHEM. Bequeathed.

1005   Nicolaes BERCHEM. Bequeathed.

1006   Nicolaes BERCHEM. Bequeathed.

1007   Lodewijck van LUDICK. Bequeathed.

1008   Jan de LAGOOR. Bequeathed.

1009   Pieter VERBEECK. Bequeathed.

1010   Dirck van DELEN. Bequeathed.

1013   Johannes SPRUYT. Bequeathed.

1015   Wybrand HENDRIKS. Bequeathed.

1021   Frans HALS. Purchased.

1879

1050   Ludolf BAKHUIZEN. Bequeathed.

1053   Emanuel de WITTE. Bequeathed.

1055   Hendrick SORGH. Bequeathed.

1056   Hendrick SORGH. Bequeathed.

1060   Philips WOUWERMANS. Bequeathed.

1061   Egbert van der POEL. Bequeathed.

1074   Dirck HALS. Purchased.

1880

1095   Jan LIEVENS. Presented.

1096   Jan Baptist WEENIX. (Transferred.)

1884

1168   Willem van der VLIET. Purchased.

1886

1221   Abraham de PAPE. Purchased.

1222   Melchior d'HONDECOETER. Presented.

1888

1247   Follower of REMBRANDT. Purchased.

1248   Bartholomeus van der HELST. Purchased.

1251   Frans HALS. Presented.

1255   Jan van de VELDE. Presented.

1256   Harmen STEENWYCK. Presented.

1277   Nicolaes MAES. Presented.

1889

1278   Hendrick POT. Purchased.

1288   Aert van der NEER. Bequeathed.

1289   Aelbert CUYP. Bequeathed.

1292   Jan van BIJLERT. Purchased.

1293   Jan MOLENAER. Purchased.

1294   Willem de POORTER. Presented.

Index by Inventory Number

551

SUPPLEMENT

Summary catalogue entries for three Dutch paintings acquired by the National Gallery between 1988 and 1990.

ALBERT CUYP, 1620–1691

For a biographical account of the artist, see pp. 86–7.

6522 *River Landscape with Horseman and Peasants*

Plate A

Signed, lower right: A cuijp

Oil on oak, 123 × 241 (49 × 96).

This large canvas was probably painted in the late 1650s.[1] Cuyp's patrons, like those of his father, the portrait painter Jacob Gerritsz. Cuyp, appear to have been members of the regent families of Dordrecht, and this large landscape was presumably intended for the house of a member of this group, which Cuyp joined by marriage in 1658.

A print made after the painting in 1764 by William Elliott shows a higher sky and in the inscription beneath gives the dimensions as 60 by 96 inches, which is 11 inches higher than the present size. For this reason it has been thought that the painting was cut down after 1764. However, after the painting was acquired by the National Gallery, the edges of the painting were carefully examined by the Chief Restorer and the unpainted edges discovered on all four sides. The painting cannot, therefore, have been cut down. There are two possible explanations: the painting may have been given a fashionably higher sky at some time before 1760,[2] or the engraver was exercising artistic licence. Whatever the explanation for the extended sky in the print, the present dimensions of the painting are original and the composition carefully balanced.

In Elliot's print, the painting is identified as a View on the Maas at Dordrecht. In fact, it is an imaginary landscape, with mountains on a scale which cannot be found in the Netherlands. Cuyp may, however, have referred to drawings of actual views he made in his sketchbooks, particularly those made on a trip to Nijmegen and Cleves in 1651–2.

The painting was purchased in the United Provinces by Captain William Baillie in about 1760. Baillie acted as an agent for John, 3rd Earl of Bute, in the formation of the collection which he hung at Luton Hoo. It was in Bute's collection by the time that Elliott's print was made in 1764. At that time Cuyp was so little known in Britain that Elliott gave the artist's first name as Adrian. In 1769 John Boydell praised the painting as 'entirely painted from nature, [it] is inexpressibly bright, clear and sunny: the choice of scene is elegant and picturesque'.[3] According to Benjamin West, it was this picture which began the rage for landscapes by Cuyp among British collectors. On 18 May 1818, Joseph Farington wrote in his diary: 'I went to the British Institution and there met Mr. West and I went round the exhibition with him examining all the pictures. While looking at Lord Bute's picture by Cuyp, he said that picture was brought to England by the late Captn. Baillie, and was the first picture by that master known in England. Having been seen pictures by Cuyp were eagerly sought for and many were introduced and sold to advantage'.[4] The painting hung at Luton Hoo, where it was seen by Gustav Waagen who praised it as 'a chef d'oeuvre by this Master . . . Few of Cuyp's large pictures are so accurately finished in the details, or unite such admirable impasto with such transparency'.[5]

ENGRAVING: By William Elliott, 1764 (discussed above).

PROVENANCE: Purchased in the United Provinces by Captain William Baillie on behalf of John, 3rd Earl of Bute, in whose possession it was when engraved by Elliott in 1764; Marquesses of Bute, Luton Hoo (Manuscript Catalogue of 1790, No. 118) and Mount Stuart, Island of Bute; On loan to the National Museum of Wales, Cardiff, 1975–87; On loan to the National Gallery of Scotland, Edinburgh, 1988–9; Purchased, with the assistance of contributions from the National Heritage Memorial Fund and the NACF, 1989.

EXHIBITIONS: BI 1818, No. 85; BI 1819, No. 37; BI 1847, No. 66; RA 1870, No. 102; London, Bethnal Green Museum, 'Collection of Paintings lent for exhibition by the Marquess of Bute' 1883, No. 38; Glasgow 1884; Manchester, Queen's Park Museum and Art Gallery, 'The Bute Collection of Pictures' (Catalogue by J.P. Richter), 1885, No. 56; London, Guildhall, 1894, No. 45; Edinburgh, National Gallery of Scotland, 'Dutch and Flemish Paintings from the Collection of the Marquess of Bute', 1949, No. 7; London, National Gallery, 'Aelbert Cuyp in British Collections' (Catalogue by S. Reiss), 1973, No. 14; London 1976, No. 31; Amsterdam, Rijksmuseum, Boston, Museum of Fine Arts, Philadelphia Museum of Art, 'Masters of 17th-Century Dutch Landscape Painting' (Catalogue entry by A. Chong) 1988, No. 25.

REFERENCES:
General: Smith, No. 264; HdG, No. 433; S. Reiss, Aelbert Cuyp, London, 1975, p. 183, pl. 140.
In text:
1. This dating was proposed by S. Reiss (Aelbert Cuyp in British Collections, London, 1973) and supported by A. Chong (Masters of 17th-Century Dutch Landscape Painting, Amsterdam/Boston/Philadelphia, 1987–8, pp. 302–4).
2. This happened, for example, to a number of paintings by Hercules Segers which were owned by the Amsterdam art dealer Johannes de Renialme in the mid-seventeenth century (J. G. van Gelder, 'Hercules Segers erbij en eraf', OH, 65, 1950, pp. 216–26).
3. J. Boydell, A Collection of Prints, Engraved after the Most Capital Paintings in England, London, 1769, pl. 12.

4. Farington, vol. 15, p. 5203. It is worth mentioning, however, that (as Chong, op. cit., points out) Noel Desenfans claimed that a certain 'Grand Jean', a Swiss dealer, imported paintings by Cuyp into England at an earlier date, some of which were sold to Blackwood who in turn sold one to Sir Lawrence Dundas (No. 53 of this catalogue) (N. Desenfans, A Descriptive Catalogue of Some Pictures of the Different Schools, Purchased for H.M. the late King of Poland, 2 vols, London 1802, pp. 142–5). Chong also notes that the first paintings by Cuyp to appear in a London auction were in Glover's sale, 16–17 March 1741, Nos. 58 (a landscape with cattle) and 115 (a seaport).
5. Waagen 1854, pp. 479–80.

JAN VAN DER HEYDEN

For a biographical account of the artist, see p. 168.

6526 *View of the Westerkerk, Amsterdam* Plate B

Signed and indistinctly dated on the lowest step of one of the houses on the right: I. vd Heijde 16(60?)

Oil on oak, 90.7 × 114.5 (35¾ × 45)

The Westerkerk is seen from across the Keizersgracht.

The date on the painting is damaged but would appear to read 1660. This painting is unusual in the work of van der Heyden by virtue of its large size. The view of the Westerkerk in the Wallace Collection,[1] which has a very similar composition, measures only 41.3 × 59 cm (16¼ × 23¼ in.), that is, about half the size of No. 6526. This size must have been specified by the Kerkmeesters of the Westerkerk who presumably commissioned the work from van der Heyden. It is recorded hanging in the Kerkmeesterscamer in 1790[2] and remained there until its sale to an Amsterdam dealer in 1864.[3]

When this view of the Westerkerk was painted by van der Heyden, it was a relatively new building. It was not, like so many others in the Netherlands, a converted Roman Catholic Church but was built explicitly for the Reformed Church. The foundation stone had been laid in 1620 and the church was completed in 1631. The architect was Hendrick de Keyser, who had died in 1621, and his plans were brought to completion by his son, Pieter. There were, however, a number of substantial changes made to Hendrick de Keyser's original designs, particularly in the tower, which was not completed until 1638, and these have been attributed to Cornelis Dankerts.

DRAWING: There is a preparatory drawing (Pen with brown ink and watercolour over black chalk, 290 × 591 mm.) in the van Eeghen collection at the Gemeentearchief, Amsterdam.[4]

PROVENANCE: The painting is described as being in the Kerkmeesterscamer in 1790.[5] It was sold by the Kerkmeesters in 1864 to an Amsterdam dealer, B.A. Hopman, who sold it to the Paris branch of the Rothschild family; Edmond de Rothschild, Paris. It subsequently passed to James de Rothschild and then to his widow. It was acquired by the National Gallery from the executors of the estate of Mrs James de Rothschild through the Acceptance-in-lieu procedure, 1990.

REFERENCES:

General: HdG, No. 23 (6); H. Wagner, *Jan van der Heyden 1637–1712*, Amsterdam, 1971, cat. no. 8.
In text: **1.** Wagner, op. cit., cat. no. 7.
2. I. Wagenaar, *Beschrijving van Amsterdam*, 1790, vol. 5, p. 451.
3. The documents concerning the sale are preserved in the archive of the Westerkerk.
4. B. Bakker et al., *De Verzameling Van Eeghen: Amsterdamse Tekeningen 1600–1900*, Gemeentearchief Amsterdam, Amsterdam, 1989, cat. no. 39. For a discussion of the drawing and its relationship with the painting in the National Gallery, see also C.P. van Eeghen, 'De Westerkerk door Jan van der Heyden', *Jaarboek Amstelodamum*, 39, 1942, pp. 1–7.
5. See above, note 2.
6. The description given by HdG is inaccurate. He notes that 'on the nearer quay in the left foreground are five mooring-posts for vessels.' In fact, these are wooden palings placed around the trunks of young trees in order to protect them. Posters have been pasted to these and on the most prominent is a torn poster advertising a sale of paintings at auction.

JAN VAN OS, 1744–1808

For a biographical account of the artist, see p. 297.

6520 *Fruit and Flowers in a Terracotta Vase* *Plate C*

Among the fruit are grapes, plums, peaches and a pineapple; the flowers include roses and carnations.

Signed, on the marble slab, at the left: iVAN Os Fecit/1777 en 1778.

Oil on mahogany, 89.1 × 71 (35 × 27⅞).

Cleaned in 1988.

It is not unusual for still-life paintings of this type to be dated in two successive years, as the artist waited for particular flowers to bloom in different seasons.[1]

PROVENANCE: Collection of Sir William Churchman, Bart (d.1947); presented by Miss Violet Churchman in memory of her sister Ida Nancy Churchman, 1988.

REFERENCE: **1.** See van Huysum No. 796 above, p.208 and p.209 (note 1).

COMPARATIVE
PLATES

FIGURE I

Ludolf Bakhuizen, *An English Hooker*. Brush and pen and brown ink, 192 × 319 m. Royal Collection. Windsor Castle, Royal Library. (See Bakhuizen No. 819.)

FIGURE 2

Attributed to Thomas Wijck, *An Astrologer*. Black chalk and brown ink, 269 × 188 mm.
Besançon, Musée des Beaux-Arts et d'Archéologie. (See Cornelis Bega No. 1481.)

FIGURE 3

Gerrit Berckheyde, preparatory study for the left half of *The Market Place and Town Hall in Haarlem* (No. 1863). Black chalk, 222 × 165 mm. Haarlem, Teylers Museum.

FIGURE 4

Gerard ter Borch, *A Lady playing the Lute*. Panel, 51 × 37 cm.
Cassel, Gemäldegalerie. (See ter Borch No. 864.)

FIGURE 5

Gerard ter Borch, *A Lady and a Gentleman making Music.* Canvas, 58 × 46 cm.
Cassel, Gemäldegalerie. (See ter Borch No. 864.)

FIGURE 6

Gerard ter Borch, *The Swearing of the Oath of the Ratification of the Treaty of Münster, 15 May 1648* (No. 896). Detail, before cleaning. London, National Gallery.

FIGURE 7

Gerard ter Borch, *The Swearing of the Oath of the Ratification of the Treaty of Münster, 15 May 1648* (No. 896). Detail, after cleaning. London, National Gallery.

FIGURE 8

Gerard ter Borch, *The Swearing of the Oath of the Ratification of the Treaty of Münster, 15 May 1648.*
Canvas, 48 × 39.5 cm. Münster, Westfälisches Landesmuseum für Kunst and Kulturgeschichte. (See
ter Borch No. 896.)

FIGURE 9

Gerard ter Borch, *The Swearing of the Oath of the Ratification of the Treaty of Münster, 15 May 1648.*
Engraving by J. Suijderhof, 46.9 × 58.8 cm. London, British Museum. (See ter Borch No. 896.)

FIGURE 10

Gerard ter Borch, *Portrait of Hermanna van der Cruis*. Canvas, 62 × 50.5 cm.
Vienna, Kunsthistorisches Museum. (See ter Borch No. 4596.)

FIGURE 11

Gerard ter Borch, *An Officer dictating a Letter* (No. 5847). Infra-red photograph.

FIGURE 12

Casp. Netscher pinxit   CASPARVS NETSCHER.   W. Vaillant fecit

After Caspar Netscher, *Self Portrait* (No. 5847). Mezzotint by Wallerant Vaillant.
London, British Museum.

FIGURE 13

Gerard ter Borch, *A Woman playing a Theorbo*. Canvas, 51.5 × 38.5 cm.
Dresden, Staatliche Kunstsammlungen. (See ter Borch No. 5847.)

FIGURE 14

Johannes Bosboom, *The Interior of the Bakenesserkerk, Haarlem.* Canvas, 88 × 113 cm. Amsterdam, Historisch Museum. (See Bosboom No. 2712.)

FIGURE 15

Johannes Bosboom, study for *The Interior of the Bakenesserkerk, Haarlem* (No. 2712). Sepia wash drawing, 280 × 440 mm. Dordrecht, D. van Houten Collection.

FIGURE 16

Jan de Braij, *Portrait of a Woman with a Black Cap* (No. 1423).
Composite X-ray photograph.

FIGURE 17

Quiringh van Brekelenkam, *The Interior of a Tailor Shop.* Panel, 60 × 85 cm. Massachusetts, Worcester Art Museum. (See van Brekelenkam No. 2549.)

FIGURE 18

Jean-Etienne Liotard, copy after Quiringh van Brekelenkam's *A Woman Asleep by a Fire, an Open Bible (?) in her Lap* (No. 2550). Porcelain, 44 × 34 cm. Vienna, Kunsthistorisches Museum.

FIGURE 19

Hendrick ter Brugghen, *Jacob and Laban*. Canvas, 123 × 157 cm. Cologne, Wallraf-Richartz Museum. (See ter Brugghen No. 4164.)

FIGURE 20

Hendrick ter Brugghen, *A Man playing a Lute*. Canvas, 100.5 × 78.7 cm. Cassel, Gemäldegalerie. (See ter Brugghen No. 6347.)

FIGURE 21

Hendrick ter Brugghen, *The Concert* (No. 6483). Composite X-ray photograph.

FIGURE 22

Abraham van Calraet, *Stable Interior with Two Dapple-Grey Horses*. Panel, 31.4 × 40 cm. Rotterdam, Boymans–van Beuningen Museum. (See Calraet No. 1683.)

FIGURE 23

Cornelis van Haarlem, *Two Followers of Cadmus devoured by a Dragon* (No. 1893). Engraving by Hendrick Goltzius, 24.8 × 31 cm. London, British Museum.

FIGURE 24

Aelbert Cuyp, preparatory study for *A Herdsman with a Cowherd* (No. 822). Black chalk, pen and wash, 147 × 191 mm. Amsterdam, Rijksprentenkabinet Rijksmuseum.

FIGURE 25

Aelbert Cuyp, preparatory study for *Ubbergen Castle* (No. 824). Chalk and wash drawing, 180 × 268 mm. Vienna, Albertina.

FIGURE 26

Aelbert Cuyp, preparatory study for 'The Large Dort' (No. 961). Black chalk and Indian ink wash, 152 × 303 mm. London, British Museum.

FIGURE 27

Aelbert Cuyp,
preparatory study for
*Peasants and Four Cows
by the River Merwede*
(No. 1289).
191 × 96 mm.
V. de S. Collection.

FIGURE 28

Olivier van Deuren, *A Young Astronomer*. Panel, 31 × 25.5 cm. New York, Private Collection.
(See van Deuren No. 2589.)

FIGURE 29

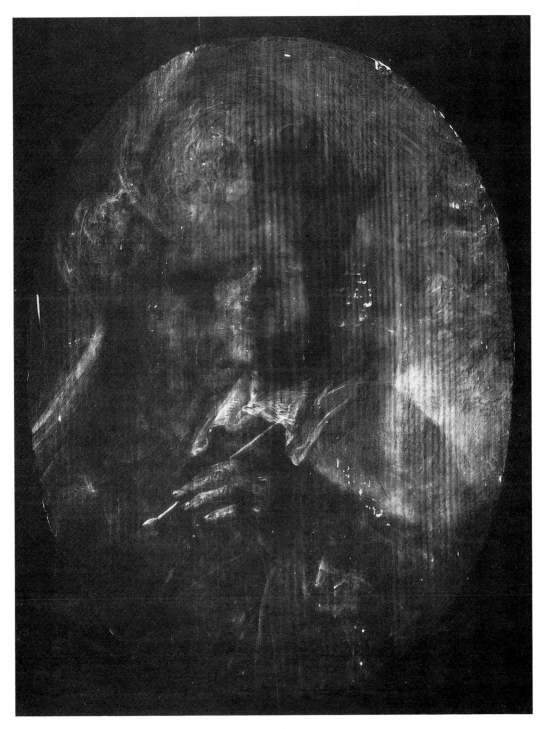

Gerrit Dou, *Self Portrait* (No. 192). X-ray photograph.

FIGURE 30

Gerrit Dou, *Anna and the Blind Tobit* (No. 4189). Engraving by Willem van der Leeuw, 30.1 × 21 cm. London, British Museum.

FIGURE 31

Willem van Drielenburgh, *A View of the Wittevrouwenpoort, Utrecht.* Canvas, 86 × 79 cm.
Utrecht, Centraal Museum. (See van Drielenburgh No. 960.)

FIGURE 32

Willem Drost, *Portrait of a Woman*. Canvas, 83 × 71 cm. The Hague, Bredius Museum.
(See Attributed to Drost No. 237.)

FIGURE 33

Karel Dujardin, *Portrait of a Young Man (Self Portrait ?)* (No. 1680). Composite X-ray photograph.

FIGURE 34

Antonio Tempesta, *The Conversion of St Paul.* Engraving. Amsterdam, Rijksprentenkabinet Rijksmuseum.
(See Dujardin No. 6296.)

FIGURE 35

Carel Fabritius, *Portrait of a Man (Self Portrait ?)*. Panel, 65 × 49 cm. Rotterdam, Boymans-van Beuningen Museum. (See Fabritius No. 4042.)

FIGURE 36

Govert Flinck, *Self Portrait*. Engraving by Blootelingh. Amsterdam, Rijksprentenkabinet Rijksmuseum. (See Flink No. 4068.)

FIGURE 37

Jacob de Gheyn III, *St Paul seated reading*. Etching, 30 × 19.6 cm. London, British Museum. (See After Jacob de Gheyn III No. 3590.)

FIGURE 38

Jan van Goyen, *River Scene with Shipping.* Panel, 39.5 × 54.3 cm. Frankfurt, Städelsches Kunstinstitut. (See van Goyen No. 6423.)

FIGURE 39

Joris van der Haagen, *The Path in the Woods.* Canvas, 114.3 × 122.5 cm. Present location unknown. (See van der Haagen No. 901.)

Frans Hals, *Portrait of Jean de la Chambre at the Age of Thirty-three* (No. 6411). Engraving by
Jonas Suijderhoef, 25.5 × 17.5 cm. London, British Museum.

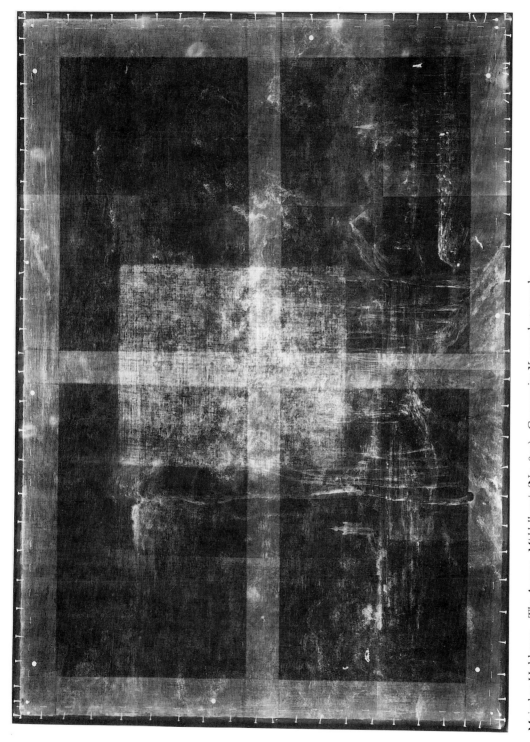

FIGURE 41

Meindert Hobbema, *The Avenue, Middelharnis* (No. 830). Composite X-ray photograph.

FIGURE 42

Meindert Hobbema, *A Stream by a Wood*. Panel, 76.4 × 110 cm. Rotterdam, Boymans–van Beuningen Museum. (See Hobbema No. 833.)

FIGURE 43

Meindert Hobbema, *A Woody Landscape with a Cottage on the right.* Canvas, 96.5 × 108 cm. Washington, National Gallery of Art, Widener Collection. (See Hobbema No. 995.)

FIGURE 44

Pieter de Hooch, *The Courtyard of a House in Delft*. Oak panel, 66.5 × 56.5 cm. Private collection. (See de Hooch No. 835.)

Pieter de Hooch, *The Courtyard of a House in Delft* (No. 835). Detail showing the inscription above the arch.

Pieter de Hooch, *The Courtyard of a House in Delft*. Detail showing the inscription above the arch. Private Collection. (See de Hooch No. 835.)

FIGURE 46

Pieter de Hooch, *A Man with Dead Birds, and Other Figures, in a Stable* (No. 3881).
X-ray photograph of bottom right-hand corner.

FIGURE 47

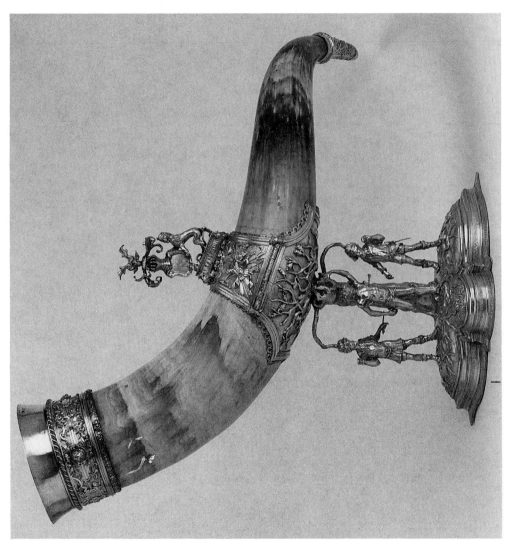

Willem Kalf, *Drinking Horn of the St Sebastian Archers' Guild.* Amsterdam, Historisch Museum. (See Kalf No. 6444.)

FIGURE 48

Judith Leyster, *A Boy and a Girl with a Cat and (?) an Eel* (No. 5417). Composite X-ray photograph.

FIGURE 49

Jan Lievens, *A Landscape with Tobias and the Angel* (No. 72). Detail of the reverse showing the Antwerp brand.

FIGURE 50

Lodewijck van Ludick, *A Castle by a River.* Canvas, 42 × 56.8 cm. Warsaw, National Museum.
(See van Ludick No. 1007.)

FIGURE 51

Rembrandt, *The Night Watch*. Canvas, 363 × 427 cm. Amsterdam, Rijksmuseum. (See Lundens No. 289.)

FIGURES 52, 53

Figure 53 Nicolaes Maes, *Seated Figure*, preparatory study for *A Woman scraping Parsnips, with a Child standing by her* (No. 159). Pen and ink with brown wash, 98 × 84 mm. New York. Ian Woodner Family Collection.

Figure 52 Nicolaes Maes, preparatory study for *A Woman scraping Parsnips, with a Child standing by her* (No. 159). Brush and brown ink, 124 × 84 mm. Paris, Institut Néerlandais.

Figure 55 Nicolaes Maes, preparatory study for *Christ blessing the Children* (No. 757). Pen, brush and brown ink, 198 × 169 mm. London, British Museum.

Figure 54 Nicolaes Maes, preparatory study for *Christ blessing the Children* (No. 757). Pen, brush and brown ink, 198 × 169 mm. Amsterdam, Rijksprentenkabinet Rijksmuseum.

FIGURE 56

Pieter van der Werff, copy after Nicolaes Maes's *Portrait of Jan de Reus* (No. 2581).
Canvas, 82 × 68 cm. Amsterdam, Rijksmuseum.

FIGURE 57

Jacob Maris, *A Drawbridge in a Dutch Town.* Watercolour, 28 × 21.5 cm.
Amsterdam, Rijksmuseum. (See Maris No. 2710.)

FIGURE 58

Gabriel Metsu, *Twelfth Night*. Canvas, 79 × 98 cm. Munich, Alte Pinakothek. (See Metsu No. 839.)

FIGURE 59

PERILLVSTRIS ET REVERENDISSIMI DOMINI D. ANTONI TRIEST GANDAVENSIVM EPISCOPI
COMITIS EVERGHEMENSIS CATHOLICÆ MAIESTATI A CONSILIIS ETC.
Auspicijs CHRISTI PATIENTIS *et in flagella parati Imago, coloribus picta, quæ in Apelleo Thefauro aulæ ipsius Epifcopalis afferuatur:
nunc ære fculpta et exprefsa, ab eius Inuentore et Pictore Gerardo Segherio, in orbis Theatrum inducta, EXPONITVR DEDICATVRQVE.
Gerardus Seghers Inuen.   *Cum Priuilegio*   *Lucas Vorfterman fculp.*

Gerard Seghers, *Christ at the Column before the Flagellation.* Engraving by Lucas Vorsterman.
Amsterdam, Rijksprentenkabinet Rijksmuseum. (See Metsu No. 5225.)

FIGURE 60

Frans van Mieris, *A Woman in a Red Jacket feeding a Parrot.* Panel, 22.5 × 17.7 cm.
Private Collection. (See van Mieris No. 840.)

FIGURE 61

Frans van Mieris, *Self Portrait*. Panel, 12.3 × 9.6 cm.
Berlin, Gemäldegalerie, Staatliche Museen.
(See van Mieris No. 1415.)

FIGURE 62

Frans van Mieris, *Self Portrait of the Artist with a Cittern* (No. 1874). Infra-red photograph showing the inscription.

FIGURE 63

Frans van Mieris, *Self Portrait*. Black chalk on vellum, 197 × 137 mm. London, British Museum. (See van Mieris No. 1874.)

FIGURE 64

Frans van Mieris, *An Old Fiddler at a Window*. Panel, 28.1 × 21 cm. Location unknown.
(See After van Mieris No. 2952.)

FIGURE 65

Peter Paul Rubens, *The Brazen Serpent.* Canvas, 186.4 × 264.5 cm. London, National Gallery. (See Netscher No. 844.)

FIGURE 66

Caspar Netscher, *Maternal Care*. Panel, 44.5 × 38 cm. Amsterdam, Rijksmuseum.
(See Netscher No. 844.)

FIGURE 67

Caspar Netscher, *A Musical Party*. Canvas, 50.4 × 45.9 cm. Munich, Alte Pinakothek.
(See After Netscher No. 1879.)

FIGURE 68

Michiel Nouts, *Portrait of a Lady*. Canvas, 108 × 50.5 cm. Amsterdam, Rijksmuseum.

FIGURE 69

Adriaen van Ostade, *A Cobbler at his Stall*. Etching, 18.7 × 14.9 cm. London, British Museum. (See After Adriaen van Ostade No. 2541.)

FIGURE 70

Rembrandt, *The Lamentation over the Dead Christ* (No. 43). X-ray photograph.

FIGURE 71

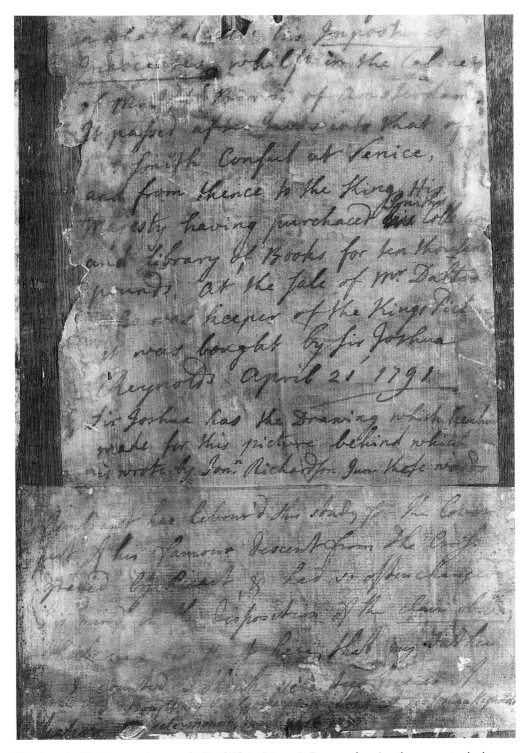

Rembrandt, *The Lamentation over the Dead Christ* (No. 43). Reverse showing the paper attached to the panel.

FIGURE 72

Rembrandt, preparatory study for *The Lamentation over the Dead Christ* (No. 43). Brown, grey and white oil colour and pale brown ink over red chalk, 213 × 254 mm. London, British Museum.

FIGURE 73

Rembrandt, *The Adoration of the Shepherds*. Canvas, 97 × 71 cm. Munich, Alte Pinakothek.
(See Rembrandt No. 47.)

FIGURE 74

Rembrandt, *Self Portrait at the Age of Sixty-three* (No. 221). Composite X-ray photograph.

FIGURE 75

Rembrandt, *An Elderly Man as St Paul* (No. 243). Detail showing the roundel.

FIGURE 76

Rembrandt, *Self Portrait*. Etching, 20.5 × 16.4 cm. London, British Museum.
(See Rembrandt No. 672.)

FIGURE 77

Joachim van Sandrart, drawing after Titian's *Portrait of a Man*. Black chalk, 225 × 180 mm. Paris, Institut Néerlandais. (See Rembrandt No. 672.)

FIGURE 78

Jan Stolker, drawing after Rembrandt's *Portrait of an Eighty-three-year-old Woman*.
Brush, Indian ink and wash, 218 × 175 mm. London, British Museum. (See Rembrandt No. 775.)

FIGURE 79

Rembrandt, *Philips Lucasz*. (No. 850). Composite X-ray photograph.

FIGURE 80

Rembrandt, *Portrait of Petronella Buys*. Oval panel, 76 × 58 cm. Formerly New York, Wildenstein and Co. (See Rembrandt No. 850.)

FIGURE 81

Rembrandt, *Ecce Homo*. Etching, third state, 54.9 × 44.7 cm. London, British Museum.
(See Rembrandt No. 1400.)

FIGURE 82

Jacob Gerritsz. Cuyp, *Portrait of Jacob Trip*. Panel, 72 × 58.3 cm. New York, Private Collection. (See Rembrandt No. 1674.)

FIGURE 83

Jacob Gerritsz. Cuyp, *Portrait of Margaretha Trip*. Panel, 74 × 59 cm. Amsterdam, Rijksmuseum.
(See Rembrandt No. 1675.)

FIGURE 84

Copy after Rembrandt, *Saskia van Uylenburgh in Arcadian Costume* (No. 4930).
Canvas, 194 × 131 cm. Kreuzlingen, Kisters Collection.

FIGURE 85

Rembrandt, *Saskia van Uylenburgh in Arcadian Costume* (No. 4930). Composite X-ray photograph.

FIGURE 86

Rembrandt, *Saskia van Uylenburgh in Arcadian Costume.* Canvas, 125 × 101 cm. Leningrad,
Hermitage Museum. (See Rembrandt No. 4930.)

FIGURE 87

Peter Paul Rubens, *Judith and Holofernes*. Panel, 120 × 111 cm. Braunschweig, Herzog Anton Ulrich-Museum. (See Rembrandt No. 4930.)

FIGURE 88

Rembrandt, *Belshazzar's Feast* (No. 6350). Composite X-ray photograph.

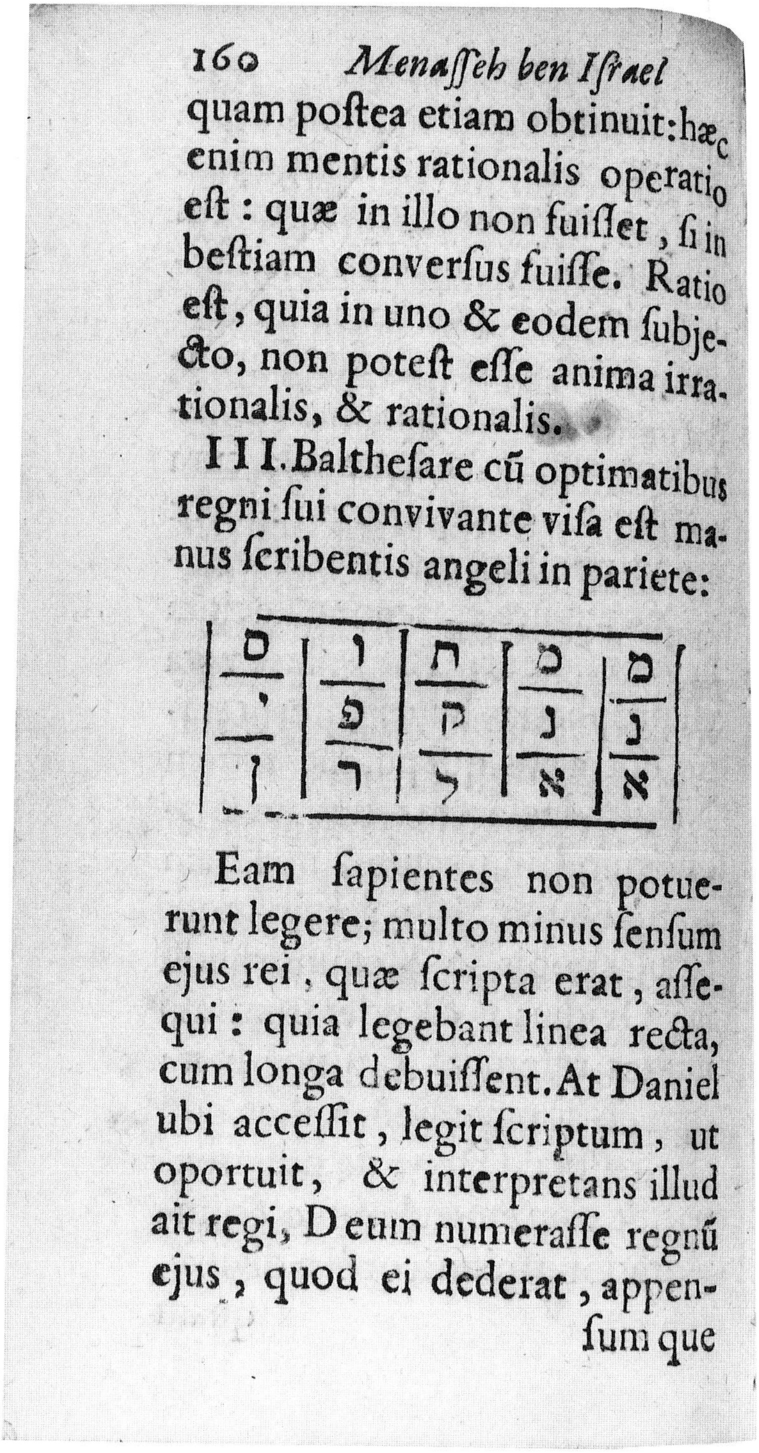

FIGURE 89

quam poſtea etiam obtinuit:hæc enim mentis rationalis operatio eſt : quæ in illo non fuiſſet , ſi in beſtiam converſus fuiſſe. Ratio eſt , quia in uno & eodem ſubje-cto, non poteſt eſſe anima irra-tionalis, & rationalis.

I I I.Balthesare cũ optimatibus regni ſui convivante viſa eſt ma-nus ſcribentis angeli in pariete:

ס	ו	ח	מ	מ
י	פ	ק	נ	נ
ו	ר	ל	א	א

Eam ſapientes non potue-runt legere; multo minus ſenſum ejus rei , quæ ſcripta erat , aſſe-qui : quia legebant linea recta, cum longa debuiſſent.At Daniel ubi acceſſit , legit ſcriptum , ut oportuit , & interpretans illud ait regi, Deum numeraſſe regnũ ejus , quod ei dederat , appen-ſum que

Mennaseh ben Israel, *De termino vitae.* London, British Library.
(See Rembrandt No. 6350.)

FIGURE 90

Rembrandt, *A Seated Woman*. Pen and wash, 165 × 144 mm. London, British Museum.
(See Rembrandt No. 6432.)

FIGURE 91

Follower of Rembrandt, *A Man seated reading at a Table in a Lofty Room* (No. 3214). Composite X-ray photograph.

FIGURE 92

Roelant Roghman, *Mountainous Landscape with Fisherman.* Canvas, 80.5 × 100 cm. Amsterdam, Rijksmuseum. (See Roghman No. 1340.)

FIGURE 93

Jacob van Ruisdael, *An Extensive Landscape with a Ruined Castle and a Village Church.* Canvas, 39.4 × 44.4 cm. Ex-Kempner Collection. (See Ruisdael No. 990.)

FIGURE 94

Jacob van Ruisdael, *A Landscape with a Ruined Building at the Foot of a Hill by a River.* Wood, 46 × 62 cm. Berlin, Gemäldegalerie, Staatliche Museen Preussischer Kulturbesitz. (See Ruisdael No. 991.)

FIGURE 95

Jacob van Ruisdael, *A Landscape with a Ruined Building at the Foot of a Hill by a River.* Canvas, 75 × 96 cm. Dresden, Gemäldegalerie. (See Ruisdael No. 991.)

FIGURE 96

Jacob van Ruisdael, *The Coast near Muiden*. Canvas, 55.5 × 69.5 cm. National Trust, Polesdon Lacey. (See Ruisdael (No. 1390.))

FIGURE 97

Salomon van Ruysdael, *A River Landscape* (No. 1439). Composite infra-red reflectogram.

Figure 98 (*Above*)
Pieter Saenredam,
preparatory study for *The
Interior of the Buurkerk at
Utrecht* (No. 1896).
Chalk and ink,
266 × 417 mm.
Utrecht, Municipal
Archives.

Figure 99 (*Right*)
Pieter Saenredam,
preparatory study for
*The Interior of the Grote
Kerk at Haarlem* (No. 2531).
Pen, 461 × 383 mm.
Haarlem, Municipal
Archives.

FIGURE 100

Pieter Saenredam, *The Interior of the Buurkerk at Utrecht*. Oak, 58.5 × 49.5 cm.
Fort Worth, Texas, Kimbell Art Museum. (See Saenredam No. 1896.)

FIGURE 101

Cornelis van der Schalcke, *A View of Haarlem from the Dunes of Overveen.* Canvas, 72 × 106 cm. Ex-Singer Collection. (See van der Schalcke No. 974.)

FIGURE 102

Frans van Mieris the Elder, *A Woman releasing a Sparrow from a Box*. Panel, 17.5 × 14 cm. Amsterdam, Rijksmuseum. (See Schalcken No. 199.)

FIGURE 103

Johannes Spruyt, *Ducks and Geese.* Canvas, 100.3 × 122 cm. National Trust for Scotland, Culzean Castle. (See Spruyt No. 1013.)

FIGURE 104

Jan Steen, *An Itinerant Musician saluting Two Women in a Kitchen*. Canvas, 46 × 36.8 cm. England, Private Collection. (See After Steen No. 1378.)

FIGURE 105

Wallerant Vaillant, *The Young Draughtsman*. Canvas, 129 × 100 cm. Paris, Musée du Louvre.
(See Vaillant No. 3591.)

FIGURE 106

Wallerant Vaillant, *The Young Draughtsman*. Canvas, 119 × 90 cm.
Maastricht, Bonnefantenmuseum. Permanent loan from Stichting Limburgs Kunstbezit.
(See Vaillant No. 3591.)

FIGURE 107

Adriaen van de Velde, preparatory study for *A Bay Horse, a Cow, a Goat and Three Sheep near a Building* (No. 983). Red and black chalk, 194 × 308 mm. Amsterdam, Historisch Museum.

FIGURE 108

Adriaen van de Velde, preparatory study for *A Bay Horse, a Cow, a Goat and Three Sheep near a Building* (No. 983). Red chalk, 193 × 298 mm. Amsterdam, Historisch Museum.

FIGURE 109

Esaias van de Velde, *A Winter Landscape* (No. 6269). Infra-red photograph.

FIGURE 110

Willem van de Velde, *The Shore at Scheveningen*. Canvas, 75 × 104 cm. Private Collection. (See W. van de Velde No. 873.)

FIGURE 113

Willem van de Velde, partial copy (?) after *Three Ships in a Gale* (No. 981). Pen and sepia ink, with wash, 154 × 189 mm. London, National Maritime Museum.

Figure 111 (*Left, top*) Willem van de Velde, partial copy (?) after *Three Ships in a Gale* (No. 981.) Graphite, 221 × 330 mm. London, National Maritime Museum.

Figure 112 (*Left, bottom*) Willem van de Velde, partial copy (?) after *Three Ships in a Gale* (No. 981.) Graphite, wash and pen, and sepia ink, 165 × 202 mm. London, National Maritime Museum.

FIGURE 114

Pieter Verbeeck, *A Horse standing by a Sleeping Man*. Etching, 16.2 × 19.3 cm. London, British Museum. (See Verbeeck No. 1009.)

FIGURE 115

Dirck van Baburen, *The Procuress*. Canvas, 101 × 108.5 cm. Boston, Museum of Fine Arts.
(See Vermeer No. 2568.)

FIGURE 116

Gabriel Metsu, *Self Portrait of Gabriel Metsu with his Wife*. Panel, 35.5 × 30.5 cm.
Dresden, Gemäldegalerie. (See Victors No. 1312.)

FIGURE 117

Jan Weenix, *The Prodigal Son.* Canvas 110.5 × 98.5 cm. Salzburg, Residenzgalerie. (See Weenix No. 6462.)

FIGURE 118

Adriaen van der Werff, *A Boy putting a Bird into a Cage*. Engraving.
(See van der Werff No. 3049.)

FIGURE 119

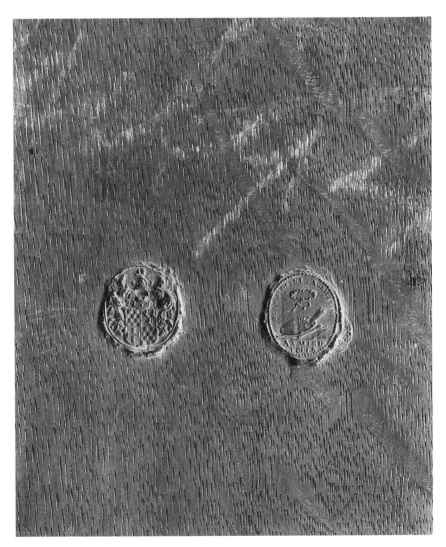

Adriaen van der Werff, *A Boy with a Mousetrap* (No. 3049). Reverse showing the stamps.

FIGURE 120

Emanuel de Witte, *Adriana van Huesden and her Daughter at the New Fishmarket in Amsterdam.* Canvas, 57 × 46 cm. Present location unknown. (See de Witte No. 3682.)

FIGURE 121

Joachim Wtewael, *The Judgement of Paris*. Panel, 81 × 104.5 cm. Present location unknown. (See Wtewael No. 6334.)

Photographic Acknowledgements

The author and the National Gallery are grateful to the following individuals and institutions for permission to reproduce material:

Amsterdam,
Historisch Museum: Figs.14, 47, 107, 108.
Rijksmuseum: Figs. 51, 56, 57, 66, 68, 83, 92, 102.
Rijksprentenkabinet, Rijksmuseum: Figs. 24, 34, 36, 54, 59.

Berlin,
Staatliche Museen, Preussischer Kulturbesitz: Figs. 61, 94.

Besançon, Musée des Beaux-Arts et d'Archéologie: Fig. 2.

Boston, Museum of Fine Arts: Fig. 115.

Braunschweig, Herzog Anton Ulrich-Museum: Fig. 87.

Cassel, Staatliche Kunstsammlungen, Gemäldegalerie Alte Meister: Figs. 4, 5, 20.

Cologne, Wallraf-Richartz Museum: Fig. 19.

Dordrecht, D. van Houten Collection: Fig. 15.

Dresden,
Staatliche Kunstsammlungen: Figs. 13, 95, 116.

Frankfurt, Städelsches Kunstinstitut: Fig. 38.

Haarlem,
Teylers Museum: Fig. 3.
Municipal Archives: Fig. 100.

The Hague, Bredius Museum: Fig. 32.

Kreuzlingen, Kisters Collection: Fig. 84.

Leningrad, Hermitage Museum: Fig. 86.

London,
British Library: Fig. 89.
British Museum, Department of Prints and Drawings: Figs. 9, 23, 26, 30, 37, 40, 55, 63, 69, 72, 76, 78, 81, 90, 114.
National Maritime Museum: Figs. 111, 112, 113.

Maastricht,
Photo: Bonnefantenmuseum: Fig. 106.

Massachusetts, Worcester Art Museum: Fig. 17.

Munich, Alte Pinakothek: Figs. 58, 67, 73.

Münster, Westfälisches Landesmuseum für Kunst und Kulturgeschichte: Fig. 8.

New York,
Christophe Janet: Fig. 28.
Wildenstein: Fig. 80.
Ian Woodner Family Collection: Fig. 53.

Paris,
Institut Néerlandais, Fondation Custodia (coll. F. Lugt): Figs. 52, 77.
Musée du Louvre: Fig. 105.

Polesden Lacey, National Trust: Fig. 96.

Private Collection, V. de S. Collection: Fig. 27.

Rotterdam. Boymans-van Beuningen Museum: Figs. 22, 35, 42.

Salzburg, Residenzgalerie: Fig. 117.

Scotland, National Trust for Scotland: Fig. 103.

Texas, Fort Worth, Kimbell Art Museum: Fig. 99.

Utrecht,
Centraal Museum: Fig. 31.
Municipal Archives: Fig. 98.

Vienna,
Albertina: Fig. 25.
Kunsthistorisches Museum: Figs. 10, 18.

Warsaw, Muzeum Narodowe: Fig. 50.

Washington, National Gallery of Art: Fig. 43. *Hut among Trees*, Meindert Hobbema, Widener Collection.

Windsor, Windsor Castle, Print Room: Fig. 1. © 1991 By gracious permission of Her Majesty The Queen.